ADVENTURE IN IRON

Adventure in Iron

The blast furnace and its spread from Namur to northern France, England and North America, 1450-1650; a technological, political and genealogical investigation

BRIAN G. AWTY

PART TWO

Prepared for publication by
J. S. Hodgkinson and C. H. C. Whittick
Index by Ann Hudson

First published 2019

Published by The Wealden Iron Research Group
8, Woodview Crescent, Hildenborough, Tonbridge, Kent, TN11 9HD, UK.
www.wealdeniron.org.uk

British Library Cataloguing in Publication Data.
A catalogue record for this book is available from the British Library.

ISBN 978-1-9160423-0-8

Cover illustration: Drome-beam hammer, with finery hearth in the background, from Diderot and d'Alembert, *Encyclopédie, Tome 21, 4me Section, Planche VI*, Paris, 1765 (Special Collections Research Center, University of Chicago Library).

Printed by ScanTech Lithographics Ltd, Hastings, East Sussex

The publishers gratefully acknowledge the receipt of grants from the Marc Fitch Fund and the Kent Archaeological Society's Allen Grove Fund towards the cost of the index.

CONTENTS

PART ONE

PART TWO

FIGURES

TABLES

7

CONSOLIDATION AND THE MANUFACTURE OF CANNON, 1525-1550

HISTORICAL SETTING

The economic factor which reshaped the iron industry of the Weald during this period was the escalation of the price of wood, especially in the 1530s, in a fashion entirely reminiscent of what happened in the Pays de Bray. The change was reflected dramatically in the experience of the Pelham family. In July 1524 William Pelham obtained licence to impark 500 acres of wood and 200 acres of land called the Verth Wood, or 'the olde Brule', in the parish of Laughton.[1] The French terminology of 'Verth', and of 'Brule', reminiscent of *Les hauts Brulons* at Forges-en-Bray, suggests that these 200 acres of land may have recently been stripped of their wood by colliers.

Although in the year ended Michaelmas 1531 the Pelham hundred court of Hawksborough received only a shilling from the sale of 'colewood' out of Dudwell Park, by October 1538, when he made his will, Sir William Pelham envisaged that a levy upon his woods would yield 1,000 marks (just less than £667) towards marriage portions for his five daughters.[2]

Up to this time licences for the export of wood, probably partly for the supply of the English enclave at Calais, had been granted with gay abandon. Sir Goddard Oxenbridge had licence in March 1517 to export three million billets of *tallwood* (a *Franglais* expression which described coppice-wood). As late as 1526 Sir Edward Nevill had licence to export six score hundred thousand (12 million) of billet wood from Kent and Sussex and in 1527 George Joiner was given leave to export eight million billets of wood.[3]

Despite an ordinance of the king made in 1533 that wood was to be exported out of Kent and Sussex only to supply Calais, the Calais governor Lord Lisle complained to the Lord Chancellor late in that year that the town was in danger of being 'quite destitute of fuel'. Earlier in the year Parliament had concerned itself with the problem, when one of the bills presented to it was for the sparing of young spring wood.[4]

The impact of the scarcity of wood on charcoal prices made it increasingly difficult, if not impossible, for ironworkers, immigrant or native, to run ironworks, except in combination with others. Landowners could still make their way, especially those who had allowed ironworks to be set up on their lands, the direction of which they could now take into their own hands, due to the insolvency of the original entrepreneurs. The opportunity for landed gentlemen to make riches out of their woodlands by becoming forgemasters had become too obvious to be ignored. However, if profits could be large, risks were incurred, as much by simple inexperience, as by carelessness and inattention to detail. The indebtedness of some made the fortunes of others. John Ashburnham was one, who entered the iron trade towards the end of this period, but was in difficulties by around 1580.

The period saw the involvement of more of the prominent Wealden gentry in iron manufacture. John Caryll had become involved at Parrock Forge in 1518. Sir Thomas Boleyn, the future earl of Wiltshire, became lessee at Newbridge in 1525. Sir William Pelham of Laughton may have had interests in ironworking, though no ironworks were mentioned in his will. His younger brother Anthony was almost certainly a forgemaster before Sir William died in 1538, his son Nicholas Pelham had become one by the following decade, and his younger son, another Sir William Pelham, was familiar enough with technical matters later to become Master of the Armouries.

Sir Roger Lewknor of Trotton, from one of the most ancient armorial families in Sussex, clearly had ironworks at his death in 1543, and his participation in the industry may go back to the early

1. *Letters and Papers Henry VIII*, **4**, no. 546.
2. BL, Add. Roll 31390; TNA, PROB 11/27/391.
3. *Letters and Papers Henry VIII*, **2** (1), no. 1641; **4** (1), no. 2002 (5); **4** (2), no. 2927 (12).
4. *Letters and Papers Henry VIII*, **6**, no. 120 (spring wood), no. 1585 (Calais).

1530s, because around 1535 he married, as his third wife, a young widow, Elizabeth daughter of Thomas Messant, apparently a member of the immigrant family of that name. By 1543 the duke of Norfolk had a furnace below Sheffield Forest and a forge on the Ouse, and it seems likely that his involvement there went back to the mid-1530s. In February 1546 Sir Anthony Browne, the Master of the Horse, was granted a lease of the king's Newbridge works following the end in September of the lease made in 1525 to Sir Thomas Boleyn. This lease of the 'iron mills and dwelling houses set within 14 acres of land in Ashdown Forest' was again for 21 years and again at the remarkably low rent of £4 a year, and Browne covenanted to maintain them, their floodgates, forge-house, furnace-house and water troughs in good repair.[5] Browne may indeed have been involved at Newbridge a few years earlier.

Lesser men, albeit parish gentry, involved before 1525, had been William Wybarne, John Barham, Thomas May, and possibly Richard Isted. Between 1525 and 1540 they were joined by John and William Levett, John Baker, John Lunsford, Richard Weekes, William Nisell, Nicholas Eversfield and Thomas Walsh. But few men of immigrant origins or descent made their way into ownership during these years. Exceptions are the mysterious Henry Lucas who appears to have run a furnace in Lindfield Arches hundred in the 1540s, the martyr forgemaster Richard Woodman, if the suggestion that he was of immigrant stock is correct, and John Harvo at Pounsley Furnace.

The socio-political event, which had an effect on the development of the iron industry as profound as the increase in the price of wood, was the dissolution of the monasteries. Some monasteries had exploited the mineral wealth of their lands in mediaeval times, especially in the Forest of Dean, the Midlands, Yorkshire and Cumbria. The water-driven forges of the abbey of Bordesley in Worcestershire are thought to have been solely mediaeval,[6] but on the monastic estates of Wenlock in Shropshire, Croxden in Staffordshire, Merivale in Warwickshire and Rievaulx in North Yorkshire, forges were already in being at the time of the Dissolution. In the Weald the immigrant Lambert Symart was resident at Bayham in 1513, closely following the expiry of his father's lease of Newbridge, which suggests that Bayham Abbey's forge, at which William Wybarne was later the forgemaster, was already in operation then.

The occasional obviously failing house, such as Bayham, had been abolished in Cardinal Wolsey's time. Only in the late 1530s under Thomas Cromwell was dissolution applied systematically and nationwide. In the Weald, the property of the priories of Michelham and of Saint Pancras, Lewes, was acquired by Cromwell himself in 1537 and 1538. Among the manors of Michelham Priory were Isenhurst and Cowden, both the sites of ironworks before 1550. Henry's attorney-general John Baker,[7] from the family later established at Sissinghurst, was granted the reversion of the New Priory, with its manor of Hasleden in Dallington and lands in Burwash, Herstmonceux, Warbleton and other places in Sussex in March 1538. In 1574 his son Sir Richard Baker had his own ironworks in Kent, but was proprietor of a furnace in Dallington and two furnaces and two forges in Heathfield and Warbleton. The site of Battle Abbey and its home estate went to Henry VIII's Master of Horse, Sir Anthony Browne, a future forgemaster, in 1538 and 1539. Robertsbridge Priory went in 1539 to Prince Edward's chamberlain and chief steward, Sir William Sidney.[8] Eighteen months later Sidney was making preparations to enter the iron trade on the Robertsbridge site.

Though Mary Tudor might burn heretics, these accomplishments of her two predecessors' reigns she found impossible to reverse and her accession may even have accelerated the speed with which owners of former monastic lands set about exploiting them, or selling them at a profit. It looks as though between one third and half the ironworks initiated in England and Wales after 1537 were built on former monastic lands.

At Merivale the grant of the abbey to Sir Walter Devereux in 1540 included an 'iron-mill' near the site, still in being in 1550 when confirmation of the grant was made to Devereux, now viscount Hereford. An 'iron-mill' will have been water powered and was certainly additional to the smithy

5. TNA, DL 14/1; I am grateful to Christopher Whittick for a summary of this lease.

6. G. G. Astill, *A medieval industrial complex and its landscape; the metalworking watermills and workshops of Bordesley Abbey*, CBA Research Report **92**, London, 1993.

7. Baker was made attorney general in 1536 (*L and P*, **11**, 202 (18)).

8. *Letters and Papers Henry VIII*, **12** (2), no. 1108 (3); **13** (1), no. 384 (74), no. 646 (34); **13** (2), no. 249 (8); **14** (1), no. 906 (7); **14** (2), no. 619 (3). Browne became Master of the Horse in March 1539; Sidney was chamberlain of the prince's household before that date (*Letters and Papers Henry VIII*, **14** (1), nos. 517 and 651 (32)).

inventoried along with the abbey buildings in 1540.[9] Croxden Abbey owned Hungarwall smithy near Cheadle at the time of the Dissolution.[10] At Rievaulx the inventory made by the royal commissioners in 1538 mentioned a rent of £1 6s 8d due from a mill within the abbey site, called *the Yron Smithes* and recently in the tenure of the ubiquitous Lambert Semer (i.e. Symart). The abbey owned a works (*fabrica*) at Laskill in Bilsdale, also called *the Yron Smithes* and leased to Richard Rawlinson for 26s 8d, though this was perhaps a smelting works only, from which the blooms were sent to Rievaulx mill for hammering. Symart's will showed that by his death in 1558, in addition to his tenancy of the Rievaulx smithy, he had *smydyes* of his own at Bolton in Craven, presumably on the estates of the dissolved priory of Bolton.[11]

At Rievaulx the bloomsmithy site was reequipped to operate on the indirect system for the earl of Rutland in 1577. However, between Symart's presence at Bayham in 1513 and Rievaulx in 1538, the subsidy rolls for Shropshire showed the presence of Hugh Morall at Lilleshall in 1525. There ironworking adjacent to the abbey went back to the 'qualmesmythe' of 1277 and Morall must be supposed to have had a hand in the development of what by 1580 were water-driven hammers at Lubstree Pool and the fully integrated ironworks leased in 1591 by Sir William Leveson to the Corbet brothers.[12]

The establishment of the Morall family in the Midlands by 1525 could be the other side of the coin which saw a member of the Welstead family from the Midlands engaged as forgemaster near Heathfield by 1524. Morall was almost certainly a member of the Morel family which had migrated to the Weald from Bouelles, near Neuville-Ferrières. Before the Dissolution, Hugh had moved on to become bailiff of Wenlock Priory's manor of Little Wenlock and in 1536 he became the lessee there of 'Calbroke smithy', the forge out of which grew the famous Coalbrookdale ironworks. It was presumably Hugh who around 1550 procured the services of John Morrell to act as founder at or near Shirlett smithy, formerly also a possession of the priory, and the site of the first English blast furnace outside the Weald.

Another immigrant family to penetrate the Midlands, even before the indirect method of iron manufacture arrived, was that of Vinton. Firstly, in 1539 John Venton married Izabell Houseman at Astley in Worcestershire, the site of a blast furnace of undetermined date.[13] A remarriage of the same man could be the first of two Ventam marriages at Solihull around 1550; John Ventam married Julyan Gibbens in 1548 and George Tomlynson married Elizabeth Ventam in 1552. Furthermore, Henry Ventam, who married Anne Peyt at Leigh with Bransford, on the lower Teme, just west of Worcester, early in 1564, and whose daughter Joan was baptised there later in the year, could have been the hammerman Henry Vinton who was buried at Buxted back in Sussex in 1590.[14]

Just as an entry of 1556 in the Much Wenlock parish register showed that the Shropshire Morrells were of French descent, quarter sessions records for Staffordshire show that Thomas Dutton, hammerman at Witton Forge on the Tame in 1590, bore the alias Tomlynson, suggesting that this family's entry into the iron trade was facilitated by its marriage alliance of 1552 with the Vinton family, whose later member, Blaise Vyntam, was finer during the 1590s, firstly at Wednesbury Forge and later at Perry Bar Forge, slightly upstream from Witton.[15]

This penetration of the Midlands by immigrant ironworkers from the 1520s onwards suggests that the Foley family, who are shown by the parish register to have been already established at Rowley Regis by 1539, could have been immigrants from the Beauvaisis, where the La Folie family had become increasingly important at Le Becquet Forge by the beginning of the century. That an unnamed member

9. *Letters and Papers Henry VIII*, **16**, no. 379 (4); *Calendars of Patent rolls, Edward VI*, **3**, pp. 432-3; W. Dugdale, *Monasticon Anglicanum*, London, 1693, p. 99.

10. *Victoria County History of the county of Stafford, vol. 2* (ed. M. W. Greenslade and J. G. Jenkins), Oxford University Press, 1967, p. 109.

11. J. G. McDonnell, 'An account of the iron industry in upper Ryedale and Bilsdale, c.1150- 1650', *The Ryedale Historian*, **6** (1972), p. 39; Borthwick Institute, Wills proved at York, 15(2), 292.

12. *Victoria County History of Shropshire, vol. 11* (ed. G. C. Baugh), Oxford University Press, 1985, p. 163.

13. Around 1660 it received 500 loads of charcoal in each of six years (Riden, *A gazetteer of charcoal-fired blast furnaces in Great Britain in use since 1660*, Cardiff, 1987, p. 18).

14. The hammerman's widow was not Anne but Margaret, but she was probably his second wife. The will shows that Vinton had already given his (unnamed) children their portions; Margaret was to have all his current goods (ESRO, PBT 2/2/1/35).

15. Burne, *Staffordshire Quarter Sessions Rolls*, **2**, pp, 73-4; **3**, pp. 204, 292, 345.

of the Foley family moved to the South Yorkshire area whilst the blast furnace was being implanted there is suggested by the burial of an illegitimate Joan Foley at Rotherham in December 1574.[16]

Lastly, purely political matters had their effect. Though the fall of Cardinal Wolsey, the architect of the peaceful policy pursued in the middle portion of Henry VIII's reign, occurred at the end of 1529, Henry's obsession with divorce from Queen Katharine ensured that the peaceful policy continued. As well as antagonising the Pope, Henry's divorce was bound to be anathema to his old ally Charles V, because Katharine was Charles's aunt. Particularly up to 1536, when Katharine died, it was necessary to tread warily and to avoid giving additional gratuitous offence.

In 1536 the Pilgrimage of Grace showed Henry that he was less than totally secure at home. By 1538 the situation seemed fraught with danger. In June Charles V and Francis I ended their wars with the treaty of Nice, designed to last for 10 years. The amicable meeting of these former deadly rivals which occurred at Aigues Mortes the following month caused panic in London. Henry and Thomas Cromwell embarked on a policy of rearmament and coastal fortification which lasted for the remainder of the reign.

The iron industry was perhaps already on the agenda at the time of the king's visit to the Weald in the summer of 1538, but in preparation for his next summer visit in 1539, Henry Polsted furnished Cromwell with two bills to be signed, one of which concerned the Forest of Ashdown, with 'a survey of the Forest and the iron mills'.[17] The indirect result was the creation of the cannon-founding industry of the Weald.

It seems probable that the successful introduction of cast-iron cannon founding to the Weald was helped by the friendly relations with some of the Protestant rulers of Germany established by Cromwell after the break with Rome. The most active of these were the duke of Saxony and the landgrave of Hessen, but it was with William de la Marck, heir to the duchies of Cleves, Berg and Jülich, who, following the death of its duke without heirs, had been elected duke of Gelders in 1538, that Thomas Cromwell suggested his master should contract marriage alliances. On his father's death in 1539, William succeeded to the other three duchies, making him a serious menace to Habsburg power in northern Germany.

Christopher Mont had been sent in January 1539 to establish friendly relations with Saxony and Hessen, from where it was hoped to recruit cannoneers and hackbutteers for the defence of England.[18] In March Edward Carne and Nicholas Wotton, already among Henry VIII's agents in the Netherlands, were sent on to Cleves to negotiate the marriages, which were to be between the king and one of the duke's unmarried sisters, and between the duke and Henry's daughter, the Lady Mary.[19] It was the first of these negotiations which prospered and in July Carne was able to return to England, leaving Wotton to complete negotiations, in which he had assistance from Dr Peter on the tricky matter of the earlier betrothal of Anne of Cleves to the son of the duke of Lorraine.

Wotton stayed on alone during 1540, acquitting himself well, especially when the marriage ended abruptly on Henry's discovery that his bride was not quite the beauty which Hans Holbein's portrait had suggested her to be. Duke William cemented his other foreign alliance in a treaty of July 1540 with Francis I of France, by which he was betrothed to Francis's niece Jeanne d'Albret, heiress to the throne of Navarre, another marriage which never actually took place.

These alliances form the context in which cannon of the new Franco-Italian denominations of culverin, saker, falcon and falconet were first made in cast iron for all three sovereigns within a few years of 1540, a coincidence otherwise quite inexplicable. In November 1539 Duke William sent the *Büchsenmeister* Hans von Homberg to his master of the armouries (*Wehr-meister*), who was to give him help in casting *Falckonetten* and other war matériel. During the winter of 1539-40, among items cast by von Homberg at the *Schevenhütte* were nine *Falckenythen*, whose average weight was around 500kg each, and the 1540 accounts for the nearby *Dollarttshütte* at Stolberg speak of the hole 'in which the vat or barrel is set in which the cannon-moulds are placed',[20] a reference to the kind of planked or stave-

16. Other Foley entries in South Yorkshire at this time appear to be entirely lacking.
17. *Letters and Papers, Henry VIII,* **14** (2), no. 29.
18. *Letters and Papers, Henry VIII,* **14** (1), no. 490.
19. *Letters and Papers, Henry VIII,* **14** (1), no. 489.
20. P. Neu, *Eisenindustrie in der Eifel: Aufstieg, Blüte und Niedergang*, Köln, Rheinland Verlag, 1989, p. 205; the reference is to a hole *da dat fass ingesaitz ist, dar man die buyssen formen insetzt.*

lined gun-pit in which cannon moulds were set for vertical casting later in the century in the Weald. At Breteuil in Normandy bastard culverins, demi-culverins and falcons of iron were all cast in 1540; at Buxted in the Weald a falconet was cast in 1543, a demi-culverin in 1544 and by 1550 all sizes of iron gun up to demi-cannon had been cast in the Weald.

No evidence has been found that Nicholas Wotton was instrumental in the transfer of this technology to the Weald. However, it is unlikely that such an intelligent man, whose family lived at Boughton Malherbe in Kent, whose elder brother Sir Edward Wotton became treasurer of Calais in 1540, and whose sister Mary had married Sir Henry Guildford, son of Sir Richard Guildford, Master of the Ordnance for Henry VII, and himself Master of the Horse and later Comptroller of the household for Henry VIII, would have been ignorant of the technological importance of the gun-casting methods being employed in Jülich. Furthermore, by July 1541, having narrowly evaded being rewarded for his services by appointment as a bishop, Wotton was back in Kent as dean of Canterbury, to whose archbishop belonged the deanery and lordship of South Malling, in which cannon-founding began at Buxted in 1543. In 1544 Wotton became dean of York, and was nominated a privy councillor in Henry VIII's will; it was he who conducted successful peace negotiations with France, for Edward VI in 1550 and for Elizabeth I in 1563. The first round of negotiations for the exploitation of English copper by German artificers was conducted between Wotton and Johannes Steinberg in 1561.[21]

It seems hardly possible that the rector and forgemaster of Buxted, William Levett, and the dean of Canterbury could have remained unacquainted. Before the end of the century the Weald had become the chief source of cast-iron guns in Europe and the Wealden industry's dominance of the English market for guns was destined to last for more than 200 years.

But Henry's immediate danger lasted for only four years. In Germany, Charles V's position, made difficult by the spread of Lutheranism, deteriorated further when his brother Ferdinand, who had been elected king of Hungary, lost almost all that kingdom to the Turks. Renewed hostilities broke out between Charles V and France in 1542, and although Charles managed to force the capitulation of the duke of Cleves, and made him renounce the duchy of Gelders, he was forced to accept Henry as his ally in the further pursuit of the war against France. The possibility of England having to face war with two major foreign powers at once had now ended. But when Henry and Charles both invaded France in 1544 cooperation between the two was minimal, and Henry contented himself with the seizure of Boulogne.

Henry died early in 1547, and his death reprieved the forgemaster duke of Norfolk from imminent execution on Tower Hill. Henry left a country religiously divided, with its government entrusted during the minority of Edward VI to a council of regency which was also at odds. The plunder from the monasteries had in no way compensated for Henry's lavish expenditure. The treasury was left so depleted that armaments could no longer be bought from abroad and even purchases from the Weald seem to have been scaled down by 1550. Peace with France had to be bought ignominiously, at the price of the cession of Boulogne.

Ironworks on the Continent

Walloons in the German Ardennes

We saw that the Rifflart family of Namur appeared in 1506 in the Hoyou basin of Liège and in 1533 in the Durbuy basin of northern Luxembourg, where that family was soon joined by Pier Le Samreu.

Further east, in the Eifel or German Ardennes, the spread of the indirect method appears also to have depended heavily on immigrants from Wallonia. In many cases it was the ironworkers themselves who appeared in leases and legal documents concerning these works, an exception being at the Dollartshammer which took its name from the copper-merchant Heinrich Dollart.

Descendants of the Walloon Johannes Servatius Pontzeler, or Puntzgen, from Limbourg, continued in the Olef valley around Schleiden, in the persons of Heinrich Poensgen at Gangfurth from 1510 onwards and Mattheus Poensgen at Wiesgen (formerly Steinenhaus) from around the same time.

21. M. B. Donald, *Elizabethan copper: the history of the Company of Mines Royal, 1568-1605*, London, Pergamon Press, 1955, p. 97.

Descendants appeared at the ironworks at Blumenthal, Hellenthal and Kirschseiffen, all in the Olef valley above Schleiden, whilst gunsmiths from this family were Balthasar Poensgen of Schleiden in the second half of the sixteenth century and Peter Pontzeler around 1630 at Gemünd below Schleiden. At Gemünd the family later acquired a wire-works which lasted until 1860, when it was closed and transferred to Düsseldorf. Albert Poensgen also transferred his wrought-iron gas-pipe works from Mauel to Düsseldorf in the same year. Both transfers were made because it had become evident that the main-line railway network would by-pass the Schleiden valley.[22]

At Kronenburg in the central Eifel, where *hutte und hammer* had been built by Johann Symar in 1464, another Walloon named Collet von der Scharten, first appeared in 1512 and was mentioned up to 1526-7. His place of origin was perhaps Sart near Spa in Franchimont and by 1520 he had an eighth share in the works.[23] The most easterly of the Eifel ironworks was at Wehr, only 10km from the Rhine. In 1606 Servatius Collett, still described as an immigrant from Sart, rebuilt this works. He died in 1623 and was followed by his son Melchior Hasenell alias Collet.

The heavy rents and the tithe payable to the abbey of Steinfeld had always been a burden to the father, but in 1624 the elector-archbishop of Cologne claimed tithes on both mining and on the ironworks, together with the water-rights, a situation which was not resolved until 1632, when a lawsuit ended in the Steinfeld claims being upheld. The only mitigating circumstance had been an order of the archbishop for cast-iron guns and shot during 1628-9. In 1649 the lease passed to Michael Bossard, who was apparently Collet's son-in-law,[24] but bore another name found somewhat earlier among immigrant ironworkers in the Weald.

At Eisenschmitt in the south of the Eifel, the presence of Walloons Peter Pyrit and of Theiss Pirrotz was noted in lists of inhabitants in 1467 and in 1581 respectively, and indeed in 1585 Pirotz Theissen of the smithy (*von der Schmitten*) was paid for coaling five loads of charcoal. Other members of this family were active in the Schleiden area, and in 1552 Heinrich Pyrotz had a sixteenth share at the Gemünd ironworks. The family persisted in the industry in the Schleiden area until around 1800.[25]

The family of Firmond or Virmond first appeared at Hellenthal above Schleiden in 1583 when Claiss Fermont was recorded as a witness. Although there was nothing to show his own origin, his two sons, *Welscher* Paulus and *Welscher* Pierath (Peter), were described as Walloons. Around 1600 the family was running an ironworks at Bruch near Blumenthal, but belonging to the lordship of Reifferscheid. Paulus Firmond worked in the ironworks of the Schleiden area in the early 1620s and the family continued as forgemasters at Hellenthal and Kirschseiffen after the Thirty Years' War. In 1653 Peter moved westwards to Monschau on the upper Roer towards the Hoher Venn and participated in a partnership at the ironworks there until 1658, but yet another Peter Virmond moved at much the same time to Luxembourg, where he was involved with Heinrich Peuchen in an ironworks at Ottweiler.[26]

An ironworks just above Stolberg on the lower Vicht was leased to Kristian Hamersmede (hammerman) van der Scharten in 1464, another immigrant apparently from Franchimont. Kristian was followed at the works by his son Dietrich. However, in 1497 Heinrich Dollart, from Aachen, took the lease. Dollart abandoned ironworking at the plant between 1510 and 1520, but it was back in production in 1535 and, together with Hens Jan, Dollart produced 142 sows there in the year 1535/6, and afterwards on his own 89 sows in 1536/7 and 55 sows in 1537/8. Stolberg belonged to the duchy of Jülich and the new duke of Cleves, who was also duke of Jülich and Berg, was the Protestant whose defence establishment (*Wehrmeisterei*) took a stake in the Dollartshammer, and in other local ironworks.[27]

The works was rebuilt in 1540 using mainly Walloon labour and it looks as though in the new dispensation Heinrich Dollart was the man described in the accounts as master of artillery (*Artillerie-meister*). The newly-built works included a boring-mill, and a payment for the digging of a hole in which 'to fix the barrel in which the cannon moulds are set', presumably a reference to the vertical casting of ordnance, and the earliest example yet known for this practice in cast iron.[28]

22. P. Neu, *Eifel*, pp. 72-3.
23. Ibid., p. 144.
24. Ibid., pp. 226-7.
25. Ibid., pp. 71-2, 102.
26. Ibid., pp. 74, 175.
27. Ibid., p. 200 and nn. 443, 444.
28. Ibid., pp. 201, 205.

In 1540 the Walloon who had stayed behind to superintend the first blast was taken ill, and his brother Myster Wylhelm *der Wale* was sent for to help out; Wylhelm also cast fire-plates (*takken*).[29] The filler at the furnace was Pontz *der Wale*, and the founder (*Massenbläser*) at the second blast was 'the Walloon's father' (*des Walen Vader*), who was the father of both Wylhelm and of the sick man.

In 1541 the founder was another Walloon, Myster Hynrich Goyrar *der Wale*, who continued in that capacity and also laid the hearth until 1546. The 1541 filler, Dederich *Wailge*, also sounds Walloon. In 1551 *der Wale* Meister Hinrich came for three days to lay the hearth and later founders with Walloon names were Lambert Huttemann who was founder in 1552-3 and Johan *der Wal* and 'the other Walloon' (*der ander Wal*), who were employed in 1559-60.[30]

Other neighbouring ironworks belonging to the Jülich *Wehrmeisterei* were the Schevenhütte on the Wehe and the Rosswerk near Eschweiler. The duke of Cleves sent Hans von Homberg to the Schevenhütte in November 1539 in order to cast items which included nine falconets (*Falckenythen*), which weighed around 500kg each.[31] The Rosswerk was built in 1555 with the help of so many Walloons - Heinrich *der Waill*, Hermann *der Waill*, Michel *der Waill*, *der Welsche* Pertzjong, Johann *der Waill*, Wilhelm *der Waill* and Gerart Schuess *der Waele* - that there was no need to attach a name to the only German (*Duitsche*) employed.[32]

To bolster his position against Charles V, the Protestant duke allied himself in 1539 with Henry VIII, who married his sister Anne of Cleves, and with Francis I, who in July 1540 cemented the alliance by offering the duke the hand of his niece Jeanne d'Albret, heiress to the kingdom of Navarre. However, Anne's marriage was short-lived and the anticipation that Henry VIII might offer effective support against his former wife's nephew, Charles V, was never likely to be realised. When war broke out again between Charles V and Francis I in 1542, French aid brought the duke of Cleves initial success but eventually proved ineffective and he had to sue for peace in 1543, the terms accepted including the duke's renunciation of his claim to Gelders. Somewhat surprisingly, cannon continued to be cast at the Dollartshammer by the duke's forgemaster there, Johann Meuthen, in 1545.[33]

That the founding of cast-iron cannon was carried on in other parts of the Eifel is substantiated by the fact that in 1538 the ironworks of the count of Arenberg in the east of the Eifel borrowed cannon moulds (*buissen formen*) from the forgemaster of the ironworks at Kronenburg in the central Eifel. At that time Lenerz was the cannon founder, but by 1550 a cannon founder named Hans Poppelruytter had been engaged.[34] Perhaps he was a son of the more celebrated Hans Poppenruyter of Mechlin.

The counts of Arenberg came from another branch of the de la Marck family, but, unlike the Cleves branch, remained staunchly Catholic and were engaged on the side of Charles V in the Jülich war. A junior branch of the Arenberg family had many properties in the southern Netherlands, where they were counts of Rochefort, and in his youth Eberhard of Rochefort, who was count from 1498 to 1524, had run the Ferot ironworks in the Durbuy basin of northern Luxembourg from 1474 onwards in company with Jehan Le Marchant and Lambert Lardinois.[35] This Rochefort branch of the family had inherited Arenberg in 1485, but in 1544 Robert III de la Marck died without heirs and through his sister Margareta, who survived until 1599, Arenberg went to her husband Jean de Ligne, count of Barbançon in Hainault. Jean de Ligne fell in battle in 1568, fighting for Philip II, but the county, from 1644 onwards a duchy, remained in the Ligne-Arenberg family.

The ironworks were two, the upper one, the Ahrhütte, and the lower one at Antweiler, which was replaced in 1642 by the neighbouring Stahlhütte. The strong connections with Wallonia of the Ligne-Arenberg family resulted in the Ahrhütte having many, and the Stahlhütte, a preponderance of Walloons among the workforce during the seventeenth and eighteenth centuries.[36] The accounts for the period after the Thirty Years' War were kept in French; they survive at Enghien in Belgium and record

29. *Takken* were not plain firebacks, but plates inserted in a cavity in the wall behind the fire so as to warm the adjoining room.
30. Neu, *Eifel*, pp. 75-6.
31. Ibid., p. 205.
32. Ibid., pp. 76-7.
33. Ibid., p. 201.
34. Ibid., p. 240.
35. Ibid., p. 231.
36. Ibid., pp. 77-8.

the names of more than a score of Walloons who were employed in the Arenberg works.

There seems to be no evidence to show whether the cannon cast at these ironworks and at Kronenburg were of the new type and were cast vertically. It is also difficult to discern how, or even whether, the founding of cast-iron guns which had been so flourishing in Bar and Lorraine towards the end of the fifteenth century, was transmitted to the Eifel. It is just possible that an Isenschmitt at Wiebelskirchen near Ottweiler in Luxembourg, which was leased in 1514 by the count of Nassau-Saarbrücken to Lux von Nassau and Johann von Lichtenstein for the casting of pots (*Heffen*), stoves, guns or gunstones (*Öfen, Büchsen oder Büchsensteine*),[37] could have formed one of the links.

Wallonia

Cannon-founding in the duchy of Jülich coincided with the start of a remarkable flowering of the indirect process in the immediate vicinity of Liège, where further cannon-founding had been prohibited by Charles the Bold in 1467 and seems never to have been resumed even after the recognition by France and the Empire of the neutrality of the Prince-archbishop in 1492.

The first furnace was that of Lize, built at Seraing just upstream from Liège in 1539. It was followed in 1548 by the furnace des Vennes built by Wathieu Godéfrin, near the confluence of the Ourthe with the Meuse in the immediate vicinity of the town. The furnace of Villencourt was built further upstream from Seraing in 1550. During the 1560s Godéfrin built another furnace at Sauheid in 1562, which was followed by a further two in the same locality by 1564. A furnace at Colonster was built in 1563. In 1566 Gilles delle Rolette built the furnace des Polets and two furnaces were built at Grivignée, quite near Les Vennes. After this burst of activity it was not until 1599 that the de Geer family built a second furnace at Les Vennes.[38]

No accounts survive for any of these works, but from the fact that a corresponding number of forges was never built it must be presumed that much of the iron they produced was used as cast iron and never converted into bars. It has been suggested that the greater water power available on the lower Ourthe and from the Meuse facilitated smelting at higher temperatures, yielding a cast iron of higher silicon content with a fluidity which was needed in the casting trade. Whether this would originally have occurred by accident or design is an interesting question.

Sow iron from these works could have been sent to the forges in Franchimont for conversion into bar iron, but in fact many of these forges had been converted into plating hammers, of which the first was built in 1498 above Theux by Pirot, son of Jean Boniver. By 1566 ten plating hammers had been created on the Hoègne, after which a further 17 appeared on the Hoègne river and on the neighbouring Vesdre by around 1630.

The first rolling and slitting mills appeared in Wallonia on the Vesdre in the 1580s, followed by others from 1625 onwards on the Ourthe, reaching a total of eight by 1650. A nail trade had existed in Liège in mediaeval times, but the rod iron available from the slitting mills now enabled it to flourish as never before and to take advantage of the market offered by the growing Dutch ship-building industry based on Amsterdam, a market to which nails could easily be shipped down the Meuse.[39]

The predominance of merchant capital in the Liège area means that the names of the proprietors of the furnaces are known because it was they who appeared in notarial contracts or leases. The absence of ironworks' accounts means that the names of the founders, fillers and colliers on the other hand are comparatively unknown. Most will no doubt have been drawn from the former ironworks in Franchimont.

Matters were somewhat different in another area of Wallonia where ironworks first appeared around the same time as at Liège. We saw that on the Luxembourg-Lorraine border ironworking had

37. L. Beck, *Geschichte des Eisens in technischer und kulturgeschichtlicher Beziehung*, **2**, Braunschweig, Vieweg, 1893-5, p. 202. The manuscript notes of the pastor of Ottweiler, from which Beck derived this information are no longer extant, so it is impossible to check the validity of the equivocal 'guns or gunstones'.

38. G. Hansotte, 'L'industrie sidérurgique dans la vallée de l'Ourthe liégeoise aux temps modernes', *La vie wallonne*, **29** (1955), pp. 117-20; G. Hansotte, 'Les fourneaux à fer dans la vallée de la Meuse liégeoise aux XVIe et XVIIe siècles', *Bulletin de la Société Royale Le Vieux-Liège*, **9** (1978), pp. 228-31.

39. G. Hansotte, 'La métallurgie wallonne au XVIe et dans la première moitié du XVIIe siècle; un état de la quéstion' in H. Kellenbenz, ed. *Schwerpunkte der Eisengewinnung und Eisenverarbeitung in Europa, 1500-1650*, Köln, Böhlau, 1974, pp. 126-46.

been carried on from early in the fifteenth century, and that by its end ironworks extended from the vicinity of Virton, along the Ton, and across through Vaux and Saulnes, just north-west and north-east of Longwy respectively, to Moyeuvre not far from Thionville on the Meuse. North of the Ton was a vast area of forest, only marginally touched so far by ironworks, which was awaiting exploitation, the future Habay basin.

The Brussels Chambre des Comptes sent Odot Viron to the Habay area in 1546 to ascertain the possibilities of raising revenue from the sale of wood. At the time the forge of Bologne, perhaps dating from around 1540, was the only one on the Rulles; by 1618 it had a furnace and two fineries. Viron met its owner and suggested the establishment of further ironworks.[40]

Following Viron's very positive report, permission was granted in April 1547 to the forgeman Gabriel de Busleiden to erect a forge, the future Forge du Prince, at a site just outside the forest of Anlier. Another forge in this region, which existed by 1562, was the Lower Forge (la Forge d'en bas) or Forge of Pont d'Oye, whose forgemasters, the Regnier family, were mentioned in the parish register of Anlier in the 1560s.[41]

By early in the seventeenth century the Habay basin had become one of the principal suppliers of cold-short bar iron to the slitting-mills of the Liège area and a mainstay of its nail trade.

Ironworks in the Weald

By 1550, sixty per cent of the sites operated on the indirect system within the ironworking area of East Sussex were probably already in operation. The Portsmen's complaints of 1548 elicited the information that within the county of Sussex the iron mills and furnaces numbered 53. Seven mills and two hammers were mentioned with their locations, in addition to the four iron mills of Warbleton. Also in 1548 the building of Alexander Collyn's new hammer mill at Hoadly in Lamberhurst drew from Thomas Darrell the information that three hammers and four furnaces already existed within the parishes of Lamberhurst and Wadhurst.[42] Many of these works seem already to have been in production by 1540.

In Hartfield hundred Newbridge and Parrock Furnaces with their forges were apparently in existence from the earliest period, the forge now linked with Newbridge perhaps being Crowborough (*Grubsbars*) Forge. By 1509 the Steel Forge at Pippingford was also in operation, whilst Stumbletts Furnace, on the edge of the royal demesne was newly erected in 1534. New works built in the area during the 1540s included the furnace in Cowden at which William Levett cast guns of up to culverin in size during 1548, and on the Cansiron Stream, the Cansiron works itself and Bassetts Furnace. Either of these could have been the Alfrey of Hartfield family's works prior to Thomas Alfrey of Battle's entry into the trade, firstly as a trustee and creditor of Bartholomew Jeffrey at Buckholt ironworks in 1575, and secondly by his purchase of Potmans Forge in 1588.

In Rotherfield, Frant, Wadhurst and Lamberhurst parishes, Birchden Forge, two forges on the Teise, which were perhaps Breechers and Benhall, Bayham Forge, Verredge Forge and Brookland Forge and Furnace each perhaps go back to before 1525, whilst John Barham was also linked with Coushopley Furnace by at least 1547. Since there was no furnace in Lamberhurst parish until 1695, two more of Thomas Darrell's four furnaces in that parish and in Wadhurst by 1548 are difficult to identify without having recourse to all the known Wadhurst sites. They seem to be Riverhall, whose forge may have been acquired by John Huggett between 1543, when his father Thomas is thought to have died, and 1550, but soon afterwards in the hands of Nicholas Fowle, and secondly Scrag Oak (otherwise Snape), not mentioned until the seventeenth century, but then supplying pig iron to Hoadly, Verredge, Brookland and Chingley forges, which sounds exactly right for the earlier period.

The subsidy roll for the hundred of Brenchley shows the denizen John Ingerfyld to have paid 2 shillings to the aid of 1550 in Brenchley borough, and it is certain that the mutilated entry recording the payment of a shilling to the subsidy of 1543 by John Ang[. . .] relates to the same man. In 1550 Angerfield was accompanied by Nicholas Colleyn, an alien who paid the poll tax. Since denizenship

40. M. Bourguignon, 'Les usines du basin de la Rulles', **1**, *Annales de l'Insitiut archéologique du Luxembourg*, **57** (1926), pp. 8-9.

41. Ibid., pp. 7, 11, 14.

42. Straker, *Wealden iron*, pp. 114, 119, 269.

is specified in Angerfield's case it looks as though Nicholas Colleyn was a non-denizen, which makes difficult the attempt to identify him with Nicholas Lawhen, made denizen for the duke of Norfolk at Sheffield in 1544, and ancestor of the Tonbridge family Lawhen alias Collyn. Meanwhile Nicholas Collen went on to work for Christopher Darrell at Newdigate in 1563 and was perhaps the Nicholas Collen buried at Tonbridge in 1580. However, the baptism of children of John Laghame at Brenchley from 1561 onwards argues in favour of the Lawhen identification, in which case Nicholas Lawhen could have been the Nicholas Colynge buried at Tonbridge in 1557.

The members of the Angerfield family whose occupations are known were all hammermen, and the John Laugham alias Collyn of Tonbridge buried in 1588 was also a hammerman. Does the Brenchley entry of 1543 mean that the furnace at Horsmonden, other than which no ironworking site from this period is known, was preceded on the same site by a forge?

The hundred of Little or West Barnfield has to be considered in conjunction with Shoyswell hundred because of the occurrence in both of workmen employed by Thomas May. The ironworks thought to exist in 1525 was Pashley Furnace, probably worked by Thomas May even before he acquired the manor of Pashley in 1543. However, the 1543 return for West Barnfield hundred included five servants of Thomas May, who were not there in 1541. It is difficult to suggest where these men could have been employed if not at Chingley Forge or Furnace. They included the English-born Bartholomew Jeffrey, who by 1549 had moved to Isenhurst, Adam Cossam, who was later at Heathfield in much the same area, and John Hoke, later of Balcombe.[43] By 1550 George Rosell was the only alien recorded at West, or Little Barnfield.

Still further into Kent, the name of Peter Hushe occurred as a poll tax payer, alongside Pawles Walter and Burkley Weston, in Cranbrook hundred in 1543 and 1544. Pawles Walter is reminiscent of 'Paul Waters the smith', who was buried at Heathfield in 1618. More importantly Peter Hushe was almost certainly the founder Peter Hese employed by Bartholomew Jeffery in Hawksborough hundred in 1549. If these identification are correct three men moved from this part of Kent to the central area of the Weald at around the same time. The works in Kent was perhaps Bedgebury Furnace, lying in Cranbrook parish, but in Barnfield hundred, where John Bousselowe paid the poll tax in 1550.

The forge at Etchingham, which ran in conjunction with Darvel Furnace in Netherfield hundred, clearly dated from at least the 1530s because in 1540, when both men died, they were held by Thomas Walsh of Etchingham under a lease granted to him by Sir Thomas Oxenbridge on 16 May 1539.[44] Bivelham was another forge just within Shoyswell hundred. At a later date it was Pelham property, and may have been so already in the 1540s, for the subsidy roll of 1550, and perhaps that for 1549, shows it was worked by Mr (Anthony) Pelham. Other forgemasters in the hundred around 1550 were Ambrose Comport (1549, 1551-2), bailiff of Anthony Browne's Battle estate, Thomas Shoyswell (1549, 1552) and John Wybarne (1551).

It looks as though Ambrose Comport could have taken over the Tyrwhitt and former Oxenbridge forge at Etchingham, following its relinquishment by Thomas Walsh's widow, Joan. Although there is no continuity between the ironworkers listed, it seems possible that Thomas Shoyswell could have shared a works with his cousin John Wybarne. However, the works cannot have been Darvel Furnace, which was in Netherfield hundred. This appears to make either East Lymden Furnace or Darfold Furnace, the histories of which remain totally unknown, the only possibilities.

Henhurst hundred contained both Socknersh Furnace and Bugsell Forge. Bugsell was Walsh property, and was perhaps built in the late 1540s, after Joan Walsh had lost control of Etchingham Forge and Darvel Furnace.

In Robertsbridge hundred the furnace and forge built by the Collyn brothers for Sir William Sidney in 1541 are well enough known from the surviving accounts.

Netherfield hundred, in which the muster roll of 1539 revealed the presence of 49 Frenchman, then clearly included one of the highest concentrations of immigrant ironworkers in the Weald. Included in the subsidy roll of 1539 were the workmen of Thomas Walsh at Darvel Furnace and those of Richard Weekes at Hodesdale Forge (complained of as 'Mountfield hammer' in 1548) and Beech Furnace. It must

43. In 1558 John Hooke of Balcombe bequeathed to his sister Alice a ton of iron at Worth, whilst debts owing to him included £7 14s 2d from Austin Mychell of Chittingly, and John Gaynsford of Lingfield, gentlemen, £1 3s 4d from John Ilman of Balcombe, and 4 shillings from Bartholomew Longly (ESRO, PBT 1/1/4/87).

44. TNA, C 78/1/57.

be supposed that all these works became operational during the 1530s. By 1549 Netherfield hundred included Penhurst Furnace at which four workers of Ninian Burrell paid the poll tax. It had been set up for Nicholas Pelham, and was run by Thomas Glazier until 1549 to supply sow iron to Brightling Forge, but reverted to Burrell after Glazier's death. It looks as though Anthony Pelham ran it in 1550 because his only two workmen of that year had both worked for Burrell in 1549. However, doubts arise about this furnace being Pelham's because, although his name did not appear as an employer of aliens there in 1551, in 1552 he employed Roger Tankerye in Netherfield hundred, and may have employed him throughout the whole period 1549 to 1552, because Tankerye, who paid a shilling on goods as Pelham's employee in 1552, paid a similar sum from 1549 to 1551 when his name appeared, not as an employee of a forgemaster, but among the Netherfield denizens.

However, from 1551 onwards Charles Gerard, in partnership with Sir William Sidney's former customer, the London ironmonger Christopher Draper, and his former ironworks manager Henry Westall, supplied sow iron to Robertsbridge Forge from a furnace on which carriage was charged at the same rate as carriage from Panningridge; the subsidy rolls show beyond doubt that their furnace was in Netherfield hundred and a site in the west of the hundred near Panningridge such as Penhurst is the only location sufficiently remote. Did Anthony Pelham therefore run some other ironworks in Netherfield hundred during the period 1549 to 1552 and perhaps even beyond those dates?

In Bivelham borough of Hawksborough hundred were found the Isted works, initially Moat Mill Forge, but shown by the 1549 subsidy roll to have included a furnace, presumably Bungehurst; both works perhaps went back to the 1520s. Not far away was Anthony Pelham's Hawksden Forge and Furnace, to which the finer John Vinton had moved from Burwash by 1534. The Collyn forge at Burwash went back to the 1520s. During the late 1540s Thomas Glazier was running Nicholas Pelham's Brightling Forge.

The works of Warbleton borough in Hawksborough hundred cannot readily be separated from those of Isenhurst borough in Dill hundred, because the Cuckmere Stream, on which four ironworks were situated, divided both the boroughs and hundreds, as well as the rapes of Hastings and Pevensey. A works run by William Woddy and John Saxby of Warbleton featured under Isenhurst in 1543 and under Warbleton in 1549. They had supplied 42 tons of sow iron to Robertsbridge Forge in 1541, and the furnace was perhaps Cowbeech.

The forge in Warbleton run by Richard Woodman from 1549 to 1552 can perhaps be identified as the site named Woodman's Furnace, but proved by archaeological investigation to have been a forge. This forge could perhaps have run in conjunction with Markly Furnace at Rushlake Green. Another forge in Warbleton from the same period belonged to Anthony Pelham and by process of elimination must have been the so called Steel Forge. In 1551 Goddard Walsh appeared in the subsidy roll for Isenhurst as the employer of four Frenchmen, perhaps having replaced Woddy and Saxby at Cowbeech, unless Waldron Furnace, which according to a 1579 survey of the hundred lay on its bounds, was already in blast.

One of the Isenhurst works, Old Mill Furnace, lay in Mayfield parish. It may have been set up by William Nisell following the acquisition of Isenhurst by Thomas Cromwell in 1537, but historically it is known as belonging to John Baker of Withyham, whose workers were noted in Isenhurst by 1543 and in Bivelham borough in 1549.

It still remains to assign Bartholomew Jeffery's Hawksborough hundred workers of 1549 and 1552 to a works. Since the borough appears to be Tottingworth rather than Warbleton and the 1549 entry included a founder, this works would appear to have been Heathfield Furnace. The fact that Heathfield was the furnace with which Jeffery's later partner William Relfe was associated in 1574 appears to confirm this identification.[45]

The presence of Giles Duffen in Bexhill hundred in 1539, and of John Rowland there in 1549 and 1550 suggests that Catsfield Furnace, a 1567 mention of which has been recently discovered,[46] might have been worked at a very early period, probably by John Lunsford.

In Foxearle hundred Panningridge Furnace is known to have been built for Sir William Sidney in 1542, whilst the presence of Mr Ashburnham's workers in the hundred by 1549 suggests that the

45. C. S. Cattell, 'The 1574 lists of Wealden ironworks', *Sussex Arch. Colls.*, **117** (1979), p. 167.

46. The furnace was recorded in a Bexhill manor field name of 1567, but has not been identified in the 1574 lists (Cleere and Crossley, *The iron industry of the Weald*, p. 322).

building of Ashburnham Furnace and Forge followed Panningridge later in the decade. Anthony Pelham's works in the hundred, in which he held Bucksteep manor from 1541, will have been Warbleton Priory Furnace, though whether it had its own forge at this time, or worked in conjunction with his Steel Forge in Warbleton itself cannot be determined. The only works left to accommodate Richard Woodman's three Frenchmen of 1549 is Kitchenham Forge, and his acquisition in 1544 of the Comphurst estate, on the border of Herstmonceux parish with Wartling, makes this suggestion plausible.

In Shiplake hundred lay Stream, the 'iron hammer of Chiddingly', complained of in 1548, at which John French employed John Scherin in 1551, the man who had appeared as 'John Sherwood' in 1550. The employment in Hoadly and Waldron borough of the alien 'Marten' by Nicholas Pelham in 1543 seems insufficient evidence to affirm that Waldron Furnace was in blast then. However, if Waldron is ruled out at this period the ironworks in the same borough at which John Rowland and three servants of Nicholas Eversfield worked in 1543 still awaits identification. Was Waldron Furnace preceded by a forge run by Eversfield?

Nicholas Eversfield was noted as the employer of Quintin Tyler in Framfield in 1551 and this identification looks at first sight almost as puzzling as the site of the 1543 works in Hoathly and Waldron. But in the aid of 1551 the entry for Tyler immediately followed that for John Harve, quite clearly the John Harvo of Framfield who had supplied eight falcons, a falconet and a large quantity of shot to the Ordnance in 1547. Harvo was certainly the predecessor of Robert Hodgson at Pounsley Furnace, which, although it cannot be identified in the subsidy roll for 1543, was probably the Framfield works complained of in 1548. No Framfield subsidy roll survives for 1549, but three aliens contributed to the aid there in 1550. It therefore seems probable that Eversfield was already the proprietor of Pounsley Furnace, with Harvo as his tenant.

In Buxted, the rating to the water-scot in 1537 of land in their respective hammer ponds shows that Howbourne, like Queenstock, was a pre-1540 site, but suggests that both were out of use in 1537.[47] Payments made by William Levett's French employees to the subsidies of 1543 under the rubric of Greenhurst and of 1550 under Buxted indicate that Queenstock was back in blast during the 1540s and that this was the site where Peter Baude, who died in 1546, cast the demi-culverin inventoried at Portsmouth in 1547. Queenstock was therefore the site of either a much enlarged hearth or even of a double furnace, before the one at Worth was built. Its sow iron could have been fined at Queenstock or at Howbourne.

Sheffield and Freshfield were the sites of other iron mills complained of in 1548. The subsidy rolls for Danehill Sheffield and Danehill Horsted show that in 1543 the duke of Norfolk employed 15 Frenchmen at Sheffield Furnace and Forge and Sir William Barrentyne 14 Frenchmen at Horsted Keynes Furnace and Freshfield Forge. The works at Sheffield perhaps date from the mid-1530s and those at Horsted Keynes and Freshfield from a year or two earlier.

The works noted in the Lindfield Arches subsidy rolls for 1543, 1550, 1551 and 1552 has still to be identified. This Lindfield works was one of the few at which an alien, Henry Lucas, achieved entrepreneurship in this period, and the fact that Nicholas Founder, mentioned in 1550 and 1551, was listed as 'The founder' in 1552, proves that it included a blast furnace. This furnace was perhaps on the site of the forge at Freshfield owned by Anthony Morley in 1574, quite distinct from the one owned by Barrentyne.[48] Straker noted that canalization of the Ouse, which at Freshfield formed the boundary between Lindfield and Horsted Keynes, had much disturbed the site and made archaeological investigation difficult,[49] so this works could remain unidentifiable.

Another furnace in being in the 1540s was that of Chittingly Manor in West Hoathly parish, from which Thomas Michell supplied 65 tons of iron to Sheffield Forge in 1546. This and the building of the Crookford double furnace and the forge at Worth by William Levett in 1547 mark the first known stages of the movement of the industry into West Sussex. This movement into west Sussex, Surrey and Kent, and to parts of England and Wales hitherto hardly touched by the indirect process was to characterize the years following 1550.

47. P. Combes and C. Whittick, 'Iron Plat, Queenstock hammer-pond and a 15th-century ironworking site at Buxted', *Wealden Iron*, Bulletin of the Wealden Iron Research Group, 2nd series, **22** (2002), p. 11.

48. Cattell, 'The 1574 lists', pp. 168-9.

49. Straker, *Wealden iron*, p. 411.

Forgemasters and their ironworkers in the Weald

The forgemasters of the period included the Bowyers, Wybarns, Barhams and Mays, who continued to play an important role throughout, whilst the Sackvilles, who have also already been mentioned, returned to the scene right at the period's end at Worth in the person of Sir Richard Sackville.

New forgemasters ranged from the most important magnates of the Weald, such as the duke of Norfolk and Sir Thomas Boleyn, future earl of Wiltshire and father-in-law of the monarch, through important county families such as the Pelhams, Lewknors, Oxenbridges and Ashburnhams, to a whole range of lesser gentry, Baker of Withyham, Isted of Mayfield, Walsh of Etchingham, Burrell of Penhurst, Michell of West Hoathly, Levett of Little Horsted, French of Chiddingly, Alfrey of Hartfield, Gavell of Westerham, Challenor of Lindfield, and Woddy and Saxbies of Warbleton.

Of these, many, such as Isted, Walsh, Woddy and Saxbies, perhaps belonged with a group of persons who really owed their positions of prominence to their participation in the trade; they included Richard Weekes, Nicholas Eversfield and Bartholomew Jeffery.

Forgemasters such as Sir William Sidney and Sir Anthony Browne achieved their positions as a reward for their services to the Crown, whilst Darrell and Nisell may have been favoured by their closeness to Thomas Cromwell.

From the immigrant community, John Colyn of Burwash was joined by Henry Lucas, and both Richard Woodman and John Harvo too may have been from the immigrant community. It seems possible that William Levett had seen service abroad, because one William Levet had been among the garrison at Tournai in 1518.[50]

Some became forgemasters by chance rather than design: Sir William Barrentyne from Oxfordshire and Sir Robert Tyrwhitt from Lincolnshire succeeded their fathers-in-law, respectively Sir Roger Lewknor at Horsted Keynes and Sir Thomas Oxenbridge at Etchingham; even William Levett perhaps became a forgemaster only due to the premature death of his elder brother.

The Newbridge works, which had apparently had no formal lessee since Humphrey Walker's death, was granted to Sir Thomas Boleyn of Hever in February 1525, on a 21-year lease commencing at the following Michaelmas, at the amazingly favourable rent of £4 per annum. The lowness of the rent was obviously not due to the fact that the works was in disrepair, because an interim 'farmer' named Ewen was required to make good its deficiencies.[51] More probably it was an attempt to renew activity at Newbridge because of a less than satisfactory relationship between the Ordnance and John Machyn, who had inherited his father Roger Machyn's leases of Buxted, Birchden and the Steel Forge ironworks, but not perhaps his capacity to meet the requirements of Sir William Skeffington, the Master of the Ordnance.

Boleyn's skill with the French tongue, his visits to Paris, in 1514 on the occasion of the marriage of Henry VIII's sister to Louis XII, and again during the period when his daughter Anne Boleyn acted as lady-in-waiting to the French queen and later to the duchess of Alençon, his probable knowledge of the Pays de Bray and its ironworks, and his link with Nicolas Bourbon, the author of *Ferraria*, the poem about ironworking, have already been mentioned. Henry had first used Boleyn in connection with firearms in September 1512 when he was sent to the Netherlands to speed up the despatch of bronze guns cast for the king in Mechlin and Germany. In January 1523 Boleyn had been to the Biscay province of northern Spain with Sir Sampson Norton, former Master of the Ordnance, to procure Spanish guns.[52]

Henry VIII's lack of a male heir, and the danger this posed to the Tudor succession, had determined him to divorce Katharine of Aragon. He had already seduced Sir Thomas Boleyn's elder daughter; in his fevered eyes, the accomplishments which Anne had acquired whilst at the French court made her desirable as his future queen. He showered favours on the father, perhaps both to secure his compliance and because he could not marry a commoner. In 1525 Boleyn was made viscount Rochford; he became earl of Wiltshire in 1529.

There is no evidence that Sir Thomas took any action himself as forgemaster at Newbridge, and his employment of Nicolas Bourbon is his only other known point of contact with the manufacture of

50. *Letters and Papers Henry VIII,* **2** (2), no. 3945 (1518).

51. TNA, DL 42/73, f. 2; I am much indebted to Christopher Whittick for making available to me a summary of both lease and inventory.

52. *Letters and Papers Henry VIII,* **1** (2), nos. 1394, 1492; **3** (1), nos. 1764, 2879.

iron. In 1534 Newbridge was in the occupation of Simon Forneres or Forniers, who had been granted the reversion of the office of royal gunstonemaker after Richard Scorer in 1529.[53] Forneres presumably cast gunstones at Newbridge. The next forgemaster at Newbridge we know of was 'oone Nysell' who held the furnace under another assignment from Boleyn, apparently made for the remainder of his lease, because according to the Survey of the Forest of Ashdown taken in 1539, it had 'yeris yet to come vij or ther aboutes'.[54] The same survey reported that the Steel Forge was by then derelict. This document was doubtless the 'Survey of the Forest and the iron mills' sent by Henry Polsted to Cromwell on 10 August 1539,[55] immediately before another of the Henry VIII's summer peregrinations through the southern counties. It also closely followed Wiltshire's death.

William Nisell was perhaps the Sevenoaks man who in 1520 had been involved in a financial dispute between the bishop of Chichester and Sir John Underhill, Nisell's brother-in-law.[56] In 1524, his name headed the Mayfield borough subsidy, to pay tax on £5 11s 0d for receipts of office, the nature of which is unknown. His name was followed by those of three English servants, none known to be connected with the manufacture of iron. In 1543 Nisell was taxed 8 pence on land at Mayfield. His will was dated March 1545, shortly before his tenure of Newbridge should have ended, and he was dead by May in the following year when it was proved.[57] The will made no reference to Newbridge Furnace or to any other works. He made Richard Holbeame his executor and Thomas Darrell the elder his overseer. After making bequests totalling more than £200 he left the remainder of his goods to be distributed to the poor for his soul's health, at the discretion of Anthony Pelham and Richard Holbeame.

Perhaps this final provision of Nisell's will was necessary because there was some truth in the claim by another forgemaster Richard Isted, against whom he had pursued a Star Chamber dispute, that he was 'a person of no good fame and name'. Isted, who lived in Bivelham borough, and John Moone, another Mayfield resident, accused Nisell of wishing to murder Isted and to bring Moone to Mayfield 'there to be bounden to a post in the myddest of the same towne'. They also accused him of assembling adherents to destroy Plashett Park, which belonged to the archbishop of Canterbury, and 'other noblemen's parks in those parts', presumably to provide charcoal for his ironworking concerns and to the detriment of the interests of other forgemasters.[58]

We shall see that in 1540 Nisell had in his possession the lease of a water-mill belonging to the manor of Isenhurst. If this was Old Mill Furnace, later in the possession of John Baker of Withyham, it would go some way to explain his wish to exploit the woods so far south as Plashett Park.

Do Nisell's friendship with Thomas Darrell and Anthony Pelham, and his enmity towards Isted indicate a division of forgemasters in the Weald into what might be regarded as an 'official' or 'court' party, and a 'local' party? The local party is perhaps indicated by the forgemasters whom Isted's daughters married: John Porter of Lamberhurst, Nicholas Fowle of Wadhurst, John Baker of Withyham and John Barham of Frant, all of them appointed her executors by Isted's widow Joan in 1557. Darrell of Scotney, on the other hand, had at one time served Thomas Cromwell, and shortly after Wolsey's fall received a grant of lands in Lamberhurst from Cardinal's College, Oxford, as part of the spoils.[59] Darrell was also appointed overseer of their wills by two other forgemasters, Thomas Walsh of Etchingham and William Levett of Buxted.[60] Probably Nisell was another of those protegees of Cromwell, to whose activities their master's sudden fall from power in 1540 put a term. But Nisell's replacement at Old Mill by Baker would certainly have been greeted with more warmth by Joan Isted than by Anthony Pelham.

The 1539 Survey of Ashdown raised another problem. It stated that sow iron from Newbridge Furnace was carried to the forge at a cost of 10 pence per ton. This would have been sufficient for a carriage of perhaps six kilometres and could help to answer the question of where the forge for the Newbridge works was situated. Straker had suggested Cotchford or Steel forge as possible sites of the 'great water hammer' used in the area in 1496. However, it seems unlikely that carriage to either of

53. *Letters and Papers Henry VIII,* **4** (3), no. 5815.
54. Cleere and Crossley, *The iron industry of the Weald*, p. 121; TNA, E 32/197.
55. *Letters and Papers Henry VIII,* **14** (2), no. 29.
56. *Letters and Papers Henry VIII,* **3** (1), no. 822.
57. TNA, PROB 11/31/148.
58. Mundy, *Star Chamber proceedings*, pp. 72-3.
59. TNA, PROB 11/41/260; *Letters and Papers, Henry VIII,* **4** (3), no. 6516(9).
60. TNA, PROB 11/28/36 (Walsh), 37/73 (Levett).

these sites could have cost so much as 10 pence the ton. Crowborough (*Grubsbars*) forge seems better qualified to meet this requirement of 1539.

The name of William Nisell failed to appear in the 1543 subsidy roll as an employer of Frenchmen, although he paid tax as a landowner at Mayfield. None of the four employers of aliens listed in the Hartfield hundred portion of the roll can readily be connected with Newbridge, unless it is parson Levett, who clearly acted for the king. However it seems possible that Levett's three employees were engaged at Stumbletts Furnace rather than at Newbridge; Stumbletts may perhaps have been returned in Hartfield hundred because according to the 1539 Survey it was part of 'the kynges Common called the Stomlett'.

However, the Westminster denization roll shows that by 1544 five French workers were employed at Newbridge. Of these, two, Thomas Layne and Peter Fremyng, had probably been among Mrs Bowyer's workers (Thomas Collyar and Peter Flemyng) at Parrock Forge the previous year. Of the other three, Nicholas Tyler, James Lenarde and Charles Mottynge, Nicholas was perhaps the unsurnamed Nicholas, coming between Robert and Anthony Tyler as a poll-tax payer at Danehill Horsted in 1543, and Charles Motye paid a shilling on goods to the 1539 subsidy in Hawksborough hundred, but Lenarde seems not to have been recorded at all. This suggests that Newbridge Furnace had been newly brought into blast again in 1544, and the tenant at this time was perhaps Sir Anthony Browne, Master of the Horse, to whom the next formal lease of Newbridge, commencing at Michaelmas 1546, was granted in February of that year.[61]

Ambrose Comport, Browne's bailiff for the Battle estates granted to him by Henry VIII in 1538, had entered the iron trade in Shoyswell hundred before 1550. The 1546 lease of Newbridge is the first proof that Browne, who son Viscount Montague was later involved in various ironworks in the west of the Weald, had himself become a forgemaster.

At Parrock in 1547 William Warner sold the Weke, with an iron mill, to William Saunders. Saunders was perhaps related to Thomas Sawnders listed, alongside William Wyllamson, as the two Englishmen whose names appeared between those of several of Roger Machyn's immigrant ironworkers, in the 1524 Hartfield subsidy roll. In the 1540s Denise Bowyer, widow of the John Bowyer who had supplied gunstones to Henry VIII in 1514, held a 10-year lease of the works apparently granted to her husband before his death. Bowyer, a Hartfield yeoman, had actually made his will in 1536, but the date of his death is unknown, and probate was never taken by his widow, perhaps because she regarded the will's terms as difficult to fulfil. Bowyer's son William took probate in May 1550, after his mother's death.[62]

John Bowyer had made his wife and eldest son William his executors and John Sackville, esquire, his overseer. He left £120 to each of his sons, John, Richard, Thomas, Henry, Simon and George, to be paid them at their majorities and his daughter Anne was to have 40 marks (£26 13s 4d). To his widow Denise he left 100 marks (£66 13s 4d) and his new house in Hartfield street.

In March 1549 Denise was in dispute with the new landlord William Saunders, who attempted to eject her. There seem to have been two separate incidents, in the first of which on 26 March Saunders and his men broke up the 'ponds and waters' so that she could not use the forge, which was perhaps the occasion when they 'did pluck up the bellows and broke the frame in which they stood and by force carried them away in the said cart, and will in nowise permit Denise to have them again'. On 31 March they 'went to the furnace myll, an arrow shot distant' and tried to stop the wheel. As to Saunders' statement that he and his cart were attacked near his home by Denise and 18 men and that she struck the oxen over their muzzles with her staff and would have turned them out of the way, shouting, 'Down with Greybeard, Down with Greybeard' and 'Shoot at Greybeard', she replied that 'she had but a small stick with her which a lame and impotent woman used to walk withall to stay her'.[63]

Denise certainly was dead within the next fourteen months and in the circumstances the Bowyer tenure of Parrock Forge was unlikely to have been renewed. In 1543 she had ten Frenchmen in her service, but her workmen mentioned in the Star Chamber case were in the first incident, Henry Tryndall, John Walter and Henry Heyward, and in the second, Christopher Tryndall, who was so wounded that he was in danger of his life. These names appear thoroughly English, but the names of

61. TNA, DL 14/1; I am grateful to Christopher Whittick for a copy of his summary of this lease.
62. TNA. PROB 11/33/222.
63. TNA, STAC 2/24/422; 25/107; 27/30; STAC3/8/38.

the aliens Simon Heyward and James Haward, who paid the poll tax in 1551 at Wadhurst and in 1557 at Cranleigh respectively, suggest that Henry Heyward could have been of immigrant descent.

The other employers in Hartfield hundred at this time were Adrian Reder and Leonard Callis, both mentioned in the subsidy roll of 1543 and John Baker, who had Frenchmen made denizens in 1544. Leonard Callis's employee Cardo Kervyle was probably Cardo Kydvilde who was made denizen for John Baker in 1544. It can be presumed that Baker employed both Callis and Kydvilde in 1543 at Birchden Forge, where the lease of both manor and forge was in Baker's hands in 1555.[64] As we have seen Baker also employed Frenchmen in Dill and Hawksborough hundreds during the 1540s, probably at Old Mill Furnace.

John Baker was mentioned in 1541 in the will of Stephen Colyn of Withyham,[65] himself the brother of and overseer to the will of the late forgemaster John Colyn of Burwash. After the fashion of a forgemaster too, Stephen Colyn left £10 for the repair of the highway between Wrythers Well and Ilfeld, provided it was repaired with flint stones. His executor was to bestow £1 on poor people each Lent for four years. He left one cow each to the wife of John Baker, and to Baker's sons John and Robert.

Adrian Reder, himself an alien, employed three other aliens in 1543. His finer, Bartholomew Pountye, appeared as Bartholomew Pountes (*Ponthieu*) in the hanaper roll. The hanaper roll also recorded Reder's name, like that of William Levett's founder Charles Gerard, among those paying for denization in 1541,[66] and all three alike failed to appear on the two surviving membranes of the denization roll.

Pountye, or Ponting, and his immediate descendants are known to have worked at Birchden Forge later on. John Godfery was also a name which appeared in the 1541 hanaper roll among those paying for denization, but whose names did not survive on the denization roll of that year. In the light of this, the failure of his and Francis Jayms' names to appear among Baker's denizands in 1544 can hardly be a convincing argument for not accepting Birchden as the place of their employment. And if Crowborough (*Grubsbars*) was the forge which at this time fined Newbridge sow iron, a possibility argued for on the basis of the Forest survey of 1539, the fact that Newbridge appears to have been put in blast again only in 1544 is the argument for Reder's men not having been employed there.

William Levett appears to have entered the iron trade on account of the premature death of his brother, John Levett of Little Horsted. Ministers' accounts of the duchy of Lancaster show John Levett to have been tenant of the new furnace at Stumbletts and of the Steel Forge in 1534. John had already made his will in 1533 in which he referred to his 'Irron mylles and furnasses',[67] so he had other works besides these. One was presumably Buxted, or Queenstock Furnace which William Levett was in possession of in the 1540s, perhaps together with Howbourne Forge.[68] But if John Levett ran Roger Machyn's former works at Steel Forge and Buxted, of which he perhaps gained possession not long after Machyn's death, then Birchden could also have been one of the forges referred to in John's will, with Baker replacing him there around 1535.

Both Levetts were apparently the sons of Robert Levett of Hollington. William Levett had been deputy to the Receiver of the King's Revenue in Sussex in the year 1533-4, so he would have had some knowledge of the Ashdown Forest ironworks before taking probate of his brother's will in May 1535. The executors, of whom William was one, were directed to take the profits of the ironworks for the fulfilment of legacies and the payment of debts only, after which they were to let them out, the rents and profits going to John Levett, who like all of John Levett's children was a minor, and who was not, according to the terms of the will, to 'occupye the said mylls himself'.

It was the Ashdown Forest survey of 1539 that first indicated that William Levett had entered the trade, when it noted that 'there is iron ore digged upon the said Ward by one William Levett, clerk, to the value of 6d'. In August of the same year William Levett was in receipt of £84 13s 4d 'for divers sundry ironwork of his wrought and made, and also delivered to Sir Christopher Morice, knight',

64. ESRO, PBT 1/1/3/186.

65. ESRO, PBT 1/1/1/37.

66. TNA, E 101/223/10.

67. E. B. Teesdale, *The Queen's gunstonemaker; an account of Ralph Hogge, Elizabethan ironmaster and gunfounder*, Seaford, 1984, p. 18; TNA, PROB 11/25/326.

68. However, both Queenstock and Howbourne ponds were reported dry in 1537 (Combes and Whittick, 'Iron Plat, Queenstock hammer-pond and a 15th century ironworking site at Buxted, p. 11).

Master of the Ordnance. In 1540 Levett's first supplies of 'gunstones of iron' to the Ordnance were noted and in 1541 he was appointed royal gunstonemaker.[69]

But it is as the first Wealden gunfounder that Levett will be remembered. Levett's new guns were muzzle-loaders, were cast in one block and, through the assistance of royal gunfounders such as the Frenchman Peter Baude and the Italian Arcangelo Arcano, on the pattern of the latest bronze ordnance.[70] In Holinshed's *Chronicles of England* the place of their first casting was given as Buxted and the date as 1543, a date validated by an inventory of the goods captured by the Spaniards at Oudewater in the Netherlands in 1575, which included an English 2-pounder of cast iron, presumably a falconet, bearing the monogram 'HR' and the date 1543.[71]

As part of his contribution to cannon founding Levett also doubled the size of the furnace hearth and used two such large furnaces in tandem. The first known double furnace was brought into blast by Levett at Worth in 1547. However, the Frenchman Peter Baude was founder of a cast-iron demi-culverin inventoried in December 1547 at Southsea Castle and since Baude was dead by July 1546, either an enlarged hearth, or alternatively a double furnace, must have been available before that date, presumably at Queenstock. Hitherto the largest castings appear to have been iron sows of around 500kg, but by quadrupling the amount of iron available to be run at one tapping Levett was able to cast full culverins and even demi-cannon. By Levett's death in 1554 something like 350 cast-iron guns of the new type had been supplied to the Ordnance.[72]

The subsidy rolls confirm that the Frenchmen listed as Levett's workmen in the Westminster denization roll worked at 'Greenherst'[73] in 1543 and Buxted in 1550. A unique feature is that in 1543 all six of Levett's workmen were affluent enough to be taxed on goods, Charles (Gerard) paying 3s 4d, (John) Perigo 8 pence, John Penyon 4 pence, Gylbert (Averell) 8 pence, John Morrell 4 pence and (John?) Angell 4 pence, in a year when the poll tax levied was only 2 pence. In the relief of 1550, when demand for cannon is known to have been much reduced due to the poverty of Edward VI's government, Charles Garrete was taxed£1 and John Penyon a shilling, but the five other men whose names followed paid only the poll tax.

Following the duke of Norfolk's attainder, Levett was given 'commission to oversee the iron mines in Sussex which appertained to the duke of Norfolk' on 27 December 1546.[74] There is no evidence for any furnace at Worth prior to the building of Crookford double furnace which was there in 1547. Although Levett had merely been given the oversight of the duke's mines, in the 1549 accounts of Worth he was styled 'one of the Mynisters of the Kinges Majestyes ordynaunce'. It was Sir John Sheryf, archdeacon of Lewes, who continued as forgemaster and who submitted the accounts for Sheffield and Worth ironworks, firstly on behalf of Thomas Seymour, the Lord Admiral and brother of Protector Somerset, to whom the forest and chase of Worth were granted in August 1547,[75] and then, after Seymour's attainder in 1549, for the Crown. In 1550 the Sheffield works were let for 21 years to Thomas Hogan and those at Worth for the same term to Clement Throckmorton.[76] However, by 1560 Sir Richard Sackville was working the furnace at Sheffield, and as early as 1552 guns produced at Worth were sold by him to the Ordnance around June 1553, which suggests he may have acquired both the duke of Norfolk's works quite soon into the Hogan and Throckmorton leases.

It seems possible that Levett continued to work Stumbletts Furnace, and that Charles and Gilbert, who were recorded as paying the poll tax under him in Hartfield hundred in 1543, were in reality his workers Charles Gerard and Gilbert Averell, who had also paid tax on goods in the same subsidy at Buxted. The identity of Levett's third alien employed in Hartfield hundred, who bore the very

69. Teesdale, *The Queen's gunstonemaker*, pp. 18-9.
70. The participation of Arcano in designing the Padstow gun was suggested in Awty, 'A cast-iron cannon of the 1540s', *Sussex Arch. Colls.*, **125** (1987), and confirmed by R. D. Smith, 'Early cast-iron guns with particular reference to guns on the Isle of Man', *Jnl. of the Ordnance Soc.*, **3** (1991), p. 43.
71. B. G. Awty, 'Parson Levett and English cannon founding', *Sussex Arch. Colls.*, **127** (1989), p. 138.
72. Ibid., pp. 138, 140, 142.
73. As mentioned when discussing the 1490 'Iernefounders of Buxtede', Greenhurst seems to have been synonymous with Buxted borough by the 1540s, but in 1525 had included wider areas such as 'Withyham Grenehurst' and 'East Grinstead Grenehurst'.
74. Awty, 'Parson Levett', p. 133; *Letters and Papers Henry VIII*, **21** (2), no. 648.
75. *Calendars of Patent rolls, Edward VI*, **1**, p. 25.
76. Straker, *Wealden iron*, pp. 414, 463-4.

Sussex surname of Scrace, cannot be determined. But Steel Forge, though it was reported by the Forest survey of 1539 to have had the capacity to make 40 or 50 tons of iron a year, was at the same time noted as 'down' (*prostrat*').

In 1549, right at the end of this period, when Levett was perhaps keen to diminish his involvement in ironworks due to the fall in demand by the Ordnance for guns, both Stumbletts Furnace and the Steel Forge were taken over by Thomas Gavell and Francis Challenor. Gavell, who was the man rather mysteriously mentioned in the Hartfield subsidy roll of 1543 as having an alien prisoner Gyllam, was a member of the English Gavell family from Westerham in Kent, and no connection of the Frenchman John Gavell who in 1544 was listed among the Sheffield Furnace denizands of the duke of Norfolk. Challenor had married Mary Levett, daughter of William Levett's deceased brother, so these two ironworks now appeared destined to revert to John Levett's descendants after all.

When William Levett made his will in March 1554 he made several bequests to the poor of Buxted, Uckfield and of Cowden. It has been suggested that guns carried for Levett from Cowden to Newhaven and to Pevensey were not from the parish of Cowden, but from the hamlet of Cowden in Mayfield parish, which would have been a convenient staging-point on the main road south for guns both from Buxted, and later from Huggetts Furnace.[77] That Cowden parish was the place involved is indicated by the cost of carriage; sow iron from Panningridge Furnace to Robertsbridge was carried at 20 pence a ton, the distance being just short of 10km. At that rate, carriage from Cowden in Mayfield to Newhaven or Pevensey would have been around 4 shillings a ton, not the actual cost of 6s 8d, only fractionally less than the 7 shillings a ton charged for land carriage of guns from the furnace in Sussex (Crookford in Worth?) all the way to Southwark in south London. Furthermore, testamentary bequests were invariably made, not to individual hamlets, but to the poor of parishes, where parish officers could administer them.

For these reasons it seems clear that William Levett had guns cast for him at Cowden. The Cowden guns sent to Newhaven were two culverins, four demi-culverins, one saker, three falcons, one falconet, total weight 11t 12cwt 1qr; and to Pevensey two demi-culverins, weight 2t 11cwt. Since elm wood to the weight of three tons was also provided to make gun-stocks for four demi-culverins, one saker and two falcons, and for pairs of wheels for five demi-culverins, one saker and two falcons,[78] it seems certain that these guns were sent for coastal defence in Sussex and not for onward shipment to the Tower of London.

The Cowden guns were paid for in January 1549, and so were presumably cast in 1548. No subsidy rolls which taxed aliens for Edenbridge borough, in which the two later Cowden furnaces lay, survive from between 1544 and 1560. No furnace appears to have existed in 1544, so it was perhaps built around 1546 or 1547. The next evidence of a furnace at Cowden came around 1558, when 'Laurence the fownder of Cowden' was referred to in the will of Katherine Tyler of Fletching, undated, but proved in April 1559.[79]

From Buxted it is a short step to Isenhurst in the hundred of Dill. The Isenhurst part of Dill hundred lay in Mayfield parish, but further south the hundred included those parts of Heathfield and Warbleton parishes which lay in the Rape of Pevensey, to the west of the Cuckmere Stream running south from Heathfield Park. Indeed, according to Budgen's map, the divide between Dill and Hawksborough hundreds followed that stream as far as Cowbeech, so that Heathfield Furnace, Woodmans Furnace (now identified as a forge), Steel Forge and Cowbeech Furnace all lay on this divide, and workers from them might well be returned in either hundred. The next borough in Dill hundred south of Isenhurst was Hellingly, but even the northern part of Hellingly parish was included in Isenhurst borough and all the aliens in Dill hundred from 1543 until 1560 were consistently recorded as belonging to Isenhurst borough.

Most noteworthy on both sides of the divide was John Baker, who in 1543 employed Gyles Myner, Peter Wete and Petter Botton in Isenhurst. In 1549 he employed a miner named David Demoyschell in Hawksborough hundred and Gawnt (probably John Sherowe alias Gownet) and John Bottinge in Isenhurst, whilst Peter White continued there, paying 2 shillings on goods to the relief. In

77. S. Barter Bailey, 'Information relating to the operation of the early cast-iron gun industry, from a manuscript account book in the collection of the Royal Armouries', *Jnl. of the Ordnance Soc.*, **3** (1991), p. 15.
78. Ibid., p. 19.
79. ESRO, PBT 1/1/3/259.

1550 Baker employed a collier named Arter in Hawksborough, whilst Peter White and John Bottinge continued in Isenhurst, though information as to their employer was withheld. In 1551 and 1552 Peter White now paid 4 shillings on goods annually in Isenhurst, and although none of Baker's workers was listed in Hawksborough hundred in 1551, he employed John Botton there in 1552.

Peter Whight and John Bottinge were two of the Frenchmen made denizens for Baker in 1544. When we remember that John Baker the younger married Joan Isted's daughter Elizabeth, it will come as no surprise that John Shermun, made denizen for Joan Isted in 1544, became Baker's worker Gawnt by 1549, a transfer of worker which also shows that the identification of this man with Sharowe alias Gownet is correct. Because the occupation of miner and ironfounder went hand in hand, it also seems likely that Baker's Gyles Myner of 1543 was Giles Lawrence, whom Joan Isted employed as ironfounder in Bivelham borough from 1549 to 1552.

The accent on mining among Baker's employees indicates that their place of work might be Old Mill Furnace which, if the boundaries indicated on Budgen's map are correct, lay on the boundary between Isenhurst borough and Dill hundred, on the one hand, and Bivelham borough and Hawksborough hundred on the other; it also belonged within Isenhurst manor and Mayfield parish. In his will dated 1555, John Baker the elder of Withyham referred to his manors of Bungehurst and Isenhurst.[80] The possibility that Bungehurst was the furnace at which John Walstedde's eight Frenchmen worked in 1524 was mentioned earlier. Maybe this was also the furnace at which Giles Laurence worked for Joan Isted around 1550.

Isenhurst had an interesting history. The manor was made over to Thomas Cromwell, together with a great many others which had belonged to the priory of Michelham, in October 1537. After Cromwell's attainder the manor was granted in January 1541 to Thomas Culpeper, who was himself soon after attainted for complicity in Queen Catherine Howard's misdemeanours. Isenhurst manor, and a water-mill in it, were bought by Richard and John Sackville along with many other properties for over £920 in July 1544. In April 1545 the Sackvilles were granted a licence to alienate Isenhurst manor and a water-mill in Mayfield to John Baker of Withyham.[81] The subtle change in status of the water-mill from being in the manor of Isenhurst to being in the parish of Mayfield, made between the documents of July 1544 and April 1545 in recognition of the difference between the manorial, parish, and administrative boundaries mentioned earlier, confirms that this mill was probably Old Mill Furnace.

The acquisition by Baker of Isenhurst manor, which lay partly in Mayfield and partly in Waldron and Heathfield parishes, took place in 1545, almost two years after the subsidy of 1543 had shown that he was employing immigrant ironworkers there. However, the Crown accounts for the estates of the late Thomas Cromwell for the year Michaelmas 1541 to 1542 show that the water-mill of Isenhurst was already in lease from Thomas Marshall to William Nisell for £1 a year.[82] Nisell we know to have been forgemaster at Newbridge by 1539; his conversion of the water-mill at Isenhurst into a blast furnace around 1541would make sense of Richard Isted's claim that he wished to destroy Plashett Park and other noblemen's parks 'in those parts', which were very distant from Newbridge. Moreover, Nisell's close proximity at Old Mill Furnace, just upstream from Richard Isted's long-established Moat Mill Forge, could account for the fierce rivalry between the two forgemasters.

The collier Robert Caron paid the poll tax, firstly in 1543 in Isenhurst borough as a workman of William Woddye, and secondly in 1549 in Warbleton borough as a workman of John Saxpes. The change of employer and location is illusory. Woddye and 'Saxbeche' were the partners who supplied 42 tons of sow iron to Robertsbridge Forge in 1541, before Sir William Sidney's furnace there was in blast; in the Sidney accounts 21 tons was attributed to each.[83] In 1555 Woddye was referred to as 'William Wooddye late of Warbleton, sometime of Buxted'.[84] Saxpes was also a Warbleton man, administration of whose effects was taken by his brother Robert Saxpes in 1563,[85] which, taken together with the fact

80. ESRO, PBT 1/1/3/186.

81. *Letters and Papers Henry VIII*, **12** (2), no. 1008 (3), **16**, no. 503 (14), **19** (1), no. 1035 (137), **20** (1), no. 282 (52, Licences to alienate lands (7th)).

82. BL, Harl. Rolls, D 21; I am grateful to Christopher Whittick for this reference.

83. KHLC, U1475 B5/1.

84. Will of John Baker the elder (ESRO, PBT 1/1/3/186). Robert Woddy of Buksted, labourer, referred to around 1512, was perhaps the progenitor of this family (Mundy, *Star Chamber proceedings*, p. 3).

85. ESRO, PBT 1/1/5/132.

that Saxpes' ironworks was located in Warbleton borough in 1549, makes it appear that their furnace should be looked for, not at Heathfield, but in Warbleton where, since the site connected with Richard Woodman is now thought to have been not a furnace but a forge, could perhaps have been Cowbeech.

The fact that Thomas Wodye of Warbleton was denominated a Frenchman in October 1538 by the Hawksborough hundred court,[86] suggests that in his case the French name Oudin had been assimilated to an apparently English name. However, the attempt to link this French Thomas Wodye with William Wooddye, 'sometime of Buxted' fails because the Thomas Wodye who was rated at £2 16s 8d for land in Greenhurst (Buxted) in 1524 appears to have remained in Greenhurst, where he paid 1s 4d on land in 1543, and there is no indication that the Buxted Wodyes were French. Nevertheless the rareness of this surname should give us pause, because apart from Henry Wodie at Lewes and William Wodye in East Grinstead Greenhurst, it remained unknown in Sussex outside Buxted in 1524.

One of William Woddye's heirs was probably John Woddye of Little Horsted, yeoman, who died in 1562 leaving a son Thomas, who was a minor. John's goods were inventoried at £201 13s 7d and he left lands in Newick and Fletching. Hints that he had been concerned in the iron industry were his bequest of 2 shillings to the repair of the highways in Horsted, debts owed to him by Peter Almunde and Robert Val[iant?], perhaps Frenchmen of those names, and the fact that his overseers were both forgemasters.[87] They were his brother Robert Woddye, to whom he left his livery coat, and his master, Anthony Morley of Isfield.

John Saxpes and his brother Robert were probably two of the sons mentioned in the will made by Robert Saxpes of Southover in 1543.[88] The links of this family with Withyham are clear from the father's bequest of 3s 4d to the church of Withyham and from subsequent testamentary material relating to the family.

It seems possible that the replacement of Woddy and Saxpes at Cowbeech Furnace is indicated by the appearance of four workers belonging to Goddard Walsh in Isenhurst in 1551. Goddard Walsh, when he made his will in 1557, left bequests to the poor of all parishes from Waldron and Heathfield southwards (Warbleton, Hellingly and Chiddingly) as well as to his own parish of Brightling, and to parishes further afield such as Penhurst, Ticehurst, Catsfield, Salehurst, Newenden and Arlington.[89] However, the immigrant Aubery Russell, who in 1550 and 1552 appeared as a Walsh family worker in Henhurst hundred, moved westwards not to Warbleton, but to Heathfield, during the 1550s, as is shown by the administration of his effects granted to his sons in 1561, which described him as being of Heathfield.[90]

Bartholomew Jeffery, who in 1543 had been amongst Thomas May's servants in West Barnfield hundred in Kent, paid 10 shillings to the aids of 1549 and 1550 in Isenhurst borough. He also appeared as an employer of immigrant labour in Hawksborough hundred, apparently in Tottingworth hundred, firstly in 1549 with the founder Peter Hese (*Hewashe*) and in 1552 with Everet and Michaell. Hewashe, like Jeffery, had perhaps formerly also been in Kent, where Peter Husshe appeared in Cranbrook subsidy rolls of 1543 and 1544. Around 1546 Jeffery delivered 12 tons of sow iron to Sheffield Forge. The Tottingworth location suggests that Heathfield Furnace might be its source. Although Straker thought that Jeffery's furnace was Chiddingly,[91] and that Heathfield, or Cowbeech (Cralle), were the possible furnaces from which William Relf supplied 15¾ tons of iron to Sheffield, it seems more likely that it was Heathfield that supplied both these amounts and that it was there that Relf and Jeffery first became partners.

Nicholas Eversfield was also a forgemaster of the 1540s. In 1510 John Eversfield had been a Buxted smith and it was at Buxted that Nicholas was assessed in 1524 at £5 in goods, paid 13s 4d on goods to the subsidy of 1543, and £1 and £1 10s 0d to the reliefs of 1550 and 1551 (there being no surviving return for 1549). He died in September 1551, describing himself in his will as 'of Poyle in the county of Surrey',[92] but it was in Buxted that his widow Joan paid 10 shillings to the relief of 1552.

86. BL, Add.Roll, 31820.
87. ESRO, PBT 1/1/5/78.
88. ESRO, PBT 1/1/1/35.
89. TNA, PROB 11/40/115.
90. ESRO, PBT 1/1/5/17.
91. Straker, *Wealden iron*, p. 414.
92. TNA, PROB 11/35/238.

John Eversfield, who was among the overseers of the will might be the man of that name who paid 14 shillings and 15 shillings to the reliefs of 1549 and 1550 in Mayfield, and 16 shillings and 18 shillings to those of 1551 and 1552 in Buxted;[93] and might also be Nicholas's eldest son. Other overseers of the will were William Alfrey the elder Thomas Alfrey and William Levett, with Levett also a witness, along with William Olyff.

Nicholas Eversfield left £2 to the poor, £2 to the highways and £2 towards the building of the church. To his eldest son John were to go the manors of Poyle in Surrey and of Tarring Peverell in Fletching, with lands in Buxted, Framfield, Maresfield and Kingston next Lewes. His lands both freehold and copyhold in Rotherfield were to go to his other son Thomas. His interests in ironworking were reflected in his gift of a cow to Lawrence Lambert 'so he contynue at the forge', in Levett's witnessing of the will and participation in its oversight, and in the proviso, that 'yf the Kinges majesteie or els any other lorde ought to have any parte or parcell of any said landes above bequeathed by reason of any statute or lawe made, Then my mynde is that the Kings majesteie or the lorde to have suche landes during suche tyme lymitted by the statute or lawe this will notwithstanding'.

As well as being the last of the overseers and the second witness, did Levett perhaps suggest the insertion of this unique clause? Government was often arbitrary, despite statute and law, and Levett had benefited from the support of the king's council, having been granted other preferments when the attempt was made to deprive him of the rectorship of Buxted, on what the council apparently considered specious grounds.

Little is known of Lawrence Lambert; he may have been the Horsted Keynes man of that name who died around 1590.[94] More is known about Eversfield's worker Quintin Tyler, who paid the poll tax as his servant in Framfield in 1551. Of Eversfield's other immigrant workers, George Morrys, John Trowley and John Cosenet, who served him in Hoathly and Waldron borough in 1543, we know virtually nothing.

Since George was not a fashionable name in the sixteenth century it is perhaps admissible to equate George Morrys with George Moryow, the first of the Frenchmen made denizen by Eversfield in 1544, and also with George Moreway, also made denizen in that year, who had been born in Beaussault in 1516 and who had come to England in 1529. By 1551 had he perhaps moved on to be 'Mowery the fyner' who paid the poll tax in the aid of 1551 at Hartfield? It may be conjectured that the original of this name was *Mauroy*.

Quintin Tyler had been born in Neuville-Ferrières in 1514 and had come to England in 1531, but in 1544 was listed last of Eversfield's six Frenchmen under the name Quintin Pyller. The fifth worker in Eversfield's list was Roger Tankerye, who appeared elsewhere in the roll as Roger Tancre, who had been born in Neuville around 1497, and had come to England around 1514. Tancre furnished yet another link with Framfield, because he married Alice Tarboyes there in October 1539.

Peter Vyllan equates with Peter Fellyn who, born at Beaubec around 1509, came to England at the age of ten, but cannot be traced in the Weald until an entry in the Maresfield parish register of 1558, only five years before he was buried at Newick.

Of the other two Eversfield denizens of 1544 even less is known: Peter Vynton, born at Neuville around 1500, perhaps the younger brother of Anthony Pelham's John Vinton, who followed John to England, has left no certain record in the Weald, and William Fremens could perhaps more properly be Freming, but is no more identifiable than Vynton.

The Framfield connections of Tyler and Tancre, together with the fact that Quintin Tyler was probably an ironfounder, suggest that one of Eversfield's works was Pounsley Furnace, complained of as the 'iron mill of Framfield' in 1548. Perhaps John Harvo of Framfield, who supplied eight falcons, a falconet and a large quantity of shot to the Ordnance in 1547 was Eversfield's tenant at Pounsley. When he was paid for the supply of five sakers, 13 falcons, one falconet and over 36 tons of shot in 1550, Harvo like Levett was styled 'the kinges gonnstone maker of Iron'.[95]

If George Morrys was in reality George Mowery, a finer, a forge site has to be found in Hoathly and Waldron, where Waldron Furnace itself is the only known site in the area from the indirect-process period. The 1551 connection with Hartfield would fit with the Hartfield slant given to Eversfield's will

93. TNA, E 179/190/191 (1543), 190/237 (1549 and 1551), 190/239 (1550), 190/247 (1552).
94. ESRO, PBT 1/3/2/88.
95. S. Barter Bailey, 'The early cast-iron gun industry', pp. 18, 20.

by the nomination of William Alfrey the elder and Thomas Alfrey as the first two overseers. When William Alfrey made his own will in 1556 he left Bassetts in Hartfield, the site of a blast furnace whose date is unknown, to his youngest son William,[96] which suggests the possibility that every overseer of Eversfield's will could have been a forgemaster. Thomas, the eldest son of William Alfrey the elder was the father of Thomas Alfrey of Battle, from whom the Alfreys of Potmans Forge were descended. The identification by Straker of Crookford Furnace and Forge held in 1574 by John Eversfield as Cotchford has now been disproved,[97] cutting away any evidence that the Eversfields ever held Cotchford, so despite the concentration of Lambert names in Hartfield both before and after this period, especially in views of frankpledge from 1576 to 1591,[98] it cannot be assumed that a forge in Hartfield was where Lawrence Lambert worked in 1551.

In Shiplake hundred the 'iron hammer of Chiddingly', very strongly complained of in 1548, was noted as being that of John French in 1551. It had apparently been built since 1543 and the lack of the 1549 subsidy roll is a sad loss. John Sherowe, who up to 1549 had worked for the Isted-Baker partnership, was undoubtedly the John Sherwood and Scherin who appeared in Shiplake in 1550 and 1551, whilst two other former Isted finers, Robert Blank and Peter Borayne (Barham), were there in 1552.

The entry into the trade of Richard Weekes perhaps came about through his affinity with the Collyn family of Burwash. In his will of 1536 John Collyn appointed Richard a'Wyke as his third overseer. The 'iron hammer of Mountfield', complained of in 1548, has bedevilled speculation about Weekes' forge. Its proximity to Battle is shown by the fact that the will made in March 1559 by James Templeir of Mountfield, one of Weekes' denizens in 1544, and among his workers in 1552, was proved in the peculiar court of Battle,[99] though the testator wished to be buried at Mountfield. The forge was undoubtedly Hodesdale and was certainly Weekes' in 1554. Hodesdale Hammer was situated in Mountfield parish on a tributary of the river Line, but close to the junction of three parishes, of which Mountfield and Whatlington lie to the north of the stream and Battle to its south. The employment of James and Hugh Turke (alias Tomplin) in Netherfield hundred already in 1539 suggests that Hodesdale Forge dated from the 1530s.

On the Mountfield site itself there was perhaps no ironworks until the late 1560s and in his will of May 1578 Weekes referred to it as 'my new yron worke or furnesse and pondes called Lyne streame in the parish of Mountfield'.[100]

However, back in 1544 Weekes' denizens, besides Lambert, Tamplier and Toulett who sound like forgemen, already included the ironfounder Warnett Geratt, together with John Vigott, whose family were also probably ironfounders. The furnace worked by Weekes was usually associated with Netherfield and the tentative suggestion of Straker, taken up by Schubert, that Beech Furnace was the one, must be correct.[101] Though apparently in Battle parish, the site was less than 2km from Netherfield and was within the bounds of Netherfield hundred. It was also well sited to provide pig iron for Hodesdale Forge. The origin of both these works needs to be looked for in the 1530s.

During the 1550s Weekes was also using Darvel Furnace, as is shown by the fact that three of the four cast-iron hursts supplied by him to Robertsbridge Forge in 1554 came from Darvel Furnace and only one, presumably taken from stock, from Hodesdale Forge.[102] Darvel Furnace had formerly worked in conjunction with Etchingham Forge, a property which may have come into Oxenbridge hands through the marriage of Anne, daughter of Sir Thomas Etchingham, to Sir Goddard Oxenbridge. The Etchingham properties descended to Thomas, Sir Goddard's son by his first wife, whilst the manor of Ford in Brede parish went to the descendants of his second wife Anne Fiennes.

96. ESRO, PBT 1/1/3/243.

97. B. G. Awty, 'Crookford Furnace, not Cotchford but Worth', *Wealden Iron*, Bulletin of the Wealden Iron Research Group, 2nd series, **23** (2003), pp.21-3.

98. ESRO, ACC 3597/8 (1576-81), 1 (1587-91)

99. ESRO, PBT 3/1/1/56B.

100. TNA, PROB 11/60/298.

101. Straker, *Wealden iron*, p. 327; Schubert, *British iron and steel industry*, pp. 367-8. Since Brian Awty wrote this the site of another furnace at Netherfield has been discovered; A. Callow, 'A blast furnace at Netherfield, Battle, East Sussex: a new water-powered site identified', *Wealden Iron*, Bulletin of the Wealden Iron Research Group, 2nd series, **23** (2003), 3-4.

102. Crossley, *Sidney ironworks accounts*, p. 114n.

In 1539 a lease of both ironworks had been taken from Thomas Oxenbridge by Thomas Walsh of Etchingham. Both Walsh and Oxenbridge died early in 1540 and the new landlord was Sir Robert Tyrwhitt of Ketsby in Lincolnshire, Oxenbridge's son-in-law. Walsh's widow and executrix Joan carried on the ironworks for a time, as is shown by the fact that her ironfounder was paid 4 pence for casting a plate to lie under the anvil of Robertsbridge Forge in 1542.[103] But Tyrwhitt obtained possession of the works from Joan Walsh by Chancery decree in return for a 13-year annuity of £24.[104] This clearly occurred in or before 1544 because in the Westminster denization roll of that year five Frenchmen were listed as being in Tyrwhitt's works. However, the subsidy rolls of around 1550 make no mention of Tyrwhitt, which suggests that he did not retain the ironworks in his own hands for long.

Darvel Furnace was in Weekes' hands by 1554 and he probably had it prior to 1550, but there is no evidence that he was also involved at Etchingham Forge. It seems possible that Ambrose Comport, bailiff of Sir Anthony Browne's Battle estate, became involved at Etchingham before 1549 because he was employer of three or four Frenchmen in Shoyswell hundred in 1549, 1551 and 1552. That Etchingham Forge was their place of work is suggested by the facts that the 1549 employees included Charles Pullyn, who in 1544 had worked for Tyrwhitt, and that the later employees included Anthony Ellys, who in his will of 1556 described himself as 'of Etchingham'.[105]

Joan Walsh was also soon involved in iron again. The Sidney accounts show that in 1546 she paid £6 6s 4d for a ton of iron had from Robertsbridge Forge.[106] The Henhurst hundred subsidy rolls also show her involvement in ironworks there from at least 1549 onwards. She was listed as employing a collier in 1549, she and her son Goddard Walsh employed four Frenchmen in 1550 and Goddard continued to employ Frenchmen in 1552. These men will have worked at Bugsell Forge.

However, the thirteen aliens listed in the 1539 subsidy roll for Henhurst are a very puzzling feature because it is not certain that even one of them was an ironworker. Nor do they show any continuity with possible workers at Socknersh, either earlier, in the 1520s, or in 1552.

Five Frenchmen 'In Master Pelhams Iron Worke' were made denizens in 1544. The reality was not so simple. For a start, although Anthony Pelham was clearly the leading forgemaster of the family, his nephew Sir Nicholas Pelham, who was its head, also played a role and in 1549, as a glance at the subsidy rolls for Foxearle, Hawksborough, Netherfield and Shoyswell hundreds makes clear, their interests were manifold. However, not only was Antony Pelham's Hawksden works sold to Thomas Morley in 1551, but the names of Nicholas Pelham and Anthony Pelham disappeared altogether as employers of alien ironworkers from two other sites in Hawksborough hundred and one in Shoyswell hundred in 1550 and 1551. Part of the reason was no doubt Anthony's involvement in the Surrey works at Ewood Park, or possibly even in unknown ironworks in the north of England.[107]

Anthony's finer John Vinton was resident in Bivelham borough by 1534. This suggests that the Pelham works in Hawksden, which in 1559 included a furnace, could date from around 1530. Since Pelham employed John Leonard as a second finer in 1549 and 1550, the forge probably incorporated a double finery, so it may have had its own blast furnace well before 1559.

Just outside Bivelham borough and in Shoyswell hundred lay Bivelham Forge, which remained in Pelham hands into the eighteenth century. In 1550 'Mr Pelham' was shown as the employer in Shoyswell of John Barden, a forgeman, and two members of the Hedoll family, thought to be colliers, whilst two members of the Hedoll family had already paid the poll tax there in 1549, though their master's name was not indicated. There is nothing to show which Pelham was forgemaster, but proximity to Hawksden and the fact that Barden had been employed elsewhere by Anthony Pelham in 1549 suggest that he may have been forgemaster at Bivelham too. Whether the forge was laid down temporarily in 1551, at a time when Hawksden was also about to be disposed of, must be a possibility. There is nothing in the subsidy

103. Cleere and Crossley, *The iron industry of the Weald*, p. 328; KHLC, U1475, B7/1.

104. A. Dalton, 'Burgh Wood Forge, Etchingham', *Wealden Iron*, Bulletin of the Wealden Iron Research Group, 2nd series, **17** (1997), p. 45.

105. ESRO, PBT 1/1/3/200.

106. ESRO, SHR 6/1/11/1.

107. Anthony Pelham's will specified lands in Westfield and Ore in Sussex bought from Mone of Mayfield, and also mentioned, without specifying, his other lands in Sussex, Kent, Surrey and Dorset, and also in Northumberland and Yorkshire (TNA, PROB 11/49/69 (1563, proved 1567)). His *inquisition post mortem* alluded only to the lands mentioned in the will.

rolls of 1551 and 1552 to suggest that some other forgemaster had taken the forge over nor, because no separate return for Shoyswell hundred survives in the subsidy rolls of 1539, does this source provide a means of tracing Bivelham back in time.

In 1549, though not from 1550 to 1552, Anthony Pelham was also shown in the Hawksborough hundred subsidy rolls as employing 'Barden hammerman' at a forge in Warbleton borough. Since Woodman was linked by tradition with the other forge on the Cuckmere Stream, Pelham's works was perhaps Steel Forge. The hammerman was presumably John Barden who was at Bivelham in 1550, and this identity is confirmed by his payment of 2 shillings on goods in each case.

Nicholas Pelham appeared in the 1549 Hawksborough hundred subsidy roll as employer of a hammerman, a finer and a collier, perhaps in Burwash borough. The forge in this case was probably Brightling, or 'Glazier's Forge'. Thomas Glazier of Brightling, who also ran Penhurst Furnace for Nicholas Pelham, had bequeathed 6s 8d to 'every one of my workemen of my forge' in his will in December 1548, but mentioned no names. Glazier left his copyhold in Burwash called Croches and a meadow called Mellordes, both held of Nicholas Pelham, gentleman, to his wife for life, and then to his son Goddard. It was on precisely these lands that he had been granted leave at Burwash manor court in April 1544 to cut down all the trees for a fine of £1, so perhaps the forge went back to around then.[108]

It was perhaps following Glazier's death that Pelham took the running of the forge into his own hands, whereas at Penhurst he released the furnace to be run by Ninian Burrell at a rent of 100 tons of sow iron a year. However, the overseers of Glazier's will had been not Pelham, but William Wybarne, gentleman, and John Wybarne his son. The executors were Thomas Glazier's son John, together with Thomas Glyd.[109] These are all names connected with the manufacture of iron and their mention suggests that the multiplicity of interests which characterized larger ironworking combinations were perhaps paralleled at this quite small forge. Nevertheless, Nicholas Pelham's name did not continue as an employer of aliens anywhere in the years 1550 to 1552.

Bearing in mind that from 1541 onwards Anthony Pelham's seat was Bucksteep manor, the ironworks in Foxearle hundred at which he had alien workers were perhaps Warbleton Priory Furnace and Forge, on the adjacent Hugeletts Stream, between the priory, which appears to have lain near the hundred boundary, and Bucksteep itself. John Lemett who worked for him in Netherfield hundred in 1549 did so perhaps at the Priory Furnace too. When still recorded in Netherfield hundred in 1550, Lamot worked for Sir William Sidney presumably at Panningridge, but in 1556 he was one of Sidney's colliers at Robertsbridge.[110] It must be supposed that Lemotte had returned to the Priory Furnace before he appeared in the Foxearle subsidy rolls for 1572 and 1576, because it was from that furnace that his body was brought to be buried at Dallington in January 1599.

Penhurst Furnace had been set up in the 1540s under a lease granted by Ninian Burrell to Nicholas Pelham, who had sublet to Thomas Glazier. About 1549, in fact probably immediately after Thomas Glazier's death, Pelham had granted the furnace back to Ninian Burrell and his son Thomas, who ran it in conjunction with Thomas Hawkins for about 8 or 10 years, selling 100 tons of sow iron a year at £1 13s 4d a ton to Pelham, which his possession of Glaziers Forge would have enabled him to fine. Four workers from Ninian Burrell's works featured in the 1549 subsidy roll for Netherfield hundred.

However, Burrell's name ceased to appear as forgemaster after 1549, which makes it difficult to know what to make of the claim that Burrell ran it in conjunction with Hawkins for as long as 8 or 10 years.[111] And two of his servants, Clement Gryans and John Bennett, appeared in Netherfield hundred in 1550 under Anthony Pelham's name. Had Pelham taken over at Penhurst temporarily, or had these men moved on to work at his Priory works? In 1563 Burrell was one of the witnesses of Anthony Pelham's will. In any case it must be suspected that Charles Gerard and his partners took over Penhurst Furnace in 1551.

It seems probable that the forgemaster Lunsford was John Lunsford of East Hoathly, Anthony Pelham's cousin. John's father William had died in 1531 and Burwash manor court noted in October

108. BL, Add. Roll, 31822.
109. TNA, PROB 11/32/414.
110. KHLC, U1475, B8/8.
111. TNA, C 3/73/58.

of that year that his son and heir John Lunsford was 11 years of age.[112] If William's servant and third executor John Fanton, whose surname was not otherwise known in Sussex, was the finer John Vinton, this could take the family ironworks back to the 1520s, but their location remains uncertain. The Lunsford family had purchased lands near Crowhurst late in the fifteenth century, and the place name 'Lunsford's Cross' is sited about a mile west of Catsfield Furnace. The 'Furnace field' at Catsfield was mentioned in a Bexhill manor document of 1567,[113] and the early use of this site as a furnace might explain some of the seven aliens, including the known ironworker Gyles Duffen, who paid the poll tax in Bexhill hundred in 1539. A location for his works in that area is supported by the mention in the Sidney ironworks accounts of charcoal which was lent to Mr Lunsford from Panningridge in 1547.[114]

Lunsford's workers cited in the Westminster denization roll also seem to suggest proximity to Sir William Sidney's works. As well as becoming denizen for Lunsford in 1544, Everode Pynion was then among the woodcutters at Robertsbridge. Lunsford's Gilham Nuffyld of 1544 seems to have had the alias Burdett and could have moved on to be the Guillam Burdett who paid 2 shillings and 1 shilling on goods to the reliefs of 1549 and 1551 in Netherfield hundred.

Lunsford's John Deforde also had an alias, that of Gillet, which he shared with his brother Giles. In 1539 he was probably the John Gyllat who paid the poll tax in Hawksborough hundred. He and his brother Giles both worked as woodcutters at Robertsbridge in 1542.[115] Giles Duffourd had paid the poll tax in Foxearle hundred in 1524, but in 1539 he appeared as Giles Duffen in Bexhill hundred among the seven aliens who paid the poll tax there. Other names among the Bexhill aliens, such as Olyver Debyll, Phylyp Mary and Nicholas Lawrens could easily have been immigrants from France, and Johnson was a common surname among ironworkers; the coincidence that Giles appeared there then, that both he and his brother worked for Sidney in 1542, and also that the other brother, John, went on to work for Lunsford in 1544 is very striking. Perhaps Giles had worked for Lunsford in 1539 and was replaced by his brother John in 1544!

If Giles worked for Lunsford in Bexhill hundred in 1539, this might indicate that his appearance in neighbouring Foxearle hundred so early as 1524 was also connected with the indirect method of ironworking, however unlikely this may seem.

The presence of John Rowland, a Frenchman, denizen and probable collier, in Bexhill hundred in 1550 and 1551, where he paid 1 shilling on goods to the reliefs of those years, suggests that the Lunsford involvement in ironworks may have extended into the 1550s, despite the apparent departure of Gilham Nuffyld to Netherfield hundred. If Samuel Rowland, the partner whom the London ironmonger James Waters nominated as one of his overseers and to whom he left £1 6s 8d in 1617,[116] was John Rowland's son baptised at Wartling in 1552, this could be evidence of a link between John Rowland's presence in Bexhill hundred and William Waters, the Bexhill forgemaster of the 1570s.

William Wybarne of Bayham did not long survive his oversight of Thomas Glazier's will. John Wybarne proved his father's will only six months later, in November 1549.[117] In it £2 was left to the poor of Ticehurst, but only £1 between the poor of Frant and Lamberhurst, where Bayham Forge was. Taken together with a mention in the will of Wybarne's 'lands at Brightling that John Walshe gentleman occupieth with the land overflowen with the pound at Dervolde and the fludegates' and his executorship of Thomas Glazier of Brightling's will, it appears that Wybarne's ironworking interests were now centred far to the south of Bayham.

And despite Schubert's identification of Gilham Holmes with 'Gyllam a Frenchman' buried at Frant early in 1559, investigation of the three French ironworkers attributed to Wybarne in the denization roll of 1544 suggests a more southerly location. Robert Holmes, mentioned in the Burwash parish register in 1559, married Alice Bussett there in 1560 as his second wife and was buried there in 1602. The earliest Gilham Bennett found in a parish register was mentioned at Brightling in 1563, and

112. BL, Add. Roll, 31818.

113. Cleere and Crossley, *The iron industry of the Weald*, p. 126; J. Upton, 'Catsfield Furnace; a new discovery', *Wealden Iron*, Bulletin of the Wealden Iron Research Group, 2nd series, **1** (1981), pp. 16-17.

114. KHLC, U1475, B10/1.

115. KHLC, U1475, B7/1.

116. TNA, PROB 11/131/218. But Samuel could have been the son not of John, but of Peter Rowland, who paid the poll tax in Foxearle hundred in 1552 as a servant of Thomas Woodman.

117. TNA, PROB 11/32/564.

later moved on to Waldron and Mayfield. Wybarne's Francis Tollett had perhaps moved further west by 1549.

In the subsidy rolls of around 1550, John Wybarne appeared in 1551 as the employer of Jakes Recrowe and his servant Nicholas in Shoyswell hundred. But it was his cousin Thomas Shoyswell who was forgemaster in that hundred, in 1549 as employer of Vincent Deproune and in 1552 as employer of the strangely named Hector and Lunto. Racreff (*sic*) and Dewprowne had become denizens in 1541. To parallel the close relationship between Shoyswell and Wybarne there is no continuity between the names of these employees to allow the inference that they were all attached to the same ironworks. Indeed Vincent Deproane was employed by Thomas May from 1550 to 1552. The only sites in the area from this period not accounted for are the furnace sites at East Lymden and Darfold.

Because several of his workmen had become denizens in 1541, Thomas May had only three workmen made denizen in 1544. He is shown by the subsidy rolls of around 1550 to have remained, as was already the case in 1524, the most considerable employer of French immigrants in Shoyswell hundred. It must be that as in 1524, these were principally employed in Pashley borough, at Pashley Furnace and perhaps at Burgh Wood Forge. May did not buy Pashley manor, including the furnace, from Sir James Boleyn until 1543.[118] But in 1543, May also employed five servants in West Barnfield hundred, none of whom had been there in 1541. In addition to an alien John Loye, they included the future forgemaster Bartholomew Jeffery, Adam Cossam who followed Jeffery's move to the Isenhurst and Heathfield area, and John Hoke, who was probably the John Hooke who died at Balcombe in 1558 and left a ton of iron to his sister Alice.[119] Although a date of 1558 for the building of the blast furnace at Chingley has been cogently argued for,[120] it is difficult to suggest where in West Barnfield hundred May could have employed these men if not at Chingley.

John Barham had three Frenchmen made denizens in 1544, of whom, provided it is realised that 'Maryon Gardyner' was an alias of Marian Lamberd, and that 'Wylliam Obery' was in reality Gilham Soberis, all appeared as poll tax payers in Wadhurst in 1543. Indeed, Lawrens Bluytt and Peter Russell, who had become denizens in 1541, and Peter Turner and John Nayler, who never became denizens, were all taxed in Wadhurst in 1543, and may all have worked for Barham in that year. Although Peter Turner had moved south to work for Sir William Sidney at Panningridge by 1549, and Bluytt had probably moved to Battle, John Nayler is rather less certainly identifiable as John Nayler alias Clotear who was at Robertsbridge from 1549 to 1560 and was clearly a nailer by trade.

In 1547 John Barham is thought to have added Coushopley Furnace to the other works, Verredge Forge and Brookland Furnace and Forge, which he already possessed. Barham made his will in 1551 and in it named David Willard as the first overseer, whilst Michael Weston was the first witness, both of them future partners and forgemasters.

It is not easy to follow the Colyn ironworking interests during this period. John Colyn the elder of Burwash had died in March 1537, leaving his lands in Burwash to his eldest son John, his lands in Brightling, which included the manor and furnace of Socknersh, to his second son Alexander, and his lands in Dallington to his third son Bartholomew. However, he expressed the wish that his three sons should 'lovingly and brotherly occupie together' his forge in Burwash and his furnace in Brightling for six years following his death. His youngest son Hugh, probably a minor then, was left a monetary bequest of £80.

Whilst Alexander and Bartholomew Colyn paid 12s 6d and 10 shillings respectively on goods worth £25 and £20 in Henhurst hundred, the only Frenchman among Colyn's family, his eldest son John Colyn the younger, was the John Colyn who paid 4 shillings on goods worth £4 to the subsidy of 1539 in Netherfield hundred. Could John Colyn the younger at this time have been in partnership with Richard Weekes, who had been an overseer of his father's will? Towards the end of the decade John Colyn appeared in Hawksborough hundred, where he employed two Frenchmen in each of the years 1549 and 1550, most notably the hammerman Adrian Hatto in 1549. Hatto had been made denizen for the duke of Norfolk in 1544, but was in 1549 presumably employed at Burwash Forge.

However the three Colyn brothers had undertaken the setting up for Sir William Sidney of both the forge and furnace at Robertsbridge in 1541 and of the furnace at Panningridge in 1542. Whilst

118. Straker, *Wealden iron*, p. 299.

119. ESRO, PBT 1/1/4/87.

120. Crossley, *The Bewl valley ironworks*, p. 3.

John and Alexander supervised the building work, Alexander acted also as founder and Bartholomew as hammerman during the early months of operation. Not only did John Colyn buy some of the iron produced at the Sidney ironworks; he also helped, presumably through contacts already established there, to sell iron in Southampton, though this is known only because 406 pounds of it remained unpaid for. That all 'the three Colyns' were recognized as regular servants in 1543 is clear from the fact that they received £3 between them in lieu of their livery coats.[121] Their role as covenant servants appeared to be coming to an end in 1543; from 1546 onwards they no longer figured in the accounts.

Objections raised by Thomas Darrell of Scotney show that by 1548 Alexander Collyn had begun building a hammer mill in the manor of Hoathly, or Hoadley, in the Sussex portion of Lamberhurst parish. The manor, which had formerly belonged to the college of Lingfield, had been granted by the Crown to Sir Thomas Cawarden in December 1546 and on 15 January 1550, almost exactly one month before Collyn's death, licence was obtained from the Crown for Cawarden to make this transfer,[122] though informal arrangements must have been agreed much earlier.

In his will Colyn called himself Alexander Collen of Lamberhurst in Sussex, yeoman.[123] His sons being minors, he left Socknersh and its furnace to his widow and executrix Julian, who was to hold it until his third son Alexander was 23. She was also to hold the farm in Herstmonceux and Hailsham before it passed to Alexander, and the lands in Lamberhurst and Wadhurst for eight years to pay bequests and debts. The woods on the rest of the estates were also reserved to her, so it is evident that she, like Joan Walsh and Joan Isted, was expected to act as forgemaster until Alexander reached the age of 23, which was also the age at which bequests made to the other sons became due. Alexander Collyn's eldest son John was to have the other lands in Kent and Sussex after eight years, but since he died in 1552, they went to Alexander's second son Stephen. Alexander made his much younger brother Hugh Collyn joint executor of the will together with his widow.

The duke of Norfolk's ironworks were a furnace below Sheffield Forest, and Sheffield Forge some distance away on the Ouse. The number of the duke's Frenchmen listed in the subsidy roll of 1543 was 15. In addition to the 14 Frenchmen listed in the Westminster denization roll as being at Sheffield in 1544, a further six workers were made denizens elsewhere in the roll, so the duke was the employer of more immigrant ironworkers than any other forgemaster in the Weald.

Although Crookford double furnace at Worth had been built on the duke's lands by 1547, there is no proof that this venture was set on foot before he was attainted and imprisoned in December 1546. On the contrary there is good reason to believe that it was the commission to oversee the duke's 'iron mines in Sussex', granted to William Levett on 27 December 1546, that gave rise to the double furnace.

At Sheffield it is the subsidy roll of 1543 that provides the earliest proof for the existence of an ironworks. However, in October 1536, at the time of the Pilgrimage of Grace, the duke already had a considerable establishment at Sheffield, because he explained his slowness in moving from his seat at Kenninghall in Norfolk to lead the royal forces north, with the excuse that his 'great horses and geldings [were] in Sussex, at Sheffield'.[124]

In the autumn of 1538, a time when preparations were set on foot to cast guns and erect new coastal forts in the face of a feared combined assault on England by the freshly reconciled Francis I and Charles V, great efforts were made by Thomas Cromwell and his son Richard for the king's reception at Sheffield, during his progress through the Weald.

However, the king's visit to Sheffield had evidently been planned well before the reconciliation of Francis and Charles, because Master Richard had already expended £100 when visiting Sussex along with the duke in November 1537. Early in 1538 Arcangelo Arcano, one of the royal gunfounders, was in Sussex to supervise for Cromwell the demolition of Lewes priory, which he accomplished by methods more usually associated with sapping and mining. It was Master Richard who authorised the payment of £30 to Arcano for this. On 1 August, immediately prior to the king's visit to Sussex, Richard Cromwell gave £4 'to the brothers and fellowship of the gunners' for undisclosed reasons, and at the same time paid £20 'for things done at Sheffeld' to William Williamson, who it will be remembered was one of the

121. Crossley, *Sidney ironworks accounts*, pp. 51 nn. 56-8.

122. Straker, *Wealden Iron*, p. 269; *Letters and Papers, Henry VIII*, **21** (2), no. 648(50); *Calendars of Patent rolls, Edward VI*, **3**, p. 247.

123. TNA, PROB 11/34/436.

124. *Letters and Papers Henry VIII*, **11**, no. 603.

forgemaster Roger Machyn's workers in Hartfield hundred in 1524.

During the visit itself £20 was given John Williamson on 22 August 'for works at Sheffelde', with a further £127 15s 0d the following day 'to Master Cofferer of the King's house for victual, and rewards to the King's chamber and household by Richard Tonyour'. The king's visit to the Weald continued via Lewes (25 August), Mr Gage's (27 August), Mayfield (28 August) and Mr Culpeper's (29 August), but with no further extraordinary expense.[125] Sir Francis Bryan had written from Lyon on 1 August that he expected to be with the king at Ewhurst or Eridge where he would 'declare to him honey with gall', which to Henry the news of the new amity between Francis I and the Emperor would no doubt be.[126]

It is obvious that the Sheffield visit was the climax of the king's visit to the Weald, transcending the usual feasting and hunting typical of such progresses. Although Arcano's visit to Sussex took place some months before the king's, and there is no proof of his visiting Sheffield at that time, or in August either, the fact that Richard Cromwell and Norfolk had visited Sussex and presumably Sheffield in the preceding November, taken with the gift of £4 made to the fellowship of the gunners immediately prior to the visit itself, suggests that the furnace could then already have been in blast and that cannon founding might have been attempted.

However, if this was the primary reason for the visit there was no immediate success. Events rapidly took a different turn: William Levett had already delivered 'sundry ironwork' to the Ordnance before August 1539, when the first payment to him of £84 13s 4d was made, and his supply of gunstones to the Crown in 1540 was followed in 1541 by official appointment as gunstone-maker to the king.

The duke of Norfolk's career as ironmaster also came to an end with his attainder in December 1546. His estates were restored after Mary I's accession to the throne, but by then both ironworks were in lease to other parties, with Worth apparently occupied by Sir Richard Sackville.

Sir Roger Lewknor of Trotton (c.1469-1543) was the last member of his line to inherit the main body of the extensive Lewknor estates. Although he was three times married his heirs were four daughters, Jane born about 1503, the daughter of his first wife Eleanor Tuchet, and Katherine and Mabel, born in 1536 and 1539, together with Constance, who may have been a posthumous child, all three the daughters of Elizabeth Messant.

Whereas Jane, until 1536 Sir Roger's sole heir, had, by the time of her father's death in January 1543, been three times married and had children by each of her husbands, her sisters were all minors and therefore wards of the king. A further complication was that after the death of her second husband Sir Arthur Pole, Jane, under pressure from her mother-in-law and from Sir Arthur's brother, had taken a vow of perpetual chastity, which threw the validity of her subsequent marriage to Sir William Barrentyne into doubt. A Royal Commission declared the marriage invalid, and its issue Drew Barrentyne therefore illegitimate. However, it is known from a letter of Lewknor to Barrentyne, written in June 1539 when he was anticipating another summer visit from the king,[127] that Barrentyne was much favoured by him, and Sir Roger appears to have secured royal involvement on Barrentyne's behalf. In 1542 the king made an award, subsequently confirmed by act of Parliament, that legitimatized Barrentyne's heirs by Jane Lewknor.

The result was a division of the estate after Sir Roger's death, by which Trotton and certain other manors were retained by his widow Elizabeth for life, but the manor of Horsted Keynes devolved on Barrentyne. Elizabeth subsequently married Sir Roger's cousin Richard Lewknor and continued to live at Trotton until her death in 1592. However, in 1546 the wardship of her three daughters by Sir Roger was conferred on Sir Henry Knyvet, who was the second husband of Ann Pickering, Jane Lewknor's daughter by her first husband.[128]

The subsidy roll of November 1543 for Horsted Keynes hundred shows that Sir William Barrentyne was the employer of no fewer than 14 Frenchmen, who included both founders, such as Anthony Fownder and Robert Tyler, and forgemen, such as David Hatto (Hawtont) and Peter Gayn. It seems clear that this workforce could not have been built up within a few months, but that Sir Roger Lewknor must have been these men's employer well before 1543, though Barrentyne might also have been somehow involved in the ironworking project before Sir Roger's death.

125. *Letters and Papers Henry VIII,* **14** (2), no. 782, 'Cromwell's accounts' (pp. 332, 336-7).
126. *Letters and Papers Henry VIII,* **13** (2), no. 8.
127. *Letters and Papers Henry VIII,* **14** (1), no. 1140.
128. E. Cobby, *The Lewknors of Sussex*, Cranleigh, 1991, pp. 14-18.

Thomas Messant, who was father of Sir Roger's third wife Elizabeth, whom he married in his 60s around 1535, was presumably from the immigrant family of that name. The contact from which such a marriage might arise appears to put the inception of ironworking at Horsted Keynes back to the early 1530s.

The forge with which Horsted Keynes Furnace was linked was Freshfield Forge, as is confirmed by the fact that one of the workers there, John Pickard, who in 1543, 1552 and 1572 paid the poll tax in the hundred of Horsted Keynes, in 1560 paid it in Lindfield Arches, on the southern side of the Ouse. By 1574 this forge may have been abandoned. In 1565, when Drew Barrentyne sold the manors of Horsted Keynes and Broadhurst to the Michelbourne family he reserved Freshfield Hammer to himself. But in 1574 he sold to Nicholas Lewknor and Richard Michelbourne not a forge but 'the . . . rent . . . issuing or going out of certain mills in Horsted Keynes called Freshfield mills'.[129] In 1574 Drew Barrentyne, along with most of the other forgemasters, signed a bond not to cast guns, but this may well have been only in respect of Horsted Keynes Furnace of which he was still the owner, although in 1574 it was tenanted by Anthony Morley.

In Lindfield Arches hundred the name of Henry Lucas headed the lists of aliens from 1550 to 1552, and, although his name occurred second in the 1543 list, the two aliens preceding and following him, John Johnson and Cornelius, were listed as his servants. John Johnson was the only alien who accompanied him throughout. Cornelius appeared in 1543 but not thereafter. Nicholas Founder first appeared in 1550, continued in 1551 and was presumably 'The Founder' who was listed in 1552. James Gascon appeared in 1550 and again in 1551, the only occasion when three servants were listed, but had disappeared by 1552.

Since the hundred at this time appears not to have included the outlier at Burleigh Arches, the site cannot have been located far from Lindfield itself, moreover Henry Lucas was an inhabitant of Wivelsfield. It seems probable that the furnace site was later the location of the forge of which Anthony Morley was both owner and tenant in 1574. This forge continued in 1602 when its current owner, John Paler alias Cooper, claimed to have bought it from Morley.[130]

The martyr forgemaster Richard Woodman had been born in Buxted, the son of Thomas Woodman. In 1544 he was not mentioned as an employer of Frenchmen in the Westminster denization roll, but in 1546 the Robertsbridge Forge accounts recorded the receipt from him of 10s 8d for the release of the covenant of the finer Nicholas Brisboye.[131] By 1549 Woodman employed three Frenchmen in Foxearle hundred, and a hammerman and a collier at a forge in Warbleton borough. Woodman held Warbleton manor under a lease assigned to him by his father. The forge in Warbleton was perhaps at the site called Woodman's Furnace, which archaeological investigation now shows was in reality a forge.[132] Perhaps Marklye Furnace at Rushlake Green was the furnace which operated in conjunction with Woodman's Forge.

The Foxearle works is also problematical because Batsford Furnace was a later foundation and Cowbeech was beyond the bounds of the hundred. Kitchenham, where a forge certainly operated later in the century, seems to be the only other available site. The fact that Richard Woodman acquired Compers (Comphurst) only 4km south-west of Kitchenham in 1544 supports the idea that this was indeed his works, an acquisition which perhaps also coincided with his entry into the iron trade.[133]

Tradition has it that among those who betrayed Richard Woodman to the authorities was his own brother, Thomas Woodman, who had perhaps taken over the ironworks during the period when Richard had sought sanctuary abroad. The subsidy rolls indicate that the works in Foxearle hundred, which were run by Richard in 1549 and 1550, belonged in 1551 to Robert Woodman and in 1552 to Thomas Woodman. These are the names of Richard's brothers, though Thomas could have been his father, and suggest that each played some role in the ironworks before 1553, the earliest date when Richard Woodman could have been driven to take refuge abroad.

By his will Richard's father, Thomas Woodman of Uckfield, who died towards the end of 1558,

129. R. Bird, 'Drew Barentyn', *Wealden Iron*, Bulletin of the Wealden Iron Research Group, 2nd series, **7** (1987), p. 20.
130. Cleere and Crossley, *The iron industry of the Weald*, p. 332.
131. ESRO, SHE 6/1/11/1.
132. *Wealden Iron*, Bulletin of the Wealden Iron Research Group, 1st series, **9** (1976), pp. 8-9.
133. ESRO, HBR 9/46/12, Tenement analysis of Wartling parish.

almost eighteen months after his son's martyrdom, granted the reversion of his lease of the lordship of Warbleton to his son Robert, although it was then in the hands of Richard's widow, Margaret, under the lease granted to her former husband. Thomas also left to Robert his house and land, presumably Comphurst, in Wartling and Herstmonceux. To his son William he left a brown cow and £20 out of the money owed to him by his son Thomas. A further £12 13s 4d owed by Thomas, to whom he made no bequests whatsoever, was to go to his executors, who were his son Robert and his son-in-law George Beaching, to be used to help clear his debts. It therefore seems certain that the younger Thomas was out of favour with his father, though nothing more sinister than debts of over £30 might have caused this.[134]

Lastly, Chittingly Furnace in West Hoathly was in blast in 1546 when Thomas Michell supplied 65 tons of iron from it at £2 the ton to Sheffield Forge. Thomas Michell of Worth, gentleman, died in 1551 and mentioned the yearly profit coming from his 'iron myll at Chidingly' in his will.[135] He was generous to his late servant Thomas Coulstocke the younger, to whom he left £10, and to 'poor Browne that worketh at the furnace', to whom he left £6 13s 4d and three kine. He had held the manor in 1536, but subsidy rolls for the northern part of Streat hundred recorded no obvious ironworkers until 1552 when Nicholas the Founder, perhaps Nicholas Tyler who had been in Buttinghill from 1549 to 1551, paid the poll tax there.

TECHNOLOGY

For the technology of ironworking at this period several documentary sources are available. At its outset, came the inventory of the Newbridge ironworks taken in 1525 when they were leased to Sir Thomas Boleyn. The 1539 Survey of Ashdown Forest also contained a few technological hints. For the 1540s there are two sources, the finest being the Sidney ironworks accounts, of which a significant proportion edited by David Crossley is in print. The main corpus is conserved at the Kent History and Library Centre in Maidstone, but the missing 1546 furnace accounts are in the Huntington Library, California, and the 1546 forge accounts in the East Sussex Record Office. In the Public Record Office are accounts and inventories for the Sheffield and Worth ironworks, belonging to the attainted duke of Norfolk, dating from the period after the attainder of Thomas Seymour, lord Sudeley, on whom they had been conferred when Norfolk was still in disfavour; these have been published by Giuseppi and Straker. The written evidence is supplemented by archaeological investigation, of which that into the furnace at Panningridge belongs to this period, in so far as it relates to the first furnace on the site.

Furnace

The only furnace remains from the period excavated in the Weald are those of Panningridge, built for Sir William Sidney under the supervision of the Collyn brothers in 1542-3. The furnace was of square section with sides measuring 5.2m.[136] This was somewhat less than at Hodeng and Les Rouges-Eaux in the Pays de Bray; at Hodeng the side between the surviving corners of the structure measures 5.7m, and at Les Rouges-Eaux the width of the surviving masonry at the top of the tapping arch is 5.2m, suggesting that at its base, now submerged, Les Rouges-Eaux was of a similar size to Hodeng.

Throughout the Weald, not much more than the foundations of furnace arches have survived, and at Panningridge, where only two foundation stones from the south side of the casting arch remain, the situation is worse. The opposite side of the casting arch and the whole of the adjacent blowing arch were destroyed when the watercourse of the Phase II furnace was driven through it. Beyond the watercourse, all that remained of Phase I was the tip of the pillar, or buttress, which separated the two arches. However, it is evident that the Phase I casting arch originally faced towards the tail race of the furnace,[137] which was presumably culverted at that point, a practice replicated at most Wealden

134. TNA, PROB 11/42A/98.

135. TNA, PROB 11/34/438.

136. Cleere and Crossley, *The iron industry of the Weald*, p. 244.

137. Crossley, 'A sixteenth-century Wealden blast furnace', Fig. 23. There are indications that, at a later stage in the life of the Phase I furnace, casting was carried out from the diametrically opposite side of the furnace (Ibid., p. 49).

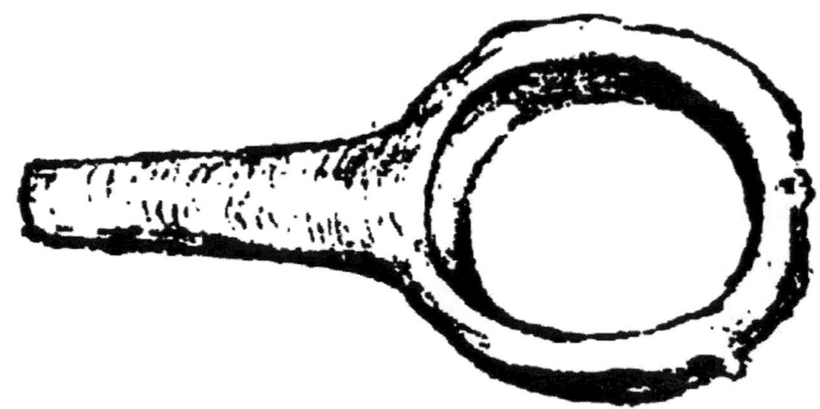

Figure 13: Seventeenth-century cast-iron hurst from Fasagh, Wester Ross (from J. H. Dixon, *Gairloch in north-west Ross-shire*, p. 158)

Figure 14: Drome-beam hammer, with finery hearth in the background, from Diderot and d'Alembert, *Encyclopédie, Tome 21, 4me Section, Planche VI*, Paris, 1765 (Special Collections Research Center, University of Chicago Library)

Key D the hammer block; E a brass; H the hammer; I the extremity of the hammer helve, with the hammer head secured by a pin; K the pane (*panne*) of the hammer; L the table of the anvil; M the hutch (*huche*) carrying the water to the hammer wheel; W the anvil; Y the hammer beam.

1 and 2 are the legs (*jambes*, 1 *sur la main*, 2 *sur l'arbre*) of the hammer assembly; 3 the gudgeon (*tourillon*) of the hammer beam; 4 the bray (*braie*) protecting the hammer helve; 7 the pig hole, through which the sow or pig of iron enters the finery hearth; 10 the key (*clé tirante*) which locks the legs into the mortices of the drome beam; 11 a wedge to secure the key in position; 12 the protecting piece (*tabarin*) between the key and the drome beam; 13 the spring beam, or rabbett (*ressort*).
hh the morris bar (*marastre*) on the fore-spirit (opposite the tuyere) side of the hearth; *d* mantle of the chimney; *bc* pillar between the fore-spirit side and the work side.
Δδ the drome beam; Ω the water-post; Σ the prick-post.

furnaces so far excavated. As the surviving arch at Les Rouges-Eaux also faces the watercourse, this pattern was perhaps a throw-back to a time when granulated cast iron was made by tapping the molten metal into a water bath, as was the case with the north Italian furnace described by Filarete in 1464.[138]

The 1525 inventory showed that at Newbridge four cast-iron sows were bedded into the furnace walls, two supporting the bellows arch, and two the casting arch. The Panningridge building accounts of 1542 hinted at the use of sows in the structure by recording the payment of 1s 4d for 'carage of sowes of iron for the said fornace', and at Crookford in Worth in 1547 'cast iron laid into the furnace' was mentioned.[139]

It was Schubert who noted that the casting aperture at Panningridge was surmounted by a timpstone, for which protective 'tymp irons' were brought from Robertsbridge Forge in 1548 and 1553, and pointed out that the presence of the timpstone was the main criterion to indicate a furnace with an open breast, or forehearth. He also averred that the interior of Panningridge Furnace could not have been lined with brick because only stones and no bricks were mentioned in the Panningridge building accounts.[140] However, the building accounts do show that a load of tiles was bought for Panningridge. Excavation has shown that the use of tiles for lining the interior of the furnace above the boshes was practised at Beaussault.

Both bricks and tiles were later used in the repair of the furnace mouth at Panningridge. In 1553, when Charles Gerard repaired it, the forehearth at Panningridge was referred to as the 'forefront of the fornes mouth'. Schubert equated 'mouth' with the charging aperture at the throat of the furnace, and thought that tiles bought in 1549 were used to floor the charging platform. However it looks as though these tiles were used at the hearth, as was again the case with a load bought in 1551 'to mend the furnace mouth'.[141] And when Charles mended the furnace 'forefront' in 1553, 400 bricks supplied by Barden were used, in addition to stone dug by Peter the Founder, Simon Spray and his son.[142]

Returning to the blowing arch, the Sidney accounts show that the tuyere was made from wrought iron, of which 9 pounds was sent from Robertsbridge in 1551 for that purpose.[143] The bellows are discussed separately.

At Panningridge the founder's tools included long ringers, bars used to move or dislodge solid matter in the furnace, made at Robertsbridge Forge. In 1553 Adrian Dogen brought two new ringers from the forge to the furnace in exchange for two old ones which he returned to the forge, and in 1554 Fylpen Tollet fetched 'great ryngars' from Robertsbridge.[144] Two ringers supplied to Panningridge in 1555 weighed 38 pounds each. At Newbridge the term 'rammers' used for ringers in 1525, seems to have continued in use there in the 'romars' mentioned in the survey of 1539, but this term was never used at Panningridge.

Furnace bellows

Furnace beams or shafts depicted in the *Encyclopédie*[145] were equipped with six cams, three to each pair of bellows, set alternately at 60° intervals, so that one pair of bellows was blown whilst the other inflated, giving six blasts to every revolution of the beam. The portion of the furnace beam excavated at Chingley Furnace, perhaps from around 1560, shows exactly this same setting of cams two centuries earlier in Kent. The Newbridge inventory of 1525 had mentioned four hoops of iron, probably set on either side of each set of cams to prevent the beam from splitting near the point where the cams had been inserted. Bound in this way, furnace beams often survived for many years.

The bellows house at Panningridge was placed close under the dam or bay, where an overshot wheel drove bellows set between the furnace and the bay. This position would be consistent with the depression of the top boards of the bellows alternately by cams set in the furnace shaft, followed by

138. R. F. Tylecote, *The early history of metallurgy in Europe*, p. 328.
139. Schubert, *British iron and steel industry*, p. 197, n. 6.
140. Ibid., pp. 196n., 198.
141. KHLC, B10/3 and 5.
142. Crossley, *Sidney ironworks accounts*, p. 44; KHLC, U1475, B10/6.
143. KHLC, U1475, B8/4.
144. KHLC, U1475, B10/6 and 7.
145. D. Diderot and J. D'Alembert, *Encyclopédie, ou dictionnaire raisonné des sciences, des arts et des métiers*, Paris, 1757, 7, pp. 134-70.

their alternate inflation by the action of the 'pole ... to lyft upe the bellows', which Hawkyns was paid for 'drawyng ... to the phurnis' in 1549.[146] At Les Rouges-Eaux on the contrary the blowing arch will have been on the downstream side of the furnace, which would be consistent with exactly similar bellows driven by an undershot wheel.

The hooks mentioned in connection with the furnace bellows at Newbridge in 1524 had no parallel at Panningridge; on the contrary, the ends of the pole which lifted the bellows were apparently connected to the top bellows boards by stirrups, two of which were made in 1550 and one in 1551 by Charles Gerard.[147] To judge from the fact that Hawkyns was paid for 'drawing' (i.e. dragging) it to the furnace, presumably with the aid of a horse or ox, the bellows pole was a very substantial piece of timber.

At Panningridge in 1551 Charles Gerard was paid 6 pence for making 'six cames for the fornes', and though later in the year he was paid for eight new cams, the extra two cams probably went into stock. The 'two plates of iron for the cams weighing 28 lb' sent to the furnace from Robertsbridge in October 1551 show that on this occasion the cams were made from wrought iron.[148]

Bellows boards were valuable, as shown by the Robertsbridge Forge accounts for 1546 which recorded that 'an old payre of bellow woods' was purchased from Richard Weekes of Netherfield for 10 shillings. To protect them from the direct action of the cams, cast-iron shammel plates were fixed to the upper boards. These probably already took the L-shaped form described in the Forest of Dean in the eighteenth century, 'which works up and down as a crank, so as for the camb to lay hold of this iron, and thereby press down the bellows',[149] because that shape enabled the furnace beam and consequently the water wheel to be set lower in relation to the hearth. This would explain the low setting of the furnace beam at Chingley, without resort to the idea that the cams had compressed the bottom boards by lifting them,[150] and that it was the upper boards that were fixed rigid. The lower setting of the furnace beam decreased the danger of the furnace being flooded, which is thought to have been the cause of the serious explosion at Coalbrookdale around 1700, when, during Shadrach Fox's lease, the dam burst.[151]

In 1555 Charles Gerard made two new 'shamowes' for Panningridge for 6 pence each, and the forge book for that year shows that these were made from 31 pounds of wrought iron sent for the purpose from Robertsbridge. His assistant Simon Spray carried the old 'shamowes plattes' and 'ryngars' to the smith of Dallington to mend.[152]

The supply by Charles of two vental boards for the 'flaps' of the bellows in 1551, shows how they were reinflated.[153]

Forge

It is easy to see from the Newbridge inventory of 1509, which listed separate bellows at the furnace, finery and hammer mill, that the forge was of Walloon type. The 1525 inventory was not so explicit.

The predominance of French vocabulary at Robertsbridge was emphasised when an English hammer mill was for the first time called a chafery. This came in the 1546 forge accounts with a reference to the 'chaverei and the fynery bellowis'.[154] The word came not from the Netherlands but from France, where it was met with in 1437 in the form of *chauffouere* at Précy in Nevers.

Hearths, hammers, anvils and tools

There are no indications of a plated finery hearth at Newbridge Forge in 1509, 1525 or 1539. At Robertsbridge, where there seem to have been two fineries in the 1550s, the evidence for plated hearths

146. KHLC, U1475, B10/3.
147. Crossley, *Sidney ironworks accounts*, p. 97; KHLC, U1475, B10/5.
148. KHLC, U1475, B8/4, B10/5.
149. Awty and Phillips, 'The Cumbrian bloomery forge in the seventeenth century', p. 33.
150. It is impossible to see how an overshot wheel above the furnace could have lifted the boards. In this position an undershot, or at least a pitch-back wheel would have been needed.
151. Raistrick, *Dynasty of ironfounders*, p. 30.
152. Crossley, *Sydney ironworks accounts*, p. 126; KHLC, U1475, B10/8.
153. KHLC, U1475, B10/5.
154. ESRO, SHE 6/1/11/1.

Figure 15: Joseph Wright (1734-97), Study for 'An Iron Forge 1772'
(© April 2019 Derby Museums Trust)

is conclusive by 1558, when Peter the founder made eight plates for the forge which he cast for 3 pence each. It looks as though these will have comprised the four side plates for each finery, without any bottom plates. However, plated hearths may have been used in the 1540s; in the last campaign at Robertsbridge Furnace in 1546 the founder Valentine cast plates, hammers and anvils for the forge to the value of 6 shillings, though their quantities were unspecified.[155]

Due to the violent stress to which hammers and anvils were subjected at each stroke of the hammer, they had a quite limited life-span. In the following century around six hammers and two anvils a year were used in the Forest of Dean.[156] Casting them was a much more skilled and costly task than casting plates; when Charles Gerard made seven hammers for Robertsbridge in 1554, followed in 1555 by six hammers and 3 anvils, the hammers cost 1s 4d each and the anvils 8 pence.[157] However, even after more than a decade of operation, the moulds for casting these items in 1555 were still borrowed from the Walsh family, at that time running Socknersh furnace.[158]

The tough cast iron yielded by some Wealden ores led to hammers and anvils made there being as highly prized as Wealden cannon were to become. Hammers and anvils were exported to other parts of England even after the indirect system had been established there, as for instance at Rievaulx in North Yorkshire, where, in 1615-16, no fewer than 40 'olde Sussex hammers' were converted into bar iron at the forge.[159]

In 1525 the great hammer of iron at Newbridge Forge had a 'hoop of iron', which may have been the protective collar of wrought iron placed round the belly helve at the point where the arms of the hammer beam impacted under the helve to raise it. This collar was termed a *braie* in French, a name which appeared in later English forge accounts as 'bray'. As it needed very frequent replacement it was one of the most commonly occurring terms in forge accounts, but the hoops and great hoops for the hammer beam manufactured at Robertsbridge in 1548, 1551, 1554, 1555 (four of them) and 1556,[160] perhaps refer to hoops used to bind the axletree of the hammer assembly and not to protect the helve. In 1551 a hoop for the hammer beam was made from 28 pounds of iron and in 1555 John Collyan made two hoops for the hammer beam from two bars of iron weighing 54 pounds.

Because wrought iron was much more heat resistant than cast iron, tools for ironworking were normally made at the forge, as the Sidney ironworks accounts constantly bear out. At Newbridge in 1525 the French terminology for tools of 1509 persisted only in the two 'stokkers' (Fr. *stoccard*) at the furnace. The 'rangardes' had perhaps evolved into 'rammers', a suggestion confirmed by the fact that the two rammers at the furnace were long and the two used by the finer were short. These 'rammers' of 1525 persisted at Newbridge in 1539 in the Forest survey's reference to 'romars', but that term was not used at Panningridge or Robertsbridge.

Forge bellows

At Robertsbridge Forge the bellows perhaps differed little from those used at Panningridge. As early as 1543 the repairs for Sir William Sidney's forge included 'a shamow and sturropis for your bellowis', as well as the making of cams, whilst in 1551 two iron pins were bought for 4 pence from Vincent Buckett to secure the 'shamoes' of the finery bellows.[161] However, the 'dobell hoke for the fynery bellowes', bought from the smith John Upton in 1555,[162] was perhaps reminiscent of the hooks used at Newbridge in 1525.

Hammer assemblies

The Robertsbridge accounts prove that the forge hammer there was a drome-beam (Old Fr. *drosme*, Fr. *drôme*) type of belly-helve, as was also probably the 'great water hammer' used at Newbridge in 1496. This type of hammer assembly went back to the *grands marteaux* first mentioned in the Netherlands in

155. KHLC, U1475, B10/10 (1558); ESRO, SHE 6/1/11/1 (1546).
156. Schubert, *British iron and steel industry*, p. 282, n. 2.
157. KHLC, U1475, B10/7 and 8.
158. Crossley, *Sidney ironworks accounts*, p. 155.
159. Schubert, *British iron and steel industry*, p. 288, n. 4.
160. KHLC, U1475, B8/1, 4, 6, 7, and 8.
161. KHLC, U1475, B2/2, B8/4.
162. Crossley, *Sidney ironworks accounts*, p. 151.

the 1390s. The 'drome' of the hammer at Robertsbridge was referred to in 1549, when two keys (*kayes*) were made for it.[163]

Oak trees were used for the two main beams of the assembly; the longest was usually the drome beam itself, which often went clean across the forge; it was about 60cm[164] square in section at the end near the watercourse, slightly less at the end beyond the anvil, and was about 9m in length, which left space beyond the hammer and anvil for the hammerman to work in. At each end it was morticed into the tops of two more stout posts, the one adjacent to the wheel-pit being called the 'water-post' (Fr. *grande attache*, but *wasser-sul* in Low German) and the one beyond the hammerman being called the 'prick-post' (Fr. *petite attache*). The water-post was about 45cm square and 5.5m in height, fixed well into the ground at its bottom end, its upper end protruding beyond the roof of the forge, so (to encourage the rain to drain off) the top was cut into a pyramidal shape. Laterally, it was supported by long diagonal braces, which were morticed into it above the level of the mortice which received the tenon of the drome. At the other end of the drome, as described in the *Encyclopédie*, the prick-post was supported by one diagonal support morticed into its side, on the opposite side to and below the mortice which received the tenon of the drome.

Beneath the drome, the hammer helve, which was between 26 and 30 cm square in section, pivoted in the ring of the cast-iron hurst (Fr. *hurasse*, or *hus*), into which it was made secure with wooden wedges. The ring of the hurst was described as being around 4 cm thick and 14 cm broad. At Robertsbridge the 'horste for to hold the homer helve' was referred to in 1555. The points of laterally placed fins on either side of the hurst allowed it to pivot in cast-iron boxes called boits or boytes (Fr. *boîtes*) morticed into the inner sides of the legs (Fr. *jambes*) of the hammer assembly. The hurst was asymmetrical, the fin towards the hammerman being around 40 cm in length, whilst that towards the axle-tree was of around 7 cm in length, so that the helve pivoted off-centre, close to the arms of the axle-tree, and leaving the hammerman with plenty of space to work in.

A hurst, apparently from an early seventeenth-century forge at Fasagh, near Loch Maree in Wester Ross, survived minus its shorter fin; the ring and surviving fin together measured around 60cm, so when complete this hurst may have been of 67cm overall, somewhat smaller than the hurst of around 77cm described in the *Encyclopédie*.[165] A hurst could weigh up to 75kg (1½ cwt)[166] and in May 1554 two new hursts, which together cost 1s 8d were cast for Robertsbridge at Darvel Furnace, whilst a further three, also had from Darvel, were bought from Richard Weekes for 2s 8d in September.[167]

Cast-iron axle-sleeves, morticed into the inside surfaces of the legs about 35cm above their bottom ends, were in the shape of boxes called boits or boytes. Though boytes were not mentioned in the Robertsbridge accounts, four 'boytes' costing 2s 8d were cast for Bivelham Forge in 1643-4, 'two new boyts' were inventoried at a forge in Frant in 1655,[168] and it would be impossible for the hurst to pivot between the legs without them.

The legs projected slightly above the drome beam, into the sides of which they were morticed and they were held in position using wooden wedges. The stability of the whole assembly was secured by drawing the legs closer together below the drome and into the mortices in its sides by a cross-piece of wood called the key (Fr. *clé tirante*), which passed through both legs to draw them together. In section the key was about 1cm high and about 7cm broad, but rather larger at the end towards the hammer beam, so that it could not completely pass through mortices of similar dimensions traversing both legs. At the opposite end it was itself pierced by a horizontal mortice, into which another wedge shaped key was hammered so as to wedge the legs firmly into the mortices in the sides of the drome. Two keys were

163. KHLC, U1475, B8/1.
164. The measurements given here and subsequently are taken, at a conversion rate of around one foot to 30cm, from the approximations given in the *Encyclopédie*, where they are given in feet (*piés*) and inches (*pouces*). The neatly measured, squared and rounded timbers depicted and described in the *Encyclopédie* surely represent an idealized picture of what ironworkers will have used in practice.
165. J. H. Dixon, *Gairloch in north-west Ross-shire*, (1886), pp. 91, 158. If, as looks possible, the surviving fin was also incomplete, Dixon's hurst could be of similar size to that described in the *Encyclopédie*. Like those at Robertsbridge, Dixon's hurst was of cast iron; those of the *Encyclopédie* were of wrought iron.
166. Schubert, *British iron and steel industry*, p. 280n.
167. KHLC, U1475, B8/6.
168. BL, Add.MS, 33,155, f. 26v.; ESRO, DYK 604.

made for Robertsbridge Forge in 1549 by Wells the carpenter, possibly a Hawksden man of that name.[169]

The legs were square in section, around 27cm square adjacent to the boyts and the key, but tapered to around 17cm in section at top and bottom. The bottom ends of the legs were morticed into a *croisée*, or cross-piece apparently called a 'plummer block' in English, set in the ground. This piece was described as being over 2m in length and somewhat more than 45cm square in section, and adjacent to the mortices which received the bottoms of the legs it was strapped with bands of wrought iron. In 1549 Unstye and his brother, probably John and Richard, were paid 10 pence for one day's work in the 'makyng of a new plommer for the halmer bealme'. A new 'legge' for the hammer had been required by 1543 and in September 1553 the carpenters at Robertsbridge were paid 11 pence for two 'new legges for the homer to work in'. The 'hamer' and the 'plomer blocke' were referred to in 1564 in the Sidney accounts.[170]

The front end of the hammer helve, in the shape of a tenon some 30cm high by 15cm wide, passed clean through the sleeve of the cast-iron hammer, and was pierced laterally on the far side by an iron pin to hold it firmly against hammer. The hammer was about 75cm in height and its head was about 30cm square; its sleeve some 15cm wide and 45cm high, and the tenon of the helve, which was less high, was made secure in it with wedges. Different sizes of wedges made it possible for the face, or pane (Fr. *panne*) of the hammer, which was about 10cm broad, to be aligned parallel to the table of the anvil. The forge hammer and anvil from Etchingham on display in the Anne of Cleves Museum at Lewes seem to differ in design very little from those depicted in the *Encyclopédie*. Hammers normally weighed around 250kg.[171]

The body of the anvil was about 45cm square in section and 60cm high, but was sunk up to about 30cm into the stock. The upper trapezoidal part was about 40cm high and the table, which was tilted slightly downwards in the direction of the hammer assembly, was about 10cm broad. Anvil pits have been excavated and they figure largely in the Robertsbridge accounts. A 'plate to lye under the handfeld' was cast for Robertsbridge by Joan Walsh's founder in 1542, presumably at Darvel Furnace.[172] The anvil also usually weighed around 250kg.[173]

The 'hammer block', which Hadlow felled in Park Wood and 'rounded' for Robertsbridge Forge in 1551, was probably an anvil block. Hadlow was paid 11 pence for his two days' labour on 28 September 1551, and on 9 October the hammerman John Collyan was paid for three days' labour in 'helpyng to sett in the homer blocke' at 4 pence a day with meat and drink. At Chingley Phase III, the wooden anvil block, a section of oak-tree trunk more than 2m high set vertically, was found still in position. It had been held in place by radial timbers wedged between the block and verticals lining the pit.[174] At Robertsbridge the plate, just mentioned, perhaps formed the foundation for the wooden block on which the anvil was presumably directly set. In 1553 the hammerman, John Collyan, was paid 4 pence for an old grindstone which he had bought 'for to drest the andvyld in the forge'.[175] This perhaps replaced the plate bought for Robertsbridge eleven years earlier.

The hammer beam was the second huge piece of timber in the drome-beam forge. It was the elongated axle of the water wheel and therefore stretched from the far side of the wheel pit to the vicinity of the anvil, gudgeons, which rested in a 'brass' on hammer blocks, being inserted at either extremity.[176] The revolving arms of the hammer beam raised the helve by their impact on the underside of the wrought-iron protective collar or bray, which encircled the helve. Two pairs of arms (*harmys*) for the 'round beam' of the forge were put in by Bodell at Robertsbridge in 1542 and 'pairs of harmys'

169. KHLC, U1475, B8/1.
170. KHLC, U1475, B2/2 (1543), B8/2 (1549) and 5 (1553), B3/10 (1564).
171. Schubert, *British iron and steel industry*, p. 282, n. 4.
172. KHLC, U1475, B7/1.
173. Schubert, *British iron and steel industry*, p. 282, n. 4.
174. KHLC, U1475, B8/4; Crossley, *The Bewl valley ironworks*, p. 26.
175. KHLC, U1475, B8/5.
176. A 'hamer blocke for the rounde bealme of the hamer' was mentioned in the Robertsbridge accounts for 1546 and another hammer block was 'set up' by Wells, the carpenter in 1549 (ESRO, SHE6/1/11/1 (1546), KHLC, U1475, B8/1 (1549)). Despite their name the 'brasses' appear to have been made at the furnace and in 1553 Richard Smyth was paid 4 pence for 'the fechyng of a brase from the fornes to the forge' (KHLC, U1475, B8/5). In the 1542 Robertsbridge accounts the 'new layng in of the gyggyn in the round bealme of the hammer wheele' was mentioned (KHLC, U1475, B7/1).

suggests that the four arms were made by driving two timbers right through the beam at right angles to each other as depicted in the *Encyclopédie*. New arms for the hammer beam were mentioned again in 1548 and 1554,[177] and their replacement probably took place rather more frequently than that, unless the practice described in the *Encyclopédie* of hooping protective shoes to the arms at the point of impact with the helve was already in use 200 years earlier.

The protective collar, or bray (Fr. *braie*) of the helve was a lozenge-shaped piece of wrought iron, one of the points of which was elongated to pass through a hole made in the opposite point. It was heated before being applied and was wrapped round the helve at the appropriate place, the elongated point being driven through the hole at the other extremity and doubled back to make it secure. The metal contracted as it cooled, forming a firm attachment. No measurements for the bray are given in the *Encyclopédie* but it must have been quite broad at its widest point to ensure that neither pair of arms, which operated in separate planes, impacted directly on the helve. 'Brayes', along with 'tew irons', figured among items manufactured at Robertsbridge in the Sidney accounts for 1563.[178]

Many of the wrought-iron hoops made for the hammer beam in 1549, 1551 and 1555 will have been strapped round the hammer beam in the vicinity of the arms, to prevent splitting, or to prevent such splits from becoming worse.[179] Even the 'great paned hoope' repaired by Vincent Bockett in 1549 was described as being 'for the rounde bealme'. The two bars of iron from which two 'hopes for the hamer beme' were made in 1555 each weighed 30 lb.

The hammer, having been thrown upwards by the hammer arms, was thrown back towards the anvil by a spring board of ash or beech named a 'rabett' (from Fr. *rebattre*, to repeat or hit again), one end of which was bedded into a mortice in the water-post. The rabett then passed through an aperture in the 'puppet' (Fr. *pouppé*), a stout beam of wood, 2m high and of square section 60cm wide. The top of the puppet was morticed into the under side of the drome beam, by a mortice 60cm long and 15cm broad, 75cm forward of the water-post, to which it was also attached about 30 cm above ground level by another block of wood called a *culard*, 75cm long, which was morticed between the water-post and the puppet by mortices 20cm wide by 15cm high. The rabett passed through the puppet by way of a mortice 30cm square placed about 60cm above floor-level, but cut in a plane rising from back to front to correspond with the rising trajectory of the rabett, which then passed forward freely between the two legs but above the hurst and hammer helve. At Robertsbridge two 'rabbettes' were felled and squared for the hammer in 1543, Wells made two 'rabettes' for the forge in 1549, three new rabetts were referred to in 1553, and the 'hewyng of a rabett and settyng in of the same', and the carriage of two further rabetts to the forge were paid for in 1555.[180]

In the *Encyclopédie* the water-post, its supporting diagonals, and the puppet were described as being bedded in or morticed through a roughly triangular framework called a 'crayfish' (*écrevisse*), to which the plummer block (*croisée*) for the lower ends of the legs was also attached. How far such a framework was used in practice and more anciently is unclear. The framework of the wheel-pit associated with Phase II of Chingley Forge extended eastwards beyond the water course in a way which suggested it might have been part of such a base.[181] However, mortices which might have accommodated the vertical pieces described in the *Encyclopédie* are notably absent, and of the verticals, only the bases of which were discovered, nos. 1-3 would clearly have supported the penstock, and 4 and 5 seem both wrongly positioned and much too slight to have formed part of a hammer assembly.

Nevertheless the 9½ foot high 'hammer-post' at Howbourne Forge, which was still standing in 1862 and was depicted in Lower's seminal article on the Sussex ironworks,[182] was clearly a 'water-post'. The end of the rabett may well have been wedged into the cut-away section depicted at its left-hand base. The pyramidal top, designed to allow rain-water to drain away, seems to have been replaced with corrugation. The mortices placed laterally above the level of the drome beam to receive the tenons of the diagonal braces, which in the *Encyclopédie* supported the water-post on either side, seem to be replaced by a mortice which passes laterally through the post at a lower level, so perhaps the Howbourne water-

177. KHLC, U1475, B7/1, B8/1 and 6.
178. KHLC, U1475, B3/10.
179. KHLC, U1475, B8/1, 4 and 7.
180. KHLC, U1475, B2/2, B8/1, 5 and 7.
181. Crossley, *The Bewl valley ironworks*, pp. 19-22, 38-40.
182. Lower, 'Historical and archaeological notices', p. 208.

post was supported in a different manner.

The fact that such timbers have not been detected in recent excavations must be due to their having been robbed out after the forges fell into desuetude. Perhaps they could yet be identified in roof timbers of buildings dating from the seventeenth and eighteenth centuries!

It is unfortunate that Joseph Wright's impressive painting *The iron forge* was used as the basis for the sketch made by J. Lewis for Charles Dawson's article of 1903 in the *Sussex Archaeological Collections*, because this has gained wide currency in Straker's *Wealden iron*, Schubert's *History of the British iron and steel industry* and elsewhere. The finished painting greatly exaggerated the size of what has come to be called 'the arm case', an item which barely exists in the original sketch discovered by Colin Phillips in Derby Art Gallery some twenty years ago. Wright exaggerated the angle of working of the hammer helve to stunning effect, whilst the bray depicted on the hammer helve was too narrow to have been capable of protecting anything. The original sketch is more realistic in many respects: there is no 'arm case', which Wright perhaps found at another forge, but the hammer-arms appear to be eating into the helve rather than impacting on the bray and the drome beam is shown bedded into the brick wall of the forge, which it would have shaken to its foundations in a few hours of use, a fault it shares with the painting. Despite this, the upper part of Wright's functionless water-post is still there in the sketch, protruding magnificently through the forge roof.

The principle on which the drome-beam forge evidently evolved was the desire to throw the wear and tear of the working parts onto small metal components, which could easily be replaced from the forge or furnace, and to preserve the expensive wooden parts from damage. In reality there was little that could be done to protect such components as the helve, the rabett and, to a lesser extent the legs, from damage, but the drome beam, hammer beam, water-post and prick-post could be preserved in action for many years. In particular, split hammer beams, the replacement of which would have entailed reconstruction of the wheel, were cobbled together with new or additional hoops, as is hinted at in the Sidney accounts, and were kept in use as long as possible.

IMMIGRANTS RECORDED IN THE DENIZATION ROLLS

Boysard, Bussard or Billing

John Boysard's denization was recorded in the roll of 1541. He had come to England around 1525 and in 1541 had an alien wife. The surname is not known to have been that of any ironworker in France, but could take its origin from the forge of Boizard, erected in 1467 at the behest of the archbishop of Chartres at Pontgouin,[183] which now lies in the department of Eure-et-Loire.

The surname Boysard failed to appear in Wealden subsidy rolls until 1576 when the alien Dynnys Bosard paid the poll tax in Bivelham borough of Hawksborough hundred. In the 1550s he may have done casual work at Panningridge Furnace, where 'Denes Frenchman' was paid for digging sand for the casting floor in 1553 and 1554. In 1554 he also received 9 pence for a day's work in helping to scour the ditch of the furnace-wheel.[184]

The family's alias stems from the French surnames Belin (which gives Billing) and its contracted form Blin (which also gives Blind) derived from *bélier* (ram). Dennis Blynne's children Audry and Peter were baptised at Waldron in 1564 and 1568, whilst Louise Denis, baptised there in 1570, was probably also his child. Agnes, daughter of 'Frenchman Denis', and William, son of Dennys Bussard, baptised at Waldron in 1574 and 1575 were also obviously his children.

Denis Bussard's move from Waldron to Bivelham borough had already taken place before May 1576, when his infant son William was buried at Mayfield. He paid the poll tax in Bivelham in July 1576 and this payment suggests that he was now a regular covenant servant at either Moat Mill or Hawksden Forge. His last child Dorothy was baptised in February 1577 at Mayfield. However, it seems possible that he was the 'Denis' buried back at Waldron in August 1588.

Another member of this family appeared in the Burwash parish register in July 1567 when John

183. Belhoste and others, *La métallurgie normande*, p. 187.
184. KHLC, U1475, B10/6 and 7.

Bozsard's son Adrian was baptised there. It seems probable that the marriage recorded at Waldron in June 1566 between John Blane and Joan Husshe may be that of Adrian's parents. However Bozsard's first wife must have died soon after 1567 because the Burwash parish register went on to record the marriage of John Byllinge (another alias of this family) and Jane Busshop in 1569, followed by the baptism of Jarman Billinge in 1570. Further baptisms of the children, Joan, Jane and John, of John Bussert, or John Bylling alias Bossard, followed between 1571 and 1574 at Warbleton.

It seems possible that John Bussard achieved employment in Bivelham borough at the same time as Dennis, because from February 1576 up to 1584 entries for more of his children, Agnes, Mary, Lawrence, Margaret, Nicholas, Rachel who did not survive infancy, and Patience, then followed at Mayfield. There seems to be no entry which records the burial of John Bussard, but if entries concerning Adrian Buzzard which occur in Burwash parish register in 1597 and 1598 relate to his eldest son, it seems possible that Jane Buzard who was buried at Burwash in 1606 was not John's daughter, who had been buried at Mayfield in 1584, but his wife or widow.

The multitude of John Boisards or Blyns in existence around 1585, even excluding the child baptised 11 years earlier at Warbleton, is confusing. Patience daughter of John Blynd alias Buzzard had been baptised at Mayfield in August 1584. John Bussard whose son Richard was baptised at Bexhill on 17 January 1585 was clearly a different man. He could possibly be John Blynd, who married Margaret Vallen of Maresfield at Mayfield in January 1585, though no entry for the burial of his former wife was recorded at Mayfield. However, John Blynd and Margaret were probably the parents of Gilbert Blyn, baptised at Mayfield in December 1585, and of Jane Bussard, baptised at Frant in 1587, but buried as Jane Blynd at Mayfield in September 1588. But which John was the father of John Bussard, William Buzzard and Katherine Blinn, baptised at Mayfield in 1588, 1590 and 1592? Again no burial entry for John Blynd occurs, but 'Margaret Billing, widow', buried at Mayfield in 1616 will have been the wife whom John married in 1585.

Another Mayfield member of this family was Anthony Blin, three of whose children, William, John and Alice, were baptised at Mayfield in 1590, 1592 and 1597, but whose son Anthony was baptised at Warbleton in 1594 under the name Bossard. Anthony's son Robert was also buried at Mayfield in 1591. Anthony himself was buried at Mayfield early in 1598 under the name Billine.

Later members of the family continued to work at forges in the capacity of hammermen. Adrian Billinge of Westfield, hammerman, will have been John's son, baptised at Burwash in 1567. He had married at Westfield in 1596, though the precise date and the surname of his wife Agnes are lost. Their children Adrian and Joan, of whom the latter did not survive, were baptised at Burwash in 1597 and 1598, their son Bennet at Brede in 1601, their daughter Ann at Salehurst in 1603 and their son John at Brede in 1606. Adrian and Agnes Billinge entered recognizances at the assizes in 1600 to give evidence against a Battle carpenter, Henry Spinner.[185] Adrian Beelinge was buried at Brede in 1609. It seems probable that Anne Billnes, widow, who married Reynold Fuller at Brede in 1618 was not Adrian's widow Agnes, but the widow of the otherwise unknown Edward Billins who was buried at Brede in 1617.

Two hammermen named John Billings, probably father and son, have left wills. The first of these was John Billings of Horsted Keynes, hammerman, who was buried in that parish in 1638. There is no doubt that he was the man who had married Anne Payne at Fletching in 1611. Their children appear to have been Elizabeth baptised at Horsted Keynes in 1614, William baptised at Framfield in 1615, Mary baptised at Cuckfield in 1616 and John, Agnes, William and Katherine baptised at Fletching between 1619 and 1626. John Billings' first wife was buried at Fletching in 1628 and in 1629 at Uckfield he married a widow named Mary Wickens. He was buried at Horsted Keynes in October 1638.

In his will John Billings left £14 10s 0d to his wife Mary, together with a featherbed, a feather bolster, a coverlet, a blanket, a fringed bed-ceiling, a holland sheet, three holland pillow-cases, all of which had been hers at marriage. His daughter Catherine was to have £20 at the age of 21, of which she was to have £5 earlier if she was sick or in need, with ashilling a year for each pound outstanding. He also left small bequests to Elizabeth and Thomas Wickens, who were probably his stepchildren. Of his own children, apart from Catherine, Billings mentioned in his will only his son John, who was to be his residuary legatee and executor. John appears to have been but 19 years of age when he took probate on 3 November 1638. Billings appointed his brother William one of his overseers. His goods were

185. Cockburn, *Sussex Assize records, Elizabeth I*, no. 1933.

inventoried at £50 17s 8d.[186]

Parish register entries do little to clarify the antecedents of the two Horsted Keynes and Fletching hammermen. The mention in his will by the Horsted Keynes man of his brother William does nothing to prove whether they were the sons of John Bussard, baptised at Mayfield in 1588 and 1590, or of Anthony, of whose sons William was baptised in 1590 and John in 1592, also at Mayfield.

The Fletching hammerman firstly followed his father at Horsted Keynes and was one of eight men, including John Duffield and John Clarke of Horsted Keynes, hammermen, who were presented at quarter sessions in 1639 for riotous entry into the home of a Lindfield widow, Joan Pegden.[187] John Billing of Fletching died in 1672, leaving only a nuncupative will. Like his father he had a daughter named Katherine; she was the wife of John Barry, to whom he left £7, with £5 to his granddaughter Jane Barry. He left three other bequests of 5 shillings and made his sons John and William his residuary legatees and executors. However, probate was granted to his sons John and Thomas![188]

Other later members of this family included Anthony's son Anthony, who married Repentance Reeve at Mayfield in 1619, but raised a family at Heathfield, before dying in 1638. His two sons Richard and Cornelius died young so he seems to have left no male heirs. William Billing, who married Mary Allen in 1621 and continued at Mayfield, may have been the man who witnessed the Horsted Keynes hammerman's will and therefore his brother. His first wife was buried at Mayfield in 1636 and he married secondly Joan Collins at Heathfield in 1638. His sons William and John, by his first wife, and Richard Billings by his second wife, may have survived him.

Outside East Sussex it seems possible that William Bossard, whose children Walter, Mary and John, were baptised at Lodsworth between 1576 and 1581, may have been from this family. However, Walter's children, William and Edward, who were baptised at Lodsworth in 1595 and 1601, were baptised under the names 'Bossom' amd 'Bossold' respectively.

Elias Billings, whose father Thomas had married Marchie Brasier at Hailsham in 1628, was baptised at Herstmonceux in 1629. His mother survived the baptism by only six months. Two children of Elias were buried at Benenden in 1653 and 1665. Both Herstmonceux and Benenden parishes adjoined ironworking areas.

Jonnett

John Jonnett was made denizen in 1544 when working at Parrock Forge. He had been born in France around 1513 and had come to England around 1525. By 1544 he had a French wife and three English-born children. Perhaps the alien John Jonner, who paid 8 pence on wages of £1 6s 0d in Netherfield hundred in 1524 was his father who had preceded the rest of the family to the Weald.

Other immigrants of this surname were possibly James Jenne, a servant of Sir William Barrentyne at Danehill Horsted in 1543, and Gloves (or Sloves?) Jonney, who paid the poll tax in Rotherfield hundred in 1551.

Andrew Gemmett of Speldhurst, who aspired to yeoman status, may have been John Jonnett's son. He may even have continued in the iron trade if it is correct to suppose that Brecher who was stated to owe him 6s 4d in one of the two copies of his will,[189] was the forgemaster Roger Breecher. The will was made on 18 January 1564 and Gemmett was buried at Speldhurst the following day. It looks as though Breecher surrendered his interest in Hungershall Forge within ten years of Gemmett's death.[190]

Andrew Gemmett's eldest son Walter and daughter Joan had died in 1562, so in his will he left Walter's heifer to his daughter Elizabeth and a black pied heifer to another daughter Margery. He had lands in both Penshurst and Ashurst parishes and these he left to his wife Joan for the duration of her life. They were then to go to his son Humphrey, and out of them Humphrey was to pay £30 to his brothers, Thomas, Andrew and James, who were all minors, at the rate of £5 yearly for six years. Joan was perhaps the widow Joan Gemmett alias Cumber who was buried at Penshurst in 1603.

Humphrey married Alice Aware at Chiddingstone in 1574; their daughters Joan and Mary were

186. ESRO, PBT 1/1/25/169a, 1/3/7/119.
187. ESRO, QR 47, m. 84; I am indebted to Brian Phillips for providing this reference.
188. ESRO, PBT 1/1/33/16.
189. KHLC, DRb/PW8.
190. Cleere and Crossley, *The iron industry of the Weald*, pp. 318, 387.

baptised at Penshurst in 1578 and 1581. Humphrey Jennet of Stonbridge, yeoman, made his will in April 1607 and wished to be buried at Chiddingstone,[191] but when or whether this occurred is unverifiable due to the lack of the parish register for that period. To his second wife Agnes he left £30 and to her son Thomas Wickenden, an apprentice in London, £20. He left £5 to Alice, daughter of his deceased brother James, and £1 to the daughter of his brother Andrew, the first bequest to be made at the age of 21 and the second at 14. He made his son Richard his executor and his overseers were to be John Turner of Bassetts in Hartfield and William Wood of Chelsham Court in Surrey. His lands in Chiddingstone, Penshurst, Speldhurst, Ashurst, Withyham and Cowden he left to his son Richard, though if Richard were to die without heirs they were to go to his wife's sons John and Thomas Wickenden and they were to pay £40 to William Wood's son Richard and £20 to his daughter Agnes.

James Jemmett had been born only in 1560 and it was not until 1590 that he married Elizabeth Tolherst at Speldhurst. However, he was buried there in 1595 after the baptism of two daughters, Alice and Elizabeth. Also presumably descended from John Jonnett was Robert Jeomett, who married Marie Crier at Goudhurst in 1580. In Sussex, Austin Jemmit was buried at East Grinstead in 1622, and on the Sussex border with Kent and Surrey the family persisted as is shown by the marriage of a second Robert Gemmet to Elizabeth Cumber at Lingfield in 1675.

In the Midlands the family was represented at Maesbury Forge in Shropshire, where the Longueville accounts mention the hammerman Abraham Jamet in 1640.[192] The disturbances of the Civil War perhaps induced Jamet to remove to the Channel Islands, where children born to Abraham Jamet and Marie Martel, a probably significant surname, were baptised from 1644 to 1666.

This family later returned to the mainland, where Renny (*recte* Remy) Jamet appeared in the parish of St Martin in the Fields in 1677, followed by Daniel Jamet, the baptism of whose first child was recorded in Threadneedle Street in 1693. In 1727, the baptismal entry for Piers son of Abraham Jamet in 1652 in the Channel Islands was paralleled by that of Pierre son of Abraham Jamet baptised at Spitalfields Artillery church in 1727.

Efforts to trace the baptism of the earlier Abraham Jamet in the Channel Islands predictably failed.

Recreff

Jakes Racreffo was made denizen in 1541. He had come to England from France about 1525 and by 1541 had an English wife. In the hanaper roll his rather unusual name was given as Jaques Recreff.[193] As Jakes Recrewe he paid 2 shillings on goods to the relief of 1549 in Shoyswell hundred as a servant of Thomas May, and his own servant Nicholas Colyar paid the poll tax. Jakes and his servant Nicholas stayed in Shoyswell hundred, where in 1550 and 1551 they paid the poll tax, in 1550 as servants of Thomas May, but in 1551 as servants of John Wybarne.

Since neither man appeared in the subsidy roll for 1552, nor in later subsidy rolls for the Weald, it looks as though Jakes must have died during 1551 or that he left the Weald. By the 1550s ironworks were being built in other parts of the country, so like John Morrell, who was last recorded in the Weald in 1549, he could have moved to the Midlands, though it is possible that he returned to France.

Harvey

John and Remy Harve were both born in Normandy at *Rosie*, a place which has not been identified. When made denizens in 1544 both claimed to have come to England around 1526. In 1544 John Harve had a Norman wife. The fact that Remy Harvie had a son named Ninian baptised at Penhurst as late as 1562 suggests that he could have been the younger man and that John may have been his father. However, John Harvie did not die until 1579, which suggests that the two denizens might have been brothers. In that case the possibility that John Darvie,[194] recorded as a servant of John Colyn of Burwash in the 1524 subsidy, was in reality John Harvie, due to the similarity in that manuscript of capital 'D' and lower case 'h', is a real one. He could have been their father and the fact that the two denizens came to

191. TNA, PROB 11/111/399.
192. Edwards, 'The early ironworks of north-west Shropshire', p. 200.
193. TNA, E 101/223/10.
194. Cornwall read 'Darme' (*The Lay subsidy rolls, 1524-5*, p. 148).

England in 1526 need not preclude their father from having arrived a year or two earlier. The suggestion that an earlier John Harvey worked for Colyn in Burwash is given support by the fact that in October 1534 John Harvye of Burwash was fined 2 pence as a defaulter at the Hawksborough hundred court.[195]

Considerable effort was made to identify 'Rosie' without success. The notarial registers of Neufchâtel contain acts relating to several families named Hervy who lived at Neufchâtel and Quièvrecourt. In the early years of the sixteenth century reference was made to Jehan Hervy the elder of Quièvrecourt and his two sons Thomassin (*Massin*) and Jehan.[196] The younger Jehan is a candidate for having been an emigrant, but how could he recently have been in 'Rosie', if his elder brother Massin made over to him property in Saint-Vincent de Nogent as early as January 1503?

A mason, Jehannot Hervy of the parish of Saint-Jacques, was referred to in 1511, and his successor in that occupation in 1537 was Loysel Hervy.[197] Colin Hervy *dit* d'Abeville who lived in the parish of Notre-Dame was referred to in 1513 and he was followed by Thomas Hervy *dit* d'Abeville at Quièvrecourt in the 1520s.[198] Gaultier Hervy of Notre-Dame parish acquired a house for leather dressing (*a facon de ouvrier de mesguicher*) in the parish of Saint-Vincent de Nogent in 1536.[199] None of these references appears relevant.

Two places in Upper Normandy are named Rosay. Rosay is a parish downstream from Saint-Saëns in the Varenne valley, for which acts can be found in considerable quantity in the notarial registers for Bellencombre from the 1480s until 1537. Although the Bellencombre acts show that secondary metal trades were prominent in the Varenne valley at the time, none referred to contemporary ironworks, nor to persons named Hervy or Hervé. Rosay-sur-Lieure is in the Forest of Lyons, but there are no extant notarial registers for the area; the notarial acts of Pont-Saint-Pierre on the lower Andelle yield a number of acts relevant to the mid-Andelle valley, but very few for the Forest of Lyons.

La Rosière is now part of the commune Beaubec-la-Rosière just north-west of Forges- les-Eaux, and notarial registers exist for the last third of the fifteenth century and for the 1550s; there is also some coverage of the area in Neufchâtel notarial registers. There are no references in either source to a family named Hervy or Hervé.

There were clear entries for both John Harvey and Remy Harvye in the Wadhurst section of the subsidy roll for Loxfield hundred in 1551. The entry for 'John Harrewe' at Wadhurst in 1550 is presumably also for the first of these men and in 1549 two badly eroded names at the end of the Wadhurst list of aliens could be theirs. Neither man had appeared in the Wadhurst section of the 1543 subsidy roll. In the entries recorded, each paid the poll tax to the reliefs or subsidies of those years.

In 1552 both men paid the poll tax in Henhurst hundred in a list of six servants of Hugh Collyn. The supposition that at this time Hugh Collyn put Socknersh Furnace in blast again is based on the fact that none of these six men had previously appeared in Henhurst; in addition to the two Harveys from Wadhurst, Simon Cleriewe had apparently been recruited from Framfield. The only one of them to continue at Henhurst in 1560 was John Harvye, who paid the poll tax there in that year and again in 1572. In 1576 he paid the poll tax in Ninfield hundred, but it was at Penhurst, close to a furnace with which Remy Harvye had been connected, that John was buried in February 1579. His goods were inventoried at only £3 14s 0d and in his will,[200] which the collier Stephen Blewett witnessed, he made his wife Catherine his sole legatee and executrix.

Remy Harvye was noticed in the Sidney ironworks accounts in 1564 when Thomas Digon, John Barbe and he supplied sows of pig iron to Robertsbridge. This was in the period when Sir Henry Sidney was no longer running his own furnace, and because the carriage of these sows to Robertsbridge was 20 pence a ton, exactly the same payment as was made for sows from Panningridge, it looks as though Penhurst was probably the furnace from which the sows came. This suggestion is supported by the fact that Remy Harvie's son Ninian, for whom Ninian Burrell could have stood as godfather, was baptised at Penhurst in April 1562. Thomas Digon died in 1565 and in that year payment for the five tons of sows

195. BL, Add. Roll 31819. It should also be noted that among the hanaper-roll denizens in 1541 was William Harvoye.

196. ADSM, 2 E 14/1144 (1 and 6 Jan 1503); 2 E 14/1146 (2 Jan 1504) etc.

197. ADSM, 2 E 14/1154 (30 Dec 1511); 2 E 14/1177 (11 Jul 1537).

198. ADSM, 2 E 14/1155 (22 Feb 1513); 2 E 14/1159 (8 Oct 1525), etc.

199. ADSM, 2 E 14/1174 (1 Aug 1536).

200. ESRO, PBT 1/1/7/137, 1/3/1/72.

supplied to Robertsbridge was made to Remy Harvie alone. This is the last known mention of Remy. His failure to appear in the 1560 subsidy rolls is not explicable. He perhaps died before the subsidies of the 1570s. Apparently his son Ninian Harvye was not the person of that name who married Elizabeth Martin at Frant in 1590.

The Harvey family throws up many more problems in addition to those of the location of 'Rosie' and the uncertainties of the relationship between John and Remy. In subsidy rolls for Framfield John Harve paid 12 shillings to the relief of 1551 and 10 shillings (as John Harvo) to that of 1552, whilst in 1560 he paid 5 shillings on goods worth £5 to the subsidy.[201] As John Harvo he married Anne Bennys at Framfield in 1558 and he was buried there as John Hervye in 1562. However, it seems from his will, dated 22 April 1562 and proved in January 1566,[202] that Harvo was the correct version of his name, and though he was listed as a native subscriber to the reliefs and subsidies, there can be little doubt that the name is of foreign origin. Perhaps the name could have been *Harvault*, *Herviou*, or some variant, in its French form.

To his wife Anne, Harvo left the lease of his house and land, the residue of his goods and chattels after payment of his debts and legacies, together with his furnace and mill. He apparently had no children and made Anne his executrix. He gave £10 to John Harvo son of William Harvo. To his brother Thomas Harvo he gave £6 13s 4d, which he had lent to him the last time they met, and he gave £2 to Gilbert, his brother's son, to be paid at the age of 20. He gave 10 shillings to be bestowed on the poor at the day of his burial and a shilling to the poor men's box of Framfield. He left a shilling to each of his godchildren, to William Barbye his best coat, to Elizabeth Alchyne (or Altham) 3s 4d and to Robert Hodgson £1. He appointed Richard Weekes of Battle his overseer, for the performance of which duty Weekes was to have £1. The witnesses were Steven Dobson, William Barbie and Robert Hodgson.

John Barbe has been encountered as a partner of Thomas Digon and Remy Harvey at Penhurst. The name will be encountered again at Mayfield towards the end of the century in connection with cannon founding and, since it is carefully distinguished from Barber, it too could be French in origin. No other person named Harvo is met with in other Wealden sources; nor is there any Gilbert Harvey. William Harvo could however have been the hanaper-roll denizen of 1541, William Harvoye.

At Robertsbridge Thomas Harvy dug at the pool in 1542. At Panningridge William Harvy cut wood and made six cams for the bellows in 1548 and 'Harvey's wife' heaped charcoal there in the same year.[203] But it was not until 1573 and 1575 that a William Harvey had children baptised at Wartling, and the only parent named Thomas Harvey encountered during the sixteenth century was a member of the gentry family of Frant in 1578. The earliest John, apart from the immigrant, or two immigrants who arrived in England in 1526, was John Harvye who married Tamson Rofe at Ardingly in 1578.[204]

John Harvo's reference to his furnace indicates that he was a forgemaster and the fact that he made a bequest to Robert Hodgson, later the forgemaster at Pounsley, suggests that Pounsley, which had already figured as 'the iron mill of Framfield' in the Portsmen's complaint of 1548, was Harvo's furnace too. His overseer, the Battle forgemaster Richard Weekes, is well enough known. As has been mentioned, Harvo supplied shot and guns to the Ordnance from 1547 onwards, and in 1550 in Ordnance accounts he was described as 'the kinges gonnstonemaker of Iron',[205] though no letters patent show that this was an official appointment.

It looks as though both Harvo and Barby may have been English-born members of immigrant families which had established themselves in the Weald around thirty or more years earlier, though why these names escaped record in the subsidy rolls of the 1520s is difficult to explain.[206]

Because in the 1520s the name Harvey was rare in Sussex, and in Wealden areas occurred only in Shoyswell hundred, it seems likely that many examples of the name found so plentifully in the Weald later in the century were persons of immigrant descent. Normally it is possible to distinguish

201. TNA, E 179/190/242, 247, 265.

202. TNA, PROB 11/49/1. The West Sussex Record Office has another copy of this will, among wills proved in peculiar jurisdictions of the archbishop of Canterbury, undated, without note of probate, and with different spellings (WSRO, STA 1/2/36).

203. KHLC, U1475, B7/1 (1542), B2/1, B11/1 (1548).

204. Another John married Clement Chittenden at Cranbrook in 1575.

205. S. Barter Bailey, 'The early cast-iron gun industry', p. 12.

206. The name John Barbile was recorded at Rye in 1525 among a list of foreigners, many of whom were unable to pay (Cornwall, *The Lay subsidy rolls*, p. 165).

indigenous families of surnames similar to those of immigrants by their relative lack of mobility. In the case of Harvey, it is only in the Cranbrook area that families display such stability. It looks almost certain that Richard Harvey, who married a wife of obviously immigrant descent, Joan Perigo, at Wartling in 1557, was an immigrant. No further mention of this man has been found.

Not so with Regnold Harve who married Margaret Dirchinge at Brightling in 1561. Brightling is where the immigrants John and Remy were last found together in 1552, so Regnold or Reynold Harvye was probably the son of one of them. The marriage was preceded at an interval of three months, and followed at an interval of three months, by two baptismal entries for Gregory, son of Regnold Harvie, or Herve. Neither of these two Gregorys, if there were in reality two of them, appears to have survived. Dirching, or rather Durkyng, was a Danehill Horsted name and it was in that direction that Regnold Harvye later moved.

Reynold Harvye was still at Brightling when his daughter Alice was baptised in 1566 but in 1567 the baptism of 'Dorothy daughter of Renould Harvye, founder in the Park', was recorded at Ardingly. The park will have been Strudgate Park and Strudgate Furnace bordered on Balcombe in the north of Ardingly parish. Reynold was still at Ardingly in 1569, when another daughter Anne was baptised there. However, when administration of his effects, which were inventoried at £14 0s 4d, was granted to his widow Margaret in 1581, the family was living in West Hoathly. Margaret's own effects were assigned to her two sons Ninian and Nicholas Harvye four years later.[207]

The Harvyes continued at Ardingly in the person of John Harvye, perhaps a son of Reynold born before his marriage to Margaret Dirching. John married Tamson Rofe in 1578 and their sons Renold and Charles were baptised at Ardingly in 1578 and 1579, after which they moved on to Worth, where Nicholas was baptised in 1584. After John Harvy's death in 1586, his widow pursued a somewhat irregular style of life for a further 36 years. Her eldest son Renold had been born within seven weeks of marriage and following her husband's death she gave birth to five more children, without ever having recourse to marriage. In the case of the second child Joan, baptised in 1592, and of the fifth child Peter, baptised in 1603, the parish register recorded the names of the fathers reputedly involved, Allen Cuddington and Peter Lockier.

Parish officials ultimately stepped in to apprentice Peter Harvye in 1617 to his legitimate half-brother Reynold Harvye, who was a Beeding finer of iron.[208] Perhaps it is not altogether surprising that Reynold, whose father had died when he was eight years of age, followed in his mother's footsteps by begetting an illegitimate child Mary, who was baptised at Cowfold in 1626, 'on the body of Mary Turner of St Leonards Forest'. If his daughter Elizabeth, baptised at Rudgwick in 1633, was also born out of wedlock, the parish register refrained from mentioning the fact.

As suggested, members of nearly all branches of the Harvye family were highly mobile. Stephen Harvie married Joan Reve at Mountfield in 1573 and Margaret, baptised there in 1574, may have been their first child. Stephen's son John was baptised at Ashburnham in 1580, but it was at Herstmonceux that Stephen was widowed in January 1587 and it was there that he was married again in February to a widow named Katheryn Dewse. Stephen brought an action for debt against the collier Peter Lamott in the Battle High court in January 1582, but at the next court in February 1582 was fined 3 pence for failing to appear to pursue the case.[209] He was buried at Crowhurst in 1596.

Giles Harvie was apparently the exception to this rule. He married Marian Lambert at Mountfield in 1582, and his three children, John, Thomas and Mary were baptised at Mountfield in 1590, 1593 and 1596, though Thomas survived only three months. Giles was buried at Mountfield in 1598. However, the years between 1582 and 1590 do remain unaccounted for. Views of frankpledge suggest that Giles was never a Battle resident, but in April 1579 the Middleborough resident William Wells was fined 20 pence for an attack on him and in September 1590 John Michell brought a suit against Giles in the Battle High court.[210]

Another member of the family in the Battle area at this period was Philip Harvey, who had a case brought against him in the Battle High court in October 1588 by the blacksmith Thomas Vipham.[211]

207. ESRO, PBT 1/3/1/101 and 139.
208. WSRO, Par 233/33/6.
209. HEH, BA Vol 97 ff 8, 9.
210. HEH, BA Vol 96 f 36, 97 f 9.
211. HEH, BA Vol 97 f 60.

Philip and his wife Elizabeth brought a case against James Boys in the same court in 1590, which was mentioned in April and July.[212] Not a Battle resident, Philip Harvey had a son named John baptised at Ashburnham in 1578, but he is otherwise unknown in the Weald.

Lewes Harvie married Joan Gringo, of obvious immigrant descent, at Mountfield in 1579. His two eldest children Nicholas and John were baptised at Mountfield in 1580 and 1582. His daughter Temperance was baptised at Crowhurst in 1587, followed by a move back to Mountfield, where Joan was baptised and buried in June 1590, and then on to Buxted, where his son Peter was baptised in 1596.

It looks as though Ninian Harvy who married Elizabeth Martin at Frant in 1590 and Nicholas Harvy who married Joan Worsley at Lamberhurst in 1599 could have been the children of the founder Reynold Harvye and his wife Margaret, who were mentioned in their mother's administration. The marriage of their sister Dorothy to Thomas Barritte at Lamberhurst in 1583 could in some way have paved the way for their move to that part of the Weald.

Ninian Harvy had two children, Ann and John, baptised at Frant in 1593 and 1597. His wife was buried at Frant in 1616 and he himself was buried there the following year. Nicholas was presumably father to Nicholas and Mary, baptised at Lamberhurst in 1602 and 1603, and was named as the father to Thomas and Richard baptised there in 1606 and 1608. Of these children only Mary and Richard survived infancy, and their parents both died in 1613, when his burial entry showed that Nicholas Harvye was a collier. Ninian's son John could have been the man who married Anne Lahan alias Collins at Lamberhurst in 1625 and whose son John was baptised at Frant in 1629. His elder sister had married Elias Russell at Frant in 1616.

Charles, the younger brother of the finer Reynold Harvie, who was baptised at Ardingly in 1579 was probably the miner, Charles Harvie of Cranbrook who married Joan Panckurst at Goudhurst in 1607. Their children, Ninion, John and Joan, were baptised at Cranbrook in 1608, 1611 and 1613. Charles was buried at Cranbrook in 1639. He was mentioned in the Cranbrook parish register in June 1655 in connection with the remarriage of Anne Austen, stated to be his widow.

It is difficult to be sure whether Peter Harvy, the hammerman who paid the hearth tax at Crowhurst in 1665,[213] was the Peter Harvey who was buried at Crowhurst in 1681, and was said in the parish register to be more than 80 years old, or his son Peter baptised at Burwash in 1629. In any case we cannot be sure whether the father was the illegitimate child of Thomasine Harvye and Peter Lockier, baptised at Worth in 1603, who would have been only 78 years old in 1681, but whom we know to have been an apprenticed forgeman, or Peter the son of Lewes Harvye baptised at Buxted in 1596, who would in fact have been around 85 years of age.

It looks as though Peter's children were Ann baptised at Salehurst in 1627, Peter baptised at Burwash in 1629, Thomas baptised at Salehurst in 1631, William baptised at Mountfield in 1637 and Walter baptised at Battle in January 1640. Peter's wife Agnes was buried at Mountfield in February 1640, the month after Walter's baptism, and in October he was married again to Martha Pookewell at Mountfield. She however was buried at Mountfield in September 1645.

William Harvie who married Clemens Pynion at Ashburnham in February 1602 was probably the father and grandfather of two Wartling forgemen, John who was mentioned in the Wartling parish register in 1637, and William mentioned in the Hailsham parish register in 1656. William's children, John, probably the first of these two forgemen, Elizabeth and Marie were baptised at Ashburnham in 1602, 1604 and 1606. Parish register entries enable the family to be followed to Warbleton in 1607, and to Wartling in 1610 and 1612, where Joan, William and Steven were baptised, and then to Crowhurst where Dorothy was baptised in 1616. However, William Harvie was buried at Crowhurst six weeks after Dorothy's baptism and his widow Clemens Harvie was buried there in 1619; of their children, Marie, Joan and William were probably the persons of those names buried at Crowhurst in 1616, 1618 and 1619, and only John, Elizabeth, Steven and Dorothy seemingly survived childhood.

John Harvey's first two children, William, apparently the second forgeman, and Anne, were baptised at Crowhurst in 1628 and 1630. In the face of a Wartling register which recorded no baptisms, but only four burials relating to this forgeman, it seems possible to bring together the entry in the Warbleton parish register which recorded the baptisms on 8 January 1637 of John and Steven, twins of John Harvy 'born at Herstmonceux', with a Wartling entry which recorded the burial of the forgeman

212. HEH, BA Vol 97 ff 81, 72.

213. TNA, E 179/258/20.

John Harvy's wife on 10 January 1637, and interpret this as a death in childbirth. The Wartling parish register next recorded the burial of the son John in December 1638, whilst at Herstmonceux the forgeman was married again to Freegift Sinden in January 1639. Their daughter Rejoyce was baptised at Warbleton in August 1639, whilst the burial of another son John, for whom no baptism has been found, was recorded at Wartling in October 1640.

It looks more likely that William Harvey of Wartling, forgeman, whose marriage to Jane Taylor of Wartling, spinster, was mentioned in the Herstmonceux parish register in 1656, was the eldest son of John Harvy, baptised at Crowhurst in 1628, than Peter Harvey's son William baptised at Mountfield in 1637.

Harvey entries occur plentifully in parish registers of the north Midlands and some of these Harveys, who were indigenous are difficult to distinguish from immigrant ironworkers. Ironworks' accounts show that John Harvy corded wood at Oakamoor in 1593, and that in 1593-4 he was employed as a collier, with Lawrence and Thomas Harvye then recorded as wood-cutters. William, Lawrence and Francis Harvye were again woodcutters there in 1598; Hugh Harvye was included among the woodcutters in 1599, and John Harvy continued to work as a collier at Oakamoor Forge in each campaign up to 1608.[214]

A hint that John Harvye may have come from the Weald along with Nicholas Lycette, who had been forgemaster at Horsmonden in 1564, and held the lease of Oakamoor Forge briefly from 1572 to 1577 before moving on to Hints, was given by John's marriage to Joan Lycette at Rugeley in 1585. The Oakamoor woodcutter William Harvye may have been the collier recorded further west at Ellastone in 1599, who fathered a son named Thomas on 'Isabell Billinge, a poor wench'. Again it is the surname of the mother which suggests that both parties were possibly of immigrant stock. A later, or the same William Harvey, who was buried in 1659 at Madeley in Shropshire, was 'a stranger and a workman at the workes in Madeley Wood'.

In Derbyshire John Harvey worked at New Mills and then at Makeney in the early eighteenth century. Whilst John was at New Mills his son John was baptised at Duffield in 1705, and baptismal entries for his children, John, Richard, Silence, Thomas and William, followed between 1708 and 1715, when he was at Makeney.

In South Yorkshire the Attercliffe bellows-maker John Harvey married Elaine Clark at Rawmarsh in 1740. The Rotherham blacksmith Vincent Harvey (1693-1742)[215] traced his ancestry back through his father Thomas and his grandfather Nicholas to another Vincent Harvey who married Joan Cussin at Rotherham in 1620.

Longley

When made denizen in 1544, John Langleys alias Margo claimed to have a French wife, to have been born at Haucourt (*Haucort*) in Normandy and to have come to England around 1526. In the French section of this work his family was traced at Beaubec-la-Ville around 1500 and members of this Beaubec family were shown indeed to have resided at Haucourt in 1495. It seems hazardous to equate a John Longlie mentioned in the Ashburnham parish register between 1543 and 1549 with the denizen, because, as we shall see, there was apparently an English John Longley in the vicinity of Panningridge Furnace, from whom the Panningridge accounts distinguished the Frenchman by using his alias Margo.

From 1549 to 1552 Langleys paid the poll tax each year in Foxearle hundred, as a servant of Sir William Sidney apart from 1550, when he was recorded as a servant of Mr Anthony Pelham. In the Sidney accounts for 1542 diggers employed at Robertsbridge for the 'amendyng of 2 pouldes (pools?) of the fynerie gatis' included John Longley. He was also among the woodcutters at Robertsbridge, whilst as John Margo he and his man were paid £8 5s 0d for getting 264 loads of mine at 7½ pence the load.[216]

In 1543 Come Longly, who was encountered at Beaubec-la-Ville as Quesm Langlais, and his son, who was presumably John Longly, were paid 7 shillings 'for Carage of Wodde owt of the ponde for safgard thereof from the water, which wodde they caryed wyth whyle borows for 7 days ether of them

214. UNMASC, Middleton MSS.5/165/52, 53, 54, 55, 59, 63, 64, 66, 68, 71, 72.
215. For his occupation see the marriage entry of 30 Mar 1719.
216. KHLC, U1475, B6/2, B7/1.

6d a day' at Panningridge. They were later paid 2 shillings for two further days of the same work.[217] Both worked as miners at Panningridge that year, and Come Langley was a filler at the furnace, whilst John Longley was a woodcutter there and was among the Frenchmen who bought white meat and milk.[218] Come Longley was not among the men made denizens in 1544 and he failed to appear in the subsidy rolls for the period 1549 to 1552. He was perhaps dead, or had returned to France.

In 1544, under the alias Margo, John Longley made a part payment of 6s 8d towards his letters patent of denization. He also continued to work as a miner.[219] Westall's 'Book of Panningridge' showed that in 1546 Margo cut 21 cords of wood, continued to work as a miner, made two coal baskets for 1s 2d, and bought apples and lent wheat; Westall's Robertsbridge book showed that Margo paid a further 11 shillings towards denization, made more coal baskets and paid for cattle sold to him.[220]

The same pattern continued in 1547 and 1548: Longley's main work was as a woodcutter and miner at Panningridge, whilst he made coal baskets for both Panningridge and Robertsbridge.[221] In 1549, in addition to his usual work, Longley was paid 'for his labor in goyng to Hawksden to speek with Wells the carpenter', perhaps in the aftermath of the destruction of Sidney's furnace by rioters who came out of Kent.[222]

The Panningridge book of 1550 showed him being paid, as John Margo, £13 0s 8d for digging 391 loads of mine out of Cressey's wood in June and £8 10s 10d for 250 loads out of Haselden Wood in September, with an additional £7 1s 8d for 170 loads which he had dug, but which had not been carried to the furnace. Later he was paid £1 6s 8d for cutting 80 cords of wood in Hordens Wood in November and 16s 8d for cutting 50 cords there in December.

After the earliest period at Robertsbridge Longley was consistently named Margo in the accounts and the suggestion that this change was made to avoid confusion with an Englishman named John Longley who lived near Panningridge seems justified by a payment made to John Longley in 1550 of 7s 6d 'for the lyberty thorow his lande for our car[ria]ge of coles'. John Margo on the other hand supplied four new coal baskets at 8 pence each and was paid 4 pence for a new 'bog' for the furnace.[223]

The same pattern of work continued in 1551, and, if the subsidy roll for that year is to be believed, during 1552, for which no furnace book survives. By 1553 however Longley was no longer at Panningridge.[224] Since he did not appear in the subsidy rolls of 1560 for the Weald, he must be presumed to have died, to have moved to another part of the country, which was becoming increasingly possible in the 1550s, or to have returned to France.

Two other immigrant members of the family, Francis and Davy Longley, were mentioned in the Sidney accounts. Both worked at Robertsbridge, where in the subsidy roll of 1552 for Staple hundred, 'Frauncis' paid the poll tax as a servant of Adrian Dogyn. He must have been the Francis who paid the poll tax there again in 1560.

Davy Longles was paid for 'cindering the ways' near Robertsbridge in 1553, and in 1554 both he and Francis were paid 'for 4 days ther workyng'.[225] That they were employed to assist Adrian Dogyn, one of the colliers at Robertsbridge, is shown in the forge book of 1555, where the receipt of £3 from Dogyn as surety for their denizations was recorded. However, Davy's failure to appear in the subsidy roll of 1560 is explained by the incidental remark 'and the sayd Davy Longley departyd within the halfe yeer folowyng'.[226]

Both surnames Longley and Langley appeared in the Wealden areas of Sussex in the subsidy rolls of 1524-5, though neither was widespread. Longley appears to be the more natural English rendering of the French *Langlais*, but in the subsidy rolls it is remarkable that it was only in 1549 that the form 'Longley' was used. In the following three years not only was the final 's' of the French original retained, but the medial 'a' reappeared, even in 1552 becoming 'Langlesse'. In Staple hundred in 1552 and 1560

217. Crossley, *Sidney ironworks accounts*, pp. 45-6.
218. KHLC, U1475, B2/2, B9.
219. KHLC, U1475, B7/3.
220. HEH, BA Vol. 97 (Westall's book of Panningridge); ESRO, SHE 6/1/11/1 (Robertsbridge).
221. KHLC, U1475, B2/1, B10/1, 2a and 3, B11/1.
222. KHLC, U1475, B11/3.
223. Crossley, *Sidney ironworks accounts*, pp. 87-8, 91, 93, 95-7.
224. KHLC, U1475, B10/5 and 6.
225. KHLC, U1475, B8/5 and 6.
226. Crossley, *Sidney ironworks accounts*, p. 119.

the problem was avoided by not using the surname.

At Brightling, the baptism in 1561 of Agnes daughter of Edward 'Loncle' suggests a French origin for this family. But there is nothing to connect this man with the later collier Edward Langley, whose son Edward Langley, a broadweaver, was married at Cranbrook in 1657. The collier can be traced from 1606 onwards at Hawkhurst where his son, Edward the later broadweaver, was baptised in 1617 and where he himself was buried in 1620. Edward Langley the collier came from Brede where he had married Annis Genner in 1594 and where the baptisms of his children show him to have stayed until 1604. Parish register entries consistently take the form Langley, so a French descent for this collier is far from certain, despite the proximity of Brede to Staple hundred where Francis Longley was last traced in 1560.

Many other persons seem better candidates for French descent. John Longley of Hartfield, for instance, a bondsman for Roger Lambert and Quintin Tyler when they took administration of the goods of Katherine Tyler of Fletching in 1559,[227] was perhaps of French descent.

Anthony Longlye of Burwash is shown by a marriage licence of 1587 to have been a blacksmith.[228] He married Elizabeth Luckas at Burwash in 1584, his children John, Mary, Goddard and Thomas were baptised there between 1585 and 1593, and he was buried at Burwash in 1608. Here French descent seems probable, but does not appear provable.

The Benenden parish register reveals that Jasper Longley's daughter Anne, who was baptised there in 1621, had been born at Henry Austen's forge at Tenterden. However, it is uncertain whether Jasper's father was Thomas Longly the younger, whose son was baptised at Ticehurst in 1586, or a 'trugger' also named Jasper Longley, whose son was baptised at Ticehurst in 1595.

In 1613 John Longley of Buxted married Ciceley Tucker, who was perhaps the daughter of the pot-founder Thomas Tucker. When he acted as bondsman in a probate administration in 1619 Longley was styled 'potter';[229] this is a case in which we can be fairly certain that the pots produced were cast-iron ones. John Longley's children, Elizabeth, John, Francis, Anne, William and perhaps Robert, were baptised at Buxted between 1615 and 1633 and he was buried at Buxted in 1639.

Their marriages make other Longleys also candidates for French descent. At Burwash Constance Longeley, who in 1563 married John Glidde, could have been of French descent. At Warbleton John Longley married Annes Pynnion in 1603. Further marriages involving two members of the immigrant community occurred in 1621 when James Spray alias Pinion married Elizabeth Longlie at Buxted and probably in 1638 when Thomas Longley married Martha Pountney at Salehurst.

The father of an ironfounder was perhaps Bartholomew Longley, who in January 1553 had married Agnes Mersall at Balcombe. After the baptism of a daughter there in December 1553 they were not mentioned at Balcombe again and next appeared at Worth, where their children Andrew and Joan were baptised in 1567 and 1569 and where their son Gerard was buried in 1575.

When he died in 1574 William Patching of Balcombe left all his property to Bartholomew Longly and his children, so it appears that Agnes Mersall was possibly his daughter. He left 6s 8d to eight of Longly's eldest children, other than William, as well as 6s 8d to Bartholomew's wife Agnes. To Bartholomew he left his best shirt and the remission of £2 13s 4d which Bartholomew owed him. To the children Patching also left three pairs of old hose (*hoosen*) and his doublet and frieze jerkin. He made Bartholomew's son William his residuary legatee and executor. William was probably Longly's eldest son, born during the 1550s, but in 1574 was still a minor and could not execute the will, so that task fell to the overseers who were Thomas Colpeper, perhaps of Wakehurst, and William Ilman, perhaps related to the forgemaster Ilman, who along with Swayne had employed two aliens in Burbeech hundred in 1563.[230]

Bartholomew Longle was buried at Cowfold in May 1596 and his will revealed the names of two more of his children: his sole bequest was of his best bed and its furnishings, which after the death of his wife Agnes was to go to his son Bartholomew; two other sons, William and John, were to act as overseers to assist their mother who was made residuary legatee and executor. Bartholomew's goods

227. ESRO, PBT 1/1/3/259.
228. Dunkin, *Sussex Marriage Licences, Lewes 1586-1643*, p. 2.
229. ESRO, PBT 1/3/4/186.
230. ESRO, PBT 1/1/6/190v.

were inventoried at £31 7s 8d.[231]

Although when he made his will in 1617 William Longley described himself as 'of Framfield, ironfounder' he was not buried at Framfield, nor were any of his children baptised there. He made the gunfounder, Richard Relf of Framfield, his executor, and Nicholas Stone and Stephen Aynscombe his overseers, appointments which suggest that Pounsley was the furnace at which he then worked. However, Relf also died in 1620, so probate was granted to Nicholas Stone on 30 December 1620.[232]

The names of William Longley's children were given in his will, and their baptisms can be traced, not at Framfield, but at Maresfield. Both his marriage and his burial took place at Maresfield in 1593 and 1620, but the marriage entry failed to name his bride. That her first name was Elizabeth can be found from the record of her burial which took place at Maresfield in 1611. From the Maresfield register it seems that his marriage to Elizabeth may not have been his first, because in July 1586 William Longly married Annes B(aylye?) there. However, no children arising from this marriage were recorded in the register, nor was there any burial entry for this first wife. The 1593 marriage therefore remains the first certain parish register entry relating to this ironfounder. It also looks as though he had formerly worked in Maresfield and that he had moved to Pounsley quite recently before 1617.

By his will William left to his eldest daughter Frances a featherbed, a feather bolster, a pillow, a pillow-coat, two pairs of sheets, two blankets, a coverlet, a joined bedstead, the bigger brass cauldron, a boarded chest, a hat and a russet gown. To his daughter Elizabeth he left the best featherbed, a feather bolster, a pillow, a pillow-coat, a joined bedstead, two pairs of sheets, two blankets, a coverlet, the other brass cauldron, a joined chest, his best hat, his best gown, and a ruff band. His executor and overseers were to sell the residue of his effects and to employ the proceeds in bringing up his youngest sons Thomas and Edward, until Edward reached the age of 21, when the residue was to be divided equally between all his sons, William, Christopher, John, Thomas and Edward.

That the eldest son William may also have been involved in ironfounding is suggested by his marriage in 1629 to a widow named Jane Guildford; the Guildfords were an English iron-founding family who worked in Mayfield.

The second Bartholomew Longley was probably the man of that name buried at Balcombe in 1605; he seems to have died unmarried. His brother Andrew's first wife Alice was buried at Worth in 1596 and neither of their daughters, Agnes and Elizabeth, baptised at Worth in 1590 and 1595, survived infancy. Andrew's second wife was Jane Parsons whom he married later in 1596 and of their children, Elizabeth, Jane, William, Joan, Susan and Francis, baptised between 1597 and 1607, all except William and Susan survived infancy. It seems improbable however, that Andrew and his family continued in the Weald.

The fourth brother John was first traced at Ardingly, then back at Balcombe and later at Horsted Keynes, where he died in 1639. By his will he left £1 to the poor at his burial, a sum increased by 10 shillings in a codicil. To his son George, who had been baptised at Balcombe in 1604, he left £40. To his granddaughters Mary and Margaret Turner he left £6 each payable at their ages of 21. They were the daughters of his daughter Margaret who had married John Turner at Horsted Keynes in 1629. Margaret had been baptised at Ardingly in 1601 and was the twin of John's eldest surviving son, William, who was appointed residuary legatee and executor. A son named John, who was baptised at Ardingly in 1598, was not mentioned in the will, so perhaps had not survived. John's youngest child was a daughter Jane who had been baptised at Horsted Keynes in 1621. Jane's grandfather Thomas Pelling had left her legacies in his will and her Longley grandfather made Jane a legacy of £100 payable at her marriage or majority, provided she made a discharge of her Pelling grandfather's legacies. He also left her an annuity of £6 until her marriage or majority, his biggest joined chest and three pairs of fine sheets. Other bequests were of 10 shillimgs to his cousin John Burte, 3s 4d each to his kinsmen William Longley, perhaps the eldest son of the ironfounder, and John Luxford and a shilling to his cousin John Comber. By the codicil, in addition to more to the poor, he left £10 to George's son John and £2 each to his granddaughters Mary and Sara Longley, who were William's daughters, all of which bequests were payable at the age of 21. John Longley of Horsted Keynes' goods were inventoried at £191 8s 7d.[233]

231. ESRO, PBT 1/1/9/393, 1/3/2/220.

232. ESRO, PBT 2/2/4/119.

233. ESRO, PBT 1/1/22/76, 1/3/7/182. This account leaves undiscussed the question of whether Jane Langley's mother was 'Eleanor, wife of John Longlye', buried at Horsted Keynes in 1624, or 'Elizabeth wife of John Longly'

Clarke

Rowland Clerke became a denizen in 1544. He claimed to have been born in France around 1511 and to have come to England around 1527. In 1544 he had an English wife and two children. He was presumably the man who paid the poll tax in the subsidy of 1543 in the same borough of Brenchley hundred as John Angerfield, but was listed separately from him. No parish register entries appear to relate to him.

The will of a Tonbridge widow, Alice Clarke, made in November 1559,[234] was witnessed by the Kent forgemaster David Willard and the ironfounder Richard Trewe. She made her two sons, William and John Clarke, her executors, but the house left her by her late husband, whose name was not disclosed, was not in Brenchley but in Bidborough.

In 1549 a Frenchman in Mr Pelham's works named Guillam Clerke paid the poll tax in Foxearle hundred. In this area Hierome Clarke's son Hugh had been baptised at Ashburnham in November 1542. It is impossible to be sure whether the marriage of Jeram Clarke to Joan Hafar at Mountfield in 1567 was a second marriage of the Ashbunrham man, or of a similarly named relative. Robert and Isabel Clarke who were baptised at Mountfield in 1569 and 1574, but whose parents were not disclosed, were perhaps their children. In 1562 the immigrant James Leonard had married Mary Clarke at Mountfield.

The finer Philip Clarke married Marion Torchyld (*Torcy*) at Maresfield in 1547. Marion was buried at Ashburnham in June 1574, when her husband was working at Kitchenham Forge. Their presence in that part of the Weald had been noticed in the Warbleton parish register in the 1560s, when the burial of 'Leonard Clarke, a French child' was recorded in December 1562 and Philip's daughter Phillis (*Felece*) was baptised in January 1563. As the Warbleton register commenced only in 1560 Clarke could very well have been working in that area during the 1550s.

In June 1575 Philip Clarke married his second wife, Alice Waters, at Ashburnham. He was next noticed in April 1578 as a defaulter in the Hartfield view of frankpledge for Birchden borough, where the original entry 'Philip fynar' was altered to read Philip Clarke.[235] The following year his daughter Jane was baptised at Frant and he later moved on to Goudhurst, where a final notice of him occurred in January 1582 at the baptism of his daughter Alice.

The marriage took place at Frant in 1563 of Joan Clarke to Thomas Hawsee, where it appears the seventeenth-century copyist read the three minims of Hanisee (for Hunnisset) as a 'w'. They were almost certainly the parents of Peter Clarke alias Honiysett who was buried at Westfield in 1632.

Another Frant marriage was that of Thomas Clarke in 1591 to Mary Angerfield. She, as Mary Lesset, had become the second wife of John Angerfield the elder in 1581. John Angerfield died in 1590, and the son Thomas Angerfield whom she bore him, his only surviving son, will perhaps have been brought up in her second husband's family, though she herself died in childbirth in May 1592, after bearing Thomas Clarke's eldest son, also named Thomas.

Thomas Clarke's second wife was Mary Peckham whom he married at Framfield in 1595. She bore him two children, Elizabeth and John, who were baptised at Frant in 1596 and 1598. Before his marriage Thomas Clarke of Frant, husbandman, had been indicted at the assizes, together with the Frant hammerman David Laffam, for an assault carried out on 13 October 1587.[236] They were found not guilty. Clarke's association with Laffam suggests he too could have been involved in ironworking.

Before his death, which occurred in 1616, Thomas Clarke had moved to Wadhurst and in his will he styled himself yeoman.[237] He left £25 to his eldest son Thomas, to which, in a codicil, was added £5 and the greatest joined chest. His younger son John and his daughter Elizabeth were each to have £20 at their ages of 23 and 24 respectively. His wife, whom he made his residuary legatee and executrix lived on until 1641. In her will she made bequests to her stepson Thomas Clarke, and to his son Thomas, as well as to her daughter Elizabeth Baldock, and her children; she made her own son John residuary legatee and executor.[238] Neither will linked this branch of the Clarke family with the manufacture of

buried at Balcombe in November 1621. The latter had married John Longley at Balcombe in 1617 as 'Elizabeth Balcomb, widow'. In any case it seems probable that Jane's mother was not John Longley's first wife.

234. KHLC, DRb/PW6.

235. ESRO, ACC 3597/8, f. 79v.

236. Cockburn, *Sussex Assize records, Elizabeth I*, no. 1931

237. ESRO, PBT 2/2/4/52.

238. ESRO, PBT 2/2/5/73.

iron, other than the fact that the forgemaster William Dyke witnessed both, which he may have done as lord of the manor rather than in the capacity of forgemaster.

Another member of the Clarke family who evidently was closely connected with ironworking was Stephen Clarke of Fletching, labourer. He was undoubtedly the Steven Clarke who married Mary Turner at Maresfield in 1586. An unbaptised child of theirs was buried at Buxted in 1588. He was charged at the assizes with the theft from George Kenion of 9 tons of iron on 2 March 1591.[239] The assize court noted that Clarke had since died and the fact that his burial was recorded at Horsham on 29 June 1591 indicates that he had ended his days in Horsham gaol. The theft of such a large quantity of iron would indicate that it was in the course of Clarke's employment that the opportunity arose, though he may have been no more than a carrier of iron.

Probably related in some way to Stephen Clarke was the Horsted Keynes hammerman, John Clarke. In 1639 he was charged, along with eight other men who included two further hammermen, with riotous entry into the house of a Lindfield widow, Joan Pegden.[240] The forge he worked at may have been Freshfield. The baptism at Maresfield of John son of John Clarke in 1608 perhaps relates to this hammerman, though whether the felon was the son or the father is impossible to say. The father was presumably John Clarke who was married in 1602 at Lindfield to Mary Hardynge, no doubt a member of the English ironworking family of that name.

Attention should also be given to the numerous parish register entries relating to persons named Clarke alias Smith. They were thick upon the ground in Goudhurst, where it will be remembered Philip Clarke the finer was last traced. However, entries relating to this family seem to go back to 1559, when John son of Thomas Clarke was buried at Goudhurst. Further entries include the baptism of Thomas Clarke's daughter Margaret in 1562 and the baptism of Steven, son of Richard Clarke alias Smythe in 1581. Richard Clarke evidently predeceased Thomas, because when the latter died in 1591, he asked his son-in-law and executor, Margaret's husband Robert Shawe, to bring up Steven Clarke. In his will, Thomas Smythe alias Clarke styled himself yeoman, left lands in Seal to his two sons John and Thomas, and in no way indicated any connection with ironworking.[241]

Not only Steven, but also John Smythe alias Clarke, who was married at Goudhurst in 1616, continued to use this alias. It had earlier been used for Thomas Smith alias Clark, who was buried at Bexhill in 1575 and by George Clarke alias Smith, who married Susan Fowling at Ashburnham in 1610, a spread which suggests that it may have had an occupational origin.

Other aliases, this time suggesting links with other immigrant families, were Milward and Fussell. John Clarke alias Milward brought an action for debt in the High court of Battle against George a'Weekes in February 1581, but failed to appear to press his suit on 11 April, so the case was dismissed.[242] The marriage of John Clarke alias Fussell to Jane Kyppinge at Tonbridge in 1591, was not followed by any appropriate baptisms. This alias suggests a former link of his family with that of Vassall or Foshall, then strongly represented in Tonbridge parish, with the lack of baptisms suggesting that he no longer lived in the parish.

A connection of the Clarke family of Battle with ironworking was made explicit as late as 1701, when the parish register recorded the burial of Sara daughter of Robert Clarke, founder, and Elizabeth his wife. Robert Clarke had married Elizabeth Walker at Battle in 1697. Whether he was the son of Thomas Clarke baptised at Battle in 1647 is rendered questionable by the fact that he would in that case have been 50 years of age at marriage. The marriage of Thomas Clarke to Mary Cole had taken place at Battle in 1626, but it was not until 1644 that Thomas Clarke was recorded as the parent of a child in the parish register, though parentage of Clarke children who were baptised in 1630 and 1638 was not disclosed.

That an earlier Thomas Clarke of Battle was a carpenter was shown in a Battle High court case of March 1586 in which he acted as surety;[243] this Thomas Clarke was presumably the Middleborough man who was fined for default at views of frankpledge in October 1583 and April 1584.[244]

239. Cockburn, *Sussex Assize records, Elizabeth I*, no. 1298.
240. ESRO, QR 47, m. 84.
241. TNA, PROB 11/78/276.
242. HEH, BA Vol. 96 ff 85, 87.
243. HEH, BA Vol. 97 f 55.
244. HEH, BA Vol. 97 ff 31, 32.

Addes, Judd or Powell

After a long gap, the arrival in the Weald around 1528 of Nicholas Uddys heralded the appearance of a few more ironworkers from the Beauvaisis. As well as being recorded in the denization roll among Master Pelham's workers, he appeared separately with four of them in a list headed by Hollowyn Belhache, as Nicholas Oddes, there claiming to have been 15 rather than 16 years in England. He had been born around 1484 at *Saucye* (Sorcy near Le Becquet?)[245] in the Beauvaisis and in 1544 had a French wife and three children.

Also included in the Westminster denization roll was Michael Oyddes; he too came from the Beauvaisis around 1532, but was still only 21 years of age in 1544, by when he had an English wife.

The French original of this name will have been Eudes, and though its rendering in English gave rise to a greater variety of options than any other French surname, there were several varieties in French, *Heudes* and *Heuldes* perhaps becoming the dominant ones as time wore on. In England 'Addes' or 'Eddes' were the commonest versions, but 'Judd' or 'Judds' and even 'Judge' and also 'Ede' occur. Other probable variants are Youd and Youds, of which the Anthony Yod who married at Fletching in 1562 is a Wealden example.

Of these surnames only Judd and Ede occurred in the subsidy rolls of the 1520s. Judd was found only in the Alciston area, whilst Ede, though well represented in West Sussex, occurred in the east only in Battle hundred. Finally, it must be queried whether Addison, of which Richard Adderson in Tottingworth was the sole East Sussex example in 1524, was another variant. The forms 'Hyndall', 'Hedowell' and 'Hedall' are surprising, but 'Heddall' is authenticated by the Mayfield parish register. From Nicholas's son Paul, other descendants took the easier surname 'Paul' or 'Powell'.

Nicholas Eudes first appeared as Nicholas Hyndall in 1543, when he paid the poll tax in Hawksborough hundred. He moved on to Shoyswell hundred, where he paid a shilling to the relief of 1549 as Nycholas Hedowell, in the company of his son Paul and a servant Nicholas Lamberd, both of whom paid the poll tax. By 1550 Nicholas had moved back to Hawksborough hundred, but the Shoyswell roll for that year showed both Paul and Michael Hedoll to be workers of Anthony Pelham, from which it can be inferred that it was at Pelham's Bivelham Forge that Michael had worked in 1549.

In Hawksborough hundred in 1550 'Hedall colyer' again worked for Anthony Pelham, but on this occasion in Bivelham borough which included Pelham's Hawksden Forge. This entry for the payment of the poll tax was followed in 1551 by an almost identical entry, though on this occasion Simon, Hedall's man, also paid the poll tax. By 1552 Thomas Morley had acquired Hawksden Forge from Pelham and 'Hedall' failed to appear among the workers employed by him. At the age of 67 Nicholas may well have died, or have become too old for such employment.

The other denizen Michael Oyddes first appeared in a subsidy roll in 1549 in Hawksborough hundred, when he paid the poll tax in the relief of that year as 'Mychell Hedhall colyar', a servant of Nicholas Pelham. In 1550 he paid the poll tax in Shoyswell hundred, alongside Paul Hedoll, probably his brother, now working for Anthony Pelham at Bivelham Forge. By 1551 he had moved on, but failed to appear in a subsidy roll until 1552, when he paid the poll tax among the Wadhurst aliens.

Nicholas's other son Paul, not recorded in the reliefs of 1551 and 1552, reappeared in Shoyswell hundred as 'Poule Judde' in 1560, perhaps again at Bivelham Forge, and then in 1572 in Hawksborough hundred as 'Powle Edolfe', a servant of Thomas Green, perhaps at Hawksden Forge, where his father had worked in the 1550s. On each of these occasions he paid the poll tax. 'Pawle Judd alias Heddall' was buried at Mayfield in March 1577.

Robert Jedd who married Gillian Tyler at Mayfield in 1573 was probably Paul's son, because their daughter Agnes was baptised under the name 'Judd alias Powle' in 1575. But by the 1580s they were settled in Waldron, where their children, Gillian, John who did not survive, Dorothy and another John, were baptised in 1583, 1586, 1587 and 1590. Robert was buried at Waldron later in 1590.

A French-born son of Paul Judd was perhaps Thomas Powle, who paid the poll tax in Robertsbridge hundred in 1576. If so, he, like his brother Robert, soon moved on to Waldron, where his sons Lewis, son of 'Thomas Powl', Jarman, son of 'Powle a Frenchman' and probably Nicholas, son of 'a Frenchman', were baptised in 1577, 1580 and 1583. Thomas will have been the 'Powle' who was buried at Waldron in 1585.

245. Page's reading of this rubbed and indistinct name was 'Stamye'.

Thomas's son Jarman is readily identifiable as Jarman Judge, whose children, William, Elizabeth, Tamesin, John, Richard, and Thomas, were baptised at Bodiam between 1607 and 1624, and whose daughters Elizabeth and Anne were baptised at Ewhurst in 1626 and 1629. Neither the first Elizabeth nor Thomas survived childhood. Jarman Judge was buried at Ewhurst in 1630. His goods were valued at £39 14s 7d. By his will he forgave his eldest son William his debts and gave him 10 shillings; he left his son Richard £5, though out of this his third wife and executrix Elizabeth was to bind the boy apprentice, and Richard was to have the residue only at 21. Jarman's daughters, Tomsine, Elizabeth and Agnes were each to have £10 at their ages of 21. A copyhold tenement in the manor of Robertsbridge occupied by Seth Davy was to be surrendered by Thomas King to the use of Jarman's wife for life, after which it was to go to his younger son Richard.[246]

The continued Robertsbridge connection of this family suggests that Nicholas Powell who married Rachel Humphrey at Salehurst in June 1600 was a son of Paul Judd. However, their first children, Margaret, Joan and Thomas, were baptised at Frant, between 1601 and 1605. Of them only Joan survived infancy. Thomas was buried at Etchingham in 1607, but their remaining children, William and Mary, were baptised back at Salehurst in 1608 and 1612. Nicholas died in 1614, but his son William continued there during the 1630s, when his children Edmund, Mary and William were baptised there, between 1635 and 1640.

Other probable descendants of Paul Judd were Henry Poole and Bartholomew Powle of Salehurst and Robert Powell of Ticehurst. Henry Poole's children, Jeremy, Ellis, Richard, Dorothy and John, were baptised between 1594 and 1603, and their father was buried at Salehurst in 1618. Robert Powell's children, Elizabeth, Alice, Barbara, Dorothy and Ann, were baptised at Ticehurst between 1599 and 1615. Robert's first wife Gilian, the mother of these children, was buried in 1622, and his second wife Joan in 1639. Bartholomew married Elizabeth Harte at Salehurst in 1623 and their children, Ann, John, Thomas, Mary and another Ann, were baptised at Salehurst between 1624 and 1635.

It looks as though Thomas Poul's youngest son Nicholas was the younger Nicholas Powell who married Mary Pannell at Salehurst in 1619. Their son Nicholas was baptised and buried at Salehurst in 1620. Their later children, John, Joan, Mary, Margaret, Nicholas and Thomas, were baptised at Ewhurst from 1621 to 1631, though of these Margaret did not survive infancy.

Another descendant of Paul Judd was George Paul alias Juds of Warbleton, who married Elizabeth Bray at Ashburnham in 1610. Their children, John, Edward, Elizabeth and Martha, were baptised at Warbleton from 1616 to 1627. 'George Juddes a married man' was buried at Warbleton in 1629. He was probably the illegitimate son of Ann Powell baptised at Mayfield in 1584. His son John, baptised in 1616, will have been John Juddes alias Powell who held a tenement in Warbleton called Turners in the 1660s and was assessed for two flues in the hearth tax of 1665.[247]

Two other members of the Mayfield family should be mentioned, though because they did not use the alias Poule there is no proof that they were descended from Paul Judd. Firstly George Judes, whose children, William, Avis, Anne, and Robert, were baptised from 1608 to 1617, though neither William nor Anne survived infancy. George Judes' first wife Dorothy was buried at Mayfield in 1635 and Christobel Ligh, whom he married later in the same year, bore him a further child named Solomon in 1636. Christobel died in 1641.

Another collier apparently from the Mayfield family was William Jude of Cranbrook, whose son Edward married Rachel Hellery of Milkhouse, widow, at Cranbrook in 1656. When this son Edward was baptised at Mayfield in 1632 the father had been described as 'William Judd junior', and was therefore unlikely to be identical with William Jude who had married Mary Gasson at Mayfield in 1606. Although the Ticehurst parish register knows no individual of that name, the younger man was probably 'William Juds of Ticehurst, collier' who in April 1635 acted as bondsman for Marian, the widow of Stephen Nash of Ticehurst, when she took administration of her late husband's estate.[248] This William Juds was undoubtedly William Jud 'a poor old collier' who was buried at Biddenden in 1679.

Another Cranbrook Judd, who was quite unrelated to the collier, but was probably also of immigrant descent, was Robert Judd, a weaver, who was buried there in 1612,[249] and two of whose

246. ESRO, PBT 1/1/21/8, 1/3/6/55.
247. TNA, E 179/258/20.
248. ESRO, PBT 1/3/6/220.
249. KHLC, PRC/17/61/103.

sons, Henry (1573-1627) and Anthony (1580-1638), were broad-weavers.[250] Their ancestor was not necessarily an ironworker.

However, Joseph Paule of Hawkhurst, gentleman, whose will was proved in 1686,[251] and two of whose daughters married members of the Tyler family of ironfounders and the Diamond family of gunfounders, may well have been descended from Paul Judd.

The ironworkers of the Eudes family so far discussed were probably all descended from the Beauvoisin family of that name, who had worked in the Pelham interest in the 1540s. It looks as though other immigrants of the surname sprang from the Eudes family of Neuville-Ferrières, and in the Weald most of these took the surname Addes or Eddes. Such would have been the collier Adrian Eddes alias Counton of East Grinstead, who appeared at Sussex assizes in 1570 on a charge of rape, of which he was convicted and thereupon sentenced to be hanged.[252] Adrian Eddes may have been descended from an immigrant named Counton, or more probably, Quintin Eddes.

Although no persons named Addes, Ades or Edes appeared in East Sussex subsidy rolls of 1524 and 1525, the names of William Addys and Thomas Addes both featured in parish register entries within 17 years of those dates, and because neither is listed as an alien in subsidy rolls, it looks as though both were English-born. If this was the case, the parents or parent of both must have been in England before 1524.

The marriage of William Addys and Agnes Stocker took place at Uckfield in 1534. Agnes was perhaps the daughter of Richard Stokker, who appeared in the subsidy roll for Buxted Greenhurst in 1525 and again in 1543, and Stokker too could have been of immigrant stock. The Uckfield man apparently moved to Westham, where William Adys made his will in 1567,[253] appointing his wife Agnes residuary legatee and executrix; all the children mentioned in the will appear to have been minors. William's only son was Thomas Addes of Westham, the administration of whose goods, valued at £16 14s 8d, was granted to his widow Mary in February 1599.[254] This family had clearly moved away from the ironworking area.

William son of Thomas Addes was baptised at Ashburnham in 1541. The father, whose wife was perhaps the Lucy Addes buried at Ashburnham in 1551, appears to have taken as his second wife Joan Woode in February 1552. This family later moved to Burwash and administration of the goods of Thomas Addes, valued at £10 0s 5d was granted to his widow Joan in 1568. She outlived her stepson, William Addes who was buried at Burwash in 1577, by five years. They were probably unrelated to the illegitimate child William Edolphe baptised at Burwash in 1576, or to Thomas and Alice Edolphe buried there in 1571 and 1579, who were probable members of the Beauvoisin family, whose Paul Hedall had appeared as Paul Edolfe in the Hawksborough hundred subsidy roll of 1572.

John and Adrian Ades, apparently very late immigrants, paid the poll tax in Foxearle hundred in 1595, but did not appear in the subsidy rolls of 1576 and earlier. John could be the man whose daughter Katherine was baptised at Ashburnham in 1579, and who was remarried to Joan Limmott (de Lamot?) at Mountfield in 1581. A further two of his daughters, Elizabeth and Joan, were baptised at Ashburnham and Warbleton in 1584 and 1592 respectively.

However, Adrian Addes was at Brede by 1597, when his unnamed son was baptised there, followed by a daughter named Joan in 1600. In 1604 John Addes also appeared at Brede, where he married Susanna Cresy, the daughter of another French immigrant, John Creasie, who had been baptised at Etchingham in 1579. In 1607 Adrian Addes witnessed the will of the Brede ironfounder, William Jarrett.[255] John Addes lived at Udimore, and since Adrian was fairly certainly the former Foxearle immigrant, it is just possible that John Ades had made a similar move, though the Udimore man might more probably have been not the immigrant's, but Adrian's son.

In 1627 Susanna Adds was left 10 shillings under the nuncupative will of the miner Thomas Creasy of Brede, in which she was described as 'the wife of John Adds of Udimer collyer'. In 1637 John

250. KHLC, PRC/17/65/10b, 70/543.
251. KHLC, PRC/17/76/428.
252. Cockburn, *Sussex Assize records, Elizabeth I*, no.304.
253. ESRO, PBT 1/1/5/484.
254. ESRO, PBT 1/3/2/265.
255. ESRO, PBT 1/1/12/235.

Ads was bondsman for a testamentary administration.[256] In 1640 he was probably John Adds of Beckley, collier, who was accused of erecting a cottage illegally at Udimore; the writ for his arrest subsequently issued by quarter sessions was more correctly directed against John Adds of Brede.[257] The Brede collier, Thomas Aeds, who paid tax on three flues in 1665,[258] was probably John's son Thomas, who had been baptised at Udimore in 1611.

Anthony Yod, who married Margaret Misho at Fletching in 1562, was probably the Anthony Hew, whose daughters Joan and Clemence were baptised at Fletching in 1563 and 1565, and the Anthony 'French', whose son Richard was baptised there in 1567. Richard may have been the Richard Ades who married Mary Harman at Buxted in 1595. She died in 1601, but there are no more certain notices of Richard unless Elizabeth Ades buried at Withyham in 1639 was his second wife.

It seems just possible that Stephen Addes of Withyham, bucket or pail-maker, who was bondsman to a marriage licence of October 1642,[259] was Richard's son. Stephen married Dorothy Lattenden at Fletching in 1632 and their children Dorothy, Richard, Sara, Elizabeth and Mary were baptised at Withyham from 1635 to 1646. Stephen's will, which was dated 1677, was proved in 1680. To his eldest son Robert he left £5 and to his youngest son Stephen £12, a featherbed, with a feather bolster and a joined bedstead. To his daughter Sarah he left 10 shillings. To his grandson Stephen, Robert's son, he left £1; to his granddaughter Sarah Orgles 10 shillings; to the children of his deceased daughter Elizabeth, Robert and Elizabeth Baker, he left £2 and £3 respectively to be paid them at their majorities. To his wife Dorothy he left the household linen, and she and their son Richard were to be residuary legatees and executors. He appointed his brother-in-law John Mainard of East Grinstead and William Baker of Withyham to be overseers.[260]

William Ades of Lewes, blacksmith, who in 1617 took administration of the goods of his father-in-law, John Foord of Fletching,[261] may also have been a member of this Fletching or Buxted family.

However, it is from members of the Beauvoisin family that ironworkers who moved to other parts of the country were descended. Francis Paul married Margaret Wheeler, the daughter of the Rotherfield finer, Thomas Wheeler, at Rotherfield in 1580. That Margaret may have been his second wife is suggested by the baptism of Richard son of Francis and Margery Paule at Worth towards the end of 1574, and the same infant's burial there in January 1575. Francis Paul was among the defaulters at Birchden in the Hartfield view of frankpledge in December 1580,[262] but soon moved on to North Yorkshire.

In Yorkshire, Ann daughter of Francis Paull of Rievaulx was baptised at Helmsley in 1589 and Francis was himself godparent for two Helmsley baptisms in 1590. By December 1591 he had moved on to Danby in Eskdale, where his daughter Maria was baptised. In 1592 he was one of the workers at the abortive blast furnace of Thomas Proctor at Brucrofts near Shipley Hirst in Airedale. His son Walter was baptised in the adjacent parish of Bingley in May 1598, but his wife was buried at Bradford only three weeks later, followed by a child in September, who may have been the unfortunate Walter.

In South Yorkshire the Powell family, like that of Mathewe, was thought to have come from Wales. In the short term it may have done so, but in the long run, unlike the Masborough finer, Howell Johnes, who was married at Rotherham in 1655, they probably came from France by way of the Weald. A finer named Edward Powell had his daughter Mary baptised at Wem in Shropshire in 1618. Like the Matthewe family of forgeman, the Powells arrived in Ecclesfield parish in South Yorkshire around 1640. Both William and John Powell had children baptised at Ecclesfield in 1643.

William Powell, apprenticed to Godfrey Mathyman of the Wheel in Rotherham, became a Freeman of the Company of Cutlers in 1673.[263] He was the son of William Powell of Wadsley Forge, finery-man, and would have been born about 1650, though his baptism appears to have escaped

256. ESRO, PBT 1/1/20/42 (1627), 1/3/7/32 (1637).

257. ESRO, QR 49, m. 33 and QR 50, m. 70.6.

258. TNA, E 179/258/20.

259. Dunkin, *Sussex Marriage Licences, Lewes 1586-1643*, p. 292.

260. ESRO, PBT 1/1/35/224.

261. ESRO, PBT 1/3/4/160. William Addes of Clive, blacksmith, bondsman to a marriage licence of 1621 (Dunkin, *Sussex Marriage Licences, Lewes 1586-1643*, p. 125), was probably the same man.

262. ESRO, ACC 3597/8, f. 173.

263. For this and subsequently mentioned Powell apprenticeships see Leader, *Company of Cutlers in Hallamshire*, **2**, p. 319.

record at Ecclesfield. The finer was presumably the man for whose children baptisms were recorded at Ecclesfield from 1643 to 1653 and who was buried there in 1657.

It seems probable that the Attercliffe forgeman Robert Powell, whose children Anne, Jane, Ruth, Robert, Mary and Samuel were baptised at Sheffield from 1677 to 1697, was the son of the Wadsley finer and had been baptised at Ecclesfield in 1652. Samuel Powell, apprenticed to Robert Powel of Wincobank in 1711, was the Attercliffe forgeman's youngest son and the second member of the Powell family of forgemen to become a freeman in 1719.

The third member of this family to be apprenticed to a cutler was Joseph, the son of an Attercliffe finer named William Powell. William Powell was perhaps baptised at Ecclesfield in 1681, the son of William Powell, who might be the cutler who had become a freeman of the Company in 1673. He married Hanna Beldon at Sheffield in 1701, but she died in childbirth in 1703 and their only son Joseph was apprenticed to Stephen Ashforth the younger in 1715, though there is no record of his becoming a freeman.

A fourth forgeman of this family who had a son apprenticed to a member of the Company of Cutlers was John Powell, a forge-carpenter of Wardsend Forge. He married Martha Jelly at Ecclesfield in 1717 and their second son John was baptised in 1722 and apprenticed to John Fletcher in 1734, although there is again no record of his freedom. Nor has a record of the forge-carpenter's baptism been found either.

Robert Powell of Wadsley Forge had daughters baptised at Ecclesfield in 1725 and 1729. Around 1730 Wadsley Forge was closed for a time and he could be the Robert Powell of Attercliffe Forge, whose children were baptised at Sheffield from 1732 to 1740. Robert was apparently the forgeman whose son Robert was apprenticed to the cutler George Wainwright in 1736 and became a freeman in 1750, though no record of the baptism of this son appears to survive at either Ecclesfield or Sheffield.

The fact that members of the Addison family of finers appear occasionally as Adamson in parish registers suggests the kind of confusion about a surname that arose from its foreign origin. William Addison's son Gilbert was baptised at Mayfield in 1606. William was subsequently at Warbleton, where his children, William, Jane and Nicholas, were baptised between 1608 and 1616. William's son John was baptised at Ashburnham in 1619, after which he moved on to Frant, where Abraham and Grace were baptised in 1622 and 1626, though his first wife died about six weeks after Grace's birth. William Addison of Buxted, finer, took Agnes Elliott of Maresfield, spinster, as his second wife in 1628, and their marriage licence disclosed Addison's occupation.[264] Their children Robert and Joan were baptised at Buxted in 1629 and 1630. William Addison was buried there in 1632.

William's eldest son Gilbert married Iden Pollard at Buxted in 1631 and their children, William, Thomas, Elizabeth and Mary, were baptised there between 1632 and 1640.

Gaege

Peter Gaege was made denizen in 1544. He claimed to have been born in Canny in Normandy around 1519, and to have come to England around 1528. There was an ancient parish named Cany in the Pays de Caux, now part of the commune of Cany-Barville, but because several other Wealden immigrants gave Canny in Beauvaisis as their place of origin, and as that place adjoins the Norman border it seems possible that there has been a mistake, and that it was also from Canny-sur-Thérain that Peter Gaege originated.

Peter Gaege paid a shilling to the reliefs of 1549 and 1550 at Danehill Sheffield, one of only three workers to do so in 1550, when the furnace was in 'ruin and decay'. He again paid a shilling to the relief of 1551 in Rushmonden hundred, but the following year he paid the poll tax only. In 1560 he again paid only the poll tax at Maresfield in Rushmonden hundred.

In Wealden parish registers he was first noted when Isabel daughter of 'Peter Gage Frenchman' was baptised in October 1549 at Chailey, the parish which abutted the south bank of the Ouse opposite Sheffield Forge. His son Stephen and daughters Dionise, Agnes and Helen were baptised at Maresfield from 1551 to 1559. However, it appears that Gagg's first wife died around 1555, because the Fletching parish register shows that he married Joan Laby (*Labe*) in January 1556. His second wife Joan was a baptismal sponsor at Maresfield in 1558, but three parish register entries from the 1560s suggest that

264. Dunkin, *Sussex Marriage Licences, Lewes 1586-1643*, p. 169.

Peter Gagg had moved permanently to Fletching by then. Firstly Elizabeth Gagg was buried at Fletching in 1561, the following year Peter's daughter Dionise was buried there and in 1565, John son of Peter Gagg was baptised there.

An entry for the baptism of Elizabeth Gagg in a bishop's transcript of 1572 for Northchapel suggests that the family had moved to the western Weald by then. She may be the same person as Elizabeth Gagge who was buried at Rogate in 1594. Despite the spelling, because the date is right, the baptism of Jane daughter of James Gaidge at Harting in October 1591 and the burial of her mother Mary four days later, may relate to the immigrant family.

In 1602 Peter Gagge's son Stephen Gagge of Horsham, founder, was a deponent in the dispute between Roger Gratwick and Thomas French about their former partnership in Gosden Furnace.[265] In the same general area, Gilbert Moth married Agnes Gagg at Horsham in 1605 and Walter Gagg married Denise Maddison at Nuthurst in 1611. The burials of Elizabeth Gagg, a child, and of an infant of Walter Gagg at Horsham in 1612 and the burials of both Walter and Denise at Nuthurst in 1639 show that Walter's family remained in the same area.

Just as Peter Gagg had been referred to as Peter Gad in the Maresfield parish register in 1559, it must be supposed that Ann Gad who married the Abinger forgeman Nicholas Gonett in 1615, and William Gadd, whose children William and Elizabeth were baptised in 1597 and 1601 at Pulborough, the parish where their father was buried in 1617, were also members of this family of ironworkers. Further afield Thomas Turner had married Joan Gadd at Haslemere in 1574, whilst back at Maresfield Joan Gad was buried in 1631. As late as 1701 a Hartfield forgeman named John Gad was referred to in the Cowden parish register.

This family helped to establish the indirect process in the Forest of Dean. Stephen Gagge, the ironfounder who was at Horsham in 1602, was almost certainly Stephen Gagge of Parkend, who was buried at Newland in 1622. Another Stephen Gagge who responded to Exchequer interrogatories in 1627 was also ironfounder at Park End Furnace, and since his age was given as 40,[266] he was probably a son of the Horsham founder and will have been born in the Weald around 1587. James Gagge of Parkend, whose daughter Prudence was buried at Newland in 1617 and whose daughter Alice was baptised there in 1620, could be the former Harting man and perhaps another son of the Horsham founder.

Margo

John Margoo was made denizen in 1544. He was then in Sir Robert Tyrwhitt's ironworks, and claimed to have been born in Normandy and to have come to England around 1528. To account for the use of Margo as an alias by John Longley it must be presumed that there was some marital relationship between the two families.

John Margo paid the poll tax in 1550 in Henhurst hundred as fourth and last in a list of alien servants of Joan Walsh and her son Goddard. After not being recorded in 1551 and 1552 he reappeared there to pay the poll tax in 1560. Rather curiously 'John [---]go', Joan Walsh's servant who paid the poll tax in 1549 was stated to be a brewer, but was almost certainly Margo. Home-brewing was not unusual in the ages before a pure water supply became available, as is evident from the numerous references to kitchen vats and furnaces in Wealden probate records. Brewing for public consumption was strictly licensed and excessive charges were the subject of manorial court fines. Perhaps Mrs Walsh had sampled Margo's produce and found it acceptable.

Whatever the nature of John Margo's services to the Walsh family, when Robert Walsh made his will in 1562 he wished his wife to 'keep and relieve in her house John Morgoo during his natural life except she fortune to break up house or he [be] willing to depart; that then to pay unto him 20 shillings a year to be paid quarterly'.[267] Margo was presumably the John Marga buried at Brightling in December 1566.

That other members of the family continued in England is shown by the baptism of James Margo, whose parentage was not disclosed, at Ewhurst in August 1569, but as the child lived for only just

265. TNA, REQ 2/166/46.
266. TNA, E 178/5304
267. TNA, PROB 11/45/27.

over a fortnight this family may have died out. Whether his father was Nicholas Morgo, who appeared briefly as a defaulter in views of frankpledge at Nutley in 1578 and at Sheffield in 1581,[268] is impossible to say.

Holmes

Gilham Holmes had been born in Normandy around 1514 and came to England around 1528. In 1544, when made denizen, he had an English wife and worked in Mr Wybarn's ironworks, which was perhaps in Shoyswell hundred. However, Schubert thought that he was buried at Frant, perhaps equating him with 'Gyllam a Frenchman', who was buried there in January 1559. Certainly, Frant borough was included in Rotherfield hundred and 'William Home alias Shynny, prisoner to Jamis Oxley',[269] who in 1543 appeared in the subsidy roll for Rotherfield hundred may be thought to have been this immigrant, especially as he paid 2 pence, the amount of poll tax paid by aliens in this subsidy. However, the roll stated that the 2 pence was paid on goods, whereas the minimum that could be paid on goods by an alien was 4 pence on goods worth one pound.

It seems possible that Robert Holmes of Burwash was of French descent. His daughter Joan was buried at Burwash in 1559 and his wife Elizabeth in 1560. Later in 1560 he married Alice Bussett, who was almost certainly of French descent. Their daughters Alice, Joan and Ann were baptised at Burwash in 1561, 1563 and 1569. When he died in 1602 administration of Robert's effects, valued at £7 19s 2d, was assigned to his widow Alice and Lawrence Bunsse, an Etchingham carpenter, signed the bond.[270]

If Schubert was correct in supposing that Gilham Homes was buried at Frant, Humphrey Holmes of Brenchley might have been his son. He was married at Pembury in 1565. His children, Richard, Alice and Sara who were twins, William, Edward, Hebricke who was a daughter, and Katherine, were baptised at Brenchley between 1570 and 1585. Humphrey Holmes was buried at Brenchley in 1587.

However, it is with John Holmes of Balcombe, who married Rebecca Tailer at Worth in 1593, that involvement in ironworking can first be proved. He was probably the son of Nicholas Homes, who had married Margaret Dossall at Balcombe in 1558, and their son John was baptised at Ifield in 1572. John's children, Elizabeth, Mary, John, Henry and George, were baptised at Balcombe between 1594 and 1617. As John Homes of Balcombe, collier, he acted as bondsman for the marriage licence of his son George Homes of Balcombe, collier, who married Eleanor Roser in 1634.[271] When he died in 1642 his goods were valued at £23 11s 0d , and in his will he made bequests of £1 each to his four Beery and his two Sherwood grandchildren, except that Elizabeth Beery was to have £2 10s 0d, all these sums payable at their ages of 21. His grandson Adrian Homes, John's son, was also to have 20s at the expiry of his apprenticeship. John made his sons John and George his executors and bestowed 20s each on their wives. James Farnes of Worth was one of the witnesses to this will.[272]

George Holmes's sons George and Walter were baptised at Balcombe in 1636 and 1639. His elder brother, John Holmes of Horsham, ironfounder, was a bondsman for Elizabeth Bull in 1640, when she took administration of the goods of her late husband, Edward Bull of Shermanbury.[273] John Holmes had married Joan Adds at Worth in 1622 and their first two children, Adrian and Eleanor had been baptised at Balcombe in 1624 and 1626. Their later children, Jane, Andrew and John, born in 1629, 1631 and 1632, were baptised at Horsham (Jane and John) and at Ifield (Andrew). The Ifield parish register noted that Holmes was at Bewbush, the site of a blast furnace, in 1631.

Mowery

When made denizen in 1544, George Moreway had an English wife. He claimed to have been born in Beaussault (*Bewsaut*) around 1516 and to have come to England around 1529. He must be equated with the George Moryow made denizen by the forgemaster Nicholas Eversfield. Was he also 'Mowery the *fyner*' who paid the poll tax in Hartfield hundred in 1551? It may be conjectured that the French

268. ESRO, ACC 3597/8, ff 87, 184v.
269. Oxley's wife was Priscilla Jackett, who was probably also of immigrant descent (see Chapter 6 p. 350).
270. ESRO, PBT 1/3/3/8.
271. Dunkin, *Sussex Marriage Licences, Lewes 1586-1643*, p. 216.
272. ESRO, PBT 1/5/413, 1/3/7/292.
273. ESRO, PBT 1/3/7/200.

original of this name was *Mauroy*.

Given that George was a quite unusual name among French immigrants, it is reasonable to suppose that the Shiplake hundred subsidy roll for 1543, which listed George Morrys as one of three alien servants of Nicholas Eversfield who paid the poll tax in Hoathly and Waldron borough, was using another variant of this immigrant's name. However, the names of neither of Eversfield's other aliens listed in Hoathly and Waldron, John Trowley and John Cosenet, corresponds with those of the other workers made denizens for Nicholas Eversfield in 1544.

The name Morye, or Moorey, occurred in West Sussex in the subsidy rolls of the 1520s, but in East Sussex only at Bexhill. Related to George Mowery was perhaps Humphrey Morrey, whose children were baptised at Mountfield from 1569 to 1584, and who was last mentioned in the Mountfield parish register in 1586, when his daughter Joan was buried there.

At Ardingly, Elizabeth Moorye married John Smith in 1565. Later, Edmund Morey of Ardingly, whose wife Margaret was appointed executor of Clement Rootes of Lewes in 1617,[274] was perhaps another descendant. Margaret was buried at Ardingly in 1626 and her busband in 1639, under the name Moorer. George Moory, who married Alice Davy at Ardingly in 1629, was buried as 'George Mory, an ancient man' in 1658. However, in none of these cases is any link with ironworking provable.

Dechyn

In French the surname was presumably Duchesne or Duquesne. An earlier ironworker of this name, Mathie du Chêne, *le marteleur* (the hammerman), together with Guillaume Le Fondeur, took over the forge at Vaux in the Barrois provostry of Longwy in Lorraine in 1451, which, since it then employed a hammerman and newly incorporated both a *fonderie* and an *affinerie*, certainly operated on the indirect system.[275] In 1474 the surname is found in connection with iron at Boizard Forge in the Perche of Normandy, when a hammerman and finer, both named Jehan du Chesne took a six-year lease of the forge.[276]

In Upper Normandy and Picardy the Duquesne form of the name predominated and Neufchâtel notarial acts were witnessed by Michel Duquesne of Compainville in 1545 and Francoys Duquesne of Compainville in 1567.[277] William Dechyn had been born around 1516 at Neuville-Ferrières, where his surname in the form Duchêne still persists, and had come to England around 1529. In the relief of 1551 he paid the poll tax in the Wadhurst section of Loxfield hundred as William Duchin.

The name is not traceable in later Wealden records. Perhaps William Dechyn moved to the Midlands during the 1550s. The possibility that the name was subsequently assimilated to the English surname Deakin, or even Dickin, cannot be lightly dismissed. The Dickin family of ironmasters is thought to have originated from the Hodnet area of Shropshire.[278]

Marian alias Dippraye and Meadow

Marian Dupre was born at La Halotière on the western escarpment of the Andelle valley in Normandy around 1511 and came to England around 1529. By 1544, when made denizen, he had an English wife and three English-born children and worked (*Deprey*) for the forgemaster Joan Isted, widow of Richard Isted. As explained in the French section of this work, Marian may perhaps have been born in a house and farmstead which Jehan Dupré bought in the rue Notre-Dame of La Halotière in 1497.

In the period 1549 to 1552 Dupre failed to appear among Joan Isted's workers in Hawksborough hundred, but was probably 'Marian' who paid the poll tax in Buttinghill hundred in 1549 and 1550, and in Hartfield hundred in 1552. In Buttinghill he probably worked at Worth; in Hartfield he was accompanied by 'Jhon his man', who also paid the poll tax.

In 1560 Dupre also failed to appear among persons paying the alien subsidy in Sussex, but if during the 1550s he had moved on to Tonbridge, the lack of subsidy rolls recording aliens there between 1550 and 1572 would account for his failure to appear. Later he perhaps moved to the Midlands, where

274. ESRO, PBT 1/1/16/63.
275. Horikoshi, 'La Lorraine pré-moderne', pp. 162-3.
276. Belhoste and others, *La métallurgie normande*, p. 187.
277. ADSM, 2 E 14/1189 (26 May 1545); 1211 (17 May 1567).
278. Awty, 'Charcoal ironmasters of Cheshire and Lancashire', p. 82.

his son Richard Marrian alias Dippery was recorded in Abbots Bromley parish register from 1573 onwards. The Bromley Forge accounts for 1575-6 mention also Hugh Marrian who 'made his morris' there,[279] and the parish register's burial entry for '[blank] Maryon de forge' in December 1578 could relate to Marian Dupre himself.

Marian Dupre's son Richard Deprye married Alice 'Lagnbre' at Worth in November 1564. In the Ardingly parish register he was described as 'Richard Dipplie of the Hamar' in 1568, and it was there that his three eldest children, Bartholomew, Charles and Ann, were baptised in 1565, 1568 and 1570. It is certain that he was one of Marian Dupre's English-born children, firstly because he was named Richard Marian when Bartholomew was baptised in 1565, and secondly because his descendants in the Midlands used both surnames Marrian and Dippery.

By the 1570s Richard Maryan was established at Bromley Forge in Staffordshire, and the baptisms of his children, Agnes, Lawrence, Margery and Richard, were recorded at Abbots Bromley in 1573, 1576, 1584 and 1586. In the forge accounts of 1574 to 1583 he appeared as a finer, and quarter sessions records of 1586 referred to him as 'Richard Moryan' of Bromley Hurst.

The ironworks accounts also show that in the period 1580 to 1583 Richard was accompanied at Bromley Forge by John Maryan, who during 1582 worked as hammerman at Cannock New Forge.[280] John Maryan alias Dipprie was perhaps Richard's brother and later moved on with Richard's son Bartholomew to the Lizard forges. Richard himself, however, was perhaps the Richard Marrian whose own burial, closely following that of his wife, was recorded at Trentham in March 1618.

The Lizard forges in Shropshire ran in conjunction with the blast furnace at Shifnal, which had been set up by the earl of Shrewsbury in 1564. Richard Marrian's son Bartholomew, who had been born at Ardingly in 1565, married Frances Emerie at Abbots Bromley in 1589. They were the parents of a daughter Frances Marrian alias Dippard who was baptised at Brewood in June 1590 and of a son named Richard. A levy shows the presence of both John and of Bartholomew Marryon at Idsal or Shifnal in 1593.[281]

A probate inventory dated April 1617, which described John Dipprie alias Marian as 'of Liziarde hombers…Fyner', showed his goods to be valued at £72 15s 0d. He left a variety of livestock, including six beasts and a yearling calf valued at £14, two mares and a yearling colt worth £3 6s 8d, 73 sheep, hogs and wethers worth £18, swine, geese, ducks, hens and other poultry worth 30 shillings. The corn upon the ground and in the barn, together with the hay was valued at £5, with bacon, beef and malt worth 30 shillings. He had pewter and brass valued at £5, with iron ware of all sorts, including pots, broches, great tongs, a fire shovel and grid-iron worth £1. Seven coverlets, ten pairs of sheets, table cloths, napkins and all the other linen were valued at £5. In the chamber over the house two featherbeds, two flock beds, pillows and bolsters were valued at £4, whilst three pairs of bedsteads, a table-board, coffers, chests and 'sawed' boards were worth £1. There was a joined bed in the parlour, perhaps the one he lay on whilst sick, priced at £1 6s 8d, two cupboards in the house and parlour worth 30 shillings, and four chests in the parlour worth 13s 4d. The yarn was worth 5 shillings, whilst the stands, barrels, looms, bowks, spinning wheels, chairs, boards, stools and forms, with all wooden wares were valued at £4. Only John's wearing apparel was strikingly modest at £1.

By his will John left to his wife Eleanor the house in which he dwelt, granted to him by the late earl of Shrewsbury; there was also pasture in Tong parish, and ground in Hales parish, near the Tern forges, granted to himself and Bartholomew Maryan by Richard Crewe. His biggest monetary bequest was of £6 to his 'cousin' William Maryan, who could have been Lawrence's son baptised at Aston in 1583, in reality perhaps his nephew, and he also left £3 to Richard Marian, perhaps his brother who died at Trentham the following year. He left £2 each to Bartholomew's son Richard, to his (Bartholomew's?) sister Katherine and to his own servant Johanna Unkell.[282]

The will of Bartholomew Dippere alias Marrian dated 1627 described him as 'of Liziarde Forge,

279. William Salt Library, D1734/3/3/190 (1 Mar 1575-28 Feb1576). A 'morris' was a *marastre*, or sow of cast iron which was placed horizontally across the top of the forge hearth to support the chimney. In English it was properly a 'morris-bar'.

280. Stanley Marrian of Aberdour, a direct descendant of Richard Marrian, very kindly provided this information from the forge accounts and drew my attention to the quarter sessions reference. His detailed knowledge of his family's history has made a large contribution to what follows.

281. Shropshire Archives, Shrewsbury, No. 4192.

282. LRO, Lichfield wills, Will and inventory of John Maryan, 1617.

Finer'. He left £20 to his son Richard, whilst his wife Frances was to have all outstanding bills and bonds and Richard and his mother were to be joint residuary legatees and executors. The will was dated March 1627 and was proved in June 1628, but Bartholomew's death probably occurred in May 1627, because his goods were inventoried on the seventeenth of that month and were valued at £68 12s 8d.[283] No record of his death survives, because the Tong parish register before 1629 is lost and there is no register for Shifnal until even later.

Entries for Bartholomew's son Richard, who was also a finer at the Lizard forges, occur in the Tong parish register from 1629 onwards. His daughter Frances was buried there in 1629 and his children, Joan, Bartholomew (also a future finer who died in 1696) and John, were baptised there in 1631, 1632 and 1635, and Vincent Marrian who was baptised there in 1638, but whose parentage was not disclosed, was probably also Richard's son. Richard's wife Elizabeth was buried at Tong in 1644 but he himself lived on until March 1667.

At almost the identical time when entries in the Abbots Bromley parish register show that Richard Marian arrived in Staffordshire, entries in the Sheffield parish register show that Lawrence Dippery, who could have been his brother, arrived in South Yorkshire. The entries commence with Lawrence's marriage to Anne Fraunce in November 1573. An entry follows in April 1574 for the baptism of an illegitimate child named Lawrence, whom he had fathered on Anne Moumforth, suggesting that he must have been in the Sheffield a few months before November 1573, unless the child's mother had travelled north along with him.

That Lawrence Dippery was not the only one of his family in the Sheffield area is suggested by the marriage of Giles Maryon and Margery Gee at Sheffield in January 1576. Giles could have been a fourth brother from this family. His stay in Sheffield was short, because he was back in the Weald by December 1577, when his daughter Jane was baptised at Buxted. Jane was buried at Buxted in April 1578. Where Giles moved during the next twenty years is not known, but the burial entry for him at Burford on the river Teme in Shropshire in 1600 shows that he was a hammerman, presumably at Burford Forge.

The Sheffield parish register entries coincide exactly with entries for other ironworkers of French descent there from 1573 onwards, and Dippery and Maryon must be regarded as two of the earliest of the earl of Shrewsbury's task force involved in the introduction of the indirect method of iron production in the Sheffield area, some ten years after Shifnal Furnace had been built.

There are no parish register entries to show that Lawrence Dippery continued at Sheffield during the late 1570s. However, he was certainly in Sheffield in September 1580, when his daughter Elizabeth was baptised there. But this entry was soon followed by others elsewhere which suggest that he quickly moved on to the Birmingham area.[284] Firstly, as 'Lawrence Marrian of Witton' he appeared in the Aston parish register in 1583, when his son William was baptised there. Secondly as Lawrence Depre he appeared in the Wednesbury parish register in 1585 for the baptism of his daughter Christian, whilst Alice Depre who was baptised at Wednesbury in 1590 was presumably also his child.

Turning back to the Weald, the first bearer of the name Dupre encountered in Sussex was Lawrens Dupre who paid the poll tax in Netherfield hundred in 1560. It must be suspected that he was also 'Laraunce Duprye a Frenchman' whose daughter Elizabeth was baptised at Waldron in 1591. Between these two dates he was perhaps Laurence, the servant of John French, who paid the poll tax in Shiplake hundred in September 1572,[285] presumably at Chiddingly. Though Laurence failed to appear in the 1576 subsidy roll, he appeared in the Waldron parish register from December 1582 until he was buried there in October 1593. The Waldron entries included the baptisms of his son Lewes in 1582 and of his daughters Margaret and Elizabeth in 1586 and 1591, whilst his own burial in 1593 was followed by that of his widow in 1597.

At some period before 1610 Lawrence's son, Lewes Dippery, moved to Mayfield where he

283. LRO, Lichfield wills, Will and inventory of Bartholomew Dippere, 1627.

284. However, the Sheffield Dippery is never called Marian in any of the three references to him. This raises the possibility that he should be identified with Lawrence Dupre of Waldron, who will be discussed later. He paid the poll tax in Netherfield hundred in 1560 and possibly in Shiplake in September 1572, but did not reappear until December 1582 at Waldron; in 1591 he was referred to as 'Laurance Duprye, a Frenchman' in the Waldron parish register.

285. Unless the Shiplake man was Lawrence Lavender, who had worked as a wood-cutter at Panningridge in 1554 (KHLC, U1475, B11/4).

appeared in 1615 as a quarter sessions surety, styled Lewes 'Dipperi' of Mayfield, iron-founder.[286] He had married Agnes Crowhurst at Mayfield in 1610 and their children, Deborah, James, Alice, and Richard, were baptised at Mayfield between 1611 and 1617. Lewes Dippery next appeared in the Heathfield parish register in 1620. If he had previously been resident in Bivelham borough this would imply no considerable move. He could have worked at any of the furnaces at Hawksden, Old Mill or Bungehurst, which were all situated not far from the boundary between the two parishes. However, by 1622 he had clearly made a larger move, because from then until his burial in 1635 all references to him occurred in his father's old parish of Waldron.

Lewes's son Henry had been baptised at Heathfield in 1621; at Waldron the baptisms of John, Agnes and another James followed in 1622, 1626 and 1629. However, out of his eight children, only two, the younger James and Agnes, survived. Alice was buried within a few weeks of her baptism at Mayfield, the elder James and Deborah were buried at Heathfield in October 1620, Richard and John at Waldron in 1625 and 1630, but the burial of Henry has not been traced.

The short lives of most of Lewes's young children cannot be ascribed to their father's poverty. Lewes had a servant named Thomas Eleman for whose apprenticeship his will provided £2, he himself was named as overseer for the will of Stephen Button of Laughton, brother of the proprietor of Steel Forge in Warbleton, whilst at his death his goods were inventoried at £89 12s 10d.[287] He left half his household stuff and £10 to his wife Annis. He bequeathed £40 to his son James and £80 to his daughter Annis, both payments to be made at their respective majorities, and they were to share the other half of his household stuff. Should his children both die an extra £60 was to go to his wife, and £60 was to be shared equally between the children of his three sisters, Annie, Margaret and Elizabeth, each of whom had three children. Finally if Henry Willard were to 'let his land fall' it was to go wholly to Dippery's daughter Annis. Lewes named his brother-in-law James Crowhurst as his residuary legatee and executor and he was buried within a few days of making this will in March 1635. His widow married William Bowyer of Wivelsfield eighteen months later.

There are some points of uncertainty concerning the Dupre family. The first concerns the identity of Lawrence Dippery of Sheffield. Was he the man who subsequently went on to the Birmingham area as suggested above, or was he the Chiddingly and Waldron man? Laurence Dupre's death in 1593 explains his failure to appear in the 1595 subsidy roll, but his non-appearance in that of 1576, which could be accounted for by his absence in Sheffield, has no other easy explanation. In fact his non-appearance in the Weald between September 1572 and December 1582 neatly covers the period when Lawrence Dippery was in Sheffield and raises the possibility that Sheffield man, who like the Waldron man was never referred to as Marian, moved back to the Weald after 1580 and not to the Birmingham area as suggested above.

Secondly, immigrants bearing the name Meadow raise the likelihood that this was a translated form of the French name Dupré. It was first found at Mountfield in 1560, when Larance Meddo married Margaret Ratte. Because Mountfield was part of Netherfield hundred it seems almost certain that this was the marriage of Lawrence Dupre who paid the poll tax in that hundred that same year. Nevertheless, Margaret Meddo who was baptised at Mountfield in 1574 is unlikely to have been Lawrence's daughter, if only because he was by then either in Shiplake hundred or in Yorkshire.

An immigrant collier, Rowland Meadow, who paid the poll tax in Staple hundred in 1576, seems a more probable parent for Margaret Meadow who was baptised at Mountfield in 1574. Rowland went on to Crowhurst, where his children Gregory and Elkanah were baptised in 1579 and 1582. By 1585 he was back in Netherfield hundred; his daughter Mary was baptised at Penhurst in 1585. He himself appeared at the assizes twice in 1589, being indicted firstly for theft, a crime of which he was acquitted, and secondly for murder, on which indictment he was found guilty and sentenced to death.[288]

Later members of this family were settled at Hastings. John Meddow the elder, who died intestate in 1620, and another John Meddow of Hastings, who left a will in 1630, had both apparently been fishermen.[289]

A final problem is the relationship between the Dupre family and the Pray or Spray family of

286. ESRO, QR 15, m. 60.
287. ESRO, PBT 1/1/24/5, 1/3/6/219.
288. Cockburn, *Sussex Assize records, Elizabeth I*, nos. 1205, 1212.
289. ESRO, PBT 1/3/5/50; TNA, PROB 11/157/373.

ironworkers, first encountered in the service of Sir William Sidney in the 1540s. The fact that there seems to be no suggestion in the Sidney ironworks accounts that anyone surnamed Dupre, Marian or Meadow worked at Robertsbridge or Panningridge during the 1540s and 1550s is the main reason for supposing that any close connection can be ruled out.

Borde

Thomas Borde, a labourer who came to England from Normandy around 1529, was enrolled in the same list of ironworkers as such well-authenticated men as the hammerman Onyan Russell and the finer Robert Blank. He was presumably Thomas Borde who paid a shilling on goods to the relief of 1551 in Danehill Sheffield hundred.

Since the furnace at Sheffield was linked by ownership with that at Worth it appears likely that Thomas Bordell who paid the poll tax in Buttinghill hundred in 1549 and 1550 (Burdel) was the same man. In that case Antoin Bordell, whose name followed his at Buttinghill in 1549, and again at Danehill Sheffield as Anthony Border in 1551, continued there as Antony Bordet in 1552, and perhaps last appeared as Anthony Burdewe at East Grinstead in 1560, was a closely related person.

Lastly, was the otherwise unknown John Bordet who preceded Antony Bordet at Danehill Sheffield in 1552 genuinely so called, or should the name have been recorded as Thomas Borde, making his last appearance in the Weald? Further consideration of this matter will be reserved until the family Nevill alias Burdett is discussed.

Blewett

Laurence Blewet was made denizen in 1541. He had come to England around 1529 and in 1541 had an alien wife. The notarial registers of Neufchâtel show that he belonged to the Bluet family of Bouelles near Neuville-Ferrières, though they throw no light on how he was related to other members of that family.

He was first noticed in the Weald at Wadhurst in 1543 and had perhaps worked for John Barham in that area from 1529 onwards, because his son Stephen claimed to have been born in Frant around 1530. In Wadhurst Blewet paid 8 pence on goods to the subsidy, but he soon moved on to Netherfield hundred where he paid a shilling on goods to each of the reliefs of 1549 to 1551. In these years he was included with the Netherfield denizens; only the relief of 1552 shows that he had moved there in order to work for Richard Weekes. He could have worked at Hodesdale Forge, which was on the border between the hundreds of Netherfield and Battle, because in a deposition dated 1584 his grandson, the Ardingly finer Abraham Bluett, stated that he had been born in Battle around 1555.[290] Laurence's failure to appear in Wealden subsidy rolls in 1560 agrees with the evidence of a French notarial act of January 1555 which referred to him as the late (*deffunct*) Laurens Bluet.[291]

In France Laurence's sons Robert and Jehan Bluet, who had probably been born in France before 1529, were involved in 1555 in the dispute in which the inhabitants contested the right of John Morel, proprietor of the corn mill at Bouelles, to enforce suit of mill. It appears that in return for a payment of 15 l.t. the brothers obtained emancipation from suit of mill. A notarial act of 1573 makes clear that Jehan Bluet was still in possession of land at Bouelles,[292] and this also agrees with English records, which make no mention of John Blewet. There is just a possibility that Robert Blow, who paid the poll tax in Rushmonden hundred in 1572 might have been the son of Laurence mentioned in the act of 1555, but it seems more likely that Stephen and Charles Blewet were Laurence's only immediate successors in the Weald. However, James Bluet who was buried at Penhurst in 1562 may have been an immediate successor too.

Stephen Blewet was a collier and was first noticed in the Weald in 1558 at Penhurst, where his younger children, Samuel, Ellis, Susan and Sara, were baptised between 1559 and 1573. In a deposition made in 1580 he stated that he had been born at Frant around 1530 and that he moved to Penhurst around 1558.[293] However, Abraham Blewett, probably his second son, was born in Battle around 1555,

290. WSRO, EpII/5/2, f. 226.
291. ADSM, 2 E 14/1212 (21 Jan 1555).
292. ADSM, 2 E 14/1212 (21 Jan 1555), 2 E 14/1218 (28 Oct 1573).
293. WSRO, EpII/5/1, f. 128.

so Stephen could have moved south along with his father. He appeared in the subsidy roll of 1560 for Netherfield hundred not as a contributor, but because two anonymous Frenchmen who were dwelling with him paid the poll tax there. He claimed that around 1573 he moved to Catsfield, a parish where in 1572 he had bought Agmerhurst, a messuage with 40 acres of land.[294] He married his second wife Lettice Wood at Ashburnham in 1577. In 1595 he paid 2s 8d to the subsidy on land worth £1.[295]

Stephen Blewet made his will in January 1605 and probably died later that year. His will was proved by his son Ellis, the residuary legatee and executor, in April 1606 and his personal effects were valued at £37 13s 8d. He left three cows, a 12-monthing bullock and 'all manner of household stuff' to his third wife Elizabeth, with £2 and all the corn both in the field, and in the house and barn. To his son Nicholas he left a 12-monthing colt, already in his son's keeping. His sons Abraham and John were each to have £1. His daughters Alice Cooper, Susan and Sara were each to have £1, but Susan was also to have a bed-covering already in her custody and a little iron pot. To his grandson Nicholas, son of Nicholas Blewet, he left £2. Rebecca Ede was to have £1. All the sums of money bequeathed were due on certain bills of account from Thomas Ashburnham of Dallington, gentleman, and were to be given when the executor had managed to obtain it. The supervisors of the will were to be Richard a'Weekes of Ashburnham and the testator's eldest son Nicholas Blewet.[296]

Stephen's eldest son Nicholas was a hammerman. He married Joan Pulleyn at Ashburnham in May 1568. Their eldest son John was baptised at Bexhill in December 1570. Nicholas Blewett and his younger brother Abraham, who was a finer, both moved to Worth during the 1570s. Abraham married Joan Rafe there in June 1572 and the subsidy roll of 1572 for Buttinghill included 'Bluett's two Frenchmen', who each paid the poll tax there, though which of the brothers employed the two Frenchmen is not made clear. The baptisms of Nicholas Blewett's son Benjamin and daughter Susannah at Horley in 1580 and 1583 suggest that earlier children may have been baptised there, but the details are missing due to the loss of the pre-1579 Horley parish register.

In 1582 Nicholas Blewett bought Cowlands in Penhurst from Thomas Cooper, perhaps in preparation for a return to the Ashburnham area, where his son Stephen was baptised in 1585. In 1586 he acquired a messuage and six acres of land in Catsfield named Stakendens. This he retained up to 1595, but he mortgaged Cowlands to William Bishop of Hastings for £130 in 1593.[297] In 1595 he paid 4 shillings to the subsidy in Foxearle hundred on land worth £1 10s 0d.[298] Further children were born to him now, another daughter Susan, his first daughter of that name having been buried at Ashburnham in 1586, Elizabeth and Nicholas, who were baptised at Ashburnham in 1588, 1591 and 1595. The only reason for supposing that he stayed in the Weald after the burial of his wife Joan at Ashburnham in 1596 is the fact that he was appointed supervisor of his father's will in 1605. The entry for his burial has not so far been found.

In a deposition made at Ardingly in 1584 Abraham Blewett outlined his moves subsequent to his stay at Worth. Around 1575 he moved to Linchmere, in 1577 to Dunsfold, about 1579 to St Leonards Forest, in 1580 to Cuckfield, and by 1584 he had worked in Ardingly for around a year.[299] However, he appears to have left his family established at Linchmere, where his daughters Elizabeth, Priscilla (her father now styled 'Goodman' Bluett) and Susanna were baptised in 1576, 1581 and 1583. By 1585 he was back in Ashburnham, where his daughter Rachel was baptised in 1585. A further foray into West Sussex followed in connection with the establishment of Rogate Forge; his daughter Mary was baptised there in 1589.

A further son of Stephen Blewett, the collier, was Samuel who had been baptised at Penhurst in 1558. He appears to have followed his brothers westwards to Worth, where in 1589 he married Bridget, widow of William Dudgin. Their son Stephen was baptised at Mayfield in 1590, after which they returned to the Ashburnham area, where their daughters Elizabeth and Christian were baptised in 1592 and 1595. Samuel Blewett of Brigden Hill House, about 1.5km west of Ashburnham Forge, predeceased his father and was buried at Ashburnham in 1598.

294. ESRO, HBR 9/11/16, Catsfield tenement analysis.
295. TNA, E 179/190/332.
296. ESRO, PBT 1/1/12/135, 1/3/3/70.
297. ESRO, HBR 9/11/19, Catsfield tenement analysis.
298. TNA, E 179/190/332.
299. WSRO, EpII/5/2, f. 226.

The English-born Charles Blewett was not mentioned in Stephen Blewett's will, and consequently may have been another of Laurence Blewett's sons. Parish register entries show Charles's move westwards to Horsham, where his son Jeremy was baptised in 1580, and back to Horley, where his son Stephen was baptised in 1585. Perhaps he replaced Nicholas at Tinsley Forge, but he was back in south-east Sussex by 1588, when both he and his son Stephen were buried at Crowhurst towards the end of the year.

Charles's son Jeremy married Beatrice Snashall at Nuthurst in 1605 and their children, Jeremy, Margaret, Elizabeth and Katherine, were baptised at Ifield in 1606 and 1609 and at Bramshott in 1615 and 1620. Jeremy Blewett was buried at Bramshott in 1620.

Stephen's youngest son Elias Blewett was another hammerman. Elias's earliest children, Marie, Sara and Margaret, were baptised at Ashburnham in 1584, 1585 and 1587. He was next found at Hawkhurst, where his children, Susan, Judith, Joan, Jane, Elizabeth, Stephen and Elias, were baptised between 1588 and 1602.[300] Finally, his children Katharine, John and William, were baptised at Goudhurst in 1603, 1605 and 1607. It is apparent, however, that between 1607 and 1618 Elias moved on to Biddenden Hammer, because it was at Biddenden that four of his children, Judith, Sarah, Joan and Stephen were married between 1618 and 1621.

Elias Blewett was buried at Biddenden in March 1622. In his will he left to his wife Margaret £20, four bushels of wheat and an iron pot, the bedstead and the bed he used to lie upon, with a new covering which was yet to wear, a joined chest, four pairs of the best sheets, all his tussom and linen yarn, four pieces of pewter and a dozen table napkins. He made his eldest son Stephen his residuary legatee and executor, left £11 each to his sons Elias and John and £10 and five sheep to the youngest son William. His daughters, Mary, Susan, Judith, Joan, Jane and Elizabeth, who were apparently all married, were to have only twelve pence each. Elias Bluatt appended his mark. The first witness Robert Pray alias Pinion made his mark, but John Stow signed.[301]

Elias's widow Margaret died in January 1625, her will being made in the previous month. She left twelve pence to her eldest son Stephen, 4 shillings to his son Stephen and a shilling to his daughter Elizabeth. To her daughter Hood she left a pair of torn sheets and to her daughter's son Robert Hood 4 shillings. To her daughters Judith Beale and Elizabeth Barre she left 5 shillings each, and to Elizabeth's daughter Margaret 4 shillings, though this was to be paid only when her executors received from David Barre £4 which he owed his mother-in-law. Her daughter Susan was to have all her woollen workday apparel and a neckerchief. She left to her daughter Jane Wood 2 shillings, and 4 shillings to Jane's daughter Margaret. Her daughter Joan (Pullen) was to have 2 shillings and Joan's daughter Margaret her best neckerchief, a sheet and a diaper napkin. To her youngest son William she left her bedstead, bed and its furnishings, with a pair of fine sheets, four napkins, a towel, a pewter plate and £2. Her other two sons Elias and John were to be residuary legatees and executors. Margaret Bluat signed her will. It was witnessed by her son-in-law Anthony Pullen, who made his mark, and John Stone, who signed.[302]

The younger Elias Blewett married Winifred Humphrey at Hartfield in 1630 and their children, William, Joan, Elias, Stephen, Elizabeth and Sarah, were baptised at Goudhurst between 1631 and 1641, though William and Elizabeth did not survive. It was perhaps this Elias who was involved in the iron industry at Thomas Culpeper's Bedgebury Furnace after the Civil War. In 1664 Culpeper himself, John Rabson of Benenden and Elias Bleuett of Cranbrook, yeoman, undertook to provide the furnace and materials at Bedgebury for the casting of 150 tons of iron ordnance at £12 per ton for George Browne of Buckland, Surrey, Alexander Courthop of Horsmonden and Thomas Browne of London, doctor of physic.[303]

The elder brother of Elias, Stephen Bluit, had married Elizabeth Cleyve at Biddenden in 1621, but by 1623 had moved to Hawkhurst, where their sons Stephen and Elias were baptised in 1623 and 1626. The antecedents of the hammerman William Blewet of Goudhurst who in 1656 married Bridget Overy at Hawkhurst are unknown.

300. Hawkhurst parish register recorded the burial of Elias son of Elias Blewet on 12 September, after his baptism on 4 Jul 1602. To accept this burial entry would necessitate the birth of a second son Elias before the baptism of John Blewett at Goudhurst on 2 June 1605, or invalidate the order of birth of their sons given in the wills of both parents. Neither register contained this baptism.

301. KHLC, PRC/17/63/307.

302. KHLC, PRC/17/65/137.

303. KHLC, TR 1295/71.

Returning now to branches of the family who remained in Sussex, in Abraham Blewett's foray of 1589 to Rogate he had been accompanied by John Blewett, whose daughter Eleanor was baptised and buried at Rogate in October and December of that year. John was perhaps the son of Nicholas who had been baptised at Bexhill in 1570 and had perhaps married Dorothy Brydale at Linchmere in June 1586, though the parish register recorded merely her marriage without naming her husband, perhaps because she was under age.

The next member of this family to come to notice was Benjamin, who was perhaps the son of Nicholas baptised at Horley in 1580. He married Joan Bound at Cuckfield in 1601. His links with the Ashburnham area were emphasized by the baptism there of his eldest daughter Judith in 1602, but he next appeared back at Cuckfield, as 'Benjamin Blewett of Moonhill', for the baptism of his son John in 1603. Moonhill is only 1.5km south of Cuckfield Forge and it seems possible that the family's ownership of local property dates back to Abraham Blewett's stay there in the early 1580s.

Between 1604 and 1614 the Cuckfield parish register also recorded the presence of John Bluet, a lawyer, whose wife Abigail was buried there in 1604. He might be the eldest son of Nicholas Blewett, the hammerman, who had been at Rogate in 1589 and was perhaps John Bluet, gentleman, who was buried at Cuckfield in 1623. Meanwhile the baptisms of three children of John Bluet and his second or third wife, also named Abigail, were recorded at Cuckfield: they were Stephen, Walter and Jane, who were baptised in 1611, 1614 and 1617.

Another of the hammerman's sons, Stephen Bluet, gentleman, and his wife Alice, also had their son Stephen baptised at Cuckfield in 1614. Through his wife Alice, who was buried at Ashburnham in 1629, he can be identified as Stephen Bluett, the Ashburnham yeoman, who in a deposition of 1626 claimed to be aged around 40, to have been born in Ashburnham and to have returned there about eight years earlier.[304] His further children, John, Nicholas, Elizabeth, Marie and Martha, were baptised at Ashburnham from 1618 to 1628. After being a widower for more than eight years Stephen Blewet married Elizabeth Southernden in 1637. She bore him further children, Benjamin and Joseph, who were baptised at Ashburnham in 1638 and 1640. However, Stephen's son John died in 1639, and then his eldest son Stephen, who had been baptised at Cuckfield in 1614, died in 1641, so when he died in 1660 it was his sons Nicholas and Joseph whom he made residuary legatees and executors, whilst to his second wife Elizabeth and her daughter Jane he left £40 in money or household stuff, between them.[305] It was in the person of Joseph Bluett that the family continued at Ashburnham after the Civil War.

The example of two grandsons of an immigrant ironworker, making it, or not quite making it, to the ranks of the gentry, is not paralleled elsewhere in the Weald. Perhaps subtle nuances between the perception of this family in Cuckfield and its perception in Ashburnham are also evident. It was however in the Cuckfield branch of the family that continued involvement in the iron industry of Sussex can best be shown.

The Cuckfield forgeman John Bluet, who married Mary Tamplin, also from a family celebrated in ironworking, at Nuthurst in 1626, was perhaps Benjamin Bluet of Moonhill's son. John's children, George, James and Jane, were baptised at Cuckfield between 1629 and 1633, the last of them posthumously, her father having been buried at Cuckfield in July 1633, a still comparatively young man.

James Blewett, the Chiddingly forgeman, who died in 1686, will have been John's son. Before moving to Chiddingly he was perhaps at Funtley Forge in Hampshire, where the baptisms of his children, Anne, William and John, appeared in the Fareham parish register in 1657, 1664 and 1667. The Chiddingly register shows him to have been married twice more after his return to Sussex, firstly to Joan Mashor in 1672 and secondly to Anne Brigham in 1683.

James Blewett left a will, of which he named John Fuller of Waldron, esquire, the overseer. His bequests were modest indeed. The largest was of 10 shillings to Andrew Powell. To his son John he left his wearing apparel and to his other children, James, William and Mary, twelve pence apiece. All his goods, chattels and credits were to be divided between his wife Anne and his son John. However, he was able to append his own signature to the will, an accomplishment that two of the three witnesses seem not to have possessed.[306]

It is not apparent that either the hammerman Nicholas Blewett, his brother the finer Abraham

304. WSRO, EpII/5/12, ff 91, 92.
305. TNA, PROB 11/300/536.
306. ESRO, PBT 1/1/37/88.

Blewett, his sons Nicholas and Benjamin, or his nephew Stephen Blewett, who had been baptised at Mayfield in 1590, ended their days in the Weald. By around 1610 one branch of the family had established itself in Gloucestershire. In January 1610 William Bluett married Joan Knight at Wotton-under-Edge and their daughter Elizabeth was baptised at Cromhall towards the end of that year. An earlier member of the family had been buried at Wotton in July 1609 as 'Bluett', without benefit of baptismal name.

Wotton and Cromhall lie respectively north and south of the Little Avon on which Thomas Hacket erected a furnace and forge in 1610, thought to have been at Tortworth. Hacket procured iron ore out of the Forest of Dean and charcoal out of Michaelwood, but did not make a success of the works and soon assigned them to Sir William Throckmorton of Tortworth. He was no more successful than Hacket, partly due to the antagonism of the forgemaster Sir Edward Winter, who had set up the furnace at Lydney in 1604, and who it seems was able to prevent Throckmorton from obtaining charcoal out of Michaelwood, so in 1612 these works were assigned to two citizens of Bristol.

It is from the *Lives of the Berkeleys* by John Smyth of Nibley, steward to the Berkeley family of Beverstone, that these facts are gleaned. John Berkeley of Beverstone was the forgemaster who set up the first ironworks in the New World at Falling Creek, near Jamestown, Virginia, in 1621. An earlier effort to start an ironworks had been made a few years earlier and the projected works may have been at the same site. In that case the leader of the party had been Captain Blewett, whose baptismal name is quite unknown, but he died not many months after his arrival in the colony in 1618. The marriage of Richard Allen to Margaret Blewet at Beverstone in 1613 suggests that a connection between the Blewetts and Berkeley may have been established soon after the start of the Tortworth works.

However, Berkeley and all the men on site were massacred in March 1622 when the local Indian tribesmen, with whom relations had hitherto been good, made a quite unexpected attack on them. The ironworks were never rebuilt. The Blewett concerned was certainly not William Bluett mentioned in connection with the Tortworth ironworks, because he survived to have a son named William baptised at Cromhall in September 1623.

The activities of the Blewett family in Gloucestershire continued, but now to the west of the Severn. Jeremy Blewett of Flaxley, perhaps Charles Blewett's grandson baptised at Ifield in 1606, married Dorothy Halstead at Westbury-on-Severn in 1631 and their son Jeremiah was baptised at Flaxley in 1635. It was at Flaxley that Jeremiah married Isabel Marshall in 1663, and Roger Blewett married Anne Steward at the same place two years later. Children of Jeremiah were baptised at Flaxley in 1664 and 1667 and children of Roger Blewett up to 1682. In 1669 Christopher Blewett appeared at neighbouring Longhope and John Blewett appeared there in 1688.

In the Midlands, the Blewett family was early into Shropshire. Nicholas Blewett, yeoman, appeared at Wem Forge in May 1612, when his daughter Jane was baptised. By October 1614, when his son Richard was posthumously baptised at Wem, Nicholas was clearly dead.

At Castle Donington, William the son of Jerome Blewitt was baptised in December 1623, and Mary and John the children of Stephen Blewit were baptised in 1629 and 1631. Stephen may have gone on to Oswestry, where his daughter Eleanor was baptised in March 1638, but where his wife was buried later that year.

Another member of the family, John Bluitt, and his wife Elizabeth, had their daughter and son Elizabeth and Simon baptised at Longnor in Shropshire in 1632 and 1635. The parents were perhaps John Bluit the elder of Winnington Forge on the river Tern, and Elizabeth Bluit, who were buried at Mucklestone in Staffordshire in 1674 and 1686.

John Blewit of Wolverhampton married Alice Naylor of Perton at Wolverhampton in January 1658. Their daughter Margery and son John were baptised at Tettenhall in 1658 and 1668 respectively. These entries do not explicitly connect Blewit with ironworking and indeed, the John Blewitt baptised at Tettenhall in 1668, who married Mary Parry at Sedgley in 1691, was stated in the Sedgley parish register to have been a nailer.

The branch of the family established at the forges on the river Tern on the Shropshire and Staffordshire border was joined by Benjamin Bluit, who appeared in the Mucklestone parish register in March 1669. He and his wife Catherine had perhaps been at Stanton by Bridge in Derbyshire in 1662, when their son Elias was baptised. It appears that two other children, Benjamin and Samuel were also born to them before they arrived on the Tern. At Winnington Forge, they seem to have joined John Bluitthe elder who was buried in March 1674.

Benjamin and Catherine's first son Elias did not survive, nor did John who was baptised at

Mucklestone in 1669, but was buried the following year, nor John who was baptised in April 1672, but died in December. On the other hand Benjamin and Samuel, together with Simon, Joseph and John, baptised between 1670 and 1675 at Mucklestone, all survived their father. The 1675 entry shows that Benjamin had now moved to Bearstone Forge, where he still worked when he died in April 1693. Administration of his goods, inventoried at £31 10s 10d was granted to his widow and one of the bondsmen was their eldest son Benjamin, who signed the bond.[307]

Benjamin Blewitt and his wife Mary were variously described as of Oakley and of Norton Forge in the Mucklestone parish register. Their children, Elizabeth, Katherine, Benjamin, William and Simon, were baptised at Mucklestone from 1690 to 1700, after which they moved to Knighton. Their son John was baptised and their son William was buried at Mucklestone in 1704. They had returned to Bearstone by 1706, when their son Simon was buried at Mucklestone, but another son named Simon was baptised there in 1709. Benjamin's mother, Catherine Blewit of Winnington, was buried at Mucklestone in 1709 and he himself was buried there in 1726. His widow was perhaps Widow Bluit of Winnington buried at Mucklestone early in 1738. The children of Benjamin and Simon Bluit baptised at Norton in Hales between 1741 and 1753 were probably their grandchildren.

Simon Bluitt of Bearstone Forge, son of the elder Benjamin Bluitt, had died in 1699, but it was not until March 1703 that an inventory of his effects was made. His wearing apparel was valued at £2 and his other asset was £17 8s 9d due to him from the ironmaster Mr Robert Slaney for iron. His elder brother Samuel Bluit of Bearstone Forge had died unmarried before this, and their mother Katherine and the next eldest son, Benjamin Bluitt of Knighton, forgeman, assigned the administration to John Bluitt of Warmingham, forgeman, the son who had been born in 1675, presumably in order to undertake the recovery of what Slaney owed them.

John Blewet 'of the forge' was buried at Warmingham in April 1705, so it must be regarded as doubtful whether he managed to recover Slaney's debt. His elder brother Joseph Blewett will have been the man of that name buried at Warmingham in 1701. Another William Bluit of Cranage had been buried at Churchhulme in 1700, so the family was well-established in the Cheshire forges, though baptisms do not appear, perhaps due to the influence of some of the Cheshire ironmasters, whose nonconformity is well attested.

From the forges in Cheshire to the Cheshire partnership's Cumbrian works was but a short step, which was one made by John Bluit, who was hammerman at Sparke Bridge Forge in 1750. He was still there in 1755, but by the 1760s Thomas Bluit appears to have succeeded him.[308] Hannah, Catherine and Thomas, the children of Thomas Blewet of Spark Bridge, were baptised at Lowick in 1763, 1765 and 1767.

By the mid-eighteenth century other members of the Blewitt family appear to have been employed on the Stour forges in Worcestershire. At Kingswinford nine children of William and Sarah Blewitt were baptised between 1731 and 1750. Benjamin and Elizabeth Blewet appeared at Wolverley in 1757 and 1758, when their sons John and William were baptised, but the father was buried there in 1758. His 80-year-old widow Elizabeth survived until 1801.

Tullet

Francis Tollett claimed to have been born in Normandy around 1516 and to have come to England around 1529. When made denizen in 1544 he was working for William Wybarne and had a French wife and one child. It seems possible Francis Tollet who was buried at Petworth in 1591 was the immigrant, but no other archival source attests his presence in the Weald. An early move to the western Weald before 1550 might account for the numerous members of the family subsequently found in central and western areas of the Weald.

Jarman Tollett claimed to have been born in Normandy around 1514 and to have come to the Weald around 1530. When made denizen in 1544 he was in Mr May's ironworks, and had a French wife and three children. He was probably Jarman Tulloke who paid a shilling on goods to the relief of 1551 in Rushmonden hundred, but no further trace of him has been found in the Weald.

Both these men were possibly sons of Anthony Tollett who worked for Richard Weekes in

307. LRO, Lichfield wills, Administration of Benjamin Blewitt, 1693.

308. LA, DDX192/1, f. 88; DDX192/2 (14 Aug 1755); DDX192/3 (11 May 1764).

Netherfield hundred in 1551. Another member of the family was Flyppyng Tollett, who paid the poll tax in Richard Weekes' works in Netherfield hundred in 1549 and 1550. He had been included as 'Philip Toulett' among the six 'Frenchmen to be made denyzens by Richard Wekes' in the Westminster denization roll. Lack of personal details for him elsewhere in the roll and his exclusion from the lists of Netherfield denizens in the years 1549 to 1551 indicate that his denization was never completed.

In the subsidy rolls Flyppyng made sure that the clerk enrolled his French name more or less correctly as Phlyppyng. Was he Phlippin Toullote of Saint-Maurice, one of the witnesses to a Neufchâtel notarial act of 1546, by which Jehan Rasset of Canchy, Anthoyne Le Fevre of Le Carrouge in Sainte-Geneviève parish, and Jehan Lambert of Fontaines-en-Bray parish, raised 200 livres through the sale to Nicolas Azoult, a Rouen merchant, of a rent charge of 20 livres?[309] Otherwise Phlippin seems untraceable in the Neufchâtel notarial records, which itself suggests that the supposition that he was the emigrant may be correct.

The Panningridge Furnace accounts show that 'Philpyn', besides working for Weekes, worked intermittently for Sir William Sidney as a woodcutter and miner in 1547 and 1548, and that in 1549 he helped to repair the furnace wall.[310] The subsidy rolls show that after working for Weekes again in 1549 and 1550, he again worked for Sidney in 1551 and 1552. In the Panningridge Furnace accounts he continued as a woodcutter and miner from 1553 until 1558, in which year 'Fylpen's servant' was also mentioned. As a miner Phlippyng was paid £11 17s 9d in 1554.[311]

It seems more likely that 'old Tullet' who paid the poll tax in Netherfield hundred in 1539 is to be identified with Anthony Tollett who paid the poll tax for Weekes in that hundred in 1551, rather than Phlippyng Tollett, who never had this epithet applied to him in the Sidney accounts. Perhaps Phlippyng was 'Flyx' (*rectior* 'Flyp'?) whose name preceded that of 'old Tullet' in the 1539 roll. At this time both men were perhaps working for Weekes at Beech Furnace.

Other Frenchmen of this name, who failed to appear in the subsidy rolls, but were mentioned in the Horsham parish register in February 1571, were Richard Tollett and Edward Tollet 'of the Forest'. Richard's daughter Joan was baptised at Horsham early in 1562. Another daughter Mary was buried at Horsham early in 1571, and Alice Towlet, who was baptised at Northchapel in October of that year may also have been his daughter. The burial of Richard Tullet has not been traced, but his wife was buried as Mary Tullet, widow, at Petworth in December 1603 and was 'Mary Tollet, widow of Richard Tolet of the parish of Petworth', whose will was proved at Chichester in September 1604.[312] She left her best gown to her daughter Joan. It is not clear whether her daughter Alice, to whom she left a heifer, was the same person as Alice Cooper to whom she left her remaining apparel.[313] Her eldest son, to whom she left a two-yearling bull, was Peter. She left a cow to another son Marian, and made her youngest son Lawrence her executor.

Marian Tollet was a Northchapel collier, who married Elizabeth Burrell at Petworth in 1611, and whose sons Marian and John are shown by bishop's transcripts to have been baptised at Northchapel in 1616 and 1622. He also had a daughter Elizabeth and, by his nuncupative will made in May 1625,[314] left £30 to be divided between these three children, but made his widow Elizabeth his residuary legatee and executrix.

Marian's elder brother was probably Peter Tullet who married Rachel Ireland at Wisborough Green in 1600, but she died in 1604 and he married secondly Margery Garton in June 1605. Their children Alice, Richard and Olive were baptised at Fittleworth between 1608 and 1612. Peter's burial has not been traced, but his widow Margery was buried at Fittleworth in 1638 and their son was perhaps Richard Tollett of Wisborough Green who was buried at Fittleworth in 1655.

Lawrence Tyllet married Mary Greenfield at Billingshurst in 1607 and their son William Tulet was baptised at Pulborough in 1610. Their later children, John, Mary and Elizabeth Tillet were baptised at Billingshurst between 1614 and 1620. Laurence Tillot of Billingshurst was married for a second time

309. ADSM, 2 E 14/1190 (7 Aug 1546). For the probable origin of this family at Trépied, see Chapter 4, pp. 74-5.
310. KHLC, U1475, B10/1, 3 and 4.
311. KHLC, U1475, B10/6-10.
312. WSRO, STC 1/15/58.
313. Stephen Blewett had a daughter named Alice Cooper (p. 492, above).
314. TNA, PROB 11/146/127.

to Elizabeth Lunne at Haslemere in 1642.

Edward Toulet had married Mary Geney at Newdigate in 1567. Of their children, Katherine and Thomas were baptised at Horsham in 1571 and 1572, though Katherine did not survive, Peter, Richard, Angell and Edward were baptised at Worth from 1576 to 1584, and lastly, Mary was baptised at Newdigate in 1587, a birth which her mother did not survive. Their son Richard may have been the Richard Tullet buried at Newdigate in April 1587. Edward Tullet was married again to Elizabeth Hollande at Newdigate in 1588, but himself did not survive the following year.

Edward Tullet, baptised at Worth in1584, was probably the man who married Elizabeth Greengow at Fernhurst in 1616. When Elizabeth's father Philip Grengoe of Dunsfold died in 1623 he left £1 to her, 5 shillings and his best ewe lamb to his goddaughter Elizabeth Tullet, and an ewe lamb to each of their other children.[315]

Edward's son Peter Tullet was probably the Ardingly hammerman who married Alice Joyse in June 1601.[316] Their children, Elizabeth, William, John, Edmond, Sarah and Edward, were baptised at Ardingly from 1602 to 1616. Soon after this they moved to Ellastone in north Staffordshire, where their son Henry was baptised early in 1621. At least a part of this family returned to the Weald as is shown by the burial entry for Henry Tullett at Nuthurst early in 1639, when the parish register specifically recorded that he was the son of Peter and Alice Tullett. In view of this it may be supposed that it was their eldest child Elizabeth who married Thomas Rowland at Horsham in 1629 and their son Edward who married Jane Stedman there in 1647.

Two of Peter's sisters had married hammermen from the White family. Firstly Mary Tullet married Nicholas White of Worth at Ardingly in 1607 and secondly Angell Tullet married Peter White at Worth in 1608. After the birth of two children, Charles and Nicholas, in Sussex, Nicholas White moved to Wem in north Shropshire, where two further children, Robert and Mary, were baptised in 1614 and 1617. The Wem parish register described Nicholas White as a hammerman.

When Peter Tullet moved to Ellastone he would have been joining his sister Mary and Nicholas White in the north Midlands. Peter White had also moved to the Midlands, but died before his brother-in-law's move north; he was the hammerman buried at Castle Donington in July 1610. His widow Aungell married William Martin at Hints in October.

The Tollitt family had been at Eckington in north Derbyshire even earlier. Both Richard Tollitt and James Tollitt, whose son Charles was baptised there in 1603, were buried at Eckington in 1613. William Tollitt's children, Mary, John, William and Charles, were baptised at Eckington from 1616 to 1623, though Mary and William failed to survive childhood. William's wife Mary was buried at Eckington early in 1627, but he married again in 1628 and a further child, William, was baptised early in 1629. George and John, the children of John Tollit were baptised at Eckington in 1642 and 1645.

Another branch of the family was found at Norton Cuckney in Nottinghamshire in 1636 and 1639, when Anne and Elizabeth, daughters of Thomas Tullet were baptised. He moved on to Attercliffe Forge near Sheffield, where further children, William who did not survive, Mary and William, were baptised from 1642 to 1645. Thomas's wife Anne was buried at Sheffield in 1652, but Thomas was not among the forgemen who paid the hearth tax at Attercliffe in 1672, though his burial at Sheffield was not recorded until 1686. Even more surprisingly, the burial of Thomas's daughter Anne at Sheffield in 1645 means that Anne Tullitt of Attercliffe Forge, who married the Attercliffe forge-carpenter Peter Vintin in 1659, cannot have been Thomas's daughter.

A second Thomas Tullet was at Melbourne in Derbyshire, where his wife Elizabeth was buried in 1657. The marriage at Edwinstowe in 1662 of Thomas Tullett, a Clipstone forgeman, to Elizabeth daughter of a tanner named Anthony Leichfield, with Robert Tullett, perhaps the man baptised at Wem in 1614, acting as bondsman for the licence,[317] could have been a remarriage of the Melbourne man. The baptisms of their sons Thomas and John occurred at Edwinstowe in 1663 and 1665, but further entries did not follow.

At least one member of the family appeared in north-east England in connection with Denis Heyford's steel mill at Blackhall. When Robert Tullit married Elizabeth Vinton at Ryton in 1704, both were stated to be of the 'steel mill'.

315. LMA, DW/PA/07/011, f 383.

316. Dunkin, *Calendar of Sussex marriage licences, Lewes, 1586-1643*, p. 37.

317. Blagg and Wadsworth, *Nottinghamshire marriage licences*, **1**, p. 214.

Nevill alias Burdett

As explained when dealing with the Bourdet family of Neuville-Ferrières, there appear to be two entries in the Westminster denization roll for the same individual who came to England in 1530, one as Gilham Nuffyld and the other as William Burdett. Gilham Nuffyld worked for Master Lunsford, had been born in Normandy, had come to England around 1530, and in 1544 was aged 30. William Burdett had been born in Normandy and had come to England in 1530, but did not give his age.

The subsidy rolls give no support to the idea that two individuals were involved. In Netherfield hundred Guillam Bordett paid 2 shillings to the relief of 1549 and a shilling to that of 1551. A marginal note made in 1566, to a Neufchâtel notarial act of 1542, shows that Guillaume Bourdet was then at Robertsbridge in England,[318] a fact reflected in his payment of 2 shillings to the subsidy of 1572 in Staple hundred as 'William the Frenchman' and his burial as William Burdett 'a Frenche man' at Ewhurst in the same hundred in August 1574. At the time of the two reliefs of 1550 and 1552 and of the 1560 subsidy he was perhaps in France, because it seems unlikely that an alien who was affluent enough to pay on goods on three occasions, could have escaped paying at least the poll tax in the intervening years. Administration of his effects was granted in September 1574 to the Robertsbridge finer, Peter Joly. The bond was for £40, suggesting that his goods were then valued at around £20.[319]

As has been shown in the French section of this work dealing with ironworkers who came from Neuville-Ferrières, Guillaume and Jehan Bourdet, two sons of the Neuville carpenter, Pierre Bourdet, made mutual procurations in 1553, the first by a notarial act of Saint-Saire dated 7 July, of which no copy exists, the second by an extant notarial act of Neufchâtel dated 7 October, both acts designed to regularize their future affairs in France on their departure to do business (*negocier*) in England. From the two denization roll entries and the subsidy rolls of 1549 and 1551 it appears that Gilham had already spent the bulk of 23 years in England, a fact nowhere hinted at in French records.

The presence of John Bourdet in England is shown in 1560, when he paid 2 shillings on goods to the subsidy in Netherfield hundred as John Nevell. However, it seems possible that, like his brother, he had made exploratory visits to the Weald before 1553. In 1549 John Bourdell had paid the poll tax in Foxearle hundred as one of Anthony Pelham's workers and in 1552 John Bordet and Antony Bordet had paid the poll tax in Danehill Sheffield, perhaps as workers of David Barrentyne. Antony Bordet was evidently the Anthony Border who had paid the poll tax in Danehill Sheffield hundred in 1551 and may have been the otherwise unknown Anthony Burdewe who paid the poll tax at East Grinstead in 1560.

Members of this, or another similarly named family, were Berry Bordett who paid the poll tax when working for the forgemaster Richard Weekes in Netherfield hundred in 1549 and Christopher Burdett who paid the poll tax in Battle hundred in 1576. The latter's son John was baptised at Warbleton early in 1577, when the parish register showed that the name of Christopher's wife's was Elizabeth.

Another member of this family was the Hartfield forgeman, John Nevell, who acted as bondsman for Margery Willett in 1595, when she took administration of the goods of her husband George Willett of Horsted Keynes. Nevell himself died around two years later, and administration of his effects, valued at £33 15s 5d, was committed to his widow Margaret, with another John Nevell, presumably his son, and John Mason, a Hartfield husbandman, acting as bondsmen.[320]

There were no entries for John Nevell in Hartfield views of frankpledge, which suggests that he had recently arrived there in 1595. However, a man of that name was consistently named as a defaulter in views of frankpledge for Short borough in Danehill Sheffield hundred from 1578 to 1591.[321] This John Nevell perhaps worked at Maresfield Forge which was situated only about 1.5km upstream from Shortbridge.

Although there was no will for John Nevell, his widow Margaret, who survived until 1620, left a will and her goods were inventoried at £16 11s 10d.[322] Her sons John, Francis and Laurence were appointed residuary legatees and executors, but it is apparent that Nicholas Nevell, to whose son John she left 10 shillings, was a fourth son who had predeceased her in 1612. She also left 10 shillings each

318. ADSM, 2 E 14/1187 (28 Jun 1542).
319. ESRO, PBT 1/3/1/3.
320. ESRO, PBT 1/3/2/210 and 237.
321. ESRO, ACC 3597/8, f. 83 (30 Sept. 1578) to 3597/1, f. 143 (21 Apr 1591).
322. ESRO, PBT 1/1/17/82, 1/3/4/45.

to John's daughter Anne and to Francis's son John and made bequests to her unnamed daughters Quittenton and Lurrett, wives of the Hartfield collier John Quittenton and of Peter Lurrett, who was of obvious immigrant descent. Her daughter Quittenton was to have £5, £4 of which was already in John Quittenton's hands, and of their daughters, Margaret was to have £1, and Alice and Catherine were each to have one pair of sheets. Her best coverlet and the sheet with tassels were to go to her granddaughter Joan Lurrett and her best gown to her granddaughter Frances Lurret; her daughter Quittenton was to divide the remainder of the linen between herself and the Lurrett granddaughters, Margaret, Mary and Anne.

Margaret's son Nicholas Nevell must be the man who married Margery Eastone at Hartfield in 1606, who was buried at Hartfield in 1612, and who also left a will. Though his goods were inventoried at only £3 2s 0d, he left a tenement and lands called Roughtye to his son John, out of which John was to pay £20 to his sister Jane at her marriage or at the age of 21. Meanwhile, because his children were both minors, his wife Margery was to have the lands until the children came of age. Witnesses to the will included John Deamond, possibly from the immigrant community, and John Nevell, who was presumably the testator's brother.[323]

The baptismal entry for Margaret daughter of John Nevell alias Burdet at Hartfield in December 1604 stated that the parental parties were French, but it seems probable that this baptism related to a granddaughter of the forgeman who died around 1597, who himself is unlikely actually to have been French. The idea that Thomas Burdett of Hartfield, whose wife Joan took administration of his effects in 1584,[324] was of English descent and was from another Burdett family of Hartfield, from which the French family needs to be distinguished scarcely holds water, because the French family was readily enough distinguished by its alias.

It looks as though the Maresfield forgeman's son Francis Nevill continued at Maresfield after his father's departure. This Francis Nevill married Joan Dobsonne in 1599; she died in 1617 and Francis married his second wife Elizabeth Beale at Fletching in 1618, though she was buried at Maresfield in 1623.

Another John Burdet who was presumably of French descent married at Warbleton in 1575; that his bride Pakat Doust was of French descent is scarcely open to doubt. For him to have been the Maresfield and Hartfield forgeman, Pakat's demise would need to have been early, because John Nevell's widow Margaret claimed parentage of five or six children.

Another John Burdet was at Hawkhurst, but his wife who was buried in 1599, was named Margery, and John Nevell or Knevell of Biddenden appears to have been single before his marriage to Elizabeth Hartridge in 1593.

Anthony Burdet, the hammerman who was buried at Tonbridge in 1620, was presumably of French descent, but was not mentioned in the will of Margaret Nevell of Hartfield. His own children were baptised at Tonbridge from 1590 to 1610, and he appeared in the subsidy rolls for South Borough in 1599 and 1600, paying 8 shillings on goods worth £3 in 1599.[325]

John Burdet who married Elizabeth Waghorne at Tonbridge in 1613 was perhaps Anthony's eldest son, baptised in the period before 1585, for which the baptismal register has been lost, or around 1592 at which point a leaf of the surviving register is missing. At his death in 1616 the Tonbridge mercer, John Laughan alias Collyn, who was also of immigrant descent, owned the messuage in Tonbridge in which John Burdet dwelt.[326]

Gardambas

When made denizen in 1544, John Gardambas was one of John Barham's workers. He was aged 33 and had been in England since around 1530. He had an English wife and one child. The surname apparently springs from 'the lower guard' (*garde de en bas*) and appeared in Neufchâtel notarial records only in the shape of a Rouen priest, Maistre Michel Gardeanbas, for whom a legal proctor was appointed in 1554.[327]

323. ESRO, PBT 1/1/14/92, 1/3/3/297.
324. ESRO, PBT 1/3/1/133.
325. TNA, E 179/127/522 and 527.
326. KHLC, DRb/PW24.
327. ADSM, 2 E 83/2 (29 Mar 1554).

In the Loxfield hundred subsidy roll for 1543 John Gardymbas appeared under Wadhurst, but no later references to him are known. After the commencement of the Wadhurst parish register in 1604, the family can be identified once more in the persons of Joseph Gardembas, whose son Joseph was baptised in March 1607, Nicholas Gardambasse who married Frances Beale in 1612, and William Gardenbash who married Mary, the daughter of John Fever, a Wadhurst collier, in 1626. In 1629 William Gardenbas was a witness to John Fever's will, to which he appended his mark.[328]

The younger Joseph Gardenbash married Joan Cobbe in 1633, and the first of George Gardenbash's children was baptised in 1637. There is nothing to connect these later members of the family with the iron industry. Outside Wadhurst an apparent member of the family, Anthony Garnebos of Little Horsted, who acted as bondsman for a marriage licence in 1625,[329] described himself as a husbandman.

Bennett alias Beeny

When made denizen in 1544 Gilham Bennet was described as a priest. He was stated to be in 'Master Wybarn's iron work', to be aged 40, and to have come to England from Normandy around 1532. Whereas all three of John Barham's 1544 denizands can be found in the subsidy return for Wadhurst in 1543, none of Wybarne's workers appeared in Rotherfield, unless Gilham Holmes was 'William Home alias Shynny prisoner to John Oxley' mentioned in 1543. It therefore seems likely that by 1544 Wybarne was running an ironworks in Shoyswell hundred as was shown to be the case by the subsidy roll of 1551, though no instance of Gilham Bennet's paying the subsidy in Shoyswell hundred or elsewhere has been found.

Gilham Bennet, a namesake of William Wybarne's immigrant, had his first son Thomas baptised at Brightling in 1563. Later he moved on to Waldron, where Joan and an unnamed daughter, probably Katherine, were baptised in 1569 and 1571. In 1575 and 1577 Mary and a further unnamed daughter, perhaps Clare, were baptised at Waldron, their father appearing as 'Gillam Bennet' in 1569, as 'Bennet Gilham' in 1571, as 'Benet' in 1575 and as 'William Bennet' in 1577. This family moved on to Mayfield parish, where Katherine Beny married the finer, Nicholas Messant or Message, in 1589.

Gilham, or William Bennet, was buried at Mayfield in 1624, and his occupation of collier was given in his own will, and is mentioned in the will of his wife Dorothy Beeny, who survived him by 12 years.[330] From the will it appears that William Binne was by no means affluent. He left 10 shillings to each of his daughters, Joan, Katherine and Mary, and to his granddaughter Clare Web. At his burial 40s was to be disbursed to the poor, with 2 shillings for the bell-ringers. His wife and son Thomas were to be residuary legatees and executors. Dorothy left £1 to her daughter Katherine Message, with 5 shillings each for Katherine's daughters Mildred and Elizabeth. She left 10 shillings each to her grandchild Thomas Collins and to her grandchild-in-law John Webb. Her most substantial bequest was of £10 to her daughter Jane Springatt, late wife of Stephen Springatt. She appointed her grandson John Tolherste of Cranbrook, clothier, her residuary legatee and executor.

It looks as though Dorothy's son Thomas Bennet, who had married Margaret Gryffyn in 1607, had predeceased his mother childless. He was buried on 4 February 1636, nine days before her. It seems possible that she had been William Bennett's second wife and he her second husband. No daughter Jane had been mentioned by her husband, nor is it clear how Thomas Collins and John Tolherste came to be her grandsons. However, both parents claimed Katherine, who had been born not later than 1571, as their daughter, so Dorothy had married William at least 65 years before her death.

In 1549 and 1550 Maryan Bennet paid the poll tax in Henhurst hundred. He was in the service, not of Wybarne, but of the Hay family of forgemasters, firstly in 1549 of William, and then in 1550 of John Hay. He appeared again in the Netherfield hundred subsidy in 1560 when he paid 2 shillings on goods.

Another early immigrant from the Bennett family, John Bennett, had also appeared in Netherfield hundred, where he had paid the poll tax as a servant of Ninian Burrell in 1549 and of Anthony Pelham in 1550, presumably at Penhurst Furnace. Was he perhaps John Bennett of Mountfield, administration

328. ESRO, PBT 2/2/5/45.

329. Dunkin, *Calendar of Sussex marriage licences, Lewes, 1670-1729*, p. 270.

330. ESRO, PBT 2/2/4/173; TNA, PROB 11/171/54.

of whose goods, valued at £36 6s 10d was granted to his widow Thomasine in May 1555?[331] The grant specified that she should 'delyver or cause to be delivered to John Bennet the Smythes Shoppe with all the toolles and implements belongyng to the seyence and occupation of a smyth' and that £1 6s 8d should be paid to Edward, Joan, Isabel and Stephen, the natural children of the deceased. John Bennet was presumably the eldest son of the deceased.

Richard and Jane Byne, a widow, who had worked for Sir William Sidney at Robertsbridge in 1549, were also presumably members of the Bennett family. Each paid the poll tax in 1549, and though Jane continued paying in 1550 and 1551, Richard had by then moved on. He was perhaps the Richard Benet who paid the poll tax in Wadhurst in 1560.

Nicholas Bennett, probably the son mentioned in the will of Henry Benett of Battle in 1559,[332] was a blacksmith who in May 1578 appeared as a surety for a defendant in the High court. The view of frankpledge of April 1578 shows him to have lived in Middleborough, and although a defaulter from the manor court in October 1577 and April 1578, he was a member of the manor court homage in October 1578 and April 1579.[333]

There are many indications that the Bennett family were specialists in charcoal burning. At quarter sessions George Bennett of Chiddingly, collier, was presented for the theft of firewood worth 2 pence from John Lulham in 1637, and George Bennet the younger of Chiddingly, collier, was presented for assault on John Pup and John Vyne in 1631.[334] George Bennett the younger was buried at Chiddingly in December 1636, whilst the older man, when buried there in 1659 was stated to be 112 years of age. This puts his birth back to around 1547 and suggests that he could have been the George Bennet who married Susan Greneleafe at Mayfield in 1576. He might be the George Bennet alias Benye whose son William was baptised at Heathfield in 1597.

Colliers of this family had become thick on the ground as early as the 1560s. Firstly, Thomas Beenye married Joan Barden at Burwash in October 1563. Their identifiable children were Gilbert, baptised at Waldron in 1568, and Simon and Thomas baptised, after the family had settled at Herstmonceux, in 1582 and 1585 respectively. In between, George, baptised at Fletching in March 1571, who may subsequently have become George Bennett the younger of Chiddingly, Elizabeth, buried at Northiam in July 1572, and Margaret, baptised at Northiam in 1574, may have been other children of theirs. Joan wife of old Bonny was buried at Herstmonceux in 1592 and Old Beney himself was buried there in 1610. Simon Bennett alias Beny, whose children were baptised at Herstmonceux from 1615 onwards, was presumably the son of Thomas who had been baptised there in 1582. He was described as a collier when warrants for his arrest and that of his wife Agnes were issued by quarter sessions in 1636.[335] The Thomas Bennet alias Beeny of Herstmonceux, for whom quarter sessions issued an arrest in 1637, was however described as a husbandman.[336] He was presumably Simon's younger brother and the man whose wife Joan was buried at Herstmonceux in 1640.

Thomas Beeny's son Gilbert married Avis Sevenocke at Heathfield in 1597. Gilbert's first son Thomas was baptised at Heathfield in 1598, after which he moved on to Chiddingly, where after a gap due to the lack of a parish register, his daughter Elizabeth and son Gilbert were baptised in 1606 and 1608. The three Chiddingly colliers, Gilbert, Thomas and Richard Beeny presented at quarter sessions in 1623 for riotous assembly,[337] were presumably Gilbert and two of his sons, Thomas baptised at Heathfield in 1598 and Richard perhaps born at Chiddingly around 1601 or 1602, before the start of the parish register in 1605.

Thomas Bennet of Chiddingly, collier, made his will in October 1667 and it was proved in the following January. He made his sons William and Thomas his executors. To his son John he left £20 and to his wife £5, though she was to retain for life her dwelling house, the bed 'that we doe usually lye upon' and 'other necessary things to keep house withall'. His daughter Elizabeth Pusteed was to have £5, his grandchild John Cooke £2, with 10 shillings each going to John Bennet, Elizabeth Bennet, Mary

331. ESRO, PBT 1/1/3/154.
332. ESRO, PBT 3/1/1/108.
333. HEH, BA Vol. 96 ff 25, 34, 30-31, 36-37.
334. ESRO, QR 39, m. 11 (1637), QI 1, f. 25 (1631); I am most grateful to Brian Phillips for these and the following Quarter Sessions references.
335. ESRO, QR 34, m. 136.
336. ESRO, QR 31, m. 94.
337. ESRO, QI 1, f. 1.

Bennet, Amos Bennet and Sara Bennet, who may have been other grandchildren. Richard Cressingham was also to receive 10 shillings.[338]

A further collier from this family was John Bennett, who, having married Collette Ransom at Ewhurst in 1565, established himself at Herstmonceux. The parish register described Steven Bennet, who was baptised at Herstmonceux in December 1567, as 'a French ladd', which suggests that both parents may have been French-speaking. Steven, whose parents were not named, was probably their first son, whilst Michael and an unnamed son, who may have been Thomas, were other sons of theirs baptised at Herstmonceux in 1569 and 1574. By 1576 John Bene had moved on to Ashburnham and there, before she died in 1589, Collette bore him five daughters. It was the burial entries at Ashburnham for his son Michael in 1581 and for three of his daughters in April and May 1584 which disclosed that John Bene was a collier.

John Bene the elder's second wife, whom he married in 1589, was Alice Horshall, also of immigrant descent. Among other children, Alice bore him three sons, George, William and Richard, baptised in 1599, 1601 and 1603 respectively, all of whom appear to have survived. The father was perhaps the John Beeny who was buried at Burwash in July 1607. Thomas Bene who married Eleanor Jud from Burwash at Ashburnham in 1600 was probably his son by his first wife. Among other children Eleanor bore Thomas five sons, Thomas, Nicholas, Richard, James and John, baptised in 1604, 1606, 1607, 1616 and 1618.

Another collier was Peter Bene who married Katherine Inglett, perhaps his second wife, at Ashburnham in December 1564. Parish register entries show that up to 1571 he worked in Brightling. Although he was never noted as an alien in subsidy rolls, the entry for the burial of his daughter Mary at Brightling in January 1564 described Peter Benet as a Frenchman. His daughter Alice and son John were baptised at Brightling in 1566 and 1571. Later in 1571 Peter's servant Richard was buried at Ashburnham, whilst he himself was buried there in 1573, and it is again these burial entries which show that he was a collier.

Peter's son John was probably John Bene the younger of Ashburnham, entries for the baptism of whose children ran from 1591 to 1609 in the parish register. They included sons named George, John, Thomas, William, James and Richard, baptised in January and December 1595, in 1598, 1601, 1603 and 1609. John Bene the younger was probably the man of that name buried at Ashburnham in 1621.

So numerous are quarter sessions entries from 1637 onwards concerning Ashburnham colliers named Beeny alias Bennett that it is impossible to be quite certain to which persons they refer. However, since John and Richard were sureties for William in 1637,[339] it looks as though these three might all have been the sons of John Bene the younger, baptised in 1595, 1601 and 1609.

In 1637 Richard Beeney of Ashburnham, collier, entered a bond for the marriage of Eleanor Beeney of Penhurst, maiden;[340] this could have been the bond of Thomas Bynney's son Richard, baptised at Ashburnham in 1607, for his youngest sister, Ellin Bene baptised there as late as 1622.

Again in 1637, George Beeny alias Bennett of Dallington, collier, and William Beeny alias Bennett of Ashburnham, collier, were presented, along with Elias Gavis alias Blackett, who had married Margerie Beenie in1636, for wounding Mathew Lambe, and were later both arrested;[341] it looks as though they could have been brothers, the sons of John Bene the younger baptised in 1595 and 1601. When George married Mary Buccoll of South Malling in 1620, the marriage licence described him as George Bennett of Ashburnham.[342] However by December 1621, when he acted as a probate bondsman for the widow Jane Dowst, he was described as a Dallington collier.[343] His wife Mary was buried at Dallington in 1634, after which he married Widow Gates.

The other George Bennett, son of John Bene the elder born in 1599, who also disappeared from Ashburnham, may have moved to Wadhurst. The Wadhurst collier named George Beeny indicted for assault on John Bonnick in 1628,, was probably the same man as George Beene, the Wadhurst collier who in 1645 entered a recognizance to appear at quarter sessions and mean-while to keep the

338. ESRO, PBT 1/1/30/384.
339. ESRO, QR 37, m. 49.
340. Dunkin, *Calendar of Sussex marriage licences, Lewes, 1586-1643*, p. 242.
341. ESRO, QR 38, m. 37; QR 39, m. 129.
342. Dunkin, *Calendar of Sussex marriage licences, Lewes, 1586-1643*, p. 266.
343. ESRO PBT 1/3/5/101.

peace towards John Dance of Wadhurst, tailor.[344] This George Beenye had married Elizabeth Yeoman at Wadhurst in 1626 and their children were baptised at Wadhurst in 1627, 1629 and 1632. However, because the Wadhurst parish register commenced only in 1604, it is impossible to prove that he was not born there.

In 1652 John Beeney of Ashburnham, collier, entered a recognizance to keep the peace, especially towards William Beeney of Ashburnham, collier;[345] these colliers may have been John Bene the younger's son John born in 1595 and John Bene the elder's son William born in 1601.

Other colliers mentioned in parish registers were Robert Bene, collier, who was buried at Herstmonceux in 1580 and John Benet 'the collier' who was buried at Stedham in West Sussex in 1593. Finally, in the case of 'Old Thomas Bennet, a smith' who was buried at Lamberhurst in 1621, the occupation of John Bennett of Mountfield, whose smith's shop had been assigned to his eldest son John in 1555, and that of Nicholas Bennett of Battle (1578), a former occupation can be seen to have continued, or been revived.

A surname so widespread makes genealogical research difficult. Even with baptismal names less common than most, the possibility of tracing the antecedents of Henry Bennet of Makeney, who was buried at Duffield in 1699 and can be traced there back to 1687, and of Samuel Bennet of Makeney, whose wife Mary was buried there early in 1705, must be thought remote.

Buckoll

Philippe Bakaell's name was recorded in the Westminster denization roll, immediately following that of Onyan Russell, as a 'hammermaker', at the head of a list of six immigrants from France and Normandy, that also included the finers John Lyonarde and Robert Blancke. By analogy with the case of Onyan Russell, it must be assumed that the abbreviated word *hammerma'* was erroneously expanded into *hammermaker* at some stage in transmission.

Bakaell had come to England around 1532, but unlike Russell he cannot be traced in the Weald. The surname Buckholt, to which it might have been assimilated, was quite rare in Sussex in the 1520s and did not occur at all in the ironworking areas.

Eventually, in February 1560 an illegitimate child named John Buckold was buried at Ticehurst, whilst it appears that Christopher Bokold, who married Joan Doggart at Benenden in 1567, lived at Hawkhurst. He was buried, as Christopher Buckholde, at Hawkhurst in March 1585, preceded by his wife Joan who had been buried there in 1581, although in the parchment register her surname was entered as Buckhall.

Henry Buckall of Frittenden, whose son Richard, a carpenter, was married at Benenden in 1656, had himself been baptised at Benenden in 1612, the son of Richard Buckall. The earlier Richard Buckall was described as a householder when buried at Benenden in 1616.

Another carpenter of this family was James Buckhould of Preston in Beddingham parish who died in 1593. He was perhaps related to another tradesmen, John Buckoll, who in 1609 was a miller at Cliffe next Lewes. However, Robert Buckoll, a tailor who died in 1632, belonged to a family for some time settled at Preston near Brighton.[346]

Andrew Bucle of Witley was buried at Haslemere in 1631, though his wife Eleanor had been buried there in 1599. An earlier Andrew Buckoll had been buried at Isfield in 1606. Richard Buckhole, whose daughter Judith was married at Buxted in 1594, was probably the Richard Buckoll who married, as his second wife, Ann Hayward at Maresfield in 1597 and was buried there in 1617 under the name Buckgold. He was perhaps the father of Mathew Bakkall who was buried at Buxted in 1625 and of William Backall, whose son Thomas was baptised there in 1632. Thomas Buckuell who married Philippa Fludd at Fletching in 1623, but who was at Lindfield from 1626 to 1640, and Peter Buckwell, who had three sons baptised at Newick in the 1630s, and was buried there in 1638, were perhaps related to the Buxted and Maresfield family. No connection with iron can be established.

344. ESRO, QI 1, f. 15; QR 69, m. 31.
345. ESRO, QR 97, m. 29; QR 97, m. 29.
346. ESRO, PBT 1/1/9/148 (1593), 1/3/3/180 (1609), 1/1/22/3 (1632).

Meryall

Henry Meryall, who had been born at 'Collo' in Normandy, which could possibly be either La Chaule in the Andelle valley, near Rouvray-Catillon, or Le Caule near Sainte-Beuve-aux-Champs on the plateau between the pays de Bray and the Lower Forest of Eu, came to England around 1532. In the Westminster denization roll his name came in the middle of a list of seven ironworkers all, of whom worked for Sir William Barrentyne.

The name did not occur in the Sussex subsidy rolls of the 1520s, but early in 1563 Francis Meriall, whose parentage was not disclosed, was baptised at Mountfield. Simon, Gregory and William Meriall had all been mentioned in the Goudhurst parish register from the 1560s onwards, and a second Henry Meriall married a widow named Katheren Loose at Goudhurst in 1603. Gregory Meriall, presumably a miner, was killed in a marl pit at Goudhurst in 1583. From Goudhurst the family spread into Horsmonden (1583), Brede, where John Meryall married Anne Jarret in 1609, Tonbridge (1610) and subsequently to Mayfield (1617) and Battle.

Although Thomas Mirriall, who was buried at Battle in 1615, was described as a mercer, and Michael Merriall, who was buried at Mayfield in 1622, was a husbandman,[347] the London ironmonger named James Waters, a Herstmonceux name, made a bequest to Arthur Meryall, a smith of Stratford Bow, in 1617.[348]

Marie or Marygold

John Marie alias Margotes from *Beauface* appeared in the Westminster denization roll under the rubric 'Sir William Sidney for six', which consisted of three Normans and three Picards. He had come to England around 1533. He first appeared in a subsidy roll, as John Marygon, when he paid the poll tax in Foxearle hundred in 1549 as a worker at Panningridge. He had earlier been recorded in 1541 as 'Margoyte', among the first miners employed by Sir William at Robertsbridge.[349] His part payment of 5 shillings towards letters of denization was recorded in Harry Westall's 1546 book for Robertsbridge, but by then he was actually working at Panningridge. The 1546 book for Panningridge notes that, in addition to mining, he also cut 32 cords of wood for charcoal and that he was among those men who paid for apples, lent wheat and malt, supplied by the management to foreign workers.[350] At this period he was styled 'John de Marye', perhaps to distinguish him from John Langlois, who used the alias Margo.

By 1550 John Mary alias Margottes had lost his letters of denization and the grant to him of a 'Constat and exemplification' of them on 25 July resulted in his becoming only the second Frenchman working in the Weald to have an individual entry in the Patent rolls.[351] By this time he had probably left Panningridge because he failed to appear in subsidy rolls in either Foxearle or Netherfield after 1549. He may have participated in the opening up of ironworks in the west of the Weald, because the burial entry of February 1561 for 'John Marrygo, *gallicus*' in the Horsham parish register probably refers to him. If so he will have been the alien 'Marygold' who worked for Roger Gratwick in the Forest of St Leonards and who paid the poll tax in Burbeech hundred in 1560.

This application of the names 'Marygon' in 1549 and 'Marygold' in 1560 to John Marie alias Margotes suggests that his descendants may have adopted the surname 'Marygold', so Peter Marygold, who paid the poll tax in Hartfield hundred in 1576 could well have been his son. Whether he subsequently moved south to Mountfield and fathered two children, Nicholas and Seles (Silas?) Marigold, baptised there in 1578 and 1580, the parish register does not disclose.

Other immigrants of this name were Philip Mary who paid the poll tax in Bexhill hundred in 1539, and Nicholas Marye who paid the poll tax in Staple hundred in 1549, but in Foxearle hundred in 1550. Some of the seven aliens who paid the poll tax in Bexhill hundred in 1539 seem unconnected with ironworking, but others such as 'Gyles Duffen', may have worked for Mr Lunsford, whose ironworks was

347. TNA, PROB 11/141/440.
348. TNA, PROB 11/131/218.
349. KHLC, U1475, B5/1.
350. ESRO, SHE 6/1/11/1 (Robertsbridge); HEH, BA Vol. 27 (Westall's book of Panningridge).
351. *Calendar of Patent rolls, Edward VI*, **3**, p. 62; Nawdyn Lucas had been granted a pardon in 1548.

perhaps Catsfield Furnace.[352]

Nicholas Marye was certainly an ironworker: in Staple hundred in 1549 he worked for Sir William Sidney, presumably at Robertsbridge, and in Foxearle in 1550 he worked for Anthony Pelham, perhaps at the Priory Furnace. He was perhaps Nicolas Marye of Le Casier in the parish of Esclavelles who in 1544 had obtained wood out of two 'ventes' farmed by Jehan Fouquier near Saint-Saëns in exchange for hay.[353] However, it looks as though members of the family could have continued in the Robertsbridge area because in 1576 John Mary paid the poll tax in Staple hundred.

In the Midlands Robert Marygold was at Oaken in Codsall parish near Wolverhampton by 1594, but this was then hardly the heart of the ironworking area. He died in 1597, but his son Robert married Joan Mason at Codsall in 1614 and the family persisted in the area between Wolverhampton and Newport.

Later connections of the family with ironworking have not been established either in the form of Mary or of Marygold.

Gayne

Peter Gayne came to England around 1534. When made denizen in 1544 he had an English wife named Agnes. In the Westminster denization roll his name came seventh in a list of 12 Frenchmen, of whom seven of the first eight are known to have been workers of Sir William Barrentyne.

Accordingly it was in the Danehill Horsted subsidy roll for 1543 that Peter Gayne's name first occurred in the Weald, when he paid the poll tax among a list of Barrentyne's servants. By 1550 he was in Netherfield hundred, where he paid a shilling on goods in the relief of that year, but by 1551 he was back at Danehill Horsted, where he paid only the poll tax. It seems possible that he was the Peter Ganny who paid the poll tax at Newdigate in Surrey in 1552. In 1560 and 1563 it was again as a poll-tax payer that he appeared at West Hoathly in the northern part of Streat hundred. Whilst at West Hoathly in 1560 he was one of the administrators of the goods of John Varnysh (*Vergnes*) of Ardingly, another former Barrentyne employee.

The Worth parish register recorded the baptism of John son of Peter and Agnes Gayne in 1565, and it is to this John Gayne that most subsequent information appertains. It must be queried whether the English wife Agnes, who was Peter Gayne's wife in 1544 was the woman named as Peter Gayne's wife at Worth in 1565, and an entry in the East Grinstead parish register for the burial of 'Mother Gayne, a Frenchwoman' in 1597 confirms that she was perhaps not.

John Gayne himself, when at Cuckfield in 1589, was father to an illegitimate child, Alice, fathered on Parnell Furye (*Furrill*), and baptised at Horsham. Little Alice followed her father to Frant and was buried there in 1592, so perhaps father and mother consummated their union properly between those two dates. John Gayne's next children were two sets of twins baptised at Frant in 1594 and 1597, of whom John, Isabel and William, appear to have survived. However, his next two children, Francis and Leonard, baptised at Frant in 1600 and at Wartling in 1603, both died young, Leonard being buried at Wartling in 1604 and Francis at Mayfield in 1618.

It must have been about 1604 that John Gayne's first wife died, because in 1605 he married Denise Comber at Herstmonceux. Their first child Joan, baptised at Wartling in 1606, was buried at Ashburnham in 1609, after which they moved to Cuckfield, where their children Thomas and Joan were baptised in 1610 and 1611, though Thomas survived for a fortnight only. However, by 1616 John Gayne was hammerman at Moat Mill Forge in Mayfield, in which parish his youngest daughter Sarah was baptised.

John Gayne the elder made his will at the end of March 1620 and was buried two days later. He made his wife Denise his executrix and left £4 each for the bringing up of her daughters Joan and Sarah. He made the following bequests to his children from his first marriage: to Isabel £2 2s 0d, a flock bed, a flock bolster, a covering, a blanket and a pair of sheets: to John £2: and to William £2, a featherbed, a bolster, a coverlet, a blanket and a pair of sheets.[354]

352. Three of these seven names, Nycholas Arysman, Dyryk Corver and Peter Johnson, may be Flemish or Dutch.

353. ADSM, 2 E 14/1188 (9 Aug 1544).

354. ESRO, PBT 2/2/4/112.

There is no proof that John Gayne the younger, the hammerman's eldest son, was an ironworker, although his marriage in 1628 to Joan Beale at Catsfield, where his younger brother William was apparently then working, perhaps suggests he was. However, by 1632 he was established in Battle where he then remained, but whether the person who married a widow, Jean Turner, at Battle in 1653 was he, or a similarly named son is unsure.

William, the younger son, married Anne Shoebridge at Mayfield in February 1620 and William Gayne 'son of a forgeman' baptised at Tonbridge in the following November was probably their son. William was next at Warbleton, where his first son William was buried in 1622 and another son of the same name was baptised in 1623. By 1624 the forgeman had moved to Crowhurst, where another son named John was baptised, but son and mother were probably John and Ann Gaine, both buried at Crowhurst in 1626 and 1630 respectively. At neighbouring Catsfield, where William's elder brother John was married in 1628, William Gayne's second son named John had been baptised in 1629.

It seems unlikely that two children of William Gayne, Margaret baptised at Laughton in July 1638 and Thomas baptised at Frant in January 1645 can have been children of the forgeman, because by January 1638 he was already established at Ashburnham,[355] where he remained until his death in 1650. They are more likely to have been the children of his sexually precocious son. In 1650 William Haynes alias Gayne of Ashburnham, hammerman, acquired an estate in Ashburnham called Coldharbour[356] and thought to embark on a new life with his marriage in September to Phillipa Wymark. However, he died in December and was buried on Christmas day of that year.

The younger William Gayne, who was still at Catsfield in June 1650, when his son William was baptised there, replaced his father at Ashburnham, but sold Coldharbour to William Gowen in 1652 for £260. Like his grandfather, he was suspected of irregularity in his sexual life and in 1657 as William Gaine alias Haines of Ashburnham, hammerman, he entered a recognizance to appear at quarter sessions on the charge of adultery with his wife's sister, Elizabeth Hampton; sureties for his appearance were Richard Weekes and Abraham Hampton of Ashburnham. By 1665 he had moved on, because when he paid the hearth tax in that year he did so at Salehurst.[357] He was perhaps the William Gain who was buried at Salehurst in 1699, whilst William Gain of Ewhurst, whose wife Elizabeth had been buried at Salehurst in 1694, was probably the hammerman's son who had been baptised at Catsfield in 1650.

The alias 'Haynes', used concerning William Gayne the elder in the Ashburnham parish register in 1650, but in 1657 applied to his son, had already been applied to him in 1638 when, as next of kin to Roger Gownut of Burwash, he was appointed administrator of the latter's goods.[358] However it goes back to 1592, when John Gaine's illegitimate daughter Alice Haynes was buried at Frant, and 1597, when his second set of twins was baptised there. It was used of him again when he remarried at Herstmonceux, and also in Cuckfield parish register.

His first use of this alias Haynes at Frant in 1592 had been preceded there by the marriage of Samuel Haynes and Joan Dimon in 1590. Joan Dimon(d) was almost certainly of immigrant descent and, although the couple's son Samuel was baptised at Hailsham in 1592, Joan was buried at Hartfield, probably her own parish, in 1594. The use of this particular alias indicates that the surname originally began with an aspirated 'g', suggesting a Flemish or low-German origin. The possibility then arises that the surname was an alternative English version of 'Haynk' or 'Hainques'.

Samuel Haines' elder brother was the Brightling miller, Alexander Haines, who died in 1588. Both had been baptised at Goudhurst in 1558 and 1561, the sons of John Haynes, who was buried at Goudhurst in 1575. Their sister Margaret had married George Ballard, a Warbleton widower in 1583, and the Ballards moved on to Heathfield and subsequently Wartling, where Ballard was buried in 1605.

Alexander Haines' goods were inventoried at £69 1s 8d, and by his will he left £4 and ten wethers to his brother Samuel, with bequests of more sheep to George Ballard's daughters and to the children of John Fryman. However, the principal beneficiary was a child named Thomas Cradocke, on whom an annuity of £5 out of the lands of Richard Browne of Warbleton was to devolve, after the death

355. In January 1638 administration of the goods of Roger Gownut of Burwash was granted to his next of kin, William Haynes of Ashburnham, forgeman (ESRO, PBT 1/3/7/66).

356. ESRO, P1/31, Ashburnham tenement analysis.

357. ESRO, QR 116, m. 47; TNA, E 179/258/20.

358. ESRO, PBT 1/3/7/66.

of Alexander's widow, Constance. Alexander appointed Constance his residuary legatee and executrix and George Ballard was to be overseer of the will.[359] Richard Browne, out of whose lands the £5 annuity was payable, was the stepson of the forgemaster Hugh Collyn, and another forgemaster, Thomas Isted, witnessed Alexander's will, together with the minister William Beell.

However, the link with Thomas Isted is not the only factor to suggest a link between the Haines family of Goudhurst and the Gaine family of forgemen. More compelling are the arrival of both the forgeman and Samuel Haynes at Frant around 1590; the marriage of Samuel to a member of the Diamond family; the fact that the forgeman's twins were baptised under the name 'Hayne' in 1597 and that one of them, the one who did not survive, was named Samuel; and lastly, by the fact that Alexander's will was witnessed by William Beell, probably of the family from which John Gayne the younger took a wife in 1628.

The name Gaine did not occur in the Sussex subsidy rolls of the 1520s, though the name William Hains occurred at Balcombe. Numerous parish register entries for Haine or Haines occurred in the parish of Seale and Beeding between 1555 and 1631, but there is no reason to think they relate to an ironworking family; indeed, John Haine who was buried there in 1590 was a shepherd.

However, it seems possible that Henry Gayne, who married Christine Smithe at Slinfold in 1614, may have been of immigrant stock. Their children, Henry, John, Nicholas and Anne, were baptised at Cranleigh from 1617 to 1623, and the marriage there of the widow Christian (*sic*) Gaine to John Weller in 1630, suggests that Henry had died before then. The Cranleigh parish register also revealed the presence there in the 1630s of John Gaines (1631) and of Alice Gaines, who married Henry Hooke in 1633.

In the ironworking area of north Staffordshire, Peter Gayne married Margaret Parker at Wolstanton in January 1631. The possibility that this Peter Gayne's descendants may be found bearing the alternative surname of Hincks or Jenks ought perhaps be considered, because explicit mentions of involvement in ironworking by members of the Gayne or Haynes family outside the Weald have not so far been found.

Raunser

In 1544 Lewis Raunser was employed in Mr Pelham's ironworks. He had been born in Normandy and had come to England around 1534 at about the age of 15. In 1544 he had a French wife and three children. He paid the poll tax to the reliefs of 1549, 1550 and 1551 in Netherfield hundred, where his name was recorded in the lists of French denizens, in the first two cases following the name of Roger Tancre and in 1551 preceding it. Lewis's name did not occur in 1552, but as Tancre was then recorded as Anthony Pelham's sole alien worker, it seems reasonable to suppose that Raunser had also worked for Anthony Pelham up to 1551.

However, in 1555 he appeared in the Sidney accounts as 'Ransell', a Panningridge wood-cutter. In both 1556 and 1558 he was paid a regular covenant servant's wage of 13s 4d a year as a collier alongside Lawrence Heynold and Thomas Dogen.[360] This wage was of course but a small fraction of what he would have earned from piecework. When he reappeared in the subsidy roll for Foxearle hundred in 1560 he was able to pay 2 shillings on goods. He was buried at Penhurst, where perhaps he had earlier lived as a Pelham employee, in January 1563.

It seems likely that Lewes Raunser's wife bore him several more children after 1544. Petronell Raunser who married John Husse at Ashburnham in 1559, during her father's lifetime, may have been one of the eldest. The subsidy rolls disclosed two more aliens of this surname who paid the poll tax: Thomas Ramset at Wadhurst in 1551 and Edward Ransome in Staple hundred in 1572. Edward Ransome may have been connected with Collette Ransom, who married John Bennett at Ewhurst in 1565, when the parish register recorded her as French. Another entry at Ewhurst for the burial of Jacqueline, 'lately wife of Charles Ranser', in 1569 implies that Charles too was dead; was he also French? And was the 'wife of old Raundsome Frenchman', who was buried at Ewhurst in 1571, Lewis Raunser's wife?

Edward Ransom married firstly Alice Fayreman at Ewhurst in 1565, but she bore him only one child, Joan, before she died in 1567. Six months later Ransome married Ann Fayreman, widow, at

359. ESRO, PBT 1/3/2/57, 1/1/8/205.
360. KHLC, U1475, B10/8, 9 and 10.

Sedlescombe, and she may have been the wife Agnes mentioned in his will and the Annis Ransor buried at Westfield in 1612. After the birth of his eldest son John in 1568, Edward had moved firstly to Brede, where Edward, Mary and Agnes were baptised between 1571 and 1577, and then on to Westfield. In 1587 Anthony Standen, presumably the Catsfield collier of that name, brought an action against Edward Raunser in the High court at Battle, but the case was dismissed in September when Standen failed to appear to press his suit.[361] Edward Rawnser was probably the Westfield husbandman mentioned in an assize court recognizance of 1600.[362]

When Edward Ranser died in 1602 he left goods valued at £119 11s 0d. By his will he left to his wife Agnes a house named Pikehole and the lands belonging to it, and Stone Croft with more lands. After her death these were to devolve on his son John.[363] His second son Edward perhaps took over copyhold lands in Ewhurst, because that is where he moved after his father's death. The younger Edward was buried at Ewhurst in 1606.

John Ransome died at Westfield in 1627, when his goods were inventoried at £78 19s 0d. By his will he left 3s 4d to the poor, £6 to his youngest son Thomas, and £8 to his second son Edward. He left £2 towards the bringing up of his son Thomas's illegitimate daughter Joan, who was the daughter of Joan Sanders baptised in 1617. He made his son John his residuary legatee and executor. Edward was to have the house in which John Jarrett dwelt and the wood or grove in which it lay, which 'abuteth to one little water course, gripe or freate which runneth from or off Westfield Down or Common'. To his son John was to go his own house, barn and lands, which also abutted on the same watercourse.[364]

John Ranson married Joan Snep and they lived firstly at Little Udimore. They had children baptised at Udimore in 1622 and 1623, at Brede in 1625 and at Westfield from 1629 to 1640. Ultimately they appear to have settled in Battle, because when Joan Ransom was buried at Westfield in 1658 she was described as 'wife of John Ransom of Battell'.

Among other members of the Raunser family was Marian Raunser, whose son Nicholas was baptised at Ewhurst in 1573. However, no more was heard of Marian at Ewhurst after the burial there of his wife Anne in 1576. Was the wife of Thomas Ramsden, a surname which did not exist in Sussex in 1524, who was buried at Ticehurst in 1583, the wife of the immigrant Thomas Ramset?

Farther afield, Gilian Ranser had been buried at Tonbridge in 1556, Carden Raunster married Hester Tayler at Worth in 1578 and Katherine Raunsome, a widow, was buried at Lamberhurst in 1583. As for Nicholas Ransom, his first son John was baptised at Salehurst in 1575, but his younger sons, Marian and Henry, and Ann his daughter were baptised at Frant between 1578 and 1586.

Henry Lesford alias Ransor, who married Margaret Mower at Frant in 1604, will have been Nicholas's son. Their children, Mary, Hester and Henry, were baptised at Frant between 1605 and 1611. Margaret died in 1616 and Henry married his second wife Dorothy Newman later in the same year. Their sons, Francis and John, were baptised at Frant in 1617 and 1619. It seems likely that at least a proportion of these members of the Raunser family were still linked in some way to the manufacture of iron.

Gumrie

When made denizen in 1544 John Gumerie was a 'finer of iron with my lorde of Norfolke'. He had been in England since around 1534 and had a French wife named Joan. Beyond the fact that he was French the Westminster denization roll had nothing to say about his origin. As it happens there is evidence to show that he was probably not from the Pays de Bray, but from the Perche.

A finer named Jehan de Gommerye had been noticed in the Perche in 1472 when he acted as a witness to a notarial act passed at Chartres. In 1478 Guillaume Berceau lord of Meaucé authorised Jehan de Gommerye to build, at a place below the *chaussee* of Meaucé where there used to be a mill, *fonte, marteau et affinerie*.[365] The hammer mill and finery are clear enough, and although 'fonte' seems to show a lack of understanding of the process involved, the forge was clearly intended to fine cast iron

361. HEH, BA Vol. 96 f 18.
362. Cockburn, *Sussex Assize records, Elizabeth I*, no. 1933.
363. ESRO, PBT 1/3/3/14, 1/1/11/178.
364. ESRO, PBT 1/3/5/297, 1/1/20/15.
365. Belhoste and others, *La métallurgie normande*, p. 47.

produced by the indirect process, so a blast furnace must be understood.

Gomery is a village adjacent to the Ton valley on the borders between the duchies of Luxembourg and Bar, in what had at one time been 'debatable ground'. During the 1430s this delicate balance of power was lost because, though Bar became an appendage of the duchy of Lorraine, Luxembourg was seized by the even more powerful duke of Burgundy, Philip the Good. Burgundian dominance had been confirmed in 1475 when Charles the Bold annexed Lorraine, but Gommery had arrived in France by 1472, shortly before that event. A descendant of a branch of the family which remained in the Netherlands was presumably Bernard Joseph Gomerée, who in July 1740 witnessed the signature of Pierre Lambert Posson, forgemaster at the Liège furnaces of Grivegnée and des Vennes, to a notarial act concerning the import of pig iron from Luxembourg.[366]

In France later notices of the Gommery family appeared to the west of Meaucé. A document of 1482 mentioned a son-in-law of Jehan de Bry, forgemaster at Bertoncelles, named Colas de Gommerye, and in the following century a citation of the heirs of Jacob de Gommerye in the seigneury of Francvilliers in 1560 carried the implication that Jacob may formerly have held the forge at that place.[367]

Documentation does not exist to establish the connections between these three Gommeryes, but there can be no doubt that John Gumerye, the duke of Norfolk's finer, was another member of their family. Interestingly enough, in England the family used an alias 'Tantas', perhaps more accurately spelled in parish register entries such as 'Tantoise' (Buxted 1575) and 'Tantois' (Chiddingstone, 1584, 1593). If the true form of this surname was the homophone 'Tontois', might it not indicate, by analogy with Langlois, Champenois, Ternois and Barrois, a person (*Ton-t-ois*) from the Ton river valley?

In the Weald the family was first encountered in 1543, when two persons named 'Tantas' were cited in the subsidy roll for Danehill Sheffield hundred. The first of these men paid 4 pence on goods and was presumably John Gumrye himself, and the second man paid the poll tax. In the relief of 1549 'John Gomer' then paid a shilling on goods whilst the second man was revealed as 'Peter Gomer', who again paid the poll tax. In 1550, when Sheffield Furnace was 'in ruin and decay',[368] neither man appeared.

Though the return of many aliens to the hundred in 1551 suggests that the furnace had by then been repaired, John Gomer was not one of them; he paid a shilling on goods in Rushmonden hundred in 1551 and paid the poll tax there in 1552. His servant Anthony (Lavender?) had also paid the poll tax in 1551.

At Sheffield meanwhile, Peter Gomer appears to have died, because in 1551 and 1552 'Comes wydowe' and 'Mother Combe' respectively paid the poll tax.[369] John Gumrye failed to appear in the subsidy roll for 1560 and by 1563 had moved on to Newdigate in Surrey, where as 'John Gomber' he paid the poll tax for the last time. There he was a servant of Christopher Darrell and had replaced at Leigh hammer another former finer of the duke of Norfolk, Marian Predome, who had been there in 1557 and 1559.

Later members of the family were John Gumrye who married Joan Lamby at Linchmere in 1572 and Charles Gomer who was at Warbleton in 1581. John Gumrye appears from parish register entries to have been at Worth in 1572, at Buxted in 1578 and at Chiddingstone in Kent from 1583 to 1593. A return to the western Weald seems to be indicated by the marriage of two of his daughters at Ifield and Nuthurst in 1607, and of his son Daniel at Kirdford in 1618. Daniel's children were baptised at Kirdford from 1619 to 1634. Joseph Gumbrill, whose children were baptised at Northchapel from 1614 to 1633 may also have been one of this second John Gumbrye's sons.

Charles Gomer had children baptised at Warbleton in 1581 and at Frant in 1590, when his wife Parnell died in childbirth. Secondly he married Mildred Garrett at Hawkhurst in 1592. His son Ruben Gumbry, who had been born at Warbleton in 1581, married Mary Nash at Lamberhurst in 1606, and their daughter Mary was baptised there the following year. Ruben then moved to Maresfield where he was in 1609 and 1612, and where his parents were buried in 1622 and 1623. Ruben next moved on to Goudhurst, where he was in 1617 and 1620, but by 1624 he was at Biddenden, where he and his wife were buried in 1626. Elias Gummerye who was married at Biddenden in 1641 may have been a son of

366. P. Pieyns-Rigo, 'Problèmes de la métallurgie liégeoise vers 1740; l'apport des actes notariés', *Bulletin de l'Institut archéologique liégeois*, **98** (1986), p. 393. Controversy centred on the excessive tolls levied by the Brabant authorities on pig iron bought for the forges in Huy.

367. Belhoste and others, *La métallurgie normande*, pp. 66-7.

368. Straker, *Wealden iron*, p. 414.

369. It seems less likely that she was the widow of the Panningridge man, Come Longley.

Ruben, whose baptism has not been discovered. Elias was buried at Biddenden, 'very poor' and 'aged' in 1683.

The movements of this family were always into parishes in which furnaces and forges were carried on, but documentary proof of their involvement in ironworking is lacking. Perhaps they did not possess the skills of their forebears and were content with wood-cutting and charcoal burning. Certainly the rather frequent moves of John and Ruben Gummrye suggest little continuity of employment. However, Daniel's stay at Kirdford and that of Joseph Gumbrell at Northchapel may indicate in their cases more permanent employment.

The occurrence of an entry for John and his wife Elizabeth Gomery in the Burford parish register in south Shropshire in 1644, following those which have been noted at Burford for Giles Maryan and John Hackwood, indicates that members of the Gummery family still participated in carrying the industry to distant parts.

Levett

At Robertsbridge in April 1536, Barden Levett and Quintin Levett assaulted Robert a'Woode, a Robertsbridge shoemaker, but a'Woode killed Barden Levett with his staff.[370] The baptismal names suggest that both Levetts were aliens. Reynold Lyvyett, who was paid 2s 6d for five days' work carrying wood out of the pond at Panningridge with his wheelbarrow during the building of the furnace,[371] is the bearer of another possibly alien name. Apart perhaps from Quintin Levett, who could have been Quinto who paid 2 shillings to the subsidy in Robertsbridge hundred in 1525, none of these men appeared in subsidy rolls.

However, in 1560 the aliens John Levee and Marian Leve paid the poll tax in Foxearle hundred. The name in French was presumably *Levée*. Further foreign sounding bearers of the name were Simon Levitte and German Levette, whose respective daughters Agnes and Marian were baptised at Brightling in 1563 and 1571. In the same parish John Freeman married another Marian Levette in 1563.

The connection with ironworking was established in 1597, when John Levitt alias Catlyn was hammerman at Etchingham Forge and was also tenant of the Forge Farm. He was paid 7 shillings for every ton of iron forged. He had been baptised in 1570, the son of Nicholas Catlin alias Levite, who died in 1572. Nicholas's effects were inventoried at £14 6s 9d and their administration was granted to his son-in-law James Lackenden and his wife Joan, apparently Nicholas's daughter, in March 1577.[372]

Four children of Nicholas were baptised at Etchingham between 1561 and 1570. John Levett's children, Anne, John, Mary, Katherine and Mary were baptised at Etchingham between 1597 and 1610. John does not seem to have remained in the parish after 1610.

Judging from the way in which the family clung to ironworking parishes, the descendants of Nicholas Levite and Parret Mose, who were married at Fernhurst in 1587 might have been from this family. Perhaps this Nicholas was a son of the Etchingham Nicholas, but was baptised before the commencement of the parish register. Their first son John was baptised at Fernhurst in 1590, and William and Edward were baptised at Kirdford in 1594 and 1596, though Edward did not survive infancy. Nicholas and Agnes were baptised at Linchmere in 1598 and 1601. Nicholas Levite the father was buried at Linchmere in 1602. His son William was probably the man who married Mary Champyon at Wisborough Green in 1636 and their children Francis and Elizabeth were baptised at Billingshurst in 1637 and 1640. The third Nicholas married Agnes Heather at Iping in 1639, and their son, a fourth Nicholas was baptised at Iping in 1640. He was perhaps the father of a fifth Nicholas baptised at Abinger in 1668.

Roboye

John Roboye, a last ironworker from Auneuil (*Owney*), arrived in England around 1536. His wife was also from the Beauvaisis, but had been in England eight years longer than he. He first came to notice in the Weald at Robertsbridge in 1542, when he helped to clear the pond at Panningridge, and in the

370. Hunnisett, *Sussex Coroners' inquests, 1485-1558*, no. 103.
371. Crossley, *Sidney ironworks accounts*, p. 45.
372. ESRO, PBT 1/3/1/55.

following year he worked both as a woodcutter and a collier.[373]

Before 1549 he had moved on to Wadhurst (*Rowbye*, *Rowbowe*, etc.) where he paid the poll tax in the annual reliefs levied in the four years up to 1552. In 1551 and 1552 he had a servant, who also paid the poll tax, whose name was Worrall. In 1557 he was briefly at Newdigate (*Roybie*) in Surrey, but by 1560 had returned to Wadhurst once more. He then moved to the Midlands, where his name occurred as John Raboye in the subsidy roll for Rugeley in Cuttlestone hundred, Staffordshire, in 1563.[374]

The name Raby is connected with ironworking in the Midlands and later again in the Weald, but there is no evidence to suggest that the name Roboye was assimilated to Raby, examples of which also occurred in the Weald around Newick.

However, in the Midlands it seems possible that Walter and Anne Robye, whose children Thomas and Mary were baptised at Mucklestone in 1634 and 1636, were descended from the French John Roboye who had moved to Rugeley early in the 1560s.

Totayn

Jeffery Totayn headed a list of workers in the Westminster denization roll which was marked 'Sir William Sidney for six'. He had been in England since around 1536 and had an English wife. The name probably derives from Toutain, which in Rouen, Dieppe and Le Havre is still vastly more common than Toussaint.

In the Sidney accounts Totayn appeared most commonly as a collier, but he seems also to have served as a furnace filler in the first campaign at Robertsbridge.[375] In 1542 he worked as a woodcutter and collier for which he was paid £1 14s 0d on a reckoning, but he was also paid 13s 4d for helping to heap charcoal (*coles*) at the furnace. In 1543 he continued as a collier, but was also a purchaser of white meat, milk and butter.[376] In 1546 he and his man cut 35 cords of wood for Panningridge, and whilst he bought cattle, apples and malt, his wife bought onions.[377] In 1547 he worked both as woodcutter and collier, he and Thomas Duggyn doing most of the coaling at Panningridge that year,[378] apparently his last work for Sidney.

Jeffrey Tootyng next paid the poll tax at Cowden in Somerden hundred, Kent, in 1560, as one of the servants of Andrew Firminger, formerly the clerk of Vauxhall Furnace near Tonbridge. His fellow workman at Cowden was a hammerman, William Brisboll, who had also formerly worked at Robertsbridge, and their place of work must have been Prinkham Farm Forge, well below the two furnaces in Cowden parish, which were located in Westerham hundred and in Edenbridge tithing.

Another immigrant member of the Totayn family who in 1576 paid the poll tax in Foxearle hundred was probably Adam Tottoe. His son Nicholas Tottie had been baptised at Burwash in 1573. No other parish register entries concerning Adam have been found. Irrespective of this it is difficult to know which members of the Totty family were of immigrant descent, because in 1524, twelve years before Jeffery Totayn's arrival in England, an apparently English-born William Toty had been taxed on £2-worth of goods in Netherfield hundred.

Edward Totty (or Totey), who worked as a miner at Panningridge in 1554 and as a woodcutter in both 1554 and 1555,[379] was perhaps more probably the man who in 1548 had married Amy Turner, the widow of the Rotherfield husbandman John Turner, than a son of Jeffrey Totayn.

Nevertheless, because Jeffery Totayn worked as a collier, it must be presumed that John Tuttye, a Warbleton collier whose will was proved in 1606, was of immigrant descent. He was obviously very moderately circumstanced and bequeathed only twelve pence each to his four daughters and his son George. Another son Richard was to have his best doublet and his daughter Elizabeth was to have a chaff bed, the best covering saving one, a bolster, two pairs of sheets, a table-cloth, a chest, a pewter platter and dish, a firkin and the least stupnet save one. His wife Mary and son John were to be residuary

373. Crossley, *Sidney ironworks accounts*, p. 45; KHLC, U1475, B9.
374. TNA, E 179/178/169.
375. KHLC, U1475, B5/1, B12.
376. KHLC, U1475, B6/2, B7/1, 2 and 3 (1542), B2/2, B9 (1543).
377. ESRO, SHE 6/1/11/1; HEH, BA Vol. 27 (Westall's book of Panningridge).
378. KHLC, U1475, B10/1.
379. KHLC, U1475, B10/7 and 8.

legatees and John was to be the executor.[380]

However, the baptisms of none of John Tuttye's eight children can be found in the parish register, though their father was perhaps the John Totain who married at Waldron in 1565.

It seems possible that some of Totayn's descendants took the name Jeffery or Jeffreys as their surname.[381] In the Midlands the first hammerman named in the Wombourne parish register, which contains entries concerning forgemen who worked at Heath Forge and Swindon Forge on the Smestow brook, was John Jeffries, whose daughter Eleanor was baptised in October 1604. Only slightly later, Alice the daughter of a finer named Robert Jeffery was baptised at Wem in north Shropshire in August 1619.

Clachoo

Joachim Clachoo claimed to have been born in *Harbfilde* in Normandy and to have come to England around 1536. He appeared in the Westminster denization roll among a list of ten Frenchmen, eight from Normandy and two from the Beauvaisis, all of whom gave their places of birth and their length of residence in England, and all of whom are proved by the Sidney iron-works accounts to have worked at Robertsbridge or Panningridge.

Herbouville, about 30km due west from Neufchâtel and about 10km south-west of Crosville seems to be the nearest likely interpretation of the English *Harbfilde*.[382]

Although Clachoo certainly worked for Sidney in 1544 as his payment of 11s 10d towards the expenses of his letters of denization shows, details are forthcoming of his work only from 1546 to 1548. In 1546 he cut 12 cords of wood for Panningridge Furnace, but thereafter worked mainly as a collier, at Panningridge in 1547 and at both Panningridge and Robertsbridge in 1548.[383]

Clachoo was clearly a skilled collier, a trade he had presumably learnt from working in the Béthune valley. After 1548 he no longer appeared in the Sidney accounts and there is no trace of him in any subsidy roll, where either of his names would have been difficult to miss. He perhaps returned to France.

Harshaw

William Harchaunt, who worked in Mr May's ironworks in 1544, had been born in Normandy around 1523 and had come to England around 1537. He cannot be traced in the subsidy rolls, but his male descendants in the Weald appear to have been three or four in number by the third quarter of the century.

It seems likely that the French original of this name was Horcholle. In 1492 Jehan Horcholle of La Rosière near Beaubec was a carpenter; the Jehan Horcholle of La Rosière in 1551 was a draper.[384] At Neufchâtel Guillaume Horcholle had an interest in one of Jehan de Quenel's butchery stalls around 1500, whilst a later member of the family, Anthoine Horcholle, was not only a butcher, but in 1540 bought the woodlands of the abbey of Beaubec at Cantecoq, Havillart and La Baltière for 290 l.t., a transaction in which Pierres Engren, a frequent purchaser of woods for the ironworks, and perhaps a Neuville-Ferrières forgemaster, was also involved.[385]

During the 1560s three members of the family, Maurice Horshall, John Horshall and Peter Hasholle appeared in the Brightling parish register, of whom Maurice was stated to be a Frenchman, although the subsidy rolls do not substantiate this. George Hasholl married at Waldron in 1570.

John's eldest son Roger was baptised at Brightling in 1566, and his second son Stephen at Ewhurst in 1572. John later moved to East Grinstead, where he was buried in 1596. Jasper Harshawe

380. ESRO, PBT 1/1/12/182.

381. However, bearers of this surname could equally have been descended from Jeffery Drewett from whom, as we shall see, finers surnamed Drewett also sprang.

382. Another similar place-name is Héberville, about 10km further west, but to accept this requires the transposition of the 'b' and 'r'.

383. KHLC, U1475, B7/3 (1544), B10/1 (1547), B8/1, 10/3 (1548); HEH, BA Vol. 27 (Westall's book of Panningridge).

384. ADSM, 2 E 83/411 (25 May 1492); 2 E 83/412 (2 Apr 1551).

385. ADSM, 2 E 14/1143 (5 Mar 1501); 2 E 14/1183 (27 Aug 1540).

who appeared as a defaulter in views of frankpledge for Brambletye in 1587 and 1588,[386] was perhaps another of John's sons, but was buried at Worth early in 1592. The entry for the burial of John Harshaw's son William at East Grinstead in 1597 shows that John had by then acquired the alias 'Minstrel'.

John's son Stephen married at Cowfold in 1597. The Warnham parish register recorded in July 1599 that he was a collier and that his son George had been born in the parish of Horsham near to Langherste Wood before being brought to Warnham for baptism.

This branch of the family continued at Warnham for at least 70 years and a note in the Sussex protestation returns of 1641 lists, 'Stephen Minstrell alias Horsie, John Stasie collier, Stephen Hersie the younger, George Hersie, Francis Herzie - These are men employed about iron workes and worke in other parishes but are not suspected of Popery'.[387]

John Stacy had married Stephen Hersie's daughter Bridget in 1623. Stephen Hersie the younger will have been Stephen Hersie's second son, baptised at Warnham in 1614. Francis Hersie's baptism has not been found, but his children, William, Dorothy, Elizabeth, John, Anne and Francis, were baptised at Warnham from 1634 to 1645. In 1655 Dorothy was married at Rudgwick to Nicholas Jarret of Rudgwick.

George Horsall married Dorothy Adds at Warnham in 1620. In 1659 George Hersie of Warnham, collier, was a surety for the appearance of John Hersie of Cuckfield, collier, at quarter sessions.[388] John Hersie will have been George's second son, baptised at Warnham in 1632. His eldest son George had been baptised there in 1628.

Thomas Hersie, who had been baptised at East Grinstead in1593 and was perhaps Jasper Horshall's son, married Elizabeth Greengow at Fernhurst in 1616. Their children William and Anne were baptised there in 1626 and 1630.

Meanwhile the descendants of Maurice Horshall, who had married Alice Measaunt at Brightling in 1562, continued at Ashburnham under the alias Horshall alias Morris. Maurice's sons, Robert, William and Nicholas were baptised at Ashburnham from 1576 to 1582. Robert Horshall married Susan Ketchlie in 1601 and William Horshall married Marie Beeching, a widow, in 1602. Robert's children, John, Richard, Edmund, and Sara, were baptised at Ashburnham from 1601 to 1618. William's children, Gilbert, Alice, William, Elizabeth, Thomas, Richard and Mary, were baptised there between 1604 and 1616.

Nicholas Morris, Maurice Horshall's third son, married Anne Cox at Dallington early in 1610. His first children, William, and the twins William and John, baptised at Dallington in 1615 and 1618, all failed to survive infancy. Anne, John and an unnamed daughter, baptised at Dallington in 1621, 1623 and 1628 all appear to have survived.

A Catsfield collier, James Morris, entered a recognizance in 1639 to appear at the next quarter sessions and meanwhile to keep the peace; an Ashburnham collier, William Morris, was a quarter sessions surety in 1662; a Dallington collier, Stephen Morris alias Usher, whose immigrant descent seems obvious, and whose arrest was ordered in 1659, was fined 6 pence at quarter sessions in 1660.[389] The mentions of colliers at Catsfield, Ashburnham and Dallington either side of 1650 suggest an immigrant family named Morris, ultimately linked with George Morris of Beaubec, but this appears impossible to substantiate in the parish registers. These colliers are perhaps more properly to be sought under those descendants of Maurice Horshall who used the baptismal name of their forebear as an alias.

James Morris of Catsfield can still not be traced, but William Morris of Ashburnham might be either William son of William Hashold alias Morris, baptised in 1608, William son of William Morris alias Harshol, baptised in 1635, or William son of John and Constance Horshall alias Morris, baptised in 1639. And Stephen Morris's alias should almost certainly have been Horshall rather than Usher, although his baptism cannot be traced.

Soberis

When he became a denizen in 1544, Gilham Soberis claimed that he had been born in Normandy, that

386. ESRO, ACC 3597/1, ff 12 (17 Oct 1587), 31, 50 (30 Oct 1588).

387. R. Garraway Rice (ed.), *West Sussex Protestation Returns, 1641-2*, Lewes, Sussex Record Society, **5**, 1905, p. 188.

388. ESRO, QR 124, m. 59.

389. ESRO, QR 47, m. 43 (1639); QR 125, m. 66 (1660); QR 126, mm. 30, 55 (1661); QR 135, m. 85 (1662); I am grateful to Brian Phillips for these references.

he was aged 18 and that he had come to England around 1537. In 1544 he was working in John Barham's ironworks and this was a fact substantiated by the 1543 subsidy roll in which he paid the poll tax as 'Wylliam Obery' in Wadhurst.

By 1549 Soberis had moved on to Netherfield hundred where he was enrolled among the alien denizens; he paid the poll tax in the relief of 1549, and a shilling on goods in that of 1550. Netherfield denizens were not enrolled under the names of forgemasters until 1552, by when Soberis had moved on. As a Netherfield denizen he could have worked alongside the non-denizen Peter Sebrys (*sic*), who paid the poll tax in 1549 as a worker in Ninian Burrell's iron-works, which would have been Penhurst Furnace.

We know that by 1556 Guillaume Desauberys was back in the Pays de Bray and his con-tinued participation in the iron industry there as late as 1570 is suggested by his support, as pledge together with Jacques Bluet, for the forgemaster François de Clery in his dispute in the court of Gaillefontaine against Charles Le Roy and Louis Pinguet.[390]

Peter Sebrys could have been the father who brought the eleven-year-old Guillaume to the Weald in 1537 and may earlier have been Pierre Desauberys cited in field-boundaries at Neuville-Ferrières in 1512. His lease from Artus Guerard of a half acre of land near La Houppelière in 1545 need not preclude his continued stay in the Weald.[391] After appearing in Netherfield as one of Burrell's workers he disappeared from Sussex, but he might be the otherwise unknown Peter Ubbris who worked for Christopher Darrell at Newdigate in Surrey in 1563. However, 'Obre' and 'Obraye' who paid the poll tax at Newdigate in 1557 and 1559 indicate Aubery Larby rather than Peter Soberis. There is no reason to presume any later participation of this family in the English iron industry.

Lygon

Robert Lyges was cited in the 1546 Robertsbridge Forge book among thirteen Frenchmen who had made full or part payments towards the costs of their letters of denization; Lyges had paid 16s 8d.[392]

His entry in the Westminster denization roll indicated that he had come to England around 1539. It was as Robert Lygeon that he appeared in the 1546 furnace book, when he cut 20 cords of wood for Panningridge.[393] However he did not appear in the Sidney account books from 1548 onwards, nor did he appear in Wealden subsidy rolls. He must be presumed to have returned to France, or perhaps, having obtained letters of denization, to have found employment elsewhere in England.

Predom

When made denizen in 1544 Marian Predome stated that he had been in England for five years. He was a finer with the duke of Norfolk and presumably worked at Sheffield Forge on the Ouse, a fact confirmed by his payment of the poll tax in Danehill Sheffield hundred in 1543, 1549 and 1551. He next appeared at Leigh in Surrey in 1557 and 1559, where he will have worked at Leigh Hammer, a fact confirmed when he was described in the second instance as a servant of Christopher Darrell. By 1571 he was at Cranleigh, where he presumably worked at John Gardener's Vachery Forge.

The other immigrant from this family was Pouncello Predom, who in January 1603, as an iron finer at Nuthurst, declared himself to be aged 62.[394] He was presumably a son of Marian Predome, born in France shortly after Marian had moved to England, but before his family had come to join him. Pouncello succeeded his father at Leigh Hammer, where he paid the poll tax as 'Pownsley Prudam' in the subsidy of 1576. He was at Nuthurst by 1583, when he witnessed, again as 'Ponsley Predome', the will of the hammerman, John Perigo,[395] though whether he too worked for Perigo's master Stephen French we cannot be sure.

Joan Predham, who married John Perigo's former apprentice Thomas Francis in 1587, will perhaps have been Pouncello's daughter, as may also be the case with Beatrice Predham who married

390. ADSM, 2 E 14/1197 (28 Mar 1556); 2 E 14/1215 (21 Jul 1570).
391. ADSM, 2 E 14/1156 (27 Nov 1512); 2 E 14/1189 (14 May 1545).
392. ESRO, SHE 6/1/11/1.
393. HEH, BA Vol. 27 (Westall's book of Panningridge).
394. TNA, REQ 2/186/35.
395. WSRO, STC 1/13/107b.

John Francis in 1597. Pouncello's wife will have been 'Mother Predham' who was buried at Nuthurst in 1598, whilst his own burial was disguised under the name 'Father Pownset' in 1615.

A third finer from this family was John Preddam of Dunsfold, who was a deponent in September 1583 in the Court of Requests case concerning Dunsfold Hammer.[396] He was aged 25 and therefore will have been born around 1558; by 1583 he had been at Dunsfold Forge for about a year.

It seems an open question as to whether this finer can be identified with John Predam and his wife Elizabeth, whose daughter Joan was buried at Worth in 1576, and whose children Bridget, Mary and Nicholas, were baptised there in 1577, 1578 and 1581. Elizabeth, another child of John Predham was baptised at Worth in 1588, and the gap between Nicholas's baptism in February 1581 and 1588, would have been ample to accommodate a stay of a few years at Dunsfold. If the Bridget baptised at Worth in 1577 was the Bridget Predham who married Edward Charman at Godalming in 1603, her father may have been the collier, John Preddam who was buried at Chiddingfold in 1614. A man who worked as a finer in the prime of life need not be precluded from taking to charcoal burning in later years.

The Predam family also appears to have spread into Kent. Here the marriages of Margery Predome to Thomas Wyborne and of Joan Predam to John Bayer took place at Horsmonden in 1565 and 1576. Entries in the Biddenden parish register for Lawrence Prowdom from 1571 to 1582 suggest his employment at Biddenden Hammer. He was twice married, firstly to Mary Poste at Biddenden in 1571, after whose death in 1572 he married Mercy Gardener at Cranbrook in 1573. Lawrence's son Richard and two of his children, baptised at Biddenden in the 1570s, were buried there before 1582, whilst another child Isabel was buried at Cranbrook in 1587. Lawrence himself had certainly died before 1598, because Mercy Prowdom was described as a widow when she was buried in that year.

Although the members of the Predam family who are noted at Horsham and Kirdford during the seventeenth century may have been descendants of Pouncello Predam, none is known to have been an ironworker. Stephen Predham who was buried at Horsham in 1655 was a 'poor carter' and another man of the same name who married at Horsham later in the same year was a husbandman.

Prudome entries commenced in 1587 in the parish register of Danby in Eskdale in North Yorkshire, where ironworking was then being carried on by Sir John Danvers. However, the will of Robert Prudome of Glaidsdale,[397] who was buried at Danby in 1595, is that of a well-established local yeoman and betrays no connection with iron. Nevertheless, in 1604 Jane Prudome married another intruder in Danby parish, William Osborne.

Collier

When made denizen in 1544 Nicholas Collier claimed to have arrived in England around 1540. He paid the poll tax from 1549 to 1551 in Shoyswell hundred as a servant of Jakes Recrewe, who in turn worked for Thomas May in 1549 and 1550 and for Mr Wybarne in 1551. Neither man appeared in 1552, or in later subsidy rolls, though Nicholas Collier was perhaps the man whose daughter Joan was baptised at Mountfield in 1559.

Another early immigrant may have been John Colyar who paid 2 shillings on goods to the subsidy of 1539 in Foxearle hundred. In this hundred lay Wartling parish where Thomas son of Thomas Collier was baptised in 1552. These two Thomas Colliers could link with the apparent three or four Thomas Colliers found in Rotherfield from 1573 onwards, though one of them might be Thomas Collyer of Boreham, who was buried at Wartling in 1580.

Clement Colyer, who was among the Frenchmen recruited by William Pepwell of Bristol, looks like the Clement Collyar who paid the poll tax in Danehill Sheffield hundred in 1551 and 1560. Unfortunately the intervening relief of 1552 was paid by Clement Malet, so it appears that in this case the name Collyar was occupational. Even in Hartfield hundred 'Peter Colyer de Newbrege', whose name appeared consistently in every subsidy roll from 1543 to 1560, twice as 'Collyar', once as 'Collyer' and in 1550, as in 1560, as 'Colyer', the suspicion that this man was in reality Peter Denwall, who had arrived in England as a four-year-old around 1507 may be considered valid.

396. TNA, REQ 2/125/14.

397. Borthwick Institute,York wills, 26/369. The Prudome family must, like Lambert and Pullen, be considered of local origin, especially as Maryan Predome had arrived in England only in 1539. The Beawshaw family of Brompton in Ryedale might more cogently be thought of immigrant origin, because Mathew Beawshaw had arrived in England as long ago as 1520, but positive evidence is lacking.

No parent's name was given to identify the Frant man whose son Jordan Collier was baptised at Pembury in May 1564, whilst even more disappointingly the Frant parish register seems quite devoid of Colliers. In this case the infant's name can hardly have been occupational.

At Rotherfield it must be questioned whether the variously expressed 'Thomas the collyer', 'Thomas Collyer', 'a Frenchman collyer', 'Thomas a Frenchman' which appear in the parish register from 1573 to 1583 all relate to the same man.

That Thomas Collyer of Rotherfield, who died in 1602, was a collier is suggested by the fact that the first witness to his will was another collier, Nicholas Millington. On the other hand, none of the entries which can be shown to relate to him describes him as a Frenchman. He left goods valued at £52 3s 0d. In his will he made no mention of his children by his second wife Elizabeth Gatland, but since he made her his residuary legatee and executrix and left only 5 shillings apiece to his five children by his previous wife, she had no cause for complaint.[398] Neither of his sons, Richard and John, appears to have continued at Rotherfield.

The last entry relating to 'Thomas a Frenchman' at Rotherfield occurred in 1583 and was the baptism of a son Robert. The father of this boy cannot of course have been 'Thomas a French-man' who was buried at Rotherfield in 1580, and who we cannot be certain actually bore the name Collyer, although he might be the son of the Thomas Collyer who was buried at Rotherfield in 1594.

However, there seems to be a possibility that some of the Rotherfield entries might relate to 'Thomas Collyar, Frenchman' buried at Sedlescombe on 9 June 1581. No other entries in the Sedlescombe parish register appear to refer to him, but 'Mother Collyer' was buried at Rotherfield on 16 June 1581, exactly a week after him.

Another man of immigrant stock at Rotherfield was perhaps William Collyer who married Katherine Harmar in 1571. Their children William, George and Christopher were baptised in 1573, 1575 and 1577. The family then moved to Buxted, where the wife was buried in 1582 and William Collier in 1589.

Their sons William and George are next traced at Heathfield, where William married Margaret Peckham in 1599. Of William's children, William baptised in 1602, Richard baptised in 1606 and Thomas baptised in 1609, appear to have survived childhood, but were left orphans when their parents died in February 1610. Thomas was still at Heathfield around 1640.

George Collier's daughter Agnes, baptised at Heathfield in 1607, did not survive infancy, and his wife Laurence died in 1612. He then married Agnes, widow of George Horshall, another man of immigrant stock whom she had married at Mayfield in 1579. But George Collier was buried at Mayfield after only six weeks of wedded life, and his wife too was buried there less than a year later.

Christopher Collier married Alice Buss at Buxted in 1609, but died in 1611 and was buried at Rotherfield, whilst his widow was probably the woman who married John Mettell, a man of fairly clear immigrant stock, at Buxted in 1617.

Deffere

When made denizen in 1544, Philip Deffere gave his occupation as collier and claimed to have arrived in England around 1541. He was undoubtedly Philip Davor who paid the poll tax in Speldhurst and Rusthall in Washlingstone hundred in 1543.

A later member of this family will have been Peter Deforre who paid the poll tax in Shoyswell hundred in 1576. It cannot be shown that the family later played any significant part in the iron industry.

DENIZENS WHOSE ARRIVAL IN ENGLAND WAS UNDATED

Joan Isted's Frenchmen

Ogier

William Ogyer was the first of three Frenchmen made denizens for Joan Isted in 1544, for whom no

398. ESRO, PBT 1/3/3/8; 1/1/11/147.

personal details are available from elsewhere in the Westminster denization roll. It seems possible that none of these denizations was ever validated.

In France in 1491 three persons named Ogier were listed in the hearth tax (*fouage*) at Rosay, downstream from Saint-Saëns in the Varenne valley.[399] To the north of the Béthune valley the late Pierre Ohier, his son Mahiot Ohier and his grandson Jehan Ohier were mentioned at Neuville-sur-Eaulne in Neufchâtel notarial acts of 1509 and 1513. Adrien Auger, son and heir of the late Ricard Auger, was similarly mentioned at Ménonval in 1553.[400]

That a French-speaking ironworking family of this name existed is shown by the fact that Henri Ogier was master finer among the largely Walloon workforce employed at the *Stahlhütte* in the central Eifel in 1648.[401]

In Sussex the name occurred as Awger at Ninfield and was possibly quite widely spread as *Wyrgar* in 1524. Unfortunately, no man named Ogier appeared among the Frenchmen who contributed to the relief as servants of Joan Isted in 1549, or in later years, and no aliens of this, or similar names were recorded in other subsidy rolls. Nor is the name connected with the iron trade by surviving records.

In fact, perhaps the only artisan of this name known is Edward Auger, a Hellingly carpenter, who took administration of the goods of his own son John Auger in 1633.[402] His antecedents are unknown but he married Barbara Scrace at Framfield in the ironworking area in 1601, and his son John was baptised at Framfield in 1602. He moved to Hellingly by way of Chiddingly, where parish register entries show him to have been from 1615 to 1618. His first wife Barbara was buried at Hellingly in 1637 and he may have been Edward Auger of Herstmonceux who was buried at Hellingly in 1640. Edward's son Edward, baptised at Framfield in 1609, was probably Edward Auger of Hellingly, who married Mary Vipham at Dallington in May 1636.

The surname does not appear to be connected with iron in any other of the ironworking areas of England.

Borayne

Peter Baynowe was the second Frenchman made denizen for Joan Isted in 1544, for whom there was no personal entry in the Westminster denization roll. However, in 1549 Peter Borayne was one of Joan Isted's two finers who paid the poll tax to the relief of that year in Hawksborough hundred. This suggests that Borayne was almost certainly the Peter Borne who had paid the poll tax in Netherfield hundred in 1539.

The similarity of the names suggests that all were one and the same and the similarity of Borayne to Beaurains, so involved with the manufacture of iron in the Beaussault area in 1477 and again around 1540, suggests this as the correct English rendering of the name.

However, the name Borayne failed to appear in later sources so it does not look as though the sojourn of this finer in the Weald became permanent.

Freeman

William Freman was the third Frenchmen made denizen for Joan Isted in 1544. Again, because there is no second entry in the Westminster denization roll, there is doubt as to whether the denization was validated. Freman also failed to appear in later subsidy rolls.

It is difficult to know what the French form of this name could have been. *Fremin* appears to have been Englished as Freming as was seen in the cases of Peter and Stephen Freming of Hartfield. The difficulty is compounded by the fact that precisely the same circumstances apply in the case of William Fremens, listed in the Westminster roll as a Frenchman to be made denizen for Nicholas Eversfield.

English families of this name were plentiful in Pevensey and Hastings rapes in the subsidy rolls of the 1520s, especially in the ironworking areas. Perhaps some are descendants of forgemen named Fremin who immigrated around 1490, but whose name was assimilated to that of Freeman, especially abundant in the Burwash and Brightling areas.

399. BN, MS Fr.25922, no. 640.
400. ADSM, 2 E 14/1153 (21 Dec 1509); 2 E 14/1156 (9 Jun 1513); 2 E 14/1193 (3 Jun 1553).
401. P. Neu, *Eisenindustrie in der Eifel*, p. 60.
402. ESRO, PBT 1/3/6/149.

One forgeman of the family is known. This was Thomas Freeman, whose son John was baptised at Frant in 1578. Unfortunately there are no other Freeman entries in the Frant parish register so it is difficult to establish links with other Freemans in the Weald. He was possibly Thomas Freman who married at Mountfield in 1559. Unfortunately, this Thomas Freman could equally well be the man of that name buried at Mountfield in 1567.

It also seems impossible to establish the provenance of Andrew Freeman, a 'furnace boy', who was buried at Northiam in 1630.

The collier William Freeman of Brightling was probably baptised at Brightling in 1564, the son of John Freeman who had married Marian Levette there in 1563. However, the eldest son of John Freeman was Abraham, perhaps born from a previous marriage. When John Freeman died in 1603 his goods were inventoried at £92. It was to his son Abraham that he left all the wood 'lying and felled about the now mansion house of me the said John Freeman . . . as well rough as hewed . . . to carry the same away within one quarter of a year . . . and one hundred of pales'. He left 10 shillings to the poor and 10 shillings to the reparations of the church, but his monetary bequests were small: only 5 shillings to Abraham, £1 each to his sons John and William, 3s 4d to his son Matthew and a shilling to his son Richard.[403]

The mention of pales in John Freeman's will suggests that he was a cooper and Abraham Freeman may well have been a cooper too. He died intestate in 1624 and his goods, which were valued at £32 16s 2d, were administered by his widow Elizabeth.[404] John Freeman of Brightling, cooper, who married by licence in 1594,[405] was probably John Freeman's third son baptised in 1565.

William Freeman, the collier, married Margaret Person at Mountfield in 1601. Their children were baptised at Brightling between 1602 and 1615. Though he did not die until 1635, he made his will in 1619. He left 10 shillings to each of his seven children. His house, barn and land were to remain with his wife Margaret during her life, after which they were to go to his eldest son Andrew. However, Andrew was to pay £5 to each of his six siblings at two yearly intervals over a period of 12 years: the two boys, Robert and Henry, were to have their money first and the daughters subsequently. It does not seem that William's circumstances improved as time went on because his goods were inventoried at only £5 11s 0d at the time of his death.[406]

Another Brightling John Freeman was mentioned as a tailor in 1574.[407] He was perhaps the man whose wife Dionise had died in 1567. Their son Peter had been baptised and buried at Brightling in September 1560.

Davy Freeman, who had figured in Battle court rolls during the 1580s,[408] was probably a son of John Fryman of Brightling whose will was proved in 1558. John Fryman left nine children and his goods were valued at £25 2s 2d.[409] Another of John's sons, William, moved to Ewhurst, where his eldest son Thomas was baptised in 1577. Davy Freeman later established himself at Ewhurst as a cooper who, when he died in 1604, left goods valued at £62 9s 1d.[410]

Nicholas Eversfield's Frenchmen

Fremens

William Fremens was the only one of Nicholas Eversfield's six Frenchmen listed in the Westminster denization roll of 1544 for whom personal details did not appear in other parts of the roll. He was not among the three aliens who served Eversfield in Hoathly and Waldron listed in the Shiplake hundred subsidy roll for 1543, nor did he appear in other sections of that subsidy roll.

The comments made immediately above concerning the difficulty of identifying Joan Isted's

403. ESRO, PBT 1/1/11/210, 1/3/3/22.
404. ESRO, PBT 1/3/5/169.
405. Dunkin, *Calendar of Sussex marriage licences, Lewes, 1586-1643*, p. 18.
406. ESRO, PBT 1/1/24/99, 1/3/7/11.
407. ESRO, PBT 1/3/1/4.
408. HEH, BA Vol. 96 f 75 (Battle view of frankpledge, 30 Mar 1581), Vol. 97.
409. ESRO, PBT 1/1/4/165.
410. ESRO, PBT 1/1/12/43, 1/3/3/39.

Frenchman William Freman apply equally here.

Richard Weekes' Frenchmen

In 1544 six Frenchmen, to be made denizens for Richard Wekes, were listed in the Westminster denization roll, personal details for not one of whom can be found elsewhere in the roll. In the cases of Peter Lambert, James Tamplier, Philip (i.e. Phlippin) Toulett and Warnett Geratt, their families are well enough known from the denization roll and other sources, so they have been dealt with elsewhere. Only in the cases of the last two men, Nicholas Kynnery and John Vigott, are family details not readily available elsewhere, but John Vigott was mentioned in court rolls and has already been dealt with.

Kellery

In general the denization rolls are to be preferred to the subsidy rolls as an accurate record of aliens' names. An exception is Nicholas Eversfield's Frenchman Quintin Pyller, though even he was correctly recorded as Quintin Tyler elsewhere in the Westminster roll.

In the case of Nicholas Kynnery, no other occurrences of this surname are to be found in any source. However, among Richard Weekes' alien servants was Antonye Keller (1549), Antony Kyllere (1550) and Antonye Kellarye (1551). Although Nicholas Kellery did not appear among Weekes' aliens, Nicholas Skellerye was listed as one of Thomas May's servants in Shoyswell hundred in 1550. In this last case it looks as though the initial 's' has been elided from the baptismal name and therefore that the correct name in all four cases should be construed as Kellery or Kyllery. In Shoyswell hundred in 1551 the Nicholas whose surname is indecipherable might also be Kyllery. The name of neither man occurs in subsidy rolls of 1552 and later.

Servant to Sir William Sidney

Torshy

The French-born collier Gillam Torshey, who in 1544 was a servant of Sir William Sidney, was listed in the Westminster denization roll without record of any personal details. No mention of him has been noted in the Sidney ironworks accounts.

The French original of the surname will have been Torcy or Torchy. Guillaume and Jehan de Torcy were among the pledges who in 1500 cautioned Robert du Templier *dit* Le Turc to pay his annual rent for the forge and mill of Hodeng. Colin de Torchy and Henry Blanche had been pledges when the forge and mill of Hodeng were leased in 1499 to Robert du Templier by Pierre Pachoult of Bouelles.[411]

Both Colin and Adrien de Torchy were resident at Hodeng. Colin de Torchy had married Marguerite daughter of Anthoine Vallery, and had a son named Jehan, but was dead by 1536. Adrien, whose wife was named Perette, also had a son named Jehan, and moved to Bosc-Roger in 1535.[412]

Earlier, unspecified property at Neuville-Ferrières had been sold in 1481 by Raoullin de Torchy to Simonnet Osmont of Bouelles for 8£ 10s 0d, the wood upon which Osmont was to be allowed to cut.[413]

In the Weald the family first appeared at Rotherfield in the 1540s. Peter Torsshe was baptised there in 1541 and Marion Torchyld married the finer Philip Clarke there in 1547. Another member of the family was John Torshye who was buried at Tonbridge early in 1571. Rotherfield was some distance from Robertsbridge, so it seems more likely that Peter and Marion were children of the man buried at Tonbridge than of Sidney's collier Gillam Torshey. He could have been one of the Jehan Torchys mentioned at Hodeng earlier in the century.

Philip Clarke went on to work at Kitchenham Forge and his wife Marion was buried at Ashburnham in 1574. Clarke later returned to Rotherfield, where he perhaps worked at Birchden Forge;

411. ADSM, 2 E 14/1143 (23 Oct 1500).
412. ADSM, 2 E 14/1172 (15 May 1535); 2 E 14/1173 (4 Apr 1536); 2 E 14/1184 (18 Dec 1540).
413. ADSM, 2 E 14/1139 (19 Dec 1481). It was usually lessees who sought permission to exploit timber, but this document firmly names Osmont as 'acheteur'.

he was noted as a defaulter in Birchden borough in the view of frankpledge of April 1578.[414]

Peter Torshee was married at East Grinstead early in 1565, but the register failed to record the name of his bride. Two of his children, Alice and John, were baptised at Frant in 1573 and 1576.

Carden Torsye, whose son William was buried at Lindfield in 1567, was perhaps a French- born brother of Peter Torshee. Carden Torch had married Alice Ifeld at Worth in December 1566. He paid the poll tax as Carden Torstet in Danehill Sheffield hundred in 1572, an indication that he was then in regular employment there. However, he soon moved on to Speldhurst, where his daughter Alice Trossett was baptised in 1575.

Another brother was perhaps Steven Tersey, whose children Alice and Richard were baptised at Newick in 1576 and 1580. The baptismal entry of 1580 for Richard was duplicated at Fletching, and it was there that Steven Torsey was buried in 1616.

Richard Tercye married Mary Fynch at Newick in 1601, and Elizabeth, Ann and Mary, the children of Richard Tersee, or Tersey, were baptised at Fletching between 1610 and 1615. His earlier children were probably Grace, Richard and Joan Terse, baptised at Fletching from 1602 to 1607, but whose parentage was not recorded. Another daughter of Richard Tersey was Maudlin, who was buried at Fletching in 1620.

The occurrence of all these names in ironworking parishes suggests that charcoal-burning continued to be the family's trade, but no firm evidence for this has so far been found.

Servants of my lord of Norfolk

Harrison

Reynold Harrison appeared in the Westminster denization roll of 1544, together with John Roberie, as 'working in my lorde of Norfolks workes', but separately from the workers at Sheffield and without any personal details. Nor is there any record of Harrison in the subsidy rolls of the Weald or in parish registers for the area.

On the other hand, parish registers further afield record the burials of persons named Raynold Harrison, at Petworth in 1616 and at Lingfield in 1637, and the link of the surname with ironworking was made explicit in Exchequer depositions by commission, to which Robert Harrison of St Leonards, mine digger, testified on 28 March 1588.[415]

The surname does not at first sight appear French, but was perhaps derived from the place name Hirson, one of the chief towns in the ironworking area of Thiérache. In its French form the surname appeared in a notarial act of 1486 by which the brothers Fremynot and Aubery Herichon of Beaussault dedicated to alms 8 sous out of a rent of 17 sous, due to them from the heirs of Pierre Le Roux the younger on certain heritages at Tréforêt.[416]

Since the name appeared at Beaussault so early in the blast-furnace period, it is worth asking whether Robert Harrison, who was in charge of Henry VII's works in Ashdown Forest in late 1491, could have been the Robin Herichon who in 1508 held land at Camp du Hault (Campdos) in Gaillefontaine parish.[417] Later members of this Beaussault family were Pierre Herichon (1509), Jehan Herichon (1539), Guillaume Herichon and Nicollas Herichon (both 1554).[418]

It seems possible that Guillaume Herichon could be Guyllam Herston who helped in the finery at Robertsbridge in 1543,[419] but is not otherwise known in the Weald. Finally, Lambert Herichon, a name which recurred as Lambert Harrison in the English Midlands in the seventeenth century, was witness to the act of August 1541 by which the forgemasters at Beaussault bought Jehan de Fry's rights in eight foundays of iron from the furnace at Neuville-Ferrières.[420]

Robert Harrison, the mine digger of St Leonards Forest, was 35 years of age in 1588 and

414. ESRO, ACC 3597/8, f. 79v.
415. TNA, E 134, 30 Elizabeth I, Easter 8.
416. ADSM, 2 E 83/411 (19 Feb 1486).
417. ADSM, 2 E 14/1152 (28 Oct 1508).
418. ADSM, 2 E 14/1152 (23 Aug 1509), 2 E 14/1182 (29 Nov 1539), 2 E 83/2 (31 Mar and 26 May 1554).
419. KHLC, U1475, B2/2.
420. ADSM, 2 E 14/1185 (7 Aug 1541).

would therefore have been born around 1553, so he could have been Reynold's son; William and Mary Harryson, who were baptised at Nuthurst in 1574 and 1577, but whose parentage was not recorded, could have been Robert's children. Other children of Reynold Harrison could have included Roger Harrison, who married Elizabeth Knight at Slinfold in 1571; Roger was buried at Slinfold in 1593 and his widow in 1599. A later Roger Harrison married Elizabeth Capelin at Warnham in 1612 and they had children named Elizabeth, Roger and Thomas baptised at Warnham between 1616 and 1623. Roger Harrison of Westminster, who was buried at Northchapel in 1669, may have been from this branch of the family too.

Other members of the family could have included Simon Herson who was buried at Framfield in 1563 and Joan Hurson who married Edward Ellis at Fernhurst in 1588.

The first Reynold Harrison mentioned in Wealden parish registers was the man who married Agnes Butcher at Petworth in 1581. He was perhaps the Raynold Harrison who was buried there in 1616. Since baptismal entries relating to the Lingfield Reynold Harrison and his wife Elizabeth were recorded at East Grinstead in 1627 and 1629 he could have worked at Woodcock Hammer. He was buried at Lingfield as Reginald Harrison in 1637 and his widow was buried there in 1638. His son Thomas, who was baptised at East Grinstead in 1627 may have been the man who had children baptised at Thursley from 1671 onwards.

Also at Lingfield, was baptised in 1630 Philip son of John Harrison. Philip Harrison was at Dunsfold, another forge site, in the 1650s, where his children, Mary, Richard, Anne, John and William, were all baptised between 1654 and 1660.

The ubiquity of the name Harrison in the Midlands makes it difficult to trace the family's arrival there. However, the Bloxwich collier Richard Harrison, whose wife Isabel was buried at Walsall in 1594, might have been of French descent. Richard himself was buried there in 1600. Ralph Harrison, whose wife was buried at Walsall in 1598, was himself buried there in 1605. In 1629 an English Lambert Harrison was baptised at Walsall, along with his twin brother Ralph, both of them the sons of Charles Harrison. Mathew Harison of Aston Furnace was buried at Aston in 1652.

John Harrison, a collier, was buried at Chetwynd in 1663 and Gilbert Harrison of Grindle Forge was buried at Ryton in 1668.[421] In the eighteenth century John Harrison 'of the Forge', who was churchwarden at Condover, was buried there in 1756. Thomas Harrison 'of the Forge', whose daughter Molly was baptised at Longnor in 1747, was probably the Thomas Harrison 'of the Forge' whose wife Mary was buried at Condover in 1778.

Miners recruited by William Pepwell

Marchant

Hugh Marchaunt was one of the miners recruited from France by William Pepwell of Bristol; indeed he headed both the lists of Pepwell's recruits recorded in the Westminster denization roll. In 1524 there had been three men named Marchant in Mayfield and Rotherfield and the name of Reynold Marchaunte, who was then at Rotherfield, suggests that there could have been earlier immigrants of this name than Hugh.

In the Weald Hugh Marchaunt was first mentioned in the 1546 accounts for Robertsbridge Forge, when he was paid 4 shillings in earnest for four years service at Robertsbridge. That year he was also among the Frenchmen who paid for supplies of apples and malt.[422] At Robertsbridge he worked in the finery. He paid the poll tax at Robertsbridge in 1549, 1551 and 1552, but not in 1550, when perhaps he was on leave in France.

Apart from fining iron, the finers were expected to keep their hearths and chimneys in repair. In 1548 this consisted only of 'dawbing' the finery chimney, but in October 1555 Marchaunt received 6 pence for repairing his chimney with stone and mortar.[423] Other casual payments he received included those in 1553 for dressing the finery bellows and heaping charcoal (*coles*), and those in 1555 of 4 pence

421. A 1626 entry in Condover parish register for the baptism of William son of 'Gilbert and Marie Harrington from the Forge' is possibly an error for this Gilbert Harrison.

422. ESRO, SHE 6/1/11/1 (Forge book, 1547); HEH, BA Vol. 27 (Westall's book of Panningridge, 1546).

423. KHLC, U1475, B8/1 (1548); Crossley, *Sidney ironworks accounts*, p. 150.

in May for half a day's labour in weighing iron, 6 pence in August for weighing iron for Mr Robarts, (when at the same time Hugh's servant received 6d); in May 1555 he received 8 pence for making a new coal basket and in September 3 shillings, when he supplied four of them.[424]

The list of finers who worked for three days helping to set in the hammer-block in 1551 was headed by Peter Gelly and Hugh Marchant, which seems to indicate that by then he and Gelly were in charge of the two fineries at the forge.[425] In August 1555 each was paid 6s 8d in lieu of a livery coat due to them the previous year, so a livery coat was clearly one of the perquisites to which their covenants entitled them. The 1555 accounts show that Marchaunt and Gelly each received covenant wages of 5 shillings a quarter, but this was negligible compared with their main income in piecework which, at 6s 8d per ton of iron fined, in 1555 yielded an income of £56 6s 2d.[426] However, this will have been divided between Marchaunt and Gelly, and out of it each will also have paid his assistants.

Already in July 1549 Marchaunt had been highly favoured in that Harry Westall had been allowed 8 pence for his expenses in going to Rye to 'speak for passage for Hugh Marchant', when he was allowed to go home on leave after rioters had temporarily put Sir William's ironworks out of action. Hugh Marchaunt's house was mentioned in the 1556 accounts.[427]

Soon after 1556 Marchant left Robertsbridge. Twice early in 1559, and again in 1561, his wife Margaret was a godparent at Horsham, as was Marchant himself in May 1563. However, only six weeks before this he had married again at Abinger, his second wife also being named Margaret, and it was at Abinger that he paid the poll tax in 1571. He finally paid an alien tax of 6s 8d on goods at Tandridge in 1576, perhaps having by then retired from ironmaking.

There seems to be no obvious link between Hugh Marchant and other persons named Marchant in the Weald, nor are there other known links with the metal industries. Silvester Marchant, who in 1588 was a Chiddingly tailor,[428] had perhaps been born at Rotherfield in 1544, and had married there in 1568. William Marchant of Buxted, sawyer, was bondsman for the marriage licence of John Marchant, a Rotherfield yeoman, in 1618.[429]

In Derbyshire Richard Marchant of Toadhole, ironfounder, was involved in 1614 in a Chancery suit between William Angrome and Robert Steward of Bringewood concerning Bringewood and Staunton Harold ironworks. In 1606 Marchant had taken a three-year lease of Staunton Harold Furnace from Sir George Sherley in trust for himself and various other partners.[430] He was perhaps descended from Sir William Sidney's former finer, Hugh Marchant. He will have been Richard Marchaunte who married Joyce Kirkam at Rugeley in 1583, rather than the son of George Marchant, baptised at Mayfield in 1577. Was he perhaps also the man of that name who married Petronella Dudley at Duffield early in 1601? Probable probate material for him at Lichfield dated 1629 no longer survives.

Malet

Clement Collyer was probably an occupational name for Clement Malet who worked in Danehill Sheffield hundred in the 1550s. He will be dealt with in a subsequent section.

HANAPER-ROLL DENIZENS OF 1541

Carpenter

The surname Carpenter was quite widespread in ironworking areas of the Weald in the 1520s. There are two reasons for supposing that some ironworkers of that name might have been immigrants. Firstly, an alien named John Carpenter was among the hanaper-roll denizens of 1541. Secondly, Dominic Russell

424. KHLC, U1475, B8/5 (1553); Crossley, *Sidney ironworks accounts*, pp. 147-9, 152.
425. KHLC, U1475, B8/4.
426. Crossley, *Sidney ironworks accounts*, pp. 134-7, 142-3.
427. KHLC, U1475, B8/3 (1549) and B8/8 (1556).
428. ESRO, PBT 1/3/2/47.
429. Dunkin, *Calendar of Sussex marriage licences, Lewes, 1586-1643*, p. 106.
430. TNA, C 2 James I, A3/31.

of Mayfield, apparently a forgeman of immigrant descent, who was buried at Pembury in 1561, named his sister Joan, wife of John Carpenter, as his executrix.

It is, however, quite uncertain whether this brother-in-law was John Carpenter of Buxted, hammerman, who in 1588 acted as bondsman when Robert Russell of Buxted was granted a licence to marry a widow named Catherine Reynolds.[431] In any case, the Buxted parish register contained entries for John Carpenter only in February 1588, when his son Richard was baptised and buried, so it is possible that he was only briefly in the parish.

Another John Carpenter lived at Mayfield, but if his first wife was Joan Russell she must have been dead before 1571, when John married Alice Darby. He was perhaps connected with ironworking because his son Samuel, baptised in July 1572, was apparently Samuel Carpenter, a Ticehurst blacksmith, who in a deposition of 1601 claimed to have been born in Mayfield around 1574.[432] The Ticehurst Samuel Carpenter was buried in 1636; he was mentioned in the will of Richard Carpenter, a Cowden husbandman, who in 1614 bequeathed 10 shillings to Samuel, son of his brother Samuel,[433] who had been baptised at Ticehurst in 1600. Richard himself had been baptised at Mayfield in 1576. Their father was presumably the John Carpenter buried at Mayfield early in 1616.

A second forgeman from this family was another Samuel Carpenter. His baptism has not been traced, but since he married Lettice Treadcroft at Ashburnham in 1590, he may have been born before 1570 when the Mayfield parish register began, and perhaps before 1568 when that for Buxted began. Samuel Carpenter's daughter Mary was baptised at Crowhurst early in 1592. His wife Lettice was buried at Ashburnham early in 1602 and later that year Samuel married Dorothy Sampson at Crowhurst. Their children Mary and Elizabeth were baptised at Heathfield in 1605 and 1607, but there appear to be no further notices of him in the Weald, so he perhaps took part in the move of ironworkers to other parts of Great Britain.

Coppyn

Almost the only suggestion that ironworking members of this family might have been immigrants arises from the inclusion of James Coppyn among the hanaper-roll denizens of 1541.

Valentine Copping, who was buried at Frant in 1558, was almost certainly the son of John Coppin of Rusthall Green in Speldhurst, who mentioned him in his will which was proved in 1508.[434] Valentine's widow, Alice Copping, who died in 1560, left 12 pence each to the children of her son John,[435] who could very well be John Copping of Petworth, hammerman. He was involved in the affray at Northchapel in 1580, in which the immigrant finer Charles Pavy was fatally wounded. He had formerly been employed at Dunsfold Hammer, and evidence he gave as a deponent in 1583, in a Court of Requests case concerning ironworking there, showed he had been born around 1533.[436] It is possible that he ended his days as a collier, and was 'Old father Coppin, collier', who was buried at Chiddingfold in 1612.

Otherwise, it appears from Alice's will that Valentine left only daughters. Their daughter Joan, formerly Joan Busse, married as her second husband a Frant husbandman, James Copping, and it is from him that later husbandmen and yeomen of Frant were descended. In 1591 their eldest son John Copping married Alice Laghen, the widow of John Laghen alias Collyn, and her son by her former husband was the Frant hammerman David Lahen or Laffam. In this case it appears that employment in the iron industry by this family may have preceded marriage to a member of an immigrant family, rather than resulting from it.

Earlier, Martin Coppin alias Harris of Salehurst, who died around 1579,[437] had worked from around 1546 to 1555 at Robertsbridge Forge, where he cut wood for charcoal and worked on the water courses.[438] It is not clear that he had ironworking skills.

431. Dunkin, *Calendar of Sussex marriage licences, Lewes, 1586-1643*, p. 3.
432. WSRO, EpII /5/6, f. 271.
433. KHLC, DRb/PW23.
434. KHLC, DRb/PW1.
435. ESRO, PBT 1/1/4/371.
436. Cockburn, *Sussex Assize records, Elizabeth I*, no. 801; TNA, REQ2/2/125/14.
437. ESRO, PBT 1/3/1/79.
438. ESRO, SHE 6/1/11/1. Crossley, *Sidney ironworks accounts*, pp. 127, 146, 147, 159, 160.

Godfrey

John Godfrye was one of the servants of Adrian Reder who paid the poll tax in Hartfield hundred in the subsidy of 1543. His name is not otherwise recorded in Wealden subsidy rolls and cannot be shown to have been otherwise connected with iron.

However, John Godfery was, like Adrian Reder, an alien who is shown by the hanaper roll to have paid for denization in 1541, but whose name did not appear on the two surviving membranes of the 1541 denization roll.

James

Francis Jayms also paid the poll tax as a servant of Adrian Reder in the subsidy of 1543 in Hartfield hundred. He is not otherwise known in the Weald. Roger Jamys had worked as a woodcutter for Sir William Sidney in 1543, and in 1554 William James was noted as serving in the same capacity in the draft furnace book of that year,[439] but there was no indication that either man was an immigrant.

It seems possible that Richard James, whose daughters, Margery, Martha and Frances, were baptised at Rotherfield in the 1560s, was of immigrant extraction. Was he 'James the Smyth' who paid the poll tax at Withyham in the subsidy for Hartfield hundred in 1576? In 1587 the youngest of Richard's daughters, Frances a'James, married William Stubberne of Mayfield, who was certainly of immigrant descent.

At this time there was also a James family which lived in Mayfield of which the head was a substantial yeoman, Nicholas James. When he died in 1589 he left £9 to the poor, houses at both Mayfield and Wadhurst, a shop in the middle of Mayfield, a yearly rent on land at Barcombe, and two pieces of land at Wadhurst, firstly a freehold of 8 acres called Barnhead and secondly Rich Fields (18 acres). His will was witnessed by John Cowper and John Gallett of Mayfield (overseers of the will), Blase Rowland, and Richard James who could have been the Rotherfield man.

Nicholas James's eldest son John, who had married Jane Edwards from the substantial Mayfield family of that name, was a tanner, to each of whose three children the grandfather left a 12-monthing bullock recently bought at Barcombe. Nicholas made his younger sons Paul and Samuel residuary legatees and executors, and the shop was to go Paul who was a butcher.[440] Samuel, whose occupation is unknown, set himself up in Brightling, and had goods worth £220 16s 0d, when he died intestate in 1611.[441] More interesting is John James's elder son, Nicholas, who in 1610 married Elizabeth Barby, from the cannon and ironfounding family of that name, who were probably immigrants. Their first three children, Mary, John and Elizabeth, were baptised at Rotherfield between 1620 and 1626, and their fourth child Nicholas was baptised at Withyham. It seems probable that Nicholas James moved on to Hawkhurst, perhaps taken there by cannon founding. In 1654 the Benenden parish register recorded the marriage of Nicholas's son Walter Jeames, a blacksmith, whose baptism has not been found, to Mary Cortney of Sandhurst, and noted that Nicholas Jeames of Hawkhurst was dead.

A forgeman named John James was buried at Monmouth in August 1608.

A family named James was involved in the spread of the slitting mill. Elizabeth daughter of John and Sara James was baptised at Edwinstowe in Nottinghamshire in 1661. When John James of Clipstone was buried at Edwinstowe in September 1663 the parish register described him as 'from the slitting milne being first inventor of it there'. A child of Thomas James of Clipstone Milne was baptised in 1670. William James was buried at Edwinstowe in 1685 and Sarah James, who may have been John James's widow, in 1686.

Reder

The hanaper roll shows that Adrian Reder paid for denization in 1541,[442] but his name did not appear on the two surviving membranes of the 1541 denization roll. He paid the poll tax in Hartfield hundred in 1543, as did three of his servants, the finer Bartholomew Pountye, John Godfrye and Francis Jayms.

439. KHLC, U1475, B9, B11/4.
440. TNA, PROB 11/74/76; ESRO, B3/131.
441. ESRO, PBT 1/3/3/238.
442. TNA, E 101/223/10.

The loss of his entry from the denization roll means that neither the date of his arrival in England, nor his country of birth is known. He may have been born in Normandy, but the name might well be of German origin. In the subsidy rolls of the 1520s the name occurred at several places in Sussex, but within the early ironworking area an instance at Mayfield is the only one. Because the first of his workers mentioned was a finer, it looks as though he was in charge of a forge in 1543. The forge may have been Birchden.

Reder could still have been in Hartfield hundred in 1549. The Hartfield subsidy roll for 1549 has been lost and it was not until 1550 that Reder appeared again as Adrian Ridleygh who paid the poll tax in Buttinghill hundred, although not among the workers at the Worth double furnace. He still paid the poll tax (without surname) in Buttinghill in 1551, but by 1552 he had left the ironworking area; in that year Adrian Reder paid a shilling on goods worth £1 at West Tarring in Bramber hundred. In 1560 he was still there but paid only the poll tax and though his name can be found on the 1563 subsidy roll for Bramber hundred, his place of residence and the tax paid cannot be deciphered. By 1572 he had either moved away or died.

The presence of a collier named Christopher Adrian alias Reder at Rotherfield proves that Adrian's descendants continued in the iron industry. At the Sussex assizes in 1593 Christopher was found guilty of theft,[443] but his literacy secured him benefit of clergy.

Two John Reders were recorded during the 1570s and 1580s, in Rotherfield and Brenchley respectively. The Rotherfield man had four children, Elizabeth, John, William and Ursula, baptised between 1575 and 1591, but then moved to East Hoathly where John and Ursula Reder were buried in 1596.

The Horsmonden John Reder married a widow, Margery Besbyche, in 1574. Their children, Mary, Sarah, Rebecca and Thomas, were baptised between 1575 and 1578, but Margery died in 1581. Mary Reder died unmarried in 1625 and left legacies of £5 to her half-brother John Besbeg, of £3 to George Hembrey of Brenchley, who as we shall see was probably of immigrant descent, and of £1 to each of his two sisters, Susan and Dorothy Hembrey.[444]

ALIENS MENTIONED IN PRE-1550 COURT ROLLS

Vouche

At the Dallington hundred court and view of frankpledge held on 5 October 1529 John Garret and George Vouche, Frenchmen (*gallici*), were each fined 2 pence for a brawl in which Vouche drew blood from Garret's face with a dagger.[445] The presence of this Frenchman in Dallington and his brawl with the ironworker John Garret suggest that Vouche too may have been an ironworker.

Unfortunately no other references to this man have been found, so nothing is available to confirm his connection with ironworking.

Gewe

At the Hawksborough hundred court in October 1530 it was presented for Burwash that Gewe, 'a Frencheman', had attacked 'Roland Frencheman' with a staff and a dagger and that Roland had attacked Gewe with a dagger worth 8 pence. Gewe was fined 8 pence and Roland 4 pence. In spite of this experience Gewe was presented again in October 1531 for carrying a dagger valued at 2 pence, with which he had made affray against another unnamed Frenchman. On this occasion he forfeited the dagger. In 1543 Gewe appeared in the Sidney accounts as a woodcutter and collier at Panningridge Furnace.[446]

In the relief of 1550 for Hawksborough hundred both John Gue the elder and John Gue the

443. Cockburn, *Sussex Assize records, Elizabeth I*, no. 1473.

444. KHLC, DRb/PW27.

445. ESRO, ASH 290; I am grateful to Christopher Whittick for a photocopy of the relevant portion of this court roll.

446. BL, Add. Roll 31818; KHLC, U1475, B9.

younger appeared as servants of John Collyn, presumably as workers at his Burwash Forge; both were colliers and both paid the poll tax. By 1551 they appear to have moved on to Isenhurst in the hundred of Dill, where their names were recorded as Gow, two aliens in the service of Goddard Walsh who paid the poll tax in the relief of that year.

Henry Gue, whose son John was baptised at Brightling in 1567, looks like a member of the Gewe family, but if he was in fact Henry Gowen, who had married Elizabeth Alland at Herstmonceux in 1562, he perhaps belonged instead with Peter Gawen and John Gawyn.

A more certain member of the family, Hanno Gewe, was cited in a Star Chamber case concerning Cowford Furnace in Rotherfield. He was among certain 'lewd and evil disposed persons' who in November 1568 in a 'warlike and riotous manner' prevented Lord Bergavenny's servants from using the furnace.[447] Hanno's employers at this time were apparently the lessees of the furnace, Bartholomew Jeffrey and William Relfe.

In January 1569, when Lord Bergavenny's servants tried to prevent the lessees' workers from cutting trees in Waterdown Forest, Hanno was perhaps the unnamed Frenchman who, together with Gilham Bygnoll alias Founder, Stephen Dennett, Thomas Weston and John Homesby, attacked them 'with eleven feet long piled staves'.

The family was already by this time represented at Lamberhurst on the Kent-Sussex border where Stephen Lambert alias Gew had been baptised in 1564, and although the father's name was not given, the alias suggests that one of the family's earlier members might have been named Lambert Gewe.

By the 1580s the Gewe family was in Cranbrook where between 1583 and 1595 four chil-dren, Priscilla, [Myhgh?], Mary and Alexander, were baptised; they then appear to have moved back to Lamberhurst where Anthony and John Gewe were baptised in 1598 and 1601. Mary Gew and Anthony Gew the younger were buried at Lamberhurst in 1598 and 1600. In none of these cases was the father's name disclosed, but he may have been Anthony Gew, whose unnamed son was buried at Lamberhurst in 1608. Perhaps later members of this family all took the surname Lambert.

Susslawe

Robert Susslawe was presented at the hundred court of Hawksborough in October 1533 for the theft of a piece of iron worth a shilling from the forgemaster John Colyn the elder. His punishment was left to the discretion of the steward, possibly in consultation with Colyn.

Masculer

The Frenchman Thomas Masculer of Warbleton was among the defaulters at the Hawksborough hundred court in October 1538.[448] Warbleton was almost certainly an ironworking parish by 1538, but no proof is available that Masculer was an ironworker. His name did not occur in denization or subsidy rolls.

Bilbow

In the Hawksborough hundred court of 26 April 1542 Antony Bylbowe, 'Frencheman', of Tottingworth was fined 8 pence for using a dagger 'contrary to proclamation'. Bylbow served Sir William Sidney both as woodcutter and collier at Robertsbridge in 1542 and was then paid £4 16s 1d on a reckoning.[449] 'Bellou, a collyer', whose son John was baptised at Frant in September 1566, was perhaps in reality 'Belbou'.

Later the family was found in the west of the Weald. Thomas Bilbowe's daughters Jane and Priscilla were baptised at Bramshott and Linchmere respectively in 1582 and 1586, whilst Alice Bilbow was buried at Linchmere in 1584. In Surrey, Robert Bylbowe was included amongst the Dunsfold gunners listed in the muster rolls for 1583-4.[450] Some members of the family continued in West Sussex until 1669, when another Thomas Bilboe was buried at Woodbeding.

447. TNA, STAC 5/A2/25.
448. BL, Add. Roll 31820.
449. BL, Add. Roll 31821; KHLC, U1475 B6/2, B7/1-2.
450. Craib, *Surrey musters*, p. 17.

In West Yorkshire among the furnace workers listed at Thomas Proctor's abortive blast furnace near Shipley Hirst in June 1593 was John Bilbowe, who had with him his wife and a boy.[451] John Bilbowe may have been the man baptised at Frant in 1566. He may have moved on to north Staffordshire and died there, because in 1599 'Widow Bilboo' from Sir Thomas Gerrard's works at Winnington was buried at Mucklestone.

This family was clearly an ironworking one. It seems surprising that further evidence is not available.

ALIENS FIRST MENTIONED IN CORONERS' INQUESTS

Milward

John Milward alias Fregman (i.e. Frenchman) of Buxted, labourer, was murdered at the house of John Foster alias Black John in the wastes (*lez Wast*) of Buxted in February 1531.[452] Though no persons of this name contributed to the alien tax in Wealden subsidy rolls, the fact that John Wildgoose engaged Thomas Millward to work as founder at his new ironworks at Iridge in Salehurst in 1584 shows that there were ironworking descendants.[453] Another, or the same Thomas Milward, a miner at Ewhurst in Surrey, was bound by the Sussex quarter sessions in 1617 to keep the peace towards a Mayfield man.[454] His sureties were two Haslemere husbandmen, Daniel Francis and John Milwarde. Thomas Milward was buried at Ewhurst in 1629.

The Mayfield connection suggests that the Surrey man may have been Thomas son of Richard Millard baptised at Framfield in 1593. There were no later entries for these men in the Framfield parish register, so Richard could be Richard Millard, who survived his son and was buried at Ewhurst in 1633.

At Buxted the family had continued in the person of Richard Milward, a Buxted yeoman who left a will when he died in 1592. Among the goods he left were an iron posnet for his daughter Susanna and an iron pot for another daughter Mary. He left his lands in Mayfield to his son John, lands both freehold and copyhold in Buxted to his son Peter, but his house and copyhold in Buxted were to remain to his wife Mary for life for bringing up his four daughters. His wife was also to have two cords of wood, and wood for house repairs out of his lands in Mayfield.[455]

It appears that there were other Milwards who were not ironworkers. One of these was the Cranbrook weaver, Thomas Mellwarde, who died early in 1576. His bequest of three acres called Salters in Buxted to his son Dunstan, whom he also named residuary legatee and executor, suggests that he may have been born in Buxted, possibly the son of the man murdered in 1531.[456]

At Battle John Clarke alias Mylward was respondent in a case of debt brought in the Battle High court by George a'Weekes, a case which was dismissed when the plaintiff failed to appear in April 1581.[457] Whether this man was related to the Battle carpenter, Thomas Clarke, the surety in at Battle High court case of March 1586,[458] or to Robert Clarke, the Battle founder of 1701, is impossible to show due to the absence of a parish register for the sixteenth century and to the failure of the seventeenth-century register to record parentage consistently until the 1640s.

In Midlands parish registers entries for persons surnamed Milward are not uncommon. A connection with ironworking can be shown in the cases of William Bloomer alias Milwarde 'de furnace', whose wife Joan was buried at Halesowen in 1658, and of Robert Millard 'of the forge' in Bringewood, whose wife was buried at Bromfield in 1661. The baptism of a daughter of Thomas Bloomer alias Milward at Wombourne in 1612 indicates that this alias had a long pedigree in the Midlands. A Robert Milward was married at Wombourne in 1587, so the alias could go back to the period of the direct system.

451. TNA, E 134/35/6 Elizabeth I, Michaelmas 34.
452. Hunnisett, *Sussex Coroners' inquests 1485-1558*, no. 79.
453. TNA, STAC 5/W2/1.
454. ESRO, QR 16, m. 107.
455. ESRO, PBT 2/2/1/71.
456. KHLC, PRC/17/42/282b.
457. HEH, BA Vol. 96 f 87.
458. HEH, BA Vol. 97 f 55.

Holgate

A Frenchman named John Holgatt was murdered at Buxted by Simon, another Frenchman, in February 1535.[459] A John Holgate had been recorded at Alciston in the 1525 subsidy. This is a very English name and it is difficult to know what the original French could have been. Perhaps the original name was *Huget* and should have been rendered as Hugget or Hewgate.

Deneuve

In September 1548 the Frenchman Martin Denewe, a Mountfield collier, assaulted a French couple, Corney and Mariette Charlowe, at Penhurst. He wounded Mariette with a meat-knife, a wound from which she died later the same day.[460] Denewe was later pardoned. Further instances of the name Deneuve seem not to occur in connection with iron either in the Weald or further afield.

ALIENS MENTIONED ONLY IN SUBSIDY ROLLS, 1539-1550

SUSSEX - HASTINGS RAPE

Foxearle hundred

The possibility that the surname of the alien John Colyer, who paid 2 shillings on goods in 1539, was an occupational one such as was used in 1543 in Danehill Horsted hundred for John and James Vergnes or Farnes, is a real one. However, it affords little support to the idea that the ironworks of Richard Woodman or Anthony Pelham recorded in the hundred in 1549 might have existed in the 1530s.

Taylor

The name of the other alien recorded in Foxearle hundred in 1539, Oliver Taylor, who paid a shilling on goods, also fails to prove a link with ironworking, though other immigrants with the surname Taylor can be traced in the ironworking area. For instance, William Taylor was among the aliens who paid the poll tax in Hawksborough hundred in 1539.

However, Martin Taillor, who was murdered at Brookland Furnace by the Frenchman William Fownder in 1534,[461] could have been English, and the surname of Peter Taylor, who paid the poll tax in West Barnfield hundred in Kent in 1541, was probably the occupational name of Peter Wyldorne who paid 4 pence on goods there in 1543, and was a Shoyswell hundred denizen by 1549, when he paid only the poll tax.

Bourdell

In dealing with the Nevill alias Burdett family the suggestion was made that this John Bourdell who paid the poll tax in 1549 in Foxearle hundred in the works of Anthony Pelham was in reality John Burdett. The variant spelling with 'll' in place of 'tt' had also occurred in the Béthune valley during the 1520s.

Chaplin

Philip Chapleyn was a Frenchman who paid the poll tax in the works of Anthony Pelham in Foxearle hundred in 1549, but failed to appear in later subsidy rolls.

Although the surname Caplin was unknown in East Sussex in 1524, but occurred quite widely in West Sussex, paradoxically it seems easier to detect descendants of this Frenchman in West rather than in East Sussex. William Chaplin married Clemence Norman at Buxted in 1575, but almost immediately moved to Lodsworth where their daughter Rose was baptised in January 1579. After the baptism of

459. Hunnisett, *Sussex Coroners' inquests 1485-1558*, no. 100.
460. Ibid., no. 144.
461. Ibid., no. 96.

their daughter Elizabeth in July 1580, they moved to Lurgashall, where their children, John, Anthony, Clemence and Thomas, were baptised between 1583 and 1593, though Thomas survived only a few days. They then moved back to Tonbridge, where William Chaplin was buried in 1595 and his wife in 1603.

Three of the children from this marriage appear to be mentioned in the Chiddingfold parish register. Clemence Capelin married William Mills there in 1609, Jane the daughter of John Capelin of Shillinglee was baptised there in 1611 and the first wife of Anthony Caplin of Combe was buried there in 1618. John was perhaps John Capline, 'servant to Mr Bettesworth', a forgemaster, and was buried at Rogate in 1639.

Curiously it was William Capline of Warnham, rather than William Caplen of Lodsworth and Lurgashall, who was descended directly from Philip Chapelyn. The Warnham man married Anne, or Annis Sloutter in 1568 and their children, Joan, Dorothy and Jane, were baptised at Warnham between 1569 and 1576. Annis was buried in 1583, and William must have married again, because his further children, Richard, Jeanne and William, were baptised at Warnham between 1589 and 1593.

This family's descent is known, because William was married in the name of Capline, but his children, Dorothy, Jane, Richard and William, were baptised under the surname Phelpe, whilst Joan and Jeanne were baptised under the surnames Capline alias Philpe and Phelpe alias Caplin respectively. William Capelin alias Philpe was buried at Warnham in 1628 and his second wife in 1630. Their daughter Dorothy married John Fiste, possibly also of immigrant descent, in April 1593; this couple's daughter Dorothy had been baptised out of wedlock one week earlier.

The woodbroker, Augustin Capline of Fernhurst, who mentioned his mansion house in his will and died in comfortable circumstances in 1600,[462] might be thought to have been of immigrant descent. However, this does not seem to be the case. Though his parentage was not disclosed in the Lurgashall parish register which recorded his baptism in 1562, his father Robert Caplyn, a Lurgashall husbandman who died in 1580, mentioned him in his will,[463] and there can be little doubt that he was of indigenous ancestry.

It looks as though only the first of the two families suggested above to have been of immigrant descent had any prolonged involvement with the iron industry. Apart from the case of Augustin Capline, most references to indigenous families named Caplin or Chaplin suggest them to have been husbandmen, or yeomen farmers.

Unckle

Peter Unckle (or Ungell) paid the poll tax as a Frenchman in Sir William Sidney's works in Foxearle hundred in 1549, and in the three subsequent years. In 1551 Unckle's servant, also named Peter, paid the poll tax alongside him, but did not appear in any of the three other years. In 1560 Peter 'Unkle' paid the poll tax in Barcombe hundred, at the time perhaps being employed at Fletching Forge, but by 1572 he had moved back to the far eastern limit of the Weald, where he again paid the poll tax as Peter 'Nonkell' in West Barnfield hundred. After this, as Peter 'Ountell' he married Agnes Browland, perhaps a second marriage, at Burwash in 1575. Agnes, the wife of Peter 'Oncklie', was buried at Ashburnham in May 1578. However, in 1580 Richard son of this or another Peter 'Ounckil' was baptised at Bexhill.

Peter Unckle first appeared in the Sidney accounts in 1548 as just one of the colliers at Panningridge.[464] However, he continued there until 1553 sharing the work with George Moryall, without any other collier being involved. In 1551 they 'coaled' 740 loads of wood at 1s 3d a load, which earned them £46 5s 0d, whilst in 1553 their work brought them £47 18s 8d.[465] Set against amounts such as these, a collier's quarterly wage of 6s 8d was minute.

It must be presumed that Stephen 'Untill', who paid the poll tax in Shoyswell hundred in 1560, was from Peter's family. Was he also the blacksmith, Stephen Ongeley of Ightham, who in March 1576 was killed by Richard Clerke of Offham, gentleman, with a hedging-bill in self defence?[466]

462. TNA, PROB 11/95/266.
463. WSRO, STC 12/157b.
464. KHLC, U1475 B2/1.
465. KHLC, U1475 B10/5 and 6.
466. Cockburn, *Kent Assize records, Elizabeth I*, no. 834.

This problem of surnames, together with the application of 'Oncklie' to this family in the Ashburnham parish register, the marriage of Clement Ungley at Benenden in 1559, the marriage of Bartholomew Bouncklie to Joan Eglis at Goudhurst in 1582 and the burial there of 'Widow Bouncklie' in 1604, raise the possibility that various forgemen named 'Onglie' or 'Ongley' might easily be of French descent, the immigrant name having been assimilated to the Wealden one, as not infrequently happened.

However, intermarriage of the English Ongley family with the immigrant Pullen family of forgemen goes back to 1587 in Frant, though here again the question of whether this marriage resulted from, or itself promoted, the involvement of the Ongley family in ironworking seems incapable of resolution.

Various parish register entries undoubtedly relate to the immigrant family. The burials of two successive John Unkylls at Newick in 1560 and 1564 are obviously linked to Peter Unckle's stay in Barcombe hundred. Michael Ounkell, shown by later evidence to have been born around 1542, whose son John was baptised and buried at Fletching in October 1566, was probably Peter's son. Since Peter Unckle himself had moved to the eastern Weald by 1572, Rafe Unkell, who was baptised at Buxted in 1570, but whose parentage was not disclosed, was perhaps Michael's son rather than Peter's. However, Edward Untyll, who was baptised at Ewhurst in East Sussex in 1567, could have been Stephen's son.

The baptism of Rafe Unkell at Buxted in 1570 gives a precious link with the move of this family to the west Midlands. In 1602 his father Michael Uncle gave evidence to Exchequer commissioners relating to the earl of Essex's blast furnace at Walford, in the Wye valley, thought by Schubert to have been erected soon after 1588. He was a collier at the works and gave his age as 60.[467] He was accompanied by another collier from the Weald, the 35-year-old Philip Arthur who had been baptised at Worth in 1566.

The will of Michael's son, the Walford collier Ralfe Uncle, was proved in 1626. The surname Uncle is also common in the neighbourhood of Cleobury Mortimer, where the blast furnace was probably introduced during the 1560s. Although their direct connection with ironworking at Cleobury Mortimer cannot be demonstrated, one member of this family who was linked to wood-related trades was the tanner Thomas Uncle, whose will was dated 1587.[468]

La Mell

Stephen Lamell who paid the poll tax in Foxearle hundred, firstly in 1549 as a Frenchman in Sir William Sidney's works and then as an alien servant of Anthony Pelham in 1550, was probably the same man as Stephen Malle who was a servant of Charles Warnet alias Gerard in Netherfield hundred in 1551, when he again paid the poll tax. In the Sidney accounts he may have been 'Stewen the filler', who was paid 8 shillings for carrying coals when Panningridge Furnace stood still for a quarter of the year in 1549, following its destruction by the rioters from Kent.[469]

However, the Gerard connection suggests that John de Mounle, one of Charles Gerard's workers at Buxted in 1550, before his move to Battle, might be connected with this man. If this is correct then Martin Le Mowle,[470] who paid the poll tax in Shoyswell hundred in 1572, and John Mowle who brought a plea of debt against Stephen Patten in Battle High court, but was fined 3 pence when he failed to appear to press his suit in December 1582,[471] could be other members of this family. Later references to the surname in connection with iron in the Weald appear not to occur.

Grewe?

Clement Grewe and Philip Grewe both paid the poll tax in 1549, the former in Foxearle hundred as a Frenchman in Sir William Sidney's works, the latter in Netherfield hundred in Anthony Pelham's works. The possibility that both men's names were in reality Growte is suggested by the fact that in 1560 Philip

467. TNA, E 134, 44 Elizabeth I, 3 Trinity.

468. TNA, PROB 11/149/97 (1626); Herefordshire Archives and Record Centre, Hereford, wills proved at Hereford (1587).

469. Crossley, *Sidney ironworks accounts*, p. 97.

470. But 'Le Mowle' could be a mis-transcription of 'Leonard'; the finer Martin Leonard was in the area before and after 1572, and was probably 'Leonard' who paid the poll tax in Shoyswell in 1576.

471. HEH, BA Vol. 97 f 21.

'Grotte' paid the poll tax in Netherfield hundred. There is no corresponding entry to confirm such a suggestion in the case of Clement. The Growte family has been dealt with earlier.

Fardell

In 1549 Phlyppyng (*Phlippin*) Fardell worked for Richard Woodman in Foxearle hundred. The fact that Gyllam Bourgonyon (Fr. *Bourguignon* = Burgundian) was employed at the Woodman works in Foxearle in 1551 shows that the possibility that Fardell was related to, or descended from, the forgemaster Claude Fardel of Bèze in Burgundy, who had been in financial difficulties in 1448,[472] must be taken quite seriously. A Rotherfield collier named George Mahoude, who was outlawed for murder in 1574, will be mentioned later. Mahoude was almost certainly connected with the forgemaster Samson Mahouard, who took a 9-year lease of the forge at Diénay north-west of Dijon in 1473.[473]

There is no subsequent record of Fardell or his descendants working in England, but two inhabitants of Battle bore the name Mahoude alias Hamon in the 1580s, one of them a tailor.[474]

Stampylyon

John Stampylyon paid the poll tax in Foxearle hundred in 1549 as a Frenchman in Richard Woodman's works. There are no other references to him or to other persons of this surname in the Weald.

Hussey

More than one French surname may have been assimilated to Hussey, the two most likely ones are Houssaye or Housset, and Hochard, Houchard or Houzard. In the Pays de Bray the name occurred at Baillolet, where Pierre Houssaye, father and son, were involved, together with Alexandre Turgis, in a purchase of bacon in 1553.[475]

In Cranbrook hundred the alien Peter Husshe paid the poll tax of 2 pence in 1543 and in 1544 the poll tax of 4 pence. He was probably Peter Hese, Benjamin Jeffery's ironfounder, who paid the poll tax in 1549 in Hawksborough hundred. In the intervening period both Husshe and Jeffery had made the move to Sussex from Kent, where the forgemaster Jeffery had previously worked for Thomas May in West Barnfield hundred. Peter Hese did not appear in subsidy rolls after 1549.

Anthony Hoyse paid the poll tax firstly in 1550 in Foxearle hundred as a servant of John Ashburnham, perhaps at Ashburnham Furnace. He later appeared at Ardingly (*Hewashe*) in 1563 and then at Worth (*Huashe*) in 1576, in each case paying the poll tax, though at Ardingly his wife was also required to pay. At Ardingly he can just possibly be equated with an otherwise unknown 'Anthony Hewet of the Park' whose daughter Alice was baptised in 1567.

Another member of this family will have been Nicholas Hoschett, who in 1551 paid the poll tax in Netherfield hundred as a servant of Charles Warnet alias Gerard. Nicholas Usher, 'a Frenchman', whose daughter Sara was baptised at Pembury in 1578, was probably the same man. Before 1583 he had moved to East Grinstead, where Sarah Hussher was buried in September of that year. In fact Nicholas may have arrived in the East Grinstead area by 1580, because a string of Hussher or Husshaw baptisms commenced in that year and continued until 1594. Although their parentage was not stated, from the burial register it appears that Nicholas Hussher was the father of Joan (*Johane*) Hushaw who was baptised there in 1586 and buried in 1592.

Nicholas Husshoe was listed among the Brambletye absentees in the East Grinstead view of frankpledge for April 1591 and was fined twopence.[476] The fact that he was not listed in views of frankpledge during the 1580s suggests that he may have previously worked at Woodcock Hammer, the parish church for which, Godstone, was very remote.

472. P. Braunstein and O. Chapelot, 'Mine et métallurgie en Bourgogne à la fin du moyen âge: première esquisse' in *Mines, carrières et métallurgie dans la France médiévale*, Paris, 1983, p. 44.

473. Ibid., p. 42.

474. John Mauwoode of Battle, tailor, was a surety in a case involving James Mauwoode, who also appeared in another case at the same court as James Mauhode alias Hamond: Battle High court, 6 Dec 1580; HEH, BA Vol. 96 f 81.

475. ADSM, 2 E 14/1193 (20 May 1553).

476. ESRO, ACC 3597/1, f. 147.

From the 1572 subsidy roll for the borough of Edenbridge it appears that Mathew Washer was an alien, perhaps working at one of the furnaces in Cowden. He will have been the father of Quintin Hoshet who was baptised at Cowden in December 1572. Earlier, Matthew and Joan Hussher had been at Worth, where their children Margaret and James were baptised in 1566 and 1568, though Margaret survived less than two months. Matthew was probably the man whose first wife was buried at Goudhurst in 1595.[477] Later in 1595 he married the widow Eve Merian. She died in 1606 and Matthew followed her to the grave in March 1608.

Matthew was therefore probably the father of James Husher, whose own son James was baptised at Salehurst in 1593, and of Quintin Husher who married Katherine Wiat at Etchingham in 1596. Eight children from this marriage were baptised at Etchingham between 1597 and 1616, whilst a daughter named Susan was baptised at Goudhurst in 1600. From a quarter sessions case brought against Quintin's 12-year-old son Charles in 1618 for larceny, it appears that Quintin was a collier. The youngster admitted stealing two puddings and a black pudding (*bloodenge*), but denied the theft of stockings.[478] Charles Husher was buried at Etchingham in 1643. Katherine Hushie, who was buried there in 1640, was probably his mother.

The Quintin Usher, whose daughter Bennet was baptised at Waldron in 1594 and who in 1603 appeared as bondsman in a marriage licence as Quintin Husher of Warbleton, husbandman,[479] will have been a different person from the Etchingham man. Either man could have been the Quinton Husher buried at Burwash in 1627.

Other immigrants of this surname included Holland Ussher and Gillam Hussher. Holland Ussher paid the poll tax at Newdigate in Surrey in 1563, when he was listed as a servant of the English-born George Laby. He was noticed again the following year at Worth, where Louise (*Lewes*) the daughter of Holand and Margaret Hussher was baptised in October 1564.

William Hoiceard, who married Joan Lambard at Goudhurst, and John Hassherd, whose son Adrian was baptised at Goudhurst, both in 1561, were perhaps descended from someone named 'Houchard'. Three daughters, the last two of whom were named Marian and Denise, were born to William and Joan, now named Hosher, between 1562 and 1569. Could William be Gillam Hussher, who paid the poll tax in Barcombe hundred in 1576?

Of John and Adrian Hassherd nothing further is definitely known. Was John the John 'Howsher' who married Alice Savage at Tonbridge in 1564, and was later married for a third time as John 'Hosharde' to a widow, Margaret Mier, in 1581?

Philip Hewashe, who married (*Hewes*) Margaret Valliance at Ashburnham in 1560, left a will which shows that at his death in December 1591 he was a Hartfield collier. However, he did not appear in views of frankpledge up to April 1591, so he had perhaps recently moved to Hartfield. He named seven children in his will, of whose baptisms only those of Agnes and Ottway, baptised at Cranbrook as Anne and Ottwell in 1576 and 1579, can be identified with any certainty. At his death Philip Hewashe's goods were valued at £52 13s 4d. He left either £4 or £5 to four sons and two daughters, though his daughters Alice and Agnes were also to have five pairs of sheets each and Agnes was to have a featherbed and a joined bedstead. A fifth son Alexander was to be residuary legatee and executor and he was to put the youngest children, Michael and Alice, out apprentice.[480]

A French member of this family was 'John Hussett a collyer dyinge at his worke on the sodaine; a Frenchman borne' who was buried at Biddenden in 1593. There are no subsidy roll entries for this man, but he was possibly John Usher, 'a Frenchman', whose daughter Mary was baptised at Rotherfield in 1566. Eleanor Hushaw and Beatrice Usher, daughters of a Frenchman, who were baptised at Rotherfield in 1568 and 1571, were perhaps his children too, though a Star Chamber case makes it clear that William Usher also lived in Rotherfield at this time. John and William Usher were among the 'lewd and evil disposed persons' who, on behalf of the forgemasters Bartholomew Jeffery and William Relfe, prevented the workmen of Lord Bergavenny from using Cowford Furnace in November 1568.[481] It will

477. Among the gunners listed at Wotton in the Surrey Muster roll for 1583-4 was Mathew Husher (Craib, *Surrey musters*, p. 24). Was this a distinct person, or did the Cowden man return to the western Weald before ending his days at Goudhurst?

478. ESRO, QR 19, m.88.

479. Dunkin, *Calendar of Sussex marriage licences, Lewes, 1586-1643*, p. 43.

480. ESRO, PBT 1/1/8/469, PBT 1/3/2/132.

481. TNA, STAC 5/A2/25.

be noted that this seems to be the second generation of the Usher or Husher family to have worked for Jeffery.

In the Battle High court, actions were brought against John Husher alias Mundo (or Minido) in 1587 by Anne Raygatt and against John Husher by George Harrison. Anne Raygatt's case was dismissed in August 1587, when she failed to appear to press her suit.[482]

Another John Hussey was perhaps the Ashurst finer, named John Huswiffe, who was killed by the Hartfield hammerman Robert Templer in 1566.[483] And Walter Hussyf's daughter Joan was baptised at Fletching in 1577, after which his further children, Elizabeth, James, Lawrence and Mercy, of whom Lawrence did not survive, were baptised at Burwash between 1579 and 1588.

Another collier, for whom defaults at views of frankpledge do not survive, was Robert Hewashe of Nutley, who was indicted firstly for the burglary in January 1587 of the house of Anthony Post at Nutley, and secondly in January 1588, together with Peter Pynion, of the house of Anthony Post at East Hoathly (*sic*). On the latter count Robert was found guilty, but was fortunate enough to be allowed benefit of clergy.[484] His son Thomas had been buried at East Hoathly in 1576, but otherwise there are no parish register entries for him.

A later Robert Usher was the Withyham blacksmith, who married Phoebe Smith of Westerham by licence in 1628.[485] Another Robert Hussey was buried at Beaulieu in Hampshire in 1687, perhaps an employee at the ironworks on Sowley Pond.

The family was well represented in ironworks in Shropshire, where at Cleobury Mortimer a Frenchman named Hussey, whose baptismal name was not disclosed, paid 16s 8d on goods worth £5 in the subsidy of 1571. Still at Cleobury Mortimer, Peter Hussie's children, Alexander and Alice, were baptised in 1649 and 1652. The earlier man was perhaps the collier John Husher, who had been given 10 shillings when sent to work for Sir Henry Sidney in Glamorgan in 1566.[486] He may have been the John Hussey whose son Nicholas was buried at Much Wenlock in 1588.

Further east near the forges on the Tern, Arthur and Margaret Hussey's children Mary and Francis were buried at Mucklestone in 1611 and 1612 and their daughter Ann was baptised there in 1614. In 1638 Elizabeth the daughter of Richard and Mary Hussey was buried at Mucklestone. Richard was presumably the 96-year-old Richard Hushy of Woore who was buried at Mucklestone in 1691. In Derbyshire Gilbert Hosey, finer, married Jane Swinscoe at Pleasley in 1615, but she was buried there in 1619.

Another Shropshire John Hussey was at Whittington near Oswestry in 1624, where the lease under which Fernhill Forge was built had been negotiated the previous year. Perhaps a collier, he was described as being 'of the cabin in Babbies Wood', when his son John was buried at Whittington in February 1624. His son Edward was baptised there in April of the same year. Perhaps he was John Husheard who was buried at Abdon in 1635. At nearby Maesbury Forge, which belonged to the same Shropshire partnership, Richard Hussey was hammerman in 1652.[487]

In Cheshire, Richard Hussey's daughter Elizabeth was baptised at Wybunbury in 1674 and his wife Amy was buried there in 1680. William Hussey was buried at Wybunbury in 1684 and his widow Anne early in the following year. Daniel Hussey's children, Anne and Daniel, were baptised there in 1681 and 1684, though Anne was buried in 1694. John Hussey was forgeman at Tib Green Forge, whose children, Mary, John, Margaret, Anne and Martha, were baptised at Wybunbury between 1688 and 1701, though Martha did not survive infancy.

At Churchhulme a child of William Hussey, a Cranage forgeman, was buried in 1693. His children, John, Hanah and Joseph, of whom only Joseph appears to have survived childhood, were baptised at Churchhulme between 1694 and 1699. William's wife Hannah was buried in 1714 and he himself in 1715.

At Wolverley on the Stour the children of Peter and Elizabeth Hussey, Elizabeth, Sarah, the twins Peter and John, William, Thomas, Mary, a second Sarah, Rebecca, and a second John, were

482. HEH, BA Vol 96 ff 12, 16.
483. Zell, *Industry in the countryside*, p. 131.
484. Cockburn, *Sussex Assize records, Elizabeth I*, nos.1069, 1091.
485. Dunkin, *Calendar of Sussex marriage licences, Lewes, 1586-1643*, p. 170.
486. TNA, E 179/167/44; Crossley, *Sidney ironworks accounts*, p. 210.
487. Edwards, 'The early ironworks of north-west Shropshire', p. 200.

baptised between 1674 and 1695. Their father, Peter Hussey, the elder, was buried there in 1707. The children of John and Martha Hussey, Peter, Elizabeth, John and Thomas, were baptised between 1724 and 1731, and their mother Martha, now a widow, was buried at Wolverley in 1740.

At Hartlebury, John, Mary, Anne, and Elizabeth, the children of Thomas and Mary Hussey were baptised from 1699 to 1706. Their father was probably the forgeman, Thomas Hussey the elder, who was buried at Lower Mitton in 1729. A gap in the parish register from 1711 to 1745 prevents our proving their connection with Thomas and Mary Hussey, whose son Francis was baptised at Hartlebury in 1759, William and Anne Hussey, whose son James was baptised there in 1765, and Samuel and Penelope Hussey, whose children, Joseph, Susannah and Samuel, were baptised there from 1765 to 1770. The Hartlebury register shows that Joseph and Samuel Hussey survived to raise families in the period between 1789 and 1811, but occupations were not disclosed, and the Wolverley parish register did not include the name Hussey among the 15 surnames of forgemen it mentioned between 1813 and 1822.

At Sheffield the Attercliffe Forge partnership employed John and David Hussey to carry on the plating trade in the 1690s.[488] Parish register entries for David Hussey first appeared in the Rotherham parish register in 1671, but by 1680 he had moved to Sheffield, where he was perhaps the hammerman who was buried in 1722. John Hussey had also appeared in the Sheffield parish register by 1683. Entries relating to an Attercliffe hammerman named Peter Hussey first appeared in the Sheffield register in 1703; his wife Ellen was buried there in 1731. A second forgeman named David Hussey married Mary Girdler at Sheffield in 1732.

The Kilnhurst forgeman Joseph Hussey, who was buried at nearby Rawmarsh in 1742, does not seem to have come from Sheffield, but was perhaps the man born at Cranage in 1699, a move that could have been facilitated because of the interest of the ironmaster William Westby Cotton in both Cranage and Kilnhurst forges.

Bexhill hundred

Rowland

The denizen John Rowland was first recorded in a subsidy roll in 1543, when he paid the poll tax in the Hoathly and Waldron borough of Shiplake hundred. He had earlier probably lived in Burwash, where, it was alleged in the Hawksborough hundred court of October 1530, Gewe a Frenchman had attacked Roland Frenchman with a staff and a dagger and the said Roland had attacked the said Gewe with a dagger worth 8 pence;. Gewe was fined 8 pence and Rowland 4 pence.[489]

In the Hawksborough hundred court it was also presented in April 1542 that John Rowland of Burwash, Frenchman, was a petty thief who had stolen four trees called 'yong Impys' worth 8 pence, the goods and chattels of Lawrence Upton,[490] an entry which suggests that Rowland might have been a collier. By 1549 John Rowland had moved to Bexhill, where he paid 2 shillings on goods to the relief, both in that year and in 1550. He last appeared in a subsidy roll in Foxearle hundred in 1560 when he paid the considerable sum of 4 shillings on goods.

Another alien from this family was Peter Rowland, who paid the poll tax in Rotherfield hundred in 1551, but by 1552 had become a servant of Thomas Woodman in Foxearle hundred, where John Rowland apparently joined him later in the decade.

No baptismal entry for John Rowland's son Richard has been found, but his son Samuel was baptised at Wartling in 1552. William Rowland, son of a Frenchman, buried at Wartling in 1553, might have been either John or Peter Rowland's son. John Rowland's wife was buried at Wartling in 1561 and in 1562 he was remarried to Joan Cade. He was buried at Wartling in February 1567 and administration of his goods was granted to his widow Joan in March. She was bound to give £3 6s 8d to each of John's sons, Richard and Samuel.[491]

Samuel Rowland, the partner whom the London ironmonger James Waters nominated as one

488. SA, SIR/1/2/1 (1690), p. 36.
489. BL, Add.Roll, 31818.
490. BL, Add.Roll, 31821.
491. ESRO, PBT 1/1/5/404.

of his overseers and to whom he left £1 6s 8d in 1617, was probably John Rowland's son baptised at Wartling in 1552. Waters was a Herstmonceux surname, and another legatee, Arthur Meryall, a smith of Stratford Bow, to whom Waters bequeathed a suit, may perhaps have been from Sussex too.[492]

An earlier alien of this surname was Roger Rowland, mentioned in the subsidy of 1524, who lived at Hurstpierpoint and was therefore not likely to have been connected with the iron industry. Possible descendants of this man and the fact that some of the descendants of Rowland Mocumble took the surname Rowland, may account for the large number of persons of that name found in the mid-Sussex area in the second half of the century.

The mention of 'Robert Rowland of the Forest' in the Horsham parish register in 1570, might suggest his possible employment in the iron industry. More certainly, John Rowland, a Lingfield collier, who was indicted for the theft of cowhides at Southwark assizes in 1597,[493] might have been descended from the earlier John Rowland. He was found guilty and sentenced to be whipped. The theft of cowhides might suggest an intention on his part to diversify into the trade of tanning.

Shoyswell hundred

Roche

Richard Roche, who paid the poll tax in Shoyswell hundred as a Frenchman and denizen employed by Thomas May in 1549 and 1550, and possibly in 1551 too, is not otherwise traceable in the Weald.

However, John Roche married Margaret Farne in the ironworking parish of Lamberhurst in 1572. James and Alexander Roche, baptised at Lamberhurst in 1574 and 1575, were presumably their children. The burial of William Roche at Goudhurst in April 1633 suggests that this family continued to inhabit the ironworking parishes of Kent.

The London ironmonger Thomas Roche, who died in 1634, had been born in Gillingham, the son of John Roche, and had married Elizabeth James, the daughter of Jonas James. In his will he left thirds of his estate to his wife and to his daughter Elizabeth, and, among other bequests, £2 to his brother John Roche and £5 to each of John's children at their majority, £3 to Jonas James, £2 to his uncle William Roche and £3 to the poor of Gillingham.[494]

Whilst these members of the Roche family may have been descended from Richard Roche, the steelmaker 'Monser de Roche' buried at Titchfield in 1624, and no doubt employed at the earl of Southampton's Funtley Forge, was presumably himself an immigrant.

Derry

John Derrye, or Dory, was an alien employed in the works of Ambrose Comport in 1549. He and his servant John Bee both paid the poll tax in the relief of that year. When workmen of Ambrose Comport next appeared in a subsidy roll in 1551, the alien named John, whose surname is illegible, might be one of these men, or alternatively John Anthony.

In France one of the blade-smiths (*taillandiers*) at Saint-Saëns in the Varenne valley during the 1530s was Pernot Doré. In the Béthune valley a family named Doré was settled at Louvicamp, the village below Compainville on the opposite bank of the Béthune from Beaussault. Jacques Doré of Louvicamp, who appeared in notarial acts of the 1550s and 1560s, was a miller.[495]

In Wealden archival sources of the sixteenth century there seems to be no record of other appearances by John Dory. However, the family may have moved to West Sussex where Richard Dorrye and Joan Dory were buried at Petworth, in 1578 and 1597 respectively.

Anthony

John Anthonye paid the poll tax as an alien servant of the forgeman Anthony Ellis in Shoyswell hundred

492. TNA, PROB 11/131/218.
493. Cockburn, *Surrey Assize records, Elizabeth I*, no. 2688.
494. TNA, PROB 11/165/321.
495. ADSM, 2 E 93/15 (3 Apr 1536); 2 E 14/1204 (11 Dec 1563).

in the relief of 1549. The subsidy roll of 1551 shows that Ellis was employed in the works of Ambrose Comport, which may also have been the case in 1549. It is uncertain whether John, with the illegible surname, who worked for Comport that year was John Derry, John Anthony, or John Bee.

Bee

John Bee was the servant of John Derry, or Dory, who appeared in the subsidy roll for Shoyswell hundred in 1549. As mentioned above, either of these men, or John Anthony, could have been John, the servant of Ambrose Comport whose surname is illegible, who paid the poll tax in the relief of 1551.

No further references to John Bee in other Wealden archival sources for the sixteenth century have as yet been discovered. Was the name actually L'abbé, or Laby?

Netherfield hundred

Collin

John Colyn, the alien who paid 4 shillings on goods in Netherfield hundred in 1539, will have been the eldest, French-born son of the forgemaster, John Colyn of Burwash. Under the terms of their father's will the Burwash estates were to go to John, and those in Brightling and Dallington to the English-born Alexander and Bartholomew respectively, but the forge in Burwash and the furnace in Brightling were to be held for six years by them all in common.[496]

In the reliefs of 1549 and 1550, John Collyn II appeared in Hawksborough hundred as a forgemaster, in each case employing two aliens, the two in 1549 including the hammerman Adrian Hatto, those of 1550 being two alien colliers, both named John Gue (otherwise Gewe), now stated to be employed in Tottingworth borough.

The forge will have been the copyhold one in Burwash, held of the manor of Brightling Prebend. It was sometimes called the Nether forge in Burwash, to distinguish it from Brightling or Glaziers Forge situated some distance upstream and belonging to Nicholas Pelham. It is evident that John Collyn II held this forge until shortly before his death. In 1574 he was described as 'an old man of 80 years and not able to travel';[497] nonetheless, he did not surrender the forge to the use of his son Henry until 1584.

John Collyns of Northiam, who died in 1586, would seem to have been the forgemaster. His goods were estimated to be worth £45 19s 4d. He left £1 to the poor at the discretion of the minister, John Frewen, and of Thomas Holman, his son in law, who had married his daughter Mary in 1575. Collyns' wife was to have £10 held by William Richardes and John Crashfield, an old bed, a coverlet and the sheets which she already had. To his son William he left 'part of his implements as were at the forge'. Collyn made Thomas Holman his residuary legatee. He mentioned his son Henry only in so far as the bequests of £8 to Thomas Holman's children and £3 to the children of Thomas Epden (Hepden) were dependent on Henry's paying this £11.[498]

In December 1584 John Collen II had surrendered to the use of his son Henry all his lands and tenements in Burwash, including three specified tenements; the last of these was 'the Millpond with one Iron Mill or Forge'. The annual quitrent was 2s 5½d, the fine was £9; for a further fine of £1 Collen was granted licence to cut and carry off within 20 years all the woods and underwoods, except 20 oaks, on his copyhold in Burwash.[499]

Of Henry's children, two daughters Mary and Constance appear to have survived. Mary married Robert Cruttenden in 1586 and in September 1596, for a fine of £4 Henry Collen was granted licence to lease the same three tenements and forge to Robert Cruttenden, his son-in-law, for eight years. But in December 1586 Robert Cruttenden was taken mortally ill; by his will he left the forge and all its profits to Thomas May of Burwash for the performance of the legacies in his will, of which Henry Collen was an overseer and, together with Richard Stollion, one of the witnesses.[500] Meanwhile in October 1596,

496. TNA, PROB 11/28/625.
497. Straker, *Wealden iron*, p. 302.
498. ESRO, PBT 1/1/8/4, 1/3/2/1.
499. ESRO, ACC 165/60 (11 December 1584).
500. ESRO, ACC 165/60 (20 September 1596); TNA, PROB 11/89/95.

Mary's sister Constance had married the same Richard Stollyan, who was the son of the forgemaster Thomas Stollyan.

Later proceedings in the manor court followed the death in 1600 of Henry Collen, now of Lewes. It appears that prior to his death he had surrendered all his customary lands and part of the forge to the use of himself and his wife Alice, with remainder to Richard Stollyan, but by agreement with Richard's father, in return for the payment of considerable sums to Robert Cruttenden's children, John and Obedience, and others, after the death of Henry's widow Alice, the forge was to remain in the hands of Thomas Hepden.[501]

John Collyn II's youngest brother Hugh Collyn, who had been left £80, but no lands, in his father's will, appeared for the only time as a forgemaster in the relief of 1552, when he employed eight aliens in Henhurst hundred, perhaps at Socknersh Furnace. The eight included John and Remy Harvey, who may have been furnacemen. Hugh later supplied 61 tons of sows to Robertsbridge Forge both in 1563, and again in 1568, in the second case Socknersh being specified as its source.[502]

Hugh Collen of Heathfield, yeoman, died in 1583. The goods left in his will were primarily agricultural; his three daughters each received only a silver spoon and a pair of sheets; his son George was his residuary legatee and executor; the ironmasters, Thomas Isted and his cousin Thomas Collen, were among his overseers. His son George, baptised at Brightling in 1562, was perhaps George Collyn of East Hoathly, yeoman, who in August 1590 took a 12-year lease from Edward Gage of Maresfield Forge or Hammer, together with the water mill, for a rent of £42 a year.[503]

But the main branches of the Collyn family were those descended from Alexander Collyn of Lamberhurst, the second and first English-born, son of John Colyn of Burwash. The freehold of Socknersh Furnace had gone along with the Brightling lands to him. It was he who acquired land at Lamberhurst around 1548 on which Hoadly Forge was built. He died, still quite young, in February 1551 and since all his children were still minors he left the ironworking interests to his widow Julian, with remainder to his third son Alexander II.[504]

However, his eldest son John, who had inherited Lamberhurst, died still a minor in 1552 and Lamberhurst consequently devolved on the second son Stephen. Stephen still held Hoadly Forge in 1574, but sold it to Robert Filmer in 1584.[505] Richard Collens of 'Hodey forge', who was mentioned in the Lamberhurst parish register in 1615, was possibly a son of William Collyn to whom John Collyn II had bequeathed his forge tools.

Alexander Collyn of Brightling and his mother Julian both died in 1566. The Lamberhurst estates having devolved on his elder brother Stephen, Alexander Collyn II left his Brightling estates to the youngest brother Thomas.[506] Socknersh Furnace remained in the hands of Thomas's descendants for many years. He married very late in life and at the time of his death in 1612 his eldest son Thomas Collins II was aged only eleven. As his second wife, Thomas Collins II married Elizabeth daughter of the forgemaster Peter Farnden of Sedlescombe, who, together with John Roberts, took a 4-year lease of Socknersh Furnace in 1671.[507]

Bredes

The alien Bormeyne Bredes paid the poll tax in Netherfield hundred in 1539. The name is otherwise unknown. It follows the name Peter 'Borne', which should probably read 'Borayne'. Has some conflation occurred?

Turner

Peter Turner had first paid the poll tax at Wadhurst in the subsidy of 1543. In 1549 he was in Netherfield

501. ESRO, PBT 1/3/2/289; ACC 165/60 (18 Dec 1600, 8 Jan and 12 Mar 1601).
502. Crossley, *Sidney ironworks accounts*, pp. 184, 191.
503. ESRO, SAS/G 13/45.
504. TNA, PROB 11/34/436.
505. Cleere and Crossley, *The iron industry of the Weald*, p. 340.
506. TNA, PROB 11/48/497.
507. Cleere and Crossley, *The iron industry of the Weald*, p. 357.

hundred, the only one of Sir William Sidney's workers there who was not made denizen. Though Turner worked for Sidney steadily throughout the period from 1549 to 1552 and paid the poll tax each year in Netherfield hundred, he was not once referred to in the Sidney accounts. This, together with the elimination from the running of Peter Unckle and Peter Cachery who were colliers, makes it virtually certain that Turner was 'Peter the founder', whose surname was never mentioned.

Nor was Peter mentioned in the 1546 book of Panningridge, but in 1548 he made his appearance when he and Richard Martyn, Harry Westall's assistant, were paid a shilling for going to Birchden to attach Gwillam Bellet, a Sidney worker who had absconded. On this occasion he was called Peter 'the filler'. However, later in the same account came a payment of 8d to Peter 'the foundre' for his labour in going with Martyn to Birchden.[508] Having worked in the High Weald, Turner would undoubtedly have been acquainted with Birchden Forge.

Peter Turner worked for much of 1548 as filler, and as founder for only part of the time, but in 1549 he did all the founding except for two foundays worked at the beginning of June by Nicholas Gerard. This amounted to 26½ foundays for which he and the filler were paid at the rate of 14 shillings the founday. Of this, 8 shillings went to the founder and 6 shillings to the filler, so that Turner's share will have been £10 12s 0d.[509]

In 1550 Peter received £18 8s 0d for 46 foundays and 5 days of 'blowing', or smelting. In addition he and John Nevyll were paid 1s 4d for mending a bridge and the ways by which sows were carried away from Panningridge, and 10 pence for digging four loads of (casting) sand.[510]

In 1551 Peter shared the founding with Charles Gerard, who had now moved to Battle. However during 1553 and 1554 the main founder was Warnet Gerard, except for October 1554 when Peter replaced Warnet as founder. In 1555 Peter appears once more to have been the main founder, though Charles did special work, such as casting hammers and anvils for the forge, and shammel plates (*shamowes*) for the bellows. That Peter was now specially favoured is shown in the 1556 accounts which were charged with 13s 8d for 'the making of Peter Founder's house', whilst in 1558 he was given a special payment of 2 shillings for casting eight plates for the forge. In 1558 he also received payments for wood-cutting and mining.[511]

After 1558 only summary accounts for the Sidney ironworks survive, but it is evident that Peter Turner did not continue at Panningridge because he failed to appear in the 1560 subsidy roll for Netherfield. A stray entry records his presence at Goudhurst in April 1559, when his son Charles, perhaps named after Charles Gerard, was buried there. Charles himself had been buried at Frant only ten days earlier and it looks as though Turner moved to replace him there because his daughter Ann was baptised at Frant in December. Finally, an entry of February 1566 records the burial at Frant of 'Peter, filler of Collin's furnace'.

A second immigrant of this surname was Robert Turner, who paid the poll tax in South-borough of Tonbridge, firstly in 1572 as a servant of Laurence Duffield, and secondly in 1598, the only one of the nine aliens listed at Southborough in 1572 still to be there. Since most of the Duffields or Dufours were forgemen, it looks as though Robert Turner may have been a forgeman too. He was perhaps the Robert Turner whose children, Margaret, Robert and Henry, were baptised at Tonbridge between 1586 and 1596 and whose wife Margaret was buried there in 1612.

The third Wealden ironworker from this family was the Speldhurst gunfounder, John Turner, mentioned in a quarter session recognizance of 1598.[512] He was perhaps the John Turner whose children were baptised at Speldhurst from 1588 to 1598 and 1607 to 1615. Lastly, Sackville Turner was a forgemaster who acquired Cansiron Forge in 1613, but sold it to the Courthopes of Whiligh in 1627.[513]

The Brenchley parish register distinguishes a sickle-maker of 1614 named William Turner, from a similarly named carpenter of 1617. In Pembury and Cowden also, Turners were thick upon the ground, but which of them were related to Peter Turner, who had ended his days at Frant, is hard to tell. Nevertheless, the two immigrants, Peter and Robert Turner, and the gunfounder John Turner, all

508. KHLC, U1475 B2/1.
509. Crossley, *Sidney ironworks accounts*, p. 78 and note.
510. Ibid., pp. 92-3, 96.
511. KHLC, U1475 B10/6, 7, 8, 9 and 10.
512. Zell, *Industry in the countryside*, p. 131n.
513. Straker, *Wealden iron*, p. 229.

probably came from the same family.

Ironworkers from the Turner family were later to be found in the north Midlands. For instance, John Turner of Keinton Forge was buried at Chetwind in 1660, whilst another John Turner had given up his lease of the Lizard forges in 1658 in order to provide capital for a new furnace at Church Lawton, which formed the basis of the later Cheshire partnerships.[514] In Cheshire, John Turner of Lea Forge on the Checkley Brook had children named William and John baptised at Wybunbury in 1659 and 1665. In Nottinghamshire William Turnor of Carburton Forge married Ruth Watson of Mansfield at Edwinstowe on 19 April 1696.[515]

Earlier than any of these, another John Turner, together with John Vinton, had been a finer at the forge at Hammersmith on the Saugus river in New England around 1650. Three of Turner's sons were also engaged in ironworking there.[516] The difficulties of determining the origins of four of these forgemen of the diaspora appear to be rendered insuperable by the fact that the name of each was John Turner. The promising fact that the Hammersmith man's son Laurence will have been baptised in England, perhaps around 1620, has not so far led to his identification.

La Mott alias Finch

John 'Lemett' was a non-denizen Frenchman, who paid the poll tax in the 1549 relief in Netherfield as a servant of Anthony Pelham. A more correct rendering of his name was given when, as John Lamot, he paid the poll tax in 1550 in the same hundred, but as a servant of Sir William Sidney. In 1556 William and John Dalamott were listed among the woodcutters at Robertsbridge and John Dalamott served as one of the colliers there.[517] However, it was neither William nor John, but Jarman Dallamot who paid the poll tax in Robertsbridge hundred in the subsidy of 1560.

John Lemotte reappeared in Foxerle hundred when he paid 2 shillings on goods to the subsidy of 1572; in 1576 he paid the poll tax there. At this time he perhaps worked at the Priory Furnace in Warbleton, for it was from there that he was brought to be buried at Dallington in January 1599. He had not appeared in the 1595 subsidy roll, so he was perhaps by then no longer a covenant servant. In 1595 Peter 'Lemote' paid the poll tax in his stead.

When making a deposition in 1586 Peter de la Mot of Ashburnham, filler, indicated that he had been born in France around 1546, and that before coming to Ashburnham around 1566 he had lived for seven years in Arundel.[518] He had therefore come to England around 1559, and indeed 'Peter Frenchman' was the last of four out of five aliens who paid the poll tax in Arundel in 1560, though he would then have been only 14 years old, and we cannot be certain that this was not his father. It seems probable that Richard Mothe of Arundel, gentleman, whose will was proved in 1615,[519] may have been descended from a member of the La Mothe family who stayed in Arundel.

The first member of the Delamote family to be noticed in the Ashburnham parish register was Marion, who in 1563 married Jarman Kyvell there. Peter Delamote married Alice Doodgyn at Ashburnham in December 1566, the year of his arrival from Arundel. His children, Gilbert, James, Peter and Marie, were baptised there between 1580 and 1590. Since Peter claimed to have lived in Ashburnham continuously for 20 years, it must be supposed that any children born before 1580 were baptised at Penhurst, whose parish register was fragmentary, or at Dallington, where no sixteenth-century register exists and where bishop's transcripts go back only to 1598. However, there must be some uncertainty about this, because he failed to appear in either of the subsidy rolls for Foxearle hundred in the 1570s, exactly the time when we would expect to find his name in the Ashburnham parish register.

Peter Lamott was mentioned on three occasions in Battle High court cases brought against him by John a'Stone in March 1582,[520] by Thomas Elyard in May 1583 and by Stephen Harvye in January 1582. Both the first and last of these cases were dismissed when the plaintiffs failed to pursue their suits.

514. Awty, 'Charcoal ironmasters of Cheshire and Lancashire', p. 74.
515. The bishop's transcript however states that it was John Turnor who married Ruth Wilson on 9 Apr 1696.
516. Hartley, *Ironworks on the Saugus*, pp. 189, 212.
517. KHLC, U1475 B8/8.
518. WSRO, EpII/5/3, f. 61.
519. TNA, PROB 11/125/570.
520. HEH, BA Vol. 97 ff 10, 24, 8-9.

Peter was buried at Ashburnham in 1622 and his widow Alice in 1627.

John Delamote married Elizabeth Ady at Ashburnham in 1585 and their son John was baptised later in that year. It seems unlikely that he was the man who had first paid the poll tax so long ago as 1549. Even the John La Motte mentioned in the subsidy rolls of the 1570s was probably the older man, as was perhaps the John Lamot who died at the Priory Furnace and was buried at Dallington in 1599. Also, the Dallington man's widow was not Elizabeth, but Annis Lamott, a 'lunatic', who was buried the following year.

A number of other members of this family featured in parish registers of the late sixteenth century. Firstly at Rotherfield, where Charles Laymoothe had a daughter Joan buried in 1564 and was probably 'Charles, a Frenchman' whose son Thomas was baptised there in 1565. If Charles was also Fynche, an alien who paid the poll tax alongside Bartholomew Ponting at Withyham in 1560, he was perhaps the progenitor of the Lamot alias Finch family later found at Worth. In fact James Le Mott and Joan Laymott, children of Charles and Joan, who were baptised at Worth in 1568 and 1570, were probably other children of the former Rotherfield man.

John Lamot alias Finch who married Alice Simons at Worth in 1589 may also have been Charles's son. Their children, Joan, John (who did not survive), John, Bridget, Jane, Mary and Richard, were baptised at Worth between 1591 and 1611. Between the baptisms of Joan in August 1591 and the first John in November 1595, there is space for them to have parented Dorothy who was baptised at Ardingly in February 1594, the daughter of John Finch 'of the hammer'. There were no La Mott entries in the Ardingly parish register and the next Finch entry is for the burial of Richard Finch, 'a hammerman', who was buried there in 1660. He could have been the Richard baptised at Worth in 1611.

It is difficult to guess what gave rise to this Finch alias. The wife of Finch, an otherwise anonymous pot-founder (*pott caster*), was buried at Fletching in 1589. It is impossible to guess whether John Finch, who married Mary Harman at Fletching in October 1591, corresponded to the second marriage of the pot-founder, or to John Finch, a carpenter, whose unnamed son was baptised at Fletching in March 1592.

At Mountfield Dorothy daughter of Richard Lamet was baptised in March 1567, but was buried the following day, nor did Richard make any further appearance, and in 1581 Joan Limmott married John Addes. At Waldron Margaret Lamooth married George Hasholl in 1570, whilst at Pembury John Lamot was baptised in 1572, without his father's name being disclosed.[521]

Steven Lemot married Dorothy Harvey at Mountfield in 1588. It seems possible that this was the same man who (Steven *Laymote*, but *Longmote* in the bishop's transcript) married Dorothy Sporr (Spurr?) at Fernhurst in 1607. The likelihood that these were the same man is increased by the fact that no children appear to have arisen from either marriage. At Haslemere Dorothy Moate was buried in 1624 and Steven De le Mote in 1633.

At Lamberhurst, a collier named Nicholas Lamote married Dorothy (Harbie?) in 1586. Their son Richard, who was baptised at Lamberhurst in 1599, became a Lamberhurst husbandman who left a will when he died in 1639. He gave his wearing apparel to his brother Nicholas, who had been baptised in 1611, and whom he made his executor. He left £3 to his sister Mercy and £4 to his sister Dorothy, both of whom were unmarried, £2 to the son of his sister Agnes Cheeseman, and £2 each to the two sons of his sister Margery Crompe.[522] Margery had been baptised in 1601, and Dorothy in 1607, but, unless Agnes were Anne Lamote baptised in 1595, the other sisters must have been baptised during the gap running from 1587 to 1594 in the parish register. Nicholas Lamote was buried in 1612 and his widow Dorothy in 1621.

Steven Finch married Joan Edsawe at Ewhurst in Surrey in 1616. Their children, Margaret, Daniel, Elizabeth and Steven, were baptised at Ewhurst between 1616 and 1622. Steven Finch was buried at Ewhrst in 1643 and his widow in 1652. The collier John Finch, 'which died at John Morlens' and was buried at Ewhurst in 1657, appears not to have been their child.

Christopher Finch, who married Elizabeth Messenger at Abinger in 1610, had children named Anne and Tamson baptised at Crawley in 1621 and 1630, and a daughter named Alice buried there in 1631. He himself was buried at Crawley in 1632.

Peter Delamote of Ashburnham's son Peter Lamote married Mary Bissenden at Salehurst in

521. The time scale would just allow John to have been Charles's son who married at Worth in 1589.
522. KHLC, DRa/PW1.

1606 and their children John Mott and Elizabeth Mote were baptised at Sedlescombe in 1609 and 1613. The long break in the parish register for Ewhurst in Sussex, which runs from 1585 to 1605, makes it impossible to know whether the Ewhurst men Stephen Moth, who married Faithful Blundell in 1615, and Edward Moth, who married Joan Martyne in 1620, were descended from Peter Delamote or were indigenous to Ewhurst parish.

In addition to the Gloucestershire forgemaster Francis Finch of Oxenhall, the Finch family of Dudley were involved in ironworking. It does not look as though there are connections between the Finches of Sussex and either of these Midland families. However, John Finch of Loscoe Furnace in Derbyshire, whose wife was named Mary, and whose daughter Mary was buried at Heanor in 1632, and John Finche, a Cleobury Mortimer forgeman of 1630, whose wife was named Anne, and who was at Kingswinford in 1639, may have had such connections, although their baptismal names do not lend themselves to easy identification. Their marriages do not seem to have been solemnized in the Wealden area.

In South Yorkshire a widow named Anne Motte of Kilnhurst Forge was buried at Rawmarsh in 1730. The forgeman Richard Motte, whose daughter Olive was baptised at Pleasley in July 1728 and was buried at Rawmarsh in March 1729, was perhaps Anne's son. At Rawmarsh his children, John who did not survive, Anne, Sarah, another John, and Mary, were baptised from 1730 to 1745, and his wife Sarah was buried there in 1747. It was probably the same Richard Mott, who with a second wife was back at Pleasley in 1752, where their daughter Frances was baptised.

Griaunt

Clement Gryans was first noticed in Netherfield hundred in 1549 when he paid the poll tax as a Frenchman in Ninian Burrell's ironworks, presumably Penhurst Furnace. In 1550 he again paid the poll tax in Netherfield hundred, but on this occasion as a servant of Anthony Pelham, who may have taken over the Burrell ironworks. Finally in 1552, as Clement Griaunt, he paid the poll tax in Foxearle hundred, again as a servant of Anthony Pelham. He perhaps appeared as a woodcutter in the Panningridge Furnace book for 1553 as Clement Gry[ant?] and Clement Greane.[523]

The attempt to link Clement with the Grint family of Herstmonceux and Arlington is difficult to sustain, because an English William Grynte paid tax on land worth four and three pounds near Arlington in 1524 and 1525, and Grints are to be found as bailiffs of Battle Abbey's manor of Barnhorn in the 15th century.

Werett

Nicholas Werett was a Frenchman in the works of Richard Weekes who paid the poll tax in Netherfield hundred in 1549, but for whom no other record survives. It seems likely that the surname should in reality be Warnet, that Nicholas was Warnet Jerratt's son and that, like his father who was buried there, he too moved to Frant, where he was first recorded in a parish register as 'French' in 1573. If so, he ultimately became the gunfounder at Horsmonden who died in 1596.

Brye

In 1550 John Brye paid the poll tax in Netherfield hundred as an alien servant of Richard Weekes. Like John Pyballyar, who also worked for Weekes in 1550, he moved to the Midlands where, among the Frenchmen employed at Cleobury Mortimer ironworks in Shropshire, he was listed in the subsidy roll as John Bray, and paid 10 shillings in 1571 and 6 shillings in 1572 on £3-worth of goods.[524] It appears that he soon returned to the Weald, because as John Braye he paid the poll tax in Buttinghill hundred in 1576.

The 1550 version of his surname accords exactly with that of Jehan de Brye, forgemaster at Bretoncelles in the Perche before 1482.[525]

523. KHLC, U1475 B10/6.

524. TNA, E 179/167/44 and 50.

525. Belhoste and others, *La métallurgie normande*, p. 66. Brye was father-in-law to Colas de Gommerye and Jehan Le Blanc.

Hawksborough hundred

Jasper

John Jespere appeared in the subsidy roll of 1539 for Hawksborough hundred, where he paid 1 shilling on goods. He was perhaps John Jasper of Burwash, whose will was made in 1547.[526] He left all his goods to a widow, Agnes Benet, 'to the comfort of her and her children'; she was to pay the rent (*farm*) of the house where his goods lay to Stephen Barham of Mayfield. The witnesses included John Fuller and Agnes his wife. Jasper's goods were valued at £2 17s 4d. He apparently had no children of his own.

Gawen

In 1539 John Gawyn paid the poll tax in Hawksborough hundred. By 1552 he had perhaps moved on to Netherfield hundred, where as John 'Quen' he paid the poll tax as a servant of Richard Weekes. He may have been connected with a French smith named Peter Gawen, who was granted letters of denization in 1542.[527]

At Fletching Nicholas Goone married Joan Combros in 1561, and their son Roger was baptised there in 1565.

At Mayfield a labourer named Thomas Gawen, who was buried in 1580, was probably another member of this family. His sons Henry and Thomas were baptised at Mayfield in 1571 and 1580. Henry continued at Mayfield and his children were baptised there from 1603 to 1622. Henry was buried at Mayfield in 1624. Thomas was perhaps the man whose children were baptised at Withyham in 1609 and at Frant from 1613 to 1617. All these parishes were connected with the manufacture of iron and as a labourer Thomas Gawen might have been an ironworker. However, there is no conclusive proof of this family's continued involvement in the iron trade.

Makkowe

The name of Peter Makkowe followed that of John Gawyn in the list of aliens who paid the poll tax in the hundred of Hawksborough in 1539. John Mocko who paid the poll tax in Ninfield hundred in the subsidy of 1560 will have been from the same family. The residence of these men in or adjacent to ironworking areas suggests their probable involvement in the iron trade. However, no proof of this is forthcoming, nor are there later sources to show that such involvement continued.

Sampton

The name of Thomas Sampton followed that of Peter Makkowe in the list of aliens who paid the poll tax in Hawksborough hundred in 1539. Unlike the surname Sampson, the surname Sampton failed to appear in the Sussex subsidy rolls of the 1520s, nor are there sources which confirm its connection with the manufacture of iron.

Wills proved in the archdeaconry of Lewes include those of Thomas Sampton of Lewes, proved in 1557, and of Thomas Sampton, a Herstmonceux yeoman, proved in 1580. Neither suggests any connection with the metal trades. In 1593 administration of the effects of Thomas Sampton of Chiddingly was granted to his brother, Henry Sampton of Staplehurst in Kent, who was a tailor.[528]

Fawke or Fakett

Guyllam Fawke paid a shilling on goods to the relief of May 1549 in Hawksborough hundred as an alien finer in the service of Nicholas Pelham. Immediately prior to this he had been among the workmen who helped to repair the furnace wall at Panningridge.[529] In 1543 he had been paid 1s 9d for three days' work digging stone for Panningridge Furnace and had worked as a miner there in 1543 and 1544.[530]

526. ESRO, PBT 1/1/1/182.
527. *Letters and Papers, Henry VIII*, **17**, no. 137 (27 ii).
528. ESRO, PBT 1/1/3/296 (1557), 1/1/7/195 (1580), 1/3/2/153 (1593).
529. KHLC, U1475, B10/4.
530. Crossley, *Sidney ironworks accounts*, p. 44; KHLC, U1475, B2/2, B7/3.

Both the Robertsbridge Forge book and the draft forge book for 1549 show Guillam Fawke or Fawkett to have been one of the finers at the forge for that year,[531] so how he came to have paid a tax of a shilling on goods as an employee of Nicholas Pelham in 1549 is difficult to understand. However, the subsidy rolls for Robertsbridge hundred concur in this, because they include William Vacket as a payer of the poll tax in the employ of Sir William Sidney in 1550, but omit him in 1549. Perhaps he moved to Robertsbridge very shortly after May 1549, the date when the relief of that year was paid.

It appears that by 1551 he had again moved on and was perhaps 'Gyllam the Fyner' who made a solitary appearance as an alien payer of the poll tax in Danehill Sheffield hundred in that year. Another move by the following year could be indicated, if the appearance of 'Gelum Fashatt', alongside Richard Woodman's hammerman 'Denys Labys' in Hawksborough hundred in 1552, is construed as Vackatt. However, it seems just as possible that this name should be construed as 'Vashall', although no other references to any Gillam Fashall are known. There is no mention of this finer in later subsidy rolls or elsewhere.

The Robertsbridge Forge accounts record payments to Goddard Fyner for the making of charcoal (*coal*) baskets, one in 1553 and six in 1555 at the rate of 8 pence each. From the 1554 book it seems that his full name was Goddard Vacket, but that he was also described as Goddard Frenchman.[532] Further identifications are difficult due to the omission of the names of finers from the accounts at this period, although the name of the hammerman John Cullyan, who took over from Gillam Hatto in April 1551, was almost always recorded. From the payment of quarterly wages of 5 shillings to Hugh Marchant and Peter Gelly it can be assumed that they were the covenant finers, with Goddard Fyner, Robert Turk and Gelly's man Mighell (Lassell) working as their assistants and receiving a proportion of the 6s 8d per ton which was paid to them.

There is no evidence that this family continued to be connected with the English iron industry after this period or outside the Weald. Nor is there any evidence that the surname of descendants was assimilated to such English names as Fawkener, the Sussex family engaged in the iron industry at entrepreneurial level, or Foulkes, as in the case of John Foulke(s), who was ironfounder at Ifton Rhyn Furnace in Shropshire around 1650.[533]

Garman

'Garman the hamerman' paid the poll tax as one of Nicholas Pelham's workers in Hawksborough hundred in 1549. A seventeenth-century hammerman at Glaziers Forge was Henry Jarman alias Mittell, and the long association of the Mittell family with the Pelhams would suggest that Jarman Mittell was the 1549 hammerman. However, Jarman Mittell was probably a miner or furnaceman, rather than a forgeman, moreover he consistently paid the poll tax as a Netherfield denizen from 1549 to 1552, so the hammerman cannot be he.

The only likely person seems to be Jarman Harby, to whom, as 'German the hammerman', Richard Porter of Bayham left a bequest in 1584. However, this raises the serious problem that Jarman Harby consistently failed to pay the alien tax, whether in the Porter ironworks in Frant, or elsewhere, and therefore appears to have been of English birth. Consequently the Glaziers Forge hammerman seems to be a third man of this name.

Minion or Monyon

The collier John Mynion paid the poll tax in Hawksborough hundred as a servant of John Collyn in 1549. Because later there was confusion between the surnames Mynion and Munnion, it must be suspected that Richard and Thomas Monyon, who paid a shilling on goods and the poll tax respectively in Danehill Horsted hundred in 1549, belonged to the same family as John Mynion. All three disappeared from the subsidy rolls in 1550 and failed to reappear, John Collyn's John Mynion having been replaced with two different alien colliers. At Danehill Horsted in 1550, out of 14 workers only the senior founder Robert Tyler was retained, but when the number of aliens rose to eight again in 1551, neither of the Monyons reappeared.

531. KHLC, U1475 B8/2 and 3.
532. KHLC, U1475 B8/5, 6 and 7; Crossley, *Sidney ironworks accounts*, pp. 146, 151, 152.
533. Edwards, 'The early ironworks of north-west Shropshire', pp. 200, 202.

The Mynion family was well represented among the workers employed by Sir Henry Sidney, Edmund Roberts and Ralph Knight in the Glamorgan ironworks in the 1560s. Old Mynion, John Mynion and William Mynion were referred to. The older man was a collier,[534] and it looks as though most of the workers of this surname referred to in the Glamorgan accounts were also colliers.

In Shropshire, John Minyan was buried at Morville near Much Wenlock in 1601. Still further north, William Mynion, a Market Drayton collier, was presumably employed at the forges on the Tern. George and Margaret, children of William Mynion and Mercy, his wife, were baptised at Mucklestone in 1599 and 1602. In 1604 their son Andrew was baptised at Drayton, but William himself was buried there in 1607. The son of another John Mynion named William was baptised at Drayton in 1609, and possibly became William Minion of Chetwind End, whose own son Thomas was buried at Chetwind in 1629.

Back in the Weald the family appears to have continued after inter-marriage with the Russell family of forgemen, in the form of at least three forgemen who bore the surnames Mynion alias Russell in the 1570s. All three appeared firstly near Hartfield.

Nicholas Russell married Alice Brysber at Maresfield in 1565, but their first children were perhaps baptised at Hartfield, for which no sixteenth-century register exists. Between 1572 and 1579 their children, Marion, Dominic, Susan and Giles, were baptised at Maresfield, a period when their father appeared seven times as Nicholas Mynion in views of frankpledge from 1576 to 1579; it was not until 1580 that his name was recorded as Russell.[535]

However, in 1581 he no longer appeared at Maresfield, so it is unsurprising to find Lawrence baptised at Lingfield in September 1581, as the son of Nicholas Russell, 'hammerman of Godstone'. After the gap in views of frankpledge for Hartfield from 1582 until the autumn of 1587, he reappeared in Lyhode borough as Nicholas Russell alias Minion. Subsequently he was named Nicholas Russell in three views of frankpledge held during 1588 and in April 1589. It seems probable that Nicholas was the 'Russell' who was fined for nonattendance in November 1590 and April 1591, his seniority as a resident with 25 years of married life behind him perhaps entitling him now to be regarded as 'Goodman Russell' and to be recorded without benefit of baptismal name.[536]

Peter Russell first appeared in views of frankpledge for Falkenhurst borough in Hartfield in May and October 1577 as the defaulter Peter Mynion (and Munnion).[537] He next appeared as Peter Russell in March 1580 in the parish register of East Grinstead, where his son Richard was buried. By September 1580 he was at Chiddingstone where his son Drew Munnion was baptised, and he finally came to rest in Buxted parish, where his son Anthony Monyon and his daughter Helen Russell were baptised in 1583 and 1586.

In views of frankpledge he was now fined in Hendall borough of Danehill Sheffield hundred as Peter Russell in April 1588 and as Peter Mynion in September 1588. As Peter Russell and as headborough he had to appear at both views held in 1589, and Russell he remained in the three remaining views of frankpledge up to the end of the series in April 1591.[538]

All later parish register entries for Peter Russell and his family appeared under the name Russell. Peter's son Drew Russell was probably the Uckfield potter, or pot-founder, who was bondsman for a marriage licence in 1616,[539] and his son Anthony Russell was the father of Ralph Russell, who around 1650 became one of the forgemen at Hammersmith in New England.

In April and November 1588 John Monyon first came to notice as a defaulter, like Peter Mynion at views of frankpledge in Falkenhurst. In November he was fined a shilling for throwing dead dogs onto the queen's highway to the annoyance of her liege men. In April 1589 he was recorded as defaulting for Parrock borough; only in October 1589 did he perhaps attend the court causing his name to pass unrecorded. In May 1590 he defaulted for Falkenhurst, but it was presented that Christopher Newman had permitted Monnion to live with him in his cottage for six months commencing at the feast of All Saints, and because the cottage did not have four acres of land attached to it a fine of 10 shillings was

534. Crossley, *Sidney ironworks accounts*, pp. 233-5, 250.
535. ESRO, ACC 3597/8, ff 6v., 29, 54v., 69v., 86v., 102, 121v. (all Mynion), 147, 170 (Russell).
536. ESRO, ACC 3597/1, ff 8 (10 Oct 1587), 28v., 53, 61v. (7 Apr 1589), 134 (18 Nov 1590), 146 (29 Apr 1591).
537. ESRO, ACC 3597/8, ff 35, 52.
538. ESRO, ACC 3597/1, ff 27, 33v., 67v., 78, 107v., 119, 143v.
539. Dunkin, *Calendar of Sussex marriage licences, Lewes, 1586-1643*, p. 101.

directed to be levied.[540] In the two remaining views of frankpledge his name was not recorded.

However, John Munnion somehow successfully raised a family, and although he died before his wife Eleanor, she was remembered in 1630 in the will of the Hartfield yeoman, William Mason,[541] from the family of smiths of that name, to the extent of £5 for herself and of £10 between her two sons William and Edward Munnyan.

William had three children, Elizabeth, Susan and Thomas, baptised at Hartfield between 1618 and 1630, and his son Richard was baptised at Chiddingstone in 1634. Edward married Joan Lurrett, of immigrant stock, in 1622 and their children, Thomas, Elizabeth and Judith, were baptised between 1628 and 1635, though Elizabeth and Judith did not survive infancy. William Munnion the elder was buried at Hartfield in 1641, and Edward Munnion at Frant in 1648.

Other members of this family mentioned in parish registers were John Monyon of Horne, whose son Thomas was baptised at Lingfield in 1566, William Moonion, whose daughter Jean was baptised at Chiddingstone in 1582, and Gilbert Minian, who married Jane Denman at Balcombe in 1590.

Maryon

The last of the four aliens who worked for Joan Isted in Bivelham borough in 1549 was John Maryon, a miner, who paid the poll tax. By 1550 he had become filler at the Isted blast furnace and, after an intermission in 1551,[542] he reappeared as 'Maryan' in 1552; he paid the poll tax on each occasion. Another man of this name was Henry Marian who worked in Danehill Horsted hundred in 1552. Richard Marion, who paid the poll tax in the hundred of Streat South in 1549 and the two following years, must be thought to have lived outside the ironworking area.

Because the immigrant Maryan Dupre had worked for Joan Isted in 1544, when he became a denizen, it could be argued that John Maryon was a member of Maryan's family left behind in Bivelham, when Dupre moved on to Worth, Hartfield, and ultimately to Abbots Bromley Forge. However, because Dupre came to England at the age of 18 and in 1544 had an English wife and three English-born children, it looks as though all his direct descendants will have been English-born. Also, where their occupations are known, they were hammermen or finers, and not miners and furnacemen like John Maryon.

Where their occupations can be identified, many of John Maryon's descendants in the Weald were engaged in mining. Unlike the remainder of Hawksborough hundred, Bivelham was in Mayfield parish and among early entries in the parish register, which commences in 1570, are those relating to Walter Marryan. He was buried at Mayfield in 1602, but two of his sons were John and William Marryan, baptised in 1572 and 1578. John Marryan married Alice White in 1595, and she bore him three sons, Walter, Thomas and Samuel, of whom Walter failed to survive infancy. There is a nuncupative will dated 1613 for John Marryan of Mayfield, 'labourer',[543] a description that is quite compatible with his having worked as a miner in the iron industry. The will was witnessed by Richard Kenwarde, yeoman, and Thomas Syslye, collier, both of Mayfield, and by it Marryan left £10, a sum which was in Kenwarde's hands, to his son Thomas, though it was first to go to his wife Alice for Thomas's bringing up. Thomas Marryan married Elizabeth Gainsford in 1626 and continued in Mayfield parish.

The Rotherfield family of Catt, to which the ironfounder Thomas Catt belonged, became related to the Marian family by the marriage of Amy Catt to Raphe Maryan. When Thomas Catt's mother Eglantine Catt died in 1593, she bequeathed a pair of sheets to Raphe Maryan's wife and 6s 8d to William Maryon,[544] the son of George Maryon, who had been baptised at Rotherfield in 1568.

William Maryon married Margaret Waters in 1594 and their children Mary and Margaret were baptised at Rotherfield in 1595 and 1597, though Mary did not survive. However around 1598, both William, and Raphe Marian's son Robert, moved to the Horsham area, presumably in search of work as miners or colliers. Robert Marian was married at Nuthurst in 1598, and William's third child, Eglantine, was baptised at Horsham in 1599. William's remaining children, Avis, Silvester, Thomas, William and

540. ESRO, ACC 3597/1, ff 28, 52v., 53v., 61, 111v., 112v.

541. TNA, PROB 11/155/206.

542. The idea that his replacement by an otherwise unknown John 'Curleggo' might be John Marian using an alias must be discounted in view of the presence of Simon Clerygo at Framfield in 1550 (Simon Cleriewe in Henhurst hundred in 1560), which suggests that there was a separate immigrant family of this name.

543. ESRO, PBT 2/2/3/151.

544. ESRO, PBT 1/1/9/187.

Joan, were baptised at Rotherfield between 1602 and 1611, but neither Avis nor Silvester survived to adulthood.

The younger William Marrian was born in 1609 and in 1629 he married Eleanor Pocock, a member of another English family of ironworkers. Their children were Robert, Eleanor, Mary, Anne, Elizabeth and Catherine, but Robert's baptismal entry has not been found; their five daughters were baptised at Rotherfield from 1633 to 1640, but Elizabeth died little more than a month after being baptised. When Thomas Pocock died in 1640, he left his smallest joined chest to the untraced Robert Marrian and a piece of pewter each to his four Marrian granddaughters. Appropriately he bestowed his axe and spade on their father, William Marrian, who was a miner.[545]

In 1655 William Marian, late of Rotherfield, miner, was charged at quarter sessions with failing to complete an agreement he had entered into on 6 July to 'draw 150 loads of mine' in the lands of Thomas Jefferay, esquire, of Chiddingly. Two years later quarter sessions were still issuing warrants for his arrest.[546]

Raphe Maryan was buried at Rotherfield in 1610. His son Robert, who had married Joan Stonestreet at Nuthurst in 1598, was by 1601, like William Maryan, back in Rotherfield, where his children, Mary, William, John, Syndeny and Robert, were baptised between then and 1618. It was probably during the 1620s that Robert and Joan Marian moved to Buxted where both were buried in 1639. Robert Maryan was described as a husbandman in his will. He left a shilling each to his sons William and John, with 10 shillings to be equally divided between William's children. He left 10 shillings each to his daughter's children, Christopher and Annis Parks, and Annis was also to have his cupboard. He made his wife and son Robert joint residuary legatees and executors, with George Cate (Catt) as one of the overseers.[547] Robert's son William had been married at Buxted in 1630 and his children, William, Robert, Mary, Nicholas and Thomas, were baptised there between 1630 and 1641.

Alongside Walter Maryan at Mayfield had been John Maryan, a carpenter, who was buried there in 1585. Two of his children, Clemence and William, had been buried at Mayfield in 1574. It seems possible that the Frenchman John Edmundes alias Marian of Frant, who was murdered by George Mahouude, a collier, in November 1574 was also from this family.[548] The baptismal entry for Giles the son of Edmond, a collier, at Frant in 1572 almost certainly referred to the murdered man and gave his occupation. No other mention of him has been found, nor does his son Giles seem to occur in later records.

Lastly, Robert Marryan of Milkhouse, farrier, who was buried at Cranbrook in 1658, must be considered, although it seems impossible to prove his link with the Mayfield and Rotherfield Marryans. His children, John, Robert, Thomas and Richard, were baptised at Cranbrook in 1620, 1622, 1624 and 1628. His son Richard Marrian of Couchman House, farrier (1657), married Elizabeth Chauntler, and the births of their daughters Elizabeth and Anne were recorded in the Cranbrook parish register in 1655 and 1657. Robert Marrian's other son Robert, baptised in 1622, was probably the Robert whose children Robert and Elizabeth were baptised at Biddenden in 1651 and 1656, but no connection with Biddenden Hammer has been proved.

Gotier

Nycolas Gottye was an alien collier who worked for Richard Woodman in the borough of Warbleton in 1549, presumably at Woodman's Furnace, now known to have been a forge. In 1550 he was joined by John Gottye, who was also a collier, and both paid only the poll tax. They were included as John Gottere and Nicholas Gotter in the lists of miners recruited by the Bristol merchant William Pepwell, though in one of those lists John appeared as 'Guntier'.

Nicholas appears to have stayed in the Weald, where he paid 6 shillings to the subsidy of 1572 at Maresfield. In 1575 a Buxted smith and a glover, John Hawkins and William Wynborn, were indicted for the theft at Buxted of Nicholas Gotier's grey horse, which was valued at £1 6s 8d. Hawkins died and

545. ESRO, PBT 1/1/27/132.
546. ESRO, QR 109, m. 17, 113, m. 77, 114, m. 59, 117, m. 64; I am grateful to Brian Phillips for all these references.
547. ESRO, PBT 2/2/6/65.
548. Hunnisett, *Sussex Coroners' inquests 1485-1558*, no. 135.

the grand jury was unable to find enough evidence to bring Wynborn to trial for the theft.[549] Presumably Gotier recovered his horse. He was buried at Horsham in 1588.

George Gotier, who married Jane Napper at Horsham in 1589, was presumably Nicholas's son. The Horsham parish register shows that this couple stayed in that area until 1604, after which they appear to have moved away. It seems possible that for a time the entire family moved to the north Midlands. George Gotier, buried in Staffordshire at Stowe near Weston-upon-Trent in 1612, could have been their eldest son, who had been baptised at Horsham in 1589. At Milwich, just north of Weston there appear to be mentions of two further sons, Thomas and John, who had been baptised at Horsham in 1597 and 1602 respectively. John, son of John and Margaret Gotier, was baptised at Milwich in 1621, and Thomas was buried there in 1623.

George's widow, Jane Gotier, returned to Sussex and was living at Duncton when she died in 1633. She left a will, which made her youngest son Richard, baptised in 1604, her residuary legatee and executor.[550] She made bequests of £10 to her son Nicholas Gotier, who had been baptised in 1592, of her best hat to his wife, of a ruff-band to his daughter Jane and of a shilling to each of his other two children. These details enable Nicholas to be identified as Nicholas Gochier of Pulborough, whose daughter Jane was baptised in 1629, his other children being baptised there between 1627 and 1640. The widow bequeathed £10 to her son John, a smock to his wife and a shilling to his son John.

The eldest surviving son William, who had been baptised in 1591, and to whom Jane bequeathed 5 shillings, had married Mary Strete at Horsham in 1619. His wife Mary was buried at Pembury in 1626, but he must soon have married again, because three of his children, Joan, William and Frances, were baptised at Pembury between 1629 and 1633. The younger William was probably the Frant forgeman who married Alice Eastland at Lamberhurst in 1655.

To her son Henry, who had been baptised in 1594, Jane also bequeathed 5 shillings. He could be Henry Gottier, who with his wife Eleanor was at Morville near Much Wenlock in the 1630s. Their children Frances, Mary and Edward were baptised at Morville in 1632, 1633 and 1638, but Frances did not survive infancy.

Edward Gothier, who was probably Henry's son, and Elizabeth 'of the Forge' appeared in the Cleobury Mortimer parish register in 1666, when their daughter Sarah was baptised there. They soon moved to Coalbrookdale, where their children Edward, Elizabeth and Eleanor were baptised in 1671, 1674 and 1675.

Anne Gothier, who must have been the eldest child of Edward and Elizabeth Gothier, married John Tyler of the Dale, the Coalbrookdale ironfounder, around 1680, during a gap in the parish register which runs from 1677 to 1683. The maiden name of Tyler's wife is known from a curious feature of Madeley parish register, a record of births of children by sex which ran from 1696 to 1706. One of its earliest entries reported the birth on 1 October 1696 of a female child to John and Anne Tyler, the report being made by 'Elizabeth Gotier the grandmother'.

A male child born to Edward and Joan Gotier on 15 October 1702 will have been another of Elizabeth Gotier's grandchildren. However, the 1678 bishop's transcript which recorded the baptism of Jane daughter of Edward Gotier and Jane (*sic*) his wife on 28 April of that year must be in error, because it is clear that Edward Gotier the elder's wife still survived in 1696.

Another member of the Gotier family who made an early move to West Sussex was the Kirdford collier, Robert Gochye, who in 1603 entered a recognizance to give evidence against three Kirdford labourers, who included Diddy Lerrett and Robert Tollett, both obviously also of immigrant descent.[551] This Robert Gotier was perhaps the man who had married Joan Bridger at Abinger in 1601.

It seems unlikely that this Robert Gotier could have been the same man as Robert Gottye or Gothewe, a defaulter at most surviving Hartfield views of frankpledge for Parrock from November 1581 to April 1591,[552] because this family continued at Hartfield in the person of John Gotty. John's first wife Mary died in 1624 and a little over a year later he married Elizabeth Iden at Battle.

Around 1630, Lawrence Gotty, whose daughter Agnes had been baptised at Hartfield in 1629,

549. Cockburn, *Sussex Assize records, Elizabeth I*, no. 550.

550. WSRO, STC 1/18/276.

551. Cockburn, *Sussex Assize records, Elizabeth I*, no.2083.

552. ESRO, ACC 3597/8, f. 210v.; 3597/1, 52v. (13 Nov 1588), 110v. (12 May 1590), 134v. (18 Nov 1590), 146 (29 Apr 1591).

moved to Battle, and it is possible that other members of this branch of the Gotier family joined him in that area.

From 1620 onwards there are entries in the Whatlington and Mountfield parish registers for another Nicholas Gottie. He was churchwarden of Mountfield in 1625. Widow Goatey who was buried at Whatlington in 1648 was perhaps his widow.

Some of the Midland members of the Gotier family could be descended from the other immigrant collier, John Gotier. He was not recorded again in the Weald after working as a collier in Warbleton borough for Richard Woodman in 1550. He (John *Gater*) appeared in Staffordshire at Rugeley in the Cuttlestone hundred subsidy roll for May 1563 in a list of three aliens.[553] From the Cannock area he was recruited as a collier in February 1569 by Rolf Engmander for the copperworks operated by German miners and smelters near Keswick. By 1577 he was apparently dead.[554]

Entries for the baptisms of Katherine, Margaret and Robert Gotyer in the Rugeley parish register running from 1575 to 1579 can consequently only indirectly relate John Gotier. They were perhaps his grandchildren and their father may have been the collier Henry Gotyer of Rugeley, who, as one of the forgemaster Fulk Greville's employees, gave evidence in 1591 to an Exchequer commission of inquiry into Bromley Forge. He claimed to be aged around 50 and to have worked in the Cannock works since around 1565.[555]

Of the children baptised at Rugeley it looks as though Robert could have been the collier named Robert Gotier who worked at Wem Forge in Shropshire from 1610 to 1620. His children Norman, Robert and Alice were baptised at Wem between 1610 and 1614, but Robert's daughter named Dorothy and his wife named Frances were buried there in 1614 and 1616. In 1617 he married Amy Neevett and their daughters named Elizabeth and Eleanor were baptised in 1619 and 1620.

Who, however, was Robert Gotier (*Goteyaw* and *Goteyeare*) whose children, Joan and Robert, were baptised at Betley in 1596 and 1598? Already noticed in 1593 in the Betley register had been George Growte, who immediately afterwards, from 1596 to 1614, worked as hammerman at Winnington Forge on the Tern, and his presence at Betley in 1593 suggests that Tib Green Forge, on the Wrinehill side of the Checkley Brook, which was mentioned in the Betley register in 1619, was where this Robert Gotier worked in the 1590s. However, if he were the man baptised at Rugeley he would have been just 17 years of age in 1596.

Very possibly Robert Gotier, baptised at Betley in 1598, was the finer of that name whose son Francis was baptised at Wombourne on the Smestow Brook north of Stourbridge in June 1629. Robert rapidly went on to Witton Forge near Birmingham, and there his son Francis was buried at Aston early in 1634. However, he and his wife Elizabeth, had another son named Robert baptised at Aston in 1635, before they moved on to Morville near Wenlock, where their son Henry was baptised in 1639.

Arthur

Arter, the collier who worked for John Baker in 1550 in Bivelham borough and who paid the poll tax there, was perhaps Hector who paid the poll tax as a servant of Thomas Shoiswell in Shoyswell hundred in 1552, but is otherwise unknown. It seems possible he could be John Artor, who paid the poll tax in Danehill Sheffield in 1560, and then in 1563, along with his wife, in Slaugham. Later he moved back eastwards to Hartfield, where in the subsidy of 1576 he paid 10 shillings on goods. In October of the same year he was fined 4 pence for nonattendance at Hartfield view of frankpledge as Arter *Gallus*, a Parrock resident, and further fines of this kind were levied in October 1578 and May 1579. In the view of frankpledge for October 1579 he was a juror in Rushmonden hundred, but in April 1580 as a resident in Maresfield he was essoined from attendance.[556] In November 1580 John Gage esquire enfranchised his messuage, garden and 40 acres of land bordering on the highway from Cowdens Cross to Lampole Green, converting the tenure to freehold at a yearly rent of 6s 9½d.[557]

It is also possible to trace John Arter in Fletching, Worth and Maresfield parish registers. His

553. TNA, E 179/178/169.
554. Collingwood, *Elizabethan Keswick*, pp. 62, 195.
555. TNA, E 178/2098.
556. ESRO, ACC 3597/8, ff 9, 92v., 115, 121v., 147.
557. ESRO, SAS/G 6/34.

son Michael was baptised at Fletching in 1562 and Margaret Arthur had been buried there in 1561. At Worth Philip the son of John and Joan Arter was baptised in 1566. John's wife Joan was buried at Maresfield in June 1580 and three months later he married a widow, Elizabeth Martin. At Maresfield he acted as godparent for baptisms in 1581 and 1582. In 1580 his son Michael acted as godparent, along with Richard Gerrat, at the baptism of Charles Gerrat's son Richard. John's second wife may have been the Elizabeth Arthur who was buried at East Grinstead in 1593.

Michael Arthur married Marie Plummer at Worth in 1584 and their sons, Peter, Nicholas and Michael, were baptised at Worth in 1584, 1585 and 1586. Michael was buried at Ewhurst in Surrey in 1591 and his widow at Lurgashall in 1593.

John Arter's other son Philip was not noticed in further parish register entries in Sussex but gave evidence in Exchequer depositions by commission of 1602 relating to the earl of Essex's ironworks at Walford in the Wye valley. In this the 35-year-old collier was accompanied by the 60-year-old Michael Uncle, who had also come from the Weald.[558] Another member of this family was John Artur, a woodcutter of Newland in the Forest of Dean, who in evidence given to an Exchequer special commission in January 1626 gave his age as 54.[559]

Back in Sussex John Arthur who married Jane Newman at Horsham in 1584 may have been another son of the immigrant John Arthur. Their two daughters Elizabeth and Joan were baptised at Horsham in 1585 and 1590, and further children were baptised at Charlwood between 1596 and 1605.

Whether Robert Arthur who was buried at Wartling in 1587, and whose widow Dorothy married Edward Wenman in 1591, and Richard Arthur, who married Jane Fiest at Kirdford in 1600, were connected with this family must be thought rather more open to doubt.

Henhurst hundred

It seems difficult to link the thirteen immigrants listed in the 1539 subsidy roll for this hundred with the manufacture of iron. The Braband and Morrant families can be traced subsequently around Salehurst and at Battle, but not in connection with iron, although in 1554 William Brabon of Salehurst bequeathed £1 to the finer Peter Jolly. In 1604 William Brabon of Wartling's will described him as a tailor.[560]

Essewe

Perhaps the three members of the Essewe family include progenitors of the Eason family who included smiths. In 1581 a son of Henry Yeston, smith, was baptised at Cowfold, whilst entries of 1603 and 1606 in the Cuckfield parish register describe Henry Essun or Essone as a smith. Another member of this family may be Thomas Esson of Rotherfield who was a tanner. He was styled 'Esson' in his will,[561] but parish register entries at Buxted gave his name as 'Eston' (1568) and at Mayfield as 'Easton' (1571), so it seems possible that there was a tendency to assimilate this name to the Sussex name of Easton, Eston or a'Neston.

Alternatively, perhaps John a'Sea, who was at Herstmonceux from 1557 to 1563 and at Wartling from 1566 to 1578 should be looked to as their descendant. There are also George Askew, whose daughter Joan was baptised at Brightling in 1566, and who was himself buried at Mountfield in 1574, and William Escu who married Elizabeth Peckam at Mountfield in 1567. In 1581 John Brissenden of Robertsbridge bequeathed two yearling steers to Thomas Haskewe alias Symon, an alias both of whose components have links with iron, and the oversight of Brissenden's will was commended to the forgemaster, Thomas Haye.[562]

558. TNA, E 134, 44 Elizabeth I, 3 Trinity.
559. TNA, E 178/5304.
560. ESRO, PBT 1/1/3/138, 1/1/12/48.
561. ESRO, PBT 1/1/9/385.
562. ESRO, PBT 1/1/7/166.

Robertsbridge hundred

Buckett

Vincent Buckett had been born in Flanders around 1508 and had come to England about the age of 10. In 1544, when made denizen he had an English wife. He was already established at Robertsbridge in 1539, before the building of Sir Willam Sidney's forge. He was described in the subsidy roll of 1549 as a nail maker and he became a purchaser of iron from Robertsbridge Forge.

The use of bellows made from animal hides at both forge and furnace in the indirect process made a ready supply of nails an essential factor in the smooth running of the iron industry. No one of the name Bockett seems to have been present in Sussex in 1524, so perhaps Vincent had come to Robertsbridge at some period during the 1530s. The building accounts for Panningridge show that he was paid 3 shillings for 1,000 bellows nails in 1543.[563]

However, he was also paid in 1548 for setting the great hoop on the hammerbeam and for renewing the ironwork of the finery bellows, and in 1549 for amending the 'great paned hoope' on the round beam of the hammer. In 1551 he was paid 4 pence for two iron pins (*peens*) for the shamell plates (shamowes) of the finery bellows at Robertsbridge and in 1553 he supplied another 400 bellows nails for Panningridge Furnace.[564]

The absence of further references to Bockett in the Sidney accounts, or in the subsidy roll of 1560 suggests he may have died in the mid-1550s. A later member of his family may have been John Buckett who in 1581 was fined 2 pence as a Middleborough defaulter in the Battle views of frankpledge of March and October 1581.[565]

Garrett

It seems extremely unlikely that this man could be Robert Gerret, who was a woodcutter at Robertsbridge Forge from 1542 onwards.[566] Robert appeared in the Henhurst subsidy roll in 1524 and his will (*Jerred*) was proved in Lewes archdeaconry in 1567, but there is nothing in any of these sources to suggest that he was other than English-born. With the death of Robert's son Thomas in 1587 this family appears to have died out.

Since the name appeared at Robertsbridge in 1539, before the building of the forge, there is no evidence to link the alien Garrett of 1539 with ironworking. However, was he perhaps, along with Peter whose surname is wanting, a servant of Vincent Bockett, who was already there?

Byne

Three members of the Byne family appeared in different sections of the Hawksborough hundred subsidy roll of 1524 without any suggestion that they were French. Richard Byne paid tax at that time on £2-worth of goods, so it is strange to find a person of this name listed as an alien in the works of Sir William Sidney, and along with Jane Byne, paying the poll tax to the relief of 1549. The forge account for 1549 also alluded to 'Byne', though without any suggestion that he was French.[567]

In 1550 Jane Byne's name occurred at Robertsbridge alone, but with the statement that she was a widow. It seems easier to suppose that she was of French nationality, and that following the death of her husband she paid the poll tax, but this leaves unanswered the problem of why Richard Byne paid the poll tax in 1549. Was his name in fact Bennett and was he Richard Benet who in 1560 paid the poll tax at Wadhurst?

Jerre

Aleyn Jerre's name appeared in the subsidy roll for 1549 as a servant of Vincent Bockett. The name is

563. Crossley, *Sidney ironworks accounts*, p. 46.
564. KHLC, U1475 B8/1 (1548) and 3 (1549), B8/4 (1551), B10/5 (1553).
565. HEH, BA Vol. 96 f 75, 97 f 3.
566. KHLC, U1475 B7/1, etc.
567. KHLC, U1475 B8/3.

otherwise unknown in Wealden sources. If the name has been corrupted he could in reality be Aleyn Jerret and therefore the Garret who had appeared after the names of Bockett and Peter in the 1539 subsidy roll. However, there seems to be no other reference to this hypothetical Aleyn Jerret.

Aliens in the works of John Philpott, smith

Like Vincent Bockett, John Philpott appeared in the Sidney accounts as a purchaser of iron and a supplier of nails. His works were mentioned in all four reliefs for the period 1549 to 1552. There is no evidence of Philpott's being a producer of iron, nor is there any suggestion that he was an alien. Of the workers mentioned as being in his works, only John Nayler, otherwise *Clotear* (Fr. *cloutier*), survived until the 1560 subsidy roll.

John Philpot of Salehurst who died around 1567 was perhaps the smith. Administration of his goods, valued at only £6 8s 0d, was granted to his widow Eleanor Philpot on 9 April, with a Salehurst weaver, Alexander Alborn, acting as bondsman. There must also have been some relationship between John Philpot and William Philpot of Salehurst, whose will was proved at Robertsbridge chapel on the same day.[568] The mention by William Philpot of his lands at Hawkhurst might indicate that both men came from Kent. Perhaps William was John's son, but predeceased his father.

Ballard

Lewis Bayard paid the poll tax as Philpott's servant in all four reliefs from 1549 to 1552, only the 1552 entry (*Berade*) presenting a significant deviation from the more usual spelling. No other Wealden source appears to contain this surname. The French original was perhaps Baillard or Baiard, more usually assimilated to English Ballard.

However, Richard Ballard of Wadhurst and his two sons Thomas and Richard, to whom Thomas Dyke made over the remainder of his 41-year lease of Chingley Furnace in 1597, were probably not of immigrant descent, but the brother and nephews of Henry Ballard, the Wadhurst yeoman, who died in 1622.[569] The lease would have run until 1620.

Lockyer

Laurence Lokear, who paid the poll tax in Philpott's works in each of the reliefs from 1549 to 1552, was presumably a locksmith by trade. His real surname may therefore have been quite distinct. He is not known from any other source.

The surname Lockier was indigenous to Rotherfield, where John and Thomas Lockyer were married in 1542 and 1546. A connection with the Baker family is demonstrated by the marriages of George Lockyer to Agnes Baker in 1585 and of George's daughter Dionice to Robert Baker in 1603. At Pembury the family of William Lockyer dated from 1573.

The earliest suggestion of any other Lockyer connection with ironworking comes from the presence of Peter Lockyer at Worth in 1603, when he fathered a son named Peter on the widow Thomasine Harvye. If he was the same Peter Lockier who married Mary Cooper at Bramshott in 1620, his presence in a second ironworking parish would tend to support the idea of a connection with ironworking.

A man rather similarly named was Thomas Looker of Cranbrook, locksmith, who secured a licence to marry Anne Standen of Ditchling in 1632.[570]

Nayler or Clotear

John Nayler paid the poll tax in Wadhurst in 1543 and was possibly the man of that name, but with the alias *Clochear*, or *Clotear* (Fr. *cloutier*, a nailer), who worked for John Philpott of Robertsbridge in 1549. He paid the poll tax at Robertsbridge in the reliefs of 1549 to 1552, and was still at Robertsbridge in 1560, when he again paid the poll tax.

568. ESRO, PBT 1/1/5/413 (William) and 428 (John).
569. TNA, PROB 11/141/475 and ESRO, SM/D148.
570. Dunkin, *Calendar of Sussex marriage licences, Lewes, 1586-1643*, p. 195.

The surname Nayler was unknown in East Sussex in 1524 and even by mid-century the burials of Peter and James Nayler at Fletching in the 1550s are two of the few Wealden occurrences that can be cited. Thomas Nayler, the baptismal name of whose father was not disclosed, was baptised at Buxted in 1586. The father could have been another Thomas Nayler, who had other children baptised at Lingfield in 1593, at Worth in 1595 and at Goudhurst from 1598 to 1602. Henry Nayler who was buried at Worth in 1595, unless a child, might be a link with an earlier generation.

Twins named James and Mary Naylor 'from Netherfield' were baptised at Battle in 1616, followed by Mercy Naillor in 1619, but again the names of the parents were not disclosed.

No long-continued links with the metal trades seem indicated.

SUSSEX - PEVENSEY RAPE

Loxfield hundred

Stoborne

Peter Stoberne paid the poll tax at Mayfield in the subsidy of 1543 and also in the reliefs of 1549 to 1552, the only substantially different spelling coming in 1550, when he was named Stoneborne.

The next generation will have been that of the English-born Richard Stubborne of Mayfield. If the parish register is correct in stating that both he and his wife Alice were over one hundred years old at their burials, in 1617 and 1608 respectively, the family will have been in England since before 1517.

An early connection with ironworking is suggested by the burial at Horsham of the child Eme Stobborne in 1555, a death by drowning, which was a continual hazard for young families living near the sluices and ponds of water-mills. John Stoborn, whose daughter Joan was baptised at Fletching in 1566, was perhaps Richard's son and Eme's father. John's daughter Joan may have married Richard Hothelye of Hellingly at Waldron in 1589.[571]

The probably 70-year-old Richard Stubbrone of Mayfield acted as bondsman for the marriage licence on that occasion, which suggests that Joan's father may have predeceased her grandfather. If this is correct she and John Stubborne who married at Horsmonden in 1582, Bridget Stubborne who married William Dudgine at Worth in 1583, Adriane Stubborne who married John Willat at Newdigate in 1585, and William Stubborne who married Frances a'James at Rotherfield in 1587, could all have been siblings. These were all ironworking parishes and the wide distribution of the marriages is typical of a family engaged in mining or perhaps charcoal-burning for the ironworks.

William Stubborne was buried at Tonbridge in 1625 and his widow, Frances Stubborne of Tonbridge, made her will in 1633; it included a bequest of 6s 8d to the poorest widows of the town, to whom was to be added Widow True of Southborough.[572] The Englishman John True had been ironfounder at Robertsbridge in 1542 and his brother Richard True at Vauxhall Furnace in the 1550s.[573] Widow True was presumably Mary Staley, who had married Robert True, perhaps Richard's son, at Tonbridge in 1576 and had been widowed in 1624. The bequest to a member of a native ironfounding family reflects the length of the Stubborn family's residence in the Weald and confirms its long connection with the iron industry.

More direct indications of the family's involvement in the iron industry are not forthcoming; perhaps the involvement did not continue.

Relf

Nicholas Relf paid the poll tax at Mayfield in 1543, but did not appear in the subsidy rolls of 1549 to 1552. Relf was far from being a widespread name in East Sussex in 1524, but it was common in Mayfield, where four English persons of the name contributed to the subsidy of 1524.

There were two later forgemaster families named Relfe. From Mayfield came John Relfe of

571. Ibid., p. 6.
572. TNA, PROB 11/164/88.
573. Schubert, *British iron and steel industry*, p. 177; Zell, *Industry in the countryside*, p. 131.

the Oak (d. 1585) and his son, the gunfounder, Richard Relfe of Framfield (1581-1620), who played a significant local role in the iron industry. In addition there was Bartholomew Jeffrey's partner, William Relfe, who had widespread interests in Sussex, but also played a part in bringing the iron industry to Wales.

There is no proof that either of these men was of French descent. Did some former member of their families move to France in connection with iron and return with a French-born child named Nicholas?

If the surname of Nicholas should really have been Rolf, there were blacksmiths of that name who could have been of French descent. Firstly, John Rolfe of East Grinstead, who died in 1570 and left his 'shop with the implements and utencils' to his son Richard, £10 to each of his other two sons and £5 to his daughter Katherine.[574] His son Richard Roffe moved at some stage to Danehill Horsted and when he died in 1607 his goods were valued at £146 8s 1d. However, his bequests were made out of £120 due to him from the forgemaster Sackville Turner of East Grinstead, so he had presumably played some role in the ironworks. As Richard had no children of his own, he left £40 to each of his brother John's three daughters, in each case £10 of the bequest was to go to his brother John and £30 was to be invested by Davy Lucas until the children's marriage or majority. Smaller bequests were to be made out of a further £4 due to him from Sackville Turner at the following Lady Day. Richard made his other brother William his residuary legatee and executor, and his overseers were to be Davy Lucas and Davy Finch, the miller.[575]

A further blacksmith of this name was Thomas Rolfe of Withyham, who died in 1633, with goods valued at £71 7s 0d. He too was childless and left his 'working tools, iron and steel in the shop and a copper furnace' to his sister's son, Richard Thomas, whom he made his residuary legatee and executor.[576]

Glade

'Glade the colyer' who paid the poll tax at Mayfield in 1543 is perhaps to be identified with Glode Aufrey who paid the poll tax in Hawksborough hundred in 1552. The latter was a servant of Thomas Morley and therefore will have worked at Hawksden Forge in Bivelham borough, which though in Hawksborough hundred, lay within Mayfield parish. He again paid the poll tax in Hawksborough hundred as Glode Avery in 1560, but by 1572 had moved on.

The probability that he was the alien Glade, who, together with his two sons, paid the alien tax at Worth in 1576 is confirmed by the marriage of an obvious descendant, John Averie alias Cloade, to Magdalyn Pytte at Worth in 1595. This man may have been the John Averey who had been included among the Cranleigh pikemen in the Surrey muster rolls of 1583-4.[577] Anthony Cludd, who was buried at Worth in February 1565, was presumably a son of Glode Avery who did not survive until 1576. Other members of this family were Richard Glode who was buried at Linchmere in 1571, the unnamed Glode whose daughter Mary was baptised at Kirdford in 1589 and William Glode who was buried at Buxted in 1599.

John Averie alias Glode moved on from Cranleigh to Chiddingfold, where his son Nicholas was baptised in 1602 and where another son Philip was buried in 1607. Parish register entries at Rudgwick which relate to him are the baptism of his daughter Grace in January 1606 and the burial of Joan Glode in February of that year. The entry for his own burial at Rudgwick in February 1612 confirms his residence in Surrey, defining him as 'Gloade of Ewhurst'.

Since no clear differentiation between Alfrey and Avery entries is made in the Wealden parish registers of the period it is often impossible to disentangle these names,[578] and bearers of either might or might not be of French descent. Marriage entries show that links between members of these families and the French community were close. This is instanced by the marriages of David Hathe (*recte* Hatto) *gallus* to Janet Averye at Maresfield in 1559, Adrian Doodgyn to Margaret Alfrie at Ashburnham in

574. ESRO, PBT 1/1/6/14.
575. ESRO, PBT 1/1/12/255; 1/3/2/115.
576. ESRO, PBT 1/1/23/39; 1/3/6/160.
577. Craib, *Surrey musters*, p. 18.
578. For instance, Elizabeth the daughter of John and Dorothy Averye was baptized at Uckfield in 1605, but when the father and mother were buried, in 1635 and 1639 respectively, both were named Alfrey.

1566, William Alberye to Joan Barden and John Alphrey to Margery Vallance, both at Burwash in 1598 and 1613, John Devale to Bridget Alphry at Hawkhurst in 1616, Thomas Lambert of Westfield to Mary Avery at Beckley in 1618 and Peter Vinten to Isabel Alvery at Mountfield in 1624.

It looks as though John Aufery, who in 1615 married Rebecca Geale at Abinger, where both were buried in 1658, may have been an ironworker and of French descent. On the other hand Abraham Aivrey who in 1579 married Elizabeth Levit, the sister of John Levit alias Catlin, hammerman at Etchingham Forge, was the eldest son of a husbandman, Richard Alphrye of Hurst Green (Herst, parish of Salehurst), probably from a family which originated in Withyham. Though a husbandman, it may have been the iron industry which induced Alphrye to move to Salehurst. Five years after his father's death Abraham married the Etchingham hammerman's sister.

At a loftier level Thomas Alfrey of Hartfield moved to Battle, where he followed in the footsteps of his father in law, Ambrose Comport, as bailiff of Battle manor, but by 1574 was involved with George May as one of the trustees for the estate of the forgemaster Bartholomew Jeffery.[579] Either he or his similarly named son acquired Potmans Forge, Catsfield, in 1588 and the family continued in the iron industry.

The name Gload or Cludd also occurs in the Midlands. Children of James and Anne Cludd were baptised at Madeley in Shropshire from 1666 until 1673. However, there were certainly indigenous Cludds in the Madeley area and when William Cludd, who was probably the eldest son of James and Anne, was buried in 1726 he was described as a weaver.

Collet

Stephen Collet paid the poll tax as an alien at Wadhurst in the reliefs of 1549, 1551 and 1552, but not thereafter. It seems likely that he worked at one of the Frant-Wadhurst forges, bought by John Barham from Humphrey Lewknor in 1521. Was he perhaps the father of Humphrey Collet to whom Humphrey Lewknor's grandson Robert sold the White Hart Inn and other properties in Southwark for £280 in 1547? In 1556 John Barham II was in dispute with Humphrey Collet of St Saviour's parish in Southwark over 92 tons of iron which had been supplied to him.[580]

The family certainly continued in the iron trade through several generations. Humphrey had a son named Thomas Collet, probably the London merchant of that name who, in partnership with the forgemaster Anthony Pelham of Bucksteep, acquired a moiety of the ironworks in Ewood Park in Surrey in 1554. The Canterbury ironmonger, Henry Collett, who died around 1650,[581] was perhaps this Thomas's son, baptised at St James Garlickhithe in July 1576.

Another son of Thomas Collet was John Collet, also a London merchant, whose son, Thomas Collet of Highgate, entered a pedigree at the Visitation of Middlesex in 1663.[582] This does not take the family back beyond Humphrey Collet, so the connection with the immigrant Stephen Collet remains likely, but not proven.

Rowe

'Rowe the colyer' paid the poll tax as an alien at Mayfield in the relief of 1550. There were no subsequent subsidy roll entries for him and the name failed to occur until 1619 in the parish register.

In West Barnfield hundred in Kent, Maryan Rawe had paid the poll tax in the subsidy of 1543. Again there were no subsequent subsidy roll mentions.

The name of Simon Rawe occurred in the Westminster denization roll of 1544 in List 11, which gives personal details for many of the men included in the ironworker lists. He came to England around 1529 aged 21 and named Bafronets (*Beaufresne*?) in Normandy as his place of birth. There seems to be no record to prove his residence in the Weald.

Thomas Rowe, 'a straunger', who was buried at Rogate in June 1596, may have been an ironworker at Rogate Forge. Apart from Katherine Rowe of Midhurst, who married Peter Massey in 1654, this appears to be the only occurrence of this surname in the early Rogate parish registers.

579. ESRO, PBT 1/1/6/103 and 321.
580. Cobby, *The Lewknors of Sussex*, p. 11.
581. Straker, *Wealden iron*, p. 452; TNA, PROB 11/220/147.
582. J. Foster (ed.), *The Visitation of Middlesex began in the year 1663*, London, 1887, p. 89.

The name Rowe was of frequent occurrence in Cranbrook parish, but Thomas Rowe of Cranbrook, who died in 1619,[583] and John Roe of Cranbrook, whose daughter Anne married William Ferrall, a Cranbrook tailor, at Benenden in 1655, were both broadweavers. Francis Rawe of Horsted Keynes was a tailor whose will was proved in 1647.[584]

Robert Rowe the younger was headborough for Telham in Battle views of frankpledge in March and October 1581. Both Robert Rowe the elder and younger were defaulters at Telham in the view of frankpledge of October 1583. One of these Robert Rowes and three other men were fined 4 pence each for digging and carrying away marl, which could be used as a fluxing agent at the blast furnace, from the lord's waste at the Manor court of December 1586.[585]

There was also a Westfield family of this name, but Robert Rowe was styled 'husbandman' in 1610,[586] and in the following generation the parish register named both Robert Rowe and John Roe as yeomen, in 1634 and 1642 respectively.

More positive indications occur elsewhere. A citizen and ironmonger of London named William Rowe was mentioned in 1580.[587]

In North Yorkshire the surname can be traced at Rievaulx: Thomas Rowe of Rievaulx was buried at Helmsley in 1580 and Francis Rawe married Grace Brand at Helmsley in 1585.

In the Midlands the hammerman George Rowe of Brewood Park was one of the sureties when another Brewood hammerman, Gilbert Roberts, was bound to appear at the next general sessions in Staffordshire in September 1603.[588] Later, Elizabeth daughter of Richard Rowe 'de Furnace' was baptised at Halesowen in 1659. A namesake of the Brewood Park hammerman, George Row, Roo or Wroo, of Makeney, had his children, Anne, Samuel, Mary, George and Benjamin, baptised at Duffield between 1688 and 1697. His wife Susan was buried at Duffield within a few weeks of the last of these baptisms.

Clerygo

Simon Clerygo paid the poll tax in the relief of 1550 in Framfield. It is almost certain that he was identical with Simon Cleriewe who paid the poll tax as a servant of Hugh Collyn in Henhurst hundred in 1552.

If so, was it Clerygo who paid the poll tax among Anthony Pelham's servants in Hawksborough hundred in 1551 on his move eastwards, as 'Simon, (Nicholas) Hedoll's man'? As a servant of Hedoll, he would have been a collier. Another possible variant of this surname occurred in the same hundred also in 1551, when John Curleggo paid the poll tax as one of Joan Isted's servants in 1551.[589] Perhaps John was Simon's son. In all cases these men are described as aliens and not Frenchmen.

It is difficult to know what the original of this surname could have been. To what name it might have been assimilated in English is also difficult to imagine. Clarke seems to be the most probable, but as this was frequently used elsewhere without any additional complications, it is difficult to understand why an exception should have been made in this case.

Hambrey

Hambrey, who was deprived of his baptismal name, paid the poll tax in the relief of 1550 at Buxted in the list of aliens headed by Charles Garrete, but the name did no appear in later subsidy rolls.

The name was perhaps one found later quite extensively in Kent parishes. During the 1560s and 1570s, Thomas, Richard and William Henberry, all had children baptised at Lamberhurst.

Thomas Henberie's son Jonas, baptised in 1570, moved on to Goudhurst, where in 1595 he married Bennett Endge. Their daughters, two Marys and Alice, all died in infancy, but John and Thomas, baptised in 1601 and 1604, apparently survived. After the burial of his first wife at Goudhurst in 1608,

583. KHLC, PRC/17/63/334b.
584. TNA, PROB 11/202/551.
585. HEH, BA Vol. 96 f 75, 97 f 3, 96 ff 19-20.
586. ESRO, PBT 1/3/3/190.
587. *Calendars of Patent Rolls, Elizabeth I*, **8**, 2514.
588. Burne, *Staffordshire Quarter Sessions Rolls*, **5**, p. 33.
589. Both Pelham's and Isted's servants were listed at the end of the Tottingworth return, but we know from the returns for other years that Bivelham was the borough in which both these forgemasters had their works.

Jonas married Anne Bine at Lamberhurst in 1609. Their first child Lucy, baptised at Goudhurst in 1610, died young, but Thomas, Anne and Mary, baptised between 1612 and 1617, appear to have survived. Jonas was buried at Goudhurst in 1633.

In the Brenchley parish register the burial of George Henbery the elder was recorded in 1593. Baptised at Brenchley in August 1597 was Alice daughter of the other George Henbery, who himself was perhaps the son of Thomas Henberry, and had been baptised at Lamberhurst in 1580. This younger George Hembrey, together with his sisters Susan and Dorothy Hembrey, was a beneficiary under the will of the Brenchley spinster, Mary Reder, in 1625.[590]

Beyond their continuing residence in ironworking parishes there is nothing to prove a link between these later Hembreys and the iron trade. However, these bequests to other descendants of immigrants by Mary Reder, who was herself probably descended from the denizen Adrian Reder, perhaps preserved the close links between immigrant families.

Hambonye

Francis and Bordye Hambonye, who were listed with their surnames preceding, paid the poll tax in the relief of 1550 at Buxted in the list headed by Charles Garrete, but the surname occurs nowhere else in Wealden subsidy rolls. By 1550 the government's impoverishment had led to a drastic diminution in the demand for cannon, but it seems likely nevertheless that the presence of these men was connected with cannon-founding. They could have been recruited at any time since the last relief, levied on 2 May 1549. However, their names do not correspond with those of any of the known gunners or gunfounders at the Tower.

Since the names were given with surname first, in Hungarian style, could they be the 'two experienced gentlemen of Hungary' by whose advice the French king had 'made many cannons of larger calibre than any before seen and avaunteth to beat this town to powder',[591] as reported by the council in Boulogne to the king's council in London in January 1546?

Hartfield hundred

More

'More', whose baptismal name was not recorded, paid the poll tax in Hartfield hundred in the 1543 subsidy at the head of the alien servants of Denise Bowyer. The surname does not correspond with that of any of the five Frenchmen made denizens at Parrock Forge in 1544.

He cannot have been 'Mores Fyner', who paid the poll tax in Hartfield in 1550, because this finer was more correctly recorded as 'Mowery the fyner' in 1551 and was perhaps George Moryow, made denizen for Nicholas Eversfield in 1544. In 1543 this man had paid the poll tax as Eversfield's Frenchman George Morrys in Hoathly and Waldron, but by 1550 had moved on to work at a Hartfield Forge.

Nothing more can usefully be said about this elusive alien.

Bordyn

William Bordyn, who was the penultimate alien to pay the poll tax in Hartfield hundred in 1543, was perhaps a member of the Barden family. Could he have been a third son of Isambard Lamy? All the later references seem to be to the English-born William Barden, who around 1580 was hammerman at Dunsfold.

Scrace

There is no baptismal name for this servant of Parson Levett, who paid the poll tax in Hartfield hundred in 1543, along with Gilbert (Averell) and Charles (Gerard), both of whom were taxed on goods at Buxted in the same year. It looks as though some similar French name must have been assimilated to

590. KHLC, DRb/PW27.
591. *Letters and Papers, Henry VIII*, **21**(1), no. 250.

this Wealden surname, or had an English forgeman returned from working in France, accompanied by his French-born child?

Perhaps the marriage of Thomas Scrace to Joan Gillam at Ardingly in 1558 should be noted.

Mores

As noted above, 'Mores Fyner' who paid the poll tax in Hartfield hundred in 1550 seems likely to have been 'Mowery the fyner', who paid the poll tax in the relief of 1551 and who has been discussed elsewhere.

Myclowe

Myclowe Colyer was the last of the aliens who paid the poll tax in the relief of 1550 in Hartfield hundred. He did not appear again in the subsidy rolls. Since the name did not occur in the Sussex subsidy rolls of the 1520s, later occurrences must be thought to be descended from the immigrant.

Richard Micklow, whose son Peter was baptised at Fletching in 1562, might himself be the immigrant. A later member of the family was John Micklow, whose children, Peter, Anne and Robert were baptised at Balcombe between 1587 and 1591.

Danehill Horsted hundred

Jenne

James Jenne paid the poll tax as a servant of Sir William Barrentyne in Danehill Horsted hundred in 1543. It seems possible that he was related to John Jonnett of Parrock Forge, who has already been discussed.

Picard

It seems fairly clear that the entries of 1543, 1552, and 1572 for this poll-tax payer in Danehill Horsted and the 1560 entry in Lindfield Burleigh Arches all relate to the same John Picard. It is less easy to decide about the validity of the entries in Danehill Horsted for Thomas Picard in 1549 and for John Pollerd in 1551. It seems probable that the 1549 entry was a mistake for John Picard. However, in the case of John Pollard, it seems possible that an immigrant of that name was present in the Danehill Horsted area in 1551.

Because no sixteenth-century parish register for either Horsted Keynes or West Hoathly survives it is difficult to put flesh on the dry bones of the subsidy roll entries. However, John Pyckard and Peter Gayne of West Hoathly were granted the administration of the goods of the collier John Varnyshe (*Vergnes*) when he died in 1560,[592] being kin to him. It also seems that the marriage of Joane (*sic*) Pickerd to Elizabeth Greene at Ardingly in 1558 and the burial of Elizabeth wife of John Pickard at East Grinstead in 1584 might relate to this immigrant or to one of his sons.

There seem to be no parish register references to Guyllam Pickarde who paid the poll tax at Newdigate in 1578.

At Rusper Richard Pickard, whose daughters Alice, Jane and Joan were baptised between 1561 and 1567, and who himself was buried there in 1578, might be a member of this family. Elizabeth the daughter of Richard Pickard, who was buried at Horsham in 1559, appears to be the first member of this branch of the family to be mentioned in a parish register.

A later Richard Pickard married Margaret Guillam at Ifield in 1616. He was buried at Ifield in 1637, leaving only one son, Richard baptised in 1624, whom Pickard wished his overseers to keep at school until the age of 14; although his goods were valued at only £29 10s 10d, he left £100 to that end. Gilbert Gillam was one of the witnesses of his will.[593]

It is not possible to show that ironworkers surnamed Picard moved to the Midlands or to other parts of the country.

592. ESRO, PBT 1/1/4/337.

593. ESRO, PBT 1/1/25/89, 1/3/7/78.

Lawnsyne and de Lawnse

It seems that this name should actually read *L'Ancien*. It perhaps appeared in disguised form in 1549 in Danehill Horsted hundred when Jorden de Lawnse paid a shilling on goods to the relief of that year, although it is difficult in that case to explain the intrusion of the particle 'de'. In the 1543 subsidy roll he had perhaps paid the poll tax in Danehill Sheffield among the duke of Norfolk's workers as Jorden 'Moyner', and it seems possible that after working for Sir William Barrentyne at Horsted Keynes in 1549 he went back to work on the Norfolk estates at Worth in 1551, when as 'Jordyn' he again paid 1 shilling on goods.

A later member of the family, who ended his days at Worth, may have been the Kirdford collier Peter Lawnsyne, who in 1580 was called on to give evidence against Roger Norres in the Northchapel affray, which cost Charles Pavy his life. He appeared as Peter Launsinge in the muster roll for Blackheath and Wotton hundred in Surrey in 1584.[594] Lawnsyne's death was recorded at Worth in June 1588, in a Latinised entry, as Peter L'Antiqua.

Later members of this family were James Lansum, whose daughter Mary was baptised at Kirdford in 1618, and Simon Lancen, who married Eleanor Smart at Petworth on 1627. Simon Launsome's daughter Mary was baptised at Lurgashall in 1629, and he was married for a second time at Kirdford to a widow named Elizabeth Tyler in 1641. He was buried at Kirdford in 1681.

John Launsum married Elizabeth Layney at Kirdford in 1634 and their son Henry was baptised there in 1640. Elizabeth was buried at Kirdford in 1679 and her husband ten years later.

It must be regarded as possible that the Old family, who were certainly immigrants, were also descended from the Lawnsins. They were first encountered in Rushmonden hundred, which is the right sort of area, in 1572, when Maryan Old paid the poll tax. However, there is no positive evidence for this and baptismal names such as Jordan, Peter, James, Simon and Henry found no place among the known members of the Old family.

Jordan

The search for immigrant families of this name is made difficult by the fact that there were several native Jordan families in East Sussex in the 1520s, and by the fact that descendants of Jordan Bully also used the surname Jordan as an alias. In the case of Bartholomew Jordan, his descendants used Bartholomew as an alias, which leads to potential confusion with descendants of Bartholomew Pullen and Bartholomew Jordan, and particular confusion with descendants of Bartholomew Ponting.

Bartholomew and Denis Jorden each paid the poll tax in Danehill Sheffield hundred in 1549, but were not recorded thereafter unless 'Jurden', who paid the poll tax in Hartfield hundred in 1552, was one of them.

John Bartholomew who was buried at Maresfield in July 1597 was probably the son of Bartholomew Jorden and was perhaps the man of that name who married Denise Richman at Uckfield in 1554. He was certainly the finer who, along with another finer Peter Gownet, witnessed the will of the hammerman Gillam Hato in 1577.[595] The first witness to Hato's will was the forgemaster Anthony Morley and from the fact that Hato gave his parish as Horsted Keynes and that he paid the poll tax in Danehill Horsted hundred in the subsidy of 1572 we can be guess that the forge concerned was Morley's Freshfield Forge.

But by the time John Bartholomew made his own will in 1597 he was a Maresfield forgeman. The forgemaster George Kennion of Maresfield witnessed the will and was the first overseer; indeed the phraseology of the preamble to the will is identical to that of another which he witnessed and was probably of Kennion's devising and writing. John Bartholomew left chests to four of his children: Peter was to have the great joined chest, Margery the lesser joined chest and £5, and Elizabeth and Joan were each to have other chests and £5. He left £1 to his son Roger and 10 shillings each to Peter's three boys, John, Roger and William. Peter was to be residuary legatee and executor. Bartholomew's goods were valued at £29 1s 8d.[596]

Because no sixteenth-century parish register for Horsted Keynes survives it is difficult to find

594. Cockburn, *Sussex Assize records, Elizabeth I*, 801; Craib, *Surrey musters*, p. 190.

595. ESRO, PBT 1/1/7/61.

596. ESRO, PBT 1/1/10/68, 1/3/1/243.

information relating to the family. However, Peter was perhaps 'Bartholomew' who was baptised at Chailey in October 1557 and the man who married Grace Newman at Fletching in March 1586. The second of Peter's sons was certainly Roger, who was baptised at Chailey in October 1587. Both the views of frankpledge of 1589 for Sheffield in Danehill Sheffield hundred recorded Peter Bartholomew as a defaulter.[597]

John Jordan, who with his wife Elizabeth, appeared at Worth in 1611 was probably the eldest of Peter Bartholomew's sons. Though their first child James was baptised in 1611 under the name Jordan, their second and third children, Mary and Elizabeth were baptised there under the name Bartholomew in 1614 and 1616 respectively. It is not easy to discern what became of this couple after this last mention in 1616. Could they possibly be 'Bartholomew a finer' and 'Widow Bartholomew' buried at Tonbridge in 1621 and 1633 respectively?

Additionally, between 1611 and 1620 the Worth parish register attributed four children to John and Mary Bartholomew, one to Roger and Mary Bartholomew, and two to Roger and Sara Bartholomew. In the case of John and Mary, in 1620 the register showed their alias to have been Ponting, but it did not enable the two Rogers to be distinguished in any other way than by the names of their wives.

The Roger Bartholomew whose wife was named Sara was clearly the man who had married Sarah Good at Maresfield in 1606, but another Roger Bartholomew, whose child John was baptised at Maresfield posthumously in May 1606, was buried there in November 1605. Most probably this Roger was Peter Bartholomew's younger brother, whilst the man who moved to Worth was probably Peter's son baptised at Chailey in 1587.

The younger Roger appears not to have remained at Worth. He was back in Maresfield by 1621, when his daughter Jane was baptised there. He was probably the Roger Bartholomew buried at Maresfield in 1622, whilst his wife was probably 'Widow Bartholomew of Piltdown' who was buried there in 1627. John the son of Widow Bartholomew, who was buried there in 1629 was their eldest son who had been baptised at Maresfield in 1607. But what of Henry, son of Widow Bartholomew, who was buried at Maresfield in 1626? If he was Henry Bartholomew, who had been baptised at Worth in 1611, the Worth register must have been in error in ascribing to his parents the names Roger and Mary, a combination otherwise unknown.

However, Roger Bartholomew buried at Maresfield in 1605 could have been Bartholomew Ponting's youngest son Roger, baptised at Rotherfield in 1553, who was shown by views of frankpledge to have been at Birchden in 1578 and 1579,[598] but whose later whereabouts are not known, though he might have left the Weald. A fourth Roger Bartholomew, who could have been the man who married Sarah Good, was Ponting's grandson Roger, the son of Peter Bartholomew alias Ponting baptised at Maresfield in 1575 and a twin of John Bartholomew alias Ponting of Worth. Peter Ponting's wife was named Mildred so it is clear that Bartholomew, who was baptised at Worth in 1589 with Peter and Mildred as parents had the alias Ponting. He was buried at Worth in 1602, so it looks as though Peter Bartholomew buried at Worth in 1613 was Peter Bartholomew alias Ponting.

By the late seventeenth century Jordan forgeworkers were widespread. Still in the Weald, the forgeman John Jordan paid tax on two hearths in 1665 at Ashburnham. In Shropshire in 1655, another forgeman named John Jordan married Ursula Worrell at Cleobury Mortimer and they were still at Cleobury in 1678, when John's wife Ursula was buried. In South Yorkshire, the Attercliffe hammerman John Jordan had his sons Thomas and Robert apprenticed to members of the Company of Cutlers in Hallamshire in 1679 and 1680.[599] If the hammerman was the John Jordan buried at Sheffield in 1696, it was probably his widow Isabella who was buried there four years later.

In the Midlands Humphrey Jorden took a lease of the blade mill on Spittle Brook at Checkhill in 1601, but it seems probable that he was from a Kinver family named Jordan.[600]

597. ESRO, ACC 3597/1, ff 68, 79v.

598. ESRO, ACC 3597/8, ff 93v. (22 Oct 1578), 115v. (11 May 1579).

599. TNA, E 179/258/20 (1665); Leader, *Company of Cutlers in Hallamshire*, **2**, p. 268.

600. *Victoria County History of the county of Stafford*, vol. 2, pp. 147, 160.

Danehill Sheffield hundred

Carler

Peter Carler paid a shilling on goods to each of the reliefs from 1549 to 1551 in Danehill Sheffield. Only for this reason does it seem permissible to equate him with Coly who had paid 4 pence on goods to the subsidy of 1543 as a servant of the duke of Norfolk in the same hundred. He did not appear in subsidy rolls after 1551, but was perhaps the Peter Calear whose daughter Parnell was baptised at Frant in January 1556.

It is difficult to find a Wealden equivalent of this name apart from Carle or Carles alias Knight. Alice the wife of William Carle alias Knight was buried at Horsham in 1541. The following year William Carle married a widow named Joan Walys, but he did not survive this marriage long, because widow Joan Carle alias Knight's bastard son John was baptised and buried in March 1544. She in turn married Philip Smythe a servant of the Countess of Arundel in November 1547. Their daughter Elizabeth was baptised in 1548, but Philip died in 1558.

Joan, the wife of George Knight alias Carle, was buried at Horsham in 1548 and George Carle married Elizabeth Trendell later in the same year. Their daughter Joan was baptised and buried in November 1552. No further baptisms were recorded, perhaps because they later lived in the Forest of St Leonards in the parish of Beeding. However, Elizabeth, wife of George Knight of the Forest, was buried at Horsham in 1572. Early in 1573 George Knight married the widow Constance Holland at Horsham, 'both of the Forest in the parish of Beeding'. George Knight 'an old man' was buried at Horsham in 1585, Constance having predeceased him in 1581.

Although John Knight alias Carles was buried at Horsham in 1557 the family was next found in the enclave of Godstone parish which contained Woodcock Hammer. Thomas Knighte of Godstone and John Knight, a sheathe-maker, were buried at Lingfield in 1574 and 1584 respectively. In 1582 Richard Carls alias Knight married Joan Wood at Lingfield and their daughter Joan was baptised there in 1589. This daughter was presumably the Joan Carls whom John Chapman married at Lingfield in 1606. In 1626 Thomas Knight alias Carles was buried at Lingfield. Had the pre-Civil War parish register for Godstone survived it might have been possible to find other entries concerning this family.

Neve

The name Neve or Neave does not occur in the subsidy rolls of the 1520s for Sussex. Nevertheless, it must be thought that a name so widespread in the second half of the century must have been represented in some way. Perhaps the two Thomas Neffes in Hartfield hundred in 1524, one of them a weaver, were the progenitors of the Neave family of Withyham.

The first immigrant ironworker bearing this name was Giles Neve, who appeared in Danehill Sheffield hundred in 1549 and paid the poll tax in the reliefs of that year and of 1551 and 1552. He was closely followed by John Neve who was a servant of Thomas Woodman and paid the poll tax in Foxearle hundred in the relief of 1552. Neither appeared in later subsidy rolls, but Giles Neve was buried at Brenchley in August 1580.

Apart from Giles and John Neve, the only evidence of the family's connection with the iron industry comes in Horsham parish register, where John the son of a collier named Roger a'Neave was baptised in June 1551. However, an occupation in the secondary metal trades was followed by the cutler, John Neave of Albourne, whose will was proved in 1633. His son Thomas lived at Hurstpierpoint and his daughters married men from Bramber and Thakeham, so he could well have been from the Horsham branch of the family. At his death his goods were valued at £53 17s 2d.[601]

Although the Withyham Neves included Thomas Neave, a weaver (1614), who followed in the profession of Thomas Neffe of 1524, and Thomas Neve, a tailor (1624),[602] there were two Gillam or Kellam Neves in that area of the Weald, whose baptismal names suggest a French ancestry. The older man was a thatcher of that name, who was buried at Rotherfield in 1635,[603] but who had perhaps moved there from Hartfield, where, according to the Rotherfield parish register, his daughter Elizabeth had

601. ESRO, PBT 1/1/23/1, 1/3/6/147
602. ESRO, PBT 1/3/4/54 and 1/3/5/157.
603. ESRO, PBT 1/1/24/49.

been baptised in 1605. The younger man, the son of Thomas a'Neve, was baptised at Rotherfield in 1594 and married Mary Sharpe at Withyham in 1618. However, he was not mentioned in either parish register after that date.

Another Thomas Neeve was buried at Burwash in 1638, but in his will described himself as 'of Little Horsted, miller'. His son Nathan married Anne Tucker, probably from a family of pot-founders, at Buxted in 1622. John Neve who married Mary Page at Buxted in 1623 and Henry Neve of Buxted, yeoman, who obtained a licence to marry Kate Overy, an Uckfield widow, at Uckfield in 1636,[604] were probably his sons too. His son Nicholas married Margaret Uridge at Burwash in 1630. The father left his house and lands at Burwash Down to Nathan and his house, 'wherein I did dwell at Burwash', was to go to Nicholas after his own and his wife's death. He made his eldest son Thomas his overseer and his wife, probably Elizabeth Burges, whom he had married as his second wife at Buxted in 1614, his executrix. His goods were inventoried at £57 12s 4d.[605]

Another Thomas Neeve, presumably from this branch of the family, held the mill at Ashburnham from 1671 to 1692.[606]

Lorman

Peter Lorman paid a shilling on goods to the relief of 1550 in Danehill Sheffield, at a time when the furnace was reported to have been 'in ruin and decay', so it is not certain that he was an ironworker at all. It is also difficult to deduce what the French version of his name could have been. Should he have been recorded as 'Lamar'? Peter Lamar worked in Netherfield hundred for Westall and Gerard in 1551 and 1552, and in 1552 there was even a second worker of that name among the servants of the forgemaster Richard Weekes. Lorman could have moved on to be one of these.

Rushmonden hundred

Richardson

The alien Barnard Richardson paid the poll tax in Rushmonden hundred to the subsidy of 1543 and to the reliefs of 1549, 1551 and 1552. He was buried at Maresfield in February 1556 and in September administration of his effects, inventoried at £6 13s 4d, was granted to his widow Elizabeth.[607] She died in April 1567, leaving goods valued at £4 6s 9d. Richardson was not stated to be of French nationality and in the 1552 subsidy roll his name was recorded separately from the aliens known, or suspected, to have been ironworkers. Elizabeth Richardson made her daughter Alice her residuary legatee and executrix and since her other bequests, each of 2 shillings, were to Margaret the wife of John Kydder and to the latter's son John, it looks as though Alice and Margaret were her only children. Her overseer was Harry Hoth, and Robert Hoth, together with John Kydder, and John Slatherford, was a witness, so perhaps Hoth was her maiden name.[608]

In the subsidy rolls of the 1520s the surname Richardson was confined to two persons at Horsham, and though the name continued at Horsham, its widespread appearance in the late sixteenth century throughout the ironworking areas is a surprise. However, apart from Humphrey Richardson, a woodcutter at Panningridge in 1547, George Richardson, married to Susan White at Worth in 1604, and 'of the Hammer' when buried at Linchmere in 1637, is the only Richardson ironworker traced in the Weald. Susan was the eldest daughter of the collier Peter White, and had been baptised at Newdigate in 1587.

The family of the Birchden forgemaster Thomas Richardson, who died in 1599, shortly after taking a lease of Birchden Forge, remains to be considered. He was probably the son of Thomas Richardson who had married Blanche Nicolls at Tonbridge in 1562. His father predeceased him and was buried at Tonbridge in 1597, but his mother survived him and was the Blanche Richardson buried

604. Dunkin, *Calendar of Sussex marriage licences, Lewes, 1670-1729*, p. 280.
605. ESRO, PBT 1/1/25/175, 1/3/7/111.
606. ESRO, HBR 9/1/14, Ashburnham tenement analysis.
607. ESRO, PBT 1/1/3/188.
608. ESRO, PBT 1/1/5/427.

at Tonbridge in 1610. Another Blanche Richardson, who had married the Tonbridge mercer John Laughan alias Collyn in 1596, may have been the forgemaster's sister.

The mercer was descended from the family of the duke of Norfolk's Sheffield denizen of 1544, John Lawhen. He was, along with William Alfraye of Leigh Green, Richard Maynard, and Walter Milles, one of the overseers of Thomas Richardson's will. It appears that Thomas Richardson's wife was a widow named Eleanor Collins, because in 1624, after her death, her son Simon Collins entered a caveat in the Lewes archdeaconry court of probate.[609] Perhaps because of the long gap in the Tonbridge baptismal register, the origins of Simon Collins have not been traced.

Although immigrant connections could arise through involvement in the iron industry, especially if this continued over some decades, the number of immigrant affinities involved here suggest an immigrant origin for this branch of the Richardson family too.

Thomas Richardson's will shows that he had taken a 21-year lease of Birchden Forge from Lord Buckhurst in June 1598, with the benefit of 420 cords of wood to be taken annually within three miles of the forge. He left a third of the stock at the forge to his son-in-law Richard Maynard. Additionally, the overseers, who included Richard Maynard, were to have his leases for four years to raise £190 for the performance of his will, after which the leases were to revert to his eldest son John.[610]

It is evident that John Richardson did not retain his interest in the forge, which was later run, together with Hamsell Furnace, by Richard Maynard in partnership with John Baker of Battle. When he died in 1614 John Richardson made Maynard his executor and, though his goods were inventoried at £202 12s 4d, some of his property was in mortgage to Maynard. Maynard in turn died in 1619 and by his will provided for payment of £30 to John Richardson's eldest son Thomas and £10 to his second son John.[611]

In 1627 this second son John Richardson married Elizabeth, daughter of the Rotherfield hammerman Nicholas Pounting, whose place of work was presumably Birchden Forge. Whether John Richardson was connected with ironworking is unknown, but most other members of his family were not.

A still younger son of the forgemaster was David Richardson, a Tonbridge shoemaker, who was also in debt to Maynard, but Maynard renounced this debt provided David would pay half the sum involved to his niece, Elizabeth daughter of Thomas Richardson, whose death in 1619 had left her an orphan. Another Thomas Richardson, a Chiddingly tailor, and yet another grandson of the forgemaster, died in 1635 leaving a bequest to the shoemaker's son,[612] another Davy Richardson who had been baptised at Tonbridge in 1610.

Lindfield Burleigh Arches hundred

In the subsidy rolls for 1550 to 1552 the aliens in Lindfield Burleigh Arches hundred were headed by Henry Lucas, who on each occasion paid 2 shillings to the reliefs of those years. To the subsidy of 1543 he had paid 5 shillings and though he did not head that list, two of the other aliens in it, John Johnson and Cornelius, were stated to be his servants. John Johnson was still there in 1552, but by 1550 Cornelius had been replaced by Nicholas Founder and James Gascon. In 1552 the words 'The Founder' were substituted for the name Nicholas Founder, so we know that the surname was an occupational one and that the ironworks in Lindfield Arch, presumably the one called the 'iron mill of Freshfield' in the Portmen's complaint of 1548, included a blast furnace.

Henry Lucas and the Lucas families of West Hoathly and Wivelsfield were treated of in the discussion of the duke of Norfolk's worker Nawdyn Lucas of Fletching.

Johnson

John Johnson's career in Sussex can be followed through in subsidy rolls from his first appearance as a servant of Harry Lucas at Freshfield from 1543 to 1552, to Worth in 1563, to Lamberhurst (John

609. ESRO, PBT 1/3/5/154.
610. TNA, PROB 11/94/4.
611. ESRO, PBT 1/1/14/267, 1/3/4/58 (Richardson); TNA, PROB 11/133/63 (Maynard)
612. ESRO, PBT 1/1/24/42.

Gunson) in 1572, and to Wadhurst in 1576. It has been suggested that he was the son of Cornelius Johnson alias Walbortson, the alien gunner and master smith of the king's ironworks,[613] who died early in 1542.

Indeed the office of gunner and master smith held by the elder man was confirmed to both men in survivorship in October 1541. Because, out of ten children, both the eldest and the third sons of Cornelius were named John, it will probably be impossible to prove whether either of them was the Sussex man. The elder John Johnson was certainly the one who succeeded his father as master smith, because Cornelius directed in his will that his freehold and copyhold land in Essex should remain first to his wife Olive and after her death to his other sons and daughters in survivorship and come to his eldest son John only in the event of the deaths without heirs of all the other children.[614] It seems likely that the elder John Johnson was Cornelius's son by a former wife.

John Johnson was perhaps married twice, his second wife Alice bearing him children from 1563 to 1575. Marion (*Marionus*), with whom in 1562 he was accused of making an affray at Waldron, for which they were fined 3s 4d, was probably his son. Specifically, the Shiplake hundred court found that on 28 May Johnson had used a dagger (*pugione*) to obstruct the headborough John Harper when trying to carry out his duties.[615] Of Marion nothing more is known, but Johnson's more famous son, Thomas Johnson, was by 1567 old enough to sponsor a baptism at Maresfield.

Johnson's presence at the gunfounding furnace at Worth in 1563 is confirmed by the baptism of Mary daughter of John and Alice Johnson at Worth on 5 December. His presence at Maynards Gate Furnace, where the excavation of the gun-pit has proved that cannon were founded, is suggested by the baptisms at Rotherfield of further daughters, Elizabeth, an unnamed child, and Friswith, between 1568 and 1575. Curiously, he paid the poll tax in the Sussex portion of Lamberhurst (John *Gunson*) in 1572 and in Wadhurst in 1576, so his gunfounding activities were perhaps not confined to Maynards Gate. He was buried at Rotherfield on 11 April 1591, but administration of his goods was not granted to his widow Alice until 15 March 1592.[616] The bondsmen were his son Thomas Johnson of Hartfield, gentleman, and William Moone of Maresfield, blacksmith, the bond being in 100 marks, which suggests that his goods and chattels were praised at around £30.

Nevertheless, Johnson had never been opulent enough to pay more than the poll tax in any subsidy. He was probably quite content to see his children well established in life. His son Thomas Johnson had become Queen's gunfounder in 1588 in succession to Ralph Hogge. Francis Johnson, who cast guns at Scarletts Furnace in Cowden between 1588 and his death in 1594, could have been another of his sons and his daughter Friswith married Peter Hook, presumably the ironfounder of that name, at Rotherfield in May 1592.

As we have seen, Thomas Johnson was mentioned in Maresfield parish register from 1567 onwards, when he was working for Hogge. As late as November 1581 he was constable for Rushmonden hundred,[617] but he described himself as 'of Cowden' in a document of 1576, when he bought charcoal from Edward Fyltness for use at Maynards Gate Furnace. At Cowden he may have worked the gunfounding furnace at Scarlets from before 1576 until 1588, when he acquired the tenancy of Horsmonden, under a lease made to John Ashburnham. An order for 'Johnson' to make his ditches from Bowery Gate to the Waterfall in Falkenhurst borough in May 1578 suggests that he had by then already acquired interests in Hartfield.[618] His definitive move to Falkenhurst occurred during the 1582-1587 gap in the court books, because from October 1587 until 1591 he was regularly cited for Falkenhurst in Hartfield hundred views of frankpledge.[619] His connection with a further ironworks is suggested in October 1587 by the order of the Hartfield hundred court that he cut his hedges near Parrock Pond, which were obstructing the highway.[620]

Thomas Johnson was buried at Brenchley on 10 March 1596. Like his father he left no will and

613. Teesdale, *Gunfounding in the Weald in the sixteenth century*, p. 132.
614. *Letters and Papers, Henry VIII*, **16**, no. 1488 (7); TNA, PROB 11/29/77.
615. BL, Add. Roll 32526.
616. ESRO, PBT 1/3/2/136.
617. ESRO, ACC 3597/8, f. 208.
618. ESRO, ACC 3597/8, f. 80.
619. ESRO, ACC 3597/1, f. 8 (16 Oct 1587) to f. 146 (29 Apr 1591).
620. ESRO, ACC 3597/1, f. 9.

administration of his goods was granted to his wife Mary in 1596.[621]

It seems that there were other ironworkers in the Weald named Johnson besides the gunfounders, though whether these were descended from Cornelius Johnson it is impossible to say. It looks as though one of them may have been Richard Johnson, who married Mary Latter at Pembury in 1568. Their children, Katherine, Joan, Ellen, Wybarn and Richard were baptised between 1569 and 1581, and Richard's wife Mary was buried at Pembury in 1584. Their father may have been the Richard Johnson who was buried at Pembury in 1612. Two of his daughters were married at Etchingham, Katherine to the hammerman John Deprone in 1589 and Ellen to Steven Valentine, Valentine Deprone's son, in 1594.

A collier, Nicholas Johnson of Biddenden, was mentioned in 1598.[622] He may have been the Nicholas Johnson who married Joan Booth at Cranbrook in 1615, and whose children were baptised at Biddenden between 1617 and 1631.

A second Francis Johnson made his way to Yorkshire. He was at Rievaulx in North Yorkshire in 1585, when his son George was baptised at Helmsley, but by 1593 he was in West Yorkshire, with his wife and two children, where he worked at Thomas Proctor's abortive blast furnace at Brucrofts near Shipley Hirst on the river Aire.[623]

In Shropshire a John Johnson who worked at Shirlett was buried at Much Wenlock in 1587. Katherine Johnson, the wife of an unnamed finer who presumably worked at Norton Forge on the river Tern, was buried at Norton-in-Hales in 1591. Since Johnson's wife had so recently died, it is far from certain that the finer named Joseph, whose son Gilbert was baptised and buried in the same parish in May and June of the following year, can have been the same man.

At Makeney on the Derwent in Derbyshire, the Duffield parish register noted the presence of Ralph, Thomas and William Johnson between 1599 and 1607. The same combination of names is found again after 1638, when William and Thomas Johnson of the 'Weare', which also seems to have been at Makeney, were mentioned, in addition to Thomas and William Johnson of Makeney, and Ralph Johnson of Makeney, whose son Ralph was baptised in 1650.

Thomas Johnson, the Wadsley forgeman who married Hannah Marriott at Sheffield in 1726, could have been Thomas son of Thomas Johnson of Makeney, who had been baptised at Duffield in 1693. Thomas's children were baptised at Sheffield between 1727 and 1730, at Ecclesfield in 1732 and 1734, and again at Sheffield between 1737 and 1743. In the Rawmarsh parish register entries concerning the forgeman Edward Johnson, who probably worked at Kilnhurst Forge, occurred in 1745 and 1746.

The continuance of the family in, or its return to Derbyshire is shown by entries in the Staveley parish register which noted the presence of Jonathan and Margaret Johnson 'of the Forge' in 1732 and 1737.

In the Weald later in the century Thomas Johnson was founder at Ashburnham Furnace during the 45-week campaign of 1763-4 and was paid £125 16s 9d for blowing, an average of £2 16s 0d a week. This presumably included payments to ancillary workers at the furnace, such as the filler and other assistants.[624]

Gascon

In discussing the role of the various branches of the Huggett family in the Weald, the suggestion was made that Nicholas Fownder who appeared at Freshfield at some time between the subsidy rolls of 1543 and 1550, might have been Nicolas Hué *dit* Le Blanc of the Glinay Furnace near Beaussault. Hué was last mentioned in notarial acts of Neufchâtel in March 1542, and, somewhat unusually, no testamentary act or acts concerning his successors occurred.

That 1550 was also the year in which the first appearance occurred at Freshfield of the alien James Gascon, whose surname is that of the family who shared the ironworks at Neuville-Ferrières and Neufchâtel with the de Fry family from 1538 onwards, cannot be merely coincidental. After paying the poll tax in 1551, James Gascon disappeared from Lindfield Burleigh Arches before 1552. Was he

621. TNA, PROB 6/5 p. 160.

622. Zell, *Industry in the countryside*, p. 132, n. 28.

623. TNA, E 134, 35/6 Elizabeth I, Michaelmas 34.

624. J. S. Hodgkinson, 'Notes on early 18th-century memoranda on the making of iron', *Wealden Iron*, Bulletin of the Wealden Iron Research Group, 2nd series, **15** (1995), p. 10.

the James Gascoyn who early in 1559 witnessed the will of the Heathfield collier Thomas a'Wood?[625] Perhaps he now lived in the Bivelham area and was ancestor to the family for which entries occurred in the parish registers of Mayfield and Heathfield.

The name Gasson or Gaston is fairly common in the Weald, and parish register entries at Lindfield used only these versions of the name. The blacksmith Francis Gasson of Horsted Keynes, who died in 1640, was the son of Thomas Gasson who was buried at Lindfield in 1610.[626] Gaps and deficiencies in the Lindfield parish register mean that the baptism of only one of Thomas's children can be found: that of Clemence, who was baptised in 1561 and married Thomas Fenner in 1591. This means that there can be no way in which Thomas Gasson or his son Francis could be thought to have been related to James Gascon.

On the other hand the alias of John Valet alias Gasken of Ticehurst appears to suggest he was perhaps not indigenous. He seems to have been well established in Shoyswell hundred in the 1520s, when he appeared in 1524 as John Gasteyn, with goods valued at £12, and in 1525, apparently more correctly, as John Gaskoyn. He made his will in 1546,[627] and left houses at Bardown and Cottenden near Stonegate, both within 1.5km of East Lymden Furnace. The movements of a later John Vallet alias Gasken, who parish register entries indicate was at Fletching from 1561 to 1579, but who was buried at Warbleton in 1581.[628]

A man who seems more likely to have been linked with the immigrant James Gascon was John Gascoin, who in 1570 was married at Mayfield to Anne Collyn of Burwash, presumably a member of the forgemaster family. However, beyond this marriage there is nothing to link John Gascoin himself with ironworking. His first children were not baptised at Mayfield, which suggests they could have been baptised at Heathfield, where no parish register survives for the 1570s. He was almost certainly the man of that name buried at Mayfield in 1601. His son John was buried at Mayfield early in 1590, so he cannot have been the father of the Mayfield mason named John Gasson, for whose marriage to Agnes Bense a licence was granted in 1602.[629]

John Gascoin's eldest son Nicholas married Elizabeth King in 1595, and their son John was baptised at Heathfield in 1598. However, Nicholas's wife was perhaps the Elizabeth Gascoin buried at Mayfield in 1602, and no further trace occurred of Nicholas or his son.

Other sons of John Gascoin were Thomas and Abraham. Thomas's daughter Elizabeth, who was baptised at Mayfield in 1603, was probably the Elizabeth Gascoin buried there in 1604. Other children of Thomas Gascoin were Ursula, Margaret, two Thomases, neither of whom survived, and Anne, baptised between 1605 and 1618. Thomas's wife Agnes was buried at Mayfield in 1623.

Abraham was possibly the Abraham Gasson who married Elizabeth Longly at Rotherfield in 1602. Their children John, Elizabeth, two Abrahams neither of whom survived, and Frances were baptised between 1604 and 1615, but Abraham himself died in 1617.

Up to 1605 all parish register entries for this family are in the form of Gascoin, but from 1606 onwards Gasson was adopted. Frances Gasson married Thomas Young at Mayfield in 1637. Nicholas Gascoin, and his son John baptised at Heathfield in 1598, and Abraham's son John baptised at Rotherfield in 1604 are the unaccounted-for male members of this family, who may of course have moved to another part of the country.

At Kingswinford in the west Midlands, John the son of a locksmith named John Gaskinne and his wife Anne was baptised in February 1619.

625. ESRO, PBT 1/1/4/307.

626. ESRO, PBT 2/2/3/83 (1610); TNA, PROB 11/184/161 (1640).

627. ESRO, PBT 1/1/1/116.

628. Although both the Valet and Gascoyn families can be found as tenants of the manor of Hammerden from the 1440s (ESRO, SAS/CO 3), and the alias first appears in 1486, the subsequent history of the family implies a link with ironworking.

629. Dunkin, *Sussex Marriage Licences, Lewes 1586-1643*, p. 39.

Shiplake hundred

Trowley

John Trowley and John Cosenet both paid the poll tax in 1543 as servants of Nicholas Eversfield in the borough of Hoathly and Waldron. Neither was among the six Frenchmen made denizens for Nicholas Eversfield the following year. Eversfield paid 13s 4d on goods to the subsidy of 1543 in Greenhurst borough of Buxted, but no ironworks site other than Waldron Furnace is known in either Hoathly and Waldron.[630]

A later bearer of this surname was John Trueley of West Firle, who died in 1571, and made his wife Thomasine his executor, both his son and daughter named John and Elizabeth, still being minors. This will was witnessed by Robert Trewly.[631]

The surname Trowley appears to have been assimilated to that of Drowley or Druley which went back to the 1540s in Surrey.[632] Richard Drowling of Dallington, whose wife Mercy gave birth to a dead female child in 1582,[633] may have moved on to be the Lamberhurst collier, Richard Drowly, who in 1594 brought an action at quarter sessions against Anthony Frelicar (*sic*) alias Lambard of Lamberhurst, another collier of immigrant descent, who had failed to honour an agreement to work for him.[634] Drowly's family appears to have persisted at Lamberhurst, where two daughters of John and Eleanor Drowly were baptised in 1616 and 1617, and six children surnamed Drowligh who were baptised from 1625 to 1637 were perhaps all the children of John and Hester Drowligh.

The family was established at Isfield by at least 1613, when George Moyse married Beatrice Druly. Her father Thomas Drewley, an Isfield husbandman, died in 1630,[635] and her brother John Druly married Joan Atterall of Fletching at Isfield in 1633.

Cosenet

The surname of John Cosenet did not recur in the Weald, but could be a diminutive of Cousin. The entry for the burial of Lawrence Cossens, Frenchman, at Heathfield in 1589 appears to confirm that French persons surnamed Cousin came to the Weald. They will be discussed later.

SUSSEX - LEWES RAPE

Buttinghill hundred

Pyballyar

John Pebealet, who paid the poll tax in 1549 in Buttinghill hundred, was almost certainly the man who later paid the poll tax in 1550 (*Pyballyar*), and 1551 (*Pyballary*) in Netherfield hundred as an alien servant of Richard Weekes. His trade was indicated earlier still when he, as John Pyball or Pybald, worked as a collier and woodcutter at Robertsbridge in 1541 and 1542 for Sir William Sidney. In 1542 he was paid £6 7s 4d.[636]

Like John Brye, who had also worked for Weekes in 1550, he was later found at Cleobury Mortimer where in 1572, as John Pybaly, he paid the poll tax of 4 pence;[637] he had not appeared in the

630. In 1551, when Eversfield paid £1 10s 0d to the aid in Greenhurst borough his servant Quinten Tyler, who had been made denizen by him in 1544, paid the poll tax as his servant in Framfield borough. The subsidies are for Pevensey rape (TNA, E 179/190/191 (1543) and 190/237 (1549 and 1551)); the second of these is ostensibly for 1549, but contains, in lieu of the 1549 return for Hartfield hundred, a second (1551) return for Loxfield hundred.

631. ESRO, PBT 1/1/6/121.

632. Benjamin son of John Druly was baptized at Limpsfield in 1541.

633. Hunnisett, *Sussex Coroners' inquests*, 1558-1603, no. 287.

634. ESRO, QR 1, m. 11.

635. ESRO, PBT 2/2/5/62.

636. KHLC, U1475 B6/2; B7/1 and 2; B12.

637. TNA, E 179/167/50.

1571 return.

Low

Gellet Low paid a shilling on goods to the relief of 1550 in Buttinghill hundred among the workers at Crookford double furnace in Worth. The name did not otherwise occur in the ironworking areas of the Weald. The French original of this name was no doubt *Bas* or *Le Bas*, though the diminutive *Basset* is also possible.

A Midlands family named Low was later involved in the iron industry at the entrepreneurial level. For instance Patrick Lowe, whose son Vincent Lowe married Anne daughter of Henry Cavendish of Chatsworth, was running Denby Furnace in 1611.[638] Richard Snape from this furnace was buried at Heanor in 1625, perhaps because he had formerly worked at Loscoe Furnace in Heanor parish, where he had married Mildred Tyler in 1598.

Neither in this case, nor in the case of Humphrey Low, who in 1606 was operating Hales Furnace on the Stour, is there any indication that the families involved were other than indigenous.

The surnames Basset and Bassock both occurred in ironworking areas of East Sussex in the subsidy rolls of the 1520s, so bearers of these names later involved in the iron industry may well have been indigenous.

However, both the miner Richard Basset of Shipley and the collier Edward Basset of Horsham came from areas not far removed from Worth. Richard Basset was aged around 40 in 1588, when he stated that he had worked in the Forest (of St Leonards) for the space of three years.[639] Edward Basset married Joan Poore at Lodsworth in 1585 and baptismal entries enable him to be traced at Woodbeding in 1586, at Maresfield in 1587, at Rogate in 1589, at Horsham in 1592 and at Fletching from 1596 to 1604. The Horsham parish register revealed that in 1592 he was 'a collier under Raffe Stones work'. His will of 1618 described him as a Fletching husbandman and his goods were valued at £61 15s 4d; he left his 'greatest iron pot' to his daughter Joan and his second iron pot to his daughter Susan.[640]

Even the surname Bassock first appeared in connection with iron not far from Worth in 1599, when John Bassocke of Nuthurst, hammerman, had to appear at the assizes.[641]

Another Richard Basset appears to have been a woodcutter. Richard Basset of Lindfield made his will early in 1593; he left £1 and one ewe sheep to each of his five children, who were presumably under age, because he made his wife Jane his executor. He had a brother named John whom he made one of his overseers. He had cut 30 'tunne' of timber for Mr Francis Chaloner of Tremans, for which 15 shillings had been paid, with 14s 6d outstanding, 10 tons for Henry Goodwyne for which 10s had been paid, with 1s 8d outstanding; he had cut 6½ tons of timber and mowed 11½ acres of grass for Richard Beves, for which 15 shillings had been paid, with 4s 1d outstanding. The timber for Mr Chaloner had been cut at 1s 1d the 'tunne' and for Goodwyne and Beves at 1s 2d; the grass had been cut at a shilling the acre. He was also owed 3s 8d by Richard Hearsee and Richard Pollard for four cords of wood cut at 11 pence the cord.[642]

Another ironworker was James Basset, a Goudhurst collier,[643] who married Mildred Stonstreat at Goudhurst in 1572 and who was buried there in 1580. Also towards the east of the Weald lived Abraham Basset, 'a single man serving at the furnace', who was buried at Dallington in 1682.

In the secondary metal trades was the Mayfield smith Alexander Basset,[644] who married Denys Daniell in 1607 and was buried in 1637. John Basset of Wadhurst, blacksmith, followed his father's trade. He married Elizabeth Upton and when her father Thomas Upton of Wadhurst died, all his 'smything tools' were bequeathed to the younger man.[645] The family was still in business in Wadhurst as farriers and blacksmiths until 1988.[646]

638. TNA, C 2 James I, C16/41.
639. TNA, E 134/30 Elizabeth I, Easter 17.
640. ESRO, PBT 1/1/17/122; PBT 1/3/4/66.
641. Cockburn, *Sussex Assize records, Elizabeth I*, no. 1839.
642. ESRO, PBT 2/2/1/87.
643. KHLC, PRC 10/13, f. 8.
644. Mayfield parish register, burials, 19 Jul 1629.
645. ESRO, PBT 2/2/6/50.
646. ESRO, AMS 6439.

Ridleigh

It seems certain that the name of Adrian Ridleygh, who paid the poll tax in Buttinghill hundred to the reliefs of 1550 and 1551, has been wrongly recorded. He was clearly the denizen Adrian Reder, who in 1543 had paid the poll tax in Hartfield hundred, but by 1552 had left the ironworking area completely for West Tarring in Bramber hundred, where he paid a shilling on goods worth £1.

KENT

Barnfield hundred

Bousselowe

John Bousselowe who paid the poll tax in Barnfield hundred in 1550 may be identical with the servant of the forgemaster Richard Weekes, John Bossell, who paid the poll tax in Netherfield hundred in 1551.

The similarity of 't' and 'c' in sixteenth-century scripts makes it difficult to be sure whether the family resident at Neuville-Ferrières at that time was 'Boucelleu', or the more usual 'Boutelleu'. However, a draft entry for a Neufchâtel notarial act of 1503 gives the version 'Bouchelleu', which suggests that the young Jehan Bouceleu of Neuville-Ferrières, who was declared to be of full age in a notarial act of March 1537, could be the man who was briefly in the Weald. By 1553 he was a collector of tax (the *taille*) in Neuville.[647]

West Barnfield hundred

Loye

John Loye was a servant of Thomas May who paid the poll tax to the subsidy for West Barnfield hundred in 1543. Although the name of John Loye did not appear in the denization rolls, Marten Loye was among the miners listed as having been recruited by William Pepwell. Either of these could be the Loye without baptismal name who paid the poll tax among immigrant workers in Buttinghill hundred in 1549 and 1550, but not thereafter.

In the Béthune valley families named Loys inhabited the parishes of Fontaines-en-Bray and Sainte-Geneviève in the first half of the sixteenth century. Jehannet Loys of Canchy in Sainte-Geneviève parish was mentioned in notarial acts from 1536 to 1546, but was dead before 1563.[648]

However, it was only in the Varenne valley that notarial acts made an explicit connection between the Loys family and metalworking. During the 1530s Jacques Loys was a smith (*mareschal*) at Saint-Saëns. In 1536 he witnessed the notarial act by which the blade-smith Pernot Doré sold a property at the junction of the rue des Forges and the rue de l'Enfer. In 1541 his son Laurens Loys married Doré's daughter Mariette.[649] It will be remembered that a member of the Dory or Derry family worked for the forgemaster Ambrose Comport in 1549.

By appearing in South Yorkshire in Sheffield early in the seventeenth century, where Richard Loy married Margaret Allen in 1616, the family continued its association with the smithing of blades. Loy was a cutler who took the apprenticeship of his own second son Richard a few years before his own death in 1652. Richard Loy II completed his term with the Wincobank cutler John Burgon, to whom he was apprenticed for two years in 1654. The records of the Company of Cutlers in Hallamshire listed 17 members of the family who were apprenticed during the seventeenth and eighteenth centuries,[650] and in the 1720s the parish register noted four cutlers named Loy, Jonathan and Joseph, mentioned in 1720, Christopher, mentioned in 1722, and William Loy of Ecclesfield, who was married at Sheffield in 1726.

647. ADSM, 2 E 14/1145 (draft) and 1146 (both 9 Dec 1503); 2 E 14/1176 (6 Mar 1537); 2 E 14/1193 (13 May 1553).

648. ADSM, 2 E 14/1174 (25 Apr 1536); 2 E 14/1190 (4 Sept.1546); 2 E 14/1203 (25 Jul 1563).

649. ADSM, 2 E 93/15 (2 Apr 1536); 2 E 93/19 (28 Mar 1541).

650. Leader, *Company of Cutlers in Hallamshire*, **2**, pp. 28-9.

Brenchley hundred

There seems to be no good reason to connect Gilbert Anderson, who paid the poll tax in this hundred in 1541 and 1550, on the second occasion in the borough of Horsmonden, with the manufacture of iron.

Fannor

The otherwise unknown Peter Fannor paid the poll tax, along with Gilbert Anderson, at Horsmonden in Brenchley hundred in 1550. In 1550 the presence of John Angerfield and Nicholas Collyn suggests that ironworking was being carried on in the Lamberhurst quarter of the hundred, although Horsmonden Furnace was not referred to before the 1560s.

Washlingstone hundred

Delamer

Mathew Delamerr paid the poll tax in Washlingstone hundred in 1543, where he appeared at the end of a list of Mr Vane's (i.e. Fane's) servants, possibly in Tudeley tithing. The Fane family were forgemasters in the second half of the century, but are not known to have had ironworking interests before 1550.

It seems possible that Peter Lamere, who paid the poll tax as a servant of Harry Westall and Charles Gerard in Netherfield hundred in 1551 and 1552, and another similarly named man, Peter Lamar, who paid the poll tax as one of Richard Weekes' workers in the same hundred in 1552, could have been from the same family.

It does not seem possible to establish a definite relationship between these men and the de la Mare family of Neufchâtel-en-Bray, members of which were involved as brewers, butchers, and in the royal sergeantry and therefore even as gaoler, in that town.

Nor can any of them be traced in the Weald after 1552. Possible descendants, who may include Edward Larmar, whose children were baptised at Petworth in 1616 and 1620, were few.

WORKERS MENTIONED IN THE SIDNEY ACCOUNTS

Lauris

This name seems first to occur in the person of Mighell Loryshe, who was among the diggers who worked on the pounding of water at Robertsbridge in 1542.[651] He was not otherwise mentioned in the Weald, but the surname is perhaps the same as that of Adrian Lauris who paid the poll tax in Rotherfield hundred in 1552.

The presence in Rotherfield in 1552 of Adrian Lauris, proves the accuracy of the name of the Lenham collier of 1562, Giles Laures, which otherwise might have been questioned as a mis-transcription of 'Laurens'. Giles Laures of Lenham was found not guilty at the Kent assizes of a theft carried out at Ospringe near Faversham in March 1562.[652] It may be supposed that Adrian too had been a collier.

Pray alias Pinyon

John Pray and his son Simon were woodcutters at Robertsbridge in 1542. In 1543, in addition to cutting wood, they were among the Frenchmen who were supplied with white meat and milk. In 1544 their names immediately preceded that of Everode Pynion in the list of woodcutters,[653] and this proximity of the two families at Robertsbridge could have been the occasion of intermarriages which would explain the appearance of the Pinnion alias Pray or Spray surname, which was frequently used from around 1560 onwards.

651. KHLC, U1475 B7/1.
652. Cockburn, *Kent Assize records, Elizabeth I*, no. 200.
653. KHLC, U1475 B7/1 (1542), B2/2 (1543), B7/3 (1544).

After 1544 there followed a gap, running from at least 1546 to 1549, during which neither family was mentioned in the Sidney accounts. Although Everode's sons William, Lawrence and John Evered were among the woodcutters at Robertsbridge in 1552, it was at Panningridge that Simon Pray, or Spray as he was now more commonly called,[654] resumed wood-cutting in 1550 and 1551.

John Pray was not mentioned again until 1555, when he was paid 8 pence for a day's work, 'the making clean of the coal house' at Panningridge.[655] This was the last clear reference to John Pray, but from 1553 to 1556 Simon Spray continued among the woodcutters. An important change occurred in 1553 when Simon was paid 3s 4d for '5 yards of frise to make a coat and his boy a coat upon a covenant to him for this year's blowing at 8d the yard' and 6 shillings 'for 3 yards of russet to make his wife a petticoat according to his covenant for this year's service at 2s the yard'. 'Blowing' was a synonym for the work of the ironfounder, so Spray was now evidently assistant to the founder, who in 1553 was Warnet, with the particular responsibility of supervising the bellows. Charles Gerard was still called upon for hearth-laying and Spray was paid 8 pence a day for five days assisting him to mend 'the forefront of the furnace mouth'. Charles's pay of 2 shillings a day reflected a differential for his greater level of skill. It was probably for this work at the furnace mouth that Spray and his son dug stone.[656]

As one of Sir William Sidney's covenant servants, Simon Spray was now in a privileged position, though only on a year-to-year agreement. The coats were referred to again in 1554 when Simon was paid 12 shillings 'for his own livery coat, his wife's and his boy's liveries, over and besides 6 shillings for every founday according to his covenants'.[657] The splendour of a livery coat was still in evidence in 1750, when even a runaway apprentice from Lord Foley's Wilden Forge was described as wearing 'a dark brown coat and grey breeches, with white metal bottons to them, and a brown waistcoat mixed with stripes of white and yellow'.[658]

During October 1554 Simon Pray was paid 2s 8d for scouring the furnace hutch (*whych*), and a further 1s 6d for himself 'and his boy' for a day and a half scouring the wheel ditch. In 1555 he was paid 1s 4d for amending the bay of the furnace pond, and 8 pence for carrying the shamell plates for the bellows and the founder's ringers to the smith of Dallington for repair. He also received 12 shillings, his wages for the 'bearing of coals' for one whole year. In 1556 he was paid 8 pence in January for going to Robertsbridge to bring two new ringers from the forge. He also received a shilling when his covenants were renewed 'before (Richard) Marten' and he was again numbered among the woodcutters and miners, but this year his son Adrian Spray was for the first time also named as one of the miners. In 1558 Simon was again among the miners and in 1561 he was again given 9 shillings for a coat.[659]

Although members of the Pray family had been at Robertsbridge from almost the start of work there, it was only as a covenant servant after 1553 that Simon Pray became eligible for payment of the alien tax. Consequently he made no contribution to the reliefs of 1549 to 1552, but in the 1560 subsidy roll for Foxearle hundred, both he and his son Adrian Spray paid the poll tax as servants of Sir Henry Sidney.

Simon did not appear in the subsidy rolls of the 1570s, so he had perhaps died by then, but Adrian (*Pynyan*) paid the poll tax in Netherfield hundred in 1572 and 1576. Adrian was accompanied in both rolls by a second John Pynyan. Meanwhile in Foxearle hundred, Simon and Adrian were succeeded by Gilbert Pynyan, but not until 1572. No member of the family was so affluent at this time as to pay more than the poll tax.

It has been suggested that the adoption of the Pinnion/Pray alias came about through inter-marriage between the two families when working at Robertsbridge. But because they appeared as aliens in the subsidy rolls in the 1570s, Adrian, John and Gilbert Pray alias Pynion must all have been born before the move of the Pray family from France. Perhaps several intermarriages took place and by the

654. It is difficult to see how real-life elision, similar to that which in the written record produced in the State papers the non-existent gunfounder Johannes Sowyn and in the Assize records the non-existent ironfounder Charles Stiller of Goudhurst (Cockburn, *Sussex Assize records, Elizabeth I*, no. 2084), could have produced the quite widespread variant 'Spray'.

655. Crossley, *Sidney ironworks accounts*, pp. 85-8 (1550); KHLC, U1475 B10/5 (1551); B10/8 (1555).

656. KHLC, U1475 B10/6 (spelling modernised).

657. KHLC, U1475 B10/7 (spelling modernised).

658. *Aris's Birmingham Gazette*, May 1750; I am indebted to Colin Lavender of Wolverhampton for kindly sending me a photocopy of this advertisement.

659. KHLC, U1475 B10/7, 8, 9 and 10, B3/10.

1560s the two families were considered indissolubly linked. By the 1570s both the Pynion progenitors, Everode and John, had been established in England for more than half a century making it quite unlikely that any further members of their family came to England from faraway Picardy.

The earliest parish register entries to reflect the union came paradoxically from West Sussex where an infant named Adrian Praye was buried at Horsham in 1560. He was probably the son of Thomas Pray whose daughter Mary was baptised there in 1565. That Thomas used the alias was shown in 1563 when at the baptism of his son Hugh his name was given as Thomas Pynion. Thomas Pray alias Pynion was probably the son of John Pynnyon, the foreigner (*vir extraneus*) who was buried at Horsham in June 1561. This John was probably the original immigrant, who had come to England around 1520, had been made a denizen for William Levett in 1544, had worked at Buxted from 1543 to 1551, but was last recorded in a subsidy roll at Wadhurst, when he paid a shilling to the relief of 1552.

Thomas Pray had married Marcia Telleth (Tullet?) at Maresfield in 1556. Children born to him during his first seven years of marriage seem not to be recorded in any parish register. Thomas's first wife had died before 1567, because when his son John was baptised in that year at Worth his wife's name was Joan. Thomas Pynion's daughter Margaret was baptised at Ashburnham in 1572, but he had returned north by 1575, when his daughter Agnes was baptised at Mayfield. His return to Maresfield was marked by the baptism there in September 1577 of his son Thomas, who perhaps did not survive infancy. Thomas was probably 'Sprey the hamarman' employed at Ralph Hogge's ironworks in the Maresfield area in 1577 and 1578.[660] Views of frankpledge recorded his default (*Pynion*) at Fletching in Danehill Sheffield hundred in May 1579, when the entry remarked that he had 'gone away'(*abiit*), but in April 1580 he (*Praye*) was fined 2 pence, when he defaulted again in the borough of Shorte in the same hundred. In 1581, as Thomas Pynton (*sic*) of Mayfield, forgeman, he entered a recognizance to give evidence at the assizes against a Burwash shoemaker, Thomas Banckes.[661]

The family can next be detected in Salehurst parish, where Thomas Spray alias Pinion was buried in April 1610 and his widow Joan in April 1611. Thomas's son Hugh Pinion married Elizabeth Beeching at Burwash in June 1610, within two months of his father's death, and this couple's son John Pinion was baptised at Burwash in August 1611. However, Elizabeth wife of Hugh Spray was buried at Salehurst the following year and Hugh Pinion was remarried at Salehurst to Mary Heade in July 1613.

The baptism at Worth of Martha daughter of Hugh and Alice Pinion in July 1614 makes it apparent that there was at least one other Hugh Pinion. Martha was undoubtedly the 'child of the Forest' who was buried at Horsham only sixteen days later, after which no more was heard of this Hugh Pinion. Was the Worth Hugh Pray the one whose son Mathew had been baptised at Luccombe in north-west Somerset in 1603? This Hugh was undoubtedly a worker at Horner Mill Forge. Although no Mathew subsequently appeared in the Weald, the first of the Salehurst Hugh's recorded marriages was contracted at the groom's age of 47, so he could easily have married and visited Somerset before that.

The Salehurst Hugh and his family next moved to Cuckfield, where Ann daughter of Hugh and Mary Pinnion was baptised early in 1617. The baptisms of their daughters Mary, Elizabeth, Joan, Dorothy and Sarah were recorded respectively, at Mayfield early in 1620, at Tonbridge early in 1623, at Frant in 1626 and 1628 and at Rotherfield in 1631.

At Frant in 1625 Hugh Pray, forgeman, entered a quarter sessions recognizance to keep the peace, with John Travett of Wadhurst, forgeman, acting as bondsman. This indication of unruly conduct was borne out both in his own case, and in that of his son John, in subsequent years. In 1636 Hugh quarrelled with John, who was almost lamed by carrying an ancony (*ankerell*) of crippling weight from Mr Luck's New forge, perhaps Eridge, to Little Buxted Forge, where it was made into dripping pans. The subsequent presentment of Hugh Pynyon alias Pray of Buxted, forgeman, and of John Pray of Rotherfield, forgeman, for the theft from John Luck, gentleman, of an 'ancorell' worth 6 shillings, left the grand jury undecided as to Hugh Pray's guilt (*ignoramus*), but the charge against his son was found to be a true bill.[662]

In 1638 George Ellis of Fletching, forgeman, was a surety for the appearance at quarter sessions of Hugh Pinion alias Pray of Fletching, forgeman, and early in the following year Hugh Pynion of

660. Crossley, 'Ralph Hogge's ironworks accounts', p. 77.

661. ESRO, ACC 3597/8, ff 113v., 144v.; Cockburn, *Sussex Assize records, Elizabeth I*, no. 886.

662. ESRO, QR 21, m. 82 (1625), QR 35, m. 91 (1636), QR 36, m. 40 (1636), QR 39, m. 47 (1637). For these and the subsequent quarter session references I am very grateful to Brian Phillips.

Fletching, finer, was one of the bondsmen for his daughter Anne's licence to marry Geoffery Millam of Ardingly, finer, at Newick.[663] By 1642 Hugh was back at Buxted, but was then again bound by quarter sessions recognizance to keep the peace towards John Wiborn, with the forgemen Peter and John Obell of Framfield as sureties. In 1648 an order was issued for the 85-year-old Hugh Spray alias Pyneon, now presumably destitute, to be sent from Framfield, to Maresfield, his place of settlement.[664]

In 1649, when quarter sessions found Hugh not guilty of the theft of two gallons of turnips, valued at 6 pence, he was still described as 'of Maresfield, forgeman'.[665] It seems scarcely credible that all these adventures and vicissitudes could have befallen one man. But the identity of the finer with the child baptised at Horsham in 1563 is substantiated by the designation of Maresfield as his place of settlement, where his father and mother had married in 1556.

Hugh's son John Pinion had married Mary Colling at Buxted in 1634 and their son John was baptised at Rotherfield in 1635. Further writs of arrest were issued in 1637, including one for the theft by John Pray of Mayfield, forgeman, from John Dicker the younger of one peck of wheat, valued at 10 pence. In 1648 John Pray alias Pinion of Wadhurst, forgeman, was suspected of stealing metal tools from Frant and selling them to a smith of Coppings Crooch in Pembury. John was ordered to be whipped.[666] In January 1650 an unbaptised child of John Spray was buried at Wadhurst.

Another family of forgemen was that descended from Robert Pray alias Pinnion. Robert was first mentioned as an inhabitant of Parrock borough in Hartfield views of frankpledge in October 1578 (*Pynion*) and May 1579 (*Pray*), when as a defaulter from suit of court he was fined 2 pence on each occasion.[667] Later Hartfield views of frankpledge failed to mention him and he was probably Robert Pynion whose son John was baptised at Ashburnham in April 1580. Robert Pray alias Pinion can then be followed in the baptisms of his children William, Elizabeth, Richard, Bridget, and the twins Quintin and Robert, in 1585, 1588, 1592 and 1595, at Hawkhurst, Goudhurst and finally Chiddingstone. Lastly, Robert's 17-year-old son John was buried at Chiddingstone in 1597.

It is easy enough to pick up Quintin Pray again in 1621 when he married Joan Valiance at Mayfield. Their first child Elizabeth was baptised at Mayfield in 1622, after which entries concerning them were made in the Frant parish register from 1628 to 1643. His sons named Quintin, Hugh, William and Thomas were buried there between 1630 and 1643, and children who survived, Sarah, Dorothy, John and Anne, were baptised at Frant between 1631 and 1638. Along with the finer Hugh, Quintin Pynyon alias Pray of Frant, forgeman, was a surety for the appearance of a witness at quarter sessions in 1636, though he himself never gave rise to any quarter session proceedings. In 1641 he was a surety when John Harden, a Frant collier, entered a recognizance to keep the peace towards another collier, John Lambert of Lamberhurst.[668] At Frant, Quintin Pray, forgeman, contributed 6 pence in 1642 towards the relief of Irish Protestants.[669]

Quintin Pray's emigration to New England brought entries for him in the Frant parish register to an end in 1643. Like his relative Hugh, Quintin was a finer of iron and in that capacity was employed at the Hammersmith ironworks in New England. There, by around 1650, he was in charge of operations at Braintree Forge. He and his son John were the progenitors of a very widespread family in North America.

Quintin's brother Robert Pray perhaps originally worked at Biddenden Hammer. His first wife was buried at Biddenden in 1617 and early in 1618 he married Ellen Cleave there. Was he the Robert Praye alias Pinnion who witnessed the will of the Biddenden hammerman, Elias Bluatt, in 1622? By 1620 he seems to have been actually resident in Hartfield, but it was at Cowden that his children Jane and Margery were baptised in 1620 and 1621, and where his daughter Mary was buried in 1626. Further daughters, Agnes, Mary and Mercy, were baptised at Hartfield between 1628 and 1635 and his son Robert was baptised there in 1641. He was presumably the Hartfield collier, Robert Pray alias Pineon who was presented at quarter sessions in 1636 for the theft of a bushel of wheat valued at 11 pence from

663. ESRO, QR 43, m. 33; Dunkin, *Sussex Marriage Licences, Lewes 1586-1643*, p. 252.
664. ESRO, QR 57, m. 47; QR 80, mm. 57 and 81.
665. ESRO, QR 82, m. 1 (1649).
666. ESRO, QR 39, m. 47 (1637), QR 80, m. 57 (1648).
667. ESRO, ACC 3597/8, ff 92v., 115.
668. ESRO, QR 35, m. 50 (1636), QR 53, m. 58 (1641).
669. M. J. Burchall, *East Sussex contributors to the relief of Irish Protestants*, (1984), col. 23.

Robert Turner. Less certainly, he was perhaps Robert Prey of Hartfield, hammerman, who in 1651, along with the Hartfield collier, Edward Fuller, was presented for having the temerity to steal a ewe from a magistrate. Edward Fuller was discharged; Pray, though convicted, could consider himself fortunate to escape punishment other than branding.[670]

Returning to Quintin and Robert's father, Robert Spray alias Pynion of Chiddingstone, there were no baptisms of further children after 1595. So although there is no record of the death of his first wife, it looks as though he may have been Robert Pynion who married Margaret Brusber, widow of Humphrey Brisboll of Brambletye Forge, at the end of 1596. It was probably as a consequence of this marriage that he moved on to East Grinstead where he was buried early in 1618. Administration of his effects, inventoried at £10 5s 10d, was assigned to his eldest son William, now a Hever husbandman, with Henry Onion, a Waldron sawyer, also signing the bond.[671] His son William was buried at Hever in 1635, [672] and William's widow Anne was buried at Cowden in 1638, when she was described as 'of Chiddingstone'.

It seems possible that the forgeman of St Leonards Forest named Richard Praye, who was buried at Horsham early in 1615, could have been Robert's remaining son.

Further forgemen of this family appear to have been descended from Dominick Pynion, who as a young man stood as godparent for a baptism at Horsham in 1563. He was next cited in the Abinger parish register, where his son Robert was baptised in September 1567. Curiously Dominick's marriage to Elizabeth Homson was celebrated at Abinger in January 1569, without any note of the burial of a first wife being recorded at Abinger. John and George, sons of Dominick and Elizabeth, were baptised at Abinger in 1569 and 1571, after which it looks as though Dominick moved on from Abinger Forge to Woodcock Hammer. Baptisms of further sons, Edward, Charles and William, were recorded at Lingfield between 1575 and 1581, the last of which described Dominick as resident in Godstone parish, in the isolated enclave of which Woodcock Forge lay.

Dominick Pinion's son born out of wedlock, Robert Pinion, was presumably the Robert Pennone listed in the Surrey Muster roll at Abinger among 'Archers selected' in1583-4,[673] and at the age of only 16 he must have been a well-built young man to stretch a bow.

Dominick's eldest son by Elizabeth, John Pinion was perhaps the man who married Mary Darret at Worth in 1597. Their sons John and Dominick Pray were baptised at East Grinstead in 1599 and 1601, which seem to be the first occasions on which the alias Pray was used in connection with this branch of the family.

In the absence of probate records it is impossible to determine what became of the two John Pinions, father and son, but Dominick Pinion II married Constance Harman at East Grinstead in 1628. Dominick's daughter Mary made objection to banns of marriage at St Michael's church, Lewes, in 1656, the record of which described her father as an East Grinstead hammerman. Baptismal records show Dominick's residence at East Grinstead in 1630, his presence at Worth in 1632 and 1634,[674] at Buxted in 1637, and his return to East Grinstead by 1639. Dominck and his son Dominick, who had been baptised at Worth in 1634, were buried at East Grinstead in 1664 and 1679, though which of the two died the earlier is not clear.

Of the first Dominick Pinnion's son George, nothing further is known. Edward's first wife Mary was buried at East Grinstead in 1610, after which he married Alice Johnson in 1611. He was presumably the Cuckfield labourer, Edward Pynyon alias Praye who killed Joan, the wife of the Cuckfield hammerman, Richard Norman, with a knife in 1613. Edward was found guilty of murder, but was allowed benefit of clergy by the assize court.[675] He was not heard of in the Weald thereafter. Dominick's son Charles was perhaps the man buried at Worth in 1600.

It seems certain that Constance Pinion, who was buried at Lingfield in 1686, was Constance Harman who had married Dominick Pinion II at East Grinstead in 1628. Richard Pinyon, who was

670. ESRO, QR 34, m. 61 (1636), QR 90, m. 59 and 98 (1651).

671. ESRO, PBT 1/3/4/167.

672. I am grateful for Mrs Garnham of Wadhurst for this information.

673. Craib, *Surrey musters*, p. 24. He could of course have been the earlier Robert, who was at Ashburnham in 1580, before reappearing at Hawkhurst in 1585.

674. Despite the insistence at Worth that his wife's name was Mary, which must be disregarded because it was there that his daughter Mary and his son Dominick were baptized.

675. Cockburn, *Sussex Assize records, James I*, no. 267.

buried at Lingfield in 1691 may have been their youngest son, baptised at East Grinstead in 1652. John Pray, who married Judith Combes at Lingfield in 1692, was perhaps their grandson. Children of John and Judith Pray were baptised at Lingfield from 1693 to 1705, but John had died before 1732, when his widow was buried at Lingfield as Jude Pinion. Their son John Pinion, who had been baptised in 1698, married Elizabeth Tidye at Lingfield in 1725, but Elizabeth was buried there in July 1727, only two days after the baptism of their daughter Elizabeth. Members of this branch of the family presumably worked at Woodcock Hammer.

Peter, the son of Peter Praye, was baptised at Crowhurst in 1570. Despite the difference in surname, it seems possible that the father was Peter Pynion whose first wife Mary was buried at East Grinstead in 1576. Pynion married his second wife, Margaret Baylie, later that year and they may have been the parents of Martin Pynion who was baptised at East Grinstead in July 1577, though the parish register did not disclose Martin's parentage.

In May 1578 Peter Pinion was resident at Falkenhurst in Hartfield hundred, where his default at the view of frankpledge went without fine on account of poverty.[676] Peter was among the prisoners in Maidstone gaol in March 1582, and although there appear to have been no legal proceedings against him on that occasion, in 1588, as Peter Pynion of East Grinstead, collier, he and another collier, Robert Hewashe of Nutley, were indicted for burgling the house of Anthony Post at East Hoathly in January of that year. They were charged with the theft of a woman's dress worth £1 10s 0d, a petticoat worth 10 shillings, a piece of diaper cloth worth 10 shillings, three kerchiefs worth 6 shillings, three shirts worth 10 shillings and a sword worth 10 shillings. Hewashe was found guilty, but was allowed benefit of clergy; Pynion was at large.[677] Perhaps he had now sought refuge in West Sussex.

Martin Pynion, who had been baptised at East Grinstead in 1577, married Joan Golding at Rogate in the western Weald in 1595, where a forge had been set up around 1588. Lawrence Pynion, who had already appeared at Rogate in 1592 could have been his brother. Lawrence had children baptised at Rogate in 1592 and 1594, and at Harting in 1596, but then moved on to Fernhurst where five more of his children were baptised between 1600 and 1613. He and his wife were buried at Fernhurst in 1629 and 1626 respectively. Martin continued at Rogate, where five of his children were baptised between 1596 and 1611. However, it was at Fernhurst that Martin's son James was baptised in 1607, whilst his last child Daniel was baptised back at Rogate posthumously, Martin having been buried there in 1610. Martin's wife survived until 1631, and his family, in the persons of his eldest son Nicholas and the latter's third son Francis, stayed at Rogate into the 1660s. No evidence to prove their continued employment as forgemen has been found.

The possibility of tracing Pray family history in the south-east of the Weald is made difficult through the failure of the Mountfield parish register to give the parents' names of nine children baptised in the parish up to 1580. In addition, the parish registers of Herstmonceux, Wartling, Bexhill, and Westfield fail to record parents' names for a further five Pray and Pinnion children before 1586.

The only sixteenth-century probate record for the family was the administration of the effects of John Spray of Mountfield, valued at £24, granted to his widow Agnes in 1592.[678] However, the Mountfield parish register recorded the death of another John Spray in 1579. The widow's name of 1592 makes it likely that the John Spray who died in 1579 was the John Pynnyon who married Alice Marten at Warbleton in 1571, but which of them was the John Pynyan who paid the poll tax in Netherfield hundred in 1572 and in 1576 is impossible to determine, especially as both had died before the next subsidy in 1595.

The marriage of John Pynnyon in 1571 at Warbleton suggests the possibility that his son Nicholas was the man who married Mary Jeselbe in the same parish in 1604. He may have been one of the Nicholas Pinions baptised at Mountfield around 1577. Children of that name were baptised at Mountfield in July 1577 and in January 1578, and although the names of the parents were not disclosed, the probability is that the father's name was John in each case. There is no possibility of determining which John was the father of which Nicholas.

The Warbleton Nicholas Pinion had perhaps been first married to Elizabeth Billin at Burwash

676. ESRO, ACC 3597/8, f. 79.

677. Cockburn, *Kent Assize records, Elizabeth I*, no. 1226; Cockburn, *Sussex Assize records, Elizabeth I*, no. 1091.

678. ESRO, PBT 1/3/2/147.

in 1600. Before she was buried at Burwash in 1602, Elizabeth bore him one child Sarah, who was baptised at Burwash in 1601. At Warbleton Mary Jeselbe bore him three more children, Mary, Nicholas and Anne, baptised in 1605, 1608 and 1611.

There seems no doubt that Nicholas Spraye alias Pinnion, baptised at Warbleton in 1608 became Nicholas Pinnion, forge carpenter at the Hammersmith works on the Saugus in New England, who, with his wife Elizabeth, was involved in several court cases in the period 1647-8. This identification is substantiated by the testimony Nicholas gave in New England in April 1661 that he was then aged around 53.[679] His wife was probably Elizabeth Starr who married Nicholas Pinnion at Burwash in 1639. Before they emigrated to New England this couple's children, Ruth and John, were baptised at Burwash in 1640 and 1642.

The name Adrian presents difficulties of identification similar to those posed by John Pinnion alias Spray. Hadrian Penion who married Katherine Olyve at Ashburnham in 1559 was presumably Simon Pray's French-born son who paid the poll tax as Spray in Foxearle hundred in 1560. Since no further parish register entries which could relate to this Adrian Spray occurred at Ashburnham, where the register appears complete and reliable, it seems possible that he too could have moved to Mountfield and have been the Adrian Pynyan who paid the poll tax alongside John Pynyan in Netherfield hundred in 1572 and 1576. Katherine Spraye buried at Mountfield in 1577 could have been his wife. Did his failure to appear in the subsidy roll of 1595 mean that he was dead before that date, or was he no longer in regular employment and no longer liable for taxation by 1595?

No burial entry or probate entry for Adrian Spray or Pynion occurred at this time and it was not until 1614 and 1619 that burials of Adrian Pinions were recorded at Bexhill and Salehurst respectively. The Salehurst man had perhaps married Joan Isaack at Udimore in 1585 and had children baptised at Westfield in 1586, 1600 and 1605, though no parent's name was specified in 1586.

But who was the Adrian Pinion who married Elizabeth Lumpier at Mountfield, only just over three weeks after Katherine Spraye was buried there in 1577? No Adrian Spray was afterwards mentioned in the Mountfield parish register until 1628, so was the 1577 Adrian Pinion the man whose son Roger was baptised at Bexhill in 1580 and who was himself buried there in 1614? Their presence in ironworking parishes is the evidence which suggests links between the Adrians buried in 1614 and 1619 and the manufacture of iron.

The Richard Pinion whose children were baptised at Bexhill from 1580 to 1592 was probably related in some way to the Adrian Pinion who was also first noticed at Bexhill in 1580. They may have been brothers, or, if it is conceivable that Adrian Pinion remarried again within four weeks of his first wife's death, father and son. Richard's sons were Thomas, and probably Richard, James, Gilbert and Stephen. Of these, Thomas, James and Stephen, baptised in 1580, 1585 and 1592 respectively, appear to have left the area. Richard and Gilbert however, who were baptised in 1582 and 1587 respectively, both married at Bexhill.

It seems possible that James may have established himself in the Buxted-Maresfield area and was the James Spray alias Pinion who married Elizabeth Longlie at Buxted in 1622. Quarter session records show that in 1637 his life was despaired of after he had been wounded during an attack made on him by John Stephens, a Buxted forgeman, and his wife Dionise.[680]

James's son Robert, baptised at Buxted in 1623, was perhaps the Maresfield collier Robert Pinyon whose children, Mary, Katherine, Elizabeth, Ann, twins John and Jane, and William, were baptised at Maresfield from 1664 to 1680. He made his will in the name of Robert Pynion alias Bray in 1701, leaving his copyhold cottage and half an acre of land at Nutley to go to his youngest son William after the death of his wife Katherine.[681]

Richard Pinion II married Ellen French in 1607. Margaret French described her son-in-law as a husbandman in 1610 when she bequeathed £7 and an iron pot to her daughter.[682] He did not move from Bexhill; his children by Ellen were Constance and Gilbert, baptised in 1609 and 1615. Ellen was buried in 1617, and by his second wife named Elizabeth, Richard Pinion II had two further children, Richard and Elizabeth baptised in 1618 and 1622. Richard Pinion II's second wife died in 1632 and he himself

679. C. H. Pope, *The pioneers of Massachusetts*, Boston, 1900, pp. 362.
680. ESRO, QR 38, m. 33; I am grateful to Brian Phillips for this reference.
681. ESRO, PBT 1/1/48/215.
682. ESRO, PBT 1/1/13/135.

was buried at Bexhill in 1643.

Gilbert Pinion, Richard's son baptised in 1587, married a widow named Joan Winter at Bexhill in 1610. Their first child Mary was baptised at Warbleton in 1612, but Gilbert then moved to Brede, where his daughter Margery was baptised in 1615 and his wife was buried the following year. He was married at Beckley later in the same year to Ann Lambert of Beckley and their children William, Gilbert, Robert, John, Samuel, Joan and Mary were baptised, mostly in the name of Spray, either at Brede or at Westfield between 1617 and 1633, though neither William nor John survived infancy. Gilbert's movements suggest a continued interest in the iron industry.

Returning to Gilbert Pynion who paid the poll tax in Foxearle hundred in 1572, he was perhaps the unnamed Frenchman whose daughter Jarmine Penyon was baptised at Wartling in 1570 and whose son Henry Praye was buried there in 1573. The fact that he failed to appear in the subsidy of 1576, or in that of 1595, suggests that he was perhaps dead before 1576, despite the fact that Margaret Pray who was buried at Wartling in 1580 was described as the wife of a Frenchman rather than his widow.

Furthermore, her burial entry of 1580 described Margaret Pray as the mother of Gilbert Pray, who was perhaps the forgeman of that name whose daughter Susan was baptised at Wartling in 1581. This 1581 entry fits nicely among other entries for children of Gilbert Pray II whose baptisms were recorded at Ashburnham in 1576, 1579, 1584, 1586 and 1592. Which of the two Gilbert Prays was father of Priscilla Pray, whose baptism was recorded at Hertsmonceux in 1573, is unclear (if indeed her father was named Gilbert at all), but it seems certain that she was the Priscilla Pynyon who married Nicholas Tomplier at Ashburnham in 1594.

During 1587 Gilbert Pynion II was mentioned in three connections in Battle manor court rolls. In the High court suit and counter-suit were exchanged between Gilbert Pray and Thomas Elvered, ended on 19 September with Elvered's failure to appear and pursue his case, and in the other case a declaration of damages of £16 and an award of 4 pence costs in favour of Gilbert Pray. Meanwhile at the view of frankpledge of 20 April 1587 Richard Todde was fined a shilling for an assault on Gilbert Pray in which he had shed the latter's blood.[683] This Gilbert Pray was probably the Ashburnham man, administration of whose effects, inventoried as worth £18 0s 2d, was granted to his widow Jarmine in 1605,[684] though a corresponding burial entry does not appear in the Ashburnham parish register.

Gilbert Pinion II's son Gilbert Pinion III, baptised at Ashburnham in 1584, married Jane May at Catsfield in 1614. Jane was buried at Salehurst in 1621, where Gilbert may have been working for some time, because Thomas Pinion baptised at Salehurst in 1620 certainly, and Catherine Pynion baptised there in 1617 possibly, were their children. As his second wife, Gilbert Pinion III married Marie Bluet at Crowhurst later in 1621. They very soon appear to have returned to Catsfield, because it was there that their son, a fourth Gilbert Pinion, was baptised in 1624. Mary, wife of Gilbert (Spray), was buried at Catsfield in 1638 and the marriage of Gilbert Pynion to Abiah Hodge recorded at both Ashburnham and Catsfield in 1640 was perhaps a third marriage of Gilbert Pinion III, rather than the marriage of his son, who will have been aged just 16. Gilbert Pinion III will have been the unnamed 'Spray' who was buried at Catsfield in 1649.

Another Catsfield forgeman was John Pineon, who in a deposition of 1616 claimed to have been born in Salehurst around 1574.[685] He was illiterate, but claimed to be worth 20 marks (£13 6s 8d). He had lived in Catsfield for only nine months and was perhaps the father of John Pinion and John Spray who were buried there, in 1616 and 1619 respectively. The baptism of neither of these children can be traced at Catsfield, nor can the baptism of the first be found at Salehurst. Their father was presumably not the son of Gilbert Pinion II, most of whose children had been baptised at Ashburnham. There were no Spray or Pineon entries in the Salehurst parish register before 1601 and no John was recorded there before 1624.

William Praye was one of two Brenchley colliers who were tried at Sevenoaks assizes in 1588 for the theft from Richard Awcock in October 1587 of two pairs of sheets worth 10 shillings, a tablecloth worth 3 shillings, a pillow case worth a shilling, a shirt worth 1s 6d and two smocks worth 2 shillings. The other defendant John Goddard was indicted for two other thefts carried out at Brenchley, and was

683. HEH, BA Vol. 96 ff 18, 24.
684. ESRO, PBT 1/3/3/58.
685. WSRO, EpII/5/11, f. 31.

found guilty and hanged. Praye was found not guilty.[686] There is no evidence to connect him with Robert Praye alias Pinnion, who early in 1622 witnessed the will of the Biddenden hammerman, Elias Bluatt.

The collier William Praye was perhaps the William Pynion who married Katherine Skeeles at Cranbrook in 1603. He was the father of a child baptised there in 1606 named Katherine Pynion, who did not survive childhood, and probably also of John Pynion who was baptised at Cranbrook in 1604, but whose parentage was not recorded. Katherine Praye, 'a wife', who was buried at Cranbrook in 1626, was presumably William's wife, but the Cranbrook parish register seems not to record William's death. Whether he was the William Pray, whose son John was baptised at Cranbrook in 1630 is perhaps doubtful, because it looks as though William already had a son named John.

Finally mention should be made of Charles Pynion alias Everet whose wife Susan was buried at Penhurst in 1613. His alias suggests his direct descent from Everode Pynion, without any admixture of Pray or Spray blood. His children Richard and Jeremy were baptised at Penhurst in 1607 and 1609, but the fragmentary nature of the earliest Penhurst parish register precludes the possibility of tracing him back to John Pynnion alias Everet who was buried at Warbleton in 1560.

In the Midlands, it was at Rugeley in Staffordshire, and in Derbyshire that early entries concerning the Pinnion family occurred. At Rugeley Francis Pynian married Elizabeth Manyfold in 1592, Gregory Pynian married Alice Haule early in 1594, James Pinion married Dorothy Wright in 1602, and Mary Pynion, whose parentage was not indicated, was baptised in 1603.

Another, or the same, James Penyon married Alice Egynton at Duffield in 1608. Back in Staffordshire, it was probably one of the Sussex Gilbert Pynions who made a brief appearance at Ellastone, where his son Bartholomew was baptised early in 1628. Later in the same year John Pinion and Margery Nelson were married at West Bromwich.

Pleasley on the Derbyshire-Nottinghamshire border was the site of an early forge, but the parish register mentioned, firstly in 1614 a husbandman named Thomas Sprey, secondly William Sprey, a labourer who married Elizabeth Mariote in 1616, thirdly Thomas Spray of Sherbrook, a cooper, in 1619, and fourthly Hercules Spray of Sherbrook and Anne his wife, who were first mentioned in 1631. Hercules Spray died in January 1641. His widow Anne married Abraham Minion in the following November and his son Robert, baptised in 1635, married Ellen Farnoth in 1660. Their son Robert, baptised in 1663, was Robert Spray of Scarcliffe who married Ellen Rag early in 1700.

In Nottinghamshire, workers at both Cuckney and Carburton forges were mentioned in the Norton Cuckney parish register. Phoebe, the daughter of another Robert Spray, was baptised and buried at Norton Cuckney in January 1677. Also at Norton Cuckney John Spray married Susanna Gamble in 1678, whilst Robert Spray's wife Joan was buried there early in 1684. Francis Spray married Mary Bruckshaw from an English family of forgeworkers, at Norton Cuckney in 1729. Another Nottinghamshire parish where forgemen from Carburton Forge and also from Clipstone Forge and slitting mill were recorded was Edwinstowe and there, the baptism of another Francis Spray was recorded in 1723, and Benjamin Spray of Edwinstowe was buried in 1726.

In Herefordshire, John son of a collier named John Pray was baptised at Leintwardine, near Burrington Forge, in 1599. This collier could also have been the father of Richard Pinion who had been baptised at Stottesden in the Rea valley, north of Cleobury Mortimer in 1597. However, it looks as though he may have moved to Gloucestershire, initially to the Tortworth area, near where Rebecca Praye married Thomas Harrington at Westbury on Severn in 1607 and the younger John Pinnion married Katherine Axoll at North Nibley in 1617. It looks as though the younger man was the John Pinion alias Pray, 'a collier living in the forest of Deane' who in July 1633 took, on behalf of his daughter Anne, a minor, administration of the goods of his servant Richard Jones, who left to his master's daughter 'his coffer (*coafer*) and all that was in it' and 'sayed unto her, Anne all that I have shalbe thine when I dy'.[687] This was the first instance of the two surnames being used in conjunction in the Forest of Dean area.

Parish register entries such as that for their son William, baptised at English Bicknor in 1624, show that the younger John and Katherine were back across the Severn in the Forest of Dean by the 1620s. Their son Thomas was baptised at Awre on the opposite margin of the Forest in 1635. In a deposition made to an Exchequer special commission of March 1639, the 40-year-old collier, John Pray

686. Cockburn, *Kent Assize records, Elizabeth I*, no. 1629.

687. GRO, GDR Wills, 1633/19. This nuncupative will of Richard Jones is wrongly indexed as that of John Pinion alias Pruy.

of the parish of Newland, an employee of William Carpender, claimed to be owed £32 4s 0d for making charcoal.[688]

John Pinnion of Awre, labourer, made his will in June 1665. He left £8 to his son William and £5 each to his son Thomas and Thomas's son John. To his daughters Anne, who had married John Robbins at Awre in 1640, and Elizabeth Edwards he left £5 each. To his daughters Margaret Bulluck and Alice James he left £8 15s 0d and £3 respectively. The many 'cousins' he mentioned in his will appear to have been his grandchildren: to his cousin Elizabeth Robbins he left his little bed, a bolster, a pair of sheets, a coverlet and a blanket; to his cousin Mary Robbins a pair of harden sheets and his second kettle; to his cousins John Robbins and Jill Robbins all his sheep that were in the custody of James Beaven of Wolleston, with 10 shillings, also in Beaven's custody, to John Robbins. To his cousin Anne Robbins he left his second best pot, his second best spit and pewter dish. His cousin John Edwards was to have his great marmite and 10 shillings. His son William's eldest daughter Anne Pinnion was to have his second best bed, his second best bolster, his second best coverlet, his second best blanket and a pair of harden sheets. William's daughter Mary Pinnion was to have his best kettle. If Thomas Pinnion were to have his dwelling house, then Thomas was to pay 10 shillings yearly to his sister Margaret Bulluck during the term of the lease, but should he refuse to live in it then Margaret was to have it, paying to Thomas 10 shillings yearly. His cousin Samuel Pinnion, who was clearly Thomas's son baptised at Awre in 1660, was to have £1. Margaret's daughter Mary Bulluck was to have his best pot, his best spit and a dish of pewter. In addition to the three pounds left to his daughter Alice James, she was to have also his best bedstead, best bed, best bolster, best rug, best blanket, and a mat. He made his daughter Margaret Bulluck his executrix.[689]

The family continued in the area in the persons of Samuel and his wife Mary, whose children Elizabeth and Thomas were baptised at Awre in 1687 and 1691. John Pray alias Pinnion who married Mary Tipping at Awre in 1689 was presumably Thomas's son.

How later members of the family, such as Hannah Pray who married Henry Neale at Thornbury in 1655, Margaret Pinion who married John Smith at Awre in 1661, Thomas Pray alias Pinnion who married Esther Lugg in 1695 and Margaret Pinion who married John Taylor in 1700, were related to the collier does not appear from his will.

Cachecoll

The baptismal name of this frequently mentioned worker in the earliest period at Robertsbridge was not disclosed in the Sidney accounts. He was a collier there in 1542, 1543 and 1544, and, in the more detailed accounts for 1543, also appeared as a woodcutter and a purchaser of milk and herrings.[690]

Confusion with the two members of the Cachery family seems to be a rather unlikely explanation for the appearance of this name. He was perhaps a forebear of the surnames Catchloe, Ketchlow or Ketslow, which did not occur in the Sussex subsidy rolls of the 1520s.

The Etchingham husbandman, William Catchlow, wrongly spelled Chatelow in 1569 in the preamble to his will, disposed of £100 which he claimed to be owing to him by Lady Henley. Out of this £60 was to go to his wife Joan, but £40 was to be held in trust for his daughters Margery and Elizabeth until their ages of 21 or marriage by Master John Roberts of Boarzell and Master Henry Garner of Etchingham.[691] Henry Garner or Gardiner was a forgemaster, and the description husbandman in no way precluded work as a woodcutter or collier in the ironworks. Should both daughters die, the £40 was to go to the children of William's brother, Thomas Catchlow. A two-yearling heifer was to go to Thomas Catchlow himself, Robert Catchlow, servant to my Lady Henley, was to have £1 10s 0d, 5 shillings was to go to Walter Tucher, and 3s 4d to the poor at William's burial.

A son of Thomas Kechlawe named William was buried at Etchingham in 1587. The name also occurs at Ticehurst, where Anne widow of Henry Ketchloe was buried early in 1619. Henry Cachelow had been baptised at Cranbrook in 1565, but his parents' names were not disclosed.

More interestingly, in 1568 the Etchingham parish register referred to a Frenchman named John

688. TNA, E 178/6080.
689. GRO, GDR Wills, 1665.
690. KHLC, U1475 B7/1 and 2 (1542), B2/2 (1543), B7/3 (1544).
691. ESRO, PBT 1/2/4/27.

Kirshley, a name variously spelled Kerlowe, Kerslowe and Kirslowe in other entries. His children named Peter, Anne and Thomas were baptised between 1568 and 1573, though Anne survived only three years. It looks as though Henry Cachelow, baptised at Cranbrook immediately before these entries, could have been another of John's children.

The family was next encountered with the marriage of John Ketchloe and Joan Stace alias Shether at Dallington in 1598. Baptismal entries enable their family to be traced at Warbleton up to 1602, at Heathfield early in 1606 and at Brightling, where John became miller, from 1607 onwards. In 1626, by the will of Herbert Hepden of Brightling, John Ketchlee received a bequest of 10 shillings.[692] He died in 1645 leaving all his household stuff and moveables to his wife, who was to dwell in the house during her natural life, after which it was to remain to his son John and daughter Mary. Mary was also to have £10 which was in the hands of John Thirshurst. Ketchloe's other daughters were all married, and he left £1 to Elizabeth Graling and £5 to Jean Brit, but nothing to Anne, who had married Robert Picknoll in 1624, but was possibly already dead.[693]

John Ketchloe's eldest son John had married Elizabeth Moore at Brightling in 1641. Baptismal entries suggest that his other son Stephen, who had been one of the witnesses to Herbert Hepden's will, was living at Ashburnham in 1632 and in Dallington from 1636 onwards.

Humfrey

In the 1520s this surname occurred as Umfray in East Sussex, whilst Humfrey was mainly confined to West Sussex. Francis and Geoffrey Omvare were among the colliers at Robertsbridge in 1542. At Panningridge Richard Humphrey cut wood in 1547 and 1548.[694]

In 1546 Thomas Humphrei was listed among those ironworkers who purchased cattle, who appeared to be entirely French,[695] though he himself was perhaps more probably English. As Thomas Hunfray he had contributed to the subsidy at Robertsbridge in 1525 and was probably the Salehurst yeoman Thomas Umfrey, who died in 1574 and whose will was proved in that year.[696]

It was perhaps Francis and Geoffrey Omvare who are more likely to have been French. However, no alien of this name was recorded until 1572, when John Humfrey appeared among the aliens who paid the poll tax in Shoyswell hundred. Perhaps he was the 'ashealer' or potash-maker of that name who was buried at Ticehurst in 1588, and whose will was witnessed by Harry Catchelow, the man baptised at Cranbrook in 1565, who was also of immigrant descent. John Humfrey wished his daughter Grace's son, John a'Nocke, to make her a jointure out of his lands in Burwash parish called Sluffames. He made his wife Parnell and younger son George residuary legatees and executors. To his elder son John, who was perhaps following his father's trade, he bequeathed ten sacks of beech ash (each sack of 200 pounds) and 3 or 400 bushels of ash at Mountfield in Richard Cresse's hands, though out of this quantity 400 of 'eled' (presumably processed) ash, together with £1 10s 0d, was to go to Braband, also a member of the immigrant community.[697]

Reynold Humfrey of Horsmonden's baptismal name suggests he could have been of immigrant descent. His children Margery and Abraham were baptised at Horsmonden in 1572 and 1575, and Robert was baptised at Brenchley in 1579. Reynold was perhaps the father of the scythe-smith, Thomas Humfrey, whose eldest son, baptised at Horsmonden in 1590, was also named Reynold.

Thomas Humfrey had evidently found scythe-smithing lucrative. Although he must have been quite young in 1601 when he died, he was affluent enough to bequeath £50 each to his three daughters, Mary, Susan and Jane, and £100 to his youngest son John, his daughters to have their portions at 21 and his son at 24. He perhaps owed some of his wealth to his wife Jane, whom he made residuary legatee and executrix, and who was to have the profits of his messuages and lands until his sons Reynold and Thomas reached the age of 30 years. After that she was to have annuities of £3 from each of them; each son was to have a messuage, shop and barn, though Reynold was also to have Pococks and four

692. ESRO, PBT 1/1/24/120.
693. ESRO, PBT 1/5/151A.
694. KHLC, U1475 B7/1 (1542), B10/1 and 11/1 (1547 and 1548).
695. ESRO, SHE 6/1/11/1 (Westall's book of Robertsbridge, 1546).
696. TNA, PROB 11/57/35.
697. TNA, PROB 11/72/499.

other pieces of land.[698] Neither Thomas Humfrey, nor his brother George, who witnessed this will, was literate. In the event Thomas's son Reynold died aged eleven in 1602.

Neither surname, Humfrey or Umfrey, was represented in Loxfield hundred in the 1520s and it was not until the 1560s that Thomas Umfrey made an appearance in the Rotherfield parish register. He died in 1570 and the fact that sums of £10 bequeathed to his son John and wife Joan were due on obligations from John a'Kent of Withyham and John Hills of Hartfield respectively, suggests that he may have had connections with Thomas Umfrey who had been assessed on £7-worth of goods in the Hartfield hundred subsidy of 1524, rather than with the immigrant community. The Rotherfield man also had dealings further afield as is shown by the fact that £20, to be equally divided between his sons Simon and Thomas and daughter Joan, was due from Mr Fryman of Hastings. Thomas made his wife Joan residuary legatee and executrix and George Maynard was to be his overseer.[699] Thomas Umfrey is of particular interest because one of his sons became a collier.

Among the wills which survive for all three of Thomas Umfrey's sons is that of Simon Humfry of Rotherfield, collier, who died in December 1621. He made his cousin John Humfry (more probably his nephew John, his deceased brother Thomas's son) his residuary legatee and executor, and John was also to have an acre of freehold in Rotherfield held by John Homsby, and the whole profits of all Simon's lands and woods in Rotherfield in the tenure of Isaac Parkes. Simon's brother John Humfry, provided he did not contest this gift, was to have an annuity of £5. As Simon had no children of his own he left £5 to his goddaughter Elizabeth, wife of Samuel Relfe, and £2 each to the wives of Andrew Moone and William Relfe, all these women apparently being daughters of his deceased brother Thomas. He also left £2 to the wife of Christopher Hider, 10 shillings to James Bachellor's wife, who was also his goddaughter, £1 to his godson Andrew Moone, 10 shillings to his godson Nicholas Puxsted and 10 shillings to Stephen Lanckeford, whom he named his overseer.[700]

As against these comparatively modest bequests, Simon's brother Thomas Humfrye, who claimed the rank of yeoman and who had died in 1614, left goods inventoried at £298 5s 10d. He left £1 to the poor, £20 to Andrew Moone and £60 to William Relf, his sons-in-law. He left £80 to each of his daughters, the still unmarried Elizabeth, and his youngest daughter Silvester, who was also to have a little heifer. His wife Silvester was to have half the household stuff, two kine, his messuage called Lugsfoord, four acres parcel of the land called Reynolds, and an annuity of £4 during her widowhood. In addition to this his son John, whom he made his residuary legatee and executor, was to pay her an annuity of £10 for life.[701]

The third brother, John Umfrey, who died in January 1622, left £2 to the poor and made his wife Mary his residuary legatee and executrix, and his brother-in-law John Puxstie and kinsman Andrew Moone his overseers. All other bequests were to be made out of his properties. Puxstie and his wife were to have the messuage called Sheriffs in Rotherfield for 12 years, out of which they were to pay his wife an annuity of £10. His grandson John Puxstie was to have an annuity of £1 13s 4d out of seven acres in Hawkhurst granted to him by James Bachelor. The freehold in Mayfield, lately bought of John Duke, was to go to Agnes wife of Andrew Moone and six of their children. Stonebridges alias Henlies in Rotherfield, which he and his brother Thomas Umfrey had purchased was to go to the other John Umfrey (probably Thomas's son) and John was also to have the reversion of Sheriffs provided he paid various legacies totalling £100 to the Relfe, Puxstie and Hider relatives and £5 to John Olliffe of Mayfield. Otherwise Sheriffs was to remain to John Puxstie.[702]

However, there was another collier named Humfrey - Matthew Humfry, who was buried at Maresfield in 1638. He was first heard of in 1595, when his daughter Mary was baptised at Newick. A deposition made in 1598, when he was living at Fletching, shows that he had been born in Hartfield around 1562. He had lived at Newick prior to moving to Fletching around 1595.[703] His four daughters Margaret, Elizabeth, Alice and Agnes were perhaps baptised between then and 1615, when his son Thomas was baptised at Maresfield. It seems likely that one or more of these daughters was baptised

698. TNA, PROB 11/98/252.
699. ESRO, PBT 1/1/6/8.
700. TNA, PROB 11/140/21.
701. ESRO, PBT 1/1/14/201, 1/3/4/40.
702. TNA, PROB 11/139/539.
703. WSRO, EpII/5/6, f. 205.

at Fletching in 1600, 1601 and 1603, when three Humfrey children were baptised, of whom only Alice, baptised in 1600, was named, and none of whose parents was named. After leaving Newick and Fletching, Matthew had presumably moved to Maresfield by 1615 and may have remained there for the remainder of his life.

No probate record mentions Matthew, even though the wills of Richard Umfrey (1575), Edward Humphrey (1617), Richard Humphrey (1631) and Thomas Humphry (1636) of Hartfield all survive.[704] However, Hartfield was the place where his daughter Margaret married Henry Burges in 1621. Perhaps these facts suggest that he was a member of the immigrant community.

Mathew Humfrey was buried at Maresfield in October 1638. A nuncupative will expresses wishes he had made to Michael Passell and Goodman Upton. His son Thomas was to have £5, with £2 towards the finishing of his house. His daughter Margaret, wife of Henry Burges, was to have £2. His daughter Mary, wife of Robert Adams of Hamsey, husbandman, was to have £5, and the same sum was to go to his unmarried daughters Alice and Agnes. Because he had nominated no executor, administration of Humfrey's effects was assigned to Robert Adams, and since the administration bond was of only £50, the effects will have amounted to not much more than the £24, a sum sufficient to discharge these legacies.[705]

A recognizance entered for the appearance at quarter sessions of the Maresfield collier William Busse in 1649 shows that Thomas Humfry still continued at Maresfield in his father's occupation of collier.[706]

Milner

Collyn Myllner was employed as a miner and filler at Robertsbridge in 1543 and 1544. As filler he was paid 4 shillings the founday. In 1543 he was included among those workers, mostly Frenchmen, who paid for cheese.[707] He did not become a denizen and by 1546 he no longer figured among the Robertsbridge work-force. The French version of this name will possibly have been *Mounier*, *Dumoulin*, *Desmoulins* or *Moulin*.

Gerlett

Although a family named Jarlett which came from the Pays de Bray was later involved in ironworking in the western Weald, Robert Jerlett, included among Robertsbridge woodcutters in 1544, was more probably Robert Jerrett, the Englishman from Salehurst who regularly cut wood during the 1540s and 50s.

Pommy

Powmye was among the Frenchmen to whom beer was supplied at Robertsbridge in 1543, but it cannot be proved that he was the Frenchman James Pomy whose daughter Clemens was baptised at Rotherfield in 1566. James was a collier and so were at least two of his sons. Later baptismal records indicate that he was at Lamberhurst from 1570 onwards, where Lawrence, Richard and Anthony Pummy were all baptised between 1570 and 1585. The sole exception was John, son of James Pome 'collier in Henlyes', who was baptised at Frant in 1576. Lamberhurst however was part of Brenchley hundred in Kent and it was there that James Pome paid the poll tax in 1598, 1599 and 1600.

James's son John Pomey married a widow named Joan Smyth at Warbleton in 1610. Their children, Mary, John, Elizabeth and Mary, were baptised at Warbleton between 1611 and 1619. When administration of his goods, valued at £46 14s 2d, was granted to his widow Joan in 1627, he was described as John Pumy of Peasemarsh.[708] John Pomey's stepson, Robert Smith of Peasemarsh, collier, acted as bondsman for his mother.

Joan Pumme made her will in 1646, and in addition to legacies to her Gates and Ashenden

704. ESRO, PBT 1/1/7/48 (1575), 1/1/16/7 (1617), 1/1/21/134 (1631), 1/1/24/134 (1636).
705. ESRO, PBT 1/1/25/188a, 1/3/7/126.
706. ESRO, QR 82, m. 39.
707. KHLC, U1475 B2/2, B7/3.
708. ESRO, PBT 1/3/5/324.

grandchildren, left £15 to her son Thomas Pummy, and five-year annuities of £1 to Margery Pummey and John Pummey, whom she described as her daughter-in-law and son-in-law. She made her son Robert Smith her residuary legatee and executor, and appointed as her overseer her landlord Thomas Theobull, who was probably of immigrant descent.[709]

John Pummy II had married Agnes Holland at Peasemarsh in 1634 and baptismal entries indicate their continued residence in that parish. However he perhaps moved on to Bexhill, where two of John Pummy's daughters were baptised in 1643 and 1646.

Richard Pummey, who had been baptised at Lamberhurst early in 1580, was next encoun-tered at Heathfield, where his son John was baptised in 1615. However, in 1617, as a Heathfield forgeman, he was in trouble with quarter sessions over the alleged receipt of stolen haberdashery.[710] He apparently moved on to Whatlington, but it was at Mountfield that his son Richard was baptised in 1619, and his first wife Denise was buried in 1622. When he married his second wife Margaret Worger, a Laughton widow, in 1625, he was described in the marriage licence as a Laughton collier.[711] His daughters Joan and Elizabeth were baptised at Laughton in 1628 and 1630, but Elizabeth died in infancy; his son Abraham was buried at Laughton in 1632 and another son Mark was baptised there in 1633. No further baptisms occurred and it appears he had died before 1637, in which year his widow married William Pup.

Anthony Pummey, baptised at Lamberhurst in 1585, married Margery Starr at Burwash in 1617. He was perhaps the Anthony Pummell whose daughter Mary was baptised at Northiam in 1618. His wife was possibly one of the two Pummey burials which occurred at Burwash in 1621 and 1622, because in 1625 he married his second wife Dorothy Chapman at Laughton. Their daughter Jane was baptised in 1626, but survived only a year. In a deposition of 1635 Anthony Pommy described himself as a collier.[712] He correctly stated that he had been born in Lamberhurst in Kent, but gave his age as 58, whilst the parish register suggests he was only 49. He claimed to have lived at Laughton for 10 years and to be worth £5 'in his own goods, debts paid'. He was not literate. He was buried at Laughton early in 1643.

James Poomy, whose baptism occurred perhaps during the ten-year gap in the Lamberhurst parish register from 1585 onwards, married Elizabeth Norden at Warbleton in 1617. Their son James was baptised at Burwash in 1620. No further baptisms appear to be recorded and James's wife Elizabeth was buried at Burwash in 1637.

Another member of the family whose baptism has not been found, perhaps also because of the gap in Lamberhurst parish register, was Peter Pummy, whose son John was baptised at Mountfield in 1631.

Herston

Guyllam Herston and the English-born Alexander Vyntam were assistants to Cardo (Boyle?), a finer at Robertsbridge in 1543.[713] The baptismal name suggests that Herston was of French nationality or descent and because the surname is not otherwise known in the Weald, he could have returned to France. However, the name could be a variant of Herichon, rendered as Harrison in the case of the duke of Norfolk's employee Reynold Harrison. If this were so and he did indeed return to France, he could be Guillaume Herychon who in 1554 was a landholder at Beaussault.[714]

Barnet

This name occurs in France in the form *Bernard* or *Bénard*, and in the sixteenth century a family named Bénard, sometimes Bénard *dit* Collart, was among the bourgeois families of Neufchâtel- en-Bray, where its members included brewers, drapers and shoemakers.[715] No member of it can be shown to have been

709. TNA, PROB 11/200/387.

710. ESRO, QR 17, m. 6.

711. Dunkin, *Sussex Marriage Licences, Lewes 1586-1643*, p. 147.

712. WSRO, EpII,5/14, f. 82.

713. KHLC, U1475 B2/2.

714. ADSM, 2 E 14/83/2 (31 Mar 1554).

715. Jehan Benard dict Collard, brewer, p. Saint-Pierre (ADSM, 2 E 14/1187 (1 Sept. 1542)); Guillaume Bernard, cordwainer, p. Saint-Jacques (ADSM, 2 E 14/1189 (24 Jul 1545)); Jehan Benard, draper (1554),

connected with iron.

In Sussex the subsidy rolls of 1524 showed two Robert Bernets in Henhurst hundred and Thomas Barnet in Staple hundred. However, Robert Barnet, who cut wood for Panningridge Furnace in 1546 and 1550,[716] was probably Robert Barnet of Warbleton, who married Ellen Browne, niece of Clement Huggett, in 1562. He owed suit of court to the manor of Battle for land at Bucksteep in Warbleton.

A man named Thomas Barnard lived in Middleborough at Battle during the 1580s and was fined 2 pence for default at the Battle view of frankpledge held in April 1584. Also mentioned in Battle was the finer, John Barnarde, for whose appearance at quarter sessions the Battle founder Peter Barnarde was a surety in 1595. This finer cannot be connected with the Warbleton man, whose son John died in infancy in 1565. Nor, in the absence of a sixteenth-century parish register for Battle, is it possible to determine whether these two ironworkers were related to the Middleborough Thomas Barnard. They may well have been connected with the Sedlescombe collier, John Barnet, who appeared with others before quarter sessions in 1595 for the theft of stockings at Ewhurst.[717]

There is no evidence to show that these men were of French descent. However, they were quite probably related to later Barnets in the Midlands. A daughter of 'Barnet of the neither (nether) Hamber' was baptised at Wombourne in 1610, and the hammer in question was probably Swindon Forge on the Smestow Brook north of Stourbridge. The name had appeared at Wombourne earlier with Bennet Barnet in 1600, and Thomas Barnet was married there in 1605. Mary the wife of Humphrey Barnet was buried at Wombourne in 1608. The family persisted in the area and a century and a half later a slitter of iron named John Barnett married Ann Burton at Kinver early in 1762.

The family appeared in the Mucklestone parish register in north Staffordshire almost equally early, presumably in connection with Winnington Forge, but Humphrey and Elizabeth Barnet the baptism of whose son was recorded in 1670 were of Norton Forge.

Daniell

The surname occurred at Chiddingly and Ninfield in the Sussex subsidy rolls of the 1520s, but not in the High Weald east of Horsham. So 'Daniell', who was paid 4 shillings in 1550 for cutting 13½ cords of wood for Panningridge Furnace out of Cops Wood in 1550,[718] could quite well have been a native of Ninfield. Nor, on the other hand, does it seem likely that the alien Nicholas Daniell, who paid the poll tax in the Lowey of Tonbridge in the same year was connected with iron, especially as he was recorded as living 'in the towne'.

However, Daniell Collyer, who paid the poll tax at Worth in Buttinghill hundred in 1563, was certainly an alien. No person with the baptismal name Daniel can be found in the Worth parish register of the 1560s and 1570s, so it seems possible that he was a collier who bore the surname Daniell.

This is rendered more probable by the fact that a Wisborough Green collier of the following century was surnamed Daniell. A writ of arrest was issued for Nicholas Daniell of Wisborough Green, collier, in 1659.[719] He was possibly the son of Philip Daniel baptised at Pulborough in October 1635.

However, Mary, the wife of an earlier Philip Danyell who lived at Ticehurst, had been called on to give evidence in an assize case in 1602.[720] Mary Danyell was buried at Ticehurst in 1619 and her husband Philip in 1635. No connection with the Wisborough Green collier has so far been proved, but because the baptismal name Philip was at the time rather unusual, some connection seems possible.

Around 1578 Robert Daniell of Wartling, yeoman, served as clerk at Panningridge Furnace. In 1586 he claimed to have been born in Ripe about 50 years earlier and the 1524 subsidy roll revealed an earlier Robert Daniell at Wilmington, so the clerk was almost certainly of English ancestry. By 1586 he had lived in Wartling for about five years, before which he had lived at Ashburnham for four years, presumably from around 1577 to 1581, the years when he must be supposed to have worked at

merchant draper (1568) (ADSM, 2 E 14/1194 (23 Feb 1553/4); 2 E 14/1212 (20 Apr 1568)).

716. HEH, BA Vol. 27 (Westall's book of Panningridge 1546); Crossley, *Sidney ironworks accounts*, pp. 83-7 (1550).

717. HEH, BA Vol. 97 f 32; ESRO, QR 6, mm. 13 and 61; I am indebted to Brian Phillips for these references.

718. Crossley, *Sidney ironworks accounts*, p. 86.

719. ESRO, QR 124, m. 139; I am indebted to Brian Phillips for this reference.

720. Cockburn, *Sussex Assize records, Elizabeth I*, no. 2070.

Panningridge. Earlier he had lived in Wartling for 15 years, presumably from 1562 to 1577.[721] However, there were no entries for him in either Wartling or Ashburnham parish registers, so he was perhaps unmarried.

It was in 1572 that a certain 'Mr Danyell' amended Sir Thomas Gresham's furnace for him. The furnace was at Mayfield and two men surnamed Daniel, Gilbert who married Alice Denysse in 1578, and William who married Tamesyn Treate in 1582, probably lived in Mayfield parish at the time. Both were apparently the sons of Gilbert Danyell of Framfield, who had married Elizabeth Swane there in 1545, and had also been buried at Framfield in 1558. Chronologically, either of these men, or even the Panningridge clerk, could have amended Gresham's furnace, but there seems to be no reason why any one of them should have been styled 'Master Danyell'.

Work as an ironworks clerk demanded literacy, rather than technical expertise; furthermore Danyell was known to Lord Burleigh, and Gresham desired his Lordship 'to geve hym your thanckes on my behalf'.[722] A man who according to the Ashburnham parish register did have reason to be called 'Master Daniel' was Mr Edmund Daniell who in 1541 married Mistress Alice Ashburnham. Perhaps he gained some knowledge of ironfounding whilst at Ashburnham.

The next Daniels to appear on the scene were certainly ironfounders and their location suggests a possible connection with the Worth collier of 1563. John Daniel of Horsham was founder at Gosden Furnace during the late 1590s and testified in September 1602, in a dispute about the quantity and quality of cast iron produced, that during his third year (1598?) he had cast 110 tons 6 cwt of sows.[723] He gave his age as around 40, and would have been born around 1562, so he cannot have been the son of either Gilbert Daniel, the elder of whom died in 1558 and the younger of whom married only in 1578.

The ironfounder could have been the son of the curate of East Grinstead, who had a son named John Daniell baptised in 1563; the name of the curate was not disclosed in the parish register, but he could have been Gresham's 'Master Daniel'; how a curate could have gained a knowledge of blast furnaces remains a problem, though Parson Levett seems to have had no problem.

The ironfounder John Daniel had six children, John, Mary, another John, Walter, Thomas and James, baptised at Horsham between 1595 and 1609, but plague struck the family in September 1610, killing Mary and three of their children. As their first child had died ten years earlier, from this substantial family only Mary, who married Francis Booker in 1619, and Walter survived. Walter Daniell married Mary Botting at Nuthurst in 1628 and four of his children were baptised there before 1641. Walter's father however had moved to Cowden and was buried there in 1631. John Daniell made bequests totalling £85 to Francis Booker of Horsham, and bequeathed £160 and his lands to Walter, whom he appointed his residuary legatee and executor.[724] John Daniell's money was all in other men's hands, £5 of it being held by Edward and John Wickenden.

It seems certain that Robert Daniell who married Mary Wickenden at Cowden in 1629 was related to John in some way and was perhaps an ironfounder too. Robert's eldest daughter Mary, baptised in 1630, married John Jarret in 1650, and his eldest surviving son Edward, baptised in 1634, became an East Grinstead ironfounder and married Mercy Desper of Cowden, from the immigrant family of pot-founders of that name, at East Grinstead in 1657.

Bannson

The otherwise unknown collier Lewes Bannson was paid £2 12s 6d for coaling 42 loads of wood out of Highwood for Panningridge Furnace in May 1550. The surname is reminiscent of Gieuffroy Bonnechon of Nesle, a rent charge on whom was among others which were sold in 1491 by Jehan Bourse of Hodeng to the ironmaster Viane de Malinguehen.[725]

721. WSRO, EpII/5/3, f. 93.
722. J. W. Burgon, *Life and times of Sir Thomas Gresham*, **2**, pp. 425-6.
723. TNA, REQ 2/166/46.
724. TNA, PROB 11/160/716.
725. ADSM, 2 E 14/1153 (10 Jan 1510).

IMMIGRANTS NAMED IN PROBATE RECORDS

Gilham

From his will of January 1546 it appears that Gilbert Ungle of Ardingly had a kinsman named Richard Guylham and a godson named Gilbert who was Richard Guylham's son. A reference in the will to Ungle's hereditaments in Kent, which he reserved to his daughter Anne, still a minor in 1546, indicates that he originated from Kent.[726]

Gilbert Gillam's son John, who was baptised at Ardingly in January 1565, survived only six weeks. Gilbert was not again mentioned in the Ardingly parish register, but was probably Guilbert Guillam who was buried at Ifield in 1615. Richard Gillam, the elder, stayed at Ardingly, was buried there in April 1582, and administration of his goods, valued at £5 6s 4d, was granted to his son Gilbert on 19 May.[727]

However, an entry in the Ardingly parish register for the burial of John, the infant son of John Gillam 'of the fornace', in December 1565 reveals that the father was French. John Gillam, founder, again figured in the parish register in January 1567, when another son of his named John, who 'died bringing to church', was baptised and buried on the same day. The founder was undoubtedly John Gillam of Awewell whose wife Joan was buried in February 1571. In 1572 he paid the poll tax in Danehill Horsted hundred. When he married a widow, Annis Beldame, in February 1572, and again when he was buried in February 1573, it was noted that this French ironfounder John Gillam was the eldest son of Richard Gillam. Before John Gillam died, his son named William had been baptised in January 1573; in January 1575 his widow Annis took as her third husband Nicholas Bankes.

It therefore appears that despite Richard Gillam's being kin to Gilbert Ungle, his eldest son was French, presumably born before his father came to England. The kinship with Gilbert Ungle must have sprung from a marriage which occurred after Richard Gillam's arrival in England; either Gillam took as his second wife a relative of Ungle, or Ungle's wife Dorothy, whom he made his residuary legatee, was related to Gillam.

William, the son of the ironfounder John Gillam, was perhaps the William Gillam who married Agnes Tankerell at Ashburnham in 1611. Their children, John and Elizabeth, of whom John did not survive, were baptised at Bexhill in 1615 and 1617. Sadly, the mother survived the baptism of her daughter by only ten days and William Gillam himself died early in 1618. Administration of his goods, valued at £11 16s 9d, was granted to a creditor, William Levett, a Bexhill husbandman, during the minority of the infant Elizabeth.[728]

Richard Gillam's second son named John Gillam, presumably English-born, married Prudence Freeman in 1568. In the period before the ironfounder's death the parish register carefully distinguished John Gillam the younger, from John Gillam the elder. The younger John Gillam's children, Joan, Annis, Richard, Thomas, Mary, Edmond, another Mary, and John, were baptised from 1569 to 1585, though John, and presumably the first Mary, did not survive infancy. His wife Prudence was buried in 1588.

It appears that the younger John Gillam married again because another son of his named John was baptised at Ardingly in 1595. However, his second marriage was not recorded at Ardingly and after 1595 no further entries for the family occurred in that parish register. He was described as an Ardingly labourer in February 1596, when Gerard Gatland gave surety to give evidence against him at the assizes.[729] He was probably the John Gillam who was buried at Maresfield in 1612, and his eldest daughter Joan may have been buried there early in 1606. If so, his widow Mary married Thomas Warner at Maresfield early in 1614.

John Gillam's son Richard, baptised early in 1574, was possibly the Hartfield collier, who was indicted for various crimes, including vagrancy, at the assizes in 1593.[730] He was found guilty, but successfully claimed benefit of clergy. He was perhaps the Richard Gilham who married Mary Tye at Horsted Keynes in 1605, and whose daughters Jane, Elizabeth and Mary were baptised there from 1606

726. ESRO, PBT 1/1/1/87.
727. ESRO, PBT 1/3/1/106.
728. ESRO, PBT 1/3/4/172.
729. Cockburn, *Sussex Assize records, Elizabeth I*, no. 1631.
730. Ibid, nos. 1405, 1471.

to 1610. Elizabeth married John Trendle of Worth in 1635 and in April 1639, Mary Gilham married Anthony Ellis of Cuckfield, son of the former Fletching hammerman Anthony Ellis, who died later in the same year.

Richard Gilham appears to have been joined at Horsted Keynes by his younger brother Edmund Gilham. The other brother Thomas married Elizabeth Sandkin at Rotherfield in 1605 and their children, Marie, John, Ellinor and Anne, were baptised at Rotherfield between 1607 and 1613. Thomas Gillam had established himself at Fletching by 1619, when a child of his was baptised there. He was buried at Fletching in 1632 and in February 1633 administration of his goods, valued at £302 9s 0d, was granted to his widow and his son John.[731] It should be noted that Elizabeth Sandkin was clearly descended from the Sandequin family of Le Becquet Forge.

The Chiddingfold blacksmith William Gillam who died in 1609 was born at Horsham in 1568, the son of William Gwyllm. Other children of Gwyllm or Gwlam were George, Clemens and Joseph, who were baptised at Horsham from 1570 to 1574.

By 1596 this family was in Chiddingfold, where George the son of William Gillam the elder was buried in 1600, and where Clemence married Thomas Harding in 1606. The younger William Gillam's children were Clemence, Richard, Marie, Joseph and an unnamed child, all baptised between 1596 and 1605, whilst his son John, who was presumably baptised before the family arrived in Chiddingfold, was buried there in 1607.

Joseph Gillam married Joan Capelin in 1597 and their children, Jackemon, George, Christopher, Joan, Thomas, Margaret and William, were baptised between 1598 and 1607. Joseph married his second wife Mary Carpenter in 1611 and their daughters, Margaret and Marie, were baptised in 1612 and 1618. Joseph Gillam was buried in 1622.

The name Jackemon suggests that this family may well also have been of French origin, and the elder William Gwyllm could have been another son of the Ardingly Richard Gillam.

The family was first noticed in South Yorkshire in 1667, when entries concerning Giles Gillam commenced in the Sheffield parish register. His two sons George and Giles were baptised at Sheffield in 1667 and 1669, followed by three daughters, Margaret, Mary and Gertrude, who were baptised at Rotherham from 1672 to 1678, of whom Gertrude did not survive infancy.

The name Gillam was new to Sheffield and its arrival there must have been connected with the iron industry, but it is difficult to connect the family with the Weald, because Giles was not a baptismal name used by the Wealden family in the pre-Civil War period. George was used by the Horsham/ Chiddingfold family, but it appears that George Gillam, baptised at Horsham in 1570 and buried at Chiddingfold in 1600, never married. Otherwise, George son of John Gilham of West Hoathly, baptised at Horsted Keynes early in 1625, was the first example of this name. His father was mentioned earlier at West Hoathly, where John son of John and Hester Gyllam was baptised in 1622.

Giles Gilham II's children, Giles, George and John, were baptised at Sheffield between 1696 and 1702. George's baptismal entry in 1699 shows that Giles Gilham II was an Attercliffe forgeman; the record of the apprenticeship of his son John to a filesmith, Luke Hellifield, a member of the Company of Cutlers in Hallamshire, shows that in 1714 he was a hammerman at Attercliffe Forge.[732]

Giles Gillam III, forgeman at Stone, or Roach Abbey Forge in Laughton-en-le-Morthen, who married Margaret Thompson of Tinsley at Rotherham in 1723, was presumably the eldest son of Giles Gillam II. Their children, Giles IV, Sophia and Hannah were baptised at Laughton from 1724 to 1727. Their son Matthias, who was apprenticed to Robert Powell in 1750, was presumably born around 1738.

The second son of Giles Gillam II will have been George Gillam I, another Attercliffe hammerman, who married Rhoda Oates [Oakes?] at Sheffield in 1724. Their children, Elizabeth, Betty, John, George and Giles, were baptised at Sheffield from 1724 to 1730, followed by Sarah, Samuel, Mary, Esther, Jonathan and Alice, baptised at Attercliffe chapel from 1731 to 1740, but of these children Elizabeth, Sarah and Samuel failed to survive infancy. In 1739 the eldest son John was apprenticed to a cutler named Edward Oakes, who was perhaps related to his mother. Jonathan was apprenticed to a scissorsmith named John Gillam, possibly his own eldest brother, in 1753.

The forgeman George Gillam II whose daughters, Hannah, Sarah and Martha, were baptised at Attercliffe between 1752 and 1759, was presumably the son of the hammerman George Gillam I,

731. ESRO, PBT 1/3/6/145.

732. For this and later apprenticeships see Leader, *Company of Cutlers in Hallamshire*, **2**, p. 214.

baptised at Sheffield in 1728.

The filesmith John Gillam, son of Giles Gillam II, married Martha Bright in 1727 and their children, Darcy, Hannah, Margaret, Charles, Rhoda and Mary were baptised at Sheffield from 1728 to 1737, though Darcy and Charles did not survive infancy. Mary and George, children of John Gillam, the scissorsmith, were baptised in 1746 and 1749.

That at least one branch of this family continued in the iron industry in the Sheffield area into the nineteenth century was shown by the baptism at Tinsley in September 1817 of Charles the son of George Gillham of Brightside, forgeman, and Hannah his wife. George Gillam had married Hannah Copley at Ecclesfield in 1805.

8

WEALDEN IRON TO ITS ZENITH AND BEYOND ITS BORDERS, 1551-1575

HISTORICAL SETTING

Government impoverishment, which characterised the reign of Edward VI, continued in that of his sister Mary I. Her Catholic faith and her marriage in 1554 to Charles V's son Philip drastically reduced the danger from abroad, so there was no pressing incentive for the Crown to call for the renewed production of guns. The abdication of Charles V in 1556 resulted in the succession of Mary's husband to both the Spanish throne and to the former Burgundian possessions in the Netherlands. The consequent English involvement in war with France was to Spain's advantage rather than to her own and ended in the loss of Calais.

Somewhat surprisingly, the return to Protestantism after the accession of Elizabeth I in 1558 brought little immediate change. Following the conclusion of peace between France and Spain in 1559, each country became embroiled in internal religious problems. In France the Religious Wars lasted for the remainder of the century. Spain's initial problem was with its own Moorish population, something finally resolved with the expulsion of the *Moriscos* from the country in 1607, but the revolt of the Netherlands, which commenced in 1567, lasted, with short-lived intermissions, as a running sore until the end of the Thirty Years' War in 1648.

On the other hand, the Heroic period of Elizabeth's reign was slow to take off. The destiny of the country as a great trading nation – Napoleon's 'Nation of Shopkeepers' – was not capable of immediate or rapid realisation. It was the sack in 1576 by unpaid and mutinous Spanish troops of Antwerp, the city which had replaced Bruges as the great entrepot of the north, that opened up for London, and later for Amsterdam, the commercial opportunities they needed. It was from Antwerp that the future forgemaster Sir Thomas Gresham, for long Elizabeth's agent there, obtained for her in 1559 the loan of £200,000 with which she financed the reform of the coinage. And Gresham's building of the Royal Exchange, opened by Elizabeth I herself in 1570, was a symbol of London's accession to financial power.

Perhaps it was the vicissitudes of her youth that made Elizabeth embrace, like her grandfather, the habits of caution and frugality. She brought an end to intervention in French affairs, and, by finally renouncing all claim to Calais in 1564, secured a payment of 220,000 crowns. The Scottish border was made safe after Mary Queen of Scots' flight to England in 1567, by Elizabeth's decision to imprison Mary, a measure which enjoyed the approval of the Protestant party in Scotland.

But this move further estranged Elizabeth from Philip II of Spain, and to placate him she delayed expressing support for the Protestants of the Netherlands until 1577. It was not until 1585 that English troops were actually committed there. That move, and Mary's execution in 1587, guaranteed the open hostility of Philip and the sailing of the Spanish Armada in 1588.

Until the mid-1580s there was therefore no crisis of military unpreparedness, such as that of 1538, to stimulate acquisition of cast-iron guns by the Ordnance. In any case, the formation in 1565 of the Company of Mines Royal and in 1568 of the Mineral and Battery Society, both intended to exploit the copper resources of the country, made the production of bronze guns a cheaper undertaking than it had been for Henry VIII. And William Winter, who had become Master of the Naval Ordnance in 1557, had no plans to equip his ships with other than bronze ordnance. The inventory of naval guns drawn up in 1558 showed 322 tons of bronze as against 56 tons of cast-iron guns on ship board and in store. By the 1570s the proportion was even less, with only four out of 24 vessels carrying cast-iron ordnance; their iron guns comprised just 8 sakers and 8 minions.[1]

William Levett had died in 1554, and Elizabeth waited a year before bestowing on his former assistant Ralph Hogge an appointment for life as Queen's gunstonemaker, with a fee of 6 pence a day,

1. Teesdale, *Gunfounding in the Weald*, p. 30.

in November 1559. Although the appointment was backdated to Christmas 1557,[2] it is clear that no immediate urgency was felt by the Crown in this matter and that, given the naval policy of the time, the concern will have been for the supply of cast-iron shot rather than of guns.

Demand for cast-iron guns from other sources cannot have been great before 1570. Throughout the whole quarter of a century now under consideration a small quantity of ordnance, estimated by Teesdale at just a few tons a year, may have gone into merchant ships in which old wrought-iron guns were replaced with guns of cast iron.[3] Because of increasing trade to Africa and the Levant, where the Barbary corsairs were making their presence felt, this demand though small was probably fairly constant.

Guns in more significant quantities would have been required for new merchant ships, but large ones were few in number until around 1570. Merchant ships of over 100 tons burden are thought to have numbered 77 around 1560, 84 in 1572, 135 in 1577, and 177 in 1582. The insignificant increase during the 1560s was later transformed by a government bounty of 5 shillings a ton on the construction of larger vessels, of which 70, totalling 12,630 tons, were built between 1572 and 1579. On this basis Teesdale calculated that from 1570 to 1585 new shipping might have required around 130 tons of ordnance a year.[4]

The impact of the revolt of the Netherlands came around the same time. In 1569 William the Silent issued his first 18 letters of marque to the privateers named 'Beggars of the Sea'; by the following year their numbers had grown to over 80 vessels. Initially they provisioned themselves with supplies of food and arms in England, but the constant importunities of Philip II caused Elizabeth to close England's ports to them in 1572. The audacious Beggars at once seized the port of Brill and proceeded to hold it against all efforts of the Spaniards to dislodge them, a first success in the long struggle for the autonomy of the United Provinces. And it is certain that even after 1572 Wealden guns managed to get through to the Dutch in one way or another in considerable quantities.

If the Crown ceased to be a major player in the expansion of the iron industry, members of the nobility, especially those who had profited from the Dissolution of the Monasteries, took its place. This was especially the case with those who were members of the king's council, such as John Dudley, who had been created earl of Warwick at the outset of Edward VI's reign. Having secured the deposition of Edward Seymour, duke of Somerset, who had been Lord Protector during the first two years of Edward VI's reign, Dudley became the head of the Council of Regency and had himself made duke of Northumberland, one of the many titles vacant by attainder at this time.

In September 1550, in exchange for property sold to the king, Dudley obtained the grant of the castle and manor of Tonbridge, formerly belonging to Tonbridge Priory but in the king's hand due to Wolsey's attainder, and also of the parks of Postern and Cage, formerly possessions of the attainted duke of Buckingham. The following July further property, the parks of Northfryth and Southfryth, became his too.[5] On these lands Vauxhall Furnace and the Postern Forge were then built.

Following Dudley's attainder and execution in 1553 his estates passed to the Crown, and it was not until Elizabeth's reign that his sons, the earls of Warwick and Leicester, resumed an interest in ironworking, Warwick through his post as Master of the Armouries, and Leicester because the exploitation of wood on his Shropshire estates led to the building of a blast furnace at Cleobury Mortimer.

Another member of Edward VI's council was Sir William Paget, the son of a Wednesbury nailer. His Cannock Wood estate was the site of the earliest blast furnace in Staffordshire. And Sir Henry Sidney, who succeeded his father as forgemaster in Sussex in 1553, was appointed Lord President of the Council of the Marches of Wales in 1559; by 1564 he had established a blast furnace at Tongwynlais in the Taff valley near Cardiff, perhaps the earliest in Wales.

A magnate more involved in the industry than even these was George earl of Shrewsbury, who not only acted as steward of the earl of Leicester's west-midlands estates,[6] but on his own account erected blast furnaces at Shifnal in Shropshire in 1564, near Sheffield in Yorkshire, probably in 1573,

2. *Calendar of Patent rolls, Elizabeth I*, **1**, p. 42.
3. Teesdale, *Gunfounding in the Weald*, p. 33.
4. Ibid., pp. 33, 50.
5. *Calendar of Patent Rolls, Edward VI*, **3**, pp. 277, 364-6.
6. S. Adams, 'Robert Dudley, Earl of Leicester and the west midlands', *Midland History*, **20** (1995), p. 36.

and at Whitchurch in Monmouthshire by 1575.

POLITICS AND IRONWORKS ON THE CONTINENT

In September 1555 the Peace of Augsburg ended Charles V's unsuccessful struggle to stifle the spread of protestantism in Germany, after which the Emperor proceeded to Brussels and in October resigned his kingdom of Spain and his dominions in the Netherlands to his son Philip II. Charles's efforts to shore up the position of the Catholic church in his dominions had always been tempered by political realism, but his son's religious bigotry would not countenance any temporisation. And whereas Charles had been born in the Netherlands, Philip, who could not speak Flemish, was there perceived as a foreigner, who in 1559 returned to Spain, never to visit the Low Countries again.

The regent of the Netherlands, Philip's half-sister Margaret of Parma, and her ministers were competent enough, but Philip kept significant decisions in his own hands and was unwilling to listen to any advice which ran counter to his instincts and prejudices. In concluding the peace of Cateau-Cambrésis in 1559, both Philip and Henri II of France embraced the opportunity that it would give them to combat religious dissent at home. A more inflexible regime in the Netherlands and a more secure one in those parts of Germany which were protestant, led to increased numbers of religious refugees leaving the Netherlands, a flow which became a flood with the arrival of the Duke of Alva's army there in 1567, Margaret of Parma's resignation, and the execution by order of Alva's Council of Troubles, better known as the 'Council of Blood', of counts Egmont and Hoorn and a great many others.

That same year a party of refugees, who included Johann Radlo, the former mayor of Limburg, set up the ironworks at Müllenborn in the central Eifel.[7] Further south, beyond the Mosel, the parish register of the local protestant community at Birkenfeld in the Hunsrück commenced in 1568 and that for nearby Achtelsbach in 1572. At Birkenfeld the names of numerous Walloon workers at the Abentheuer furnace, traditionally started in 1499 by *Meister* Hans and his son Mathes from Eisenschmitt in the Eifel, were now recorded.[8] This was an 'Adventure' indeed for those ironworkers who left Wallonia.

In 1569 Johannes Eisenschmitt, 'the old Master', the Walloon (*der Welsch*), married Eva the daughter of Nikolaus Helleisen 'at the Abentheuer'. His mother, Katharina Eisenschmidt, and his brother, Hans Caspar Eisenschmidt, both died in 1576; he himself died in 1613 and his wife in 1611. Three children of 'Old Eisenschmitt' who were first mentioned around 1605, were Niklaus, who died of the plague in 1633, another Hans Caspar, who died in 1632, and Anna, who in 1606 married *der welsche Meister*, Johannes *Formenmacher* (mould-maker).

Caspar Barth, commonly called *Welsch* Caspar, a pot-moulder (*Döppenformer*), was first mentioned in 1573 and died at the age of 78 in April 1607. A collier named Lorentz Buss, from Remsfels was mentioned in 1574, but died the following year. Other Walloon colliers were Kilian Burgo (1601), and Johannes Friedrich from Arlon in Luxembourg (1612). The places of origin of three other workers were indicated, all of them straddling the border between Wallonia and the Eifel; they were Paulus Eisenchmitt from Schleiden, who was mentioned in 1560 and died in 1610, Wilhelm, a founder (*Schmelzer*) from Monschau (*Montjoie*), mentioned in 1587, and Heinrich Beyer, *vulgo Welsch*, from Stavelot (*Stablo*), mentioned in 1605.[9] Of them *Meister* Paulus is known to have been an Anabaptist.[10]

The Frankfurt-am-Main area was one to which many refugees were drawn, in what has been described as a mass-emigration. Hans Caspar, whose family came from Liège, and in all probability from Sart in Franchimont, was a refugee first known to have worked at the Michelstadt ironworks in the Odenwald, south of Frankfurt. Heinrich Caspar, who was perhaps his brother, had formerly worked in the Saarbrücken area. By the 1580s both were working in ironworks north of Frankfurt and in 1584, Heinrich, who had married a widow from the city, became one of Frankfurt's burghers.[11]

There followed an explosion of furnace-building in the Nassau-Dillenburg area north of Frankfurt, which can best be explained by the need of the Dutch for matériel to support their war of

7. Neu, *Eisenindustrie in der Eifel*, p. 149.
8. Böcking, *Abentheuer*, pp. 16-17.
9. Ibid., pp. 17, 138-140.
10. Neu, *Eisenindustrie in der Eifel*, pp. 89, 165.
11. Schubert, *Vom Ursprung und Werden der Buderus'schen Eisenwerke*, **1**, pp. 56-8.

independence against Spain. In the Netherlands all the ironworking areas were firmly in Spanish hands or belonged to the prince-archbishop of Liège. It was in his native Dillenburg, with his younger brother, John count of Nassau-Dillenburg that William the Silent, prince of Orange-Nassau, sought refuge in April 1567, just prior to Alva's arrival. There he gathered men, arms, and financial help to prepare for his return to the Netherlands. His early efforts came to nothing, but encouraged by the capture of Brill by the Beggars of the Sea and their subsequent seizure of Flushing, the Prince made his return in July 1572, and was at once acclaimed Stadtholder by eight towns of Holland. He established himself at Delft, and there he lived until his murder in 1584, despite all the vicissitudes which intervened.

The Saarbrücken branch of the house of Nassau, like the Dillenburg branch, traced its descent from Henry count of Nassau who died in 1251. The production of guns or gunstones in 1514 at Wiebelskirchen near Ottweiler in Nassau-Saarbrücken has been mentioned. Ten kilometres west of Saarbrücken, the town of Geislautern, also within the bounds of Nassau-Saarbrücken, was the site of a blast furnace (*Schmeltz*) first mentioned in 1572.[12] It could have been at Geislautern that Heinrich Caspar worked before his move east across the Rhine. From Geislautern, or from other furnaces near Saarbrücken, cannon shot could as easily be shipped to Holland down the Moselle and the Rhine, as it later was from the Dillenburg area itself down the Rhine.

In 1581 Heinrich Caspar was at Vockenhausen near Eppstein, just west of Frankfurt, a furnace which belonged to the electoral bishop of Mainz, where he and Wilhelm Wilken, whose origin is not known, worked as stove-founders (*Ofengiesser*). Before 1589 both Hans and Heinrich Caspar had moved further north: in February 1588 Hans Caspar joined another stove-founder, Heinrich Olivy, who came from Spa in Franchimont, and Wilhelm von Liere, in the construction of a *hoher Giessofen*[13] and a *Hammer* near Wetterfeld in the county of Solms-Laubach; Heinrich Caspar had worked firstly at a furnace at Landenhausen, secondly in the county of Solms, possibly at Kraft-Solms, and in 1589 he joined his brother Christian Caspar, a pot-founder, in building a furnace at Weinähr, 5km east of Nassau in Nassau-Orange territory. This he left in 1590, following a dispute with his brother over the first year's accounts. After living in Nassau for five years he built a new furnace in 1595 at Dillhausen north of Weilburg, again on Nassau-Orange land. This works was laid down in 1606, after which Caspar lived in retirement at Biskirchen on the Ulm.[14]

The division of the greater Nassau estates was complicated and Nassau-Saarbrücken still had properties east of the Rhine on which the furnace at Emmershausen in the Weil valley was built in 1599. Ebersbach Furnace built in 1587, Oberscheld built in 1589, Hirzenhain built in 1608 and Fellerdilln built in 1609, all belonged to Nassau-Dillenburg; the Weinähr and Dillhausen furnaces built, as we have seen, in 1589 and 1595, and Bad Ems built in 1600, belonged to Nassau-Orange; the furnace at Kraftsolms which is shown by a dated stove plate to go back to at least 1585, and that of Asslar, built in 1587, which produced both guns and shot, was built for Konrad, count of Solms, but passed to his fifth son, Count William of Solms-Greifenstein, who became son-in-law to John, count of Nassau-Dillenburg.[15]

Whilst the furnaces towards the south of the region, at which Walloons played a leading role, specialised in the production of a fluid cast iron from which stove plates and pots were cast, those in the north, where workers of German nationality from Westphalia and Waldeck were employed, produced mainly sow iron for conversion at the forge. And the furnaces in both areas produced munitions, but whereas the Walloon furnaces produced only shot, those in the north produced both shot and guns, the casting of the latter a technique which they had apparently acquired in Westphalia, presumably in the service of the Catholic elector-archbishop of Cologne, and in Waldeck, whose count had earlier been bishop of Münster.

Only a few accounts showing what was produced at these furnaces have survived. The following can be cited: in 1598 at Audenschmiede Count Louis of Nassau-Saarbücken placed an order for 101 cannon balls, with a total weight of over two tonnes (40 *Zentner*), therefore intended for large 40-pounder guns. At Asslar where Johannes Hüttenhenn, a man from Siegen who had gained his

12. A. Hasslacher, *Beiträge zur älteren Geschichte des Eisenhüttenwesen im Saargebiet*, pp. 75-8.

13. A *Giessofen* suggests a furnace which specialised in casting-irons, whereas a *Hochofen* might produce merely 'rough iron' for conversion at the forge.

14. Schubert, *Vom Ursprung und Werden der Buderus'schen Eisenwerke*, **1**, p. 58.

15. Ibid., pp. 58-59, 65; F. Geisthardt, 'Fruhe Eisengewerbe an Sieg, Dill und Lahn', in H. Kellenbenz, ed. *Schwerpunkte der Eisengewinnung und Eisenverarbeitung in Europa*, pp. 194, 197.

Figure 16: Iron stoveplate showing Elisha and the miracle of the oil (2 Kings ch. 4, 1-7), made by Peter Sorges at Kraftsolms, 1585 (photo: Shubbay)

experience in electoral Westphalia and in Waldeck, was the founder, Count John of Nassau-Dillenburg placed an order in the spring of 1614 for 1270 16-pounder cannon balls and 250 12-pounder grenades, hollow shot designed to splinter on impact. In July 1615 he ordered a further 502 cannon balls, two chamber-cannon and three mortar guns from Asslar. Whilst the guns were all for his armoury at Siegen, the greater part of the shot was sent on to the Netherlands. The quantities of guns produced at Asslar for the Netherlands are not known, but when Nassau-Dillenburg ordered 20 cast-iron guns from Asslar for the elector of the Palatinate in October 1614, he remarked that the order was placed there because 'the iron was the best made in Germany', and that 'a very good Master' (Hüttenhenn), who had already delivered 'many hundreds of guns' to the Netherlands, was the man who made the moulds and cast the guns.[16]

Many other Walloons were in the area: Wilhelm Kemmerling alias Kolmuth, a stove-founder, whose family had fled from Delft to Neu-Hanau in 1537, and who worked at Wetzlar Furnace from 1588 onwards and at Weinähr from 1595 to 1597; Bartel Thumann, who worked at the *Schmeltze*

16. Schubert, *Vom Ursprung und Werden der Buderus'schen Eisenwerke*, **1**, pp. 82-3, 98.

near Ruppertsburg in 1589; Caspar Mohser, a stove-founder from On in Luxembourg, who worked at Audenschmiede in 1601; Rupprecht Class, who worked at Wetterfeld in 1603, and whose sons were Jakob Class who worked at Dillhausen in 1606, and Johannes Class who worked at Wetterfeld in 1609, and from 1625 to 1631; Julius Gilson, an ironfounder employed at Audenschmiede between 1615 and 1625; and Johann Caspar, probably Heinrich Caspar's son, who worked at Audenschmiede from 1601 to 1615.[17]

During 1599 Heinrich Caspar himself was as far afield as Bohemia, where at Strasice, between Prague and Pilsen, he converted the smelting hearth of a bloomery into the first blast furnace in the country, from which he cast sows of between 12 and 14 hundredweights.[18]

The duke of Lorraine had two *fourneaux de fonderie* built in 1565 near Moyeuvre, where one of the finers at the forge was Pierre Grantpierre.[19] Was he descended from *Grant* Pierre Roberdes, who had worked in the Weald during the 1490s and had perhaps in the first place come to England from Hainault?

In the Habay basin more ironworks were built in the first quarter of the seventeenth century, that at Houdemont in 1613 by Tilman Poncelet and his partners from Saint-Léger, La Trapperie, which took its name from its founder, Herman Trappé, a former mayor of Liège, also in 1613, and Mellier in 1617, founded by two men from Thiérache, François de Gozée, lord of Macquenoise, probably the son of Quentin de Gozée, who had started the ironworks at Macquenoise in 1548, and Pierre Goens, a merchant from Desiny. At this time the works at Bologne, at Pont d'Oye, La Trapperie and Mellier each had a furnace and two fineries. No plating- or slitting-mills are known to have existed in the Habay basin and almost all its output, which was cold-short bar, went by way of the slitting-mills of Liège into the nail trade.[20]

IRONWORKS IN ENGLAND AND WALES AND BEYOND

This period saw the spread of the indirect process further into Kent, where with the possible exceptions of ironworks at Horsmonden and Bedgebury, only the streams near the borders of the county had hitherto become the sites of ironworks. To the west the first ironworks on the indirect system were established in Surrey, whilst more gradually ironworks spread further to the west in Sussex. Outside the Weald the indirect process appeared firstly around 1550 in Shropshire, before spreading in the 1560s into Staffordshire, South Wales and Herefordshire, and in the 1570s into Yorkshire.

The Weald

Denization rolls were now often bare lists of names, and that of 1550 did not even mention the denizand's nationality. Subsidy rolls also become less helpful and the main source which reveals the names of forgemasters and ironworks is the series of lists compiled in 1574, near the period's end, at the instance of a government anxious to establish some control over cannon founding. These lists have been used by all historians of the iron industry in the Weald from Straker onwards, and new detailed analyses have recently been provided by Cattell and Teesdale.[21] Further analysis of these lists scarcely falls within this work's scope.

In most of East Sussex the subsidy rolls rarely gave the names of forgemasters after 1552, and ironworks were already so thick on the ground that it is often impossible to assign aliens recorded in

17. Ibid., Anlage 2.
18. I. Krulis-Randa, 'Le développement des fourneaux à fer et l'introduction du haut fourneau wallon en Bohême', *Revue d'Histoire de la Sidérurgie*, **8** (1967), pp. 247-8.
19. A. Weyhmann, 'Geschichte der älteren lothringischen Eisenindustrie', *Jahrbuch der Gesellschaft für Lothringische Geschichte*, **17** (1905), pp. 72-3.
20. M. Bourguignon, 'Les usines du basin de la Rulles', **2**, pp. 41-4, 107-8, 143, 161-2.
21. C. S. Cattell, 'The 1574 lists of Wealden ironworks', *Sussex Arch.Colls.*, **117** (1979), pp. 161-72; E. Teesdale, 'The 1574 lists of ironworks in the Weald; a re-examination', *Wealden Iron*, Bulletin of the Wealden Iron Research Group, 2nd series, **6** (1986), pp. 7-44.

the subsidy rolls, as well as those mentioned in parish registers, to particular sites. For Kent there are no relevant subsidy rolls between 1550 and 1572, except in the lathe of Sutton at Hone, where rolls for both 1560 and 1563 have survived.

For East Sussex, replies to an inquiry of around 1570 into wood supplies in the Framfield area given by the forgemaster Richard Leech listed the works within 3 miles of Pounsley Wood and Echingwood;[22] these were Ralph Hogge's furnace, perhaps Queenstock, and his two unnamed hammers; Nicholas Pope's furnace (Hendall), Little Buxted Hammer, Howbourne Hammer, and Huggetts and Pounsley furnaces; listed within three miles of Langhurst Wood and Barnet Wood were John French's hammer (Chiddingly) and Waldron Furnace. The works which took wood 'most years out of most of these woods', Leech singled out as Pounsley and Huggetts furnaces and Howbourne Forge.

Here then, were the furnaces of Arthur Middleton (Huggetts) and Robert Hodgson (Pounsley), both of whom, according to Hogge's complaint of 1573 (along with himself) daily cast guns and shot, and had continued long in cannon-founding, having begun in Parson Levett's time. But Hodgson had apparently worked originally for John Harvo and in 1562 was a witness to, and beneficiary under his will to the extent of £1,[23] evidently taking over at Pounsley only after Harvo's death.

The use by Middleton of the Little Buxted site as a forge and his building of Huggetts Furnace outside Buxted/Greenhurst borough, as well as the building of new furnaces, by Nicholas Pope at Hendall, and by Hogge, perhaps both Langleys and Marshalls furnaces in Maresfield,[24] is partly reflected in the run-down of aliens in the Greenhurst/Buxted borough of Loxfield hundred (7 in 1550, 4 in 1551, nil in 1552) and their increase in Rushmonden hundred (nil in 1550, 7 in 1551, 11 in 1552).

Chiddingly Hammer dated from the 1540s and Waldron Furnace was mentioned in the Framfield inquiry of around 1570, but the Waldron site might, as has been seen, already have been in existence in 1543, as an Eversfield forge, or around 1550, as Goddard Walsh's furnace. Another furnace which was Middleton's in 1574 was Maynards Gate where the gun-casting pit has been excavated. This is thought to have been the furnace which Anthony Fowle worked in 1562. Although Fowle's will, made in 1567, did not mention iron, his servants George Collyn[25] and Richard Woodman, to each of whom he left £1, were probably connected with ironworking; Fowle's goods were inventoried at an impressive £1,141 4s 0d and the four men whom he appointed overseers to assist his widow Margery in the execution of the will included his brother the forgemaster Nicholas Fowle, and John Stapley, one of the purchasers of the manor and the new ironworks at Newdigate and Leigh, Nicholas Burges, possibly the Rotherfield man whose son Henry Burges was hammerman at Abinger in 1595, and George Maynard, from another family connected with ironworking in the Rotherfield area.[26] Maynards Gate presumably came under the control of Arthur Middleton in 1568, when he married Fowle's widow Margery.

Reverting to Hogge's complaint of 1573, four other forgemasters were mentioned in it: Sir Thomas Gresham, Nicholas Fowle, Alexander Fermor and Michael Weston, who had all begun to cast guns and shot within the last five or six years, and therefore under the stimulus of the Dutch uprising which began in 1567.

John Gresham's licence to alienate the manor of Mayfield (including Wadhurst) and the parks of Mayfield and Frankham to Sir Thomas Gresham was granted in January 1567,[27] but Mayfield Furnace is not known to have existed either in John Gresham's time, or in the days of the archbishops of Canterbury, whose lordship of South Malling had previously included Mayfield as a bailiwick. However, it was certainly in being in March 1572, when Gresham wrote to Lord Burleigh, 'Mr Danyell departs this daye; who haythe shewed me great friendship wyth his coming, in amending my furnace, and melting of my irone: for the wyche I shall desire your Lordeship to geve hym your thankes on my behalf'.[28]

22. ESRO, SRL 13/1.

23. Will of John Harvo of Framfield (TNA, PROB 11/48/340).

24. The two furnaces which Hogge claimed by 1568 to have built at his own expense for the service of the Crown are thought to have been Marshalls and Langleys (Teesdale, *The Queen's gunstonemaker*, p. 50), though in the lists of 1574 only Marshalls was attributed to him.

25. Could this be George Collyn of East Hoathly, yeoman, who in 1590 took a lease of Maresfield Forge and a water mill? In 1645 this forge was in the hands of a later Anthony Fowle (ESRO, SAS/G 13/45 and 49).

26. ESRO, PBT 1/1/5/508. Henry Burges took administration of his father's estate early in 1595 (ESRO, PBT 1/3/2/204).

27. *Calendar of Patent rolls, Elizabeth I*, **4**, 647.

28. J. W. Burgon, *The Life and times of Sir Thomas Gresham*, **2**, London (1839), pp. 425-6.

Nicholas Fowle's furnace was at Riverhall, above the site acquired by John Huggett of Riverhall before 1550, but both in Fowle's hands very soon afterwards.

In 1574 the furnace of Alexander Fermor, whose family later had interests in Wales, was Hamsell in Rotherfield, which like the nearby Birchden Forge was Waller property, and as recently as December 1567 had been in the hands of John Baker of Battle.[29] Hamsell Furnace could have been built much earlier to link with Birchden Forge, which Baker also held from Waller. Fermor may have temporarily taken over the lease of Hamsell. Baker's Withyham furnace of 1574, thought to have been Crowborough Warren, could have been built to replace Hamsell around 1570.

In 1574 the furnace of Michael Weston of Leigh was at Cowden, but which of the two furnaces there is hard to determine. A furnace at Cowden had produced cannon for William Levett in 1548, but by 1574 Cowden had two furnaces, the upper furnace named Scarlets and the lower one nearer Cowden itself; both lay in the hundred of Westerham and the borough of Edenbridge. A gun pit has been excavated at Scarlets furnace, but a map of 1743 depicts a 'boring house' at the lower site, so both had been cannon foundries.[30] The identity of the forgemasters at these furnaces must be considered later. Michael Weston, who occupied one of them in 1574, also had Cansiron Forge in Hartfield.

It now appears that there was no forge adjacent to Scarlets Furnace despite the references quoted by Straker.[31] The subsidy roll of 1560 appears to corroborate this and shows that Cowden Forge was in Somerden, not Westerham, hundred. This means that the site was the one near Prinkham Farm on the Kent Water, well below the township of Cowden. Two Frenchmen, formerly workers at Robertsbridge, William Brisboll and Joachym Tootyng (Totayn), were employed there by Andrew Firminger, who in the early 1550s had acted as clerk at the duke of Northumberland's ironworks in Tonbridge. The forge had perhaps changed hands by 1563 when four different aliens were employed there, including Peter Russell of Cowden, hammerman, who in 1564 took administration of the goods of his intestate brother Jordan Russell of Salehurst.[32] No aliens were returned for the forge in the subsidies of 1572 or later, which suggests that Cowden Forge may then have been out of use, though probably only temporarily.

The six aliens listed for the Lowey of Tonbridge in 1550, five of them living in the town itself, do not seem to include any names connected with ironworking. This is no surprise because Northumberland's ironworks were sited on lands he did not acquire until 1550 and 1551.

Following Northumberland's execution early in the new reign, the grant made by Queen Mary to Edward Nevill in November 1553 of the manor and Chase of Southfryth and the parks of Postern and the Cage shows that the furnace, usually called Vauxhall furnace, was sited within the Chase of Southfryth and that the iron mill called 'a hammermill' and the mills or offices called 'fyneres' were in Postern Park.[33]

A 40-year lease of these works had been granted by the duke towards the end of 1552 to George Harper and Thomas Culpepper, who were to be allowed to build an additional furnace and forge. They in turn under-leased the works to David Willard, who may have built Barden Furnace and Old Forge in Southborough as the additional furnace and forge.[34]

In 1574 John Stace and an otherwise unnamed Thomas held Ashurst Furnace and Forge near the confluence of Kent Water with the Medway.[35]

The possibility that Horsmonden Furnace could have been the site of a forge in the 1540s has been explored. By 1564 Shirrenden Furnace, as it was then called, was certainly in being, because Michael Collen or Collyn of Horsmonden, founder, was accused of stealing various items from Nicholas Leysard or Lewshoodd, the owner, or more probably lessee, of the furnace. This case appeared before the assizes at both East Grinstead and Dartford in July of that year, before being referred from the

29. Will of John Waller of Leigh (TNA, PROB 11/50/322).

30. KHLC, U650-P1. A map of 1641 showing Scarlets Furnace also shows a building which may have been a boring house; ESRO, ACC 9639/1.

31. Straker, *Wealden iron*, p. 225.

32. ESRO, PBT 1/1/5/155.

33. *Calendar of Patent rolls, Mary*, **1**, p. 286.

34. S. M. Jack, 'Sources for the History of the Wealden Iron Industry in the Public Record Office, part 3', *Wealden Iron*, Bulletin of the Wealden Iron Research Group, Second series, **2** (1982), p. 24.

35. TNA, SP 12/95/15 f. 48v; 61 f. 131; Cleere and Crossley (1995, 311) assumed that Thomas, for whom no surname was given, was Stace's kinsman when it would seem likely that he was a lessee.

Dartford assizes of April 1565 to the court of King's Bench.[36] Its records show that Collen was outlawed on two indictments, as was his accessory to the first charge John Winter of Horsmonden, labourer,; John Comden of Goudhurst, yeoman, was eventually pardoned.[37]

Continuity between Nicholas Colleyn, the alien of the Brenchley hundred subsidy roll in 1550, and Michael Collen in 1564 is impossible to substantiate from parish registers, partly because that of Horsmonden starts only in 1558 and that of Brenchley only in 1560, but also because, apart from the burial at Horsmonden of Joan Colen in September 1559, the name Collyn failed to occur in either register during the sixteenth century.

It is impossible to verify from parish registers the suggestion that the ironworks at Bedgebury could date from the 1540s, because the register of Cranbrook dates from September 1559 and that of Goudhurst from November of the same year; moreover, Cranbrook baptisms failed to record parents' names until 1603.

Evidence from the Goudhurst register is unclear because although it recorded men with French surnames such as John Hassherd and Peter Degoye in 1561, John Garett and William Hosher in 1562, and John Millam in 1563, all of them might be recent arrivals, like Degoye who had newly moved to Goudhurst from Shoyswell hundred since 1560. The remaining men, John Capell, who was buried at Goudhurst on 7 April 1559, and Peter Turner, whose son Charles was buried there on the same day, who were each possibly French or of French descent, could also have been recent arrivals in Goudhurst. Turner, for instance, had been employed at Panningridge during most of the 1550s.

None of the four Cranbrook aliens of the 1572 subsidy roll is known to have been connected with iron, and although the five aliens who paid the poll tax in West Barnfield hundred in 1572 were probably ironworkers, there is no way to determine whether they, or indeed the workers named in Goudhurst parish register, worked at Bedgebury rather than at Chingley. Works at both places were in existence in 1574: Bedgebury belonged to Alexander Culpepper, and Thomas Darrell was the owner of Chingley, with Thomas Dyke as tenant.

The Hawkhurst parish register recorded the baptism in September 1550 of Robert Turke's son Peter, who was buried at Ashburnham in 1562, and the burial in January 1554 of his daughter Faith. The movements of this forgeman, Robert Turke alias Tomplin, can be followed from Netherfield hundred, where he had worked for Ninian Burrell in 1549, to Shoyswell hundred, where he worked for Thomas May in April 1550, to Goudhurst later in 1550, where he still was in January 1554, and back to Sussex later in 1554, where in 1555 he did casual labour at Robertsbridge Forge. The only known forge in Hawkhurst parish was the one near the later Furnace Mill, called Wenebridge Forge in 1579;[38] on this evidence the forge went back to 1550.

Frith Furnace in Hawkhurst parish is thought to have been the one operated by Sir Richard Baker in 1574, but nothing so precise as the movements of Robert Turk seems to relate to furnacemen living in Hawkhurst parish. There is no reason to link the alien Thomas Vinsenall, who paid the poll tax in 1572 and was buried at Hawkhurst in 1584, with the manufacture of iron. James Florence, a Frenchman who married the widow Elizabeth Stone at Hawkhurst in 1579, and John Santo, a Frenchman who moved from Frant to Hawkhurst around 1574 and was buried there in 1587, seem more likely furnacemen.

Biddenden Hammer, which was probably Sir Richard Baker's hammer of 1574, was undoubtedly the forge at which the English-born hammerman, Borden (*recte* Barden?) paid a shilling to the subsidy of 1572 in Berkeley hundred. Its pond had been built around 1570.[39]

In the areas of East Sussex where indirect-process ironworks were already thick on the ground, further ironworks appeared. On the southern fringe, a Crowhurst court roll of 1591, by referring back to an iron mill of 1556, implied that Crowhurst Furnace or Forge was already in existence then.[40] Batsford Furnace was built on land belonging to lord Dacre in 1571 by Thomas Glydd and Simon Colman. Since Batsford was probably abandoned before around 1620,[41] its enlargement for use as a gunfoundry most

36. *Cockburn, Sussex Assize records, Elizabeth I*, no. 123. Cockburn, *Kent Assize records, Elizabeth I*, nos. 259, 321.
37. TNA, KB 29/199 m56.
38. Cleere and Crossley, *The iron industry of the Weald*, p. 334.
39. Ibid., p. 316.
40. Ibid., pp. 326-7.
41. O. Bedwin, 'The excavation of a late 16th-century blast furnace at Batsford, Herstmonceux, East Sussex,

probably occurred during the last quarter of the century. In 1574, also in the southern area, Bartholomew Jeffery held Buckholt Furnace and Forge from lord Dacre. Of the older ironworks, John Gardener now held Kitchenham Forge, formerly probably Richard Woodman's, from John Ashburnham, and Thomas Stollyan now held the Priory Furnace from Sir Richard Baker.

In Netherfield hundred Ninian Burrell's Penhurst Furnace was run by its owner in 1549, and perhaps by Anthony Pelham in 1550. On the basis of the fact that the cost of carriage of sows to Robertsbridge was the same from Panningridge as from the furnace used by the Draper, Westall and Gerard partnership from 1551 onwards, it can be argued that Gerard's works in Netherfield hundred was Penhurst. However, Anthony Pelham still employed Roger Tankerye in the hundred in 1552, and may have employed him there earlier, because Tankerye paid a shilling to reliefs in Netherfield from 1549 onwards. Can Pelham and Gerard both have used Penhurst around this time, or were some of Anthony Pelham's Netherfield workers employed at the Warbleton Priory works, as was apparently the case with John Lamott in 1549?

In Henhurst hundred the works continued to be Socknersh Furnace and Bugsell Forge. John Collyn's youngest son Hugh had six workers in the hundred in 1552 and these must clearly have been employed at Socknersh, in lease from his elder brother Alexander, with Goddard Walsh's two workers of the same year just as clearly at Bugsell. But was Socknersh the ironworks at which Maryon Benett was employed? He had paid the poll tax as a servant of William Haye in 1549 and, together with James Frencheman, of John Haye in 1550. The return of hammer and anvil moulds, borrowed for Robertsbridge Forge from 'Mr Welch', from Glottenham to Socknersh Furnace in 1555, suggests that Collyn had held the furnace only briefly. However, before 1559 Joan and Goddard Walsh had let Bugsell Forge to Collyn, and the Sidney accounts mention the supply of 61 tons of sows for Robertsbridge by Hugh Collins from Socknersh both in 1563 and in 1568, which suggests that after the death of Goddard Walsh, Socknersh was permanently in Collyn's hands.[42]

Another supplier of pig iron to Robertsbridge Forge during the 1560s was Richard Weekes, who in 1568 supplied 40 tons from Netherfield, presumably from Beech Furnace, and 12 tons from his new furnace,[43] which would be Mountfield and perhaps dated from around 1567, but was still referred to in his will in 1578 as 'my new iron work or furnace and ponds called Lyne stream', which, in contrast to his Beech Furnace in Netherfield perhaps dating from the 1530s, it was.

'Mr Gardiner', who in 1563 supplied 5.75 tons of sows to Robertsbridge, was Henry Gardiner, described as Tyrwhitt's servant in a Chancery case concerned with the water supply to Bugsell Forge.[44] The sows were probably supplied from Darvel Furnace in Tyrwhitt's interest rather than Gardiner's own. Gardiner is not thought to have been of immigrant descent and he probably ran Darvel Furnace until 1568, when Tyrwhitt leased it to Thomas Glydd, who still held it in 1574 and 1588.[45]

In Waterdown Forest Cowford Furnace was set up in 1562 by William Relf and Bartholomew Jeffery on land belonging to lord Bergavenny, and Schubert argued that the furnace and forge at Eridge which Bergavenny had in 1574, were already in existence when Cowford was set up in 1562.[46] Lord Bergavenny was also landlord at Hungershall, or High Rocks Forge, on the border between Frant and Speldhurst, the lease of which was transferred in 1568 from Roger Breecher to James Ellis.[47]

A hitherto undated furnace in Frant is Tollslye; could this be 'Collin's furnace', whose filler Peter was buried at Frant in February 1562? Also in Frant, Henly or Brinklaw, a forge rather than a furnace, could have been the ironworks at which John Carpenter employed Peter Lambert in 1572, though these works might be considerably older, because Carpenter had acquired the Henley estate in 1547.[48]

1978', *Post-Medieval Archaeology*, **14** (1980), pp. 93-4.

42. ESRO, PBT 1/1/4/491; Crossley, *Sidney ironworks accounts*, pp. 184, 191.

43. Ibid., pp. 191-2. Weekes also agreed to supply 210 tons of sows by the following Michaelmas, for which he was to be paid with 70 tons of bar iron, half the estimated yield. A further amount of 88 tons of wrought iron was supplied to Weekes in 1572-3 on similar terms, which suggests that he had supplied 264 tons of sows on that occasion (Ibid., pp. 196, 197, 202).

44. TNA, C 3/13/103.

45. Cleere and Crossley, *The iron industry of the Weald*, p. 328.

46. H. R. Schubert, 'A Tudor furnace in Waterdown Forest', *Jnl. of the Iron and Steel Institute*, **169** (1951), pp. 241-2.

47. Cleere and Crossley, *The iron industry of the Weald*, pp. 325-6, 387.

48. Straker, *Wealden iron*, p. 275.

In Ashdown, Peter Collyar of Newbridge, possibly the former Parrock denizen Peter Denwall, paid the poll tax, and Dawne, perhaps Maryan Downe, hammerman of Parrock paid 2 shillings on goods; they were among four aliens listed in the 1560 Hartfield subsidy roll. The two ironworks passed unnoticed through most of this period. A Court of Requests case brought by Lord Buckhurst in 1573 indicated that John Wiken had been granted a 21-year lease of Parrock Forge from Lady Day 1571 by William Saunders, shortly before his death in 1570. The current landlord was William's son Nicholas Saunders.[49] By 1574, however, George Bullen of Hartfield was running Parrock as Lord Buckhurst's tenant.

The lease of Newbridge granted to Anthony Browne in 1546 would have expired at Michaelmas 1567, and in 1574 the tenant was Henry Bowyer, who was variously credited with a double furnace, and a forge and a furnace in Ashdown, specified in one of the lists as the Queen's furnace and forge. Perhaps the Bowyer tenure at Newbridge ensued during Browne's lease, but after the Parrock dispute of 1549, which probably saw the end of the Bowyer tenure there.

South of Ashdown, Woolbridge Forge was suggested by Cattell as one of the Mayfield forges mentioned in 1574, but given no further attribution. In the central belt, new ironworks additional to those already mentioned in connection with the Framfield survey of 1570 and Hogge's complaint of 1573 were naturally few, but included Gage's Maresfield Furnace and Forge which in 1574 were in lease to John Fawkner.

Moving westwards to the East Grinstead area, the possibility that Bower Forge may have been in existence in the 1550s is suggested by the will of Hugh Botting, who had recently bought the Bower estate; it showed that in August 1558 he was owed two tons of iron by his son Henry.[50] Nearby, Mill Place Furnace could have been the furnace at which the founder John Brokes worked, to whose son, another John Brokes, John Homwood of East Grinstead left £1 in 1560 by a nuncupative will, of which the furnace's landlord Richard a'Myll was both witness, along with his wife, and overseer.[51] By 1574 Robert Reynolds was lessee of this furnace and also of Brambletye Forge, which had been built by Thomas Lutman, and in 1562 leased to Henry Bowyer.[52]

Also in the East Grinstead area, John Payne's Stone Furnace and Forge were worked in 1574 by Thomas Duffield of East Grinstead, perhaps a native of the area rather than a man of immigrant descent. Tinsley Forge at Worth was run by Henry Bowyer in 1574, but Tilgate Furnace could also have been in operation then. Tilgate may have been Ninian Burrell's unnamed furnace of 1574.

The most westerly ironworks in Sussex recorded before 1550 were Worth, and Thomas Michell's Chittingly Manor Furnace. Chittingly lay in West Hoathly in the northern part of Streat hundred and it seems possible that Chittingly was the furnace at which 'Nicholas the Founder' paid the poll tax in 1552. He was perhaps Nicholas Tyler, who had been at Worth in 1550 and 1551, but who, when he made his will around 1556, had moved on yet again and was a Fletching parish founder, presumably at Sheffield Furnace.[53] Michell's Chittingly Manor Furnace was perhaps the one held in 1574 by John Blacket (alias Gavis) in [West] Hoathly and owned by 'Mr Michael'.

However, the ironworks at Ardingly was almost equally old and Ardingly Hammer was first referred to in the parish register in 1568, but Richard Maryan alias Dipplie (*recte* Dipperye) whose son Charles was then baptised, had been mentioned in the register in 1565, when his eldest son Bartholomew was baptised. The forge went back to at least 1558, when Joan the wife of John Barden was buried, Barden being the Ardingly hammerman who in 1559 was surety for the appearance of another hammerman, George Tyler of Worth, at the assizes.[54] .

Ardingly Furnace was first mentioned in the parish register in December 1565, when John Gillam, an infant, son of John Gillam, 'Frenchman of the furnace', was buried. When the French John Gillam was remarried in 1572 to Annis Beldame, widow, he was stated to be Richard Gillam's eldest son. But from the will made in January 1546 by Gilbert Ungle, a Kentish man who then dwelt at Ardingly, it

49. TNA, REQ 2/272/1.
50. ESRO, PBT 1/1/4/113.
51. ESRO, PBT 1/1/4/496.
52. Cleere and Crossley, *The iron industry of the Weald*, pp. 317-8.
53. ESRO, PBT 1/1/3/225.
54. *Cockburn, Sussex Assize records, Elizabeth I*, no. 16.

appears that Richard Gillam had another son Gilbert who was Ungle's godson and therefore English.[55] If Richard Gillam the elder, and Ungle, who could have been father of his second wife, had been brought to Ardingly by the establishment of ironworking there, this might mean that iron production at Ardingly started in the 1540s.

There were however two blast furnaces in Ardingly parish. The older furnace, at which John Gillam and Charles Tiler worked according to the parish register in 1565 and 1569, was probably the one near Saucelands, which Francis Chaloner confusingly had *de novo* in 1592; it was just less than 2km north of 'Awewell', where John Gillam of the furnace was living when his first wife was buried in 1571. But Renolde Harvye the 'founder in the park', John Morgaine, Warnet Dogion, Nicholas Hoock and Thomas Kerbee 'of Strudgate furnace' referred to in 1567, 1578, 1581, 1584 and 1591, clearly worked at a different site, almost a further 4km to the north; Strudgate was lord Bergavenny's furnace near Wakehurst Park run by Henry Bowyer in 1574.

In comparison with the wealth of information about forgemen conveyed in the Ardingly parish register, other registers in this area are comparatively unhelpful. The Worth reference of 1584 to 'the old forge comenlie called Worthe hamer' implied the existence of a further forge at Worth, but both Rowfant, built around 1556 by Robert Whitfield, and Tinsley forges had been referred to earlier, so was perhaps Blackwater Green Forge the original 'Old Hammer'? The reference of the Worth register in 1587 to 'Crookeford fornace' was also to the furnace held by John Eversfield in 1574, and therefore to the double furnace built in 1547.

Bolney and Balcombe parish registers, which begin around 1540 are devoid of references to ironworks and almost devoid of occupations. Slaugham's register is too late and the Cuckfield register, which occasionally mentioned occupations, started only in 1598.

Sows were supplied by Sir Walter Covert from Cuckfield Furnace to Roger Gratwick's St Leonards Forge in 1576, so both Cuckfield Furnace and Forge probably started during this period. They may even go back to the 1560s because the subsidy roll of 1563 put John Carye at Cuckfield, where Peter Lurye [Lurrett] also then was. However, these men could have been at Blackfold Furnace, which was worked by Nicholas Chalenor in 1574, possibly along with Holmsted Forge. Slaugham Furnace was run by Ninian Chaloner and Walter Covert in 1574.

Further to the west the Nuthurst register, which started in 1559, could have been of help had its baptisms mentioned parents' names. The voluminous parish registers of Horsham which date from 1540, include references to many persons described as 'of the Forest', often belonging to Lower Beeding, who will have included ironworkers and colliers. The register mentioned a collier named Roger a'Neave as early as 1551, and the first French ironworker who can be positively identified, the collier Lewis Buttre, a former servant of the duke of Norfolk, mentioned together with Milicent his wife, had his son John baptised at Horsham in June 1553, though as recently as 1551 he had paid the poll tax as 'Lewes' at Worth. It looks then as though Straker was correct in surmising that the first ironworks in St Leonards Forest were set up during the period after the duke of Norfolk's estates were sequestered and before the act of attainder against him was reversed by Mary's first parliament, which met in October 1553.[56]

In the subsidy rolls, the ironworkers in the Forest of St Leonards were not identified until 1560, when Marigold and Jocab [*sic*] paid the poll tax as servants of Roger Gratwick in Burbeech hundred. Marigold did not appear again in Burbeech hundred and was perhaps the man who paid the poll tax as Peter Marygold in Hartfield hundred in 1576, but Jacob still served Roger Gratwick in 1563, and was probably Jacob Missian who was buried at Horsham in 1565. Adrian, Gratwick's other servant who paid the poll tax in 1563, was probably Adrian Duddinge who continued at Ifield in the 1570s, and paid 6 shillings in 1572 and 10 shillings in 1576 to the subsidies of those years.

Thomas Ilman of Ifield, whose sows were sold to Thomas Blackwell of Mitchellpark Forge in 1567, but in 1569 were sent to Darrell's Leigh Forge,[57] was probably one of the two forgemasters Swayne and Ilman who in 1563 employed the poll-tax payers William Panny (Pavy?) and John Parrys in Burbeech hundred. Thomas Fenner also had an iron mill at Ifield before 1569. There were furnaces and forges at both Bewbush and Ifield within 1km of each other and earlier ownership of the sites cannot be determined, but by 1574 Roger Gratwick held both.

55. ESRO, PBT 1/1/1/87.
56. Straker, *Wealden iron*, p. 434.
57. Cleere and Crossley, *The iron industry of the Weald*, p. 162.

Also in the Burbeech subsidy roll of 1560 was Jamys Hennesey (Hunnisett), the finer, who paid 8 shillings on goods. No forgemaster is indicated, but he too could have worked for Gratwick, because Birchenbridge Forge, though the nearest ironworks to the tithing of Sedgwick in which he lived, did not appear in the 1574 list and could be a later creation.

The earliest indication in parish registers of ironworkers further west in Sussex occurred in 1566, when at Kirdford the finer Bartholomew Deboncorte married Jane Otta in May. The ironworks in Petworth great park were Mitchellpark Forge in Kirdford and Frith Furnace in Northchapel which in 1574 belonged to the earl of Northumberland. Subsidy rolls show that in 1572 the finer Charles Payve and another alien named Nicholas Mores were at Northchapel. Mitchellpark will have been the forge to which sow iron was taken from Bewbush in 1567 for Thomas Blackwell. Blackwell having died, in 1574 both works were occupied by William Walpole, in lease from Mrs Blackwell. Later ironworks in the area were the furnace of Thomas Smith of Petworth in Shillinglee Park, recorded as a double furnace in some of the 1574 lists, and Wassell Forge, which was then still under construction.

Also in 1566 Katherine Perigo was baptised at Linchmere in April, though the name of Katherine's father was not recorded. The Linchmere parish register follows the name of Perigo with those of Lamby and Jolly in 1569, and shows that the finer Blaise Briday, who appeared in the subsidy roll at Linchmere in 1572, had arrived there by 1570. They were joined by other bearers of French forgemen's names, Barton, Laby and Doogyne (1570), Glode (1571), Gummrye (1572), and Larby (1573), with other possible men of French descent, such as Charles Pellam (Pullen?), William Balden (Barden?) and John Sporr, also appearing.

The Linchmere forge will have been Pophole which in 1574 was described as lord Montague's furnace. Nevertheless, in their wills the hammermen, Charles Barden in 1631 and his grandson Charles Bredah alias Blaze in 1703, described themselves as of 'Linchmore', whilst the 1703 man's other grandfather, Blaise Bridae, who had been at Linchmere in 1570, still wished to be buried there in 1608, though he had moved on to Bramshott by the time he made his will. Despite the 1574 list only forge cinder has been found at Pophole, now thought to be the site of 'Lord Montague's forge' which still produced 50 tons of iron a year according to the 1717 list.

It might be thought that North Park Furnace, which in the eighteenth century was let along with Pophole,[58] was the furnace which provided sows for Pophole from around 1570. However, a court roll for Linchmere and Shulbrede manor refers to the completion of an iron mill on the site in 1614. The other suggested site is Imbhams in Chiddingfold parish, which Straker thought was built around 1570, but which in the preamble to one of the 1574 lists seems to be 'a new furnace sett upp in Haselmoore by my L. Montague which as yet hathe never wrought and whether they shall blow sowes for Iron or ordenance I know not'. The list itself says 'The Ld Montague one forge and one furnace in Haslemeere or thereabouts',[59] a qualification which makes the identification with Pophole and Imbhams more tenable, but fails to explain why after four years of existence it was not known whether Imbhams would produce sow iron or ordnance.

Further east, in Surrey in the hundred of Reigate, a furnace at Ewood in Newdigate and a forge in Leigh were set up in the early 1550s. The Leigh site, whose owner was Henry Lechford, was let to Richard Wheler and William Hawthorne in 1551, but was transferred as a forge to George and Christopher Darrell, London merchants and members of the Darrell family of Scotney, in 1554. The Ewood site belonged to the Nevill family, but works had also been built there before 1553, when lord Bergavenny sold Ewood manor to the Darrells too. The presence of forge bottoms indicates that the Ewood site at one time had its own forge, thus confirming that the works were at first separate creations. In 1554 the Darrels leased Ewood manor and Leigh Hammer to John Stapley of Framfield and Gregory Newman, a London grocer. Immediately afterwards moieties of the freehold were also disposed of, George Darrell's to Anthony Pelham and Christopher Darrell's to Thomas Collet of London. Thomas Collett was probably the son of Humphrey Collet, landlord of the White Hart Inn in Southwark, where iron from Worth and Sheffield ironworks had been stored in the late 1540s. Collett held his moiety until 1567, when he sold it to John Heathe of King's Lynn, from whom it was acquired again by Christopher Darrell and Thomas Browne of Betchworth in May 1574. Darrell had already reacquired the other

58. C. Barnes, 'Iron-working sites in the Haslemere area', *Wealden Iron*, Bulletin of the Wealden Iron Research Group, 2nd series, **11** (1991), pp. 27-8.

59. Straker, *Wealden iron*, p. 421-2.

moiety of the works from Anthony's son Herbert Pelham somewhat earlier and signed the bond for the works in April 1574.[60]

Passing on to the hundred of Blackheath and Wotton, it looks as though sites in Cranleigh and Dunsfold had by the early 1550s become the most westerly in the Weald to be equipped with ironworks using the indirect process. The 1587 renewal of the lease of Vachery Forge to John Lambard alias Gardner included the 'furnace pond', demonstrating that the earliest works on this site included both furnace and forge. Indeed the presence of three aliens, Charles, Crystyan and Adryan Huysson, at Cranleigh in 1551 suggests that ironfounding may have been well enough established at Vachery Furnace for gunfounding to have been attempted there. The middle of these three names was probably Christian Hewgynson, a 'gonmaker', who in 1561 was made denizen. He had been a subject of the Emperor.[61]

These names have to be taken in the context of Hambonye Fraunces and Hambonye Bordye, who were at Buxted in 1550, and who, I have suggested somewhat tentatively, might have been Hungarians, and of John and Christopher Hans, the gunners who were sent from the Tower to Worth in 1552 to prove the guns cast there for Sir Richard Sackville.

In 1552 the collier John Mocomber paid the poll tax at Cranleigh, where he was followed by James Haward and John Myles in 1557 and by James Wayner in 1559, all three of them probably ironworkers. The readily identifiable denizen Marian Predam was at Cranleigh in 1571; he had previously served as a finer at Sheffield (1549-52) and Leigh (1557-59) forges. James Wayner perhaps resurfaced as James Wheler in 1589, with a wife who also paid the poll tax.

These quite early Surrey ironworks had spread even more spectacularly west by 1551 when Bardyn, specified more closely the following year as Izambard Lamye alias Bardyne, was at Dunsfold. There he presumably inaugurated Dunsfold Hammer at the Burningfold site, where his relative the hammerman William Barden was to work around 1580. Izambard was accompanied by an unknown alien named Roger in 1552.

In Tandridge hundred aliens who paid the poll tax at Crowhurst were John Johnson in 1551 and John Joly and Charles in 1552, of whom John Joly certainly bore the surname of an ironworker. The discovery of a forge established in the parish by Thomas Gaynsford in about 1550 confirms this.[62] Some ten years later the hundred of Tandridge included Woodcock Hammer, the forge which operated in conjunction with Warren Furnace in Worth, both of them established around 1560 on Gage family property. 'Swanne of the Hammer Mills' was referred to in the Lingfield parish register in 1561, because though the forge lay in an enclave of Godstone parish, the churches of Lingfield and Horne, and indeed of East Grinstead, were closer to it than the mother church.

Although Abinger Hammer is thought to date from 1557 no aliens were listed there in the subsidy roll of 1559. The aliens listed in 1571 included Hugh Marchaunt, who had worked as a finer at Robertsbridge 20 years earlier, and Oberie Larbie, who had been at Newdigate in 1557 and 1559. The Abinger parish register mentioned Oberie Larbie already in 1563 and John Larbie in 1564. The other alien from the 1571 subsidy roll, Stephen Macie, had married Katherin Tollett at Abinger in 1567.

Beyond the Weald

Outside the Weald we saw that in the Midlands members of the Morrell family had established themselves in Shropshire by 1525, whilst in even more remote North Yorkshire, far from any industrialised area, Lambert Seimar was already working the abbey forge at Rievaulx in 1538.

In Shropshire we know that Hugh Morall, who first appeared at Lilleshall in 1525, obtained a lease of the famous Coalbrookdale works, 'le Newhouse and Calbroke smithy', for 63 years in 1536, at a time when he was already bailiff of Wenlock Priory's manor of Little Wenlock in which Coalbrookdale lay.[63] Iron was worked in the Lilleshall area both before Morall's stay, in the form of the 'qualmesmythe'

60. Ibid., p. 451.
61. *Calendar of Patent rolls, Elizabeth I*, **2**, p. 2.
62. J. S. Hodgkinson, 'Crowhurst Forge, Surrey – a new site identified', *Wealden Iron*, Bulletin of the Wealden Iron Research Group, 2nd ser., **32** (2012), 5-10.
63. *Victoria County History of Shropshire*, **11**, p. 48. Dugdale, *Monasticon Anglicanum*, **5**, p. 79.

of 1277, and after. Lilleshall Priory and its lands were granted to William Cavendish for 21 years at it dissolution in 1538. The following year a Wolverhampton merchant James Leveson purchased the reversion of Cavendish's lease for £1,173 16s 8d,[64] which should have brought him these estates in 1559. Water-driven hammers at Lubstree Pool were noted in 1580 and a fully developed ironworks was leased by Sir William Leveson to the Corbet brothers in 1591, so it appears a valid inference that Morall's presence at Lilleshall was also connected with the manufacture of iron.[65]

Seimar's agreement of 1541 with the agents of the earl of Rutland, who had acquired Rievaulx Abbey at its dissolution, shows that Seimar was to make iron in the traditional direct method, the only novelties being the installation of a water-powered hammer, presumably on the pattern of the Walloon drome-beam hammer and of 'too bloome smythes' instead of one, to produce blooms for the 'stryngharth'. Rutland's agents signed the agreement 'per me', and Seimar signed it 'De per moi', but the only foreign nomenclature in the agreement was the use of a 'forgayn' (Fr. *fourgon*) among the tools, not at Rievaulx, but at the smithy in Bilsdale.[66] In the event it was not until 1577 that a blast furnace was eventually built at Rievaulx.

The Midlands

In the Midlands events moved much faster. Following the dissolution of Wenlock Priory the manor of Madeley was granted to Robert Brooke in July 1544, on which occasion specific mention was made of 'Cabroke Smethe' as part of the manor.[67] The Brooke family became heavily involved in the iron industry in the seventeenth century, especially in the Forest of Dean, where Sir Basil Brooke firstly managed the royal ironworks and later became their lessee. At Madeley Robert Brooke will have been entitled to appoint his own bailiff, but how far the change of ownership of the manor affected Morall's lease of the smithy, scheduled to last until 1599, we do not know. However, it seems that by the 1540s Morall was at Much Wenlock where he paid 6 shillings on goods worth £3 to the lay subsidy of 1544. Now, as bailiff of Much Wenlock, he submitted accounts for repairs carried out on the estate between Michaelmas 1544 and Michaelmas 1545,[68] repairs which included tiling the roof of the tenement of Christopher Morall, who may have been his son.

There had already been two smithies in Shirlett Forest in 1532, the one occupied by John Myston and Thomas Venymer, and the other near the house of Thomas Ellestone in Marsh manor, let to Thomas Munslowe of Caughley. After the Dissolution the Court of Augmentations account roll for 1541 shows that the Shirlett estate included iron mines yielding a rent of £2 6s 8d, a workshop called an 'Irone Smythee', alternatively a 'Smyth's Place', yielding a rent of £12 8s 0d and another ironworks (*fabrica ferri*) whose rent was £2 13s 4d.[69] Much Wenlock, Rievaulx and an entry under the Staffordshire abbey of Croxden relating to Hungarwall smithy near Cheadle,[70] are three of the few instances which show ironworking as a source of monastic revenue at the Dissolution.

The books of the Court of Augmentations show that a 21-year lease of the 'iron smithy in Shurlet in the lordship of Marshe in Much Wenlock parish' was granted to Reginald and Thomas Rydley of Caughley in May 1541. The reversion of this lease was granted in November 1554 to Stephen Hadnoll, gentleman, one of the grooms of Queen Mary's Privy Chamber. The 1554 recital of the 1541 grant shows that the smithy had then been 'late in the tenure of Thomas Monsloo'. Hadnoll was also granted another smithy in Shirlett which was in the tenure of Alexander Wood and a pit called a 'cool dolfe' in Broseley

64. *Letters and Papers*, **14** (2), no. 780 (39).
65. *Victoria County History of Shropshire*, **11**, p. 163. It should be noted that in 1541 the rents yielded by two mills belonging to Lilleshall Abbey, those of Attingham (£6 13s 4d) and of Longdon in Staffordshire (£6) (where a forge had existed in 1306 (*VCH Staffordshire*, **3**, p. 108)), were much higher than those of normal corn mills (Dugdale, *Monasticon Anglicanum*, **6** (1), p. 265).
66. Schubert, *British iron and steel industry*, p. 148 and Appendix VII.
67. *Letters and Papers, Henry VIII*, **19** (1), no. 1035 (144).
68. *Letters and Papers, Henry VIII*, **21** (2), no. 185.
69. *Victoria County History of Shropshire*, **10** (ed. G. C. Baugh), Oxford University Press, 1998. p. 228. Dugdale, *Monasticon*, **5**, pp. 80-1.
70. *Victoria County History of Shropshire*, **3**, p. 109.

held by William Adams.[71]

The importance of the area can be judged from the fact that in recognition of his services against the Scots at the battle of Pinkie in October 1547, John Dudley, earl of Warwick and future duke of Northumberland, was granted the wood called Shirlett Wood alias 'the forest of Shorlett' in Morville parish, comprising 140 acres, though he rapidly disposed of it in December 1547 to George Willoughby, esquire, and Robert Longe, citizen and mercer of London, who in turn passed it on in February 1548 to William Acton of Aldenham.[72]

By 1545 a former watermill of Wenlock Priory in Broseley had also been leased to Reginald Ridley, but around 1550 the actual possession of this mill was in the hands of John Munslow.[73] What happened next can be conjectured from the transcript of a burial entry at Much Wenlock which runs as follows: '20 Jan. 1555[/6] Here was buried out of Caughley Wood the body of John Morrell, a frenchman born, the headman or chief workman of John Munslows Smithies, called the founder thereof'.[74]

John Morrell had been born at Neuville-Ferrières around 1514 and had come to England around 1532. When made denizen in 1544 he had an English wife and three children. He had paid 4 pence on goods to the subsidy of 1543 at Greenhurst/Buxted where he will have worked at the cannon foundry of the rector of Buxted, William Levett. He was not among the Frenchmen made denizen for Levett in 1544, though his older relative James Morrell was, but John had perhaps already moved on to Danehill Sheffield where he paid a shilling on goods to the relief of 1549. There he will have worked at Sheffield Furnace, which had belonged to the duke of Norfolk.

The 1549 record is the last mention in the Weald of John Morrell and came at the start of a period when there were annual subsidy rolls for Sussex; his failure to appear in any of these rolls from 1550 to 1552 makes it reasonably certain that by 1550 he had already left the area. He could consequently have had around five years in Shropshire during which to set up a blast furnace in the Shirlett area, in Caughley Wood. Whether Hugh Morrell was also involved in the setting up of Shirlett smithy, perhaps around 1540, is impossible to say, but it seems certain that he was behind the move of the Frenchman to Shropshire.

It must be noted that there was a discrepancy between the new grant of Shirlett smithy to Stephen Hadnoll in November 1554, which conveyed (1) 'the mill of the iron smithy called "an iron smythye place" in Shurlett and liberty of mining and digging in the mines within Shurlett wood in the tenure of Reynold Ridley'; (2) 'the iron smithy in Shurlett in the tenure of Alexander Woode'; (3) 'a pit (*puteum*) called "a coole dolfe" in Burwardisley (Broseley) in the tenure of William Adams', and the parish register entry which specified that Morrell was head workman of John Munslow's smithy, and could be interpreted as indicating that this was a different works in Caughley Wood. We know that Munslow held the manors of both Broseley and Caughley, because in 1563 he paid £10 for a licence to alienate both to Richard Cupper.[75]

A letter of July 1564 which reported to the earl of Shrewsbury that 'the two new fineries at the smithy in Lyssard which Monslow made will be finished not long' perhaps explains his departure from the Wenlock area.[76]

There were certainly other ironworks in the Shirlett area because William Acton of Aldenham Hall, who had acquired the Forest of Shirlett in 1548, was active too. In August 1561 'in consideration that he has lately built two iron mills in Moreveld . . . and has bought a great quantity of timber for fuel, and that many poor men have little or no livelihood other than by making coals for the said iron mills or working in them', he was granted a licence to 'convert to coal (charcoal) or any other fuel for the making of iron, timber trees of oak, beech and ash within the parish of Morveld' in contravention of the recent act of Parliament, despite the fact that the parish was within 14 miles of the river Severn.[77]

71. *Letters and Papers, Henry VIII*, **17**, p. 696. *Calendar of Patent rolls, Mary and Philip*, **2**, p. 21.
72. *Calendar of Patent rolls, Edward VI*, **1**, pp. 171, 199, 280.
73. *Letters and Papers, Henry VIII*, **20** (2), no. 496 (49); *Calendar of Patent rolls, Edward VI*, **3**, pp. 213-4.
74. W. A. Leighton (ed.), 'The Register of Sir Thomas Botelar, Vicar of Much Wenlock', *Transactions of the Shropshire Archaeological Society*, First series, **6** (1883), p. 110.
75. *Calendar of the Patent rolls, Philip and Mary*, **2**, p. 21; *Calendar of Patent rolls, Elizabeth I*, **2**, p. 551.
76. S. Watts, 'Shifnal ironworks accounts, 1583-90' in *Shropshire historical documents; a miscellany*, Keele, Centre for Local History, 2000, pp. 4-5.
77. *Calendar of Patent rolls, Elizabeth I*, **2**, p. 96.

One of William Acton's furnaces is thought to have been at the Hurst (SO 671959), about 600m north of Aldenham Hall, identified on Morville tithe map by the place names, Furnace Pool and Furnace Coppice.[78]

Other entries in Much Wenlock parish register linked to ironworkers or ironworking probably included the following, who have surnames which may be Wealden in origin: 1559, Mathew Curbiton, a labourer who was 'killed by a lump of earthe that fell upon him as he digged in the moyns at Shirlette'; 1560, the burial of Richard Heyward or Heaywod, 'collier from Linley Greene'; 1561, Christopher Morall, 'tanner', whose daughter Joan was baptised, and who was probably related to Hugh Morrell. Heyward, and also Thomas Habburley 'of Sheinton streete, laborer', who was 'killed by earth that fell upon him . . . in the moyns in Shurlett' in 1561. Just beyond this period 'John Morain a Frenchman was slayn in the Southe Field by a blackamore and others of that company' and was buried on 2 April 1577. The parish register had also mentioned Muckley 'smithyes' from where Francis Crump was buried in April 1571.

The reversion of Shirlett smithy to Stephen Hadnoll will have become operative in 1562. It is noteworthy that Stephen Hadnoll was apparently involved in the next major move of ironworking into Shropshire at Cleobury Mortimer during the 1560s. His interest in the area had commenced in July 1557 with the purchase of the manor of Cleobury Barns, which had fallen to the Crown in 1549 by the attainder of Thomas Seymour, lord Seymour of Sudeley.[79]

The indirect process had meanwhile spread into the neighbouring county Staffordshire during the 1560s. Here lands had been granted by Henry VIII to another of his councillors, Sir William Paget, whose origins as the son of a Wednesbury nailer have already been alluded to. Involved were Abbots Bromley and Bromley Hurst, possessions of the former college of Burton-on-Trent, granted to him in 1544, and Cannock Chase and Rugeley, formerly belonging to the now much-reduced bishopric of Lichfield, granted to him in 1546.[80]

At Risom Bridge on Cannock Chase, Paget confirmed the lease of a bloomsmithy, together with iron mines in Beaudesert Park, granted in 1542 for ten years to William Fletcher at a yearly rent of £20. There was also a forge at Rugeley, held by Thomas Chetwynd in 1555.[81] In January 1560 Paget and his son Henry were granted a licence to cut oak, beech and ash of whatever breadth on the Chase, at Rugeley, Longdon, Heywood, Pagets Bromley and Abbots Bromley, because they were not within 14 miles of the sea or any navigable river.[82] The indirect process then appeared in the form of a blast furnace on Cannock Chase and a forge at Abbots Bromley between 1560 and 1563. Later in the 1560s Old and New forges were in operation, and the reference in 1568-9 to the Old Furnace indicates that a second furnace had by then been built. Another furnace at Teddesley came into use in 1578.[83]

The appearance of the names of the aliens John Raboye, John Gatier and Nicholas Regell in the subsidy roll for Cuttlestone hundred in May 1563 will have been connected with these developments.[84] These names came under the heading 'Ridgeley', but it seems likely that this comprehended workers at Cannock Furnace as well as at Rugeley itself.

John Roboye, it will be remembered had come to the Weald from the Beauvaisis in 1536, had been at Robertsbridge in 1542, had worked at Ewood in Newdigate as recently as 1557, and in 1560 had paid the poll tax in Wadhurst. There is no sign that he ever returned to the Weald.

John Gotier had worked as the collier John Gottye for Richard Woodman in 1550 at Warbleton in the Weald. In 1569 he was recruited as a collier to work in the copper works run by German miners in the Keswick area, but by 1577 was reported dead. John's son was perhaps another collier, Henry Gotyer of Rugeley, who in 1591 worked for the forgemaster Fulk Greville and gave evidence to an Exchequer commission of inquiry concerning Bromley Forge; he had been born around 1540 and claimed to have worked in the Cannock works from around 1565. In 1590 Henry Gotyer paid 3 shillings to the subsidy

78. I am grateful to Mrs Janet Swabey for this information, and for a photocopy of the tithe map.
79. *Calendar of Patent rolls, Philip and Mary*, **3**, p. 288.
80. *Letters and Papers, Henry VIII*, **19** (1), no. 80 (27) and **21** (2), no. 332 (76).
81. *Victoria County History of Shropshire*, **3**, p. 109.
82. *Calendar of Patent rolls, Elizabeth I*, **1**, p. 326.
83. *Victoria County History of Shropshire*, **3**, p. 111 and n. 45.
84. TNA, E 179/178/169. Assessment details and payments made on this roll are unfortunately not legible.

on goods worth £3.[85]

Entries for the baptisms of Katherine, Margaret and Robert Gotyer in Rugeley parish register running from 1575 to 1579, their parentage not recorded, presumably relate to children of Henry Gotier. Robert Gotyer was probably the collier who worked at Wem Forge from 1610 to 1620, and possibly fathered the children of Robert Goteyaw or Goteyeare baptised at Betley in 1596 and 1598.

Nicholas Regell had moved on to work at Cleobury Mortimer by 1572, when his surname was recorded as Regyn. That a family named Collyns also worked on Cannock Chase is evident from the statement by Nicholas Collyns, who also moved into Shropshire, and in April 1610 testified, as a yeoman of Harley near Much Wenlock, that he had been born on the Chase 50 years earlier.[86]

At Abbots Bromley Lawrence Hatto was married in July 1562; his bride was Margaret Pegg, an indigenous surname which rapidly became widespread in English ironworks. Their children, Mary, Richard, George and Elizabeth, were baptised at Abbots Bromley from 1567 to 1579. John Mathew of the forge's son Lawrence was baptised in August 1566, but died the following year, whilst Mathew himself died in 1569. Richard Marian's children, Agnes, Lawrence, Margery and Richard, were baptised at Abbots Bromley from 1573 to 1586, after which he moved on and was eventually buried at Trentham early in 1618.

To the west of Cannock Chase a forge had operated at Brewood on the Penk in 1485. This was distinct from the site south of Somerford Hall at which Thomas Chetwynd and Walter Coleman built a forge around 1620, because several hammermen of Brewood Park were referred to in Staffordshire quarter sessions books of 1603.[87] That the forge had continued during the intervening period is suggested by the appearance there in subsidy rolls of the 1560s of Andro the Frenc[hman] (1563) and Andrewe Frenchman (1568), who in 1568 paid a poll tax of 2 pence.[88] He was perhaps Andrew Cornua alias Frenchman, who in 1592 married Ursula Yate, and who died in 1627. The parish register also shows the appearance of immigrant names such as Dofill or Duffeild from 1574, Furnace (*Vergnes*?) from 1577, and Lenard from 1579.

More specifically, Frances Marrian alias Dippard, who was baptised at Brewood in 1590, was the daughter of the finer Bartholomew Dipperie who had married Frances Emerie at Abbots Bromley in 1589 and later moved on to the Lizard forges. Moreover, although Hincks was a Midlands surname, it appears possible that the Hynckes entries recorded in this register from 1570 onwards could be those of the immigrant Haynk family.

At Cleobury Mortimer we saw that Stephen Hadnoll arrived on the scene in 1557. However, it was only when reversions of the leases of Cleobury Foreign and Cleobury Borough made to Sir George Blount in 1550 were granted to Robert Dudley, earl of Leicester in 1563, that exploitation of the woodland resources of these properties commenced. His surveyors estimated that £400 a year could be obtained from the export through Bristol of barrel staves, for which he received a licence in November 1565.[89]

The ironworks were perhaps built later in the decade, but they were certainly in being by April 1571, when seven Frenchmen, paid the alien tax there. Four of these men who again paid tax the following year were 'Hewgate Founder', who was assessed at £10 in goods, John Done and John Bray, who were each assessed at £3 in goods, and Glowde Trunchyn who paid the poll tax of 4 pence. On this assessment Hewgate, whose baptismal name was sadly not revealed, paid £1 13s 4d in 1571 and £1 in 1572, payments surpassing even what had been paid by the ironfounder Charles Gerard in the Weald. Done and Bray paid 10 shillings in 1571 and 6 shillings in 1572. Hewgate we know to have worked for Sir Henry Sidney in Glamorgan during the previous decade. Bray returned to the Weald, where he paid tax in Buttinghill in 1576. Glode Tronchin moved on to Rievaulx in North Yorkshire, where the Helmsley parish register shows he was in 1587 and 1588. Hewgate's later movements are unknown.

These four men were supplemented in 1571 by Hussey, who paid 16s 8d on goods worth £5, by a finer named Gyllam who paid 10 shillings on goods worth £3, and a collier named Gillam who paid

85. TNA, E 178/2098 and E179/178/225.

86. TNA, E 178/4533.

87. Burne, *Staffordshire Quarter Sessions Rolls*, **5**, p. 33.

88. TNA, E 179/178/169 and 184 (Cuttlestone hundred).

89. *Calendar of Patent rolls, Elizabeth I*, **2**, pp. 534-42. S. Adams, 'The earl of Leicester and the west midlands', *Midland History*, **20** (1995), p. 35.

the poll tax. Bereft of full personal details, of these men only Hussey appears identifiable as John Husher who in 1566 had been paid 10 shillings at Robertsbridge 'at his goinge (into) Walles to colliar' for Sir Henry Sidney.[90] By 1572 they had been replaced by three other Frenchmen, John Sherley, Nicholas Regyn and John Pybaly, who each paid the poll tax. As Regell, Regyn had been at Rugeley in 1563, and John Pybaly had a long history in English ironworks, having worked as a woodcutter for Sir William Sidney in 1542, paid the poll tax, presumably as a worker at Worth Furnace, in Buttinghill in 1549, and been one of Richard Weekes' servants in 1550 and 1551 in Netherfield hundred.

Rowley Forge at Cleobury was demised to Stephen Hadnall in October 1571 and he in turn obtained a licence to alienate it to William Morton in October 1576.[91] The ironworks as a whole were leased to John Weston in June 1576, and a survey of 1584 referred to two iron mills there called 'furnasses'.[92]

Meanwhile, George Talbot, earl of Shrewsbury, set up a blast furnace at Shifnal in Shropshire in 1564, together with a forge at the Lizard site near the Staffordshire border. It looks as though John Munslow, at whose Caughley smithy the French founder John Morrell had worked in the early 1550s, was involved at the forge, because it was reported to the earl in July 1564 that 'the two new fineries at the smithy in Lyssard which Munslow made' were nearly finished, though a second forge soon had to be built because of the inadequacy of the first one.[93]

Talbot had married Gertrude Manners, the daughter of Thomas, earl of Rutland, in 1539. Rutland had died in 1543, and because his successor Henry was still a minor, it was Shrewsbury's mother-in-law 'my lady Rutland' who had the 'iron maker' Lambert Symar made denizen in 1544. The seat of the Rutlands was Belvoir Castle in Leicestershire, so Talbot need not necessarily have known anything of what was afoot at Rievaulx, but his own home was at Sheffield in South Yorkshire, where he must have been well acquainted with the metal trades, especially in the shape of bladesmiths and knife-grinders.

Shrewbury's Shifnal Furnace and Lizard Forge of 1564 had presumably been intended to compete with Paget's Cannock ironworks in the Birmingham market, but perhaps also to find an outlet on the Bristol market by transport down the Severn. Shrewsbury was appointed chief steward of the earl of Leicester's lands in Warwickshire, Shropshire, Denbighshire and Yorkshire in February 1566, and although this seems to have been a purely honorary appointment,[94] it could perhaps have been prompted by his knowledge of the iron industry. In Sheffield the Shrewsbury ironworks, as we shall soon see, dated from the early 1570s and his other furnace at Whitchurch and its forge near Goodrich Castle on the Wye were in production by 1575, possibly on lands formerly belonging to the monastery of Flansford, which had been granted to his grandfather in 1538.[95] These would also presumably have supplied the Bristol market.

South Wales

Sir Henry Sidney became Lord President of the Council in the Marches of Wales in 1559. Accounts for his Welsh furnace, that at Tongwynlais, six miles above Cardiff on the eastern side of the Taff, survive for 1564-5 and since these do not include items for its erection, it had perhaps been built a year or two earlier. In addition to sow iron, the furnace produced iron plates which were shipped to Sussex and there converted into steel at Sidney's Boxhurst steelworks. The local finery forge is thought to have been at Rhyd-y-Gwern in the Rhymney valley, 5km east of the furnace.[96] Evidence for the continuance of the furnace after 1568 is not available in the Sidney accounts and since the Rhyd-y-Gwern Forge was taken over by the Company of Mineral and Battery Works in 1569-70 and afterwards used for the production of osmund iron, it looks as though Tongwynlais Furnace could have been temporarily laid down.

Almost coeval with Tongwynlais must have been the furnace at Pentyrch, on the western side

90. Crossley, *Sidney ironworks accounts*, p. 210.
91. TNA, E 179/167/44. *Calendar of Patent rolls, Elizabeth I*, **7**, p. 95.
92. Schubert, *British iron and steel industry*, p. 371.
93. Watts, 'Shifnal ironworks accounts', pp. 4-5.
94. S. Adams, 'The earl of Leicester and the west midlands', p. 41.
95. *Letters and Papers, Henry VIII*, **13** (1), no. 1309 (12).
96. Crossley, *Sidney ironworks accounts*, pp. 32-3.

of the Taff, which belonged to the Mathew family of Radyr, and was mentioned in a law suit in May 1565.[97] This furnace was presumably of local origin, established under the stimulus of the Tongwynlais operation, and perhaps the one used by Edmund Mathew for gunfounding from the late 1590s onwards.

In Monmouthshire events were heavily influenced by the Worcestershire forgemaster, Richard Hanbury, who in 1570 became one of the lessees of the Tintern wireworks, which belonged to the Mineral and Battery Works. Another early foundation, Monkswood Furnace established in 1564, was from 1570 operated by Hanbury. Cwm Frwd-oer Furnace near Pontypool was leased by the Mineral and Battery Works to Richard Martin, Andrew Palmer, John Wheeler and Richard Hanbury in 1570, but from 1577 onwards it was in Hanbury's ownership.

Thus, out of four ironworks started in south Wales before 1575, only one owed its foundation to Wealden entrepreneurs. On the other hand a fifth, started in the early 1570s, owed its conception to immigrant forgemen and its execution to Wealden forgemasters. Jordan Russell II, probably the grandson of an immigrant, claimed to have initiated the setting up of ironworks in Glamorgan in the Forest or Chase of Glin Cynon (*Lyncommon*).[98] The ironworks in question was Dyffryn Furnace, near Aberdare in the Cynon valley, an upstream tributary of the Taff, but this was linked to two forges, one in Llanwonno parish and another called the 'New forge', perhaps at Mountain Ash.

In a Chancery bill dated 23 November 1584 Russell claimed that the ironworks in this area grew out of a visit he and the late Richard Bennett had made to Wales some '10 or 11 years last past'.[99] This fits neatly with the dates of 1574, in which Dyffryn Furnace is thought to have been built, and between 1575 and 1578, when it first produced shot for ordnance.[100]

During their visit to Glamorgan, Russell and Bennett made a bargain with the earl of Pembroke's agent, Edmond Morgan, to buy a 21-year lease of all the earl's woods, underwoods, timber and trees within the Forest, with all its water, watercourses, mines of ironstone and coal for £300, but without rent. They were to be at liberty to divert the water and watercourses, to make dams, erect and build iron mills, houses and forges for the getting of ironstone and coal and all other things necessary for the melting and making of iron. Payment was to be made, £150 at 1 May, with the remainder at St James' tide (25 July).

After his return to Sussex, Russell acquainted William Darrell of Litlington with the scheme. Darrell expressed himself eager to enter into partnership with them, and since the time was approaching when they would have to find the money, Russell and Bennett agreed to this. Darrell was to advance the £300, to build the mills, houses and forges, and was to enjoy the works until he had made good the £300 together with his costs and charges, after which he was to have half the profits, the other half going to Russell, Bennett, and George Coucheman, an Ardingly draper, who had now entered their partnership. By 1569 Coucheman was an intermediary in the transaction by which a property in Buxted, later part of the Hogge House estate, was sold to George Burgess.[101]

Unfortunately, due to the lameness of his horse, Russell was unable to accompany Darrell when he visited Wales to seal the bargain and to pay the money. However, Bennett, who was there, advised Darrell that there was much more wood available than they could ever use in 21 years, so Darrell returned with the idea of building a double furnace and two forges, of which he proposed that Russell, Bennet and Coucheman should have the one forge to their own use, together with half the sows produced at the furnaces, without paying any part of the £300. Subsequently Darrell made different proposals: firstly, that he should take over the whole project, but pay the three other partners £100 a year in recompense; secondly, he prevaricated about giving sureties for the £100 and tried to treat with Russell separately, suggesting that he should enter Darrell's service and make merchantable iron of the best sort for him.

After this, the partners complained of their treatment to Thomas Lewis, a Llandaff justice of the peace, whose service Bennett had now entered. Lewis advised them to try once more to persuade

97. P. Riden, 'Early ironworks in the lower Taff valley', *Morgannwg; the journal of Glamorgan history*, **36** (1992), p. 70.

98. W. Llewellin, 'Sussex ironmasters in Glamorganshire', *Archaeologia Cambrensis*, 3rd series, **34** (1863), p. 84.

99. TNA, C 3/216/15.

100. Schubert, *British iron and steel industry*, p. 374.

101. ESRO, AMS 6888/1/32-33.

Darrell to make assurance of the annuity of £100, but in this they were unsuccessful. Lewis then revealed that he had a lease of the herbage and pannage of the Forest of which 18 years were unexpired, which he could use to prevent Darrell from cutting wood, breaking the ground, or building any ironworks. They agreed to pay Lewis a £20 fine and a yearly rent of £10 for his permission for them to do all these things. Lewis then rode out into the Forest and stopped Darrell and his workmen from felling wood and breaking the ground.

Next to be involved was Anthony Morley, who was the younger brother of William Morley of Glynde, the forgemaster at Hawksden. When made privy to proceedings by George Coucheman, he offered to buy their agreement with Thomas Lewis on favourable terms. Coucheman took a letter to Lewis which contained Morley's proposals and his request that Lewis should persuade Russell and Bennett to give their agreement. Morley was to take over the partners' obligations to Lewis, pay Lewis £30 for his agreement, and to pay the partners £20 down, with annuities of £20 each to Russell and Bennett and of £30 to Coucheman. They having agreed to these proposals, Morley came to Wales and indentures were drawn up in the manner suggested, except that they included the transfer to Morley, not only of the partners' agreement with Lewis, but also of their former agreement with Darrell.

But Russell was concerned that the indentures did not lay down the precise dates and places at which Morley was to make payment of the various sums involved. Morley assured them that he would come to Wales again at May Day following, provided with the necessary assurances for each of the parties. The articles of agreement were left in the hands of Thomas Mathews who lived about three miles from the Old Forge near the forest, perhaps Llanwonno.

Meanwhile Darrell had bought an old forge about three miles outside the bounds of the Forest and had built a furnace between the forge and the Forest, which he was able to run for about three years with wood from elsewhere, hoping thereby to weary the partners into treating with him. Nor did Morley appear again in Wales to make any of the payments due to either Lewis or the partners. But Darrell found himself unable to make the anticipated profit because of his difficulty in obtaining fuel and iron ore, so he invited Russell, Cocheman, Morley and his own new partner, William Relfe, to a meeting in London, which took place in Southwark during the winter.

Darrell estimated the works he had built under the first agreement to be worth £600 a year and he agreed to rent it to Russell and Coucheman, together with the old forge and the second furnace which he had built, for £300 p.a., along with all his stock of wood, charcoal, mine, sows and all his wrought iron lying between the works and Bristol, which he reckoned to be worth £300, or, if they so preferred, he would give them £300 instead of this stock. Russell and Coucheman thought that the stock would be useful to them and at Anthony Morley's persuasion they agreed that he should replace Bennett in the partnership, provided that Morley would indemnify Bennett according to the terms of the earlier agreement. The indentures were to be drawn up and to be presented at a further meeting at the Talbot Inn in Southwark fixed for a fortnight's time. However, the indentures were not then produced, on the excuse that Thomas Lewis's agreement had not been secured, and to lend further colour to this pretence Morley, Darrell and Relfe each contributed fo[rty shillings?] to send Russell on a fruitless errand to Wales, where Lewis refused to sign the proposed agreement because Morley had not performed his earlier agreements. By these devious means, Russell alleged, the original protagonists of this Welsh ironworks had been deluded, and cheated out of their just deserts.

Edward Cavell, the ironfounder at Dyffryn, was also a Sussex man; he died in 1578.[102] His family is unlikely to have been of immigrant origin, because John Cavyll the younger, who (transcribed as Canyll) paid tax on goods worth £1 at Buxted/Greenhurst in 1525, was not an alien.

South Yorkshire

Whilst many of the nobility saw ironworks as a means to finance their social extravagances or political careers by raising capital from the sale of woodlands, the earl of Shrewsbury appears to have had the welfare of local people much at heart. He was buried at Sheffield in 1590 and in his will left bequests of £200 per annum for the benefit of artificers in the towns of Pontefract and Rotherham.[103]

102. Schubert, *British iron and steel industry*, p. 374.

103. TNA, PROB 11/76/425.

In 1803 'A Descendant of a Refugee' communicated to the *Sheffield Iris* the story of how George, sixth earl of Shrewsbury, as commissioner for the settlement of Huguenot refugees in Yorkshire, had contributed greatly to the growth of the cutlery trades around Sheffield. Later elaborations of this story gave 1570 as the date of the refugees' arrival. But Professor Lloyd, historian of the cutlery trade, who subjected this story to examination in 1913, came to the conclusion that, 'The only scraps of local evidence of a positive character that can be adduced are derived from industrial terminology and technique'.[104]

However, the real aims of the earl of Shrewsbury in the Sheffield area are perhaps illustrated by the first question, which according to the correspondent of the *Sheffield Iris*, he addressed to the prospective immigrants of the 1570s, 'not Can you make a knife?' but 'can you make anything in the iron steel way?'.[105] And it would have indeed been strange for the introduction of the indirect process of ironmaking near the earl of Shrewsbury's home in Sheffield to have been delayed beyond the 1570s.

A gap of 30 years between the lay subsidy rolls of 1568 and 1598 for the wapentake of Strafforth and Tickhill eliminates evidence for the presence of foreign refugees in the Sheffield area at the precise period involved.[106] Fortunately, the parish register for Sheffield shows that during the 1570s members of the immigrant families Dippray (1573), Allen (1575), Maryon (1576), Valliance (1576) and Russell (1577), all of them well enough known in the Weald, were present in Sheffield. Of these surnames, Allen seems indigenous to the town, but the baptismal names of Ralph Allen's sons, Bastian in 1577 and Michael in 1579, suggest his French descent. Michael was the baptismal name of an alien surnamed Alyne who had paid the poll tax in Danehill Horsted hundred in Sussex in 1551, moreover the Sheffield Michael Allen moved on later to the ironworks at Rievaulx, from where he was married at Helmsley in 1606 to Isabella Russell, who had herself been baptised at Sheffield.

Many surnames similar to those borne by immigrants to the Weald can be found in the Sheffield parish register already during the 1560s, in particular Peter Pynion who married Agnes Jane early in 1567. However it was from 1570 onwards that new names, some of them foreign and others associated with the Weald and with ironworking, started to appear. Firstly Laurence Cheyney was buried, and Silvester Huit was baptised, on 20 and 24 June 1571 respectively. The first child of Bastian Pagez, or Pagions, Anne Basten, was baptised, and Robert Braydow was buried, on 14 and 17 October respectively. Lawrence Totte, possibly Totain, was baptised on 1 January 1572. In June 1573 Thomas Freeman and Henry Steele were buried at Sheffield, the Freeman entry the only sixteenth-century occurrence of this surname in the Sheffield parish register, though he obviously cannot have been the forgeman of that name who was mentioned in the Frant parish register in 1578.

Men probably from the Weald who were married in Sheffield during the 1570s were Lawrence Dippray (1574), Ralph Allen (1575), Thomas Good and Gyles Maryon (both January 1576), John Valyance (1576), and possibly Christopher Waddye (1578).[107] Dippray also gave rise to the baptism of an illegitimate child in 1574, as had Nicholas Steede and William Burgesse in 1573, and as did Robert Barton in 1578. Other men from the Weald may have been William Gee and James Barton, who were buried in 1577 and 1581 respectively; Margery Gee, whom Gyles Maryon married, could have been Gee's daughter.

Disruption caused by the introduction of ironworks into the area was not confined to the births of illegitimate children. The diary and accounts of William Dickenson, bailiff of Hallamshire, show that, as the earl's mills were turned over from corn milling to the metal trades, compensation had to be paid to persons displaced. It was precisely in 1574 that such payments were made to Thomas Chapman of Heeley, to John Garlick, and to William Greaves of Charnock Hall; the payment to Greaves was of £1.[108]

That ironfounding was indeed being carried out in the Sheffield area at this time, perhaps on

104. B. G. Awty, 'French immigrants and the iron industry in Sheffield', *Yorkshire Archaeological Journal*, **53** (1981), p. 57; G. I. H. Lloyd, *The cutlery trade; an historical essay in the economics of small scale production* (1913), p. 105.

105. Awty, 'French immigrants', p. 61.

106. TNA, E 179/208/230 (1568) and 271 (1598).

107. That this surname occurred elsewhere in South Yorkshire is shown by the marriage of Nicholas Waddye at Silkstone in May 1573.

108. SA, RC/159/12001, f. 68v.

the Kimberworth manor site granted to the earl's father in 1552,[109] is confirmed by the amercement in 10 shillings in the Sheffield manor court in April 1578 of James Tyler, *founderer*, for 'a Fraye made upon Nicholas Sanderson of Sheffield and for blood drawen at the same Fraye'.[110] The accounts for 'bothe your Lordships Hammers' show that a production of 220 tons 4 cwt of bar iron was achieved at Attercliffe in the year beginning 14 November 1585, when Roland Revell and Martin Ashe took charge there. Nicholas Smyth, who had previously run the forges, had left owing £386 5s 11d in debts. The two hammers and the high output of 1585-6 suggest that both Kimberworth and Wadsley furnaces were by then in blast. The largest customers were Robert Fletcher of Makeney in Derbyshire, who owed £36 for iron in 1586 and William Fletcher and partners (*cum sociis*), owing £57 7s 6d in 1587. However, a local man, Richard Houghton of Howbrook owed £25 4s 0d in 1586.

After Revell and Ashe left Attercliffe forges in 1590, they were run for nine weeks between 22 March and 24 May by Francis Storth, Anthony Robertes and Thomas Twigg. The payment made to the hammerman was of 13s 4d for each ton of iron drawn out.[111]

Men associated with Attercliffe Hammers were the hammerman Hugh Bamford, who in 1586 owed 12s 1d for iron supplied to him,[112] Thomas Fraunce of Attercliffe who owed a similar debt of £2 17s 8d, John Swann 'de Atterclyffe' who was buried at Sheffield in 1587, and John Vallyance, who was described as being 'of Attercliffe' in 1601, four years after his death, when his daughter Alice was buried at Norton Woodseats. Maurice Lawrence, whose son George was baptised at Sheffield in 1587, probably also worked at Attercliffe, because he was the finer employed at Oakamoor in Staffordshire in 1593 when the ironworks there first went over to the indirect method.

Hugh Bamford was of course of English descent, but there were two men of that name in Sheffield at the time. By his marriage to Mary Swinden in 1580 the hammerman Hugh Bamforth probably became related to Ralph Allen, who had married Elizabeth Swinden in 1575. At Whitsuntide1588 he paid a half yearly rent of £4 15s 0d for Attercliffe mill, which cannot be the Hammers. At the mill he perhaps processed the iron which he had bought at the Hammers. His payment of the same sum in 1589 was accompanied by a note that the mill had now been leased to John Royles.[113]

Thomas Fraunce had married Anne Staniforth at Sheffield in 1579. The question as to whether he was a local man, or of immigrant descent, cannot be resolved. Fraunce baptisms occurred in Sheffield from 1562 onwards and the marriage of Hugh Fraunce preceded that of Thomas Fraunce by 10 years. Thomas's children, Laurence and John, were baptised in 1580 and 1584 respectively, but Laurence did not survive childhood.

The Swann connection with ironworking was established early in 1585 when the parish register named the putative father of Jenett Swann's illegitimate child as Richard 'Ironmann', a description rather than a surname. An earlier forgeman named Swann had worked at Woodcock 'Hammer Mills' in Godstone, but his baptismal name was not given in the entry of July 1561 in Lingfield parish register, which recorded the baptism of his son Reginald. In later parish register entries Reginald, or Reynold, was often surnamed Soane.

John Valyance moved on from Attercliffe to Royston parish after 1591 and was buried there in August 1597. The Doncaster deanery act book described him as of 'Monckbretton smithies' when administration of his effects was granted later that month.

A deposition made by John Boyne, a former tenant of these smithies, dated April 1588, related that they had been demised by the Crown to Robert Thwaytes in 1548. Boyne had held the smithies for four or five years in the early 1580s, but they were in such disrepair that he could make only three blooms of iron in a whole year. Around 1586 the remainder of the lease had apparently been transferred to George Woodruffe, esquire, and John Valyance. A smithyman named George Truelove deposed that two new water wheels which they had installed took all the water of Dearne, so that whereas previously the water had sufficed for five wheels, including two corn mills and a fulling mill, these new wheels took

109. *Calendar of Patent rolls, Edward VI*, **4**, p. 407. The grant included a water (corn) mill and two fulling mills.

110. SA, ACM/6/4/4 f. 1v

111. Op. cit.

112. Op. cit.

113. SA, ACM/6/4/5.

all the water.[114]

Within a year or two of John Valyance's death, his family had moved to Norton Woodseats, where in 1601 his daughter Alice was buried, where in 1604 his daughter Mary married the scythesmith John Parker, and where in 1621 his son Jasper Valiance was buried. His youngest son George, who had been baptised at Royston in 1595, found his way into the Company of cutlers in Hallamshire, perhaps through John Parker's agency, and in 1633 became the first Master Cutler from the immigrant community.

Cheyney was a Wealden name and Laurence Cheyney, who was buried at Sheffield in 1571, was perhaps the father of John Cheaney, whose children, Laurence, Elizabeth and Roger, were baptised between 1576 and 1581. It seems probable that John Chennye, who was baptised in February 1574 but whose parentage was not disclosed, was the first of John Cheyney's children.

Another family which appeared in Sheffield during the 1570s was that of Raynold. James Raynold was buried at Sheffield early in 1577 and his wife may have been the widow Alice Raynold, who was buried there in November 1586. John Raynold was perhaps the man who married Elizabeth Bearde at Ecclesfield in November 1572 and their children, John, Thomas, Edward and Elizabeth, were baptised at Sheffield between 1578 and 1586, though Thomas died in February 1587.

Of French origin were Bastian Pagez, or Pagions, Peter Roolett and Piers Adryan. Roolett and Adryan were each denoted *gallus* in the parish register; the former at his burial in September 1574 and the latter at the burial of his son Arnold in November 1583. There were numerous references in the parish register to Bastian, whose children, Anne, who did not survive, Anthomete, Anne, Jane and Elizabeth were baptised between 1571 and 1581, though Elizabeth too failed to survive. The attribution of the title 'Master' to Bastyan, when his daughter Jane was baptised in October 1579, suggests he was perhaps a cutler rather than an ironworker.

The arrival in Sheffield of the hammerman Jordan Russell II by 1577 is noteworthy. He had married Margery May of Frant at Maresfield in 1562, his first children, Valentine and Rebecca, were baptised at Frant in 1566 and 1569, and his daughter Elizabeth at Buxted in 1571. The early 1570s had seen him engaged in the frustrated attempt to set up ironworking in the upper Cynon valley in Glamorgan. He was at Sheffield from 1577 to 1582, a period when his children Christian, John and Isabel were born. By November 1584 he had moved to Duffield parish in Derbyshire, from where he initiated his Chancery suit concerning events in Wales.

Jordan Russell's departure from Sheffield was perhaps preceded by the arrival there of Peter Russell, who had left the Weald after 1580. He had been at Worth in 1566, at Crowhurst from 1570 to 1578 and at Speldhurst in 1580. His move to Sheffield occurred between the baptism of his daughter Katherine at Speldhurst in March 1580 and the baptism of his daughter Elizabeth at Sheffield in May 1583. The identity of the Crowhurst and Speldhurst man with the Sheffield Peter Russell is established by the marriage of his daughter Joan, who had been baptised at Crowhurst in 1578, to Robert Wightman at Rotherham in 1596, and by the burial of his infant daughter Katherine at Sheffield in September 1583.

Whereas Jordan Russell was presumably employed at Attercliffe Hammers, Peter Russell took a lease of Brightside Mill at a rent of £16 a year from Christmas 1585, presumably to set up his own works in the Don valley. The Shrewsbury accounts, which end in 1590, show half-yearly payments of £8 still being made by Russell in 1588 and 1589.[115] His son Nicholas was baptised at Sheffield in August 1586, but Peter Russell himself was buried at Sheffield in January 1593.

As former ironworkers moved on others replaced them. They included John Morrell who in 1586 owed £2 2s 9d for iron had from Attercliffe Hammers;[116] this he had apparently acquired 'for Barden'. Barden was presumably of immigrant stock, but his name cannot be found in the Sheffield parish register, unless in the corrupted form of Barton. John Morrell was the father of Mary Morrell, who was baptised at Sheffield early in 1587, and probably also of William Morrell, who was baptised there in 1583, but whose parentage was not disclosed.

Another ironworker was perhaps John Lambert, who married Isabel Barker at Norton in 1587

114. TNA, E 134/Elizabeth I/Easter 28.
115. SA, ACM/6/4/3.
116. S, ACM/6/4/4.

and whose sons John and Francis were baptised at Sheffield in 1588 and 1592. John Lambert and his wife were both buried at Sheffield in 1634 and 1628 respectively, and his second son Francis had four children baptised there between 1616 and 1634.

Wadsley Furnace which was mentioned in the Attercliffe Forge accounts of 1585 to 1590, was perhaps set up around 1580, because two members of the Bartholomew family, Alice and John were buried at Ecclesfield in 1581 and 1582. Another name of immigrant origin at Ecclesfield may be that of Thomas Potter, five of whose children were baptised at Ecclesfield between 1607 and 1618. A Wealden name which appeared briefly at Ecclesfield was that of Relf. Richard Relf married Alice Bromhead in 1594 and William Relf married a woman surnamed Bower in 1603. Richard Relf of Ecclesfield's wife Alice was buried at Ecclesfield in 1603 and in 1617 he, or another Richard married Dorothy Goulding.

The name Bartholomew rapidly became established at Rotherham, where William Bartholomew married Alice Hall in 1588. As at Ecclesfield, Bartholomew entries in the Rotherham parish register commenced in 1581, with the baptism of Margaret Bartholomew, followed in 1582 by the baptisms of Alice and Ellin, probably twins, and of Mary Bartlmew in 1586, but parents' names were not indicated in this parish register until 1604. The marriage of 1588 probably came to a rapid end, because William Bartolmoew was buried in 1591, and the only child baptised during the brief period of their marriage was Agnes Bartlmew in 1589. Alice Bartelmewe, perhaps William's widow, was buried early in 1607. Quinton Bartellmow who was buried at Rotherham in 1613, was the son of William baptised at Rotherfield in 1575. He was finer at Kimberworth Forge and his will was made in the name of Pountinge, which proves his descent from Bartholomew Ponting, though it does not prove that all the local Bartholomews were descended from him.

Norway

Remarkable though the expansion of the indirect process throughout the southern half of the British Isles may have been, it was outstripped in the last quarter of the century. And already by the 1570s the reservoir of talents and expertise nourished in the Weald spread outside these islands when a party of Wealden ironworkers embarked for Norway, and set up a blast furnace in the Hakedal, a valley to the east of Oslo itself. It seems likely that they intended to build a complete indirect-pattern ironworks consisting of furnace, finery and hammer mill, but in effect they were remembered chiefly as having been able to produce cast-iron goods.

This enterprise seemed to have ended in complete failure when the bulk of the workmen, whose names are unknown, returned to the Weald soon after 1580.[117] However, the seeds of future success had apparently been sowed and from the fact that the main partners in the 'Great Iron-company' (*Store jern-kompagni*) which in 1624 took over from royal control ironworks at Baerum, on Hadeland, in Hakedal and at Ski, were Johan Post and Herman Krefting,[118] it must be inferred that a member of the Post family stayed on in Norway.

FORGEMASTERS

The numbers of forgemasters having become very numerous, and because the sources used in this work, such as denization and subsidy rolls and parish registers, from this point onwards yield little new information about them, attention will be concentrated mainly on those forgemasters who were of immigrant stock and on forgemasters from the Weald who carried the indirect process beyond its borders.

It was suggested that John Collyn of Burwash, Richard Woodman of Warbleton, John Harvo of Framfield and Henry Lucas of Lindfield were members of the immigrant community who in the period before 1550 established themselves as forgemasters in their new Wealden environment. In the period

117. G. Thuesen, 'Bergverksdrift i Oslo området', *Volund* (1988), p. 69; A. den Ouden, 'The introduction and early spread of the blast furnace in Europe', *Wealden Iron,* Bulletin of the Wealden Iron Research Group, 2nd series, **5** (1985), p. 35.

118. J. H. L. Vogt, *De gamla norske jernverk* (Norges Geologisk Undersögelse, No. 46), Kristiania, 1908, p. 7.

between 1550 and 1575 this phenomenon showed further development.

In 1550 Charles Garrete was still at Buxted, where he paid £1 on goods to the relief of that year. Having entered into partnership with the London citizen and ironmonger Christopher Draper, and Henry Westall, Sir William Sidney's former ironworks' clerk, he very soon moved to Battle. No subsidy return survives for Battle for 1551, but Charles Jerett paid 8 shillings to the relief of 1552. Draper, from being a customer of Robertsbridge Forge during the 1540s, became in this new partnership a supplier of sow iron to Robertsbridge. In 1551 the partnership supplied 100 tons of sows at £2 12s 4d the ton; however, in 1553 Draper was still a customer for Robertsbridge bar iron, of which he bought 80 tons.[119] Draper and company's furnace seems to have been Penhurst; this can be deduced firstly, because in 1551 and 1552 their alien workmen appeared in the subsidy rolls for Netherfield hundred, which proves that the furnace was located west, and not north or east, of Robertsbridge, and secondly, because transport costs of sows at £1 the ton were identical to costs for those brought from Panningridge, which suggests a source not far distant from Panningridge.[120]

Draper's business was apparently still expanding in 1555 when he and a citizen and cooper of London, John Heth, acquired 'a great tenement with houses, shops, solars, cellars and wharf called Asshelyngwharff', which abutted on the Watergate in the parish of St Dunstan in the East.[121] He reappeared as a purchaser of iron in 1570, long after his partnership with Gerard had ended.

Gerard still did repairs for Sir Henry Sidney at Panningridge up to July 1558,[122] but in the Battle hundred court of 30 March 1559 his 'heirs' were referred to.[123] He was apparently 'Charle a Frenchman' who was buried at Frant on 27 March 1559. Whether his former partnership carried on until his death is quite unsure.

The burial at Frant in December 1557 of Warnet Charles, who may have been Charles's son, a man usually styled Warnet Jeratt, together with the presence at Frant of Peter Turner, probably Sidney's former alien worker ('Peter the founder'), suggests that several former Panningridge employees had moved to Frant, perhaps in connection with (Stephen) Collin's furnace, the filler of which, Peter [Turner?] was buried at Frant in February 1566.

Though later members of the Gerard or Jarrett family continued as ironfounders and gunfounders in the Weald throughout the seventeenth and into the eighteenth century, none is known to have done so in an entrepreneurial capacity. However, the gunfounder Jarrett Holloway, who in 1711 purchased wood from Lord Montague,[124] perhaps for use at Beech Furnace, may have been a descendant too.

It has been assumed that John Harvo of Framfield, the gunfounder at Pounsley Furnace, who supplied smaller guns and shot to the Ordnance from 1547 onwards, was of immigrant descent. No trace has been found of his brother Thomas Harvo, of John son of William Harvo, or of his brother's son Gilbert Harvo, persons all named in Harvo's will. Robert Hodgson, a witness and a beneficiary under Harvo's will to the extent of £1, was the later gunfounder at Pounsley and presumably followed Harvo there, though Richard Weekes of Battle, whom Harvo made his overseer, may have had a role to play there. Both these men were of local origin.

However, William Barbye, to whom Harvo left his best coat, and who as 'Barbie' witnessed the will, was probably of immigrant descent. He was a gunfounder, and in 1592 worked for Henry Nevill, Sir Thomas Gresham's successor at Mayfield. But because the Dickinson list of gunfounders was deficient in baptismal names, 'Barby works for Mr Nevill' has been taken to refer to Robert Hodgson's son Barnaby, who did indeed cast guns at Mayfield Furnace, but a decade later, from 1599 to 1609.[125]

John Barbile, who was too poor to contribute to the subsidy at Rye in 1525, was probably an immigrant. James Barbye was among the hanaper-roll denizens of 1541. The first Barbye mentioned in the Framfield parish register was Nicholas Barbye, who married Joan Turner in 1558. But John, Thomas and William Barbye, who were baptised at Framfield between 1561 and 1566, were perhaps William's

119. Crossley, *Sidney ironworks accounts*, pp. 101, 108n.
120. Ibid., p.102n.
121. *Calendar of Letters patent, Philip and Mary*, **2**, p. 232.
122. Crossley, *Sidney ironworks accounts*, p. 177n.
123. HEH, BA Vol. 95 f. 18.
124. Straker, *Wealden iron*, p. 315.
125. Teesdale, *Gunfounding in the Weald*, p. 96.

sons, though their parentage was not indicated in the parish register. In any case the elder William Barby was at Mayfield by 1571, where three of his children were baptised between that date and 1577. He could have moved to Mayfield in order to cast guns for Gresham.

A second William Barby, presumably the man baptised at Framfield in 1566, had a son John baptised at Frant in 1592, followed by Mary and Margaret baptised at Mayfield in 1593 and 1596. Mary Barby will have been the woman for whose marriage to the ironfounder John Gurr of Mayfield a licence was granted in February 1621.[126] Two William Barbys were buried at Mayfield, the first in April 1598 and the second in January 1602, but which of these was the gunfounder cannot be determined. Probate records can be found for neither man.

John Barby, baptised at Framfield in 1561, was married at Mayfield to Elizabeth Relf in 1588. John Relfe of the Oak had a daughter of that name, perhaps baptised before the start of the parish register in 1570, and this marriage would have made Barby the brother-in-law of the future gunfounder, Richard Relf.. However, John Barby died in 1593 and Elizabeth in 1596, leaving just two children, William and Elizabeth, baptised at Mayfield in 1589 and 1593.

An earlier man from this family was probably 'John Barbe', who along with the immigrants Thomas Digon and Remy Harvye, had supplied sow iron to Robertsbridge Forge in 1564. They were perhaps successors to Draper, Westall and Gerard at Penhurst Furnace, and Remy Harvie, who had been a servant of Hugh Collyn in Henhurst hundred in 1552 when he presumably worked at Socknersh Furnace, had moved to Penhurst before 1562, when his son Ninian was baptised there. Thomas Digon died in 1565, in which year it was Remy Harvey alone who supplied 6 tons of sows to Robertsbridge. The other Harvey immigrant, John, had continued at Henhurst from 1552 to 1572, had paid the poll tax in Ninfield hundred in 1576, but was buried at Penhurst in February 1579. Whether the Harvey family continued as forgemasters at Penhurst throughout this time is impossible to say. There were no further mentions of this 'John Barbe'

At the Vachery ironworks in Cranleigh, which were started around 1550, a rent roll for 1571 named Richard Gratwick and John Gardner as liable for 'the forge and the ground which they have by lease'. Richard Gratwick was the son of Roger Gratwick of Sullington, who had purchased the attainted duke of Norfolk's manor of Beeding from the Crown in April 1553,[127] and may have run the ironworks in St Leonards Forest from their inception. From later evidence it is clear that Richard Gratwick's partner at Vachery, John Gardner, bore the alias Lambert, which linked him with the immigrant Frenchmen John and Marian Lambert alias Gardner, who had paid the poll tax in Hartfield and Wadhurst respectively in the 1540s.

In 1573 John Lambert was accused, together with Richard Weste of Rudgwick, of felling 837 oak and beech trees, within 14 miles of navigable water,[128] and in 1581 he was subject to a similar charge, on this occasion in concert with the forgemaster John Thorpe, who had acquired the Vachery works in 1580, when the former landlord Edward Bray defaulted on mortgage repayments. In 1574 a letter from Edward Bray to a local Justice, William More of Loseley, about the threatening behaviour of William Heyward, a collier at the works, included the complaint that John Gardner of Cranley 'by his own speech in a common ale house doth seem to be a maintainer of the said Heyward in his lewdness'.[129]

In 1571 John Gardner had been rated to the Cranleigh subsidy at £4 in goods, on which he paid 6s 8d. The payment had increased to 10 shillings by 1589, and in 1593, the year of his death, he paid £1 6s 8d on £10.[130] In this final assessment Gardner's partner and cousin John Gavis alias Blacket was rated to the same amount. When John Gardiner alias Lamberd died in December 1593 he bequeathed to John Gavis alias Blacket the lease of his forge to satisfy the debts which he owed him 'till the said debtes by the yearlie rent of the said forge shalbe worne out, the rent to be as myne overseers and the praisers of my goodes . . . shall finde and value the same'.[131]

There is no evidence for the continuance of John Gavis at Vachery. However, William Gardner,

126. Dunkin, *Sussex Marriage Licences, Lewes 1670-1729,* p. 267.

127. J. English, 'Vachery Forge and Furnace, Cranleigh, Surrey', *Wealden Iron,* Bulletin of the Wealden Iron Research Group, 2nd series, **19** (1999), p. 25. *Calendar of Patent rolls, Edward VI,* **5**, pp. 124-25.

128. Straker, *Wealden iron*, p. 446.

129. English, 'Vachery Forge and Furnace', pp. 26-7.

130. TNA, E 179/185/301 (1571), 185/336 (1589), 186/351 (1593).

131. LMA, DW/PA/05, 1593/176.

who in 1619 took a lease, along with the forgemaster Sackville Crowe, of land at Vachery which included a 'parcel of land and pasture that the pond called the furnace pond overflows', may have been the ironmaker's younger son of that name. William Gardner of Albury's burial at Wem in Shropshire in 1644 suggests that he had some connection with the forge which was mentioned in the parish register of Wem from around 1608 to 1624.

Despite the alias and the unusual name Gavis, there seems to be no proof of an immigrant origin for John Gardner's cousin. Indeed, the name Blakett had occurred in connection with ironworking in North Yorkshire in the 1540s. There, although Lambert Symar continued at Rievaulx after he had rebuilt the forge, by 1545 an ecclesiastic named John Blakett, who later became vicar of Helmsley, was manager of the works at both Laskill and Rievaulx.[132]

The name seems first to be met with in the Weald at Horsham early in 1561 when Anne daughter of John Gavis was baptised, with Anne Henwysey (Hunniset), widow, acting as godmother. Gavis was probably the John Blacket, who in 1574 had a furnace in 'Hodly', probably not Gravetye as suggested by Straker, an attribution questioned by Cattell,[133] but Chittingly Manor in West Hoathly of which Mr Michael (Michell) was the owner. Gavis's wife was buried at Balcombe in 1598, and he himself was buried at Slinfold in 1614, leaving a will which styled him John Gavis alias Blacket of Slinfold, ironfounder. He made Katherine Blount, youngest daughter of Mr Richard Blount of Dedisham, his sole legatee and executrix.[134] The 'attached' list of debtors mentioned in the will was not reproduced with its registered copy. The Slinfold location suggests that Gavis may have worked Dedisham Furnace and that it was from there that Vachery Forge could have taken sow iron after its own furnace at Vachery was no longer in blast.

Michael Gavye (Gavis) first appeared as a sponsor for a Maresfield baptism in 1566. His son John was baptised at Worth in November 1567, but survived only until August 1568. Michael's son Thomas was buried at Worth in January 1568, followed by his wife Joan in February, though the baptismal entry of 1567 which had given her name as Marie was perhaps more correct. In effect he married a second wife named Joan Vowsden in May 1568 and their first child Alice was probably the girl baptised at East Grinstead in 1569. Their second child Michael was baptised at Worth early in 1571.

Participation of the family in the move of the industry to the extreme west of Sussex is indicated by the burial unbaptised of a son of Michael Blackett at Rogate in 1595, but whether the father was the Michael baptised at Worth in 1571, or his father, cannot be determined. Michael Gavys alias Blackett was buried at Rogate early in 1604. The widow named Alice Blackett buried at Lurgashall in 1610 was perhaps the Rogate man's widow. Another member of this family was Nicholas Blacket, who married Frances Whyte at Kirdford in 1589.

Ellis Gavis alias Blacket married Mary Quittenden at Dallington in 1621. Their daughter Elizabeth was baptised at Dallington in 1623, but whether Alice Blackett alias Gavis, buried there in 1630, was their daughter, or was the woman baptised at East Grinstead in 1569, was not disclosed. Ellis's wife Mary was buried at Dallington early in 1636 and in May of that year Ellis married Margaret Bernie (Beenie?) at Catsfield. Their son John was baptised at Dallington in 1637, and there 'Ellis Gavies commonly called Old Blackett' was buried in 1667. A quarter sessions warrant for his arrest, issued in 1637 for reasons unknown, referred to him as an Ashburnham labourer.[135]

The next generation of this family seems to be indicated at Mountfield, where Richard and Anne, children of Richard Gavis alias Blacket, were baptised in 1668 and 1670. The Brightling tithe book listed a founder at Darvel Furnace named Richard Blackett in 1665 and 1666, and the founder named Blacket who was listed among payers of the hearth tax at Battle in 1665 was possibly the same individual.[136]

John Collyn I's eldest French-born son John was presumably the John Collyn II who employed two alien colliers, both named John Gue in Tottingworth hundred in 1550. The forge will have been the copyhold one in Burwash previously held by his father, sometimes called the Nether forge in Burwash

132. J. G. McDonnell, 'An account of the iron industry in upper Ryedale and Bilsdale, c. 1150-1650', *Ryedale Historian*, **6** (1972), p. 44.

133. Cattell, 'The 1574 lists of Wealden ironworks', pp. 168-9.

134. TNA, PROB 11/124/5.

135. ESRO, QR 38, m. 37.

136. ESRO, PAR 254/6/7; TNA, E 179/258/20.

to distinguish it from Brightling or Glaziers Forge situated some distance upstream and belonging to Nicholas Pelham. As the forge lay in Burwash it devolved with Collyn's lands in that parish on his eldest son. It is evident that John Collyn II held this forge until shortly before his death. In 1574 he was described as 'an old man of 80 years and not able to travel', but nonetheless he did not surrender the forge to the use of his son Henry until 1584.[137]

Of Henry's children, two daughters Mary and Constance appear to have survived. Mary married Robert Cruttenden in 1586 and in September 1596 Henry Collen paid a fine of £4 for a licence to let the forge and other copyhold lands in Burwash to Cruttenden. But in December Robert Cruttenden was taken ill and by his will left the forge and all its profits to Thomas May of Burwash for the performance of the legacies in his will, of which Henry Collen was an overseer and together with Richard Stollion, one of the witnesses.[138] Meanwhile Mary's sister Constance had married Richard, the son of the forgemaster Thomas Stollyan, in October 1596.

Later proceedings in the manor court followed the death of Henry Collen of Lewes in 1600. It appears that prior to Collen's death he had surrendered all his customary lands and part of the forge to the use of himself and his wife Alice, with remainder to Richard Stollyan, and had also come to an agreement with Richard's father by which, in return for the payment of considerable sums to Robert Cruttenden's heirs and others, the forge devolved on Thomas Hepden.[139]

Socknersh Furnace went with John Collyn I's Brightling lands to his second, and first English-born son, Alexander I. It was he who acquired land at Lamberhurst around 1548 on which Hoadly Forge was built. He died in February 1551 and since his children were all still minors he left the ironworking interests to his widow Julian, with remainder to his third son Alexander II.[140] However, the eldest son John died still a minor in 1552 and Alexander and his mother Julian both died in 1566. The Lamberhurst estates had devolved on Alexander II's brother Stephen and by his will Alexander II left his Brightling estates to his younger brother Thomas.[141]

Stephen held Hoadly Forge in 1574, but sold it to Robert Filmer in 1584.[142] Richard Collens of 'Hodey forge' who was mentioned in the Lamberhurst parish register in 1615 was possibly a grandson of John Collyn II.

Socknersh Furnace remained in the hands of Thomas Collins I's descendants for many years. He married very late in life and at the time of his death in 1612 his eldest son Thomas Collins II was aged only eleven. As his second wife, Thomas Collins II married Elizabeth daughter of the forgemaster Peter Farnden of Sedlescombe who, together with John Roberts alias Callis, took a four-year lease of Socknersh Furnace in 1671.[143]

The forgemaster at Horsmonden, according to assize court records concerning the alleged theft from Horsmonden Furnace of various goods by the ironfounder Michael Collyn in 1564, was Nicholas Leysard or Lewshodd. His name had already appeared in the Weald in February 1556 as Nicholas Lewsad, the fourth overseer appointed by Goddard Bachelor of Etchingham to assist his executors, his wife Maryan and son Thomas, in the administration of his will.[144] The forgemaster Thomas May was the first witness to Bachelor's will. A further link of Nicholas Lesard with both Echingham and Thomas May came in April 1560 when he and his wife Mildred were granted a licence to alienate to May unspecified lands in Etchingham for a payment into the hanaper of five marks.[145]

By 1559 Lesurde had already left the Etchingham area and was at Wadhurst, and therefore already perhaps linked with Horsmonden. In 1560 as Nicholas Lesset he paid 9s 4d to the lay subsidy in Wadhurst on land worth £7,[146] a figure which was only £1 less than Stephen Collyn of Lamberhurst's assessment.

The different ways in which this forgemaster's name was written support the idea that he might

137. Straker, *Wealden iron*, p. 302; ESRO, ACC 165/60 (11 Dec 1584).
138. ESRO, ACC 165/60 (20 Sep 1596); TNA, PROB 11/89/5.
139. ESRO, PBT 1/3/2/289; ACC 165/60 (18 Dec 1600, 8 Jan, 12 Mar 1601).
140. TNA, PROB 11/34/436.
141. TNA, PROB 11/48/497.
142. Cleere and Crossley, *The iron industry of the Weald*, p. 340.
143. Ibid., p. 357.
144. ESRO, PBT 1/1/3/182.
145. *Calendar of Patent rolls , Elizabeth I*, **1**, p. 383.
146. TNA, E 179/190/265.

have been of foreign descent. He was perhaps the son of Nicolas Leysure, a German to whom Henry VIII had awarded an annuity for life of 200 crowns of the sun in July 1539, payable half-yearly, for services not specified,[147] and Nicholas Lisarde, presumably the same man, who in November 1554 was made the 'king's and queen's serjeant painter' at £10 yearly, payable half-yearly, an appointment extended for the term of his life in April 1556.[148] This link with the former Roman Catholic monarchs would explain the fact that among those named in the first pardon roll of Elizabeth I's reign dated January 1559 was Nicholas Leusod alias Lesard of Wadhurst, 'yoman'.[149]

Other members of this family seem to have been centred on Hadlow in Kent. The will of Alice Lesset of Hadlow was proved in 1547 and, although Thomas Lezard was a witness, Alice mentioned only her Tirry relatives. Two brothers, John Lewsode, labourer, and Ralfe Lewsarde, both of Hadlow, whose wills were proved on 24 March 1571,[150] mentioned their sisters Deborah and Mary Lewssarde, and their brother Fisher Lessarde, perhaps named after the Catholic bishop and martyr, but none of these testators mentioned any relative named Nicholas.

After 1565, Nicholas Lycette next appeared in the Churnet valley of north Staffordshire, where he took a lease of the earl of Shrewsbury's forge at Oakamoor in 1572. In 1577 he passed this lease on to Richard Weston of Rugeley and Peter Growt, and under the name Nicholas Lesurde accepted a tempting offer to build a new hammer mill for Sir Francis Willoughby at Hints.

Peter Growt will have been descended from one of the immigrants of that surname. He was mentioned in parish registers neither at Abbots Bromley nor at Rugeley. However, in 1576 'Growt' paid 5 shillings to the subsidy at Rugeley on goods worth £3, and in 1590 Richard Weston paid 2s 8d at Rugeley on land worth £2.[151]

Perhaps related to Peter Growt were Lawrence Growte, the finer at Bromley Forge in 1575, who had married Helena Mathew at Abbots Bromley in 1565, and John Growte alias Paradice, an alias unknown in the Weald, who had been at Abbots Bromley as early as November 1562, when his daughter Margery was baptised there. Catherine, wife of John Paradice was buried at Abbots Bromley in 1592 and Lawrence Growte in 1597.

IMMIGRANT WORKERS MENTIONED IN THE SIDNEY ACCOUNTS AFTER 1550

Rossett

John Rossett, who in 1551 was paid a shilling for his help in breaking the furnace mouth at Panningridge,[152] later paid the poll tax in Buttinghill hundred in 1576. He, or another John Russett, married Mary Morgyn at Worth in January 1580.

He was perhaps Jehan Rasset of Canchy, who along with Anthoine Le Fèvre of Le Carrouge, both of the parish of Sainte-Geneviève, and Jehan Lambert of Fontaines-en-Bray, raised 200 livres in August 1546 by the sale of a rent of 20 livres to Nicolas Azoult, a Rouen merchant.[153] The sale was witnessed by Phlippin Toullotte of Saint Maurice, who worked for Richard Weekes up to 1551 and for Sir William Sidney from 1551 onwards.

That a later member of this family involved in the English iron industry may have worked at Kirkstall is suggested by the baptism of Peter son of Peter Russet 'of the forge' recorded on 25 May 1617 at Leeds.

147. *Letters and Papers, Henry VIII*, **14** (2), 781 (p. 314).
148. *Calendar of Patent rolls, Philip and Mary*, **2**, p. 221 and **3**, p. 227.
149. Ibid., **1**, p. 195.
150. KHLC, DRb/PW3 (Alice), DRb/PW9 (John, Ralph).
151. TNA, E 179/178/199 (1576); 178/225 (1590).
152. KHLC, U1475, B10/5.
153. ADSM, 2 E 14/1190 (7 Aug 1546).

Lassoll

Myghell Lassoll, who assisted Peter Jolly in 1552 at one of the fineries of Robertsbridge Forge,[154] was perhaps from the Loisel family of Neuville-Ferrières and Bouelles. Miquelot Loisel of Neuville had died around 1528 leaving two sons: the elder, Colin Loisel, lived at Bouelles, apparently in right of property inherited through his wife Perette Baart; the younger, Anthoine Loisel continued at Neuville.

Colin's connection with iron is evident through the marriage of two of his daughters to ironworkers: his daughter Jehanne's husband was the forgeman Bardin Poullin; in 1536 another daughter Romayne married Robert Videbout from Graval, whom Colin allowed to set up a smith's hearth (*une feuge a usage de mareschal*) in his own house. Since Colin, who died around 1538, left only daughters, Myghell was perhaps a younger son of Anthoine Loisel, who was also dead by 1540.[155]

Lassoll never appeared in Wealden subsidy rolls, so he perhaps moved to another part of the country, along with other immigrant ironworkers who left the Weald in the 1550s and 1560s. The family is picked up again in connection with Makeney Forge in Derbyshire in 1606, when Francis Lassells of Makeney's son Brian was baptised at Duffield. Francis moved on to North Wingfield, where his daughter Marie was baptised early in 1610. An entry for Paul Lassells of Heage in the Duffield parish register in 1726 suggests that one branch of the family went to ground in Derbyshire.

However, Robert Lacells appears to have moved on to Stone Forge in Yorkshire, because his son John was buried and his daughter Elizabeth was baptised at Laughton-en-le-Morthen in 1652 and 1657 respectively.

Henold

Lawrence Henold, Henowe or Henno [Hainault?] worked as a woodcutter and collier at Panningridge during the 1550s. As a collier he was one of Sir Henry Sidney's covenant servants and in 1554 and 1555 he and John Pollyn shared the charcoal burning between them, earning £47 10s 0d in 1554 and £39 10s 8d in 1555. In 1556 and 1558 he and Ransell (Lewis Raunser) were the colliers who as covenant servants had annual wages of 13s 4d, sums which were of course dwarfed by the amounts they earned by their piecework. However, they shared the work with John Pollyn, Thomas Dogen and Philip Growte in 1556 and with Dogen, Gyllam Ullard and John Grevatt in 1558.[156]

The subsidy rolls do not record Henold's presence in Foxearle or Netherfield hundreds in 1552 or 1560, so either he was English born, or he was employed only briefly as a covenant servant in the mid 1550s. Later bearers of this name connected with the iron industry are not known, so Henold may have returned to France.

Foster

George Fostard worked as a woodcutter at Panningridge in 1554 and 1556.[157] It is quite uncertain whether this man was of immigrant descent. The French name assimilated to Foster was probably *Forestier*.

John Foster, known as Black John, who could have been both French and a collier, had a house in the Wastes (*lez Wast*) at Buxted in 1531. In February John Milward alias Frengman of Buxted, labourer, came to his house late at night and Foster murdered him with a blow to the stomach with a knife. Foster fled and was outlawed the following year.[158]

A Frenchman named Peter Foster was mentioned in the Mayfield parish register in 1585. The first notice of him had been his marriage to Maryan Botrys at Balcombe in 1566. His movements during the next 12 years are unknown, but in 1578 his daughter Eleanor was baptised at Etchingham. His first wife was buried at Goudhurst in 1583, but early in 1585 he was married again at Maresfield to Alice

154. KHLC, U1475, B8/5. He was named alternatively 'Myghell Fynar', 'Mygell, Peter's man', 'Myghell Lasso', 'Myghell Lassall'.

155. ADSM, 2 E 14/1165 (3 May 1528); 2 E 14/1164 (16 Apr 1529); 2 E 14/1173 (8 Feb 1536); 2 E 14/1174 (17 Jun 1536); 2 E 14/1184 (1 Feb 1541); 2 E 14/1184 (2 Apr 1541).

156. KHLC, U1475, B10/7, 8, 9 and 10.

157. KHLC, U1475, B11/4 (1554), B10/9 (1556).

158. Hunnisett, *Sussex Coroners' inquests, 1485-1558*, no.79.

Lynnett. Their daughter Joan was baptised at Mayfield later in 1585.

The surname Foster was widespread across the Weald, and was particularly common in the Burwash area. There seems to have been a close relationship between the family of a Burwash ashealer or potash-maker named Robert Foster and the Cruttenden family, who in turn were closely allied to the Collyn family, forgemasters at Burwash. Another link between Robert Foster and the iron industry is perhaps indicated by the probate in 1552 of his will in the 'usual dwelling house of William Blacknoll in Robertsbridge at the sign of the Black Bull'.[159] William Blacknall was at the time the clerk of the Robertsbridge ironworks.

Robert Foster left what money could be made from his 'ash which lieth out at plots' to be divided between his sons Richard, John and Thomas, who were presumably his sons of full age. To his younger son William he left Strowdes (9 acres) to the south side of the king's highway and 'part of' his tenement at Fontridge, but the eldest son Richard was to possess the remainder of the Fontridge property and the 'custody and rule' of William until the boy was 12 years of age. Robert left a tenement and lands called Plotts to his wife Joan for 16 years, after which it was to go to his son Goddard, presumably his youngest child. John and Thomas were to have his messuage and garden called Grays 'nigh to the town of Burwash'. He made his wife and his eldest son Richard residuary legatees and executors and appointed as his overseer Goddard Cruttenden, who had performed the same service for John Collyn of Burwash in 1536. The witnesses were Goddard and William Cruttenden and John Hepden.

When Thomas Foster died in 1566 he left to his eldest brother Richard 'all my ash that I have in all places', to his brother John a two-yearling heifer, to his younger brother William £1, and to his sister Elizabeth £5, with £3 which he owed her. All of this last bequest was in the hands of Henry Dennet. Thomas made John Cruttenden, whose wife was Odiana Collyn of Burwash, his residuary legatee and executor. His goods were valued at £14 0s 3d.[160]

The close relations of this family with the iron industry continued in the next generation, when in 1587 Richard Foster's daughter Joan, who had been baptised in 1567, married the ironfounder Henry Gunter of Burwash. Her elder sister Eleanor, who had been baptised in 1560 had married William Middleton in 1586. Another of Richard's daughters married George Wenham.

When Richard Foster made his will in 1607 his goods were inventoried at no more than £13 17s 8d.[161] Nevertheless he managed to find 3s 4d for the poor, and in view of their quality he left 10 shillings each to the four children of George Wenham and the six children of William Middleton. The children of Henry Gunter the ironfounder fared less well: each had ashilling, except for Richard's godson Richard Gunter who received 4 shillings. To the children of his son John who had probably predeceased him, he left to the two daughters £2 each and to the son John £6. To his son Richard, whom he made executor, he left all his household stuff, his corn and hay, all his lands and tenements, orchards, house, barn, buildings, closes, woods and underwoods. The will was witnessed by Samuel Cruttenden, who signed, and his relative Elizabeth Valance, who had married 'Old Valance' in 1581, and who made her mark.

It looks as though Richard Foster of Fontridge, who died in 1629 represented the next generation of this family. His goods were valued at £22 15s 0d. He made his wife Elizabeth executrix and left to her all his cattle and corn during her widowhood and the rents and profits from all his lands and tenements until his son William, who had been baptised in 1618, was of age. Elizabeth was also to bring up his three younger children, who were each to have £10 from William when he was of age, or 16 shillings a year each until it was paid. When William came of age, all the household stuff was to be divided equally between his wife and the children. The overseers were Anthony Cruttenden and Thomas Collins.

It was inevitable that some Foster families who were more peripheral to the ironworking community should have been drawn into the metal trades. For instance David Foster, a Burwash blacksmith, was appointed overseer of the will of Simon Byne in 1616.[162] He was probably the son of Henry Foster of Burwash, and had been baptised at Brightling in 1574. Henry was probably the youngest son of Stephen and Denise Foster of Burwash, who died in 1559 and 1574 respectively, both leaving wills.[163] Stephen had land near the church of Burwash which he left to his eldest son Reynold,

159. ESRO, PBT 1/1/3/35 (*in domo solite mansionis Willelmi Blacknoll de Ponte Roberti ad signum negritauri*).
160. ESRO, PBT 1/1/5/360.
161. ESRO, PBT 1/1/12/319, 1/3/3/143.
162. ESRO, PBT 1/1/15/193.
163. ESRO, PBT 1/1/4/482, 1/1/6/358.

land in Hailsham which he left to Alexander, and a tenement called Tharlskeyr in Burwash which he left to Henry.

The names Stephen, Denise, Reynold, Alexander and Henry, might of course suggest a French origin for this family too. It was at Warbleton that Alexander next appeared in 1576, when he married a widow named Elizabeth Gytard. Their son John, who was baptised in 1577, found employment in cutting wood and as a collier, so that when he died in 1619 another collier, Anthony Fevers, owed him £1 for cutting around 20 cords of wood.[164] John's son George Foster, baptised at Warbleton in 1612, was buried at Dallington in 1631, being at the time apprenticed to Fevers. George's father and grandfather may of course also have been colliers.

Involved in the affray at Plaistow which cost Charles Pavy his life in 1580 was William Foster, a Northchapel finer.[165] He could have been the younger son of the Burwash ashealer, Robert Ashburner, mentioned above, though there is nothing to prove such a relationship. No parish register for Northchapel survives for this period and the Petworth register, which included entries for some of the Northchapel residents carried no entry for a William Foster before 1606.

If William Foster left the area after the affray he could be the man whose son Leonard was baptised at Leigh in 1581, and whose son Lawrence was buried there later in the same year. He could be the William Foster who married Mary Ilands at Newdigate, the adjoining parish to Leigh, in 1589, but neither parish register recorded the burial of his first wife. In 1592 William and Mary Foster, styled 'of the Forest' to distinguish them from an indigenous couple of the same name, were mentioned in the Horsham parish register, when their twin sons Steven and Thomas were baptised there, though Thomas did not survive infancy. If these identifications are correct, the finer could have been the William Foster whose son John and wife Mary were buried at East Grinstead in 1598.

A cutler named Robert Foster was bondsman for a Hailsham probate administration in 1614.[166] Robert appears not to have been baptised at Hailsham, though he might be the son of a couple named Robert and Agnes Foster, who were also intrusive in the parish register, but were both buried at Hailsham in 1611. The cutler probably married Ann Drewe at Hailsham in 1605 and their children were baptised at Hailsham from 1608 until 1615. The cutler was perhaps the 'Foster' who was buried at Hailsham in June 1640. His son Robert, baptised early in 1610, was perhaps the Robert who married Elizabeth Wheatly in October 1640.

In the Midlands John Foster, a forgeman at Perry Bar was sponsor to a baptism at Handsworth in March 1599. Further north Black Thomas (Foster) was a collier at Oakamoor Forge from 1594 to 1608.[167]

Lavender

It has proved impossible to show that John Lavander, born in France around 1522, who came to England around 1529 and was made denizen in 1544, was the progenitor of this ironworking family. The surname seems not to occur in the Pays de Bray so the family may have come from the Perche area on the southern border of Normandy. The duke of Norfolk's finer, John Gommery or Gomer, is known to have come from the Perche, and it seems just possible that his servant Anthony, who paid the poll tax in Rushmonden hundred in 1551, was Anthony Lavyntor who paid the poll tax in Hartfield hundred in 1576.

But the intervening silent quarter-century discourages such an identification and it is only with Lawrence Lavander, who was named amongst the woodcutters at Panningridge Furnace in 1554,[168] that firm evidence of the immigrant family's connection with the Weald and the iron industry has been found. As a woodcutter Lawrence was not employed under covenant, but would have been a day-labourer; this would have precluded his appearance, even as a poll-tax payer, in the subsidy rolls. It also prevents our proving that Lawrence was already resident in the Weald in 1550 and earlier.

However, Peter and Anthony Lavender, who were perhaps Lawrence's sons, both paid the poll

164. ESRO, PBT 1/1/17/18.
165. *Cockburn, Sussex Assize records, Elizabeth I*, no. 801.
166. ESRO, PBT 1/3/4/38.
167. UNMASC, Middleton Papers, 5/165/53-66.
168. KHLC, U1475, B11/4.

tax in 1576 and were young enough to be married in 1576 and 1582 respectively. Such evidence suggests that both could have been born in the early 1550s and does not conflict with the supposition that in 1554 Lawrence Lavender was a newcomer to the Weald. Simon Lavender on the other hand, who married at Worth in 1580, but did not pay the poll tax in 1576, could have been the first member of the family to have been born in England. Another child of Laurence Lavender, Katherine, was baptised at Waldron early in 1565, and this suggests that 'Laurence', an alien servant of John French, who paid the poll tax in Shiplake hundred in 1572, might have been Lawrence Lavender too.

Peter Lavender had married Elizabeth de Vereye at Mayfield early in 1576. Though he paid the poll tax in Shoyswell hundred in 1576, by March 1577 he had moved to Warbleton, where his daughter Elizabeth was baptised. His next two children, Margaret and John, were baptised at Burwash in 1579 and 1584. The burial of Margaret at Mayfield in 1581 may have come about through the wish to have the child buried in the mother's parish, or being cared for by her grandmother, rather than indicating yet another change of residence. However, an unnamed son, who was perhaps Gilbert Lavender, was baptised at Warbleton in 1586, followed by the baptisms of Adrian and Mary, back at Burwash in 1590 and 1593.

Apart from the forays into Warbleton, Burwash would seem to have been Peter Lavender's usual place of residence. From the assize rolls we learn that his home there was burgled by Elizabeth Tomlyn of Burwash in June 1617.[169] His wife Elizabeth had been buried at Burwash in 1616 and Peter himself was buried there in 1623.

Two of Peter Lavender's children were married at Burwash – Elizabeth to Peter Jollye in 1596 and Adrian to Elizabeth Duffell in 1616, whilst a third, John, was perhaps the man who married Elizabeth Clarke in the adjacent parish of Heathfield in 1611.

Adrian Lavender was a Burwash collier and it was at Burwash that his two sons and a daughter, Simon, William and Elizabeth were baptised in 1621, 1627 and 1635, though a third son, Thomas, was baptised at Heathfield in 1629.[170] Adrian Lavender's son Thomas will have been Thomas Lavender of Burwash, who married another Burwash resident Elizabeth Levis, at Brightling in 1656.

The Warbleton parish register shows that Adrian's two sons, Simon and John, for the latter of whom no baptism has been found, were married in 1654 and 1656 to Anne and Elizabeth Sanders respectively, both the daughters of a Warbleton carpenter named William Sanders. It also shows that Simon was resident in Warbleton, but had followed in his deceased father's trade of collier; nothing however was divulged concerning John Lavender's occupation.

Simon and Anne Lavender's sons, William, Adriell, John and Peter, were baptised at Warbleton between 1655 and 1662. However, Anne was buried in May 1663 and the mother of Simon's later children, Simon, Thomas, Mary and Peter, who were baptised between 1667 and 1672, was Alice, whose marriage has not been found. Simon Lavender, buried at Warbleton in 1675, was probably the son baptised in 1667, whilst his father was probably the man of that name buried there in 1688.

It appears that John Lavender was not the only son of Adrian Lavender of Burwash whose baptism has not been found. The Warbleton collier Peter Lavender was apparently Adrian's son too. He had married Mary Tisehurst at Warbleton in 1667. He died childless in 1680 and left to his wife for life all his 'household stuff, bedding, pewter, brass, working tools and implements of husbandry' and all his other goods and chattels, together with the 'use, profit and yearly advantage' of the house, lands and tenements in which he dwelled. After Mary's death all this property was to be shared among Peter's two brothers, who can only have been Simon and John Lavender of Warbleton, and his sister, who was perhaps Elizabeth. However, if his widow descended into want and poverty through sickness 'or any other casualty' she was empowered to sell part of this inheritance.[171]

Gilbert Lavender married Susan Bluet, daughter of the Goudhurst hammerman Elias Bluet, at Goudhurst in 1609, but their first three children, Mary, Susan and Peter, were baptised at Burwash in 1610, 1612 and 1614. It looks as though Bluet the hammerman, who had by then moved on to Biddenden Hammer, was godfather to their fourth child Elias Lavender, who was baptised at Cranbrook in 1616.

169. Cockburn, *Sussex Assize records, James I*, no. 426.

170. Another baptismal entry at Heathfield of June 1632 for 'Athrell the son of Athrell Lavender of Burwash' apparently relates to another son of Adrian Lavender. The younger Adrian Lavender will perhaps have been the man buried at Brightling in 1681.

171. ESRO, A35/322.

Gilbert Lavender moved to Battle, where the burial of his wife Susan was recorded in 1645, but whether they had moved to Battle by 1622, when Nicholas Lavender was baptised there, without his parents' names being recorded, is impossible to determine. Gilbert's daughter Mary, baptised at Burwash in 1610, could have been the woman of that name who married John Miles at Battle in 1640. Gilbert's occupation of collier was disclosed when he was a quarter sessions surety in 1641.[172]

A further Peter Lavender married Anne de Verry at Mayfield in 1621. His children, Elizabeth and John, were baptised there in 1622 and 1623. The Mountfield parish register recorded the baptism at Whatlington in October 1632 of another of Peter Lavander alias Hannoway's daughters, Mary, who had been born at Mountfield. Other baptisms, of Gilbert son of 'Hanna alias Lavender' at Battle in 1625, of Margaret daughter of Peter Hannaway at Mountfield in 1629, of two Elizabeth's daughters of Peter Lavender, neither of whom survived, at Mountfield in 1634 and 1638, and finally the baptism of Peter Lavender's daughter Martha at Mountfield in January 1641, followed three days later by the burial of his wife Anne, suggest that all these entries relate to the couple married at Mayfield in 1621.

The concentration of these later baptisms in Battle, Whatlington and Mountfield, near the junction of which three parishes Hodesdale Forge was situated, suggest that it was there that Peter Hannoway alias Lavender was employed. To suppose that he was a son of Peter Lavender of Burwash, the record of whose baptism has not survived, leaves the alias Hannoway unexplained.

It seems possible that this Peter Lavender was married again to Margaret Bywood at Mountfield in 1641. They had a son named Peter baptised at Battle in 1648, but Margaret, Peter's second wife, was buried at Battle in June 1649. Though Peter's son John was possibly the man who married Mary Stevens at Mountfield in 1645, he is unlikely in that case to have been the John Lavender whose son George was baptised at Battle in 1643.

Other John Lavenders of East Sussex are also difficult to sort out. The immigrant Peter's son, John Lavender who married at Heathfield in 1611, may have been the man whose daughter Mary was baptised at Waldron early in 1617. But who was the John Lavender who married Sarah Lavy at Mayfield in 1631? Finally, which of them was the man whose 'Goodwife Lavender' was buried at Battle in 1620?

Anthony 'Lavyntor', who paid the poll tax in Hartfield hundred in 1576, did not appear in contemporary views of frankpledge for Hartfield, but was perhaps 'Anthony *gallus*', who was fined 2 pence for default in its Rottingham Fletching borough in April 1577.[173] In May 1582 he married Joan Furner at Balcombe and their son Robert was baptised at Buxted early in 1584. Elizabeth, 'daughter of Lavander', who was baptised at Buxted in 1585, was perhaps their child too. Thereafter, Anthony was not heard of again in the Weald, so he may have joined the large number of ironworkers who were around that time helping to establish the indirect process of iron manufacture in other parts of the country.

Nevertheless, it is evident that some members of the Lavender family, in addition to the descendants of Peter Lavender of Burwash, stayed on in the Weald. In Surrey, the 1583-4 muster rolls included Richard Lavender among the pikemen of the parish of Ewhurst.[174] No parish register for Ewhurst survives before 1615, by when most of the Lavender family seems to have moved on, but a solitary member, Margaret Lavander, was buried there in 1644.

In West Sussex, Agnes, the wife of Humfrey Lavander was buried at Linchmere early in 1619, and in 1620 a second Lawrence Lavander married Elizabeth Stonam there. At Cuckfield, three children of George Lavender, Anne, Elizabeth and John, were baptised from 1628 to 1633. These members of the family could, of course, all be descended from Anthony Lavender if after 1585 he had moved to some Sussex parish such as West Hoathly, Horsted Keynes, or even Wadhurst, or to Ewhurst in Surrey, none of whose sixteenth-century parish registers survives. An isolated entry for the baptism of his daughter Mary, shows that in 1616 an otherwise unknown Benjamin Lavender lived in Wadhurst.

At a later period a Heathfield collier Thomas Lavender married Catherine Smith at Waldron in 1725, but their son John, baptised at Heathfield in 1727, cannot be the forgeman John Lavender of Ewhurst in Sussex who was first married in 1738. This forgeman is more likely to have been the son of John and Anne Lavender baptised at Ewhurst in 1702.

John Lavender, bachelor, iron forger of Ewhurst, Sussex, was first married to an Abinger widow Jane Vice at the Fleet prison in London in July 1738. Jane and her only child by John, Mary Lavender,

172. ESRO, QR 54, m. 47.
173. ESRO, ACC 3597/8, f. 30.
174. Craib, *Surrey musters*, p. 19.

were buried at Ewhurst in April and July of 1740; John Lavender married his second wife Mary Watson at Ewhurst in 1741.

Towards the end of his life John Lavender and his family were enumerated in a settlement certificate of 1764, by which they were returned from St George's parish Southwark to Ewhurst. Lavender was obviously at Ewhurst from 1742 to 1748, when his children Mary, John, Joseph, Margaret and George were baptised there. George (aged 16) was the eldest of John and Mary Lavender's children to be enumerated in the removal certificate. The others were Robert (13), Thomas (11), Elizabeth (9), James and Sarah (twins) (near 5), Edward (near 3) and Jane (near 6 months). Of these, the baptism of only Elizabeth can be traced in neighbouring parish registers.

A letter written in May 1754 by John Churchill of Hints in Staffordshire, who was negotiating for the lease of Robertsbridge Furnace and Forge, to their owner Sir Whistler Webster, indicates that John Lavender was then in the Midlands. This would explain why the baptisms of Robert and Thomas, born around 1751 and 1753, cannot be found in Wealden parish registers. Churchill wrote, 'I hope there will be no dispute about putting up another finery as John Lavender tells me there was always two till one was pulled down by Mr Jewkes's (the former tenant's) order and an air furnace built in the place which is since taken away'.[175]

By May 1756, when his daughter Elizabeth was baptised at Salehurst, Lavender had clearly returned to the Weald. By 1759 he was probably working at Woodcock Hammer, because his twins James and Sarah were baptised at Lingfield in May 1759, and then in February 1761 his son Edward was baptised at Godstone, and his 18-year-old daughter Mary was married there to Thomas Collins. John Lavender's wife Mary had been brought home to Ewhurst for burial in August 1764, before the issue of the Southwark removal order in December of that year. He himself was buried at Ewhurst in 1780, but his sons Edward and James had predeceased him in 1765 and 1769.[176]

There appears to have been some connection between John Lavender of Ewhurst and Andrew and Sarah Lavender who lived in the Surrey ironworking parish of Abinger in the late 1730s. Andrew and Sarah's sons Andrew and John were baptised there in 1738 and 1740, and Sarah Lavender, baptised there in 1736, was also their child. The baptisms of their children Joseph and Mary, around 1731 and 1733 respectively, cannot be found at Abinger. That Andrew was a forgeman is suggested by his move around 1740 to Fareham. The connection with the Ewhurst man is suggested by the fact that during Andrew Lavender's absence the parish overseers paid 14 shillings on 1 May 1741 to his eldest son Joseph for keeping the children of Richard Vice, who will have been the former husband of Jane Vice, whom John Lavender had married in 1738. At the end of May 1741 an order was obtained for the removal of Sarah and her five children to Fareham, which will have been done, not because Andrew was there searching for work, but because that was the family's place of settlement.

The Fareham parish register was searched for Lavenders without success, but the removal order proves that the marriage of Andrew Lavington in 1731 and the subsequent baptisms of Joseph and Mary Lavington are the missing entries actually relating to the Lavender family. From 1743 to 1751 three more children, two Annes and Margaret, were baptised at Fareham. Andrew Lavender later worked at Titchfield and Funtley forges and was buried at Fareham in 1780.[177] His son Andrew married Jane Mannings (formerly Bartholomew) at Titchfield in 1760, but is next traced back at Abinger where his daughter Ann was born in 1764. However, she was baptised not at Abinger but at Lingfield in November 1764, near Woodcock Hammer where John and Mary Lavender had formerly resided. The younger Andrew later returned to Titchfield where three further children of his were baptised from 1769 to 1775.[178] In the 1780s the overseers of the poor of Fareham and Ewhurst were in correspondence over John Lavender, employed in 1789 at the iron mills in the Hampshire town.[179]

But it was in the north of England and in the Midlands that the Lavender family made its

175. C. Whittick, 'Wealden iron in California - the Huntington Library, San Marino, California', *Wealden Iron,* Bulletin of the Wealden Iron Research Group, 2nd series, **12** (1992), p. 62.

176. I am greatly indebted to Mrs Janet Swabey of Great Ayton for the bulk of the information in the previous five paragraphs.

177. The Abinger overseers' disbursements are SHC, P1/7/1; I am grateful to Martin Lavender of Ramsgate for this valuable information, and for a photocopy of the removal order.

178. My thanks are due to Martin Lavender of Ramsgate for information on this branch of the family.

179. ESRO, PAR 324/35/2.

greatest contribution to the iron industry. Surprisingly, the descendants of Simon Lavender, who moved to remote North Yorkshire, can be traced relatively easily. He was married to Joan Obeit (*recte* Obell) at Worth early in 1580; their son Charles was baptised at Worth in 1582, but by 1589 they were at Summerbridge Forge in Nidderdale. Their son Marian was baptised at Pateley Bridge in April of that year, but the baptism of their daughter Rebecca at Helmsley in 1592 shows that they had already by then moved on to Rievaulx ironworks. Among the sponsors of this baptism was Rebecca Browne, the daughter of Jordan Russell II, who had been baptised at Frant in 1569, but was now wife of Thomas Browne, ironfounder at Rievaulx. Simon Lavender was still at Helmsley in June 1595, when he in turn stood as godfather to Thomas and Rebecca Browne's daughter Elizabeth.

A few years later Simon was back in Nidderdale, but at a perhaps hitherto unidentified ironworks some 8 or 9km downstream from Summerbridge; his children Hermon and Elizabeth were baptised in 1601 and 1604, at Ripley and Hampsthwaite respectively.

Lastly came this family's second major move which took them to Shropshire. In April 1606 Simon's son Hermon was buried at Morville, south of Much Wenlock, and in 1609 Thomas, another son of his, was baptised there. It was at Morville that Simon Lavender himself was buried in August 1628. The family of Simon's son Marian Lavender can also be traced with certainty at Morville, whilst John Lavender, whose eight children were baptised at Morville from 1621 onwards was probably Marian's brother, baptised in North Yorkshire at some parish other than Pateley Bridge, Helmsley, Ripley and Hampsthwaite, which had each recorded the baptism of one of Simon's children.

Eight children of Marian and Judith Lavender, were baptised at Morville from 1617 to 1629, including four sons, William, John, Richard and Simon, of whom the two last did not survive. By 1630 the family had moved on to Oldbury, near Bridgnorth, where their children, Enoch and Alice, were baptised in 1630 and 1634. Their son Richard was buried at Oldbury in 1639, whilst Marian and Judith themselves were buried there in 1668 and 1669.

That Simon Lavender and his descendants were up to this point employed in the iron industry can be inferred from the parishes in which they lived and by their association, particularly at Rievaulx, with other ironworking families. An entry of 1656 made in the register of the Worcestershire parish of Halesowen on the occasion of the marriage of his son Joseph, states that John Lavender was hammerman at Kingswinford in Staffordshire. John's children had been baptised at Morville from 1621 onwards, and in addition to Joseph who had been baptised there in 1634, were John, two sons named Simon, neither of whom survived infancy, and Nicholas.

As far as ironworking is concerned almost all the later history of the Lavender family is bound up with the forges on the river Stour around Stourbridge and Kidderminster. Iron was brought across the Severn at Bewdley, from the ironworks at Cleobury Mortimer and in Bringewood Chase, for onward transmission to the markets of the Birmingham area. Nailmaking had been a long-established occupation in the Midlands and it was almost inevitable that the river Stour would become the site of the earliest slitting mills in the Midlands, where bar iron was cut into rods for the use of nailers mechanically, rather than by hand as formerly. Stourton Mill was set up around 1614,[180] and the great forgemaster Richard Foley established his mill at Hyde some years later. Locally the impact was such that by 1616 a third of the children baptised at Kingswinford were recorded as being born to nailers.[181]

Confirmation that John Lavender the Kingswinford hammerman was the Morville man is found in the parish registers of both places which name Frances as his wife. John and Frances Lavender and their family had evidently moved to Kingswinford in the late 1630s, and in 1641 their twins Edward and Eleanor were baptised there.

John Lavender II, the eldest son of John and Frances Lavender, baptised at Morville in 1621, was probably the John Lavender of Kingswinford, whose son Francis was baptised at Rowley Regis in 1651 and whose wife Alice was buried there in March 1652. John Lavender, whose son John had been baptised at Rowley Regis in 1645, was presumably also this same man. It looks as though he may have twice remarried, because in 1653 an unnamed daughter of John and Catherine Lavender was baptised at Rowley Regis, and Mary and Moses, children of John and Anne Lavender, were baptised at Kingswinford in 1657 and in 1658; Thomas, baptised at Rowley Regis in 1661, was perhaps also their

180. TNA, C 21/W53/8.

181. In 1616, 13 fathers out of 40 were nailers, in 1618 the figure was 19 out of 48, a proportion which remained little changed in 1686, when 23 fathers out of 66 were nailers.

child, though on that occasion the mother's name was not recorded.

John Lavender III, baptised at Rowley Regis in 1645, is thought to have been the man who married Anne Browne at Wolverley in 1681. This 'John Lavinder, of Cookley, forgeman', was buried at Wolverley in 1720, and his goods were appraised at £134, though the largest part of this was made up of debts due on bond, which totalled £80. John's son Richard had predeceased him. In 1705 Richard had married Anne Hutt, from a family which included the forge carpenter William Hutt, buried at Kinver in 1692, and Richard had three daughters, Mary, Ann and Sarah, to each of whom their grandfather John Lavender left £5.[182]

When Joseph Lavender's daughter Mary was buried at Halesowen in December 1660 her parents were stated to be of 'Clebury' and it was at Cleobury Mortimer that Thomas, 'son of Joseph and Mary Lavender of the Forge', was baptised and buried in 1661. Joseph's future movements are unknown. However, both his elder brother Nicholas and his younger brother Edward, one of the twins born in 1641, appear to have stayed at Kingswinford. Nicholas's wife was named Joyce and their sons, William and Edward, were born or baptised at Kingswinford in 1658 and 1664. Edward was probably the forgeman Edward Lavender, whose wife's name was Margaret, and whose children, Jane, Mary, Edward, Margaret and John, were baptised at Kingswinford between 1671 and 1685.

Reverting to the family of Marian Lavander, it seems probable that William Lavender who was at Kinver in 1642, was Marian's son of that name baptised at Morville in 1617. William and Elizabeth Lavender's son Edward was baptised at Kinver in 1642. They also had a son named William, whose baptism perhaps fell during the 1645-1653 gap in the Kinver parish register. However, by 1650 William and Elizabeth had moved on to Cleobury Mortimer, where their children Hannah, Charles, Elizabeth and Anne were baptised between 1650 and 1661; Charles did not survive infancy and it was at Cleobury that their son William was buried in 1662. Remarkably, although the parish register had firmly designated his cousin Joseph Lavender as being 'of the Forge', it attached the description 'artist' to William Lavender's name in 1650.[183] He was buried at Cleobury Mortimer in 1670, as was his widow, Elizabeth Lavender, in 1671. Their daughter Hannah married Edward Bateman in 1676, but there is no further record of their son Edward, who had perhaps been buried at Kinver between 1645 and 1650.

It is in trying to trace the movements of Simon's son Thomas, and Marian and Judith's son Thomas, baptised at Morville in 1609 and 1618 respectively, that severe problems are encountered. It is fairly certain that they too moved to the area of the Stour forges. Since baptismal names often run in families, likely clues are the baptisms of Simon at Kingswinford in 1646 (the son of Thomas and Lawre Lavender), and of Judith and Marian Lavender at Hartlebury in 1656 and 1665 (both the children of Thomas Lavender, though the mother's name Elizabeth was recorded only in the case of Marian). It seems certain that two different Thomases were involved, whilst the number of Thomas Lavenders actually residing in the two parishes may have been three.

The Thomas Lavender who married Elizabeth Gelly at Burrington in 1633 was presumably Simon's son, baptised at Morville in 1609. But Elizabeth did not survive beyond September. Thomas may have worked at Burrington Forge in Bringewood Chase before moving to the Stour forges whose relationship with the Bringewood ironworks is clear enough. It seems possible that he was at Kingswinford early in 1638, when a Thomas Lavender married Margery Mullinax, but neither she nor her child Margery survived the year. More certainly he married Lowrye Jones at Longnor early in 1642. Their first son John, baptised at Kingswinford in August 1644, was recorded as the son of 'Thomas and [blank] Lavender', perhaps because the parish clerk was unfamiliar with the name Lowry. More of their children, Simon, Lowre[184] and Jane, were baptised at Kingswinford between 1646 and 1652.

Turning to Hartlebury parish, where a new forge and slitting mill at Wilden were probably set up in the late 1640s, at least two more Thomas Lavenders seem to be involved. Thomas Lavender, whose son James was baptised at Hartlebury in 1650 could have been the Thomas whose wife Eleanor was buried there in 1653.

The other couple Thomas and Elizabeth Lavender were not actually mentioned until 1659,

182. A. T. C. and E. M. Lavender, *Our Lavender forgemen*, pt. 1 (1999), p. 27.
183. The original of this part of the register no longer survives, so it is impossible to check whether the transcriber of the published version has wrongly expanded an abbreviation intended to read 'artisan'.
184. The Kingswinford register named Lowre's mother Joan (14 Oct 1649), which it seems legitimate to denote as an error.

when the birth of their daughter Margaret was recorded, but could have been Thomas Launder (a name otherwise unknown in the parish) and Elizabeth Stephens, who were married at Hartlebury in 1646. Other entries perhaps take them back to 1656: when their child George Lavender, who had been born in 1657, was buried in 1661, the register named his mother as Elizabeth, and since it seems likely that Judith, born in 1656, had the same parentage as Marian, we can suppose that Elizabeth was her mother too. This Thomas Lavender was probably Marian's son baptised at Morville in 1618; he was presumably buried at Hartlebury in March 1665, because the Lavender children baptised at Hartlebury from 1668 onwards had Thomas and Anne as their parents.

Whilst it is certain that Anne, whose children were baptised at Hartlebury from 1668 onwards, was Anne Parker, sister to Humphrey Parker of Elston Hall, Bushbury, near Wolverhampton, her marriage to Thomas Lavender has not been traced, perhaps because of the loss of the early parish registers of Bushbury. Though James Lavender was one of Thomas's children mentioned in the administration granted to Humphrey Parker following Thomas's death in December 1680, James who was baptised at Hartlebury in 1650 cannot have been he, because the 1680 child was still a minor. However Anne Parker's husband could still have been the man whose former wife Eleanor was buried at Hartlebury in 1653.[185]

If Anne, the daughter of Thomas and Anne Lavender, whose birth on 27 March 1655 was registered at Kingswinford, was their child too, Thomas Lavender must have married Anne Parker quite soon. However, if the Kingswinford birth relates to them, Timothy son of Thomas Lavender born on 17 November 1655 and registered at Hartlebury, can hardly be their child too. It looks as though the earliest entry attributable to them at Hartlebury may be Mary daughter of Thomas Lavender baptised and buried on 2 February 1663, after an unlikely eight-year gap, then followed by another five-year gap before the baptism of another Mary in April 1668, on this occasion unambiguously attributed by the register to both parents. This Mary also failed to survive long, because in November 1669 a further child named Mary was attributed to them, followed by Thomas, Samuel and Humfrey, who were baptised at Hartlebury between 1671 and 1680, though Humfrey did not long survive.

Many later forgemen of the family were certainly descended from Thomas Lavender of Wilden, who died intestate in December 1680. His wife Anne had predeceased him by a few months, so during the minority of his surviving children, Thomas, Samuel, James and Mary, administration of his estate was assigned to his brother-in-law, Humphrey Parker. One of the appraisers of the inventory was Thomas Lowbridge, Lord Foley's manager at Wilden Forge, and the goods totalled £44 16s 1d, including two hogs worth £3 and 10 sheep worth £2. Other possessions included a clock, two guns, a belt and rapier, and a crossbow. The rooms included the hall, parlour, pantry, kitchen, with chambers over the hall, parlour and kitchen, a cellar and a barn.[186]

Thomas Lavender's eldest son, Thomas Lavender of Oldington Farm, near Wilden, had been baptised in 1671. He was twice married and among his eleven children were seven sons. Like his father and his eldest son he probably worked at Wilden Forge. When he died in 1729 he left his 'dwelling house and farm ... in Oldington' to his wife Mary and to his second surviving son Samuel Lavender. They were to pay an annuity of £2 to his surviving son by his first wife, John Lavender, who was master hammerman to Lord Foley at Wilden Forge. Though the rooms mentioned in Thomas's inventory seem to tally with those enumerated in his father's will and the clock still survived, the house seems to have been less sumptuously furnished than in 1680 and the total of goods inventoried amounted to only £16.[187]

John Lavender, master hammerman at Wilden Forge, had been baptised at Hartlebury in 1698. He died in 1751. From May 1750 an interesting side-light is thrown on life at a Stour forge by the advertisement which he had placed in *Aris's Birmingham Gazette* concerning a runaway apprentice named Francis Jones.[188] The 18-year-old Jones left during the night of 1-2 May, having about three

185. Lavender and Lavender, *Our Lavender forgemen*, pt. 1, p. 14-7.

186. Ibid.

187. Ibid., p. 18.

188. If Thomas Lavender who married Lowrye Jones at Longnor was the master hammerman's ancestor, Francis Jones may have been a cousin. William Jones, who was buried at Kinver in May 1700 was clerk of Whittington Forge. At Longnor Margaret daughter of William and Martha Jones 'of the forge' was baptised early in 1756.

years of his service left to run. He was promised to be 'entertain'd' as before in the event of his return; otherwise all 'Gentlemen belonging to forges' were desired not to employ him. He was described as 'a strong-made, well-set lad', with 'his hair lately cut off his head' and had departed wearing his Lordship's rather splendid livery coat, 'a dark brown coat and grey breeches, with white metal buttons ... and a brown waistcoat mixed with stripes of white and yellow with metal buttons'.

Though John Lavender was married he appears to have had no children. He made his will in May 1751 and died later that year. He left his household goods and £20 to his wife Mary and she was to have the interest, twice yearly, from a sum of £500 which was to be invested on her behalf. His half-brother Samuel and a cousin were to be executors, and after his wife's death his estate was to be divided equally between his half-brothers and sisters.[189]

Of the master hammerman's younger brothers, Samuel Lavender (1705-1779) married Ann Hillman at Oldswinford in 1738. He served as churchwarden of Hartlebury in 1754 and it was he who acquired Bury Hall in Wolverley, a property which continued in his family for several generations.[190]

The next brother James Lavender (1707-1762) married Mary Hudson at Kidderminster early in 1731. His eldest son Thomas was baptised out of wedlock at Lower Mitton in 1730, but the remaining children were baptised regularly at Hartlebury. From the will of James's sister Elizabeth, drawn up in 1783, it appears that her nephew Thomas, who married Margaret Beech at Bedwardine in 1753 and who was a hammerman at Wilden until after 1770,[191] was by 1783 working at Burton-on-Trent.

Of Thomas's sons, Elizabeth's great-nephews, George Lavender was a Stourport cooper, and James was apprenticed to a Kidderminster carpet weaver. However, James was bought out of his apprenticeship, and worked firstly at Wilden Forge where his father had been hammerman. By 1787 he had moved on to Bradley where John Wilkinson had his works. He married Mary Green at Wolverhampton and then moved to Monmouthshire where he worked for three years at Llangrwyney Forge in the Usk valley and for five years at Beaufort ironworks above Ebbw Vale. By the end of the 1790s he had moved to a forge at Machen and in 1811 he was working at Pentyrch, where three sons worked alongside him. He was buried at Machen in 1839.[192]

On the other hand, it appears from his aunt's will that in 1783 James Lavender, the fourth surviving son of James and Mary Lavender, baptised at Hartlebury in 1748, was living at Broadwaters, near Kidderminster, where there were both Upper and Lower forges. It is thought that he was the ancestor of John Herbert Lavender (1882-1957) who set up the firm of aluminium founders of that name in Crankhall Lane, Stone Cross, West Bromwich.[193]

The next brother, William Lavender (1711-1761) was probably a forgeman too. This can be judged from the fact that, after he had married Ann Shepherd at Cannock in 1736, his sons William and Samuel were baptised at Brewood, where there were also forges, in 1737 and 1739. He was buried at Hartlebury in 1761.

The next brother, George Lavender (1714- c1808), is the only one known not to have been involved in the iron trade. He married Mary Parr at Hagley in 1738 and became a wheelwright. His children were baptised at Kidderminster between 1739 and 1760, but at some stage he moved to Wribbenhall near Bewdley. His will, dated 1791, described him as of Knighton upon Teme, 'late of Wribbenhall, wheelwright'.

The youngest brother, Joseph Lavender (1717-1787), married Frances Andrews at Worcester in 1737. Their children Mary and John were baptised at Hartlebury in 1738 and 1740, when Joseph was probably still working at Wilden Forge. The baptisms of Thomas and William at Shenstone in 1743 and 1745 suggest that he worked at Little Aston Forge during the 1740s. Finally, another five children were baptised at Wolverley between 1750 and 1758, and he was described as being of Cookley in his sister's will of 1783, and as a forgeman when he was buried at Wolverley in October 1787.

James Lavender, baptised at Hartlebury in 1650, may have been the man of that name whose sons James and Samuel were baptised at Wolverley in 1681 and 1682. Subsequently three further

189. Lavender and Lavender, *Our Lavender forgemen*, pt. 1, p. 21.
190. Ibid., pp. 31, 35-7.
191. Burial entries for his daughter Betty and wife were entered at Hartlebury in 1770 and 1771 respectively.
192. C. Evans, 'A skilled workforce during the transition to industrial society: forgemen in the British iron trade, 1500-1850', *Labour History Review*, **63** (1998), p. 145-6.
193. Lavender and Lavender, *Our Lavender forgemen*, pt. 1, pp. 22-3, 29.

children of his were baptised at Kinver between 1683 and 1690. He was perhaps remarried to Sarah Baker at Kinver early in 1693. His son Thomas, baptised at Kinver early in 1685 was probably the man who in 1725 married Sarah Richards at Kinver. He died early in 1739, his inventory totalled over £16 and by trade he was a carpenter.[194] This need not necessarily have meant his exclusion from the iron trade, because the proliferation of forges and slitting mills in the area made the profession of forge-carpenter an essential one.

Ullard

Gyllam Ullard was one of the men who shared the work of charcoal burning with Laurence Henold, Lewis Raunser, Thomas Dogen and John Grevatt at Panningridge in 1558.[195] Though he did not appear as an alien in any subsidy roll the baptismal name Gyllam certainly suggests he was of French origin or descent.

Could the name have been assimilated to Willard? Apart from the forgemaster Davy Willard, other Willards were blacksmiths, and Raphe Willard of East Grinstead, who died in September 1599, was an armourer. Raphe left goods valued at £129 11s 4d and 20 marks (£13 6s 8d) each to six of his Willard relatives, including Edward Willard of Coldwaltham and Mary Castley [Castlen?] of Cralesdowne.[196]

IMMIGRANT WORKERS MENTIONED IN SUBSIDY ROLLS AFTER 1550

SUSSEX - HASTINGS RAPE

Foxearle hundred

Burgonyon

The alien Gyllam Burgonyon who paid the poll tax in Foxearle hundred in 1551 as a servant of Robert Woodman may have been of Burgundian origin, or he might have been from the family of Charlot Bourguygnon, record of whose apprenticeship in 1479 as an ironfounder survives in the archives of the department of Eure et Loire.[197] In either case the family may have originated in Burgundy. It seems possible that Gyllam Burgonyon stayed in England for some years because early in 1570 a child named Steven Burgonion was baptised at Mountfield. However, the parents of this child were not named so the entry is all but useless for genealogical purposes. No other examples of the use of this surname have been traced, so perhaps the family more commonly used an alias which has not so far been deduced.

Coupled with the names of Phlippin Fardell, who worked for Richard Woodman in 1549, and of George Mahoude, the Rotherfield collier outlawed for murder in 1574, a case can be made for the arrival in the Weald, perhaps in the 1540s, of a number of immigrants whose ancestors had been ironworkers in Burgundy. Unless all came together, they may be thought to have come, as seems possible in the case of Bourgonyon, indirectly after residence in Normandy.

Seddes

This name appears in various forms, occurring first at Herstmonceux in the 1550s, when Annis the daughter of Michael Dissedede was baptised on 29 December 1556. Michael Seade's son Thomas was baptised there the following year. It must be presumed that Michael Seddes was employed under covenant only around 1572, the sole occasion when he paid the poll tax in Foxearle hundred. He was a collier and was buried at Herstmonceux under the name Ezeedes in August 1576, but a nuncupative will dating from the previous December gave his name as Seddes. His goods, administration of which

194. Ibid., p. 24.
195. KHLC, U1475, B10/7, 8, 9 and 10.
196. ESRO, PBT 1/1/10/206, PBT 1/3/3/272.
197. Belhoste and others, *La métallurgie normande*, p. 249.

was assigned to his son Ambrose, since no executor had been named, were inventoried at £15 15s 6d.[198] Michael's wife had been buried as 'Mother Ezeedes' at Herstmonceux in 1574, and by his will 'all goods moveable and unmovable (were) to be equally shifted' between Michael's sons Ambrose and Thomas.

Ambrose Zedes had married Agnes Sawyer at Warbleton in 1572 and their first two children, Eleanor and Giles Ezeedes, were baptised at Herstmonceux in 1576 and 1578. Giles did not survive more than a few weeks, whilst in Warbleton, to where the family appears to have moved soon after Michael's death, a son named William who was baptised in 1579 survived not much longer. However Eleanor, and the twins William and Katheren, who were baptised at Warbleton in 1581, all reached maturity. Ambrose's younger brother Thomas Zedes, still a single man, was buried at Warbleton in 1582.

Ambrose Zeeds was buried at Warbleton in 1611, his wife having predeceased him by around eight years. In his will he was described as Ambrose Seeges of Warbleton, husbandman. He made his second wife Joan executrix and residuary legatee, his goods being inventoried at £39 3s 6d.[199] He left a shilling to the poor and £2 to his only son William. He left £2 to each of his three surviving daughters: they were Katherine, who had married John Wood at Heathfield in May 1608, to whose child a lamb was left; Eleanor, who had married Thomas Cade at Warbleton in the same month, and to each of whose two children a lamb was left; and Elizabeth, who married Richard Woode at Warbleton in September 1611, only a month before her father's death.

Other members of this family included Thomas Sudds alias Bardon [Barden?], who was sentenced to be hanged for a theft carried out at Withyham in June 1601.[200] John Seede married Bridget Larence at Rotherfield in 1584, and their daughter Alice was baptised at Maresfield early in 1585, with other children including Dorothy and Joseph, baptised at Mayfield in 1596 and 1599, and John baptised at Hartfield in 1606, though Dorothy survived only a week and John less than ten days. By 1610 the father was clearly dead, because his widow Bridget Seeds married Nicholas Care at Hartfield in October of that year.

Ambrose Seedes' son William perhaps followed the iron trade into West Sussex. In 1602 Anne wife of William Seades of Stoughton was indicted for recusancy.[201] William could perhaps in his 60s have been William Sudds of Chailey, who together with Nicholas Grant (*recte* Grout?) of Fletching, forgeman, entered a recognizance in 1645 for the appearance at quarter sessions of Margaret Sudds, charged with the theft of a goose.[202]

Perhaps the Hartfield collier, William Sudds, who, in a deposition of October 1640, claimed to have been born at Rudgwick some 32 years earlier, was a son of the man later found at Chailey.[203] The Hartfield collier was probably the William Seedes who had married Mary Hartnope at Brenchley early in 1629. By 1640 he had lived in Hartfield for around ten years. Under the style of William Sudds of Hartfield, forgeman, it was presented at quarter sessions in the same year that he, along with two other men, had been involved in hunting in the Maresfield portion of Ashdown Forest. Quarter sessions writs of arrest still included his name up to 1646,[204] showing that he was successful in avoiding apprehension for some years.

Sellen

The alien John Sellen paid the poll tax in Foxearle hundred in 1572, 1576 and 1595. He was already in the Weald by 1565, when his son William was baptised at Wartling. Others of his children, James, Elias, Cuthbert and Joan, were baptised at Herstmonceux from 1567 to 1577, though of these Elias died around the age of 20 and Cuthbert failed to survive infancy. Sellen's wife Annys was buried in 1579 and later that year he took as his second wife Margaret Dennit. Herstmonceux parish register recorded that John Sellwyn was an aged man (*senex*), when he was buried in 1610. The following year his widow married John Baker.

In addition to Sellwyn, the Herstmonceux parish register used the form Selandes as a surname

198. ESRO, PBT 1/1/7/16, 1/3/1/47.
199. ESRO, PBT 1/1/13/178, 1/3/3/256.
200. Cockburn, *Sussex Assize records, Elizabeth I*, no. 1995.
201. Ibid., 2068.
202. ESRO, QR 69, m. 40; I am indebted to Brian Phillips for this and the following references.
203. WSRO, Ep II/5/17, f. 53.
204. ESRO, QR 48, m. 10; QR 49, m. 104; QR 65, m. 124; QR 72, m. 150; QR 73, m. 125.

for the family in 1579, at the burial of John's first wife and at his remarriage. His son William Sellwyn married Elizabeth Snayle at Herstmonceux in 1590 and their children, Richard, Mary, Elizabeth, John, Susan, William, Margaret and Thomas, were baptised there between 1591 and 1610, though Richard, Mary and Thomas all failed to survive infancy. Willam Selwin was buried at Herstmonceux in 1615.

In 1578 William Judde of Alciston left bequests to his brothers John Sellyn, Giles and Edward Sellin.[205] In parish register entries at Laughton (1588-1600), Ashburnham (1599) and Dallington (1613, long after his death) Giles was always referred to as Selwyn or Selwin and a single reference to Edward Sellwyne is found at Hailsham in 1594. It looks as though these men were descended from Englishmen of that name recorded at Fryston, and Natewood and Wilmington, in the subsidy rolls of the 1520s, rather than from immigrants. The name Selden was common in West Sussex in the 1520s and so probate references to the blacksmiths Richard and William Selden (1566, 1608) of Crawley,[206] also probably refer to men of English descent.

Though William Sellynge who married Mary Aspes at Ticehurst in 1576 and John Sellen who married Mary Baldock at Wadhurst in 1612 may have been additional men of this surname of immigrant stock, only the fact that they were settled in ironworking areas suggests their involvement in the iron industry.

Bexhill hundred

Growshe

William Waters' man who paid the poll tax in Bexhill hundred in 1576 perhaps worked at Buckholt, of which Waters obtained the lease in 1575 from Bartholomew Jeffery's overseers. He may have been Growshe, who paid the poll tax along with his wife in Bexhill in 1572, when Jeffery was still alive.

No such person appears in Bexhill parish register, nor is he otherwise known.

Shoyswell hundred

Capper

John Capper, an alien who was servant to Thomas May in Shoyswell hundred in 1552, perhaps worked at Pashley Furnace. No parish register entry relating to him has been discovered. The name could be occupational and in a period when the wearing of hats was a sign of gentle, or noble birth, it is possible that Corneles Capper of Battle, a *Dutchman* [German?], and Charles Capper, an alien of Lewes, who were listed in the subsidy rolls of 1524, were immigrant makers of caps.

John Capper of Ringmer, the only Englishman who bore this name in East Sussex in 1524, was perhaps the ancestor of Robert Capper, who married Mary Lullingham at Fletching in 1611, and John Capper, who married Margaret Burrow at Little Horsted early in 1621, but nothing connects any of these persons with the manufacture of iron.

Another occupational name, that of Cooper, was widespread in Sussex. It is connected in two cases with the manufacture of iron. The Cooper alias Paler family of Rotherfield were forgemasters and Richard Cooper (alias Steyning) was ironfounder at Lurgashall in the 1620s.

In 1524 the name Paler did not occur in the Sussex subsidy rolls, nor was the name Cooper present in Loxfield hundred. However, there had been Coopers in Shoyswell hundred at that date and the forgemaster John Cooper alias Paler married Eleanor Hayward at Rotherfield in 1569. This appears to have been a second marriage, because John son of John Cooper was baptised at Rotherfield early in 1565 and William son of John Paler alias Cooper in 1568. No children appear to have survived from the second marriage, because Elizabeth daughter of John Paler was baptised and buried on the same day in March 1575.

John Paler witnessed the will of the Withyham smith, Robert Elyard, in 1565, that of William Alchen, a Rotherfield smith, in 1580, whilst in 1588 he was one of the overseers for the will of his cousin,

205. ESRO, PBT 1/1/7/133.

206. ESRO, PBT 1/1/5/280, 1/1/12/270.

Stephen Lorken of Rotherfield,[207] presumably from the English ironworking family of that name. In 1593 he owed £4 to Eglantine Catt, the mother of the Rotherfield and Maresfield ironfounder Thomas Catt and widow of George Catt.[208] Perhaps her late husband, George Catt, had worked for Paler. By 1574 Paler was tenant of Howbourne Forge, presumably in succession to John Relfe and Robert Olyffe, who held it in 1568,[209] and it was perhaps because of this involvement at Howbourne that he appeared as sponsor to a Buxted baptism in November 1572. He later bought Freshfield Forge from Anthony Morley and his sale of it to Stephen Penkhurst resulted in a Chancery case in 1602, due to the encumbrances placed on it in favour of Paler's son, William Cooper, William Crowe and David Middleton.[210] John Paler himself had been buried at Rotherfield in April 1592.

At Lurgashall the name Cooper goes back to the 1570s, when Peter, Agnes and Elizabeth Cooper alias Stening were baptised in 1570, 1573 and 1576, the father's name, Richard Cooper alias Steninge, being given only in 1576. He could have moved to Worth, where Elizabeth daughter of Richard and Margaret Stenynge was baptised in 1579, and where Richard Stenynge was buried in 1593. The furnace at Lurgashall is known to have been built by Peter Young of Midhurst before 1585,[211] and the association with iron can be proved in the case of Thomas Cooper alias Stening, who married Joan Chalwen at Lurgashall in 1581. Their children, Elizabeth, Richard, Joan and Thomas, were baptised at Lurgashall between 1583 and 1594. Thomas made his will in 1597 and enjoined his sons 'not to vex John Smith of Kirdford gentleman ... for any manner of iron mine, or any manner of wood or timber growing, or [that] did grow or have been taken out of any parcel or part of that land called Greene Lands'. Both his sons were still minors: to Thomas the father left an annuity of £1 10s 0d out of Paynes in Chiddingfold and to Richard he left Nether Rownderst in Lurgashall.[212]

The ironfounder Richard Cooper alias Stening whose children, John, William, Richard, Rowland and Marie, were baptised at Lurgashall between 1620 and 1629, was presumably Thomas's son; the children John and Richard failed to survive infancy. His first wife appears then to have died, because in 1633 he was married to Marie Tribe and their children were Joan, Margaret, Mary and Elizabeth, baptised between 1634 and 1640, though again Joan and Mary failed to survive.

Allow

Allo, who paid the poll tax in Shoyswell hundred in 1552, and was listed as one of Mr May's servants, was probably the same man as Allo Fyllet, who paid the poll tax in the same hundred in 1560. He was presumably at Rotherfield in June 1566, when Julian, daughter of 'Allo, a frenchman', was baptised. Perhaps 'Laurence Vlow [*sic*] child of a Frenchman' who was buried at Frant in May 1571 was his child too. Alloe, who paid the poll tax in Henhurst hundred in 1576, was also almost certainly he. In June 1583, according to the Salehurst parish register, the wife of Allowe Philot was buried at Etchingham, but the Brightling parish register noted this burial a day earlier and gave Allo's wife's name as Moiren. In December 1583 he (Allo Philiet) was again married at Mountfield to Marian Phiret. This second marriage can have lasted only a few years, because Maryan Allo, widow, was buried at Mountfield in August 1594.

Allo Fyllet may well have been a collier, because no fewer than five of his descendants followed that occupation. As far as can be ascertained all Allo's descendants took the surname Allo rather than Fylet, Philiet or Phillip, perhaps because of the risk of confusion with the family of Valet alias Gasken, already well-established in Ticehurst by the 1540s. Indeed, John Valet alias Gasken, who died around 1546, left houses at Bardown and Cottenden near Stonegate, both within 1.5km of East Lymden Furnace.[213]

It looks as though baptismal entries at Salehurst of January 1593 for children of both Nicholas Fylet alias Allow and John Fylet alias Allow must both relate to grandchildren of Allo Fyllet. Baptismal entries in the case of John occurred in 1581, 1589 and 1593 and in the case of Nicholas in 1593, 1599

207. ESRO, PBT 1/1/5/279, 1/1/7/200, 1/1/8/197.
208. ESRO, PBT 1/1/9/187.
209. Straker, *Wealden iron*, p. 389.
210. Cleere and Crossley, *The iron industry of the Weald*, p. 332.
211. Ibid., p. 342.
212. TNA, PROB 11/91/561.
213. ESRO, PBT 1/1/1/116.

and 1605. But other baptismal entries relating to another John Allowe occurred at Burwash in 1587, at Brightling in 1589 and at Etchingham in 1591, 1593, 1594, 1596, 1598, 1602 and 1604, suggesting that Allo Fyllet perhaps had two sons named John.

To make confusion worse confounded it was not until 1619 that any member of the family was buried at Salehurst. Both John Allowe of Hurst Green in the parish of Salehurst, buried at Etchingham in 1606, and Nicholas Allowe, buried there in 1608, appear to be the two Fylet alias Allows whose children were baptised at Salehurst. In addition Thomas Allowe of Kentbridge, buried at Etchingham in 1613, was perhaps one of the two children baptised at Salehurst 20 years earlier.

Among the children of John Allowe alias Fylet was Robert, baptised in 1593. He will have been the father of John, Robert, Elizabeth, Sara, Ann and Elizabeth, baptised at Salehurst from 1622 to 1639, of whom Robert and the first Elizabeth did not survive infancy. Robert Ollow of Salehurst, collier, was fined 6 pence at quarter sessions in 1642.[214]

The occupation of John Ollow of Catsfield, collier, was given in the licence for his marriage to Denise Hales of Catsfield in 1639.[215] He was possibly the John Aloe whose son Laurence was baptised at Battle in 1642. He could have been the son of Robert Allow who was baptised at Salehurst in 1622, though a third John Allow had a son of the same name baptised at Salehurst only three weeks earlier.

The occupation of John Allowe of Etchingham, collier, was mentioned in the survey of Etchingham manor made in 1597. He occupied a tenement and backside near Church Stile and three little meadows of 5 acres worth £5 a year.[216] Both his eldest surviving son Nicholas, baptised at Brightling in 1589, and his eldest surviving daughter Joan, baptised at Etchingham in 1594, were mentioned in the probate administration of the effects of John Alowe of Etchingham granted in July 1616.[217] His goods were inventoried at £29 10s 11d and administration was granted to Nicholas Alowe of Etchingham, collier (*carbonarius*), the bond being signed by Nicholas and by John Dad of Salehurst, finer, who was the husband of John's daughter Joan.

John Allow of Etchingham's son Thomas was baptised at Burwash in January 1587 and buried at Brightling less than three months later. Of his seven children baptised at Etchingham between 1591 and 1604, the first, another Thomas, survived until 1615, but John, baptised in 1593, lived for only four months. Joan, as we have seen, Richard and another John all survived, but the last two, Deborah and Mary, died at their ages of two and four respectively. There seems to be no burial entry for John Allow, the collier, to correspond with the administration granted to his son Nicholas in 1616, but Tamson, wife of John Allowe, buried at Etchingham in 1615, may have been his wife.

John's son Nicholas was perhaps both Nicholas Allowe alias Phillip, whose son John was baptised at Ticehurst in 1610, and Nicholas Alloe, whose son Thomas was baptised at Burwash in 1613. He may also have been Nicholas Aller, who was buried at Etchingham in 1632.

It becomes difficult to differentiate the parentage of Richard Alloe, who married Mary Tuckneys at Hawkhurst in 1629 and whose seven children were baptised at Hawkhurst between 1630 and 1640, from the parentage of Richard Aller or Allow, whose children were baptised at Etchingham from 1633 to 1644. When the Hawkhurst Richard Alloe was married for the fourth time, to Sarah Ellis in 1659, he was stated to be a husbandman, as was John Alloe of Hawkhurst, who married Mary Burden in 1655.

However, Thomas Alloe of Brightling, collier, who married Elizabeth Fernden of Hawkhurst, widow, at Hawkhurst in 1655, was probably Nicholas Alloe's son, Thomas, who had been baptised at Burwash in 1613.

There seems to be no record of the Allow family of colliers in other English ironworking areas.

Lunto

Thomas Shoyswell employed two strangely named aliens in Shoyswell hundred in 1552, Actor and Lunto. Lunto is less easily explained than Actor, who it has been suggested might be John Arthur whose first appearance in the Weald apart from this was as John Artor in Danehill Sheffield hundred in 1560.

Lunto can hardly have been a forebear of the Lyntot family of Horsham, with which the

214. ESRO, QR 58, m. 128.
215. Dunkin, *Sussex Marriage Licences, Lewes 1586-1643*, p. 225.
216. S. P. Vivian, *The Manor of Etchingham cum Salehurst*, Lewes, Sussex Record Society, **53**, 1953, no. 137.
217. ESRO, PBT 1/3/4/118.

ironfounding family of Tyler alias Quintin of Shipley and West Grinstead became allied by marriage. That family was already established at Horsham by 1524, when Thomas Lyntott was assessed at £2 to the subsidy.

There seems to be a possible reference to Lunto in Ralph Hogge's accounts in September 1578 in the reckoning with Jeffery Bell and John Kydd for cutting wood, mining and other work, 'whereupon I must answer to Lautto for him 6s 8d'.[218] This name could presumably be transcribed 'Lantto'. It does not occur elsewhere in the accounts.

Degoye

Peter Degoye or de Guye was first noticed in the Weald when he paid the poll tax in Shoyswell hundred in 1560. In October 1561 he allied himself with the distinguished Leonard family of ironworkers, through his marriage to Rowland Leonard, who had also paid the poll tax in Shoyswell in 1560. He next paid the poll tax in Little Barnfield hundred in Kent in 1572, and parish register entries for the baptisms of his children, Ellin, Samuel, Nicholas, Adam, Anthony, Margaret and Joan, occurred at Goudhurst between 1562 and 1573, though Adam survived only a few days and Margaret was buried on the day of her baptism. Although Peter de Goye paid the poll tax in Staple hundred in 1576, it was at Hawkhurst that Peter de Guyse (*de Guize* in the paper register) was buried in 1590.

Because the surname Guy was unknown in Sussex in the 1520s it looks as though Richard Guye, mentioned in the Warnham parish register from 1573 to 1585, may have been of alien origin too. Also probably connected with him were an unmarried woman (*virgo*) named Kateryn Guy, who was buried at Horsham early in 1561, and Elizabeth Guye, who married Thomas Lambard, a man of probable alien descent, at Warnham in 1576.

The children of Richard and Annis Guye, Joan, Jean, Francis, Letitia and Elizabeth, were baptised at Warnham from 1573 to 1584, with the baptism of just one child, Anne, being recorded at Horsham in 1575. Richard's wife Annis was buried at Warnham in 1585, but Richard met a violent death when he was 'slain with a dagger' in 1591 and buried at Horsham on 2 May of that year.

Richard's family continued at Warnham in the person of Francis Guy, who married Joan Cobb in 1605, their children, Elizabeth, John, Richard and Mary, being baptised at Warnham between 1605 and 1612. John Guie married Marie Steere in 1637 and their children John and Henry were baptised at Warnham in 1638 and 1639, the second of these entries recording that the family still resided at Broadbridge Heath within 1.5km of Warnham Furnace.

To return to the children of Peter de Guye, Ellen Deguyse married Anthony Farmer at Hawkhurst in 1591. Of Samuel Guyse' twins, one was buried at Goudhurst in September 1594, and the other, Nicholas, was baptised there ten days later. Samuel's son John was baptised at Hawkhurst in 1599 and his daughter Elizabeth at Ewhurst in 1607. Samuel himself was buried at Ewhurst in 1619. Nicholas Guye married Martha Benton at Cranbrook in 1595, his servant Michell was buried at Biddenden in 1597 and he himself was apparently the Nicholas Guise buried at Beckley in 1624.

With Anthony Guise comes a first confirmation of the family's role in the iron industry. He married Dorothy Young at Cranbrook in 1594, but they soon moved north into Staffordshire, where their daughter Dorothy was baptised at Rugeley in January 1602. In January 1608 the parish register for Ellastone recorded the baptism of German the son of Anthony Guyes, hammerman, and named his wife as Dorothy, so confirming the identity of the couple.

By 1614 they were back at Cranbrook, when the collier Lambert Fashall bequeathed a lamb to Anthony's son Lambert Guise. Anthony's wife Dorothy was buried in January 1616 at Cranbrook. Anthony himself may have married again, because his burial at Westfield in 1624 was followed by the burial of Widow (*Vidua*) Guyes in 1628. There was no mention of German Guyes in the Weald, but Lambert Guise married Elizabeth Taylour at Wadhurst in 1648.

Richard Goye, who married Elizabeth Patche at Goudhurst in 1575, was apparently another member of this family. Their children, Robert, John, Richard, Hugh, Stephen (who died aged nine) and Job, were baptised at Goudhurst between 1576 and 1591. Richard Goye, 'poor', was buried at Goudhurst in 1611 and his widow was buried there the following year.

Richard's son Robert married Elizabeth Meere in 1604, and their children, Marie, John, Robert

218. Crossley, 'Ralph Hogge's ironworks accounts, 1576-1580', p. 74 (text modified).

who did not survive infancy, Richard, a second Robert and Alexander, were baptised at Goudhurst between 1605 and 1620. Robert's wife Elizabeth was buried at Goudhurst in 1634, and her children Marie and John also predeceased their father.

Richard Goye's second son was John Guy, the Crowhurst husbandman who married Isabel Clarke at Whatlington in 1600. They had three children, John whose baptism has not been found, and Elizabeth and Mary, who were baptised at Sedlescombe in 1609 and 1612. In 1622 John Guy made his will: he left £10 to each of his three children, but the money was to remain in the hands of Isabel his executrix and legatee during her widowhood. John's burial has not been found but probate was granted in June 1625 and his goods were valued at £45 3s 0d.[219] Isabel was buried at Beckley in 1639 having survived her son John. He married Elizabeth Rootes at Catsfield in 1626, had children named John and Elizabeth baptised at Crowhurst in 1628 and 1631, and was buried at Crowhurst early in 1635 leaving his wife to administer goods valued at only £14 7s 0d.[220]

Richard's youngest son Job married Elizabeth Geale at Goudhurst in 1615. Their children William and Job were baptised at Goudhurst in 1617 and 1620, but their father was buried at Heathfield early in 1620, leaving his son Job a posthumous child.

Alexander Guyse, a Goudhurst collier,[221] whose baptism has not been traced, married Dorothy Fletcher alias Ridley at Ticehurst in 1620 and their children, Mark, Martha, Richard, Thomas, John, and the twins Joan and Mary, were baptised at Goudhurst between 1622 and 1640, whilst other children of theirs, Margaret, Nicholas and Alexander, were baptised at Goudhurst in 1620 and at Ticehurst in 1622 and 1627 respectively; Margaret and John did not survive infancy.

Nicholas Guise of Ewhurst, who married Annis Adams of Beckley at Beckley in 1619, will have been the survivor of Samuel Guise's twins, born in September 1594. A son of Nicholas and Annis was buried unbaptised at Ewhurst in 1621, and a daughter Amy who was baptised there in 1624, may have been their child too. However, the wife of Nicholas Guise buried at Ewhurst early in 1629 was named Mary, so Annis Adams had not survived as his wife very long. In November 1629 Nicholas was married for the third time at Udimore to a widow named Elizabeth Andrews.

Another member of this family was an earlier Alexander Gouy 'a porter at the place', who was buried at Herstmonceux in 1611.

Apart from Anthony Guyes' years in Staffordshire no other members of this family are known to have participated in the spread of the iron industry to other parts of Britain.

Prevaute

John Prevaute who paid the poll tax in Shoyswell hundred in 1552 is not otherwise known in the Weald. In the Pays de Bray the family was well represented at Bouelles, where names listed in the *rôle de fouage* for 1497 included Henry Prevaut.[222]

Since the name does not appear in other Wealden sources, Prevaute's stay in Sussex was perhaps short.

Minnage

This family perhaps lived at one time near Longmesnil between Forges and the Picard border. Gregoire Manant of Le Becquet granted a three-year lease of the *pré des Mares* (5 acres 20 perches) to Jehan Menaige of Criquetot in 1503. Early in 1505 Manant obtained 15 livres from Pierres Dugardin of Neufchâtel by selling him a rent of 30 sous on meadow (*pré*) of five acres in the hamlet of Hupignys (Dupigny in the parish of Longmesnil), which was perhaps the same land; Colin Mesnage of Le Plix, east of Serqueux, acted as a pledge for this rent payment.[223]

It seems possible that members of the family who remained in France were progenitors of the Ménager, or Le Ménager family of slitters of iron who worked at numerous mills in the Perche in the

219. ESRO, PBT 1/1/19/29, 1/3/5/211.
220. ESRO, PBT 1/3/6/212.
221. ESRO, PBT 1/3/5/242 (administration of Mark Fletcher alias Ridley of Ticehurst, 1626).
222. Bibliothèque Nationale de France, Paris, MS. Fr. 25924, no. 1152.
223. ADSM, 2 E 14/1145 (3 Oct 1503); 2 E 14/1148 (1 Feb 1505).

sixteenth and seventeenth centuries.[224]

Nicholas Mynnage was first noted as a poll-tax payer in Shoyswell hundred in 1560. He was married to Denise Robard at Goudhurst in 1567.

Although James Minidge did not appear in a subsidy roll until 1576, when he paid 3s 4d on goods in Battle hundred, he may have been the head of the family. As a resident in Mountjoy he defaulted from Battle views of frankpledge in April and October 1578.[225] He retired from ironworking to end his days as a Rye resident, where in 1597 James Menadge's widow Collette was granted administration of his goods, which were inventoried at £26 10s 6d.[226] Beyond the marriage of Nicholas Minnage, no parish register entries from the ironworking areas seem to refer to these two men.

Meanwhile in the High Weald, Richard Mannadge had married Joan Hayward at Speldhurst in 1577. Their children Thomas, John and Eleanor were baptised in that parish between 1578 and 1582. In 1582 Anne Mennadge married Thomas Waller at Speldhurst. No entry for the burial of Richard Manadge has been found, but 'Widow Mannage' was buried at Speldhurst in 1603. Richard's eldest son Thomas married Celia Gilnet at Tonbridge in 1603 and their son Thomas was baptised there in 1606.

Back in Sussex the baptisms of, Dorothy, John, twins named Benjamin and Susan, and Annis, children of the hammerman Peter Mynidge were recorded at Ashburnham between 1604 and 1616, and another son named John was baptised at Penhurst in 1606. By 1619, when his wife Susan was examined at quarter sessions,[227] Peter had moved to Westfield. Susan was buried there in February 1621, followed to the grave by her husband twelve days later, both perhaps victims of some infection.

Peter Minage left goods valued at £36 0s 10d. He made his eldest son Roger, whose baptism has not been found, his executor and left £2 to each of his other children, to be paid to them at 21. His eldest daughter Dorothy was to have her mother's best petticoat and waistcoat, two of her best neckerchiefs, coifs and cross-cloths, two aprons, two pairs of her best stockings, a pair of shoes, her best hat and a little joined chest. Roger was to bring up Anne (or Annis) and also Benjamin 'till he be able to shift, or else to provide for him a Master'.[228] The unfortunate Benjamin did not live to see either, because he was buried at Westfield at the age of nine.

Roger Minnedge married Anne Slater at Ashburnham in 1622 and their children, William, James, Elizabeth (who survived less than two years), John, Anne, Elizabeth, Peter and Roger, were baptised at Westfield between 1623 and 1638. Roger's wife Anne was buried in January 1640 and he survived her by only five months. His daughter Elizabeth married Thomas Bishop at Westfield in 1656, and Peter married Joan Mittenden at Heathfield in 1664.

John Mynage, Peter Minage's younger son, married Alice Bray at Westfield in 1630. Their son John was baptised at Westfield in 1631, but a daughter named Anne who had been baptised at Crowhurst in 1634 was buried at Brede in 1635. John Minnage's first wife Alice was buried at Catsfield in 1636 and later in the same year he married Elizabeth Taylour, also at Catsfield. John was buried as 'John Minnage the elder' at Westfield in 1679 and his will shows that, like his father Peter, he was a hammerman.[229] It does not appear that he had any children by his second wife, to whom he left £30, as much household stuff as should be necessary for her housekeeping and a red cow. To his brother Roger's sons John and Peter he left £10 and £3 respectively. He also mentioned his cousins, James, Roger and Elizabeth Bishop in his will, the mention of the latter proving that by 'cousins' he implied his nephews and niece, more of Roger's children. To James's daughter Susan and Roger's daughter Anne he left £3 each and to Elizabeth Bishop £1. He made his son John his residuary legatee and executor.

A second James Mynage married Joan Martin at Westfield in 1618, but sadly he was buried at Catsfield in September 1619 on the day on which his only daughter Katherine was baptised. He could have been another of Peter's untraced sons, not mentioned in his father's will because his death occurred before that of his father. However, his daughter Katherine received no mention in Peter's will either.

In the hearth tax of 1665 a finery man named John Minnage was taxed on two hearths at

224. Belhoste and others, *La métallurgie normande*, pp. 156, 305-6.
225. HEH, BA Vol. 96 ff 34-35.
226. ESRO, PBT 1/3/2/241.
227. ESRO, QR 19, m. 93; I am indebted to Brian Phillips for this reference.
228. ESRO, PBT 1/1/18/5, 1/3/5/84.
229. ESRO, PBT 1/1/35/205.

Westfield.[230] It seems probable that he was the son of John the hammerman, baptised at Westfield in 1631. Although this finer could have been Roger's son John baptised in 1629, to whom the hammerman had bequeathed £10, it seems more probable that Roger's son was the John Minedge who was buried at Hawkhurst in 1684. The Peter Minnage who occupied Westfield Forge with Thomas Western in 1692 cannot be positively identified but was undoubtedly a member of this family.[231]

Cressey

The aliens John Cracye, John Cressye and John Cressie, who paid the poll tax in Shoyswell in 1572 and 1576 and in Netherfield hundred in 1595, will have been one and the same man. They were undoubtedly 'John Creasie a Frenchman' whose daughter Susan was baptised at Etchingham in February 1579.

However, it appears probable that Cressie was married again in 1580 at Mountfield to Parnell Vinton (born Perigo), the widow of the Westfield finer Alexander Vintam. In addition to Susan, John Cressie probably had two other children, but perhaps because for a time he lived in Battle, whose sixteenth-century parish register does not survive, their baptisms cannot be found. Nor have burials for John and Parnell Cressie been found, so they too were perhaps buried at Battle before 1611. Alternatively it is possible that the immigrant was the John Cresey who was buried early in 1625 at Catsfield, where his son later worked.

The eldest of John Cressie's children was certainly Thomas Creasy, who in 1599 married Joan Harrow, from another Mountfield immigrant ironworking family. They had one son Thomas, who was baptised at Mountfield in 1600, and it is possible that Constance, daughter of Thomas Cresy, who was baptised at Brede in 1602 was their child too, but Constance does not seem to have survived. The elder Thomas Cresse was buried at Mountfield in 1603 and five years later his widow Joan married the Mountfield ironfounder Richard Gunter, who later moved to Robertsbridge.

The younger Thomas Cressie eventually found himself at Brede, where his aunt Susan had married the collier John Addes in 1604, and where he himself found employment as a miner. However, like his father, he failed to survive his twenties and was buried at Brede unmarried in 1627. His goods were inventoried at £11 10s 10d. He left £1 to his mother, the same amount to his half brother Henry Gunter, and 10 shillings to John Adds' wife.[232]

John Creasey of Catsfield, forgeman, was probably another son of the immigrant John Cressie. In a deposition of November 1616 he stated that he was aged 23 and had been born in Battle, presumably around 1593. He had lived in Catsfield for about 10 months and before that in Ashburnham for about a year and a half. He had been a covenant servant of the forgemaster Richard Alfrey for the last year, worked at Alfrey's forge, which would be Potmans Forge in Catsfield, and lived 'in his house', one of the workmen's cottages provided at the forge. Creasey was illiterate, but claimed to be worth £7 'in his own goods, debts paid'.[233] In 1629 he acquired three roods of land and a house at Penhurst and was still at Catsfield in 1633 when he entered into a bond in £30 with Edward Elphick; the documents involved show that though he had styled himself a forgeman in 1616, his actual occupation was that of collier.[234]

John Creasey had evidently married whilst he lived at Ashburnham, where the parish register recorded his marriage to Marie Waters in July 1615. Their children, John, James, another John, Thomas, Mary, Richard and Hester were baptised at Catsfield between 1616 and 1637, but both the Johns and Richard died within a year of baptism, as did yet another son John, baptised at Ashburnham in 1621. Thomas too died around the age of 12, so by 1640 James, Mary and Hester were the sole survivors out of all these children. John Cresey was buried at Catsfield in 1643 and his widow was buried there the following year.

In addition to this small family of forgemen, there were other Cressies involved in the metal trades is Sussex, which raises the question as to whether there had been earlier immigrants of this name. In the 1520s Cresses mentioned in the subsidy rolls were confined to East Sussex, but most were in peripheral areas, with only Richard Cresse of Mountfield, rated at £17 in 1524 and £15 in 1525,

230. TNA, E 179/258/20.
231. ESRO, DUN 27/7.
232. ESRO, PBT 1/1/20/42, 1/3/5/310.
233. WSRO, Ep II/5/11, ff 25-6; I am grateful to Brian Phillips for this reference.
234. ESRO, ASH 4501/514, 537.

inhabiting an ironworking area, a circumstance which does not properly resolve the issue.

An ironworking family which can first be detected in Mountfield was that of Christopher Cressey. His daughter Elizabeth was baptised at Mountfield in 1585 and his son Richard was buried there in the following year. By the 1590s he had moved on to Maresfield, where he fathered a son named John, baptised in 1593, and possibly Charles Cresse, who was baptised there in 1594. In 1602 Christopher Cressey of Cranbrook, furnace filler, was bound to keep the peace, along with Roger Cressey, who may have been another son whose baptism has not been traced, but who was also a furnace filler.[235] Christopher Cressey was buried at Salehurst early in 1612. Roger Crecie's marriage to Martha Jerrarde at Cranbrook in 1602 linked him with another ironfounding family, but his later occupation as a locksmith is revealed by an entry in the Cranbrook parish register for the burial of his son Richard Cressee (1615-1658) early in 1658.

William Cressy, the Hastings blacksmith, made a deposition in 1581 which indicated that he had been born in Pevensey around 1530, but had lived for a time in Hampshire before coming to Hastings about 1561.[236] He died later in 1581, leaving a will in which he mentioned his son John, probably the Hastings blacksmith of that name who in 1584 took administration of the goods of Edward Pontte of Wartling, as next of kin, Pontte's widow Thomasine having renounced .[237]

Netherfield hundred

Fever

Nicholas Fewer was perhaps the man whose son William Faver was baptised at Rotherfield in 1540. After paying the poll tax as a worker of Charles Warner (i.e. Gerard) in Netherfield hundred in 1551, Fewer or Fever perhaps went north again to Tonbridge, where another Nicholas Fever was baptised early in 1557.

Other Frenchmen of this name were Anthony Favor who was buried at Burwash in 1578 and Charles Fever who paid the poll tax in Robertsbridge hundred in 1576.

Anthony Favor perhaps came from Le Carrouge in the parish of Sainte-Geneviève. He was possibly the eldest son and heir of Jehan Le Fèvre of the adjoining hamlet of Canchy, who had been mentioned in a notarial act of 1512.[238] Anthoine himself was first mentioned in a notarial act of 1535, an act by which he raised 20 livres by the sale of a rent of 2 livres to the Neuville carpenter, Pierre Bourdet. In 1537 he raised a further 1£ 19s 0d by an exchange of property with Robinet Langloys of Sainte-Geneviève, and by then selling to Robinet the property that should have accrued to himself. In April 1544 he was indebted in 15£ 10s 0d to Guillaume Le Roy for a loan and other affairs, and in July 1544 he made a gift of land in Sainte-Geneviève which belonged to the lordship of Bosc Herault to his younger brother Michel, perhaps the first indication that he intended leaving France.

In June 1545 Anthoine bought out the rights of his stepfather, Christofle Acard, in his father's estate, by agreeing to pay an annuity of 1£ 5s 0d to his mother Collette. A week later he raised 40 livres by selling a rent of 4 livres to Guillaume Rasset of Neufchâtel. The following month he sold lands held of the lordship of Canchy to Colin Rasset dit Petit of Canchy for 30 livres In May 1546 he and Nicolas de Choppin engaged to deliver a hundred (*cent*) of wool to Lucas de Guerres of Bully for 16 livres. In August 1546, together with Jehan Rasset of Canchy and Jehan Lambert of Fontaines, he raised 200 livres by the sale of a rent of 20 livres, to Nicolas Azoult, a Rouen merchant.[239] This sale was witnessed by Phlippin Toullotte of Saint-Maurice, who worked for Richard Weekes up to 1551 and for Sir William Sidney from 1551 onwards. This sum of 200 livres was perhaps intended to finance their expedition abroad. The final notarial act concerning Le Fèvre was the procuration he made in 1552 to his wife Perette and her father Henry Acard to realise all his assets in France.[240]

235. L. A. Knafla (ed.), *Kent at law, 1602*, London, HMSO, 1994, 694.
236. WSRO, EpII/5/1, ff 109-10.
237. ESRO, PBT 1/3/2/77.
238. ADSM, 2 E 14/1154 (10 Apr 1512).
239. ADSM, 2 E 14/1171 (19 Jun 1535), 2 E 14/1176 (3 Feb 1537), 2 E 14/1183 (19 Apr and 3 Jul 1544), 2 E 14/1189 (23 and 30 Jun, 18 Jul 1545), 2 E 14/1190 (1 May and 7 Aug 1546).
240. ADSM, 2 E 14/1192 (4 Jul 1552).

Before he died Anthony had almost certainly become the father of Francis Favers, who was baptised at Burwash in 1574, and perhaps the man whose son Anthony 'Yufavoine' (*sic*) was reportedly baptised in 1568 at Frant, the vagaries of whose parish register have already been the subject of comment.

That Charles Fever may have been the son of Michel Le Fèvre and the grandson of Jehannequin Le Fèvre of Neuville-Ferrières, is suggested by his inexplicable disappearance from the French scene after 1544. In 1505 Jehannequin, along with Jacquet Le Tieullier, had witnessed the act by which Jehan d'Angreville purchased the estate of Pierre Nazet, a man involved in the running of Anthoine Doullé's forge. The sale of a rent of 14£ 12s 6d on Jehannequyn by the forgemaster Doullé to the cleric Aubery Dufour in 1508 confirms that Le Fèvre could have had a close connection with ironworking.[241]

By 1528 Jehannequin was living in the parish of Saint-Pierre of Neufchâtel and bore the sobriquet alias (*dit*) Tallon.[242] In 1536, when Charles Le Fèvre was engaged to Alizon daughter of Rommain Bouceleu, he and his father Michel Le Fèvre dit Tallon were living in the farm of Saint Anthoine, on the plateau above Neufchâtel, and bordering on the forest of Ménonval, but Michel's father Jehannequyn had now apparently returned to Neuville-Ferrières. Jehannequin died around 1540 and during the 1540s there were numerous notarial acts dealing with the properties of Michel and Charles Le Fèvre at Neuville-Ferrières.[243]

However, following the gap between 1546 and 1551 in the notarial acts, the sole reference to Charles appears to concern a rent of 2£ 5s 0d owed by Charlot Le Fèvre and Charlot Cousin to Pierre Le Noble of Bures, which Nicollas Boissay dit Frerot of Mainières had acquired from Le Noble in 1554 and which he sold for 22 livres to Robert Boissay of Mainières in 1559. Finally in 1566, a case before the bailie of Gaillefontaine in which the parties were Christiane, widow of Michel Le Fèvre, and Adrien Dupont, on whom the Le Fèvre properties in Neuville-Ferrières had devolved,[244] indicates, not only the death of Michel Le Fèvre, but the disappearance without explanation of his son.

In England Charles Fever was perhaps the man who in 1576 paid the poll tax in Robertsbridge hundred. In 1590 Charles Feever was cited in the will of Thomas Bourne of Crowhurst,[245] among a list of debtors mainly of French descent, of which Charles's debt amounted to 4 shillings All were presumably employed at Crowhurst ironworks by Gregory Relfe, who himself owed an unspecified amount 'in accounts and reckonings' to Thomas Bourne, perhaps the forge clerk. Charles Fever's wife was buried at Crowhurst in 1598, after which he was briefly married to Agnes Gabriel in 1602, but died in 1606.

The Nicholas Fever baptised at Tonbridge in 1557 was the Nicholas Favoure who married Mary Blynd at Mayfield in 1582 and whose daughter Dorothy was baptised there early in 1584. It looks as though he went on to Brede where his son James was baptised in 1588 and another child was buried in 1590. He was next found at Warbleton in 1593, where in December his child Lidia was buried only six days after baptism, and where his first wife died in childbirth. By 1595 Nicholas was married again and further daughters, Margaret, Denise, Joan, Elizabeth, Martha and Mary, were baptised at Warbleton by 1605, followed by Nicholas, Charles and Anne, baptised between 1607 and 1614. Many of these children appear to have died in childhood, but James Fever married Mercy Muza in 1616, and after her death in 1618 he married a widow named Susan Fox. Nicholas Fever buried at Warbleton early in 1649 was perhaps the man baptised in 1607, rather than his father, who would have been over 90 years of age.

Also at Warbleton was Anthony Fevers, who was perhaps the man baptised at Frant in 1568. His children, Elizabeth, Anthony and John, were baptised at Warbleton between 1599 and 1606. In 1619 Anthony Feaver was mentioned in the will of John Foster of Warbleton as owing him £1 for cutting 20 cords of wood 'or thereabouts',[246] so in this case Feaver was an employer of labour.

Anthony's sons Anthony and John were probably also master colliers and appear to have moved via Heathfield to Dallington. Anthony had married Joan Enscombe at Warbleton in 1623 and their daughter Elizabeth and son Anthony were baptised at Heathfield in 1627 and 1630. Bishop's transcripts for Dallington record the death of George Foster, apprentice to Anthony Fever, in 1631.

241. ADSM, 2 E 14/1150 (29 Dec 1505). 2 E 14/1152 (25 Nov 1508).

242. ADSM, 2 E 14/1164 (1 Apr 1528).

243. ADSM, 2 E 14/1173 (24 Feb 1535/6), 2 E 14/1185 (28 May and 4 Jun 1541), 2 E 14/1186 (15 Nov and 3 Dec 1541).

244. ADSM, 2 E 14/1198 (18 Nov 1559), 2 E 14/1209 (23 Jul 1566).

245. ESRO, PBT 1/1/8/413.

246. ESRO, PBT 1/1/17/18.

John Fever married Martha Waters at Heathfield in 1630, but their twin daughters Elizabeth and Joan were baptised at Warbleton in 1637. The Warbleton tenement analysis shows that it was John Fever of Dallington, collier, who owned Wyatts in Warbleton from 1652 to 1664. When he acquired the leasehold in 1646 it had been wasteland. When he died in 1664 it was divided into three 'moieties'.[247] In 1656 the marriage of John Weekes of Warbleton to Mary, daughter of John Fever of Dallington, collier, was recorded at Warbleton.

Meanwhile Francis Feaver, who had been baptised at Burwash in 1574, married Mary Linche at Framfield in 1603, though they do not appear to have continued in the parish after 1605.

John Fever of Wadhurst, collier, is the only member of this family for whom a will, made in 1629, has survived. He was first noticed at Tonbridge, where his daughters, Annis and Mary, and son Nicholas were baptised between 1594 and 1600. He then moved to Wadhurst, where his sons Anthony and Abraham were baptised in 1605 and 1607, two other children, John and Elizabeth, apparently having been baptised there before 1604, when the earliest parish register to survive starts.

John left his working tools to his second son John, whom he made his residuary legatee and executor. His other sons and his unmarried daughter Annis each received £5 and Annis was also to share half the household goods with John. However, the coppice woods, which he held by lease from William Fowle of Lightlands, were to be equally divided between his four sons. His other daughters, Elizabeth wife of George Chapman, and Mary, wife of William Garnebas, were to have the money due to him from John Luck of Mayfield, yeoman. This nuncupative will was witnessed by Thomas Gilber[t], Alexander Collin, and two of Fever's sons, Anthony and Nicholas, who all entered their marks. It was countersigned by William Russell and William Hosmer, and William Gardenbas appended his mark.[248]

John Fever's eldest son Nicholas Fever had married Dorothy Leaver in 1626 and by 1640 eight of their children had been baptised at Wadhurst. His second son, John Fever, whom he had made his heir, married Susan May at Frant early in 1644. His fourth son Abraham Fever moved to Beckley, where he married Ann Brunnell in 1641. Their daughter Mary was baptised at Beckley early in 1642.

Polvo

The surname of John Polvo, who paid a shilling on goods among the Netherfield denizens in 1551, is otherwise unknown in the Weald. Perhaps Polvo is an alias for a man better known under some other name. The surname seems not to occur in any surviving denization roll.

Pavy

The surname Pavy did not occur in the Sussex subsidy rolls of the 1520s, but a citizen and skinner of London named Nicholas Pavy made his will in 1538,[249] so it cannot automatically be assumed that all Wealden parish register entries for this surname relate to the ironworking family. Indeed, the citizen and merchant tailor of London, Robert Pavie, who was buried at Penshurst in October 1600, was clearly from the London family, and Frances the wife of Robert Pavie, buried there early in 1597, was clearly his wife, rather than the wife of the Frant immigrant of the same name.

The first immigrant of this family was William Pavy, who, together with his wife and son, paid the poll tax in Danehill Horsted hundred in 1560. It must be suspected that entries for William Pawyer, who had paid the poll tax in Netherfield hundred in 1551 as a servant of Charles Warnet (Guerard), and also for William Panny, who paid the poll tax in Burbeech hundred in West Sussexas a servant of Swayne and Ilman in 1563, relate to the same man.

Other immigrant members of the family mentioned in subsidy rolls were Charles Payve, who paid the poll tax at Northchapel in 1572 and Anthony Pavye,[250] who paid the poll tax as a servant of John Porter in Rotherfield hundred in the same year.

247. D. Martin and B. Martin, *Tenement Analysis, Warbleton*, Robertsbridge, Rape of Hastings Architectural Survey.
248. ESRO, PBT 2/2/5/45.
249. TNA, PROB 11/27/413.
250. Since the Pevensey rape subsidy for 1572 was levied on 30 September of that year, it is theoretically possible that Anthony Pavy could have been the shipwright of that name who arrived in Sussex on 1 September 1572 from Rouen with other Huguenot refugees, but it seems rather unlikely.

In the Pays de Bray the family was widespread between the Béthune and Varenne valleys, on the outskirts of the Forest of Eawy. A dressmaker (*cousturier*) named Jehan Pavet, of Morimont in the parish of Esclavelles, was also a dealer in wood and he and his son Guillaume were involved in a legal dispute against the *verderer* of the Forest, Anthoine Bourgoise, in 1536. In 1542 Jehan Pavet's sale of five and a half hundreds of billet-wood (*buche*) was witnessed by his son Guillaume Pavet, but the latter was already a dealer in wood on his own account, having sold a puncheon of cider and four hundreds of billet-wood to Cardin Le Fevre, a Neufchâtel ironmonger, in 1541.[251]

By 1541 Jehan Pavet had acquired a house at Les Hayons in the parish of Esclavelles. Whilst his younger son Jehan followed his father's profession, his elder son Guillaume, who continued at Morimont, became a smith (*mareschal*) and may have been the man who came to the Weald. In November 1554, perhaps significantly, he made over to his younger brother Jehan their late father's house, farmstead, garden and *heritages* at Les Hayons, in return for which Jehan renounced all claim on the remainder of their father's estate.[252]

There is no evidence that William Pavy remained in the Weald after 1563, or that he ended his days there, which agrees with his initiation of a rent sale of 6 livres which he made at Neufchâtel in 1565 and his purchase in 1567 of a rent of 13 sous which the late Pasquet Pavet held on Jehan Gressent.[253]

Further members of the Pavye family mentioned in notarial records of Saint-Saëns were Robert and Adrien Pavye, the sons of the former sergeant of La Haye de Saint-Saëns, Jehan Pavye, who died around 1541.[254] Both these men may have emigrated to England. Robert Pavy, the Frenchman whose daughter Mary was baptised at Frant in 1572, was not afterwards heard of, and if he was the elder of these brothers, had more reason to return to France than Adrian.

Adrian Pavey was at Horsham in September 1559, when his son Peter was baptised there. Adrian Pavey and his wife Joan, whose daughter Katherine was baptised at Horsham in 1589, were perhaps from the next generation of this family.

It looks as though one branch of this family moved north around 1570, because in South Yorkshire, Edward Pavye was enrolled in the Sheffield Easter book in 1572.[255] Later Peter Pavye, who was probably the child baptised at Horsham in 1559, was among other Frenchmen employed in Eskdale in North Yorkshire: his daughter Katherine was baptised at Danby in October 1586. He perhaps moved south to Makeney in Derbyshire around 1590: there the burial of his wife Elizabeth in 1602 and his remarriage to Joan Watters early in 1603 are among the first entries in the Duffield parish register. Elizabeth Pavie, 'an oulde woman borne in France which died in Codnor Park' and was buried at Heanor in Derbyshire in August 1596, may well have been the elder Adrian Pavey's widow and Peter's mother, and possibly the mother of Edward too.

Back in the Weald the family was next found at Worth in the persons of the second Adrian Pavy, and Charles Pavy who paid the poll tax later at Northchapel. Adrian married Agnes Marten in 1562 and Charles married Dorothy Predam in 1566, both marriages taking place at Worth; and it was there that Charles's daughter Catherine was baptised in 1567. Around the same time a deceased member of the family, Richard Payve, was referred to in the Balcombe parish register. His widow Margaret was buried there in March 1566, and her daughter, named Katherine Powlter, was buried there a week later.

Since no more Pavy entries occurred in the Worth parish register until 1589 it looks as though both Adrian and Charles moved westwards in the Weald around 1570, and that Charles was the unnamed father of Alice Pavy who was baptised at Northchapel in March 1572. On 2 March 1580 both men were involved in the affray at Plaistow which arose when a Dunsfold hammerman, Nicholas Unyon, pulled Roger Noras alias Norris, a Northchapel miner, off the back of a horse on which he was riding behind Richard Cowlstock of Kirdford. Other persons who became involved included James Bewsar, a finer, and Peter Madbow, a collier, both of Kirdford, John Coppyn, a hammerman, and William Foster, a finer, both of Northchapel, Charles Foxe of Dunsfold, a finer, and a servant of John Smith, the forgemaster of Kirdford, named Alexander.

In the assize proceedings which followed, both Pavyes were stated to be finers, Charles Pavye

251. ADSM, 2 E 14/1174 (4 Nov 1536); 2 E 14/1186 (8 Oct 1541); 2 E 14/1186 (11 Mar 1542)
252. ADSM, 2 E 14/1184 (22 Jan 1541); 2 E 14/1195 (10 Nov 1554).
253. ADSM, 2 E 14/1208 (7 Sep 1565); 2 E 14/1211 (19 Jul 1567).
254. ADSM, 2 E 93/19 (12 Aug 1541).
255. Sheffield Public Libraries, ACM/S62.

at Northchapel, and Adrian Pavye alias Foye at Kirdford. Charles Pavye sustained a wound to the head, as a result of which he gradually became insane, became paralysed down one side on 26 March and eventually died on 4 April. Though this fatality was judged to have been due to the 'Visitation of God', the affray was considered a serious matter and Norris seems to have been thought in some way culpable, because 'his escape' was alluded to, and various persons entered recognizances to give evidence against him, and against Adrian Pavye 'and others'.[256]

It looks as though Adrian Pavy's wife Agnes had died, because early in 1579 he married Margaret Leonard at Worth. Adrian's son John Pavy was baptised at Wisborough Green in 1582, but may have been the boy of the same name who was buried at Horsham in December 1589. In the previous month Adrian's daughter Katherin had been baptised at Horsham, though on this occasion his wife's name was stated to be Joan. Adrian Pavy's burial has not been traced, so perhaps he returned to France.

A second Charles Pavy from this family was a Horsham collier, and he, together with two other colliers, David Powell and Peter Dugeon of Shipley, was indicted in 1605 for riotous assembly at Shipley and an attack on John Lucas. The verdict is unknown.[257] Charles's son Richard was baptised at Horsham in 1604, but the baptism of his other son Charles has not been found. His wife was stated to be Agnes in 1604, but she may have been married to him under the name Ann Holte at Shipley in 1601 and it was as Ann that she was buried at Shipley in 1649.

Charles Pavy's two sons, Richard and Charles, both continued at Shipley, where Richard married Joan Towne in 1637. Charles predeceased his brother, apparently unmarried, in 1652. In his nuncupative will he was described as a husbandman.[258] Though he left only a shilling each to his brother and sister-in-law, he left £10 to each of their five children, to be paid them at their majorities. He appointed his father overseer of his will, who was to be succeeded on his death by Richard's eldest son, another Charles Pavy, who had been born in 1640.

The Frenchman Marian Pavy acted as a godparent when Susan daughter of the hammerman Nicholas Russell was baptised at Maresfield in 1576. The following year he married Mary Farrard at Mayfield. It seems possible that Jane daughter of Marian the hammerman, baptised at Frant in October 1572, and who married John Lamy at Frant in 1590, was his daughter by a former wife. He was described as French when his daughter Mary was baptised at Frant in 1578. Mary survived only one week, and John, who was baptised in 1580, for not much longer, but his daughter Alice who was baptised in 1582 may have fared better. No further mention of Marian Pavy occurred at Frant and the family may have moved to Surrey, where Alice Pavie married Richard Harding at Chiddingfold in 1605.

Mary the daughter of John Porter's French servant Anthony Pavy was baptised at Lamberhurst in 1579. Anne and Adrian Pavy, who were baptised at Lamberhurst in 1575 and 1585, but whose parents were not disclosed, were also probably Anthony's children and it seems possible he can be identified with Anthony Pavie, whose wife Julian bore him a daughter Katherin, baptised at Worth in 1588. Anthony's widow, whose name was unfortunately not given, was buried at Lamberhurst in 1624, but the parish register contains no record of the burial of Anthony himself. Perhaps it occurred towards the end of the nine-year gap in the Lamberhurst parish register between 1587 and 1595. The ill fate which afterwards befell two Lamberhurst spinsters, of whom at least one was his daughter, was sometimes the lot of fatherless children.

Anthony Pavy's children who clearly continued at Lamberhurst were Adrian and Mary. Adrian married Ann Daye in 1610, but no mention of their children is found at Lamberhurst. However, Adrian appeared there early in 1619 with a second wife named Elizabeth, and their children John and Dorothy were baptised at Lamberhurst in that year and in 1622.

Mary Pavy of Lamberhurst, spinster, was indicted along with William Baker, a labourer, for the theft of a bushel of wheat worth 4 shillings from the forgemaster John Porter in 1598. It was Baker who was found guilty of this theft and he was hanged. Mary Pavy was found not guilty.[259] However, the Lamberhurst parish register recorded the baptism of Mary's fourth illegitimate child, Moreshame, early in 1612 and another illegitimate child, Ann who did not survive a month, was fathered on her by the Frant collier Richard Horden. Another member of the family, Agnes Pavye of Lamberhurst, spinster,

256. Cockburn, *Sussex Assize records, Elizabeth I*, no. 801.
257. Cockburn, *Sussex Assize records, James I*, no. 80.
258. WSRO, STC 1/21/470.
259. Cockburn, *Sussex Assize records, Elizabeth I*, no. 1782.

fared even worse. In 1612 she was sentenced to be hanged for strangling her illegitimate child.[260]

It seems possible that Richard Horden's name should be read as 'Harden', and that he was the Richard Harding who had married Alice Pavy in 1605, and belonged to an English family of colliers. A Frant collier named William Hardinge had been indicted of involvement in a theft at Lamberhurst in 1596, but evaded arrest. The marriage of Alice Pavy to Richard at Chiddingfold in 1605 already alluded to, was followed in 1609 by that of Margaret Pavy to John Harding at Lamberhurst. It seems possible that they too moved temporarily to Chiddingfold, because Edward, the son of the collier John Harding, was buried there in 1616. If John Harden, the Frant collier towards whom the Frant founder John Lullam was ordered to keep the peace in 1640,[261] was Margaret's husband, the couple had perhaps by then returned to Frant.

Another member of this family who married a forgeman from an English family was Katherine Pavie, who married Gregory Rive at Lamberhurst in 1601. 'Gregory Reeve, forgeman', was buried there in 1620.

Yorkshire and Derbyshire members of this family have already been dealt with. The burial of the hammerman, Steven Pavie, at Wombourne early in 1640 indicates a presence at one of the forges on the Smestow Brook, north of Stourbridge in the Midlands. It seems possible that John Pave of Kinver, who married Mary Hodgetts at Kingswinford in 1652, was also a member of this family. He was buried at Kinver in 1659. Little else has come to light concerning the family's participation in the spread of the indirect method to other parts of the Midlands.

Peter

Peter Petyre and Martin Peter, who paid the poll tax in 1551 in Netherfield and Danehill Sheffield hundreds respectively, have left no further record in the Weald. Their appearance in the same year suggests that they perhaps arrived in the Weald together and did not stay long in England. The possibility that both were sons of an immigrant ironworker whose baptismal name was Peter is made less likely by the coincidence of their appearance in separate rapes in the same year.

Persons surnamed Peter appeared quite widely distributed throughout Sussex in the subsidy rolls of the 1520s, which makes it difficult to establish whether later bearers of the name in the Weald were descended from either of these men.

Latornys

There is no further mention in the Weald of Peter Latornys who in 1551 paid the poll tax as an alien servant of Charles Warnet in Netherfield hundred. A surname which appears similar to it is Lardenois, borne by some ironworkers in regions close to the Ardennes, but any really exact French parallel is difficult to find.

Pettit

English persons of this name had been located at Buxted and in Hawksborough hundred in the 1520s, but not in Netherfield. Parish registers for the second half of the century indicate that this concentration in Buxted and Warbleton continued.

The immigrant Nicholas Pete or Petit paid the poll tax in Netherfield hundred in 1572 and 1576, and it was in Mountfield parish that he married Tomasin Stonham in 1584. The only other Pettit entry of the period in the Mountfield parish register was the marriage of Iden Petit to German Kennet, who was almost certainly of immigrant descent, in 1581. No contemporary records show that Nicholas Pettit was involved in the iron industry, but a descendant may have been Thomas Pettit of Buxted, cutler, who married Anne Burge in October 1688.[262]

260. Cockburn, *Sussex Assize records, James I*, no. 227.
261. Cockburn, *Kent Assize records, Elizabeth I*, no. 2447; ESRO, QR 49, m. 48.
262. Dunkin, *Sussex Marriage Licences, Lewes 1670-1729*, p. 304.

Hawksborough hundred

Fasshatt

The name of Gelum Fasshatt, who paid the poll tax alongside the hammerman Denys Lebys as one of Richard Woodman's workers in Hawksborough hundred in 1552, did not occur elsewhere in the subsidy rolls. The surname could possibly be a mis-transcription of Fashall or Vassall, in which case he may be an otherwise unknown relative of Woden Vassall.

However, as he worked alongside a hammerman, the works was probably a forge, which increases the likelihood that he is to be identified with William Fawket who worked as a finer for Sir William Sidney in 1549. This possibility has already been considered when rendering an account of Gillam Fawke.

Haunyng

The surname of John Haunyng, who paid the poll tax in Hawksborough hundred in 1552 as a servant of Joan Isted, has already been discussed under the account of the family of Hunnisett. In Rotherfield hundred in the reliefs of 1549 to 1552 that name was recorded as Hamyng, Hanyng or Honynges; only in 1543 was the name correctly rendered as Hanizett.

On this evidence, it seems permissible to suppose that this servant of Joan Isted belonged to the Hunnisett family. He was perhaps the alien John Hauneng who had paid a shilling on goods at Worth in 1551, but failed to appear there in 1552.

Gringo

The surname Gringo did not figure in the Sussex subsidy rolls of the 1520s. It first appeared in subsidy rolls in 1560, when John Gryndegore paid the poll tax in Hawksborough hundred. Warbleton was within Hawksborough hundred and the immigrant was perhaps the father of John Gryngoe, whose son Philip was baptised there in June 1565. The immigrant then passed on to Baldslowe hundred, where as John Grengell he paid the poll tax in 1572 and may have worked at Crowhurst Forge. He did not appear in the 1576 subsidy roll, evidently because he was the John Greengood buried at Crowhurst on New Year's Eve 1572.

No immigrant of this name appeared in contemporary denization rolls. However, a Pevensey rate book shows that John Grenegore paid 6 pence a year on a messuage in the quarter of Westham from 1521 until 1526. From 1527 onwards he took a messuage in Pevensey quarter 'lately held by Osbarne', at a rent which was soon reduced to 2 pence a year. He died around 1542, after which the payment was continued by his heirs, who were unfortunately not named, up to 1548, when the rate book ended.[263]

The wide spread of the name in the second half of the sixteenth century, the fact that around 1560 there were two Henry Gringos, and in the 1580s and 90s two separate John Gringos, and the fact that none of these was listed as an alien, all suggest that the family had been resident in Sussex for some time before 1560 and this seems to be confirmed by this rate book.

The first named member of the next generation was Henry Gringo who married Joan Bayly at Bexhill in 1559. Joan died soon after bearing Henry two children, Jane and Walter, of whom Walter did not survive, in 1560 and 1562. In October 1563 Henry married a widow named Agnes Colbrand at Bexhill. The widowed Agnes Gringord was buried at Bexhill in November 1587 and in her will mentioned her two Colbrand sons, but no child named Gringo.[264]

The Bexhill man had a contemporary of the same name, Henry Grengoo, who succeeded Nicholas Norton as tithing-man for Heathhatch in the manor of Godstone or Walkhamstead in April 1559. He continued as tithing-man at Heathhatch until he was succeeded by John Lusted in April 1561. Heathhatch is a placename now lost, but was apparently the detached part of the manor and parish which incorporated the highway from Woodcock Bridge by way of Hedgecourt Park (*cf.* Park Farm) to Felbridge Heath, from which the tithing of Heathhatch perhaps took its name. Henry Grengor was one

263. ESRO, PEV 513.
264. ESRO, PBT 1/1/8/365.

of the jurymen for the manor in April 1564,[265] and he paid 4 shillings on land worth £1 to the subsidy of 1593. He was still at Godstone in October 1595, but had disappeared by 1599.[266]

Woodcock Forge was first mentioned in July 1561, when a son of 'Swanne of the Hammer Mills' was baptised at Lingfield. It and Warren Furnace, higher up the watercourse in Worth parish, were Gage property, first run in the 1560s by John Fawkner and John French, and then in 1574 by John Thorpe of Hedgecourt. It seems possible that Henry Grengor could have worked there.

Children of a third Henry Grengoe were baptised at Buxted from 1590 to 1607, and perhaps in 1613. Henry's wife was the daughter of the Waldron yeoman Richard Brightredge, who in 1611 left his son-in-law Henry Grengow £4 in his will.[267] Henry himself was buried at Buxted in 1614 and his unnamed widow in 1625. He may already have been at Buxted in 1588, when a child named Elizabeth Grengoe had been buried there.

John Gryngoe, who perhaps married Denise Boxe at Warbleton in 1561,[268] and whose son Philip was baptised there in 1565, was apparently the man shown by views of frankpledge to have been bailiff of Lindfield hundred right through from 1578 to 1590.[269] As bailiff in an adjoining hundred he was pardoned for failure to appear at views of frankpledge for his residence at Barkham in Danehill Sheffield hundred from September 1579 to April 1589, and then at Maresfield in Rushmonden hundred in October 1589 and April 1590. He was also pardoned for unlicensed brewing in Maresfield in October 1590.[270] He was most likely the John Gringoe whom in 1594 the Buckhurst Terrier named as a former tenant of Black Venn Farm in Fletching.[271]

In Maresfield parish John Gringo was a sponsor, along with Margaret Hogge and Elizabeth Fowle, to a Rigson baptism in September 1580 and, along with Bridget Gavell and Joan Page, to a Bryan baptism in March 1584. His wife Denise was sponsor to a Catt baptism at Maresfield in 1580 and to Davy and Bartlett baptisms in 1583. She was buried at Maresfield in 1597. John Gringoe was overseer to the will of Thomas Galloppe of Fletching in 1582.[272] He was also presumably the Fletching gentleman who was bondsman in 1607 for the marriage licence of Thomas Fletcher and Winifred Norris.[273] He was perhaps the John Gringo who married the widow Anne Coomber at Lindfield in May 1609, but was buried there towards the end of that year.

John's son Philip was perhaps the man who was listed in the Surrey muster rolls for 1596 at Dunsfold.[274] He was perhaps the man who married Anne Furrell at Cuckfield in 1621 and was buried there in 1623.

The other contemporary John Gringo took part in setting up Rogate Forge around 1590. His son, another John Gringo, was perhaps the child baptised at Mountfield in 1568, whose parentage was not stated. Possibly the Rogate man was also the John Grengowe who married Mary Dobet at Tonbridge in 1576, though no burial entry for his first wife has been found. It is only with his son Philip's baptism at Rogate towards the end of 1589, that rather firmer ground is reached. His daughters Elizabeth and Mercy were also baptised at Rogate in 1594 and 1598, whilst Anne and Mary Gringoe, who married John Page and Charles Younge respectively at Rogate in 1611 and 1613, were presumably daughters born to him during the 1580s before his move to Rogate. He was buried at Rogate in 1612.

John Gringoe who married Mary Lipscom at Rogate in 1613 was presumably the man baptised at Mountfield in 1568. His children, Elizabeth, Anne, John, Joan, Arthur, Mary, Patience, Roger and Peter, were baptised at Rogate between 1614 and 1625, though Mary did not survive infancy. It was this branch of the family which later moved into Hampshire with considerable success. Of John's four sons, John, Roger, and possibly Peter, are known to have moved to Hampshire.

The eldest of these three brothers was presumably the John Gringo who held Funtley Forge

265. Surrey History Centre, 6511/1/1. The manor of Walkhamstead was held from 1559 to 1565 by Sir John Harcourt, MP, of Ellenhall, Staffordshire, whose family set up ironworks in that county, apparently in the 1570s.
266. TNA, E 179/186/352 (1593), 346 (1595) and 373 (1599).
267. ESRO, PBT 1/1/13/179.
268. The bridegroom's name in this marriage on 16 Nov 1561 was recorded as John Smythe.
269. ESRO, ACC 3597/8, f. 68v. (14 Jan 1578) to 3597/1, f. 116 (14 May 1590).
270. ESRO, ACC 3597/1, f. 128v.
271. ESRO, DLW 392 ff 389v, 390 (published as Sussex Record Society, **39**, 1933, p. 73).
272. ESRO, PBT 1/1/7/240.
273. Dunkin, *Sussex Marriage Licences, Lewes 1586-1643*, p. 61.
274. Craib, *Surrey musters*, p. 241.

in Titchfield, which ran in conjunction with the earl of Southampton's furnace on Sowley Pond, near Lymington. In 1647 he also took over the earl of Southampton's tinplate works at Wickham, but this seems to have been abandoned after the earl's death in 1667,[275] which was when it perhaps became a forge. John Gringo was buried at Titchfield in 1681 and his rather damaged will still survives. After his death, and that of his second wife Elizabeth, his tenement at Wickham and £10 were to go to his 'godson and loving kinsman' John Gringo, apparently the son of his brother Peter. To the three sons of his brother Roger, John, Roger and Robert, he left £1 apiece, and he made further monetary bequests totalling £8.[276]

In 1679-80, and again in 1696, Roger Gringoe paid the half-yearly rent of £25 for Funtley Forge, which his family held during most of the following century.[277] He had three sons, Robert, John and Roger, and the birth of the last was registered at Southwick in Hampshire in June 1659. But the elder Roger became a Quaker and it was in the Friends' Swanmore burial ground near Swanwick that his wife Joan was buried in 1671. His own burial took place there in 1703. At Funtley Forge he was apparently followed by his son Robert.

The younger Roger Gringo appeared in the Sowley area in 1687, when his daughter Jane was buried at Beaulieu. His son John and another daughter named Jane were baptised at Lymington in 1688 and 1692. But the younger Roger predeceased his father in 1693 and was buried at Lymington, and it was his 25-year-old son John who took over 'all that ironworks called Titchfield Hammer, together with a tenement, orchard and garden, with a meadow and three parcels of land in Titchfield aforesaid, now or late in the occupation of Robert Greengoe or his assigns' at Lady Day 1712.[278]

John's uncle John was buried at Titchfield later in 1712, and his other uncle Robert, who had been referred to as an 'ironmaker' in 1710, and who handed the forge over to him in 1712, was styled 'gentleman' in his will, and was buried at Fareham in 1715. The family had prospered in Hampshire, and set up Bursledon Furnace, on the river Hamble not far from Swanwick, from which pig iron was landed at Fareham quay, which they also built, for onward transmission to Funtley and Wickham.[279]

John Gringo, who was referred to as an 'ironmonger' when he married Elizabeth Dimmock at Easton in 1715, seems to have had no male heirs. His wife was buried at Winchester in 1771 and he made his will, as 'John Gringo of Fareham . . ., esquire', in May 1773. He left his 'Estate Right Title and Interest in and to three Ponds a Furnace and yard with the Appurtenances in Bursleden' to Peter Barfoot of Bishops Waltham, gentleman, but beyond a reference to the former tide mill of Fareham he mentioned no other industrial interests whatsoever, probably because Henry Cort had taken over Funtley Forge in 1775. Nor did he mention any other members of the Gringo family, being perhaps the last of his line. He was buried at Fareham on 5 November 1773 and his will was proved the following day.[280]

To return to the Weald, a more ancient Roger Gringo first appeared in the Bexhill parish register when his son James was baptised there in 1581, though James survived a few weeks only. The Bexhill location suggests that Roger might have been Henry Gringoe's son, but if the Roger Gringore baptised there in 1577, whose parents were not named in the parish register, was his son, and perhaps even if James was Roger's first child, that would entail supposing that Joan Bayly, whom Henry married in 1559, was his second wife and Agnes Colbrand his third.

Roger Gringo married Ellen,[281] daughter of the Robertsbridge finer Peter Jelly, and between 1581 and 1584 they moved to Salehurst parish. When Jelly died in 1594 he left a pair of sheets, a pillow, a pillowcase, two table-napkins and a towel to Alice Gringoe, who was presumably his granddaughter,

275. G. Watts, ed. *Titchfield; a history*, Titchfield History Society, 1982, p. 68.
276. I am grateful to Tony Greengo of Longfield for a photocopy of the will.
277. R. A. Mott, *Henry Cort, the great finer*, ed. P. Singer, The Metals Society (1983), p. 24.
278. Ibid., p. 23. This citation obviously refers to 1712, rather than 1671.
279. Ibid., p. 26.
280. I am indebted to Tony Greengo of Longfield, Kent, for the genealogical details of the Hampshire branch of this family. These cast doubt on some aspects of the account given by Mott. Both Roger Greengos were dead by 1703 so it was perhaps Robert Greengo who handed the forge over to John Greengo in 1712 (Cf. *Henry Cort*, p. 24). John was son and grandson of the two Rogers and the nephew of Robert, which better fits his description as 'cousin' of the former proprietor.
281. Roger was the only Gringo known to have fathered children in the Salehurst area around 1590.

and £1 to his daughter Ellen Gringoe.[282] The baptism of Alice Gringo, who married William Startup at Salehurst in 1604, has not been found, but Roger's children baptised at Salehurst from 1584 to 1602 were John, James, Joan, Mary, Anne and Elizabeth. He was buried at Salehurst in 1616.

There is no documentary proof that Roger Gringo of Salehurst was engaged in the iron industry, but his marriage to a finer's daughter and the possibility that his son John fathered two forgemen and was grandfather to a gunfounder, suggest that all were employed in the ironworks. Roger's eldest son John, who had been baptised at Salehurst in 1584, married Elizabeth Greene in 1605. She was the daughter of Richard Greene, a Salehurst yeoman, whose other daughter Mary later married the finer John Allen.

John and Elizabeth Gringo's children, Joan and John, were baptised at Hawkhurst in 1606 and 1607, but it was at Etchingham that John Gringow was recorded as being a churchwarden in 1611 and John's son James was baptised at Etchingham in 1617.[283] James will have been the forgeman who, along with other workmen of Mr Higham, was a witness to a sheep-rustling incident at Burwash in 1644. Early in 1645 he signed a testimony at quarter sessions that the poachers had confessed their guilt to his father, who was too ill to appear.[284] James's mother was buried at Etchingham in 1636, but his father was clearly not the man buried there in May 1644. Perhaps his father was buried at Salehurst in 1653. His sister Joan had married Henry Cruttenden at Etchingham in 1627.

The marriage licence of John Gringo, probably James's brother, who married Anne Dunke at Etchingham in 1640, shows him to have been a hammerman.[285] Their children, Anne, Judith and John were baptised at Etchingham between 1641 and 1644. Was he the John Greengow who married Anne Traffick, as his second wife, at Biddenden in 1650?

John Gringo, the child baptised at Etchingham in 1644 ended his days as a Catsfield gunfounder. By his will dated 1720 he left his messuage and tenement in Catsfield to his sister Judith, after whose death it was to go to Elizabeth, the wife of John Benge, a Catsfield wheelwright, and her heirs. He also made bequests of £50 to John Sinden, a Dallington collier, of £20 to William Sinden, a Penhurst husbandman, and of £30 and £5 respectively to his two godsons, John and Edward sons of James Daw, a Penhurst husbandman.[286] Both John Gringo and his sister Judith were buried at Catsfield, he in 1721 and she in 1730.

Drowsh

This name had first occurred as Drush at Fletching in 1566, when Margery daughter of John Drush was baptised. By 1570 John Thrushe had moved to Burwash, where he paid the poll tax in Hawksborough hundred in 1572 as a servant of John Glasyer and in 1576 as resident in Burwash borough. His sons Richard and John were baptised in 1570 and 1574 at Burwash, where on the second occasion he was specified as French (*gallus*). Margaret and Joan Thrushe, who were baptised at Burwash in 1575 and 1578, were undoubtedly his daughters though the parish register failed to note the parents' names.

During the 1580s John Drush's name failed to appear at Burwash but his daughters Margery and Joan were noticed again in 1593. Margery's illegitimate child James was baptised in February 1593 but was buried in January 1594. Joan Thrush was buried in May 1593. Why the two daughters stayed in Burwash when the remainder of this family apparently moved on, or returned to France, is not explained.

Henhurst hundred

Mallet

Clement Malet, who paid the poll tax in Danehill Sheffield hundred in 1552, was presumably identical

282. ESRO, PBT 1/1/9/257.
283. ESRO, Challen Bishop's transcripts.
284. ESRO, QR 66, mm. 78 (evidence of John Wood) and 80 (evidence of James Gringoe); I am indebted to Brian Phillips for this reference.
285. Dunkin, *Sussex Marriage Licences, Lewes 1586-1643*, p. 265.
286. ESRO, PBT 1/1/51/43.

to Clement Collyer who paid the poll tax, using an occupational surname, in the same hundred in 1551 and 1560. As Clement Collyer he had appeared among the Frenchmen recruited by William Pepwell to work in mines. Could Clement Malet have been the Clement Mole who married Joan Godward at Fletching in 1563? He was presumably related to Collen Mallet who paid the poll tax in Henhurst hundred as a servant of Goddard Walsh in 1552.

The name occurred rather sparsely in the Pays de Bray. Michellet Mallet witnessed a notarial document in 1501, Adrien Mallet was the heir of Guillaume Mallet of Bailleul in 1540 and another Guillaume Mallet lived at Perduville in 1567.[287] There is no suggestion of any link with the manufacture of, or trade in iron.

On the other hand in the mid-1530s Pierre Mallot *dit* Sauvage of Vatierville was a partner with the forgemasters Guillaume and Robert de Fry in wood purchase and in the disastrous encounter with Pierre Le Noble of Bures, their creditor. The sobriquet took its origin from the tavern named the *Wild Man* (*Homme sauvage*) which Jehan Mallot, perhaps Pierre's grandfather, had owned in the Neufchâtel parish of Saint-Pierre in the early years of the century.[288]

Parish register entries for the name also occurred only sparsely in the Weald, though it is possible that Joan Molet who married Michael Vyllaine at Newick in 1563 was from this family. If so entries in the Mountfield parish register for the baptism of Acalig (Atalig?) Molett in 1568 and for the burials of Peter Molet in 1558, and of German Moolett and Joan Molet in 1574 might be connected with Collen Mallet, Goddard Walsh's servant of 1552. If the version Molet or Moolett was correct any connection with Mallot *dit* Sauvage appears ruled out.

In 1574 Roger Mallet married Agnes Scott at Cranbrook, and Agnes Mallet baptised there later in 1574 and Rose Maylet baptised there in 1579, may have been their children, though parentage is not indicated.

Further west Martin Mallet was buried at Kirdford in 1589. Later Elizabeth Mallett married Isaac Hugatt at Abinger in 1616 and William Mallet was buried at East Grinstead in 1630.

John Charterye and Gyllam Detrove

Charterye and Detrove are surnames which seem not to occur in other Wealden sources. The idea that they might be garbled versions of Cacherye and Deprone cannot be substantiated because the names John Cacherye and Gyllam Deprone do not occur in other sources either.

Tassell

John Tassell paid the poll tax in Henhurst hundred in 1572. At Beaussault in the Pays de Bray Robert Tassel and Robert Tassel the elder occurred in numerous notarial acts from 1506 until 1542.[289] Jehan Tassel was referred to from 1535 onwards, but by 1539 there were two men of this name, because in that year Jehan Tassel the younger pledged himself to pay unpaid tithes, whilst two years later Jehan Tassel *dit* Robert (and therefore probably the son of one of the Robert Tassels) was involved in a lawsuit. The forgemaster Anthoine de Beaurains acted as pledge for the younger Jehan Tassel in both this case and one of 1539 in which he was engaged in a dispute with the lord of Beaussault.[290] Such legal troubles could have persuaded Jehan Tassel to seek his fortune abroad.

John Tassell was first encountered in Etchingham where his daughter Marian was baptised in 1566. Another daughter Anne was baptised at Brightling in 1570 and a daughter named Agnes was buried there in 1572. A fourth daughter named Susan was baptised at Penhurst in 1576.

A second member of this family was Nicholas Tassell, against whom the widow Margaret Ellyarde brought an action in the High court of Battle in November 1586. He was discharged *sine die* when she failed to appear to pursue her case in February 1587. Neither John, nor Nicholas Tassell, who could have been his son, appeared in Battle views of frankpledge in the late 1580s.[291]

287. ADSM, 2 E 14/1143 (5 Mar 1501); 2 E 14/1183 (4 Sep 1540); 2 E 14/1211 (19 Jul 1567).
288. ADSM, 2 E 14/1152 (21 Oct 1508); 2 E 14/1169 (22 Jun 1534); 2 E 14/1172 (1 and 11 Jul 1535).
289. ADSM, 2 E 14/1151 (6 Jun 1506); 2 E 14/1187 (29 Apr 1542).
290. ADSM, 2 E 14/1171 (15 May 1535); 2 E 14/1180 (10 Jan 1539); 2 E 14/1182 (29 Nov 1539); 2 E 14/1185 (6 Aug 1541).
291. HEH, BA Vol. 96.

In the next generation, John Tassill married Joan Henisett at Westfield in 1604, where the parish register survives in a damaged condition: it perhaps recorded the baptism of one of the younger John Tassell's children in 1605. Marie, John and Anne were other children of his baptised at Westfield between 1613 and 1617, whilst Jane, Joan and Eleanor were his children who were buried there between 1617 and 1623. His wife Joan was buried at Westfield in May 1623 and in the following October at Battle he was married again to Joan Kidder. It is uncertain whether his son John, who had been baptised in 1615, survived, because by his second wife John had sons named John and George baptised in 1624 and 1626. His son John buried in December 1625 was presumably the John born in 1624. John Tassell of Westfield was buried early in 1655. Before then he appears to have married a third time, because in June 1655 Caleb Turner, a widower, married a widow named Constance Tassell.

A bishop's transcript of 1607 for Penhurst shows that Adam Tassell married Anne Rogers alias Twist. From a deposition he made in 1617 it appears that Adam was a Battle collier,[292] and his descendants continued in that occupation for at least half a century. Nicholas Tassell who was baptised at Battle in 1611 was presumably his child, and eight other baptisms followed in regular succession, five of them stated to be Adam's children, but the parents unnamed in three cases.

William Tassell of Battle, collier, who in 1644 entered a quarter session recognizance to give evidence against Edward Carter, who had allegedly broken into his house and stolen money and goods,[293] was baptised at Battle in 1620. Was it by coincidence that he married Anne Carter in the year following the theft? Their son John was baptised 5 February 1645 only four days after their wedding, but was perhaps the John Tassel buried on 25 February. Their daughter Dorothy was baptised in 1647.

The Battle collier, John Tassel, who was in a reasonable degree of prosperity when taxed on four hearths in 1665,[294] was perhaps another son of Adam Tassell. He may have been the man who married 'Widow Barden' at Battle in 1638.

Levyvache

Charles Levyvache paid the poll tax in Henhurst hundred in 1572. He was perhaps 'Charles a Frenchman' whose daughter Faith was baptised at Brightling in 1575. The surname is not otherwise known in the Weald. Was its French original Larchevesque or Levesque?

Neufchâtel notarial records show that in 1528 Simon and Gieuffroy Larchevesque were both bakers. The family was found earlier outside the walls of the town in the suburb of Saint-Pierre of Neufchâtel, in the persons of Jehan and Robin Larchevesque, but by the 1530s Simon was established in the parish of Saint-Jacques and Gieuffroy in Notre-Dame parish.[295]

A notarial act of 1482 shows that in 1482 Jehannot Levesque held property not far from the *Vivier* of Neuville-Ferrières.[296] Jehan Levesque of Bouelles, who lived at Cornemesnil, was mentioned in notarial acts which ran from 1504 to 1529, and was followed at Cornemesnil by Cristofle Levesque, mentions of whom ran from 1528 to 1554, by a second Jehan Levesque, mentions of whom commenced in 1555, and Pierres and Anthoine Levesque, mentioned from 1568 and 1573 respectively.[297]

Beyond their residence in Cornemesnil, home to many colliers and miners serving the ironworks, there was nothing to suggest an industrial connection for this family, but in 1553 both Marin Levesque and his son Guillaume, were living at Longpaon in the Rouen industrial suburb of Darnétal. Already a widower, in that year Marin quitclaimed his lands and his *heritages* of every kind to his three children Guillaume, Robert and Jehanne, and in 1555 was cited as living in Bouelles. This family still had rights in a house, farmstead and garden adjoining the Philbert stream in Brémontier, sold to Jehan Descordes in 1533, his own share in which Guillaume Levesque renounced in 1553.[298] No mention of any Charles Levesque is forthcoming.

292. WSRO, EpII/5/11, f. 47.
293. ESRO, QR 65, m. 102; I am very grateful to Brian Phillips for this reference.
294. TNA, E 179.258/20 (1665).
295. ADSM, 2 E 14/1139 (6 Jan 1482); 2 E 14/1140 (5 Nov 1486); 2 E 14/1167 (2 Dec 1528); 2 E 14/1177 (1 Dec 1537); 2 E 14/1182 (17 Dec 1539).
296. ADSM, 2 E 14/1139 (10 Feb 1482).
297. ADSM, 2 E 14/1146 (17 Feb 1504); 2 E 14/1165 (20 Apr 1528); 2 E 14/1164 (15 Mar 1529); 2 E 14/1195 (21 Jan 1555); 2 E 14/1196 (10 Aug 1555); 2 E 14/1212 (22 Feb 1568); 2 E 14/1217 (19 Nov 1573).
298. ADSM, 2 E 14/1193 (12, 13 Apr and 25 May 1553); 2 E 14/1196 (15 Jul 1555).

Baldslow hundred

Theobald

In Baldslow hundred in 1572 James Tubull was listed as a poll-tax payer alongside the ironworker John Grengell, who was buried at Crowhurst towards the close of the year. The hundred extended eastwards to Westfield, which was where the Theobald family was established from 1598 onwards, so it seems possible that James lived there.

The first member of the family about whom something definite is known was Christopher Tibball, who married Gillian Wighorne at Northiam in 1590. According to his will, made in 1611, Christopher Theobald was a 'kemmer', perhaps akin to the feminine *kempster*, a wool-comber. His children were William, Francis, John, Thomas and Christopher, of whom William was baptised and buried at Benenden in 1591, Francis was baptised at Northiam in 1593, John's baptism has not been traced, and both Thomas and Christopher were baptised at Westfield, in 1598 and 1602 respectively. In his will Christopher left 5 shillings to the poor, and £5 for each of his sons, to be paid them at their majorities. His wife was to be the residuary legatee and executrix, and his goods were inventoried at a very respectable £107 10s 0d. Christopher appointed his brother Richard his overseer.[299] He was buried at Westfield early in 1613.

Christopher Theobald's brother Richard was presumably the man whose daughter Deborah was baptised at Benenden in 1589 and whose son Samuel was baptised at Biddenden in 1593. Richard's servant Alice Tollerst was buried at Benenden in 1620 and he himself, described as a 'householder', was buried there towards the end of the same year. Richard's son Samuel married Mildred Burden at Benenden in 1616 and their children Richard, Samuel and Margaret were baptised there between 1617 and 1621.

Francis Theobald had married Elizabeth Row in 1618. Their children, Elizabeth, John, Martha, Peter and Walter, were baptised at Westfield from 1621 to 1633, but Elizabeth did not survive infancy. Francis Theobald was buried at Westfield in 1634. His son Peter Theobalds was buried at Udimore in 1658 at the age of 30 and was described in the parish register as a smith. This, the fact that Joan Gringoe had witnessed the will of the younger Christopher Theobalds in 1629, and that Thomas Theobald of Westfield, yeoman, acted as bondsman in 1632 for the pot-founder, Richard Coulstock, when he took administration of his sister-in-law's goods,[300] are the rather tenuous hints of links between this family and the manufacture of iron.

John Theobalds, the second son of Christopher Theobalds the kemmer, left a will which claimed for him yeoman status. He died in 1643 leaving bequests totalling over £40, secured on bonds owed by William Keete, Thomas Butcher, Moses Purphle and Mrs Mary Breame of Hastings. The most substantial of these was £20 owed by Moses Purphle, which was to go to John's brother Thomas to be equally divided between the latter's children. The £10 due from Mrs Breame was to go to Elizabeth, Francis Theobalds' widow.[301]

Although Christopher Theobald's son Christopher died in 1629 at the age of only 27, his goods were inventoried at £254 6s 4d. He left 3s 4d to the poor. His overseers were to take £20 to be paid to his one-year-old son John at 21, and meanwhile the profit from this sum was to go his grandmother Gillian during her lifetime, which in the event extended up to 1637, and only afterwards to John. His wife, whom he made his residuary legatee and executrix, was Mary Gilbert, a widow whom he had married in 1627. His brothers Francis and Thomas were to be overseers of the will.[302] His widow took Nicholas Fowl as her third husband in 1630.

In East Grinstead Tibbal baptisms commenced in 1565. Between then and 1573, William, John and Marie Tibbal were baptised, but the register did not disclose their parentage. Perhaps Margaret Tybball and Edward Tubball, who were buried at Horley in 1578 and 1579 respectively, were their parents.

William married Katherine Tomplyn alias Turke, who was obviously of immigrant and

299. ESRO, PBT 1/1/14/104, 1/3/3/4.
300. ESRO, PBT 1/3/6/117.
301. ESRO, PBT 1/5/1/230.
302. ESRO, PBT 1/1/20/180, 1/3/6/42.

ironworking stock, at Cowden in 1601. She died in 1608 after bearing William's children Jane, John and Edward, of whom only John survived infancy. William was subsequently married again and a daughter named Ann was born to him, the baptismal entry suggesting that William was actually resident in Hartfield. William Tibballs himself returned to East Grinstead where he was buried in 1629. By a nuncupative will he bestowed £3 on Ann and made his son John his residuary legatee and executor. His goods were valued at £17 16s 0d.[303]

William's son John Theobals married Phillis Jelite at Horsted Keynes early in 1630, and their children, Katherine and Ann, were baptised at East Grinstead in 1630 and 1633.

The marriage of two successive generations of this family to wives fairly certainly of immigrant stock makes it probable that this East Grinstead family was also immigrant. This is emphasised by the move from East Grinstead to Worth of Thomas Tibball, who in 1580 had married Elizabeth Harraud. Their first child Thomas was baptised at East Grinstead and another child of theirs, Elizabeth, was buried there early in 1582. However, their third child Alexander was baptised at Worth in December 1584. Sadly his mother was buried six days after this baptism and Alexander himself survived only two years. In 1585 Thomas Tybbold married Agnes Kent and their children, Anne and Elizabeth, were baptised at Worth in 1586 and 1595. Thomas Tibboll himself was buried at Worth in 1610 and 'Widow Tibball' in 1625. Their daughter Elizabeth had married William Welling at Worth in 1623.

Battle hundred

Byman

The name of Peter Byman, who in 1552 paid the poll tax at Battle, is not otherwise found in the Weald. His surname is not dissimilar to that of William Boynam, a forgeman who was buried at Pitchford in Shropshire early in 1725.

Giles

The surname Gyles occurred widely across Sussex in the 1520s. In the Wealden area two men of that name contributed to the 1524 subsidy in Rotherfield. The possibility that forgemen of this name were descended from Giles Glodde, or from other immigrants bearing the baptismal name Giles, has already been mentioned.

Among immigrants recorded in the subsidy rolls were Antony Gyles who paid the poll tax at Battle in 1552 and George Gyles recorded at East Grinstead in 1572. Antony Gyles could have moved to Tonbridge where the burial of Lambert Gyles in 1566 suggests the presence of immigrant members of the Giles family in that parish during the sixteenth century. However, the loss of the baptismal register from 1558 to 1585, and the lack of subsidy rolls between 1550 and 1572, makes this almost impossible to substantiate.

But some confirmation is provided by the 1624 burial entry at Tonbridge for 'Marian brother of Anthony Giles', the latter baptismal name being popular among the French community and the former, for male children, entirely confined to it. This later Anthony Gyles was buried at Tonbridge in 1635.

In the adjacent area the Frant parish register mentioned Stephen Giles, whom it described as 'a stranger' in the entry which recorded the baptism of his son Richard early in 1578. Stephen Gyles had married Elizabeth Kitchinam at Frant in 1577 and their first child Richard, who had been baptised only three months after their wedding, survived only a fortnight. A further child of the same name, a future hammerman, was baptised in 1579. Of their next children, two Johns, baptised in 1580 and 1581, the first died in infancy and the second did not survive to adulthood.

Stephen's first wife died in 1585. He married his second wife Eleanor Davy in 1586 and their children, Stephen, Thomason and William, were baptised between 1588 and 1591, though of them Stephen died young. Stephen's second wife Eleanor died in 1602 and by his third wife Lettice, whom he married at Lamberhurst in 1603, Stephen had another child baptised Margaret in August 1606, but Lettice died in childbirth. His fourth wife, Annys Wakelin of Wadhurst, whom he married in December 1606 appears to have survived him. Stephen was buried at Frant in 1611.

303. ESRO, PBT 1/1/20/185, 1/3/6/44.

Richard Gyles, Stephen's eldest son, was a hammerman, whose eldest child Stephen was baptised at Rotherfield in 1613. Another child William, mentioned in Richard's will, was perhaps his unnamed child baptised at Rotherfield early in 1615. When twins were born in June 1620, one was buried unbaptised, and Richard, the other child, was not mentioned in his father's will. It seems unlikely that Richard's first wife survived this tragedy because in April 1621 he married his second wife, Isabell Harman, at Speldhurst. They appear to have had but one child, Sara baptised at Rotherfield in 1622.

Richard Giles of Rotherfield, hammerman, made his will in 1638. He made nominal bequests of a shilling to his sons by his first wife, Stephen and William. The household stuff was to be divided equally between his wife Isabel and her daughter Sara; Sara was to have £30 and Isabel was to be residuary legatee and executrix. The overseers, who were also among the witnesses, John Baker of Gildredge in Withyham and John Burges of High Green, were each to have 5 shillings in addition to their expenses. Richard's goods were inventoried at £78 18s 2d, but this included £50 18s 6d, an astonishing amount, in 'ready money in the house' and an additional £3 2s 0d.[304]

Richard's eldest son, Stephen Giles, married Amy Cox at Maresfield in July 1641, a wedding also recorded in the bride's parish of Withyham. The marriage licence showed that Stephen had followed his father's occupation of hammerman. His occupation as a Rotherfield forgeman was confirmed in a quarter session roll for 1641 when he was surety for a recognizance.[305]

Richard's younger son was probably the William Gyles who married Susan Rolfe at Withyham in 1637. His residence at Rotherfield was confirmed by the baptism of his daughter Joan there in 1638, though she survived barely more than a month.

George Gyles who paid the poll tax at East Grinstead in 1572 may have been the father of Juliana Jyles who was baptised at Newdigate in 1576 but was buried there the following year. Also buried at Newdigate in 1590 was Elizabeth the wife of Peter Jyles, and this burial was followed in 1594 by that of Peter Gyles himself. He was probably the Peter Gillis or Gylles whose children Alice and John were baptised at Abinger in 1565 and 1567, though John failed to survive the day of his baptism.

Finally, two men named Giles took brides from the immigrant community. They were Francis Giles, who married Marie Foshall at Cranbrook in 1600, but did not otherwise appear in that parish register, and Thomas Gyles who married Agnes Jarret at Brede in 1607. Their daughter Elizabeth was baptised at Brede later in 1607, but Agnes wife of Thomas Gyles was buried at Sedlescombe in 1610.

SUSSEX - PEVENSEY RAPE

Loxfield hundred

Trantham

John Trantham paid the poll tax as an alien in Wadhurst in 1551. The surname appears as native to England in other parts of the country, but was not recorded in the Sussex subsidy rolls of the 1520s. It is difficult to know what the foreign original of the surname could be.

The manuscript reading is not in doubt, but it seems easiest to suppose that at some stage in transmission the surname more usually rendered Tronchin, possibly from the French original of Tranchepain, has been corrupted. Tronchin appeared firstly at Cleobury Mortimer in 1571, but in Sussex it occurred only briefly at Fletching in 1589, before establishing itself in Maresfield in the following decade. Members of this family will be discussed later.

Worrell

Though only the 1551 entry in Loxfield hundred is evidence for this immigrant poll-tax payer, the absence of the surname in the subsidy rolls of the 1520s suggests that the Richard Warrells or Worrells of Heathfield and Lingfield towards the end of the sixteenth century were both of immigrant descent.

It is uncertain whether Richard Worrell, who was buried at Lingfield in 1612, left any descendants.

304. ESRO, PBT 1/5/1/102.
305. Dunkin, *Sussex Marriage Licences, Lewes 1586-1643*, p. 279; ESRO, QR 52, m. 87.

When Richard Warrell of Heathfield's wife was buried in 1617, he was reputed a 'householder', but when he himself was buried at Heathfield in 1620 no description was entered in the parish register. However, his will shows him to have been a husbandman, and his goods were inventoried at £60 18s 10d.[306]

Richard Worrall the younger, who had been baptised at Heathfield in 1581, was shown by the licence issued for his marriage to Elizabeth Fuller of Hellingly in 1612 to have been a shoemaker. He predeceased his father in 1613 leaving goods worth £32 11s 0d.[307] His younger brother Josias was a Burwash husbandman, but also died young and was buried at Heathfield in 1622. Josias' goods were inventoried at £94 1s 0d.[308] A later member of this family, Jo Worrell, who paid the tax on two hearths at Heathfield in 1665 was a thatcher, whilst Roger Worrell of Lewes who had been surety for a marriage bond in 1615 was recorded as a butcher.[309]

Possible connections with iron were the entries concerning Richard Worrell in Lingfield parish register, which might indicate his involvement at Woodcock Forge, the burial at Rogate in 1605 of Alice Warroll, widow, without any indication of who her husband might have been, and the burial of Mr Ainscome's servant, John Worell, at Battle in 1611.

Even the 1551 entry in Loxfield hundred for 'Worrell, Robey's man' gave no indication of this ironworker's baptismal name. The lack of further entries for him in the Weald could have been due to a decision by him to follow John Robey to the Midlands, where Robey appeared in 1563 among three aliens listed in the Staffordshire subsidy rolls for Rugeley.[310]

The name appeared in conjunction with iron in Derbyshire. Between 1651 and 1665, Joan, Mary, John and Charles, the children of Thomas Worrill of New Mill, which in the seventeenth century was the site of a forge, were baptised at Duffield. Worrill's wife was buried in 1667. Ann, daughter of Charles Warrill was baptised at Duffield in 1668.

However, it should be borne in mind that in the South Yorkshire area the surname was derived from a local place name.

Tosain

It is difficult to identify Tosain, John Roboye's other man, who paid the poll tax in Loxfield hundred in 1551. It is just possible he could have been Toussains Holland, as mentioned earlier. A more plausible suggestion is that he was James Tussan, whose son John was baptised at Horsham in 1561. However, among the sponsors for this baptism, alongside the young Thomas Pynion and Hugh Marchant's wife Margaret, was John Tussan, who could equally well have been this poll-tax payer.

Evidence has not been found for the continued residence of either man in the Weald. The surname has not been found in other areas of Britain in connection with iron.

Heyward

Lay subsidy rolls show that this surname was very widespread in Sussex in the 1520s. In the late 1540s it was borne by workers at Parrock Forge, so it is a surprise to find two Heyward aliens in the subsidy rolls as late as the 1550s. These were Simon Heyward at Wadhurst in 1551, and James Haward at Cranleigh in 1557, a parish where ironworks had apparently been set up earlier in the decade.

If it is correct to identify the 1557 James Haward with the occupationally named James Wayner and James Wheler who paid the poll tax at Cranleigh in 1559 and 1589, he is likely to have been a cartwright or wheelwright rather than an ironworker. However, three later Cranleigh Heywards, two colliers named William Heyward, perhaps father and son, and the hammerman Robert Hayward, were indicted for a burglary carried out at Cranleigh in 1596.[311] Robert was found not guilty, but the two colliers were found guilty and were remanded in custody.

No other record from East Sussex appears to confirm the existence of Simon Hayward in that area, so possibly he belonged to a family which in the early 1550s moved westwards to Cranleigh. It

306. ESRO, PBT 1/1/17/77, 1/3/5/45.
307. Dunkin, *Sussex Marriage Licences, Lewes 1586-1643,* p. 83; ESRO, PBT 1/1/14/120, 1/3/4/12.
308. ESRO, PBT 1/1/18/50, 1/3/5/109.
309. Dunkin, *Sussex Marriage Licences, Lewes 1586-1643,* p. 97.
310. TNA, E 179/178/169.
311. Cockburn, *Surrey Assize records, Elizabeth I,* nos. 2681, 2745.

has recently been pointed out firstly, that Simon Heyward's name occurred in the same subsidy roll which included Marian Lambert alias Gardner of Wadhurst, who was clearly related to the immigrant-descended John Lambert alias Gardner, forgemaster at the Vachery ironworks in Cranleigh, and secondly that Robert Haward, who in 1593 witnessed the will of John Lambert alias Gardener, was probably the hammerman known from the assize court proceedings of 1596.[312]

The new lease of Vachery Forge made to Gardner in 1578 included two cottages, one of which, to the north of the forge pond, was inhabited in 1580 by the collier, William Heyward. In 1574 Edward Bray, the lord of Vachery manor, had written to William More of Loseley, to complain both of a specific instance of William Heyward's suspicious and hostile behaviour and of John Gardner of Cranleigh who 'by his own speech in a common ale house doth seem to be a maintainer of the said Heyward in his lewdness'.[313]

Although no Cranleigh parish register survives to furnish sixteenth-century references to the Heyward family, it seems possible that the isolated Heywarde entry at Newdigate which records the baptism of Robert son of Robert Heywarde in July 1580 could relate to the hammerman.

The East Sussex connections with ironfounding which do exist appear to be two in number, but they may be closely connected. Firstly, at Rotherfield in 1569 the forgemaster John Cooper alias Paler married Eleanor Hayward. She was a daughter of Thomas Hayward of Rotherfield and had been baptised there in 1548. Her brother James Hayward, a Rotherfield yeoman, died in 1581. His goods were appraised at £118 11s 6d and his only connection with iron, beyond the 'fire plate in the hall' and a spit, which he bequeathed to his young son, was his close relationship with John and Eleanor Cooper, whom he made responsible for his son's 'education, rule and governance', should his wife soon die. References to all his 'timber-like wood ready felled', which he left for the maintenance of his house and buildings, indicate, not a smith, but a carpenter or timber merchant.[314]

In the eastern Weald, John Hayward, a Battle ironfounder, went surety for a quarter session recognizance in 1640.[315] This John Hayward was probably the son of another John Hayward of Burwash, who married Margaret Baseden at Hawkhurst in 1603. Their ironfounder son John was baptised at Burwash in 1605, but his father died in 1611 and in 1613 his mother Margaret married the Brightling founder Thomas Jarret at Burwash. When Jarret made his will in 1634 he left his little red colt to John Hayward, son of John Hayward, his son-in-law (i.e. stepson).[316]

It would have been natural for Jarrett to bring up his 8-year-old stepson in his own trade, especially as he had only one son from his own first marriage. The younger John Hayward married Elizabeth Start at Mountfield in 1628 and their son was probably the John Hayward baptised at Battle in January 1630, whose parentage was not given in the parish register.

A connection between the two East Sussex families lies in the possibility that John Hayward, the Burwash man married at Hawkhurst in 1603, could have been the son whose education had been confided by the Rotherfield James Hayward to the forgemaster John Cooper in 1581,[317] and it would explain the absence of further Hayward entries in the Rotherfield parish register after that date.

Another Hayward involved in the metal trades was John Hayward, a Lewes wire-drawer, who in 1629 was bondsman for a marriage licence.[318] Among ironworks-related trades there were two bellows-makers named Hayward whose occupations were revealed by their wills. The will of John Haywarde of Fernhurst was proved in 1610 and that of William Heyward of Haslemere in 1619. Because William asked to be buried at Fernhurst, it seems likely that both men were originally from Fernhurst, where the position is made complicated by the existence of an indigenous family named Hayward.

The indigenous Hayward family at Fernhurst can be traced back to 1547. From 1577 onwards new names appeared in the parish register in the persons of Nicholas Hayward, said to have been 'of Lurgashall' in 1579, but whose name cannot in fact be traced at Lurgashall, and Simon Hayward, a

312. J. English, 'Vachery Forge and Furnace, Cranleigh, Surrey', *Wealden Iron*, Bulletin of the Wealden Iron Research Group, new series, **19** (1999), pp. 26-7.
313. Ibid.
314. ESRO, PBT 1/1/7/218, 1/3/1/98.
315. ESRO, QR 49, m. 51; I am very grateful to Brian Phillips for this reference.
316. ESRO, PBT 1/1/23/132.
317. ESRO, PBT 1/1/7/218.
318. Dunkin, *Sussex Marriage Licences, Lewes 1586-1643*, p. 172.

name reminiscent of the man who perhaps moved from Wadhurst to Cranleigh in the 1550s. Both these men were married at Fernhurst, Nicholas to Elizabeth Bignolde in 1577 and Simon to Perret Cottes in 1578. Simon was buried at Fernhurst in 1603 and Nicholas in 1622. It seems possible that both were of immigrant descent.

There seems to be no link between Nicholas and Simon Hayward and the two bellows-makers. In his will John Haywarde of Fernhurst made his sons Thomas and George his executors, but did not name his other children, though he left a fustian doublet to his son-in-law John Bridger. George son of John Hayward was baptised at Fernhurst in 1581 and Thomas could be one of two Thomas Haywards baptised in 1583 and 1584, whose parents' names were not recorded. This will was proved in 1610.

The bellows-maker William Heyward asked to be buried at Fernhurst and left 3s 4d to the church there. Accordingly, 'William Hewarde of Holfast in the parish of Haselmere was buried amongst his ancestry' at Fernhurst in 1618, a statement which neatly distinguished him from the immigrant Heywards. His will mentioned two sons, Thomas and Robert, and seven daughters, of whom Thomas and Joan could be the son and daughter baptised at Fernhurst in 1595 and 1598 respectively, and Katherine the daughter baptised at Haslemere in 1601, leaving six children unaccounted for. William appointed his brother Edward Heyward of Northchapel one of his will's overseers, and it is the will of this Northchapel dish-maker, made in 1617 which proves that they were the sons of the Fernhurst bellows-maker; Edward left 10 shillings to Alice Bridger, his sister Agnes's daughter, though John Heyward had mentioned none of these three children, but only his son-in-law John Bridger, in his will.[319] Edward Heyward was buried at Northchapel early in 1619.

Quintun

It will be recalled that we identified Quintin Pyller, made denizen for Nicholas Eversfield in 1544, with Quintin Tyler, whose personal details were recorded elsewhere in the Westminster denization roll. Tyler's misfortunes continued in 1550 when his name appeared as Menten Tyller, alongside that of Reme Tyller, at Framfield, presumably for Pounsley Furnace, of which the Eversfield family held the freehold.

After paying the poll tax correctly as 'Quinten Tyller alien servant to Nicholas Eversfelde' at Framfield in 1551, it seems certain that Peter Quintun the alien who paid 2 shillings on goods to the relief of 1552 at Framfield was Quintin too, and that his fortunes in material respects had taken the upward curve which led to his being the 'Quyntin' who held a furnace at Cowden by 1574.

Smith

As was the case throughout England, this surname was widespread in the Weald. Because so considerable a number of persons named Smith was engaged in the iron industry in the sixteenth and seventeenth centuries it would be unwise to try to determine what proportion of them was immigrant in origin.

For immigrants the name must be considered the equivalent of *Le Fèvre*, or *Le Fèbvre*, but attempts to establish a genealogical link between the families of Smith and Fever, or Favor, fail. For instance, Nicholas Smythe, whose daughters Patience and Faithful were baptised at Warbleton in 1588 and 1590, disappeared from the parish register and was replaced by Nicholas Fever, a string of whose children were baptised between 1593 and 1614. However, as we saw, Fever had married at Mayfield in 1582, was in Brede in 1588 and 1590, and arrived in Warbleton only between then and December 1593, when he lost both his first wife in childbirth and his daughter Lidia within a week of each other.

The widow of Thomas Smythe paid the poll tax at Framfield as an alien in 1560, and although this entry does not prove that Smythe himself had been an immigrant, an entry of 1574 for the burial of a Frenchman named William Smith at Mayfield shows that he could have been. The Thomas Smyth in question was either the man of that name buried at Framfield in August 1558, or Thomas Smythe alias Peckes buried there in December 1558.

There are no probate acts connected with the Mayfield burial and since the Mayfield parish register commenced only in 1570 the chances of establishing William Smith's family connections are

319. WSRO, STC 1/15/355 (John Haywarde) and 16/72 (Edward Haward); LMA, DW/PA/07/009, f 307v. (William Heyward).

not good. However he could have been the William Smyth who married Ciceley Meppam at Framfield in 1562, neither of whom was subsequently mentioned in that parish register.

Robert Smith, who married a woman of obvious French descent, Dorothy Lammye, at Mayfield in 1584, may have been the Frenchman William Smith's son; they certainly named their son, baptised at Mayfield early in the following year, William. However, they seem not to have stayed in Mayfield and it looks as though Robert's wife Dorothy was buried at Chiddingstone in 1590, together with an infant son named Thomas. The long gap in the Chiddingstone parish register prevents our knowing whether Robert Smith continued at Chiddingstone. William Smith baptised at Mayfield in 1585 could be the man referred to in 1618 in Shropshire, when Jane daughter of William and Anne Smith of the 'Iron Mylles' was baptised at Condover on 29 March of that year.

A move in the reverse direction occurred in 1644, when a Shropshire collier named Thomas Smith was examined by the Sussex magistrates on a charge of vagrancy. He claimed to have been on a visit to his uncle John Smith at Upottery in Devon, when he was pressed for military service, from which he had deserted.[320] Smith probably formed part of Hopton's west-country army which in December 1643 captured Arundel, but then was driven into retreat by Sir William Waller. The collier perhaps made the most of this opportunity to desert. So it is by no means certain that this man's presence in the Weald had anything to do with members of his family having formerly lived there, or living there still.

Richard Smith, a servant of the forgemaster John Fawkner of Waldron the elder of Waldron, who was buried at Kirdford in August 1587, left no children of his own but made Fawkner responsible for the bringing up of his deceased brother's children, John and Joan. To them he left £40 and £30 respectively, to be paid them at their marriages out of a tenement in Framfield held on mortgage from Robert a'Brooke. To his mother he left £10 and to his brother Olive's children £1 each. Smith also left £10 to the vicar of Framfield and £1 to the poor of that parish as well as to the poor of Waldron. He also left £6 13s 4d to each of the two sons of Sampson Coulstock.[321]

The names Olive and Coulstock mentioned in this will further consolidate Richard Smith's connections with the iron industry. Robert Olyeve had married Isabel Smyth at Framfield in 1562 and was probably the forgemaster Robert Olyffe who held Howbourne forge in partnership with John Relf of the Oake in the 1560s. Samson Colstock had been one of Ralph Hogge's clerks during the late 1570s and in 1579 and 1580 witnessed two deeds at Fletching,[322] but followed the industry along with Richard Smith westwards to Kirdford, where Coulstock too died in 1594.

Richard's mother was apparently the Isabel Smith buried at Framfield in 1593. In her will, among the iron goods which she bequeathed were an iron mortar, an iron pot, a pair of brandirons, a war-bill, a fire-prong, a pair of pot-hangers and a pair of pot-hooks, a frying pan, a saw, three iron wedges, an auger, a wimble, a plate (fireback) and a spit with a foot, which went to her grandson John Smith, and an iron posnet for her granddaughter Bridget Smith.[323]

Payments were made on behalf of the gunfounder Ralph Hogge around 1578 to another Framfield branch of the Smith family. Those made to John a'Smyght of Blackboys and to John A smyght 'the Carppenter' probably referred to the same man; those made to Robard a'smyght were for the carriage of mine, probably out of Etchingwood.[324] The mine carrier was perhaps the Framfield yeoman Robert Smith who died in 1615 possessed of the 'house and land called Tickerridges'.[325]

Specifically named ironworkers commence with the Ashburnham miner Ralph Smythe, who in 1567 was found not guilty at the assizes on an indictment of raping his servant Catherine Burrell.[326] He was presumably identical with the man who in 1579 married a widow named Joan Ellis at Ashburnham and with 'Old Ralph Smythe' who was buried there in 1604.

In chronological order the next ironworker of this surname to be noticed was Richard Smyth,

320. ESRO. QR 65, m. 93; I am indebted to the kindness of Brian Phillips for this reference.
321. TNA, PROB 11/71/289.
322. Straker, *Wealden iron*, p. 389; Crossley, 'Ralph Hogge's ironworks accounts', p. 50; ESRO, SRL 1/4/9-10.
323. ESRO, PBT 2/2/1/105.
324. Crossley, 'Ralph Hogge's ironworks accounts', pp. 61, 78.
325. ESRO, PBT 2/2/4/41. Slag and cinders found at the Tickerage site indicate the presence of both a furnace and forge; the 'hammer' was referred to in 1617 (Cleere and Crossley, *The iron industry of the Weald*, p. 360-1).
326. Cockburn, *Sussex Assize records, Elizabeth I*, no. 251.

hammerman at Hoadley hammer, who was involved in a coroner's inquest in 1589.[327] It seems possible that he could have been the Richard Smith whose daughter Elizabeth was baptised at Frant in 1581. He could also have been the father of Stephen Smith who was baptised at Lamberhurst in 1584, but whose parentage was not disclosed in the parish register. It seems probable that he was the Richard Smith buried at Lamberhurst in February 1604.

The name Stephen, more widely used among French immigrants perhaps than among the native population, was surprisingly common at this period. It is impossible to trace the antecedents of Stephen Smith, whose children, Joan, Philip, John and Stephen, were baptised at Maresfield between 1583 and 1590. He was probably employed in the ironworks because his son Philip, baptised in 1584, was the gunfounder of that name who in 1617 obtained a licence to marry a widow named Mary Pescod.[328] The gunfounder's daughter Mary was baptised at Maresfield in 1618, after which they seem to have moved on because the names do not recur in the Weald. The father was perhaps the Stephen Smith buried at Maresfield in 1612.

Thomas Smith, whose children, Robert, William and Richard were baptised at Heathfield between 1603 and 1606, and whose son Thomas was baptised at Warbleton in 1608, was perhaps a member of the French community. His infant son William was buried at Heathfield in March 1605 and his sons Richard and Thomas at Warbleton in 1608. Thomas Smith's own death followed in 1609 and in 1610 his widow Joan married John Pomy, who was certainly of immigrant stock. After the baptism of their daughter Mary in 1619 this couple moved on to Peasemarsh, where John Pomy died in 1627. When administration of his goods, valued at £46 14s 2d, was granted to his widow Joan in 1627, John's stepson, Robert Smith of Peasemarsh, collier, acted as bondsman for his mother.[329]

Another Robert Smith was a Frant forgeman who in 1642 contributed 2 pence to the relief of Protestants in Ireland.[330] Baptismal entries for the children of Robert and Jane Smith commenced at Lamberhurst in 1615 and continued until 1623, though Richard son of Robert Smith baptised at Frant in 1616 was perhaps their child too. However, it is difficult to determine whether entries for Dinah, Alice and Katherine, daughters of Robert Smith baptised at Frant in 1633, 1641 and 1642, none of whom survived childhood, relate to the same Robert Smith, since mothers' names were no longer indicated. It is also unclear whether this Robert Smith was related to Richard Smith, the Hoadley hammerman of 1589, who was perhaps buried at Lamberhurst in 1604.

Another forgeman was James Smyth of Wartling, whose marriage to Anne Smyth, a Heathfield widow, was recorded in the Hailsham parish register in May 1657. This James Smith was possibly James son of John Smith baptised at Burwash in 1634.

Among related trades occurred the nailer, Richard Smith of Horsted Keynes, who in 1592 obtained a licence to marry Jane Lambard, the widow of the Horsted Keynes forgeman Laurence Lambert.[331] Bishop's transcripts show that Richard's wife Jane was buried at Horsted Keynes in 1610 and that he was buried there in 1616.

The Herstmonceux smith, Abel Smith, was bondsman for another marriage licence in 1603.[332] His children were baptised at Herstmonceux from 1595 to 1611, though in the last entry he was named Abell Smyth of Wartling. However, both he and his widow Martha were buried at Herstmonceux in 1614 and 1617 respectively, and claimed to be of Herstmonceux in their wills. Abel Smith's goods were inventoried at £84 6s 8d and his widow's at £54 15s 10d respectively.[333]

Hartfield hundred

Curlyffe

There is no further record of Leonard Curlyffe, an alien who paid the poll tax in Hartfield hundred in

327. Hunnisett, *Sussex Coroners' inquests, 1558-1603*, no. 397.
328. Dunkin, *Sussex Marriage Licences, Lewes 1586-1643,* p. 105.
329. ESRO, PBT 1/3/5/324.
330. M. J. Burchall, *East Sussex contributors to the relief of Irish Protestants, 1642* (1984), col. 20-3.
331. Dunkin, *Sussex Marriage Licences, Lewes 1586-1643,* p. 13.
332. Ibid, p. 43.
333. ESRO, PBT 1/1/14/269, 1/3/4/59; 1/1/16/90, 1/3/4/163.

1551. The surname seems clearly distinct from Curleggo, which occurred in Hawksborough hundred in 1551, which in turn was closer to Clerygo and Cleriewe, the surnames used in Framfield in 1550 and in Henhurst in 1552 by Simon, who in Henhurst became a servant of Hugh Collyn. Positing the corruption of a double long 's' leads back to an original not unlike Calisse, but Leonard Caliss who was buried at Rotherfield in 1577 was almost certainly English born.

It is not evident what a French equivalent of this surname could be.

Jurden

Jurden who paid the poll tax in Hartfield in 1552 cannot be identified. As earlier suggested, he might have been either Barthelmew or Denys Jorden, who both paid the poll tax in Danehill Horsted hundred in 1549, but of whom there was no further record. The name could just possibly be a baptismal one.

Kerwyn

It must be supposed that Kyrwyn Carde who paid the poll tax in the relief of 1552 in Hartfield hundred was in reality Cardo Kyrwyn, probably the progenitor of the Kerwyn family of forgeworkers.

The family had already been noted in the Weald when the sons of Thomas Kyrwyn, Thomas and Daniel, were baptised at Rotherfield in 1544 and 1548. In his will, made at Burwash, where he was buried in 1559, Thomas was styled Thomas Kerey. He asked for 6s 8d to be expended at his funeral. His son Robert was to have 6s 8d and all the tools belonging to his occupation. His younger sons, Thomas and Daniel, were to have £1 6s 8d and £2 13s 4d respectively put out at interest at their ages of 16, and the proceeds were to be paid them at their ages of 21. Kyrwyn's three daughters, Joan, Eleanor and Mary were each to have 6s 8d. Kyrwyn's son(-in-law), William Stammenord, was to be residuary legatee and executor and the witnesses were Richard Barham and Peter Benett, who was probably the immigrant collier of that name. Kyrwyn's goods were inventoried at £11 5s 6d. In 1561, in his turn, William Stammyner of Mayfield remembered the young Robert Kyrwyn in his own will, of which Robert was a witness, with the bequest of a 'horse-cloth'.[334]

Two of Thomas Kyrwyn's children were at Ashburnham in 1589. Daniel was buried there in August 1589, the parish register noting that he was 'a servant to John Ashburnham, esquire'. It appears that he was still unmarried because administration of his effects, valued at £7 18s 0d, was granted to his sister Helen, in the person of her husband, Robert Berche, an Ashburnham husbandman. Bondsman for this administration was the Ashburnham collier Simon Morrell.[335]

It is uncertain whether Daniel's brother Thomas was Thomas Kere, whose children, Mary, Margery and Ann were baptised at Maresfield between 1571 and 1575, or Thomas Kerin who married Marie Plomerden at Goudhurst in 1573. Thomas and Marie had six children baptised at Goudhurst between 1574 and 1590 and Thomas Kerrin was buried there in 1616.

The Maresfield Thomas Kere was perhaps the Thomas Kyrwyn whose daughter Sapphira was buried at Mayfield in 1580. At some stage Thomas Kyrwyn had a son named Edward, but his wife Elizabeth was buried at Mayfield in 1584 and in 1586 he took as his second wife a widow, Iden Chillye, whom he married at Heathfield. Their son Thomas was baptised at Mayfield in 1596. Iden was buried in 1607, but Thomas lived on at Mayfield until 1615.

Thomas's son Edward was also twice married. The Mayfield parish register shows his daughter Marie to have been baptised in 1604, but another child and his first wife Joan were buried there in January 1607. In April 1608 he married Joan, daughter of Christopher Bodel, at Waldron. However, Edward was buried at Mayfield in the following June, his wife was buried at Waldron in February 1609, within a fortnight of the baptism of Edward's posthumous child Rebecca, whilst Rebecca herself died at the age of five in 1614.

Other members of the family continued at Burwash after the death of the first Thomas Kerwyn. Jordan and Catherine, children of Jordan Kirrin were baptised there in 1572 and 1574. Also at Burwash, James, son of William Cary, Frenchman (*gallus*) was baptised in 1578, followed by Audiana (Odiana) daughter of William Kerren in 1580. From Burwash both Jordan and William Kerwyn moved on to

334. ESRO, PBT 1/1/4/442; WSRO, STA 1/2/29.
335. ESRO, PBT 1/3/2/82.

Mayfield.

Jordan's son William and William's son Anthony were both baptised at Mayfield in 1582, but William moved next to Buxted, where Alice his daughter was baptised in 1585, and then back to Mayfield where his son Jordan was baptised in 1588. William Kirwin was buried at Mayfield in 1590.

Another French member of this family who moved to Mayfield was the forgeman John Kyrrin, whose daughter Katherine was buried at Ashburnham in 1580. The baptismal entry for his second child Robert at Mayfield in 1583 disclosed that the father was French. John then seems to have married his second wife Mary Relfe at Mayfield in 1588, after which his other children, Margaret and John, were baptised at Mayfield in 1590 and 1592.

Another Mayfield member of this extensive family was Giles Kyrrye, who in 1581 married the widow Audrye de Verey. Their daughter Joan was baptised at Mayfield before the end of the year, but died early in January 1582. Giles may have been Giles Kirrell who was buried at East Grinstead in 1596.

In North Yorkshire the Pateley Bridge parish register showed that two members of this family were in Nidderdale by the 1580s. When his unnamed son was baptised in February 1588, it noted that James Kirring was hammerman at Sommerbridge, the forge of the Sussex forgemaster Thomas Dike. This son may be identical with 'the child of one James a workman at the forge' who was buried in August 1590. The other member of the family in Nidderdale was Margaret Kirrin, who married Giles Garrit, also from the Wealden French community, at Pateley Bridge in December 1589.

Jordan Kirrin, who married Susan Russell at East Grinstead in 1597, was probably the man baptised at Burwash in 1572. Jordan's daughters Margaret and Joan were baptised at Burwash in 1604 and 1609. However, this family moved on to the western Weald. Susanna wife of Jordan Kirrie was buried at Rudgwick in 1625. In May 1630 Jordan Kerrine of Horsted Keynes, hammerman, married his second wife, a widow named Margaret Luxford, and the licence for this marriage divulged his occupation.[336] Jordan Kerrin moved on to Thursley, where his second wife Margaret Kerrin was buried in 1639.

The will of William Kerring alias Jordan, a Rudgwick finery man, was proved in the Surrey archdeaconry court in 1661. The alias suggests that he was Jordan Kirrin's son. He married Mary Midhurst at Cranleigh in 1640, though she was perhaps his second wife. In his will he mentioned his son William, who was to retain a messuage or tenement, gardens, orchards and barn in Rudgwick known as Butlers Garden. Out of this William was to pay £5 to his sister Anne. Out of the proceeds of the lease of Gingerberrys in Ewhurst was to come £2 10s 0d a year for four years, to provide a further £10 for Anne, but the remainder was to go to William's other daughter Elizabeth and her husband Edward Thornden. Kerring made Elizabeth Thornden his residuary legatee and executrix and appointed his neighbours Richard and Mathew Napper as overseers.[337]

At Mayfield the Kirrin family continued in the person of Jordan Kerry, son of the Frenchman William baptised in 1588. Jordan died unmarried in 1627 and left £3 to his sister Alice, who had married Edward Andrew at Mayfield in 1616, but was now married to Thomas West. He left £5 to her son Jordan Andrew, and £6 each to her other children, Edward Andrew and Debora West, to be paid them at 21. To his sister Audiana (called Andrew in the registered copy of the will), wife of Richard Weld,[338] he left 10 shillings, with 5 shillings to each of her children. To Anthony, son of Robert Kerry, he left 10 shillings. To Martha, wife of Anthony Kerry, he left a shilling and the same sum to each of her children. But Jordan's brother James, his residuary legatee and executor, who was to have his lands and tenements in Mayfield, was the main beneficiary under the will.[339]

Because of the bequest made by Jordan Kerry to Anthony son of Robert Kerry, it is seems probable that Anthony Kerry buried at Maresfield in 1624 was his own brother. Anthony's children, Elizabeth, William and Joan, had been baptised at Maresfield between 1617 and 1622, but William died within a few weeks of birth. Anthony Kerry himself was buried at Maresfield in June 1624, and his daughters Elizabeth and Joan were buried there in August and September.

Anthony son of Robert Kerry lived at Mayfield. His children Robert and John were baptised there in 1612 and 1614, and on the second occasion Anthony Kerry was given the alias 'Robins',

336. His name was then recorded as Kerrine Jordan (Dunkin, *Sussex Marriage Licences, Lewes 1586-1643,* p. 182).

337. LMA, DW/PA/05, 1661/61.

338. But Richard Willard married Auderia Kirrin at Goudhurst in 1610.

339. TNA, PROB 11/152/499.

obviously a patronymic. Anthony was clearly still alive in 1627, but received no further mention in the parish register. His son Robert Kerry married Mary Martyn at Maresfield in 1636 and their daughter Joan was baptised there the following year.

Jordan and Anthony's brother James had married Mary Gatlin at Mayfield in 1604. His daughters Anne and Jane were baptised there in 1604 and 1605. It looks as though he may have been married three times because an otherwise unknown second wife, Margaret, was buried at Mayfield in 1615. He then married Joan Rofe at Framfield in 1616 and their children, Mary, Thomas and Elizabeth, were baptised at Mayfield between 1617 and 1621. It was James Kerry who was beneficiary under the will of his brother Jordan Kerry in 1627, but of the five children mentioned in the parish register it was only Anne, the first child of James's first wife, and Marie, the first child of his third wife who were singled out for bequests of £5 and £6 respectively. After 1621 no further baptisms for children of James Kerry were noted in the Mayfield parish register and it is possible that he moved to Barcombe, where in 1634 a collier named James Kerry was bondsman for a marriage licence.[340]

Downe

Maryan Downe was probably the poll-tax payer recorded as Marian Dawe in the relief of 1552 in Danehill Horsted hundred. He was almost certainly 'Dawne the hamerman' of Parrock who paid 2 shillings on goods in the Hartfield hundred subsidy of 1560. In parish registers his sole appearance was apparently his burial as Maryan a'Downe at Frant in May 1568. The family has to be distinguished from the Rotherfield family of a'Downe, to which the surname was evidently often assimilated.

Nicholas Downe, who paid the poll tax at Charlwood in Reigate hundred in 1576, was perhaps Maryan's son. As a 54-year-old Beeding collier he was a deponent in the 1585 inquiry into the ironworks in St Leonards Forest.[341] From this it must be inferred that he had been born about 1530, presumably in France. He had married Clementia Wauklyn in November 1566 at Balcombe, though his daughter Alice had already been baptised there in September. His house at Beeding was burgled by three fellow colliers in 1580.[342]

Moyses Downe, who married Joan Missho at Wisborough Green in 1605, was perhaps Nicholas's son. Moyses' son Samuel was baptised at Alfold in 1606 (according to the Wisborough Green parish register), his son Peter at West Chiltington in 1611, but the twins Davy and Moyses, baptised there in February 1617, cost Joan her life, because her burial followed just over a fortnight later.

Another son of Maryan Downe was probably the forgeman Richard a Downe, who in 1567 married Alice, a widow rather unreliably surnamed 'Tenate' in the Frant parish register. The baptism of their daughter Alice was recorded at Frant in 1573, their daughters Mary and a second Alice were baptised at Mayfield in 1574 and 1576, followed at Burwash by a daughter named Catharine in 1578. The sequence of daughters continued at Wartling with the baptisms of Sara and Joan in 1580 and 1581, the father being styled 'Adowne a frenchman' in 1580 and 'Richard a'Downe forgeman' in 1581. Sara survived less than six months, but a further daughter named Dorothy was baptised at Warbleton in 1584.

In May 1584 John Wenham brought a case against Richard a'Downe in the High court at Battle, but Wenham failed to appear in June to press the suit and so a'Downe was discharged *sine die*.[343] It looks as though the family had returned to the High Weald by the 1590s, because Richard's wife Alice was buried at Frant in 1592.

There are tenuous references in probate records to Richard a'Downe in 1558, when he received a heifer and a calf as servant of John Fermar of Rotherfield, and in 1567, somewhat before his marriage, when he and William Marryon witnessed the will of Thomas Plom[er]den of Heathfield, who made the forgemaster Thomas Isted his executor.[344] a'Downe may well have worked for Isted at Moat Mill Forge from 1574 to 1576, when two of his children were baptised at Mayfield.

Bartholomew Downe, perhaps another of Maryan's sons, married Mary Panckhurst at Mayfield

340. Dunkin, *Sussex Marriage Licences, Lewes 1586-1643*, p. 213.

341. TNA, E 134, 27 Elizabeth I, Easter 16.

342. Cockburn, *Sussex Assize records, Elizabeth I*, no. 911. This seems to be the only occasion when the name 'a Downe' was applied to Nicholas.

343. HEH, BA Vol. 97 ff 39-40.

344. ESRO, PBT 1/1/4/305; 1/1/5/479.

in 1579. A first son Thomas was baptised at Heathfield in 1581, but no further children appear to be recorded until the baptism of Richard Downe at Mayfield in 1590. Bartholomew Downe was buried at Frant in 1592. The form 'a Downe' was never used with reference to Bartholomew in these parish register entries.

It is not certain that Bartholomew's sons Thomas and Richard Downe can be later identified. Thomas Downe, buried at Westfield in 1619, was probably the man who married Joan Byshoppenden at Sedlescombe in 1589, and was therefore too old to have been Bartholomew's son. Thomas appears to have moved to Westfield between 1592 and 1600. However, the isolated entry in Newdigate parish register early in 1616 for the baptism of Elizabeth daughter of Richard Downe, could relate to Bartholomew's other son.

Jeffery Downe, buried at East Grinstead in 1579, may have been another son of Nicholas Downe. His sons, Thomas and Francis, closely followed him to the grave and it is not certain that there were other descendants.

There does not seem to be any justification for supposing that the name Downe was in any way connected with the English surname Downer. The Chiddingly forgeman John Downer, mentioned as a surety in a quarter sessions roll of 1640,[345] was the son of John Downer, baptised at Chiddingly early in 1609, and he in turn may have been the unnamed son of John Downer and Alice Dawe baptised at Heathfield in 1582.

Gifford

The surname Giffard does not occur in the Pays de Bray or at Dieppe, but can be found extensively at Rouen and to a lesser degree elsewhere in the Seine valley. It is perhaps of English origin, and may well go back in Normandy to the Lancastrian occupation.

Gyfferd, the colyer, who paid the poll tax in Hartfield hundred in 1560 has not been traced elsewhere in the Weald. The surname was that of Mr John Gifford, who in 1651 succeeded Richard Leader as the agent managing the Hammersmith works in New England on behalf of the Company of undertakers, but intervening links between the Hartfield collier of 1560 and John Gifford are not evident.

Pykes

This surname seems to be Wealden rather than French. Three apparently English persons named Picas were mentioned in the subsidy rolls of the 1520s, including John Pykas in Streat hundred and Roger Pycas in Danehill Horsted. In 1574 Drewe Pickhayes held Brambletye Forge which was then in lease to Robert Reynolds.[346] Views of frankpledge show the mill of Brambletye to have been held by James Pycas gentleman and William Burnett in 1577, with John Harte succeeding Burnett in 1579 and Drewe Pyckas succeeding James in May 1590.[347]

The alien Gyllam Pykes, who paid the poll tax in Hartfield hundred in 1572 is not encountered elsewhere. The original surname is not immediately obvious. The nearest French equivalent might be *Pigache*, the name attached to a garden at Neuville-Ferrières which Almaury Roussell leased to Merigon Lambert in 1487.[348]

This raises the possibility that having been assimilated to the Wealden name Pycas, the original surname adopted in place of Pigache was gradually abandoned in favour of Pyke, which we have seen was used by forgeworkers from the Tyler family both in the Weald and in South Yorkshire. The name Pyke had been confined to West Sussex in the 1520s, but by the end of the century was being used at Frant and in adjacent parishes. For instance John Picks married Margaret South at Frant in 1591.

345. ESRO, QR 48, m. 37.
346. Cleere and Crossley, *The iron industry of the Weald*, p. 318.
347. ESRO, ACC 3597/8, ff 49 (1577), 127 (1579); 3597/1, 114v. (1590).
348. ADSM, 2 E 14/1140 (21 Feb 1487).

Rotherfield hundred

Lucian

The list of six aliens in Rotherfield hundred in 1552 ended with John and Anthony Lucian who each paid the poll tax. It seems probable that one of these men was Lucyan, who in 1572 paid the poll tax in Shoyswell hundred.

It seems very probable that work in the iron industry drew these men to Rotherfield, but there is no proof of this and the surname seems not to have later links with the history of iron.

Pygot

The name was perhaps *Picot*, or even *Pigault*, in French. Entries for the immigrant family have to be quite carefully separated from entries for the Chiddingstone family of Piggott, which flourished in the same general area. Even the blacksmith, Richard Pigott of Cowden, whose eldest son William married Annis Tyler, and whose grandson was named Drew Pigott after his grandfather, the ironfounder Drew Tyler, belonged to the Chiddingstone family.[349] Further Drew Piggotts were baptised at Cowden in 1638 and at Lingfield in 1668 and 1695, whilst another branch of the family, headed by Anthony and Baptiste Pigott, established itself at Biddenden, another ironworking parish.

The alien Mighell Pycot, a servant of the forgemaster David Willard, paid the poll tax in the South Borough of Tonbridge in 1572. Michael Piccat had earlier married Joan Leonard at Pembury in 1561, but further traces of him in the Weald have not been found. Perhaps he was the ancestor of Stephen Picket who flourished in the 1630s in Wadhurst.

Guilam Pygot, or Pycott, paid the poll tax alongside Hugo (Huggett?) in 1560 in the South Borough of Rotherfield hundred, which would be the part adjacent to Rotherfield itself. In 1572 he paid the poll tax alongside the pot-founder, Remy Durrant, who featured in the Rotherfield parish register around that time. However, there seems to be no mention of Pygot in that register.

Durrant

Remy Durrant paid the poll tax in Rotherfield hundred in 1572 and again in 1576, on the second occasion being listed under Rotherfield, whilst the other aliens were employed in Frant. He appeared in the Rotherfield parish register for the first time early in 1564, when his daughter Gillian was baptised there. Further children, Sylvester, John and Thomas, followed in 1566, 1567 and 1570. Early in 1575 Remy married his second wife Audrin Bysse (Busse?), and a first son, Francis,[350] was baptised within a month of the marriage. Further children, Richard and Margaret, were baptised in 1577 and 1579. Remy's second wife Adrian was buried at Rotherfield in 1582, but between that date and 1591, when he made his will, Remy had moved on to Horsmonden.

His will shows that Remy Durrant was a pot-founder, a profession unlikely, as explained in the technological section, to have been widespread in the Weald before the 1540s. That this was a family of pot-founders is shown by the fact that Remy's son Anthony Durrant of East Grinstead and grandson Humphrey Durrant of Rudgwick were also pot-founders. Even one of Remy's younger sons, Thomas, whose children were baptised at Brenchley, was, in parish register entries of 1604 and 1621, given the alias 'Potter'. Remy perhaps cast pots at Maynards Gate Furnace.

The baptismal name Remy was popular in the Béthune valley, where in the earlier part of century the priest Remy Crespin had been rector of Bouelles. But the surname Durant was not common in the Pays de Bray, so it seems possible that Remy came from elsewhere. The Liège area, where potfounding came into vogue from around 1540 onwards, in blast furnaces specifically set up in the vicinity of that city to produce foundry pig iron,[351] at once suggests itself. However, it seems to have

349. See the will of John Pelling of Lindfield, who married Margery Pigot at Chiddingstone in 1577. He nominated Richard Pyggott of Cowden, smith, his brother-in-law, and Henry Pygott of Chiddingstone, yeoman, his cousin, as overseers (ESRO, PBT 2/2/2/89).

350. The parish register made an otherwise unknown Reynald Durrant his father, but Remy claimed Francis as his son in his will.

351. G. Hansotte, 'La métallurgie wallonne au XVIe et dans la première moitié du XVIIe siècle', p. 130. Since

been from Martigny-en-Thiérache that a collier actually named Anthoine Durant was recruited in 1621 for Guillaume de Bèche in Sweden.[352]

In his will Remy bequeathed to his daughter 'Gwillian' £8, to his youngest daughters Margaret and Joan all the linen and £10 each, to his son John £20 and a 12-monthing colt, to Thomas £10 at 21 and a 3-yearling colt, to Francis £10, and to the children of his daughter Marie Jarrett £10, of which £2 was already in the hands of her husband Nicholas. His remaining moveables were to be divided equally amongst all his children. He made his son Anthony executor.[353] Remy was buried at Horsmonden in May 1591 and probate was granted to Peter Johnson, proctor of Anthony Durrant, in April 1592. Peter Johnson was presumably related to Thomas Johnson, the Queen's gunfounder, who was forgemaster at Horsmonden at this time.

If Remy enumerated all his children, it is evident that Sylvester and Richard must have died. Additional to the children whose baptisms have been found were Anthony, Marie and Joan. Joan was one of the youngest children, but it is evident that Marie, who married Nicholas Jarrett in 1578, must have been born before 1564 and therefore before Remy's arrival at Rotherfield, and it seems probable that the same applies to Anthony, one of whose children was baptised at Ifield as early as 1586.

Since the gunfounder at Horsmonden was named Nicholas Jarrett, it would be natural to suppose that it was his son-in-law's move to that furnace which encouraged Remy Durrant also to move and end his days there. However, cogent reasons have been advanced for supposing that the gunfounder at Horsmonden was actually Warnet Gerat's son, Nicholas Jarrett alias Warner, whose wife was named Joan and not Marie.

Remy's younger children accompanied him to Horsmonden. As already noticed, his younger son Thomas Durrant alias Potter stayed in the area. He married Mary Akers at Horsmonden in 1594 and their children were baptised at Brenchley from 1597 to 1623. Mary was buried within a month of the last of these baptisms and Thomas himself was buried at Brenchley in 1626.

Remy's son John Durrant married Alice Laughen at Speldhurst in 1591, but their daughter Elizabeth was baptised at Brenchley in 1596. He was the John Durant numbered among the furnacemen of the gunfounder John Browne at the end of the 1620s.[354] It seems possible that Repentance Durrant who married Alice Lowdwell at Brenchley in 1621, whose children were baptised there from 1622 to 1634, and who was buried at Brenchley in 1658, could have been John Durrant's son, but there is no evidence of his involvement in ironfounding.

Anthony Durrant, Remy's eldest son, had an unnamed child baptised at Ifield in June 1586, but by October 1587 he had moved to the borough of Ashurst in East Grinstead, where he was recorded as a defaulter in views of frankpledge up to the end of the series in 1591. He sometimes paid the regular fine of 2 pence, but equally as often he was essoined.[355] The East Grinstead parish register recorded the burial of his son Remy in 1588, followed by the baptism of six further children from 1589 to 1600. He too was a pot-founder and was buried at East Grinstead early in 1613, his wife Mary having predeceased him by over two years.

There seems to have been no furnace within the bounds of Ashurst borough, which, taken in conjunction with the fact that the ironfounder Charles Tyler had preceded Durrant in the same borough for the period May 1579 to May 1580, just prior to his move to Loscoe Furnace in Derbyshire, is hard to explain. Perhaps an outlying part of Ashurst borough was located near to Mill Place Furnace. More probably, Durrant habitually cast pots at various furnaces in the High Weald between which Ashurst lay centrally placed.

Anthony made his eldest son Humphrey his residuary legatee and executor. He bequeathed £10 to each of his other seven surviving children. In addition Richard was to have a chest, Anthony a red cow 'with some white upon her' and a 'joyned' chest without hinges, John a bucking chest, Francis a

1974 Hansotte has shown that the Lize Furnace at Seraing was set up in 1539 (G. Hansotte, 'Les Fourneaux à fer dans la vallée de la Meuse liégeoise aux XVIe et XVIIe siècles', p. 229).

352. E. W. Dahlgren, ed. *Louis de Geers brev och affarhandlingar*, pp. 50-1. The transcription 'Montregny' cannot be right, nor can J. Yernaux's correction 'Montigny' (*La métallurgie liégeoise*, p. 296).

353. TNA, PROB 11/79/295.

354. *Acts of the Privy Council*, **44**, pp. 71-2; I am indebted to David Crossley for communicating this list of furnacemen.

355. ESRO, ACC 3597/1, f. 12 to f. 147v.

table cupboard, Katheryn her mother's joined chest, Martha a red cow with a white star on its forehead, a featherbed, a bolster-tick and the greatest joined chest, and Elizabeth was to have a pair of hook-seamed sheets. The remaining linen (except for three pairs of sheets, which will presumably have gone to Humphrey) was to be divided among his three daughters, who were also to share the pewter. The brass and iron vessels were to be divided between all Anthony's children. He also left 5 shillings to the poor.[356]

Anthony's eldest son Humphrey followed in his father's trade of pot-founder. He married Joan Jenner at West Hoathly in 1614, but by 1617 had established himself at Rudgwick, where he was buried in July of that year. He made his wife Joan his residuary legatee and bequeathed a shilling each to his seven brothers and sisters, who corresponded exactly to those named in his father's will. To the poor he left 3s 4d.[357]

Anthony's second son Richard appeared in the Cuckfield parish register as 'founder at the Furneis' there in 1614. His wife Eleanor gave birth to twins, Richard and Jane, in May of that year. Richard survived only four months and his sister for only three years. Further twins, Anthony and Elizabeth who may have survived, were baptised in November 1615. By 1617 the couple had moved back to East Grinstead, where Jane was buried in July and where a further son named John was baptised in December, but failed to survive the month. His mother was buried two days later. It is not known whether Richard Durrant married again.

Anthony's third son, Anthony, had been baptised in 1595. He may have been the Anthony Durrant who married Parratt Hodson at Stedham in 1616. Children named Anthony, Mabel, Thomas and Margaret were born to them by 1622. Parratt was buried at Stedham early in 1629 and Anthony married his second wife, Elizabeth Laker, at Stedham in 1631. It seems possible that Anthony Durrant of Chiddingfold, who married Mary Betsel at Linchmere in 1645, was the child of that name baptised at Stedham in 1617, and Elizabeth the wife of Anthony Durrant buried at Chiddingfold in 1659 will have been his stepmother.

A further generation of Anthonys is indicated by the baptism of Anthony son of Anthony and Ann Durrant at Northchapel in 1676. One of these Anthonys was buried at Northchapel in 1694. The continued residence of these men in ironworking parishes and the continued use of the same baptismal name suggests that a connection with ironfounding may have continued and that all were members of the family descended from Remy Durrant of Rotherfield.

That the two youngest sons of Anthony Durrant, John and Francis, could both have moved to Isfield is suggested firstly by the fact that John Durrant, whose children were baptised at Isfield from 1621 to 1633, is shown by a marriage bond of 1631 to have been a blacksmith,[358] and secondly by the marriage in the same parish of Anthony Durrant's youngest son Francis to Elizabeth Martin early in 1638.

Furr'

Along with David Willard's servants William and Nicholas Furrie, who paid the poll tax in Southborough of Tonbridge in 1572, Furr' the servant to Alexander Fermor, who paid the poll tax in Rotherfield in the same year, perhaps bore the surname Furrill.

Nicholas Furrye was perhaps the man who moved on to pay the poll tax in Buttinghill hundred by 1576, but there is no means of tracing the later history of Alexander Fermor's servant.

Danehill Horsted hundred

Pollard

John Pollerd paid the poll tax in Danehill Horsted hundred in 1551. He was perhaps the father of Richard Pollard, a future miller at Waldron, who was baptised at Maresfield in 1566.

The suggestion will be remembered that Peter Villain, for whom and for whose family there

356. TNA, PROB 11/121/222.
357. TNA, PROB 11/130/362.
358. Dunkin, *Sussex Marriage Licences, Lewes 1586-1643*, p. 193.

are entries in the parish registers of Maresfield and Newick, was the son of Thomas Le Villain who originated at Gratenoix in Beaussault parish, but after he had established himself at Illois, just north of the Pays de Bray, by around 1510, was not heard of again in Neufchâtel notarial records. The elder brothers of Thomas were both wheelwrights: Jehan Le Villain who had moved to Neuville-sur-Eaulne near Londinières by 1526 and Jehannot Le Villain, who from 1509 onwards lived in Saint-Pierre parish in Neufchâtel.

The grandson of the Neuville-sur-Eaulne man was Jehan Le Villain *dit* Polourde, who in 1540 was miller at the windmill of Sainte-Beuve-aux-Champs, and in the 1550s disposed of rights, possibly only leasehold ones, in the Claqueret watermill at Vatierville and in the windmill of Nullemont.[359]

Although there is no proof of a similar relationship between the names Villain and Pollard in the Weald as obtained in France in the case of Jehan Le Villain *dit* Poullard, it is striking that in the Weald a member of the Pollard family was a miller.

This was John Pollard's son, Richard Pollard of Waldron, who died in January 1589. He appears to have died young, because neither wife nor children were mentioned in his will and his first bequest was of £5 to his father John Pollard. His brother Stephen also died young leaving but one child, to whom Richard bequeathed 10 shillings. Richard's unnamed sister was married to Nicholas Hoth, to whom Richard bequeathed £1 10s 0d, a cloak and a pair of leather breeches. His sister's children were each to have ashilling and she was to have four pairs of sheets. His goods were valued at £20 17s 4d.[360]

If John Pollard, the father, was employed at Maresfield Forge, it seems likely that it was through the patronage of the forgemaster there, John Fawkener of Waldron, that his son Richard's employment as miller at Waldron was secured. And Richard Pollard did enjoin Fawkener his executor 'to distribute the rest of my goods at his discretion'.

The son of Pollard's brother Stephen was presumably Stephen Pollard, who was baptised at Framfield in February 1587, and the father Stephen received no bequest in the will because he had died, buried there, albeit as Stephen Pullen, in November 1587. He had been married, also erroneously as Stephen Pullen, in 1585 to Eleanor [*blank*], but when she was remarried to the tailor Mathew Freman in October 1592, her name was correctly recorded as Elleanor Pollard.

'Pollard the Frenchman' was first mentioned in the Waldron parish register in January 1604, when his daughter Joan was baptised. Was he the John Pollard, who married Mary Kennet at Waldron in 1595, and whose son Mathew was baptised there in 1613? The baptisms of three other Pollard children, besides Joan and Mathew, were recorded at Waldron in 1598, 1608 and 1610, without mention of their parents' names. It seems difficult to imagine that the 'Frenchman Pollard' could still be the alien of 1551, but he had certainly died before 1618, when Mathew son of 'Widow Pollard' was buried. Their daughter Iden Pollard, baptised in 1598, produced an illegitimate child in 1625, but finally married Gilbert, the son of the finer William Addison, at Buxted in 1631.

Rushmonden hundred

Tullock

It seems safe to identify Jarman Tulloke, who paid a shilling to the relief in Rushmonden hundred in 1551, with Jarman Tollett who had been made a denizen for Thomas May in 1544.

Coulstock

In the subsidy rolls of the 1520s the names Holstoke and Cowstoke both occurred, though the latter was confined to Hurstpierpoint. Peter Gostocke's name occurred only once in the subsidy rolls, when in 1552 he paid the poll tax in Rushmonden hundred, an area first substantially penetrated by alien names in 1551. The surname originated in the Low Countries and the aspiration of the initial 'G' will perhaps have given rise to the Holstoke variant. However, Peter Gostock's descendants' surname seems ultimately to have been assimilated to Cowlstock or Coulstock.

The father of the Brede pot-founder Richard Cowlstock was apparently John Coustock (1592)

359. ADSM, 2 E 14/1182 (6 Mar 1540), 2 E 14/1192 (22 May 1552), 2 E 14/1197 (24 Nov 1555).
360. ESRO, PBT 1/1/8/260, 1/3/2/69.

or Costock (1596) whose children, Jane and Richard, were baptised at Framfield in 1592 and 1596. Both Framfield versions of the name, especially that of 1596, are closer to that of the surname of the 1552 alien, than Coulstock(e), which was used for the pot-founder in the Brede parish register in 1624 and in an administration bond of 1632.

John Colstocke was buried at Brede in 1613, his burial followed shortly afterwards by that of his wife Elizabeth. This couple can hardly have been John Colstocke and Elizabeth Longe who married at East Hoathly in 1563. Their daughter Jane married Henry Sloman at Brede, just after her mother's death in 1613, and Richard, the pot-founder, married Anne Turner at Battle in 1623. Their parents were far from indigent, because John's goods, assigned for administration to his widow Elizabeth, were inventoried at £102 8s 8d, with Stephen Collins, a Brede husbandman, acting as bondsman, and hers, valued at £103 12s 0d, were assigned to her son Richard.[361]

Richard Coulstock's occupation was revealed when he took administration of the effects of his sister-in-law, Dorothy Turner of Westfield, in 1632.[362] His children, John, Frances, Marie who did not survive infancy, Elizabeth, Richard and Agnes, were baptised at Brede between 1625 and 1633. Of them Frances married the ironfounder Richard Gunter of Dallington at Brede in 1656.

The name Coulstock had occurred frequently in Fletching parish register from 1548 onwards. The 1557 will of Richard Cowstocke of Fletching indicated that his daughter Margery had married William Collen and among bequests to Margery's three children was that of an iron pot to Eleanor Collen.[363]

Thomas Mychell of Worth, gentleman, died in 1551 and mentioned the profit yearly coming from his 'iron myll at Chidingly' in his will.[364] He was generous to his late servant Thomas Coulstocke the younger, to whom he left £10.

One of the clerks of the gunfounder Ralph Hogge in the late 1570s was Samson Coulestoke.[365] The fact that he was not mentioned in the will of Richard Cowstocke of Fletching, or in other Coulstock wills of the period could indicate that he was related to the immigrant. Since he worked for Hogge it is not surprising to find that Sampson Cowstocke's marriage to Margery Mychelborne took place at Maresfield in October 1579. Curiously however, it was John Coulstock who appeared among the defaulters for Nutley borough in Rushmonden views of frankpledge from October 1579 until April 1581.[366] Perhaps he was Sampson's elder brother; John was normally essoined.

Sampson Coulstock must have moved west soon after Ralph Hogge ceased trading. The baptism of his eldest son Thomas took place at Lurgashall in 1583 and of his third son William at Kirdford in 1590, so the baptism of his second son John must have taken place between those two dates. Samson Cowlstock must have died at a quite young age because his burial occurred at Kirdford in 1594.

From Coulstock's will dated 3 September 1594 it looks as though since Hogge's death he had been a supplier of wood or charcoal to the late John Fawkenor the younger of Waldron, and to John Thorpe of Hedgecourt, who were forgemasters. £590 was due to him out of Fawkenor's lands and tenements by 2 May 1596 and this sum was to go to Coulstock's eldest son Thomas. His son John was to have £200 due from his landlord William Brown. An unspecified sum, which was due to Coulstock from Robert Sherlock of Tangmere and from John Thorpe, was to go his son William. Coulstock's sons were to give half the interest on all these sums to their mother Margery, who was also to have Coulstock's term of years in Ifold farm (except its woods and timber) in Kirdford, held of William Browne and his mother Annis Browne, together with all the household stuff, corn and cattle. Margery was to bring up their sons during their minorities. Coulstock left £1 to the poor, styled himself yeoman and elected to be buried in Kirdford church.[367]

The will also contained a list of debts: £25 was due at Christmas from Mr Bongard, the master of the glasshouse, for 1,000 cords of wood, for which £25 had already been paid, and which Bongard was to have up to Midsummer 1596 to clear. Among other debts, Coulstock owed £10 to the hammerman

361. ESRO, PBT 1/3/4/5 and 17.
362. ESRO, PBT 1/3/6/117.
363. ESRO, PBT 1/1/4/19.
364. TNA, PROB 11/34/438.
365. Crossley, 'Ralph Hogge's ironworks accounts', p. 78.
366. ESRO, ACC 3597/8, f. 122 (9 Oct 1579) to f. 179v (10 Apr 1581).
367. TNA, PROB 11/84/294.

Charles Barden, £100 due at Christmas to Mr Thomas Cooper of Godalming, which was to be paid in wood at 1s 4d a cord, and £3 6s 8d to be paid 'to the farmer at Lee (Leigh?)' for a debt owed to 'my hosts at Leatherhead for my son John's board ever since he came thither'.

The overseers of this will were Edward Mychelborne, gentleman, Richard Willson of Uckfield, yeoman, and Coulstock's brother John. Sampson Coulstock appointed his eldest son Thomas residuary legatee and executor, but during his minority Sampson's brother John was to act as supervisor. John Coulstock took probate of this will in October 1594, his nephew not taking execution until October 1605.

If the Nutley borough man of around 1580 was Sampson Coulstock's brother, he could have been the John Colstock who married Alice Atherall at Maresfield in 1578. It is not evident that members of either of these families became involved in the iron industry outside the Weald.

Debewe

In dealing with the family Dubusc in the Pays de Bray, it was suggested that Pierre Dubuscz, who married Noëlle Maubert in 1544,[368] was perhaps the Peter Debewe who came to England and paid tax as an alien in Rushmonden hundred in 1572.

The family had first been noticed in England in John De Vewe, who worked as a miner at Panningridge in 1547-8.[369] John Dewewe, a Frenchman who paid the poll tax in Richard Weekes' works in Netherfield hundred in 1549, was probably the same man. Since he was not at this time included among the Netherfield denizens he cannot have been John Debowes who was born in Normandy around 1522, came to England in 1532, and was made denizen in 1544, but he may have been the John Deboyse who paid the poll tax in Shoyswell hundred in 1576.

In 1562 Anthony Debew married Joan Villayne at Newick. The marriage of Peter de Bewe to Alice Vyllayne at Maresfield in 1571 could have been the immigrant's second marriage. Alice de Bewe, baptised in June 1572 and buried already in August of that year, may well have been their child. After his payment of the poll tax in Rushmonden in 1572, Peter was not subsequently traced in the Weald.

It is unclear whether John de Bewe, who appeared briefly in 1569 at Maresfield as sponsor to a Snashall (*Le Seneschal*) baptism was the former Netherfield man. Related to Peter and John may have been Richard Debyes, who was sponsor to a Gotcher (*Gotier*) baptism in July 1569, but was himself buried at Maresfield in December.

In contrast, Anthony Debew can be traced in parish registers from 1562 right up to his burial at Mayfield in 1610. His first three children, Charles, Peter and John, of whom Peter did not survive infancy, were baptised at Maresfield between 1565 and 1569. He was later encountered at East Grinstead, where his daughters Marie and Margery were baptised in 1573 and 1577, but where his wife Joan was buried within two months of the baptism of her last child. Anthony next moved to Goudhurst in Kent, where three more children, Andrew, who did not survive infancy, Anne and Anthony, were baptised between 1579 and 1586.

John Debewe, who married Mary Bewe at Speldhurst in 1592, will have been Anthony's second surviving son. John's children, John, Agnes and Alice, were baptised at Mayfield between 1593 and 1603. It seems probable that Anthony had accompanied this move made by his son to Mayfield, because that was where he himself was buried in 1610. The widow Clemence Bue who was buried at Mayfield early in 1612, will have been Anthony's second wife.

Assize rolls show that John Debewe of Frant, who was the victim of theft in 1601, was a collier. Thomas Sudds alias Barden was found guilty of the theft from him at Withyham of a blue coat valued at 6 shillings, a waistcoat (6 shillings) and a flitch of bacon (13s 4d) and another waistcoat (3s 4d) and was sentenced to be hanged.[370]

In 1637 John Bew the elder of Mayfield, collier, was himself presented at quarter sessions for the theft of five geese, valued at 2 pence each. John Bew the younger of Mayfield, yeoman, who went surety for his appearance,[371] will have been his son, baptised at Mayfield in 1593.

368. ADSM, 2 E 14/1188 (17 May 1544).
369. KHLC, U1475 B2/1.
370. Cockburn, *Sussex Assize records, Elizabeth I*, no. 1995.
371. ESRO, QR 37, mm. 31 and 42.

Blowe

Other than his payment of the poll tax in Rushmonden hundred in 1572, there seems to be no mention of Robert Blowe in the historical record. Could the original French name have been Bleu? The suggestion that the intended name was Blewet, and that Laurence Blewett's son Robert made a short visit to the Weald almost 20 years after his father's death seems highly unlikely.

Lawnsyn or Old

Just as we saw that the French surname L'ainé (Old Fr. *L'aisné* or *L'ainsné*) is translatable as 'the Elder' or 'the Older', the name L'ancien is translatable as 'the Old'. Bearing this in mind, it seems possible that the first member of this family to come to the Weald was Peter Lawnsyne, the Kirdford collier, who in 1580 entered a recognizance to give evidence against the Northchapel miner, Roger Norris, the assault on whom resulted in the affray at Plaistow in which Charles Pavye was fatally injured. Later he may have been in Surrey, where the muster roll of 1583-4 listed a gunner named Peter Lansatt at Ockley.[372] The assize court had sought perhaps to reproduce the French form of this name, but in 1588 he was buried at Worth where the clerk used Latin and styled him Peter *Lantiqua*.

Entries in the West Chiltington parish register for the baptism of Edward Lanset in 1594 and for the burial of Ciceley Launsat in 1599 probably relate to this family. There is then a gap until Mary daughter of James Lansum was baptised at Kirdford in 1618. She married John Stacey at Kirdford in 1640.

It seems certain that Simon Lancen who married Eleanor Smart at Petworth in 1627, and whose daughter Marie Launsome was baptised at Lurgashall in 1629, was from this family. He was married again at Kirdford to a widow named Elizabeth Tyler in December 1641, and was buried there in 1681, whilst Elizabeth Lansom who was buried there in 1684 was probably his second wife.

Whether John Landsden who married Sarah Bennet at Stopham in 1628 was from this family seems less certain, but John Lausum who married Elizabeth Layney (Laisné?) at Kirdford in 1634 almost certainly was. John's son Henry was baptised at Kirdford in 1640, Elizabeth his wife was buried there in 1679 and he himself was probably the John Lansome buried at Kirdford in 1689. Another member of the family was probably Richard Lansome, who was buried at Northchapel in 1670.

Beyond their persistence in ironworking parishes, there is nothing to prove the link of this western branch of the Lawnsyn family with the manufacture of iron. However, a branch in more central areas, but which also made a brief foray into the western Weald, was certainly of French origin and certainly worked in iron; it was among those families which adopted a translated form of its original name in its new surroundings.

Maryan Old paid the poll tax in Rushmonden hundred in 1572 and 1576. He also appeared in the Maresfield parish register from 1572 to 1589 for the baptism of four children and the burial of one. These entries were for the baptism of Nicholas in 1572, of Alice in 1575, of Eleanor in 1585 and of Steven in 1589, and for the burial of Colletyce in 1574. The only entry for which certainty is lacking occurred in 1585 when Eleanor's father was stated to be 'Maryon, a Frenchman'. Ellen Old and Margaret Old were buried in 1593. Since Maryan was not heard of again it seems safe to assume that 'Father Maryon', who was buried at Maresfield in 1595, was Maryan Old. Another son of Maryan Old was Walter Old, who in his will left a bequest of £1 to his brother Stephen Old.

Whilst Maryan's son Walter moved eastwards and married a widow named Elizabeth Woodgate, born Bennet,[373] at Salehurst in 1609, his two other sons moved to the west of the Weald: Nicholas married another widow, Rose Barden, at Linchmere in 1601, and Stephen married Mary Knight at Bramshott in 1615. Unfortunately, Nicholas came to a sudden and violent end in June 1604, when the parish register of Linchmere recorded the burial of Nicholas Olde 'that was slayne'. Nicholas left two young daughters, Jane and Elizabeth.

After the baptism of his daughter Mary at Bramshott in 1616, Stephen Old moved back to Kirdford, where his daughters Anne and Elizabeth were baptised in 1618 and 1619. In 1622 another daughter Susan was baptised at Linchmere, but Stephen later moved eastwards to Cuckfield, where his

372. Cockburn, *Sussex Assize records, Elizabeth I*, no. 801; Craib, *Surrey musters*, p. 25.
373. She was the sister of William Bennet of Fletching, yeoman, who died in 1628 (ESRO, PBT 1/1/26/190).

son Stephen was buried in 1627. By September 1636 he was at Fletching, where his wife was then buried. He was still described as a Fletching hammerman in 1657, when his daughter Elizabeth's intention of marriage to Gregory Parker, a Chiltington husbandman, was entered at St Michael's church, Lewes.

Walter Old was perhaps slightly older than Stephen, born possibly in the gap between the Maresfield baptisms of 1575 and 1585. He moved to Fletching where he was in 1632, when as a Fletching forgeman he was bondsman for a marriage licence.[374] The year 1632 was also that of his wife's burial there, and his own burial followed in 1639. His will reveals that he was, like his brother Stephen, a hammerman.

Walter Old left to his wife Elizabeth the joined bedstead and the bed he lay in, two pairs of sheets, two blankets, two coverlets and other bedding, for life. In addition she was to have his best horse with a side saddle and bridle, a flock bed standing in the outermost chamber, with its 'steddle' and other items, three kine called Shell, Whiteface, and Brown Cow, 10 tegs, 'none of the worst nor all of the best', a sow now with farrow, one of the sheats, quarters of wheat and of malt and 'so much of other my household stuff as for brewing and baking and such like offices will be only necessary for the manner of the housekeeping and doings she shall go forth with all and so much wheat now on the ground as will keep her house during . . . one year and likewise so much malt'. These items she was to have 'if she continue the said year a widow', with £10. However, should she marry again or die these items were to devolve on the children of Walter Dennat, 'which he hath by Elizabeth daughter of her the said Elizabeth my wife'

Although it sounds as though Elizabeth was Old's stepdaughter, he nevertheless made Dennat, whom he called his kinsman, his residuary legatee and executor, and bequeathed £5 to Dennat's son William. To his brother Stephen he bequeathed £1 and to each of his two daughters the same amount. He left £2 each to Isaac and William Halfpenny, who appear to have been related to him in some way. Anthony Knight of Framfield, who may have been related to his brother's wife, and Anthony's wife and two daughters were each to have 5 shillings. Finally he left 5 shillings for his apprentice Charles Growt, to be had at the end of his term. His goods were inventoried at £81 1s 0d.[375]

It seems clear that neither Nicholas nor Walter Old were survived by male children, so the family may have died out in the male line with the death of Stephen Old, the surviving brother.

East Grinstead hundred

Burdewe

The suggestion that Anthony Burdewe who paid the poll tax in East Grinstead hundred in 1560 was Anthony Border or Bordet, who had paid the poll tax in Danehill Sheffield hundred in 1551 and 1552, was made earlier.

Buss

This name was relatively uncommon in the Sussex subsidy rolls of the 1520s: in the eastern Weald it appeared only at Wadhurst, where John Busse was taxed on £10 of goods and his servant William Busse was taxed on wages of £1. A single example of the name Buste occurred at Ringmer. It must be suspected that immigrants from the Pays de Bray bearing the name Beuse, whose surname had been assimilated to that of Busse or Bust, were responsible for the wide spread of these surnames in the eastern Weald by the end of the century.

In the Pays de Bray the family included technicians, possibly ironworkers, but certainly millers, from early on. Such involvement on the part of Jehan Beuse the elder of Fontaines-en-Bray came in 1495 when he paid 37£ 10s 0d for a twelve-year lease of the township's mill from Guillaume de Fry, the annual rent being only 1£ 10s 0d.[376] By 1528 his son Colin Beuse was dwelling in the Varenne valley at La Boissière in the parish of Saint-Martin-le-Blanc, and an act of 1534 shows that he was miller there. The important mill at La Boissière belonged to the count of Auxerre and in 1538 its rent was 90 livres a

374. Dunkin, *Sussex Marriage Licences, Lewes 1586-1643*, p. 196.

375. ESRO, PBT 1/1/26/28, 1/3/7/158.

376. ADSM, 2 E 14/1142 (21 Jun 1495).

year. However, Colin Beuse seems to have temporarily lost this mill in April 1539, when it was let until April 1540 to Jehan Humart *dit* Le Coq and his son Laurens. In March 1541 Colin Beuse was described as 'miller of Fontaines', so it seems that this family then still held its lease of de Fry's mill at Fontaines.[377]

By 1544, when he acquired the house named L'Angleterre in Esclavelles parish and replaced its thatch with tiles bought from Loys Vigot of Brémontier, Colin Beuse was again at La Boissière. His eldest son Raoullin appears to have followed him at La Boissière, dying around 1563, whilst his younger son Jehan sold the lease of the mill at Fontaines in 1548 and was presumably the miller of Vaudichon on the Varenne referred to in 1549. From 1553 to 1555 Jehan was back at Fontaines, but was in September 1555 perhaps the man 'at present' dwelling at La Rosière, who acquired from Pierre Mauroye the lease of the monastic corn mill on the Sausson river, formerly held by the Vincent family. Jehan was again referred to as 'of Fontaines' in notarial acts of 1556, but from 1561 onwards, following his marriage to Marion daughter of Michel Le Baucher, resided at Brémontier, close to the house named L'Angleterre, which his father had acquired in 1544.[378] Following the death of Raoullin Beuse, an exchange was effected in 1564 of the lease of the mill at La Boissière with that of Brémontier, and Jehan Beuse was referred to in 1566 and 1567 as miller at Brémontier. He was dead by 1573, by when he had been succeeded at Brémontier by his son Nicollas, a husbandman (*labourer*).[379]

It is not at all clear whether Guillaume Beuse, the miller of Fontaines referred to in 1567,[380] was a member of this branch of the family.

In February 1487, well before he became miller at Fontaines-en-Bray, Jehan Beuse the elder acquired from Mathelin Beuse the third share of a 60-acre field called the Three Ears (*Le Camp des Trois Oreilles*) in Neuville-Ferrières, which together with Perrin Beuse of Neuville-Ferrières and Rasset de Montfort of Fontaines, Mathelin had leased from the lord of Neuville, Aubery Doullé, at a rent of 7s 6d per acre, with the obligation of building three houses on it within four years.[381]

Because he appears to have financed his activities by selling or leasing portions of the Camp des Trois Oreilles, it seems possible that Nicollas Beuse de Haut was descended from Jehan Beuse the elder. His appellation 'de Haut' distinguished him from Nicollas Beuse de Bas, who dwelt in Le Bas de Fontaines-en-Bray. However, whilst de Bas continued at Fontaines, Nicolas Beuse de Haut had moved to Randillon in the parish of Mauquenchy by January 1534 and was at Sommery in September 1534, where he collected a debt for Jehan Le Lasnyer, the Neufchâtel smith and ironmonger, from Adrien Le Hideux, lord of La Ferté-en-Bray.[382] From 1535 until 1540 Nicollas was at Le Carreau in Beauvoir-en-Lyons, and from 1540 to 1545, and possibly beyond that date, at Gournay.[383] Although notarial records give no hint that he was involved in the iron industry, it is apparent that at Beauvoir Beuse de Haut would have been situated just less than 6km to the west of the *fonderie* of Mont-Louvet, and at Gournay, just less than 5km south-east of it.

Another branch of this family which may have been connected with the iron industry was settled at the hamlet of Les Monceaux in Neuville-Ferrières parish. It is possible that Perrin Beuse who had been a partner in the *Camp de Trois Oreilles* lease in 1486 was a member of this family, because notarial acts of 1494 and 1495 associated him with Neuville-Ferrières.[384] However, a family settlement of 1504 which named the 22-year-old Jehan Beuse as head of the family, first associated it with Les Monceaux. A livre rent on him was sold in 1505 by Jehan Hellebault of Neuville and Robinet Mensire of Saint-Saire to Aubery Dufour and in November 1508, around the time, following the death of Jehan Lucas, when the Dufour family appears to have acquired an interest in the forge at Neuville, Aubery

377. ADSM, 2 E 14/1166 (25 Jun 1528); 2 E 14/1168 (16 Jan 1534); 2 E 93/16 (30 Apr 1538), 2 E 93/17 (21 Apr 1539); 2 E 14/1184 (19 Mar 1541).

378. ADSM, 2 E 14/1188 (22 Mar 1544); 2 E 93/23 (23 Oct 1548, 23 Jan 1549); 2 E 14/1193 (16 May 1553); 2 E 14/1195 (23 Mar 1555); 2 E 14/1196 (15 Sep 1555); 2 E 14/1197 (4 Mar 1556); 2 E 14/1201 (3 Jun 1561).

379. ADSM, 2 E14/1205 (2 Jan 1564); 2 E 14/1209 (27 Aug 1566); 2 E 14/1211 (12 Apr 1567); 2 E 14/1217 (29 Sep 1573); 2 E 14/1220 (21 Feb 1575).

380. ADSM, 2 E 14/1211 (24 May 1567).

381. ADSM, 2 E 14/1140 (17 Nov 1486, 6 Feb 1487).

382. ADSM, 2 E 14/1168 (16 Jan 1534); 2 E 14/1169 (7 Sep 1534). Beuse paid Le Lasnyer 16 livres for a bond in which Le Hideux was obliged to Le Lasnyer for a larger sum.

383. ADSM, 2 E 14/1171 (3 Jul 1535); 2 E 14/1183 (3 Apr 1540); 2 E 14/1184 (23 Oct 1540); 2 E 14/1189 (26 May 1545)

384. ADSM, 2 E 14/1141 (22 Dec 1484, 9 Jan 1495).

Dufour took over from Anthoine Doullé another rent of 8£ 17s 6d due from Jehan Beuse, one of three rents passed on by Doullé to Dufour at that time for 260 livres.[385]

At least one member of the Les Monceaux Beuse family was involved with milling. In 1545 Colin, son of Perrin Beuse, sold to Bertin Digon, bourgeois and merchant of Neufchâtel, a house, farmstead, garden and heritage in the parish of Saint-Pierre, adjoining the road from Neufchâtel to Neuville, together with a windmill which had been built on the site, for 45 livres with 3 livres for the wine of the purchase.[386]

In the Weald four immigrants of this name paid the poll tax: they were Peter Busse in East Grinstead in 1572, and Robert Buse and his two sons in 1576 in Buttinghill hundred. Frustratingly, the names of Robert's two sons were not disclosed and they did not appear in the 1595 subsidy, of which only the roll for Hastings rape survives. Perhaps either William, Thomas and Dominick Bust, who will shortly be dealt with, were among Robert's sons.

The East Grinstead collier William Bust and two Hartfield colliers broke into the house of Frances Onyon at East Grinstead in 1582 and stole various items. Bust was found guilty, but was literate and able successfully to invoke benefit of clergy.[387] Curiously, no person of this surname was recorded at views of frankpledge for East Grinstead after the death of the husbandman George Busse in March 1577, though in his will George referred to his brothers John and William and their children. His son George, baptised in 1562, appears not to have survived.[388]

After 1582 isolated entries occurred in the parish registers of Kirdford and Rogate, for the respective baptisms of Lawrence Busse in 1587 and Robert Busse in 1594, both sons of William Busse, who could be the former East Grinstead collier. It looks as though Lawrence Busse could have stayed in West Sussex because in 1620 Joseph son of Lawrence Busse was baptised at Kirdford.

In October 1590 Thomas Buste, founder, was fined 2 pence for defaulting from the view of frankpledge at Maresfield in Rushmonden hundred.[389] Thomas Busse had married Mary Norman at Maresfield in 1576. In September 1577 he was a defaulter at Barkham in Danehill Sheffield hundred, and, after the gap in the series, he defaulted again at Maresfield, firstly in October 1587, when his poverty allowed him to escape fine, in April 1588 when he was essoined, and in October 1588 when he was again recorded as a pauper. In June 1589 he was pardoned for nonappearance at Lindfield, but in May and October 1590 he was again at Maresfield where his nonappearance incurred a fine of 2 pence on each occasion and where his occupation of founder was recorded in October.[390]

In fact parish register entries show that from 1580 to 1584 Thomas Busse was at Buxted, where his children, John, William and Mary, were baptised. His return to Maresfield was corroborated by the parish register which showed that his daughter Anne was baptised there in April 1589. These children were referred to in 1591 in the will of their grandfather Thomas Norman of Maresfield, yeoman,[391] who left £2 to be divided equally between the four, payable at their majorities or, in the case of the girls, at marriage. Two further sons who were baptised at Maresfield in March 1591 and May 1592 were both named John, but the first survived baptism by only 24 hours and the second was probably the John Bust buried in November 1592. The founder himself was probably the Thomas Busse buried at Maresfield in January 1599.

Dominic Buste of Framfield married Susan Water at East Hoathly in 1594. His disappearance that same year may have been occasioned by the issue by quarter sessions of warrants for the arrest of 'Dominic Busse, late of Framfield, collier'.[392] He had moved to West Sussex, where his son John was baptised, and also buried, in April 1595.

By 1599, when he entered a recognizance to give evidence in a Little Horsted larceny case, he had returned to Little Horsted.[393] Dominacle Buste who was baptised at Framfield in 1600 may

385. ADSM, 2 E 14/1152 (25 Nov 1508).
386. ADSM, 2 E 14/1189 (23 Jul 1545).
387. Cockburn, *Sussex Assize records, Elizabeth I*, no. 911.
388. ESRO, PBT 1/1/7/56.
389. ESRO, ACC 3597/1, f. 128v.
390. ESRO, ACC 3597/8, f. 45v.; 3597/1, ff 14v., 24, 47, 76, 109, 128v.
391. ESRO, PBT 1/1/9/99.
392. ESRO, QR 1, m. 1 and 2, m. 27; I am indebted to Brian Phillips for these references.
393. Cockburn, *Sussex Assize records, Elizabeth I*, no. 1915.

have been the collier's child. His first wife was buried at Little Horsted in 1609. The following year Dominickell Busse married Mary Muncke at Maresfield and their children, William, Dominic, Thomas, Mary, Nicholas, and twins named Elizabeth and Anne, were baptised there between 1610 and 1625, though the last three did not survive infancy. Their mother was buried at Maresfield in 1639.

Dominick Busse of Maresfield, now described as husbandman, was bondsman for the licence of William Busse, husbandman, to marry Dionise Pollard of East Grinstead in 1632. However, William Busse of Maresfield, collier, was bondsman in marriage licences dated 1636 and 1643, the latter for the marriage of Thomas Busse of Maresfield, collier, to Margaret Pannet of Newick, maiden.[394]

It must appear probable that both these colliers were the children of Dominickell and Mary Busse, and they continued at Maresfield. Firstly, William Busse of Maresfield, collier, was presented for the theft of hop poles valued at 3 pence, a crime of which he was acquitted. Later he was presented for the theft of a sheep valued at 10 pence. In this case William Busse of Mayfield, husbandman, entered a recognizance to appear, when his sureties included Thomas Busse of Mayfield, collier, whilst William Busse, husbandman, was one of the sureties for the appearance of Thomas Busse. Ultimately, William Busse, the collier, was sentenced to be whipped. However, the story did not end there, because warrants for the arrest of William Busse of Maresfield, collier, continued to be issued up to 1652. Had he somehow evaded being whipped?[395]

Other persons perhaps linked with these immigrants included Richard Busse, who was buried at Heathfield in 1595, and administration of whose goods was assigned to the smith Thomas Fuller of Heathfield,[396] for whom he may have worked.

Emanating from Warbleton was Nicholas Busse, who married Elizabeth Cobb in 1580, but by 1584 had moved to Ashburnham. His son Miles, baptised at Warbleton in 1581, apparently (as *Milo Busted*) married Katherine Kettell at Cowden in 1598. Nicholas's son Francis, baptised at Ashburnham in 1591, may have been the man who later appeared at Mayfield, where his children, Martha, John, Thomas, Margaret and Francis, were baptised between 1617 and 1627.

Lawrence Busse, whose daughter Elizabeth was baptised at Warbleton in 1584, had earlier been at Buxted, where his son James was baptised in 1583, and where his daughters Ciceley and Margaret were baptised in 1590 and 1594, the latter posthumously because her father was evidently the man buried at Maresfield in July 1593. Lawrence's brother James Busse stayed in Warbleton and died in 1603, with goods inventoried at £80 13s 6d, and made provision for Lawrence's children in his own will. When Lawrence's son, James Busse of Hollington, made his will in 1605, he ordered the house at Warbleton, which had come to him on the death of his uncle's daughter Mary, to be sold for the benefit of his three sisters. Of male descendants there were none.[397]

Members of the Busse family in Wadhurst and Frant were probably descended from the Wadhurst men listed in the subsidy roll of 1524. William Busse of Wadhurst, who died in 1560, made his son Henry his executor. Henry married Joan Golde at Pembury in 1566 and their daughter Margaret was baptised at Lamberhurst in 1567, followed by Thomas and Mary baptised at Speldhurst in 1569 and 1572. Thomas was the Pembury clothier, who in 1617 took administration of the goods of his cousin Alice, daughter of Richard Busse of Frant and widow of Robert Baker.[398] In 1618 Alice's brother John married Margery Paler, from the ironworking family of that name, although it is not evident how this was a marriage of significance for the iron industry.

Some members of the Busse family in Kent were also engaged in the clothing trade. Richard Busse of Cranbrook, who died in 1615, was a clothier.[399] His grandson was probably James Busse, the son of James Busse (1604-1632), baptised at Biddenden in 1627 and buried there in 1689, whom the parish register reveals to have been a broadweaver.

However, Mathew Busse, whose children, Thomas, Mathew and John, were baptised at

394. Dunkin, *Sussex Marriage Licences, Lewes 1670-1729*, p. 274; Dunkin, *Sussex Marriage Licences, Lewes 1586-1643*, p. 228, 295.

395. ESRO, QR 82, mm. 7, 25, 39, 51, 94; QR 86, m. 161; QR 89, m. 74; QR 90, m. 95; QR 91, m. 89; QR 92, m. 54 (if living); QR 94, m. 74; I am most grateful for all these references to Brian Phillips.

396. ESRO, PBT 1/3/2/218.

397. ESRO, PBT 1/1/12/ 6 and 46, 1/3/3/29.

398. ESRO, PBT 1/3/4/21.

399. KHLC, PRC/17/60/85b.

Cranbrook between 1632 and 1636, was described as a cooper when his wife Elizabeth was buried in 1655. He was probably descended from the alien Mathew Busse, who had paid the poll tax in Cranbrook hundred in 1550 and who had been buried at Cranbrook in 1560. Another worker in wood was John Busse, the Ticehurst carpenter, who married Alice Alchin at Ticehurst in 1656. He was the son of Nicholas Busse and had been baptised at Ticehurst in 1627. Nicholas Busse had married Jane Rabson at Ticehurst in 1623, but his origins have not been traced.

Dill hundred

Potell or Post

It seems fairly certain that this name derives from the French surname Postel. One family of that name inhabited the parishes of Sainte-Geneviève and Saint-Saire, where among those mentioned were the heirs of the late Roger Postel in 1489, and Colin Postel in 1495.[400] Jehan Postel of Saint-Saire, who in 1537 was stated to be a tanner, was probably the Saint-Saire notary (*tabellion*) of around 1540.[401]

However, it seems possible that Anthony Pottell could have originated from a family which included corn millers, who usually operated watermills, but occasionally leased windmills. In 1534 Pierre Postel of Esclavelles took a four-year lease of the windmill at Massy, but this he soon passed on to Collenet Le Villain of Conteville.[402] In 1576 the inventory of the late Jehan Potel, miller at Richemont, taken on behalf of his heirs, his eldest son Thomas Postel, miller at Ellecourt, and his daughter Binette, included an iron pot and an iron frying pan (*paielle*).[403]

A miller named Anthoine Postel was first mentioned in 1513. His family lived at the mill of Roncherolles-en-Bray, and his father Pierre Postel had died around 1509. In 1513 his mother Jehanne made an agreement with Pernot Seur of Roncherollles for the marriage of Anthoine to his daughter Jehanne. In 1533, when Anthoine Postel was miller at Neuville-Ferrières, he took a lease of the windmill at Vimont from the lord of Vimont, Jehan de La Mothe.[404]

Anthoine Postel was not mentioned in later notarial registers at Neufchâtel, so he could very well have been Anthony Pottell, who paid the poll tax in Isenhurst borough in 1560, alongside Roger Tankerell, who was also from Neuville-Ferrières, and Nicholas Forrell. However, Anthony Pottell of Maresfield, who married Parnell Auverey at Maresfield early in 1561, was probably the immigrant's son. By the end of the decade the son had moved on to Ifield, where his daughters Susan and Jane were baptised in 1569 and 1570 under the surname Postle. He then moved to Mayfield where in 1572 the baptism of Moyses son of Anthony Pustill was recorded.

The name, having first assumed a more French form as 'Postle' at Ifield, seems now to have been rapidly assimilated to the surname 'Post'. It looks as though the West Firle collier Anthony Poste, who was indicted for recusancy at the assizes in 1586,[405] may have been the immigrant father.

Meanwhile, the younger man had reestablished himself as Anthony Post at Nutley in Maresfield by January 1587. His house was alleged then to have been burgled by another Nutley collier, Robert Hewashe. Hewashe was indicted for this theft in January 1588, but was then at large. Curiously enough, Hewashe and the East Grinstead collier, Peter Pynyon, were indicted in 1589 for a similar offence alleged to have been carried out in January 1588, in which a woman's dress (£1 10s 0d), a petticoat (10 shillings), a piece of diaper cloth (10 shillings), three kerchiefs (6 shillings), three shirts (10 shillings) and a sword (10 shillings), items almost exactly similar to those stolen the previous year, were again alleged to have been stolen. On this occasion Hewashe was found guilty, but was allowed benefit of clergy, whilst Pynyon was still at large.[406]

Anthony Post was registered as a Nutley defaulter at several views of frankpledge, from 1587 up to the end of the series in 1591. He twice escaped fine on account of poverty, in October 1589 he was

400. ADSM, 2 E 83/411 (23 Jul 1489); 2 E 14/1141 (23 May 1495).
401. ADSM, 2 E 14/1175 (4 Jan 1537); 2 E 14/1185 (27 Apr 1541).
402. ADSM, 2 E 14/1168 (19 Jan and 28 Mar 1534).
403. ADSM, 2 E 83/5 (5 Aug 1576).
404. ADSM, 2 E 14/1152 (10 Feb 1509); 2 E 14/1157 (29 Oct 1513); 2 E 14/1168 (29 Nov 1533).
405. Cockburn, *Sussex Assize records, Elizabeth I*, no. 1341.
406. Cockburn, *Sussex Assize records, Elizabeth I*, nos. 1069, 1091.

sick, and only finally in April 1591 was he charged the customary 2 pence fine.[407]

The family, or two members of it, Daniel and Moyses Poste of Buxted, was among a party headed by Richard Maynard of Buxted, which disrupted the efforts of the forgemaster, William Bassett of Withyham, to obtain charcoal out of Buxted Wood for his ironworks, which included Oldlands Furnace, Ashurst and Grubsbars forges, and two other forges in Hartfield. Bassett complained that they, 'to the number of fortye persons and upwards the seconde daye of August [1591] . . . being weaponed with swords, daggers, staves and other weapons . . . did pull up a Bridge standing over a River there, beinge the necessarye and usuall carryinge waye of . . . coles unto divers of his aforesaid Ironworkes and after this donne, the said ryottous persones upon the said seconde daye of August in riottous and terrible manner did enter . . . Buxstede woode . . . and there did make an assault upon one William Growte Collyer and servant unto your said Subiect and him did beate and greveously wounde and mayme in one of his handes by reason whereof he is not able to worke to gett his livinge and . . . did take and carrye awaye Tenne loads of Cole and fowerscore and tenne Cordes of woode . . . in waynes and cartes', whilst on the following day they 'did enter into . . . Buxstede woode and .,. . did take and carrye awaye . . . two and twenty Cordes of woode and two loades of Cole . . by reason whererеof (*sic*) his said Iron Workes were unstocked to the greate losses and hindrances of your said Subject'.[408]

By the time this case came before Star Chamber in 1593 Moyses Post was dead; he had been buried at Rudgwick in July 1592, aged only twenty. Daniel Post, who was possibly Moyses' brother, moved on to Rotherfield, where his children, Mary, John, twins named Anthony and William, Richard, Anne and Susan, were baptised between 1602 and 1618. William died in 1620 before attaining his majority, but otherwise all this family survived. Daniel Post's occupation as an ironfounder was disclosed in 1637 when he entered a recognizance for the appearance at quarter sessions of Mary Post, presumably his daughter.[409] He was buried at Rotherfield in 1641.

Licences were issued for the marriages of two of Daniel Post's sons. In 1635 Anthony Post, an Uckfield hammerman, obtained a licence to marry Anne Mason of Rotherfield at the Cliffe church.[410] However, it was at Rotherfield that his children, Mercy, Anne, Richard, John and Anthony were baptised from 1635 to 1647. Anthony's mother was buried on the day of his baptism and the child himself died less than two weeks later.

Richard Post was several times married: firstly to Elizabeth Palmer at Rotherfield in 1632, but this marriage cannot have continued long because 'Richard Post of Rotherfield, founder', was granted a licence in July 1636 to marry Mary Hooke of Rotherfield at the church of St John, Lewes.[411] Mary was the widow of the Tonbridge ironfounder, Charles Hooke. As well as a wife, Richard Post acquired by this marriage three young stepchildren.

Richard Post was a major participant in the establishment of the indirect process of iron manufacture in the New England colonies. He was first mentioned at Hammersmith in New England in February 1649, when in the county court held at Salem he was fined for drunkenness. By 1653 Post, and his stepson Charles Hooke, were owed £20 13s 4d, for 248 loads of bog ore dug at £1 the load.[412] In March 1648 Hooke had witnessed a Pynion marital misdemeanour, so it seems probable that Richard Post too was already at Lynn by that date.

Eventually Richard Post succeeded Roger Tyler as ironfounder at Hammersmith, where by 1657 he was recorded as doing the 'blowing'. He was married twice more in New England, firstly to Susanna Sutton in February 1650, and again in November 1662 to Mary Tyler, possibly the daughter of Roger Tyler.[413]

Remarkable though the New England enterprise in which Richard Post participated may have been, his adventures were anticipated by another branch of this extraordinary family, who took part in a much earlier attempt to spread abroad the techniques perfected in the Weald. In the 1570s a party

407. ESRO, ACC 3597/1, ff 15, 88v., 109, 144v.
408. TNA, STAC 5/B90/39.
409. ESRO, QR 39, m. 54; I am indebted to Brian Phillips for this reference.
410. Dunkin, *Sussex Marriage Licences, Lewes 1670-1729*, p. 278.
411. Dunkin, *Sussex Marriage Licences, Lewes 1586-1643*, p. 231.
412. G. F. Dow (ed.), *Records and files of the quarterly courts of Essex county, Massachusetts, 1636-1656, vol. 1*, Salem, Essex Institute, 1911, pp. 157, 292.
413. Hartley, *Ironworks on the Saugus*, p. 188; Pope, *The pioneers of Massachusetts*, p. 369.

of Wealden ironworkers embarked for Norway, and in Hakedal, the next valley to the east of Oslo itself, they set up a blast furnace. It seems likely that they intended to build a complete indirect-pattern ironworks of furnace, finery and hammer mill, but in effect they are remembered chiefly as having been able to produce cast goods. The bulk of the workmen, whose names are unknown, returned to the Weald soon after 1580.[414]

However, the seeds of future success had been sowed and we know that some member of the Post family stayed on in Norway, because the main partners in the 'Great Iron-company' (*Store jern-kompagni*) which in 1624 took over from royal control the ironworks at Baerum, on Hadeland, in Hakedal and at Ski, were Johan Post and Herman Krefting.[415]

There may have been other descendants of the first Anthony Pottell, though proof of their involvement in ironworking is not forthcoming. Richard Post, who married Alice Chownyng at Tonbridge in 1566, could have been one of these. Further west, the Slaugham husbandman George Poste, who at the assizes in 1569 confessed to poaching deer in St Leonards Forest,[416] could have been another member of this family, the Forest being a regular haunt of colliers and woodcutters. George Poste survived this brush with the assize court to marry Anne Habchyll at Balcombe in 1578. Jonas Post, whose marriage to Katherine Knowler at Chiddingfold in 1612 was short-lived, could have been from this family too. Katherine died the following year.

Another, perhaps remote possibility for the continued participation of the Postel family in the Wealden iron industry is through assimilation to 'Potwell'. This surname, which in 1524 had been confined to the single example of Simon Potwell, perhaps a Hollington man, became much more widespread later in the century. A case in point was the Battle collier, Isaac Potwell, who in 1585, along with a Mayfield collier named John Robson, was indicted at the assizes for making and issuing six counterfeit shillings. Robson was found not guilty, but Potwell was remanded in custody.[417]

A Hampshire member of this distinguished family was undoubtedly another Daniel Post, whose daughter Joan was born in November 1658, a birth recorded in the Beaulieu parish register. But Joan's burial was recorded only six days after her birth. This Daniel Post will have been a worker at the Sowley ironworks. His wife Joan was buried at Beaulieu in 1678 and Daniel Post himself was buried there in 1694. John Post's son Jonas was buried at Beaulieu in 1655, and his or another John Post's children, Mary and John, were baptised there in 1677 and 1679. The name Jonas perhaps links this Beaulieu branch of the family with Jonas who had married at Chiddingfold in 1612.

Outside the Weald, the name occurred at Duffield in Derbyshire, where Anne and John, the children of John Post were baptised in 1625 and 1632. This John Post could have been Daniel's son, baptised at Rotherfield in 1602.

Furrell

Numerous notarial acts of Neufchâtel show that the Fourrell family was well established at Fontaines-en-Bray during the sixteenth century.[418] Other branches of the family flourished as merchants and butchers in Notre-Dame parish at Neufchâtel,[419] and in the hamlet of Les Hayons in the parish of Esclavelles. At Les Hayons Jehan Fourrell of 1533 was followed by Nicollas Fourrell in the 1560s.[420]

In the Weald Nicholas Forrell first paid the poll tax at Isenhurst in 1560, before soon moving on to Penhurst, where he paid the poll tax in Netherfield hundred (*Furre*) in 1572 and (*Furry*) in 1576.

414. G. Thuesen, 'Bergverksdrift i Oslo området', Volund (Norsk Teknisk Museum, 1988), p. 69. A. den Ouden, 'The introduction and early spread of the blast furnace in Europe', *Wealden Iron,* Bulletin of the Wealden Iron Research Group, 2nd series, **5** (1985), p. 35.

415. J. H. L. Vogt, *De gamla norske jernverk* (Norges Geologisk Undersögelse, No. 46), Kristiania, 1908, p. 7. That the surname is not indigenous is confirmed by the fact that only one person named Post is recorded in the Oslo telephone directory (1995).

416. Cockburn, *Sussex Assize records, Elizabeth I,* no. 310.

417. Ibid, no. 995.

418. At Fontaines, Protin, Jehan and two successive Colins Fourrell were mentioned (ADSM, 2 E 14/1151 (5 Mar 1506); 2 E 14/1187 (15 Jul 1542)).

419. Jehan Fourrell dit Servent (ADSM, 2 E 14/1161 (6 Feb 1528)) and Guillaume Fourrell (ADSM, 2 E 14/1195 (12 Nov 1554)).

420. ADSM, 2 E 14/1168 (22 Nov 1533); 2 E 14/1204 (28 Feb 1564).

However, in 1572 two more aliens named William Furrie and Nicholas Furrye paid the poll tax in the South Borough of Tonbridge, so there were clearly two Nicholas Furrills in the Weald at this time. Perhaps the Tonbridge Furries were French-born sons of the Isenhurst and Penhurst Nicholas Furrell. The Nicholas Furrye who paid the poll tax in Buttinghill hundred in 1576 was probably the Tonbridge man. At Tonbridge he had worked for David Willard in 1572, perhaps alongside Laurence Duffyll, the name of whose master was not given in the subsidy roll because he paid tax on goods. The suggestion that it was this Nicholas Furrell who moved to Buttinghill is given verisimilitude by the fact that Laurence Duffield moved there too, and was buried at Worth in 1585.

The Buttinghill man may have given rise to the entry in Worth parish register of 1579 which recorded the baptism of Susan daughter of Nicholas and Agnes Furrell. The burial of Agnes Furrye shortly after Susan's birth may account for the fact that no further children of Nicholas Furrell were recorded at Worth. On the other hand, the baptism of Sara daughter of Steven and Alice Furrell followed at Worth in 1590, and Steven Furrell may have been the child baptised at Penhurst around 1560, whose father was the Netherfield Nicholas Furrell.

Indications that a Furrell presence was still maintained in the Penhurst area are given by the marriages of Margaret Furrye to John Ballan at Burwash in 1584, and of Anne Ferral to Richard Baleden at Brightling in 1592.

At Worth, in addition to the entries concerning Nicholas Furrell in 1579 and Steven Furrell in 1590, there were also a burial entry of 1577 for John son of John and Elizabeth Furrell, and baptismal entries, in 1589 for Alice the daughter of Philip and Agnes Furrel, and in 1601 for Thomasyn daughter of Peter and Elizabeth Furrell, which might relate to children of three separate brothers. Peter Furrell remained at Worth, where his second wife Mary was buried in 1619.

At Cuckfield John son of John Fourrell was baptised in 1598 and Susan Furell married James Groute in 1599. The parent John Fourrell might have been the man, whose earlier son named John had been buried at Worth in 1577. Susan was probably Nicholas's daughter and, as seen earlier, she accompanied her husband James Groute to Worth and then to Cowden, where she was buried in 1628.

When John Garston the elder, a Cuckfield yeoman, made his will in 1624 he awarded the rent out of his lands held by Nicholas Fourrell to his grandson Henry Spurling for five years. His other grandchildren were Anne and Mary, the daughters of Thomas Fourrell, who had married his daughter Agnes. To each of them he left £2 and to their mother he left 'all the household stuff in two (bed-) chambers which they use, with a flock bed, a coverlet, blanket and bolster, an iron pot, two little iron pots, a posnet, four tubs and two firkins'.[421]

Thomas Furrell's daughters, Ann and Mary, had been baptised at Cuckfield in 1621 and 1622. His later children were Robert, baptised at Cuckfield in 1625, Joan baptised at Ifield in 1628, and Philip and John baptised at Dunsfold in 1630 and 1638, of whom Philip died in 1635. Thomas then moved on to Thursley, where his wife was buried in 1639 and his daughter Anne married John Morrell in 1640. Their two sons, Edward and Thomas Morrell, baptised in 1644 and 1656, were hammermen according to entries of 1685 and 1687 in Thursley parish register. John Furrell, was also at Thursley in 1616, when his unnamed son had been baptised there.

Stephen had meanwhile moved on to Ifield, where his daughter Susan was baptised in 1601. Susan Furrell married Edward Scott at Worth in 1620 and her cousin Thomasyn married John Butcher there in 1622. Philip Furrell had also moved to Ifield. His daughter Alice married Richard Dench at Ifield in 1610 and he himself was married again to Elizabeth Rickman at Newdigate in 1615. Philip and Elizabeth's son Philip Furrell was baptised at Cuckfield in 1617. It seems probable that the father of this child was the Philip Furrell buried at Cuckfield in 1623.

Meanwhile another Philip Foorie had married Joan Denier at Thursley in 1615 and Alexander Forrey had married Elizabeth Collins there in 1616. It looks as though both men subsequently left the parish, but in May 1627 Philip reappeared there. His sons John, Anthony and William were baptised there between 1627 and 1631, although Anthony did not survive. Philip Fory was buried at Thursley in 1653 and two years later his widow Joan married Richard White of Bramshott.

When the widowed Joan married Richard White, some relationship between the Furrells or Fouries and the Pavy family was indicated by the description of her as 'Joan Pavy alias Foury, widow'.[422]

421. ESRO, PBT 1/1/18/163.

422. It should be remembered that the finer Adrian Pavy bore the alias 'Foye', or should that be 'Forye'?

This is confirmed by the fact that when her son John made his will in 1697 he described himself as 'John Pavie alias Forie the elder of Thursley, blacksmith'. He had married Elizabeth Glazier in 1652, but the baptism of his son John is not recorded in the parish register.

On the other hand, the children of John Fory the younger, John, Richard, Elizabeth, William and Thomas, were baptised at Thursley between 1676 and 1688. Only Richard appears to have died young: the other sons were all remembered with the gift of lands in their grandfather's will, but John Fory the younger was to hold them for the grandchildren's maintenance and for raising a sum of £10 to be given to Elizabeth at her age of 24.[423]

Shiplake hundred

Varyet

Nicholas who paid a shilling on goods to the relief of 1551 in Hoathly was clearly Nicholas Varyet who paid only the poll tax there in 1552. The name is unknown in connection with the iron trade.

Varyet shows complete discontinuity between Nicholas Eversfield's three or four workers of 1543 in Hoathly and Waldron and the later occupants of the Waldron Furnace. Nicholas was clearly recorded separately at Hoathly.

SUSSEX - LEWES RAPE

Streat hundred: north borough

Tulley

Because the will of Simon Tyler recorded him as Tulye it is tempting to identify the West Hoathly George Tullye, who paid the poll tax in 1560, 1563 and 1572 with George Tyler, the Worth hammerman, who in 1559 was indicted for the theft of five bars of iron from the forgemaster Robert Whitfield.[424]

However, George Tyler's survival of this episode and his payment of the poll tax at Worth in 1563 invalidates the identification, because George Tullye continued to pay the poll tax up to 1572, and his wife survived him to pay that of 1576.

The name is not known in connection with the iron industry.

Homan

It appears likely that Nicholas Homan who paid the poll tax in the northern borough of Streat hundred in 1560 is identical with Nicholas Hune who paid the poll tax at Balcombe in Buttinghill hundred in 1563. He was perhaps the Nicholas Home who had married Margaret Dossall at Balcombe in October 1558.

The name has to be distinguished from the indigenous surname Holman which could be found in Staple hundred and surrounding areas, as also at Hartfield, in the 1520s. The immigrant name seems not afterwards to occur in the Balcombe parish register.

John Homan, whose son John was baptised at Mayfield in 1588, perhaps moved on to Ticehurst where his daughter Mildred was baptised in 1592. The names Thomas and William Homan occurred at Hartfield in 1615 and 1616, but then again at Horsted Keynes in 1624 and 1626.

Beyond the recurrence of the surname in ironworking parishes there is nothing to link it with the manufacture of iron, but the possibility that the family was engaged in woodcutting and in charcoal burning is a real one.

423. LMA, DW/PA/05, 1697/62.
424. Cockburn, *Sussex Assize records, Elizabeth I*, no. 16.

Demerowe

Again there is nothing to connect Nicholas Demerowe, who paid the poll tax in the northern borough of Streat hundred in 1560, with the manufacture of iron other than the occurrence of his name alongside those of known ironworkers. He too was perhaps a collier.

He might be the hanaper-roll denizen of 1541 Nicholas Damery.

Obell alias Francis

In France the name occurred as *Lobel* in the Eaulne valley to the north of Neufchâtel-en-Bray, especially at Epinay, but also at Vatierville, Sainte-Beuve-en-Rivière and later at Auvillier. In the upper Béthune valley Thomas Lobel is shown by Neufchâtel notarial acts to have been at Saint-Maurice in the 1540s.[425] In the 1560s the name was found in a slightly different form, near Neufchâtel, where Ancelot Aubel, an archer in the company of the Sieur de Sénarpont, inherited in the right of his wife property in Brémontier which had formerly belonged to Yvon Le Boullenger; by the 1570s Andrieu Aubel lived at Les Hayons in Esclavelles.[426] However, nothing in any of the acts involved indicates links with the iron industry or with emigration to England.

Francis Obell first paid the poll tax along with his wife in 1563 at Ardingly, and their eldest child, David was born in England, probably in that year, or in 1562. Their daughter Joan, who as Joan Obeit married Simon Lavender at Worth in 1580, was probably Joan Fraunces who was baptised at Ardingly early in 1565. Between 1582 and 1589 Simon and Joan Lavender moved to Nidderdale in North Yorkshire in the service of Thomas Dyke, the Frant and Pembury ironmaster, and it seems probable that Joan's brother David accompanied them to Yorkshire. Later the Lavenders moved on to Morville near Much Wenlock in Shropshire, but David returned to the Weald, where he married in 1598.

By 1568 the family was established in Worth, where in 1576 both Francis and Joan paid the poll tax in the hundred of Buttinghill. Their son Marian was baptised at Worth in 1568, but when their children John, Richard and Mary, of whom Richard did not survive, were baptised between 1571 and 1578, the surname appeared in a slightly different guise as Obeth(e) and Obeit. It was perhaps these difficulties with the name Obell that induced some descendants to adopt the surname Frauncis.

In 1590, when Davy Frauncys was domiciled at Warsill near Ripon, he gave evidence before an Exchequer inquisition into an allegation that his master Thomas Dyke had cut trees within 14 miles of the river Ure, which was navigable as far as Boroughbridge. He had worked for Dyke as a collier at Dacre and near Warsill and was then aged 27, which means he would have been born around 1562.[427] After moving back to Sussex he married Amy (Emie) Skinner at Mayfield early in 1598. She died in childbirth and was buried four days before the baptism of her son William, early in 1599. However, Davy Frauncis must soon have married again because his daughters Elizabeth and Alice were baptised at Mayfield in 1601 and 1605.

Because no evidence can be found for the presence of the Obell family in the Weald between 1580 and 1620, it is tempting to believe that other members of the family had also temporarily left the area. However, the Framfield parish register shows that during the whole of this period the family used the alias Francis. Only as late as May and September 1670 did the alias finally become explicit, firstly with the burial at Framfield of John Francis alias Obell, and secondly with the baptism of George son of John and Elizabeth Francis alias Obel.

Francis Obell's son Marian, baptised at Worth in 1568, was married as Maryan Francis to Jane Moncke at Buxted in 1596. His son Denis was baptised at Cuckfield in 1612, but other mentions of Marian have not been traced in the Weald.

Philip Frances, who married Agnes Thousand, another member of the immigrant community, at Shipley in 1594, may have been another son of Francis Obell. Agnes, or Anne Frances, bore Philip Frances seven children, Mary, Philip, Leonard, William, Mary, Richard and yet another Mary, between 1594 and 1615. Philip Frances was buried at Shipley in 1617 and his widow married Antony Bradfold

425. ADSM, 2 E 14/1183 (20 Sep 1540); 2 E /14/1187 (15 Jul 1542).

426. ADSM, 2 E 14/1207 (20 Jun and 7 Aug 1564); 2 E 14/1210 (11 Mar 1568); 2 E 14/1218 (30 Jan 1574); 2 E 14/1220 (13 Feb 1575).

427. TNA, C 183/7/1055.

there in 1618.[428] His son Philip was probably Philip Francis, whose children, Mallin, Philip, Walter, Jane who did not survive, and John, were baptised at Burstow between 1631 and 1640.

The first member of the Francis family noted in the iron trade of the Weald was Thomas Frances, an apprentice to whom the Nuthurst hammerman, John Perigo, bequeathed £1 in 1583, in addition to his 'wages afore bargained'.[429] The hammerman was probably the son of John Perago, who had come from Picardy around 1514 and in 1544 had worked for Parson Levett. The apprentice Thomas Francis was probably another child of Francis Obell, baptised around 1566 or 1567, before the arrival of the family in Worth. He was the Thomas Francis who married Joan Predham at Nuthurst in 1587. His bride was probably the daughter of the immigrant finer Poncelet Predham, who, as Ponsley Predom, had witnessed Perigo's will.

Formal apprenticeship of children within the iron industry was comparatively rare because skills were normally passed on informally from one generation to the next. This did not happen in the case of Thomas Francis because his father, Francis Obell, probably died around 1580.

Later mentions of Thomas Francis have not been traced in the Weald. However, an iron-working family can be traced there which was descended from John Francis, who married Beatrice Predham at Nuthurst in 1597, and just as Beatrice may have been the sister of Joan Predham, so John Francis was probably the younger brother of Thomas Francis, baptised at Worth in 1571. Parentage of children was not recorded by the Nuthurst parish register of the sixteenth century, but daughters Mary and Anne Francis, baptised there in 1598 and 1599, were almost certainly those of John and Beatrice Frances.

There is a gap of five years before the family can next be traced at Maresfield, where John's children, Peter, Thomas and Agnes, were baptised in 1605, 1607 and 1609, after which he moved on to Framfield, where his daughters Ruth and Jane were baptised in 1612 and 1617. The name Obell was first used again in 1620, when John's daughter Mary married John Wever at Framfield, and again in 1633 when his daughter Ruth married John Chapman. In 1637 John Obell, now of Mayfield, forgeman, obtained a licence to marry the Mayfield widow, Mary Woolman, at Uckfield.[430] But it was at Framfield that Goodwife Frances was buried in 1642 and her husband in 1643.

John's son Peter Frances continued at Framfield. There is no record of his first marriage, or of the burial of his first wife, but in 1625 his son John was baptised at Framfield. Then in 1627, as Peter Obell, he married Joan Ginner and went on to raise a family. The twins Peter and Thomas Obell were baptised at Framfield in 1630, whilst Philip, Jane, Ruth and William were baptised there in 1636, 1640 and 1642, under the name Frances, and finally their son William was baptised there under the name Obel early in 1647. In 1659 various persons had to enter quarter sessions recognizances to keep the peace towards the collier Peter Frances,[431] who was buried at Framfield in 1681.

Another member of this family was John Francis, who married Mary Wever at Framfield in 1623. The likelihood that he was Peter's elder brother is increased by the fact that their eldest sister, Mary Obel, had married John Wever there in 1620. After the baptisms of their children John and Mary, of whom John did not survive, in 1625 and 1626, John and Mary moved on to Chiddingly, where their daughter Elizabeth was baptised in 1628. Mary, 'wife of John Francis of Chiddingly, hammerman', was a deponent in an ecclesiastical inquiry of 1634.[432] He was probably 'John son of John Fraunces' who was buried at Framfield early in 1640, and had perhaps been born at West Hoathly or Horsted Keynes during the gap of 1599 to 1605, between the baptisms of the first John Francis's children.

However, if Peter's brother John had died in 1640, was the John Obell of Framfield, forgeman, who together with Peter Obell of Framfield, forgeman, went surety at quarter sessions in 1642 for Hugh Pynion of Buxted to keep the peace towards John Wiborn, their father?[433]

The other son of John Francis, Thomas, established himself at Mayfield, where as a forgeman

428. The male baptismal name Maryan was used exclusively by immigrant families, whilst the names Philip and Denis were uncommon among the English population at this time. Thousand was a translated name, adopted by some members of the immigarnt Millam family in England.

429. WSRO, STC 1/13/107b.

430. Dunkin, *Sussex Marriage Licences, Lewes 1670-1729*, p. 283.

431. ESRO, QR 124, m. 62-4; I am greatly indebted to Brian Phillips for this reference.

432. WSRO, EpII/5/14, ff 54-5.

433. ESRO, QR 57, m. 47; according to the scenario outlined above John, although ultimately buried at Framfield, was 'of Mayfield' in the 1640s.

he entered a recognizance as a quarter sessions informant in 1632.[434] His wife's name was Sindony and their children, Mary, John, Thomas, Henry, Elizabeth and Francis, were baptised at Mayfield between 1631 and 1643, though Francis did not survive infancy. At Mayfield Thomas worked from 1642 until 1662 as hammerman at Bivelham Forge. His annual standing wage was one pound, but at the hammer he received 7 shillings for every ton of bar iron hammered, which amounted to £19 11s 0d (should have been £17 17s 0d) for 51 tons of bar iron in 1657-8, £15 1s 0d for 43 tons in 1658-9, and £19 12s 0d for 56 tons in 1659-60. He also worked as a collier there, and in 1645-6 was paid £3 for making 24 loads of coals from 55 cords of wood, and in 1657-8 10s 4d for cording 62 cords of wood, and £29 10s 0d for coaling 236 loads of coals from 487 cords and 6 foot of wood.[435] Thomas was perhaps the Thomas Frances buried at Framfield in 1681.

Thomas Francis's son John, baptised in 1633, was almost certainly John Obill of Mayfield, hammerman, who married Anne, the daughter of William Muckumble of Goudhurst, at Benenden in 1662. Could he earlier have been married to Marie Martin at Heathfield in 1652? After 1662 John and Anne Obel continued at Mayfield, where their children, Mary, Sindenith and John, were baptised early in 1664, in 1665 and in 1668.

Thomas's second son Thomas probably married Mary Bacheler at Burwash in 1669 and predeceased his father in February 1677, being distinguished from him in Mayfield parish register as 'Thomas, husband of Mary Obell'. His third son Henry was presumably Henry Obell of Mayfield, who married Susan Morris at Heathfield in 1682.

It is difficult to discern why another John Obell, who in 1654 married Elizabeth Hemsley of Framfield, did so at Chiddingly rather than at Framfield. He was perhaps the only son of the Framfield forgeman Peter Obell by his first wife. Their child was perhaps one buried at Framfield in 1655, whilst others of their children baptised at Framfield between 1656 and 1670 were Mary (1656), Elizabeth (1658), John (1661), Philipa (1664), Joan (1667), George (1670) and Suzanah (1674). That in the cases of the last three of these four baptisms the mother's name was recorded as Elizabeth seems to prove that their mother was Elizabeth Hemsley.

Philip Obell, who with his wife Philipa appeared at Framfield in the 1660s will have been Peter's son Philip Frances baptised there in 1636. Philip Obell, baptised there early in 1660 may have been their child, though his parentage was not revealed in the parish register. Philip's daughter was buried at Framfield in 1664, and their children Elizabeth and Jane were baptised there in 1665 and 1668, though Jane too failed to survive infancy. However, it was probably the Philip Obell born in 1660 who was the father of Anne, buried at Framfield in 1685, and of Elizabeth baptised there in 1686.

Still to be accounted for is John Francis, hammerman at the chafery of the Hammersmith works in New England. The 1653 accounts show that he also worked as a collier there. He stayed on in New England, but when he died in 1668 owned goods worth only £18 10s 0d, although the debts owed to him amounted to £25 4s 0d.[436]

Buttinghill hundred

Hauneng

John Hauneng, who paid a shilling on goods in Buttinghill hundred in 1551, was probably the man who in 1552 paid the poll tax in Hawksborough hundred as a servant of Joan Isted. The fact that Jakes Hunnisett had been recorded as Hanyng and Honynges at Rotherfield around the same time suggests that this name is a garbled form of Hunnisett, borne by that important family of forgeworkers, which originated in Namur and has already been dealt with.

Bylwarn

At first glance it is difficult to equate the surname of Peter Bylwarn, an alien who paid the poll tax

434. ESRO, QR 33, mm. 70, 77.
435. BL, Add.MSS, 33,155, ff 40v, 91v, 92, 92v, 94, 95.
436. Hartley, *Ironworks on the Saugus*, pp. 189, 211; Dow, *Records and files of the quarterly courts of Essex county, Massachusetts, 1636-1656, vol. 1*, p. 292.

alongside known ironworkers in Buttinghill hundred in 1552, with any other name connected with ironworking. It has earlier been suggested that this rather strange name is a corruption of Byllouard, itself a possible variant of the more common Byllard.

Dawes

It is tempting to equate the hammerman Dawes, who paid the poll tax in Buttinghill hundred in 1552, with Dawne the Parrock Forge hammerman, who paid 2 shillings on goods in the Hartfield hundred subsidy of 1560. However, the Parrock man was probably Maryan a Downe, who was buried at Frant in 1568, and who in 1552 had paid the poll tax as Marian Dawe at Danehill Horsted. This leaves the 1552 entry at Buttinghill as the sole reference to this hammerman in the Weald.

That he was an alien cannot of course be in doubt. He should probably be regarded as a member of the Doust family, whose progenitor was apparently Robert Dows, who had come from Picardy in 1515, worked for the Sidney family at Panningridge, and was buried at Ashburnham as Robert Dowlce in 1568.

Against this must be set the fact that the Dawes or Dawse family played a prominent part in the British iron industry, especially in the Midlands, both on the shop floor and at the entrepreneurial level. The name did not occur in the Sussex subsidy rolls of the 1520s, but by the second half of the century it was well-established along the northern borders of Sussex with Kent and Surrey: at Ticehurst, Tonbridge, Lingfield, Horley and Worth, and at Cowfold.

Dawe, a surname perhaps related to Dawes, was borne by Richard Dawe who appeared in the 1524 subsidy in Henhurst hundred. Intermarriage with immigrant families is suggested by the marriage of a woman with an immigrant baptismal name, Audiana Dawe, to Godfrey Foster at Burwash in 1563. William Dawe of Burwash married at Mayfield in 1581. Around the same time the surname also occurred in the adjacent parish of Ticehurst, and in the parishes of Benenden and Cranbrook just north of the Kent border.

Involvement in the metal trades eventually followed, with Thomas Dawes of Lewes, 'mettleman', witnessing a marriage bond in 1639 and Abraham Daure (i.e. Dawe) of Hawkhurst, 'mettall founder', marrying at Benenden in 1653.

In Shropshire, much earlier than this, Robert Dawe, a finer, rented a cottage, and pastures on both sides of the brook at Lubstree Park, in 1595; he presumably worked at Lubstree Forge near Lilleshall. The pastures were retained around 1660 by a 'hammersman' now named as Thomas Dawes.[437] In 1707 the parish register of Wrockwardine, where the name can be traced back to 1603, referred to Edward Dawe of the Moss in Wrockwardine Wood, collier. In 1720 Winnington parish register referred to William and Margaret Dawes of Winnington Forge. As late as 1770 the forgeman John Daws married a widow named Elizabeth Nelson at Penkridge in Staffordshire. Another, or the same, forgeman named John Daws was buried at Wolverley in 1794, whilst in the next generation Edward the son of the Cookley forgeman John Daws and his wife Mary was baptised at Wolverley in 1814. In Nottinghamshire Jeffrey Dawes 'of Bulwell forge' had been buried at Bulwell in 1657.

This confusion of the two surnames Dawe and Dawes, whilst not proving conclusively that the two Shropshire men were descended from the Worth hammerman of 1552 named Dawes, certainly makes this more likely. In that case all these forgemen sprang from one branch of the immigrant Dowse or Dowst family, whose surname was less than successfully assimilated to two rather similar English surnames.

Colbor or Calober

Among the aliens contributing to the relief of 1552 at Crawley and Worth, James Colbor's name followed those of six probable ironworkers and preceded those of two provers of guns for the Office of Ordnance. After he had paid the poll tax in that year his name did not appear in subsequent subsidy rolls. James was perhaps related to Peter Calober who paid the poll tax in Shoyswell hundred in 1576.

The surname seems not otherwise to be found in the Weald, nor is there evidence of its otherwise being found in connection with iron. Its French original might be a name similar to *Callebert*, *Callebaut*

437. *Victoria County History of Shropshire*, **11**, p. 163.

or *Caillebaud*, which are unusual but occur at Rouen and Le Havre.

Hans

There is no doubt that the two aliens, John and Christopher Hans, who terminated the list of aliens at Worth in 1552 were on secondment from the Tower of London. Hans probably was the correct version of Christopher's surname, but as Christopher Hane he had been paid among Henry VIII's Almain (German) armourers as long ago as September 1539. He later became one of the gunners at the Tower and as Christopher Haues [*recte* Hanes?], his death was reported in 1555.[438]

Their presence at Worth on 1 April 1552 coincided with the time when Sir Richard Sackville produced the guns made at Worth, which the Ordnance paid for in 1553. The book of payments at the Royal Armouries shows that £1 12s 0d was paid to two anonymous gunners sent to Worth to prove the guns,[439] and the subsidy roll proves that the guns concerned were cast around a year before payment was made and furnishes the names of the gunners involved.

Brydale

Blase Bryda, an alien who paid the poll tax in Buttinghill hundred in 1560 and 1563, had presumably arrived in the Weald during the 1550s. Though there is no evidence in the notarial records of Neufchâtel-en-Bray to indicate that any member of the Bridoul family left the Pays de Bray around that time, Blaise's original name was undoubtedly Bridoul or Bridoulet. The family originated near Beaussault, but by 1487 had established itself in the parish of Notre-Dame at Neufchâtel, and played a major role in the commercial life of the area.

Brydale was first noticed at Worth when Margaret daughter of Blase the Frenchman and Joan his wife was baptised in December 1559. When their daughter Joan was baptised in 1562 the surname was given as Breder, but established itself as Brydale when John and Alice were baptised in 1565 and 1568. Of these four children, Margaret was buried at Worth in 1565 and 'John Blease, a French boy' at Petworth in 1575. Meanwhile, the family had moved to Linchmere, where firstly an unnamed child, who was perhaps Dorothy, was baptised in 1571 and further children, Samuel, Joseph, Rachel, two Johns, and finally twins named Joan and Jane, were baptised between 1573 and 1583. The burial of Blase Briday was recorded at Linchmere in April 1610, and the bishop's transcript gave the additional information that Blasse was 'dwelling in Bramshott'.

'Blaise Bridae, finer, of Bramshot' made his will in July 1608 and it was proved in October 1610. He made his wife Joan and his eldest surviving son Samuel his residuary legatees and executors. All bequests were limited to a shilling each and were made to Bridae's sons Joseph and John and to his five daughters, all of whom were married. The inventory, one of whose appraisers was the hammerman Charles Barden, totalled £22 13s 4d.[440]

Of Bridae's daughters, Alice had married the finer George Larber of West Hoathly at Linchmere in 1584, Dorothy had been married there in June 1586, according to Bridae's will to John Bluett, but the parish register recorded merely her marriage without naming her husband, possibly because the bride was underage. If this was Nicholas Bluett's son he too will have been aged only sixteen. Rachel had married Edward Horne at Bramshott in 1600. The marriages of Joan to Thomas Abram and of Jane to Thomas Simones have not been traced.

Samuel Briday married Elizabeth Farnden at Bramshott in 1600 and their children, Samuel, Elizabeth, Thomas, Roger, Agnes, another Samuel, Sibel and Edward, were baptised between 1601 and 1618 at Bramshott. Their mother was buried early in 1620 at Linchmere. Thomas Breda of Bramshott, who married Elizabeth Simmons of Haslemere at Haslemere in 1640, will have been Samuel's son. They had moved on to Frensham by the time that their son Thomas was baptised at Haslemere in 1641, but the son survived only two months, whilst his mother died in the following year.

John Bryday married Anne Barden at Linchmere in 1604 and their children, Charles, William, Gain (i.e. Jane), Anne and John, were baptised there between 1610 and 1622. In 1633 they were among the main beneficiaries under the will of Anne's father, the hammerman Charles Barden of Linchmere.

438. *Letters and Papers, Henry VIII*, **14** (2) no. 781 (p. 314); *Calendar of Patent rolls, Philip and Mary*, **3**, p. 49.
439. Royal Armouries Library, Tower of London, RAR.0119 – Ordnance accounts book 1547-1553.
440. Hampshire Record Office, Winchester, 1610B/07.

By this will Charles Bryday, who was Charles Barden's grandson and godson, received £30, all Charles's apparel and two firebacks. He raised his own family at Linchmere, where his sons Charles and Edward were baptised in 1634 and 1636. The younger Charles Bridah alias Blaze followed in his great-grandfather's trade of hammerman at Linchmere and made his own will in 1703,[441] in which year he died. Having no children of his own, he made most of his bequests to his sister Joan, who had married Gregory Hoad, a Frensham blacksmith, and to their children. Joan herself received £5 and her five daughters £5 each. Her son Gregory Hoad, who was a Linchmere miller, was also given £5, his two daughters, Sarah and Joan, were each to have £10 when 21, and his son, a third Gregory Hoad, was to be residuary legatee on reaching the age of 21, whilst a cousin, Richard Bayly, a Fernhurst yeoman, was to be the executor.

Charles Bridah's uncle, William Breda alias Blase, had married Joan Balden (Barden?) at Haslemere in 1644 and, like his cousin Thomas, Samuel's son, moved to Frensham, where he was living in 1650, when his son Thomas was baptised at Haslemere. William's wife Joan was buried at Haslemere in 1652 and the infant son of 'William Blase of Pitfold', who was buried later in the same year, will have been Thomas.

Another descendant of Blaise Briday was perhaps John Bradwall, Braddow or Braddy, of Staveley Forge in Derbyshire. In 1668 Richard Bradwall was buried at Staveley and John son of John and Margaret Bradwall was baptised there. In 1688, John Braddow, a hammerman and widower of Cuckney Forge in Nottinghamshire, married Martha Turner of Welbeck, and in 1691, John Braddy, of Cuckney hammerman, who was perhaps his son, married Margaret Norman.[442] Both marriages were celebrated at Norton-Cuckney, and both men were possibly nonconformists, because corresponding baptisms failed to appear in the parish register. The variations in orthography of these recorded names perhaps support the suggestion that they were not indigenous.

Starr

Richard Starre had figured in the subsidy rolls of the 1520s at West Street in Horsham, but not as an alien. He was undoubtedly the tailor Richard Ster, who was buried at Horsham in 1545, and whose son William, also a tailor, was buried there in 1550. However, the name did not occur in the whole of East Sussex in the 1520s, so the evidence of the 1560 subsidy roll for Buttinghill that Peter Starre was an alien must be accepted. An initial 'St' is very rare in French, which begs the question of whether Starr can have evolved from *Estrade* or *Estrée*.

Peter Starre paid the poll tax in Buttinghill hundred in 1560 and had been in Worth the previous year, where the parish register recorded the baptism of Nicholas son of Peter and Joan Starr in March 1559, followed by his burial in August of that year.

However, it was in the south-east of the Weald that the name appeared later in the century. John Starr of Waldron died in April 1567. His goods were inventoried at £12 0s 8d, he left three young daughters, and he appointed his son Richard as his residuary legatee and executor, but left the lease of his house to his wife Joan.[443] Richard did not appear in the contemporary Waldron parish register so it is not certain that John had any further Starr descendants.

However, Robert Starr married at Waldron in 1573 and he and his wife Dorothy had a daughter named Dorothy baptised at Etchingham in 1579. They soon moved to Burwash where their children, Peter, John, Robert, Catherine and Starr [*sic*], were baptised between 1581 and 1596. It was at Burwash that John Starr married Elizabeth Milton in 1613 and their children, John, Susan, Peter, Alice, William and Nicholas were baptised at Burwash between 1614 and 1628.

Peter Starr on the other hand married Grace Pryor at Brightling in 1615 and it was at Brightling that his descendants continued for most of the century, including a grandson Peter Starr, who was baptised there in 1642 and who was probably the man who married Constance Bachelour at Heathfield in 1674.

Robert Starr married Susan Haws at Ewhurst in 1618 and they continued at Ewhurst, where their son William was baptised later in that year and where Susan was buried early in 1629.

441. WSRO, STC 30/618.

442. Blagg and Wadsworth, *Nottinghamshire marriage licences*, **1**, p. 417, 439.

443. ESRO, PBT 1/1/5/427.

As will be noticed, the name Peter was much in favour in this family suggesting that all may have been descended from the Worth man of that name. Another Peter Starr was at Burwash in the 1580s, where his son Peter was buried in 1587 and his daughter Margery was baptised in 1588. Margery was probably the woman who married the collier Anthony Pummey at Burwash in 1617.

There was also a Starr family in Mountfield parish. James Starr's daughter Mary was baptised there in 1603, although he apparently moved to Burwash, where his daughter Margaret was baptised in 1605. James was next found in Brightling parish where he married Katherine Harmar in April 1613. Their son James was baptised at Brightling in January 1614, but the mother died in childbirth, and the infant James died in March. James Starr next married Joan Waterman at Brightling in October 1614 and their children, Elizabeth, Thomas, Joan and Anne, were baptised at Brightling between 1615 and 1620. Thomas, Joan and Anne all died in infancy, but it was at Mountfield that Anne was buried in 1622.

The family was now reestablished at Mountfield, where James's son James was baptised in 1623. In 1624 James and Joan Starr were fined at quarter sessions, on which occasion James's occupation was disclosed as that of collier.[444] The elder James Starr was buried at Mountfield in August 1645, shortly after the birth of the younger James's daughter Joan, whose baptism had taken place in June.

George Starr was first encountered at Cranbrook, where in 1599 his son William was baptised. By 1605 he was at Goudhurst, where his son John was baptised in June of that year. In 1606 his daughter Mary and the 18-month old John were buried at Goudhurst. George Starr was at Warbleton in 1610, where his son Richard was baptised, but had soon moved on to Waldron, where his sons Abraham and Thomas were baptised in 1612 and 1618. He was buried at Waldron in 1628. Meanwhile his sons Abraham and another John had been buried at Heathfield, in 1615 and 1620 respectively, and his wife was buried there in 1621, though in two of these cases it was noted that Waldron was George Starr's place of residence.

Another branch of this family was established in Battle. Roger Starr, a carpenter, was an inhabitant of the borough of Sandlake in 1554, and in 1563 he and his wife Margaret bought Mordants Field and Clerkenland from John and Katherine Morris. In 1571 they leased it for 10 years to John Turner. Roger Starr died in 1581.[445] Margaret Starre, his widow, left a will dated 1584, which was proved the following year. Their son Richard Starr, who was also a carpenter, left a will dated 1609, which was proved in January 1610.[446] Richard's wife Rabidge was buried at Beckley in 1616.

Devall alias (G)ounyon

Neither of these two surnames can be found in the Sussex subsidy rolls of the 1520s, except for two Gunwens at South Bersted in 1524. By the 1540s the surname Unwyn was well-established at Herstmonceux, where John Unwyn the elder was buried in 1544. The name Devall occured by 1560 at Worth, where Agnes daughter of Peter and Joan Devill was baptised in 1559 and where Peter Devall paid the poll tax in the following year. By 1576 further immigrants of this name were paying the poll tax in the easternmost parts of the Weald. In that year Robert Devall appeared in Shoyswell hundred, disguised as Robert 'Dooall' in the subsidy roll, but in Staple hundred Stephen appeared more regularly as 'de Voye'.

The surnames *Deval*, *Deveau*, *Duval*, *Duveau*, etc., are various possibilities for the original of one of these French surnames. During the 1550s Denys Duval was an inhabitant of Neuville- Ferrières and Michel Duval of the hamlet of Trépied in Beaussault.[447] Nicholas Devild alias Deviell was a hanaper-roll denizen of 1541.

The second surname also occurred at Neuville-Ferrières in the persons of Noël Gounyon around 1510-13, Thomas Gounyon (*fl.* 1526-1546) and Aubery Gounyon, the husband of Jehan Lerbier's sister Collette. Aubery Gounyon died around 1554; Nicollas Gounyon who was mentioned there from 1564 onwards was apparently Aubery's son.[448] He appears to have divested himself of his assets at Neuville-

444. ESRO, QI 1, f. 5; I am indebted to Brian Phillips for this reference.

445. Battle hundred court, 4 Oct 1554; HEH, BA Vol. 95 f. 7; Vol. 5 3551, 3756; Roger was last fined as a defaulter by the manor court of 4 Apr 1581, and his son Richard was fined as a defaulter for Sandlake at the view of frankpledge of 5 Oct 1581; HEH BA Vol. 96 f. 77, Vol. 97 f. 3.

446. ESRO, PBT 3/1/1/182, 250.

447. ADSM, 2 E 14/1193 (10 Aug 1553); 2 E 14/1195 (12 Nov 1554); 2 E 14/1196 (4 May 1555).

448. ADSM, 2 E 14/11 (23 Mar 1510), 2 E 14/11 (10 Mar 1513), 2 E 14/11 (31 Aug 1526), 2 E 14/11 (18 May

Ferrières in favour of Symon Feuldrix and Michel Le Clerc in the 1570s.[449]

There seems nothing to suggest that John Honwyne of Herstmonceux who died in 1544 leaving a will, and whose Ounwyn descendants continued there, was an immigrant. However, the collier Martin Gunwyn of Burstow, who was indicted at the assizes as accessory to a burglary at Horsham in 1578, and was then reported to be at large, could very well be connected with the Neuville-Ferrières family.[450]

The appellation Divall alias Oynyan was first used in 1599 when Margaret wife of Drew Divall alias Oynyan was buried at East Grinstead. Drew Onyan had been baptised in 1571 at East Grinstead, where his father, whose name was not disclosed, could have been the immigrant Peter Devill. Mother Divall, who was buried at East Grinstead in June 1597, could have been Peter's wife Joan. Drew was married under the name Divall to Margaret Harborow in 1596. Peter de Vale, who married Catherine Marshall at Rogate in 1596, may have been another of Peter's sons.

At East Grinstead, Divall entries continued in 1575 with the marriage of Nicholas Divall, but neither the exact date of the marriage nor the surname of his wife Joan survived. Nicholas was not again mentioned in that parish register and it must be supposed that by 1580 he had become the Dunsfold hammerman, Nicholas Unyon, who sparked off the celebrated affray at Plaistow by pulling Roger Norris, a Northchapel miner, off the back of a horse on which he was riding behind Richard Cowlstock, a Kirdford yeoman.[451]

The marriages of two John Divalls took place at East Grinstead in 1587 and 1592. The first man of that name married Maudlyn Aylard and the second Marie Russell. Though the two John Divalls were occasionally distinguished in the parish register as 'the younger' and 'the elder', this was not done in any consistent manner. From the evidence available it looks, somewhat unexpectedly, as though it was the first married of these John Divalls who was the younger man.

The collier John Onnyon alias Divoll, who was buried at East Grinstead early in 1630 and left a will which was proved in the Prerogative court of Canterbury,[452] was certainly the man married in 1587 because he appointed his wife Magdalen his executrix and residuary legatee. He does not seem to have lived in opulence because all his quite small bequests were to be made good only after the death of his wife. His four sons, Richard, John, Edmond and Francis were to have £1 each; his unmarried daughters Annis and Marie were to have £5 each, whilst his daughter Alice, the wife of William Awstin, was to have a shilling, and three of his grandchildren 10 shillings each. The master whom he served was probably one of three witnesses to his will, John Cripps of Homstall, later shown by his own will to have been the proprietor of the blast furnace at Horsted Keynes.[453]

Richard Divoll, John Onyon's eldest son, married Judith Bennett in 1610 and continued to practise his father's trade of collier in East Grinstead. From Richard's will, made in 1661, it appears that of his children only his son John and his daughter Mary, who had married Richard Best, a carpenter, survived. Richard's wife Judith was to have his messuage, tenement and lands in East Grinstead for life. Then Newmans Slype (3 acres), which Richard had purchased from Sir Thomas Gage in 1650, and a two-acre field of meadow adjoining the Slype, were to go to his grandson Richard Best, with permission to use the oast-house for a dwelling house and to remove it onto this land. Should Richard Best wish to sell the pieces of land, Divoll's own son John was to have the first option on their purchase for £60, and John was to have the remaining lands after Judith's death. Richard left to Richard Best his cupboard, his bedstead, a featherbed with a flaxen tick, a feather bolster, a chaff bolster, a red and yellow coverlet, a blanket, two pairs of sheets, a feather pillow, a little spit, a little table made by Richard Best the elder, an iron plate which stood upright, the best pair of pot-hooks and a little boarded chest. To his son John he left the (brewing-) furnace, the cheese press with the gun-head, the stone hog-tub, the trough to powder bacon in, and the benches and shelves as standards to the house. The remaining household stuff was to be divided equally between John, Mary and Richard Best the younger.[454]

1546), 2 E 14/11 (11 Jan 1555), 2 E 14/1197 (22 and 25 Feb 1556), 2 E 14/1207 (17 Jun 1564), 2 E 14/1215 (17 Sep 1570).

449. ADSM, 2 E 14/1215 (4 Dec 1570), 2 E 14/1217 (18, 26 Jul and 13 Oct 1573).

450. Cockburn, *Sussex Assize records, Elizabeth I*, no. 722.

451. Ibid, no. 801.

452. TNA, PROB 11/157/432.

453. TNA, PROB 11/201/570.

454. ESRO, PBT 1/1/29/32. The gun-head was the extraneous mass of metal formed at the top of the mould

John Onyan's son Edmond married Mary Payne at Fletching in 1621 and subsequently lived at Bolney. He too was a collier and by the time he made his will in 1663 he had returned to live at Forest Row in East Grinstead, which had been the dwelling place of his father-in-law, Richard Payne.[455] Edmond left his messuage and tenement in Forest Row to his son Francis, whom he made his residuary legatee and executor. His other sons John, Edmond and Thomas each received a shilling, but Thomas was also to have a featherbed and bolster.[456]

John Onyan's son Francis, who also followed in his father's trade of collier, married Elizabeth Earl in 1625, and their children were baptised at East Grinstead between 1626 and 1636. His wife Elizabeth died in 1638 and Francis pronounced his own nuncupative will in August 1644.[457] He wished his brother Richard, and William Wickens of East Grinstead to act as executors, managing his estate 'to the benefit of his three children . . . John, Elizabeth and Francis'. They were to 'bestow some reasonable breeding upon Francis his youngest son till he be thought fit to be put forth apprentice, over and above his third part'.

The elder John Divall alias Onyon was perhaps the man buried at East Grinstead in 1627. His younger sons, Adam, Hugh and Henry, baptised between 1601 and 1607, due to the singularity of their names can all be traced. Hugh was buried unmarried at Cowden in 1625, but Adam and Henry both married into well-established Wealden families.

Adam married Anne Michelborne at West Hoathly in 1629. Parish register entries enable them to be traced at East Grinstead in 1630, at Newick in 1631 and 1633, at Little Horsted in 1636 and 1638 and at Wadhurst in 1639 and 1640. This peripatetic career may indicate that Adam too followed the occupation of collier. His wife ended her days in 1663 as a Lewes widow, leaving only a shilling to each of her four eldest children, and making her two youngest sons, Gabriel and David, her residuary legatees and executors.[458]

Henry married the widow Margaret Delve at Newick in 1635. Their daughter Jane was baptised at Newick in 1636, but Margaret was buried at Buxted in May 1640 and in November of that year Henry was again married, still at Buxted, to Joan Bennett.

Another son of the elder John Divall was Drew Onyane, baptised at East Grinstead in 1596. However, it is difficult to distinguish him from Drew Onyane's son of the same name, baptised at East Grinstead in 1605. Nevertheless, the facts that Hugh Onion was buried at Cowden, and that William Deval who married Dorothy Picknell at Cowden in 1634 could be their elder brother baptised in 1599, support the idea that the Drew Devoll who married Catherine Humfry at Hartfield in 1632, might be the elder Drew. Drew Devall of Hartfield, yeoman, made his will in 1675. He had settled his copyhold land on his wife for life, but bequeathed £100 to his granddaughter Elizabeth Care, and made his son-in-law and daughter, Simon and Catherine Care, his residuary legatees and executors.[459] The younger Drew may have been the Drewe Divoll who married Anne Harling at East Grinstead in 1637.

The children of William and Dorothy Divoll, John, Robert, Sarah and Mary, were baptised not at Cowden, but at East Grinstead. He ended his days at Horsted Keynes and also claimed yeoman status in his will, which was proved in 1679.[460]

Notwithstanding this claim to yeoman status asserted by or accorded to members of this family, charcoal burning may still have been the major occupation of some of them. The Horsted Keynes parish register for 1705 contained an entry for the burial of Jane, the daughter of Edmund Divall, of Maresfield, collier, and Mary his wife.

The Maresfield furnaceman, John Carpe alias Devale, claimed in a deposition made around the end of the year 1600 to have been born in Cowden 33 years earlier. He had lived in Maresfield, where he was married in 1592, around nine years. In 1594 he was obliged to enter a quarter sessions recognizance

above the muzzle when ordnance was cast; containing voids and slag it comprised less dense and inferior metal and after cooling was labouriously cut off, a task which could take 24 hours.

455. ESRO, PBT 1/1/20/110.
456. ESRO, PBT 1/1/32/182.
457. ESRO, PBT 1/5/1/64.
458. ESRO, PBT 1/1/29/95.
459. ESRO, PBT 1/1/34/108.
460. ESRO, PBT 1/1/35/150.

to keep the peace against the Maresfield pot-founder Thomas Tucker.[461] Divoll's children were baptised at Maresfield from 1593 to 1607. How long beyond 1607 he lived is difficult to say. Widow Devall was buried at Maresfield in 1617 and Widow Carpe in 1631, but the latter had already been a widow in 1622, when Annys daughter of Widow Carpe alias Devall was buried.

Neither of these women can have been the widow of Abraham Devall, who married Anne Newman in 1612 and whose children were baptised at Maresfield from 1612 to 1625. Abraham was not among the children of the furnaceman baptised at Maresfield, nor was William Devall who married Eme (Amy?) Ebbs at Maresfield in 1624. William Devall's wife was buried at Maresfield in 1635. It seems possible that Abraham Devall could like the furnaceman have originated in Cowden, though whether William Devall had done so too is quite uncertain.

The Frenchman Robert Dewall's son John was baptised at Etchingham in 1577. However, Robert Dywall, who had been baptised there only nine months earlier, was more probably a son of William Devell, whose wife Jane was buried at Etchingham in August 1582, or of Thomas Devell, whose wife Margaret was buried there in the December following, than of Robert. In May 1583 Thomas Devell married a local woman, Anne the daughter of Robert Border.

Robert Devall was buried at Sandhurst in October 1610 as 'Robert Dervale, a frenchman'. He left three sons, John, Thomas and James, and two daughters who married shortly after his death. A will and inventory for him survive and his estate was valued at £234. Because Robert's sons were all colliers, it seems probable that it was to that trade that the father also owed his wealth.

When Robert's son Thomas died in 1631 he owned his own house, and debts owed to him on bond were £55 15s 0d in Kent and £19 in adjoining parishes of Sussex. His brother John had died the previous year and in his will bequeathed land called Tillies to his son John and made legacies totalling £150. Their brother James, who died in 1638 was perhaps the wealthiest of the three, and caused controversy by making bequests to the children of his brothers in preference to his own children.

John's son John Devall married Jane Rogers at Cranbrook in 1640 and moved to Hawkhurst parish about the same time. Their children were baptised there between 1642 and 1664. He had only a small 18-acre farm at his death, but described himself as a clothier. He had evidently moved into a different trade from his forebears as the main source of his income.[462]

It looks as though Robert Duvell whose children were baptised at Ticehurst from 1624 to 1637 and Thomas Divall or Devall who had two daughters baptised at Mountfield in 1649 and 1652 may have been descendants of the immigrant Robert buried at Sandhurst.

Stephen de Voye also soon moved on from Staple hundred into Kent, where Nicholas the son of 'Steven Diffold frenchman' was baptised at Brenchley in 1580. The baptisms of two more of his children, Alice Divold and Stephen Devole, followed in 1585 and 1590. An otherwise unknown John Divold was buried at Brenchley in 1599, but it appears that this family must have moved away from Brenchley.

Rafe

Gillome Rafe, who paid the poll tax at Worth in Buttinghill hundred in 1563, was almost certainly an ironworker. The surname Rafe is not otherwise known in connection with ironworking, but was that of Joan Rafe, whom the finer Abraham Blewett married at Worth in 1572.

Dermetond

No further references to Gillome Dermetond, who paid the poll tax among the ironworkers at Worth in 1563, are known. The surname should no doubt be read as D'Ermetond, which appears quite unknown. Perhaps it is a garbled version of D'Ernemont, from a place-name which occurs on the southern fringes of the Pays de Bray, but not elsewhere in France, as both Ernemont-sur-Buchy and Ernemont-la-Villette near Gournay. Although the surname is reminiscent of Gyllam Detrove, who had paid the poll tax in Henhurst hundred in 1555, the names are sufficiently different to make suggestions of a common

461. WSRO, EpII/5/6, f. 261; ESRO, QR 4, m. 51; I am grateful to Brian Phillips for both these references.
462. KHLC, PRC/32/41/247b (Robert), 50/129 (Thomas), 49/258b (John I), PRC/32/52/325 (James) and PRC/17/73/184 (John II). The inventories are PRC/27/1/181 (Robert 1610), PRC/28/18/302 (Thomas 1632), and PRC/28/18/253 (John 1631); I am deeply indebted to Tony Singleton for all these references and my account of the Sandhurst family is based on a kind communication from him.

derivation difficult.

Lurrett

Robert Loret owned property at Neuville-Ferrières in 1546. Thomas Loret acquired further property at Neuville in 1555 and 1570. In 1567 he acted as guardian of the children of John Morel, lately farmer of the lord of Orbec's estate at Vatierville.[463]

In Buttinghill hundred in 1563, Peter Lurye paid the poll tax in Cuckfield, and Nicholas Lurie, who could have been Peter's brother, and his wife, both paid the poll tax in Balcombe.

Peter will have been the man whose first wife was buried at Balcombe in 1568. The Peter Lurret whose children were baptised at Hartfield in 1594, 1604 and 1608, and whose French nationality was affirmed in the 1604 entry, was presumably the same man. Because his name was listed in none of the views of frankpledge for Hartfield up to April 1591 it seems he arrived in Hartfield between 1591 and 1594.

At this time Peter Lurrett's wife was Anne Nevell, whose mother Margaret Nevell made bequests in 1620 to four of Peter Lurrett's daughters, which Anne had born him. To Joan she left her best coverlet and the sheet with tassels, 'conditionally that she shall lend it to any of my children at their need'; to Frances she left her best gown; her linen was to be divided between Margaret and Mary Lurrett.[464] She made no bequest to her daughter Anne, because Anne had been buried at Hartfield in 1612.

Peter Lurrett's children baptised at Hartfield had been Laurence (1594), Elizabeth (1604) and Edward (1608). Edward was buried in 1615, but since they were not named in Anne's will it is evident that Laurence and Elizabeth had also died, their burials, and the baptisms of the five named daughters not being recorded, because before 1608, bishop's transcripts for the years 1594, 1604 and 1606 are the sole records to survive.

Nicholas Lurye, who had formerly been at Balcombe, probably married Mercy Gamer at Worth in 1579 as his second wife. In the guise of Nucholas Loes he had paid the poll tax in Buttinghill in 1576. Four children, Mary, Joan, John and Annes,[465] baptised at Nuthurst between 1586 and 1596, were probably those of Nicholas, who as Nicholas Lurrett was buried at Nuthurst in 1611. Though the parentage of these children was not disclosed in the parish register, when Mary was buried at Nuthurst in 1611, less than six weeks after her father, she was confirmed as Nicholas's daughter.

Nicholas Lurrett's daughter Joan married John Duffeild in 1607, and in 1614 Anne Lurret married Nicholas Good, though the bishop's transcript more correctly gave the bride's name as Annes Lurret. Nicholas's son John may have been the John Lyrret who fathered an illegitimate daughter named Elizabeth, buried at Ewhurst in 1620. In 1628 Nuthurst parish register recorded the baptism of William an illegitimate child of Agnes Lurrett, the mother perhaps being Nicholas's unnamed widow who was buried at Nuthurst in 1632.

The next member of the family to come to notice was Anthony Lerrot or Lurate, whose son Avery was baptised at Ockley in 1583, shortly after which Athony Lurratt was listed among the Ockley billmen in the Surrey muster rolls of 1583-4.[466] In 1589 his son Peter was baptised at Warnham, but by 1595 Anthony Larrett was back in Surrey, where at the assizes he was indicted as a Wotton collier for the theft of a sheep. He was found guilty of this offence and was sentenced to be whipped.[467] The burial of his wife Adrian at Shere in 1602 shows that he had continued in Surrey, but as a widower he may have joined Nicholas Lurrett at Nuthurst, where the parish register recorded the burial of Antony Lurrocke in 1602.

Anthony's son Peter was perhaps Peter Luret whose children, Peter, Anne, Jane, Alice, and John, were baptised at Cranleigh between 1612 and 1629. Peter's wife was buried at Cranleigh in 1660. Their son Peter, after begetting an illegitimate child on Suzanne Cheseman in 1637, married Mary Deaven in 1641, and John married Anne Tanner in 1652. The younger Peter's son Anthony, baptised in

463. ADSM, 2 E 14/1190 (18 May 1546); 2 E 14/1196 (27 May 1555); 2 E 14/1211 (3 Jul 1567); 2 E 14/1215 (17 Sep 1570).

464. ESRO, PBT 1/1/17/82.

465. In 1586 and 1588 the name was reproduced as Lurrocke, but changed to Lurrte in 1592 and Lurrett in 1596.

466. Craib, *Surrey musters*, p. 25.

467. Cockburn, *Surrey Assize records, Elizabeth I*, no. 2556.

1642, was buried at Cranleigh in 1645. His wife was buried at Cranleigh in 1654, whilst John's wife was buried there in 1659.

Also at Cranleigh was Richard Lorat, whose daughter Winifred was baptised there in 1612. He may also have been a son of Anthony Lurrett. No baptisms of further children of Richard were recorded at Cranleigh. Perhaps Anne daughter of Richard Lure baptised at Rotherfield in 1618 was his child. However, by the 1630s he had returned to Cranleigh. In 1634 his daughter Winifred gave birth to an illegitimate child, fathered on her by John Ridgell, and in 1637 Richard was married again to a widow named Margaret Graffam. She was buried at Cranleigh the following year.

Another member of this family who worked in Surrey was the collier Dedy or Digill Lerrett. He was indicted at Surrey assizes on two occasions. In 1597 he and two other Albury colliers were arrested for thefts carried out at Ockley and Dorking, but they escaped the constable's custody. In 1600 he and another Ewhurst collier were indicted for the theft of lambs from Thomas Stride, were found guilty and were whipped.[468]

The ultimate fate of Dedy Lerrett is unknown, but he was presumably the father of Roger Lurritt alias Diddye who was buried at Maresfield in 1639. Roger's daughter Susan was baptised at Hartfield in 1605. Roger had presumably already moved to the Maresfield area by 1625, when Henry Cooper married Susan Lurret at Fletching. Roger's former wife will have been 'Widow Lurrett' who was buried at Maresfield in 1643.

Michael Lewrye who married Joan Greenfilde at Pulborough in 1592 will have been another member of this family. Michael and Joan were perhaps the parents of Richard Lure who was baptised at West Chiltington in 1595. Their daughter Anne was baptised at Pulborough in 1607. Michael's wife Joan was buried at Pulborough in 1626. It seems possible that Michael Lewry married again because the Itchingfield parish register recorded the burial of Elizabeth wife of Michael Lewry in 1634.

Michael's son Richard was almost certainly Richard Lewer who married Elizabeth Michell at Pulborough in 1624. Their children, Richard, John, Alice and Elizabeth, were baptised at Pulborough between 1627 and 1636. The Pulborough parish register recorded the burial of Elizabeth, Richard Lury's wife, in 1639, an entry which showed that they lived at Nutbourne. Their son Richard Lewrye was perhaps the father of an unnamed daughter buried at Kirdford in 1670.

Also resident at Pulborough was another Nicholas Lewry. His daughter Anne was baptised there in 1606. It is impossible to be sure whether Anne Lury who married Anthony Turner at Pulborough in 1633 was the daughter of Nicholas or of Michael Lury.

Quynale

This surname, which we have met at entrepreneurial level as *Quenel* and *Quesnel* at Neuville-Ferrières, appeared without baptismal name as the middle one among five poll-tax paying aliens in Buttinghill hundred in 1572. It is possible, but far from certain, that Markes Quenill, who appeared in the Surrey musters as a Dunsfold billman in 1596 was also an immigrant.[469]

Imbhams Furnace was referred to as 'Mr Quynell's furnace in Chiddingfold' in the Haslemere parish register in 1608 and again in 1609. Later Peter Quennell cast guns and shot there in the Royalist cause in the Civil War.[470] However, there can be no question of any links between the Quennell family involved, that of Lythe Hill, and the Brayon ironmasters, Anthoine and Jehan Quenel, lords of Quenel, the Isles and of La Houppelière.

Although the surname was apparently an intruder in Surrey, and in Sussex no person of the name appeared in the subsidy rolls of the 1520s, Henry Qwennell of Horsham, who died in 1554, left all his lands and tenements to his 'well-lovyd' Joan Dewke, and his sword and dagger to Thomas Tradcroft.[471]

Perhaps the four Quinney girls baptised during the 1560s at East Grinstead, whose parentage was not disclosed, relate to an immigrant family. However, evidence for continuing links with ironworking

468. Ibid, nos. 2790, 3031.
469. Craib, *Surrey musters*, p. 241.
470. Straker, *Wealden iron*, p. 420.
471. WSRO, STC 1/8/111b.

are absent: Thomas Quennell of Lodsworth, who died in 1580, was a weaver,[472] and the Haslemere parish register recorded the burials of two Richard Quennells in 1635 and 1638 as those of a butcher and of a tailor respectively.

Later Quynall entries at Horsham occurred only after the marriages of Henry Quinnell (the elder) and Henry Quinnell in 1585 and 1586, before which the name had appeared at Petworth by 1559, at Lodsworth from 1567, at Linchmere from 1568, and at Wisborough Green from 1579. Most of these occurrences must also relate to families of indigenous origin.

However the baptism at Lodsworth of William Quenyll's daughter Jackomyn in April 1588 probably relates to an immigrant. He was perhaps the William Quennell who married a widow, Margery Harowden of West Grinstead, at Lodsworth later in that month; their son Peter was baptised at West Grinstead in 1591. William Quennell was buried there in 1608 and his widow Margery in 1614. Their son Peter moved to Selhurst in East Dean and, when he made his will in 1620, described himself as a husbandman.[473]

Samuel Harmer alias Quinnell, mentioned in the Rotherfield parish register in 1635, was possibly of immigrant descent, but the alias apparently sprang from the marriage of John Harman of Rotherfield to Mary Quinel of Frant at Tonbridge in 1593.

SUSSEX - BRAMBER RAPE

Burbeech hundred

Heath

The description of Martin Heath as a 'howsholder' when he paid the poll tax in Burbeech hundred in 1560 seems to preclude his being an ironworker, although some immigrant ironworkers certainly became householders. However, an instance of this surname being applied to a member of the Hatto family has been noticed.

Parris

Aliens named Thomas Paris and John a Parys were listed at Lewes in the subsidy rolls of the 1520s in the parishes of St Andrew and St Michael respectively. Because Swayne and Ilman were forgemasters it is virtually certain that John Parrys, the alien who was their servant and paid the poll tax in Burbeech hundred in 1563, worked in the iron industry in some capacity.

It seems possible that John Paris, whose daughter Joan was baptised at Horsham in 1562, could have been the ironworker in question. He may have been the husband of 'Joan Parrish, a wife' who was buried at Buxted in 1568. John Paris was married again to Joan Frier at Buxted in 1573,[474] and went on to Maresfield, where their children, Suzanna, John, and Mary, were baptised between 1574 and 1580, Ralph Hogge's wife Margaret being among the sponsors in 1574, Hogge's clerk George Kenyon among those of 1577, and Jillian Frier among those of 1580. In December 1573 John Paryse had acted as a sponsor for an Upton family baptism at Maresfield,[475] along with John Caslyn and Margaret Hogge. John Parysh was buried at Buxted in 1587.

There is no further evidence of the participation of the Paris family in the primary iron industry. However, Christopher Paris, an Isfield man, who married Joan Haselgrove at Newick in 1558,[476] was father of Roger Parys, baptised at Newick in 1574, who became a Hamsey blacksmith. Roger Parishe made his will in 1631 and his goods were inventoried at £23 13s 6d.[477]

The baptism of Joachym Paris at Framfield in December 1558 and his burial in the following January should also be noted. The significance of the fact that Abraham and William Parris of Worth

472. WSRO, STC 1/12/177.
473. WSRO, STC 1/16/162b.
474. Frier was an alias used by John Lammyn at Maresfield in 1579.
475. Upton was the surname of an English family of ironworkers.
476. An English family of colliers was named Haselgrove.
477. ESRO, PBT 1/1/21/174, 1/3/6/111.

both used the alias Russell during the 1590s is not so far explained.

Millam alias Thousand

The French surnames *Mille* and *Millon* derive from the baptismal name Emile, but are quite uncommon in the Pays de Caux. However, two examples of Mille and one of Millon survive at Neufchâtel-en-Bray.[478] The name appeared in a supposed translation as 'Thousandman' in Burbeech hundred, but as 'Myllam' in West Barnfield hundred, in both cases in 1572.

At Worth, the earliest member of the family to be mentioned was John Myllam who married Catherine Payne in 1565, but John soon moved on to Horsham where he had three children, John, Anthony and William, baptised between 1566 and 1571. In 1569 he was styled 'John Myllion of the Forest' (of St Leonards) and in 1571 John Thowsandine. He paid 6s to the subsidy at Ifield in 1572, but only the poll tax in 1576, his contributions being made as Thousandman in 1572 and as Towsand in 1576.

It is difficult to understand why John Myllam's wife should have contributed to the subsidy in 1576, when she appears to have been English born. Perhaps she was actually surnamed Catherine Payve and not Payne. His two servants contributed to the subsidy in 1576, but their names were withheld.

Unfortunately, the Ifield baptismal register contains no entries for 1573 to 1578, exactly the period when John Myllion was there. At Nuthurst no parentage was given for the baptisms, which took place there from 1584 to 1588, of Pauncelet, Mary, and George and Alice Millam, the last two of whom were twins. They were very possibly later children of John Myllam, but there is no proof of this.

The family can be picked up again at Ardingly, where John's son Anthony married Joan Lucar, an Englishwoman whose family worked at the forge, in 1592. Their children, Elizabeth, Joan, William, Catherine, Mary, Margaret and Anthony, were baptised from 1593 to 1603, but Joan and William did not survive infancy, and Anthony's wife Joan died in 1605. Anthony married again and further children named Jane and Susan were baptised at Ardingly in 1606 and 1609. The licence for the marriage of the Ardingly hammerman Peter Tullet, for which Anthony Millam was one of the bondsmen in 1601, shows that Millam too was a hammerman.[479] He was descibed as 'an old man of the Hammer' when he was buried at Ardingly in 1638. The old woman, Elizabeth Millam, who was buried at Ardingly the following year was his second wife, to whom administration of his goods, valued at £38 1s 4d, had been assigned in 1638.[480]

George Millam, baptised at Nuthurst in 1588 and therefore possibly Anthony's younger brother, married Cicely Ponting, the daughter of the hammerman, Nicholas Ponting of Rotherfield. She had been baptised at Buxted in 1591 but her marriage has not been found. Of their children John was baptised at Worth in 1611, George at Mayfield in 1617, and Elizabeth and Cicely at Buxted in 1622 and 1628. Their son John was perhaps the man of that name buried at Buxted in 1636. When Nicholas Ponting made his will in 1638 he left a shilling to each of his four sons-in-law, including George Milham alias Thousand.[481]

Another forgeman from this family, whose baptism has not been found, was Geoffrey Millam of Ardingly, who married Anne Pynnion, daughter of Hugh Pynion of Fletching, finer, at Newick in 1639. The marriage licence showed that Geoffrey too was a finer.[482] His daughter Anne was baptised at Buxted in 1640. The Framfield parish register records the baptism of his daughter Elizabeth in 1643, and his son John was baptised at Buxted in 1647, after which further children, Mary and Thomas, were baptised at Framfield in 1650 and 1655. In 1655 wages of £7 6s 0d owed to him by Robert Hammand of Waldron were the subject of a quarter sessions case.[483]

John Millions, who appeared at Lingfield in 1685, could have been Geoffrey's son. His children, Susannah, William, Mary, and the twins Thomas and Sarah, were baptised at Lingfield from 1685 to 1692, but Thomas survived baptism by only four days. Both parents died in 1692, John Millions being buried in March and his widow Bridget in June. He may have worked at Woodcock Hammer.

478. *Seine-Maritime: annuaire officiel des abonnés au téléphone; alphabétique*, Rouen, 1986, p. 678.
479. Dunkin, *Sussex Marriage Licences, Lewes 1586-1643*, p. 37.
480. ESRO, PBT 1/3/7/117.
481. ESRO, PBT 1/1/25/126.
482. Dunkin, *Sussex Marriage Licences, Lewes 1586-1643*, p. 252.
483. ESRO, QR 108, m. 34; I am indebted to Brian Phillips for this reference.

If Leonard Thousand, who never paid the alien tax, was a son of the immigrant John Myllam, he must have been born prior to the latter's marriage at Worth in 1565, and therefore his son by a previous marriage. He did not figure in any sixteenth-century parish register, but was old enough to receive £3 10s 0d and a 12-monthing calf in 1577 by the will of Leonard Luke of Worth, who appointed him overseer of the will, alongside Thomas Lambert.[484] Leonard's son Nicholas Millin was baptised at East Grinstead in 1589, though parents' names were not recorded. Leonard was at Shipley in 1606, when his son Edward was buried there. He made his will after the burial of his wife Margaret in 1646 at Shipley, and seven sons or daughters were mentioned in it, in addition to the by then defunct Nicholas, so that it seems possible that Leonard had been absent from the Weald for some years between 1590 and 1605.

Leonard's son Nicholas married a widow named Agnes Sherwood at West Grinstead in 1628. Their children, Leonard, Katherine and Margaret, were baptised there from 1629 to 1634, but Katherine did not survive infancy. Nicholas was buried at Shipley in 1635, but his wife and the remaining two children survived their grandfather Leonard, who did not die until 1646.

In his will Leonard Millom the elder left £10 to each of his sons Anthony, John and James, £3 each to his daughters Katherine wife of Thomas Parker and Angell wife of John Ansell, and £5 to his daughter Mary wife of Richard Ledbeater. He left a shilling to his grandchild William Thorpe. To his daughter-in-law, widow of Nicholas Millam deceased, he left a shilling and to her children Leonard and Margaret he left £1 each, at 22 and 21 respectively. He also made bequests of 5 shillings each to his grandchildren by John Ansell, Thomas Parker and Richard Ledbeater at their ages of 21. To Thorpe's child he left 5 shillings to be paid at 21. He wished his friends James Hurst the elder and John Hill to divide his household goods between his son Leonard and his three other sons. He made his son Leonard his residuary legatee and executor.[485] He was buried at Shipley in May 1648 and his will was proved at Petworth the following month.

Leonard Millam had both a son and a grandson named Leonard, the latter being the son of Nicholas, who had been baptised at West Grinstead in 1629. His own son Leonard was probably the Shipley yeoman who made his will in 1666, leaving 10 shillings to the poor and £30 each to his three children, Joan, Nicholas and Richard, the bequests to his two sons to be paid only at their ages of 24. He made his wife Joan and his eldest son Leonard his residuary legatees and executors. Leonard was to have his farm and 'all the leases and dealings' which were in his occupation.[486]

The other Leonard Millam, a smith who paid tax on two hearths at Heathfield in 1665,[487] was perhaps Nicholas's son. He married Bridget Weekes of Wartling at Warbleton in 1655 and their son Nicholas was baptised at Warbleton in 1657. He was married twice more at Heathfield, firstly to Elizabeth Kent in 1664, secondly to Elizabeth Mepham in 1677.

Though no connection can be proved between John Myllam alias Thousand of Ifield and John Myllam, the alien who paid the poll tax in West Barnfield hundred in Kent in 1572, the fact that both first appeared in the subsidy rolls in 1572 suggests that their arrivals in the Weald must have been linked in some way. The Goudhurst John Millam appears to have had four children baptised at between 1564 and 1577. He was clearly recorded as the father of Stephen and William baptised in 1564 and 1574, whilst Marie the daughter of 'Millam the Frenchman', who was baptised in 1571 was almost certainly his child too. The baptism of Margaret daughter of 'Millam alias Hosher' in 1577 shows that John Millam also had the alias Hosher. Additionally, a son of his named John, whose baptism has not been found, was buried at Goudhurst in 1583. His wife was apparently buried at Goudhurst in 1597, but in that case, who was 'Old Mother Millam - poor' buried at Goudhurst early in 1604? His own burial was the one recorded in 1615, with the note that he too was poor.

Later records are not forthcoming. Perhaps further entries were entered under the name Hosher or Usher.

484. ESRO, PBT 1/1/7/61.
485. WSRO, STC 1/21/248.
486. WSRO, STC 1/23/318.
487. TNA, E 179/258/20.

Cranbrook hundred

Walter or Waters

On the three occasions when it occurred during the 1540s, firstly as a poll-tax payer in 1541, and in 1543 and 1544 as a payer on goods, the final 's' of the baptismal name suggests that the immigrant Paulus Walter m,ay have originated in Germany. He may well have been a metalworker, but was perhaps unlikely to have been employed in the indirect-process ironworks brought from Normandy.

The surnames Walter and a'Water were widely spread in Sussex in the 1520s, but gradually the form Waters became more common. The similarity of the name of the Battle blacksmith, Paul Waters, who in 1600 had to appear at the assizes,[488] to that of the Cranbrook immigrant makes it seem possible that it was to Waters that the surname of the Cranbrook man's family later became assimilated.

The blacksmith may have first appeared as Paul a'Water, who in 1576 married Elizabeth Colman at Herstmonceux. Their children Agnes and Richard were baptised at Brightling and Salehurst in 1577 and 1579 respectively, and their son John was buried at Penhurst in 1582. Residence in Battle precluded further parish register entries, but in 1614 Paul Waters married his second wife Alice Nicholas at Heathfield. The burials of both Waters, his wife Alice, and of a son named Walter all at Heathfield in February 1618, appear to be evidence of pestilence striking, a possibility not entirely ruled out by the fact that Paul's body was found drowned in a ditch.

In 1597 Paul Waters' father-in-law, Richard Coleman of Brightling, made bequests of £1 to his grandson Richard Waters, and of 10 shillings each to his granddaughters Agnes and Elizabeth. To Paul's younger children, Walter, Mary and Joseph, he left 6s 8d each.[489]

Paul's son Richard Waters, a Brightling husbandman, took administration of his father's effects, valued at £31 2s 5d.[490] His children Martha and Thomas were baptised at Brightling in 1610 and 1616. In 1630 Martha married the collier John Fevers at Heathfield, to which parish her father had moved before 1621, when his son Richard was baptised there. Richard Waters was probably 'Waters' who was buried at Heathfield in 1629. His son Richard probably married Elizabeth Tapsell there in 1643.

Joseph Waters appears to have been the man whose children, Mary, Joan, Stephen and John were baptised at Warbleton from 1608 to 1619. He was buried there in 1622. His son John was probably the Warbleton collier, who was a quarter sessions surety in 1654 and was subsequently fined 2s 6d.[491]

It seems clear that Walter Waters of Hastings, blacksmith, who in 1618 joined Richard Waters in the administration bond for Paul Waters' effects, was related to this family in some way. Another member of the family was the forgeman, Adrian Waters of Battle, who was a quarter sessions surety in 1641.[492] He and his wife Mary had children named Robert and Margaret baptised at Mountfield in 1642 and 1644. It seems possible that Thomas, son of Athering (*sic*) Waters baptised at Battle in 1639, was their child too.

With the mentions of Adrian, the forgeman of 1641, and John, the collier of 1654, the family appears finally to have become engaged in the iron industry proper, but there is nothing to suggest that this family participated in the spread of the industry to other parts of Britain.

West Barnfield hundred

Weldern

This name is not known to be connected with ironworking. Peter Wyldorne first appeared as an alien in West Barnfield hundred in 1543, when he paid 4 pence on goods. By 1549 he had moved into Sussex, where, as the denizen Petre Weldern, he paid the poll tax in Shoyswell hundred. On this occasion his

488. Cockburn, *Sussex Assize records, Elizabeth I*, no. 1933.
489. ESRO, PBT 1/1/10/148.
490. ESRO, PBT 1/3/4/167.
491. ESRO, QR 102, mm. 40 and 91; I am grateful to Brian Phillips for this reference.
492. ESRO, QR 54, m.47; I am grateful to Brian Phillips for this reference.

name was recorded separately from those of the ironworkers. It seems possible that he was Peter Weaver who paid the poll tax in Netherfield hundred in 1595, an entry which perhaps recorded his occupation.

Michell

John Michell paid 2 shillings to the subsidy in West Barnfield hundred in 1572. He was perhaps the joiner, John Michell, a Norman who became a denizen in 1544, and who at that time dwelt in Cranbrook. It is uncertain that he had any connection with the iron industry.

Ponynges

There seems nothing to show that John Ponynges, an alien who paid the poll tax in West Barnfield hundred in 1572, was an ironworker.

The Lowey of Tonbridge

Dufour or Duffield

The name Dufour first appeared in Wealden parish records when Dominic du Four married Margery, the daughter of Cardin Quydeville, at Rotherfield in August 1554. This marriage was part of a double transaction by which the two families were linked, the second strand being the marriage of the widowed Cardin Quydeville to Joan Du Four, which followed two months later. It seems possible that there had already been close ties between the two families in the Pays de Bray.

At Neufchâtel-en-Bray members of the *Duquiefdelaville* family had been linked with the metal trade since at least 1452, whilst by the 1490s both families were involved at Neuville-Ferrières, where Aubery Dufour was mentioned as chaplain in 1494. Aubery's brother, the merchant Jehan Dufour, moved from Neufchâtel to Neuville around 1509, a move which coincided with the death in that year of the forgemaster Jehan Lucas.

The late Laurens Dufour, mentioned in a document of 1509, was perhaps the father of both Aubery and Jehan, and also of a third brother, Colin Dufour, who in 1509 was also initially living at Neuville, and whose sons Laurens and Anthoine Dufour may have held an interest in the forge following the deaths of their uncles Jehan and Aubery in 1522 and 1525 respectively.

Whilst Dominic du Four, who can be traced at Fletching from 1560 to 1570 and at East Grinstead in the 1570s, failed to appear as an alien in subsidy rolls at either place, Lawrence Duffyll, who married the widow Mercy Maryan at Tonbridge in 1561, paid 2 shillings on goods in 1572 as an alien in the subsidy for South Borough of Tonbridge, where he was recorded alongside his servant Robert Turner, who also paid the poll tax. So whereas Lawrence Duffyll had been born in France, Dominic was English-born. It seems possible that there was an additional immigrant belonging to the Dufour family who paid the poll tax in Netherfield hundred in 1595. This was John Defect, whose name can be more easily recognized, among a number of persons ordered by quarter sessions to be arrested in 1594, as John Duffield, late of Dallington, miner.[493] He seems to have left no trace in any of the parish registers of Netherfield hundred, so he perhaps returned to France, or moved on to some other English ironworking area. There is also a George Duffell, tenant of Drew Barrentyne's suggestively-named Calehyll in Horsted Keynes in 1565, but his place in the family is unclear.[494]

Another early, but unknown member of the family in England was the former husband of the widow Barbara Duffill, who in October 1571 married Thomas Weston at Lamberhurst.

The lack of further documentation about Colin Dufour at Neuville-Ferrières after 1509 suggests that he might have been the first member of this family to come to the Weald. However, it seems rather less certain that his son Lawrence could have been the Tonbridge alien.

Following his move to the cure of Grandrû in the diocese of Noyon in 1513, Aubery Dufour appointed his nephew Laurens as procurator for his affairs in Neuville, but Lawrance Duffell was not buried at Worth until 1585 making a stretch of adult life of at least 72 years. On the other hand,

493. ESRO, QR 1, m. 1 and QR 2, m. 27; I am grateful to Brian Phillips for these references.
494. ESRO, GLY 2047.

documentation for Laurens Dufour at Neuville-Ferrières, which had been plentiful up to February 1528, became very sparse afterwards without any reference to his death occurring.

In common with several immigrant families, the Dufours, or Duffills and Duffields, as it became more usual to call them, adopted a number of aliases. Firstly, descendants of Dominic du Four often used the alias Dominick alias Duffill. Another alias was that used by Margaret Duffell alias Peters when she married Henry Simons at Worth in 1593. Margaret may have been a child of Peter Duffielde, whose daughter Joan was baptised at Buxted in 1588. The only other possible reference to this man would seem to be the burial at Maresfield in 1601 of Peter Domynockle, which would suggest that he himself used the surname Duffill alias Dominic.

Another potential difficulty is the need to differentiate the immigrant family from that of the 1574 forgemaster John Duffield of Nayland in East Grinstead. This family may have been descended from Thomas Duffeld, 'a northern man', who was buried at East Grinstead in 1589.

It seems possible that the first child of Dominic du Four was John Domynycke who was baptised at Tonbridge in 1554, less than three weeks after the marriage of his parents. Thereafter, the lack of the Tonbridge baptismal register for the period 1558 to 1585 precludes further information until Dominic appeared at Fletching, where his son Lawrence was baptised in 1562. Dominic's other children, Gyllam, Elizabeth, Joan, Agnes and James, were baptised at Fletching between 1564 and 1572. Afterwards Dominick Duffort, baptised at East Grinstead in 1577, with no parent's name cited, was perhaps his child, and he cannot be definitely identified again until 1579 at Pembury, where his daughter Joan was baptised.

Dominic's son Laurence can be identified at Hartfield in 1595, when his son Thomas Domynack was baptised, and again at Mayfield in 1600, when his daughter Elizabeth Dominick was baptised in October. However, although the baptism took place at Mayfield, the assize court recorded Lawrence Duffell as a Rotherfield forgeman in June 1600 when he entered a recognizance to give evidence in the prosecution of the Frant forgeman Leonard Saxbies.[495] There seems to be no record of Laurence's burial in either parish, but the widow Mary Duffeild alias Dominacle, buried at Mayfield in 1613, may have been his former wife. His son Thomas might be the Thomas Duffeild buried at Mayfield in 1627.

It seems possible that the hammerman James Duffield, for whom entries in the Mayfield parish register commenced in 1609, could have replaced Laurence at Mayfield. He was probably the son of Dominic du Four baptised at Fletching in 1572. His nuncupative will, witnessed by the hammerman Roger Sherroe and by Duffield's eldest daughter Elizabeth, was proved in April 1618. He left all his goods and chattels to his children, but the younger ones were to have the 'better portions'. The trustees were two finers, Nicholas Pullen of Frant and Thomas Cox of Mayfield, and it was to Cox that administration of Duffield's goods was assigned, with power reserved to Pullen.[496]

Fortunately the probate administration named Duffield's children, which was not the case in the will: they were Elizabeth, Dominaculus, Alice, Agnes, John and William. It was William who had been baptised at Mayfield in 1609, the other child of James and Elizabeth Duffield, James, who was baptised there in 1612, having survived only a month. Dominic, son of James Duffill had been baptised at Frant in 1598. Dominic or Dominacle not having attained his majority in October 1617, it was Duffield's eldest child Elizabeth who had witnessed his will. She had been baptised as Elizabeth Dominacle at Lamberhurst in May 1595, though her parents were not named in the parish register. The baptisms of the other children, Alice, Agnes and John have not been traced, but perhaps occurred at Hartfield, where bishop's transcripts for 1604, 1606 and 1608 alone survive from the period 1598 to 1609.

James Duffield's will having been proved in April, his eldest daughter Elizabeth appears to have taken an early opportunity to marry Adrian Lavender at Burwash in May 1618. Such a move might have contributed to the marriage of her brother Dominic to Susanna Dennat at Salehurst in 1620. Dominic's son William was baptised at Salehurst in 1621, followed by an unnamed child, and John and James, baptised at Etchingham between 1623 and 1628, and Mary, baptised at Goudhurst in 1630. Mary survived only six months and it looks as though Dominic's family moved to Mountfield, where his son James was buried in 1632 and his wife in 1638. He was probably the Dominic Duffield who married Elizabeth Pooke at Beckley in 1639.

John Duffield of Horsted Keynes, hammerman, was presented at quarter sessions in 1639 along

495. Cockburn, *Sussex Assize records, Elizabeth I*, no. 1933.

496. ESRO, PBT 2/2/4/90.

with seven other men, including two more hammermen, for riotous entry into the house of a Lindfield widow, Joan Pegden.[497] Because the marriage licence granted for his marriage to Joan Picknell in March 1638 had described him as a Mayfield forgeman,[498] it seems probable that he was a son of James Duffield of Mayfield, whose baptism has not been traced. The fact that no other family named Duffield or Duffill had appeared in the Mayfield parish register after 1618 makes this the more likely. John the son of John and Joan Duffeild was baptised at Horsted Keynes early in 1641.

Gyllam, the son of Dominic Duffit baptised at Fletching in 1564, may have been William Duffill, whose son Richard was baptised at Shipley in 1593. Both men were subsequently traced at Thursley, where Richard Duffell married Catherine Winchester in 1617 and William Duffield was buried in 1625. Richard's children, Jane and Richard, were baptised at Thursley in 1624 and 1626, but not before Richard had been married twice more, if the burial of Jane Duffeild wife of Richard Duffeild in 1623 is to be credited.

Perhaps William was ancestor in some way of Philip Duffill, whose children, Philip, Mary and Elizabeth, were born at Witley in 1654, 1656 and 1657. Elizabeth could be the woman who married Henry Haloway at Thursley in 1692.

Dominic Duffort, who was baptised at East Grinstead in 1577 was perhaps the man whose son Edmund Duffell alias Dominacle was baptised at Cuckfield in 1603. As his second wife Dominacle married a widow named Ellen Martin at Bexhill in 1606. When Dominacle Duffell died in 1627 he made only two bequests of 10 shillings each to his kinsmen Ninnian and Dominacle Duffell. He made his wife Ellen his executrix and left his house and land to her for life; afterwards it was to go to her grandchild, who in the will was misnamed Ellen too, and to her heirs.[499] Further confusion arises from a burial entry for Edward Dominackle alias Duffet in the Westfield parish register on 19 March 1627. Dominacle's will had been dated 15 March and it was proved on the 12 April next following. From his will it is clear that the son Edmund (or Edward?) born to him at Cuckfield in 1603 was no longer alive. Were both of them mortally ill on 15 March and both buried in the same grave?

In addition to the Mayfield hammerman who died in 1617, there were two other James Duffills. Firstly, in 1582 a daughter named Annis, who was born to James Duffill and Margaret Stallworth out of wedlock, was baptised at Lamberhurst. Secondly, a Cuckfield forgeman named James Duffell alias Dominacle had a daughter named Elizabeth baptised in 1610. The Cuckfield man is probably to be identified with James Duffell, whose children, Mary, James and Sarah, were baptised at Maresfield from 1613 to 1622, with James Dominacle whose son James was baptised at Uckfield in 1615, and with James Dominickell whose children Alice and Richard were baptised there in 1623 and 1624. Possibly Thomas son of James Duffell baptised at Framfield in 1627 was his child too. His first son James and his daughter Elizabeth were buried at Maresfield in 1617 and 1629 respectively, whilst his daughter Mary was buried on the day after her baptism. This forgeman was buried at Maresfield in 1635. Since he also bore the Dominacle alias, his father was perhaps the Peter Domynickle who had been buried at Maresfield in 1601.

Another branch of this family moved at an early date to the west of the Weald. John Duffill of Lurgashall made his will on 14 March 1595 and it was proved at the end of the month. He left £10 to each of his children, John, Peter, William and Dennis Duffill, to be paid them at their ages of 21, and made his wife Margery his residuary legatee and executrix.[500] His son William had been baptised at Lurgashall as recently as December 1592, so it seems possible that the child Dennis was in fact a girl named Denise. Though the parish register did not give the parentage on this occasion, Michael Duffill baptised at Lurgashall in November 1591 and buried there in the following January could have been another of John Duffill's sons. It seems possible that this man was John Domynycke, baptised at Tonbridge in 1554. He could have accompanied Lawrence to Worth, and despite the lack of exact correspondence in the wife's name, have been the father of John, the son of John and Margaret Duffell, buried at Worth in 1580.

There seems also evidence that the next generation of this family may have moved back to Worth. In 1621 George the son of John Duffeild was baptised at Kirdford. It seems possible to trace both father and son at Worth. In 1623 Edward son of John and Joan Duffell was baptised at Worth. It is

497. ESRO, QR 47, m. 47; I am grateful to Brian Phillips for this reference.
498. Dunkin, *Sussex Marriage Licences, Lewes 1586-1643,* p. 246.
499. ESRO, PBT 1/1/20/20, 1/3/4/298.
500. WSRO, STC 1/14/368.

unclear whether the father was the same man as the John Duffell who in 1624 married Elizabeth Simons at Worth, because the register fails to record the burial of his wife Joan. The marriage licence described this John Duffell as a Worth hammerman.[501] However, his wife, Elizabeth Duffell, was buried in 1625 and he himself was perhaps the man buried at Worth in 1627. Entries for George Duffield followed later in the Worth parish register, when his unnamed daughter and his son named George were buried in 1645 and 1647 respectively.

George perhaps ended his days in Hampshire, where George son and Eleanor daughter of George Duffell were baptised at Beaulieu, in 1676 and early in 1678 respectively, Eleanor being born posthumously, because her father had been buried at Beaulieu in September 1677. George Duffell will presumably have worked at the ironworks on Sowley Pond.

Another member of this family who moved across the full length of the Weald was Michael Duffell of Goudhurst who had married Katherine Baker at Lingfield on Whitmonday 1584. Due to the rarity of the name Michael, and the close way in which some of the dates follow one another, it is possible to trace the baptisms of his children Elizabeth and Henry at Goudhurst in 1586 and 1587, of Denise and Charles at Warbleton in 1596 and 1598, of Edward at Kirdford in 1600 and of Dorothy at Rogate in 1603. Another member of the family who appeared at Rogate around the same time was an otherwise unknown Adrian Duffyll, whose wife Margaret was buried there early in 1607.

Michael Duffell's father was possibly Joseph Duffell who was buried at Goudhurst in 1617. Another Joseph Duffell, who might have been Michael's younger brother, married Marie Sabb at Goudhurst in 1604. They had nine children baptised at Goudhurst between 1604 and 1621. The younger Joseph Duffell was buried at Goudhurst in 1627 and his widow married Solomon Walter in 1629.

Another John Duffeld, this time of Beeding, gave evidence in Exchequer depositions by commission in Easter term 1588 about the ironworks in St Leonards Forest.[502] He gave his age as 23 and so would have been born about 1564 or 5. It looks as though he may have been the man whose children, Jane Duffield and Benjamin Duffill, were baptised at Horsham in 1583 and 1585 respectively. He was clearly distinct from the Lurgashall man because not only did the names of the children not correspond, but the parish register named his wife Jane on both occasions. This man may later have moved on to Morville in Shropshire.

At Morville around the end of the sixteenth century John son of Stephen Duffell was baptised in 1598, and the baptisms of Cisily, William and John Duffell followed in 1600, 1604 and 1608. The parentage of William was not disclosed, but John Duffell was the father of Cisily and John, his wife's name being given as Jane in 1608, thus corresponding with the couple who had been at Beeding in the 1580s. William, a base son of Denise Duffell, was baptised at Morville in 1620, but the last mention of this family there was when the bloomer, Michael Duffill, was buried in 1625.

The intrusive Stephen Douffeld, who was buried at Titchfield in Hampshire in 1612, may have been employed at the earl of Southampton's Funtley Forge, which had been set up around a decade earlier. He was perhaps the man who had been at Morville in 1598. The last two Morville entries remind us of Denise the daughter of Michael Duffell baptised at Warbleton in 1596, but the remaining names do not agree. However, Michael's son Edward baptised at Kirdford in 1600 could be the founder Edward Duffield mentioned at Redbrook in Newland in the Forest of Dean in February 1659.[503] The subsequent occurrence of the baptismal name Charles among the Forest of Dean branch of this family perhaps confirms that they were also descended from Michael Duffell of Goudhurst, who failed to be noticed again in the Weald after the baptism of his daughter Dorothy at Rogate in 1603.

Another member of this family was Nicholas Duffett, whose children, Edward, Joan, another Joan, Mary, Charles and Adrian, were baptised at Hartfield between 1609 and 1620. Edward and Joan were twins, neither of whom survived for long and the second Joan was buried at Hartfield in 1629. Mary, Charles and Adrian seem all to have survived. The latter will have been the Maresfield collier Adrian Duffeild who in 1655 was a quarter session surety for John Reade of Rotherfield, husbandman.[504]

The baptisms at North Nibley from 1597 to 1606 of George, William, Anne and Sarah, the children of William Dyffolde, are perhaps the earliest trace of this family in Gloucestershire. North

501. Dunkin, *Sussex Marriage Licences, Lewes 1586-1643,* p. 142.
502. TNA, E 134, 30 Elizabeth I, Easter 17.
503. ESRO, SAS/G 55/934.
504. ESRO, QR 107, m. 45; I am indebted to Brian Phillips for this reference.

Nibley was immediately north of Tortworth, where ironworks are known to have been operated in the first decade of the seventeenth century.

Just to the north of Redbrook, at Staunton by Monmouth, John Duffield's son Thomas was baptised in 1638. At Newland itself Henry son of John and Mary Duffield was baptised in 1662. The will of Charles Duffield shows that he died in April or May 1663, but does not disclose his place of residence. He made his wife Margaret executrix and left to her all his goods, cattle and chattels together with his livelihood in the expectation that she, his son Charles and daughter Mary would live there together, and that 'if it should happen that my son Edward Duffield should at any time . . . be out of employment or have any need, that he may have a home there with my now wife and my son Charles'.[505] Whether the Redbrook founder of 1659 was the man baptised at Kirdford in 1600, or the man mentioned in the will cannot be determined, but the latter was presumably the father of Jane and Francis, the children of Edward and Elizabeth Duffield, who were baptised at Newland in 1682 and 1685.

Later members of the family were located in the parishes of Lydney, Flaxley, Newnham and Westbury on Severn (each only 3km distant from Flaxley), and at Oxenhall (Newent Furnace), also within the ironworking area. At Lydney John Duffield's children, Thomas, Sarah and John were baptised from 1674 to 1689, and the children of James and Margaret Duffeild, Margaret, Anne and John, were baptised from 1679 to 1689. From 1680 to 1701, Mary, William, Sarah, James, Henry, Charles and Thomas, the children of William and Anne Duffield were also baptised at Lydney.

Charles, the son of Charles and Abigail Duffield, was baptised at Flaxley in 1699, but their subsequent children, Mary, Abigail and Edward, were baptised at Westbury on Severn from 1701 to 1705. The children of a later Charles Duffield and his wife Mary [Seville?], Anne, Mary and Sarah, were baptised at Newnham from 1742 to 1747, but their later children, Edward, Catherine and Duffield, were baptised at Flaxley. The use of the baptismal name Edward by both families suggests a link with the former Redbrook founder.

At Oxenhall the children of John Duffield, John, Elizabeth, Margaret and Anne, were baptised from 1674 to 1682.

Brook

The family Broke, or a'Broke, was shown by the subsidy rolls of the 1520s to be widespread in Sussex.

The alien John Broke, who paid 2 shillings on goods to the subsidy of 1572 in South Borough of the Lowey of Tonbridge, was possibly John Brokes, the founder, to whose son John 10 shillings had been bequeathed in 1560 by John Homwood of East Grinstead. The will was nuncupative and the forgemaster Richard a'Mylle and Agnes his wife were the witnesses.[506] Both Homwood and John Brokes were therefore probably workers at Mill Place Furnace.

It seems impossible to establish whether there was any connection between the alien Broke and Jeremy Philpott, the Burwash founder, whose will was proved in 1615.[507] Philpott had married Joan Hyland at Wartling in 1578. He was probably baptised at Herstmonceux in 1548 as Jerome a'Broke alias Philpot, the son of John Fylpot alias Brokes, who had married the widow Joan Bonyface as his second wife in 1547.

In the Midlands John Brooke 'from the Forge', who was buried at Condover in 1629, and Humphrey Brooks, a forgeman who married Susanna Tullitt at Cuckney in 1645, may both have been of immigrant stock.

Dabat

Maryan Dabat paid the poll tax as a servant of the forgemaster Davy Willard in South Borough of the Lowey of Tonbridge in 1572. He had married Agnes Turner, perhaps also of immigrant stock, at Tonbridge in 1567, but the loss of Tonbridge baptismal entries between then and 1585 prevents our tracing their children.

Another member of this family will have been Julian (i.e. Gillian) Dobet who in August 1573 married the forgeman Nicholas Good at Tonbridge. She ended her days at Horsham as Gillian Good,

505. Gloucestershire Record Office, GDR wills, 1663/28, Duffield.
506. ESRO, PBT 1/1/4/496.
507. ESRO, PBT 1/1/14/16.

'an old widow' who was buried there in March 1614.

The Dabat or Dobet family has not been traced elsewhere in the Weald, or further afield, in connection with iron.

Geering

A connection with James Geryng, one of Davy Willard's workers who paid the poll tax in the South Borough of Tonbridge in 1572, seems to have been established when Matthew Fuller of Waldron married Margery Gerynge at Rotherfield in 1566.

Berehowse

There seem to be no further references to John Berehowse, who in 1572 paid the poll tax in the South Borough of Tonbridge as a servant to David Willard. Could the name have been assimilated to Peareshouse? In the Midlands John Peareshouse *de Furnace* was mentioned in the Halesowen parish register in 1678.

Somerden hundred

Bonford

The baptismal name of Bonford, the last of four aliens who paid the poll tax in the borough of Cowden in 1563, was not revealed in the subsidy roll. The only known ironworking site is the one at Prinkham Farm Forge.

Further references to Bonford or to his family are not known in the Weald and it is difficult to know what the French original of the surname could have been.

Westerham hundred

Crippen

There is no evidence that Stephen Crippyn, who paid the poll tax in Edenbridge borough in 1560, in that case with a servant, and in 1563, was employed at either of the two furnaces above Cowden on Kent Water. The Edenbridge collier who died in 1633 was not Edward Crippin, but Edward Crips.[508]

SURREY

Reigate hundred

Le Jean or Young

Robert Le Jean who paid the poll tax at Newdigate in 1557 did so again as Robert Younge, servant to Mr Dorrell, forgemaster in 1559. He has not been traced with certainty in parish registers.

The surname Young became connected with ironfounding at Lurgashall, where Peter Young had a furnace built before 1585. Other ironworking connections have yet to found.

Parish register entries for Edward Lejune at Beaulieu from 1656 onwards suggest that later members of the immigrant family may have continued in ironworking at the Sowley Furnace.

Symons

An alien surnamed Symons, whose baptismal name was not recorded, paid the poll tax at Newdigate in 1557, but had moved on or died by 1559, unless he had become the Adrian who paid the poll tax

508. KHLC, DRb/PW29.

at Newdigate in that year. No person named Symons was recorded around that time in the Newdigate parish register, which commenced in 1560, and no person named Adrian Symons is known from other sources.

Nevertheless, three persons, a collier, a hammerman and an iron finer, all named John Simons, operated in the area between Abinger and Ardingly in the last quarter of the century, and the fact that an immigrant had been present so close to this area as Newdigate only 20 years earlier suggests that all of them may have been of immigrant descent. The area is quite distinct from the Plumpton, Ringmer, Barcombe and Lindfield area in which a similarly named family of blacksmiths flourished, and the Buxted and Mayfield area in which a similarly named family of wheelwrights operated towards the close of the century.

John Symons of Abinger, collier, was the first of these men to appear, when he was charged in 1574 along with others of riotous assembly at Shere and of entering the estate of the local forgemaster Sir Edward Braye.[509] The other offenders included a blacksmith and two more colliers, one of whom, Peter White, married Susan Symond four years later.

Alice, John and Joan, the children of John Symonde, were baptised at Abinger between 1569 and 1574, after which he moved to Worth, where the parish register noted the baptism of Joan and Margaret children of John and Helen Simons in 1577, of whom Margaret did not survive infancy. The Abinger man's identity with the Worth man was established by the burial entry for his wife Eleanor in 1584, which also confirmed that he was a collier. It is not clear what subsequently became of him but he was presumably still at Worth in 1589 when John Lamot alias Finch married Alice Simons.

The second of these men was John Simmons, a hammerman, the baptism of whose son Joseph was recorded at Ardingly in 1580. The hammerman is not subsequently traceable, but his son Joseph married Margaret Lucar at Ardingly in 1605. Their daughter Anne was baptised at Worth in 1606. In 1608 their son John was baptised at Bramshott, but they soon returned from the western Weald to Cuckfield, where Susan the daughter of Joseph Symons, forgeman, and Margaret his wife was baptised in April 1610. He was perhaps back at Worth in 1615 when the baptism of Elizabeth daughter of Joseph and Mary [*sic*] Simons was recorded. Joseph seems not to be traceable later in the Weald.

The forgeman Thomas Simons, whose son Henry was baptised at Cuckfield in 1626, was perhaps a son of Joseph Simons, whose baptism has not been traced. Joseph's son John, baptised at Bramshott in 1608, was possibly the man who in 1640 married Susan Messence at Maresfield. This John Symons of Maresfield, forgeman, along with Nathaniel White alias Angerfield, a butcher, presumably also of French descent, was acquitted of the theft of geese from William Delve of Isfield in 1643.[510]

The last of the three John Symons was the iron finer, who was buried at Worth in September 1607. By his will he left the farm he occupied to his wife Gylmet for life; after her decease it was to go to his sons Thomas and Hugh and to their best use and profit. No executor was named in the will and, Gylmet also being deceased, probate was granted in October 1607 to Hugh Simons.[511] The administration bond was for £70 suggesting that Symons' goods had been inventoried at around £35.

Despite being mentioned second in the will, Hugh was perhaps the elder of these two brothers and the family can already be traced in 1591 at Worth, where Hugh had married Elizabeth Streater. The administration bond recorded Hugh's occupation as that of hammerman. His children, Richard, Elizabeth, John, Alexander and another Elizabeth, were baptised at Worth from 1594 to 1603. Hugh died intestate early in 1612 and administration of his goods, valued at £57 18s 1d, was granted to his widow.[512]

Hugh's son John married Mary the daughter of the Ardingly hammerman Anthony Milham at Ardingly in 1620. Their children, Elizabeth, Thomas, John, Hugh and Mary, were baptised at Ardingly between 1620 and 1629. John Symons was perhaps the married man of that name who was buried at Ardingly in 1635. He was one of the few members of this family whose occupation was not recorded. Probably he was a hammerman like both his father and his son Hugh, who as Hugh Simons of Ardingly, hammerman, married Anne Newman of Balcombe at Horsham in 1655. Hugh's elder brother Thomas was perhaps Thomas Simmons belonging to the 'yron works' who was buried at Ardingly in 1644.

509. Cockburn, *Surrey Assize records, Elizabeth I*, no. 746.
510. ESRO, QR 59, m. 2; I am indebted to Brian Phillips for this reference.
511. ESRO, PBT 1/1/12/237, 1/3/3/107.
512. ESRO, PBT 1/3/3/260.

The other child of Hugh Symons who remained in the immediate area was Elizabeth, who had been baptised in 1603 and married John Duffield at Worth in 1624.

No further trace at Worth or Ardingly can be found of Hugh's eldest son Richard who had been baptised in 1594 nor of Alexander, who had been baptised in 1601, unless Alexander was the man who married Joan Gallop at Ardingly in 1637. However, it appears more likely that the husband of Joan Gallop was Alexander, the son of Thomas Simmons, baptised at Cuckfield in 1616.

Missing members of the family can be traced in north Shropshire. The first mentioned in Shropshire was the forgeman, Francis Simons, whose daughter Elizabeth was baptised at Wem in 1612. The Wealden origin of Francis has not been traced, but Richard and Alexander, the missing sons of Hugh Symons, can be found in Shropshire. At Wem the marriage of Richard Symmons to Jane Hardinge was recorded in February 1621, and the parish register revealed that Richard was a hammerman when his daughter Eleanor was baptised in October of the same year; Eleanor was buried at Wem in December 1621.

Both Richard and Alexander Simons were at Condover around 1627. Alexander Simons 'from the Forge' was buried there, probably unmarried, in March 1627. Anne, the daughter of Richard and Jane Simons 'from the Forge', was baptised there in October 1628.

We now return from this family of hammermen to follow the fate of John Symons' younger son Thomas, who followed in his father's trade of a finer of iron. Thomas's occupation was revealed in the will of Thomas Wright, an Ifield husbandman, who died in 1610; he bequeathed £10 to his daughter Eleanor,[513] who had married Thomas Symons at Worth early in 1606. Their daughter Bridget was baptised there in May of that year and their son William in 1611. Whether Alexander son of Thomas Simmons, baptised at Cuckfield in 1616 was their child too is impossible to say. Eleanor, wife of Thomas Simons, was buried at Worth in April 1626 and Thomas Simons himself was perhaps the man of that name buried at Worth in May 1627.

However, Thomas Symons of Frant, forgeman, gave evidence in 1636 concerning the alleged theft of two ringers or furgons from the forge of Mr William Fowle.[514] Whether this Thomas was the man whose son Henry had been baptised at Cuckfield ten years earlier, or the Worth man is impossible to say with certainty. The Frant parish register seems to know of no such person, so perhaps this Thomas Symons was at that time unmarried.

This is not the place to review the families of the blacksmiths and wheelwrights mentioned earlier. Perhaps, however, a Worth nailer named John Simon, a contemporary of the two forgemen and the collier named John Symons who worked at Worth and Ardingly, should be mentioned. His wife was named Margaret and their two sons Hugh and Thomas were baptised in 1587 and 1588, though Hugh survived only four months. It is possible to distinguish between all these men, primarily because the Worth parish clerk took the trouble to record mothers' names; an effort to distinguish between Simon and Simons, or Symons seems also to have been made.

The link between the Wealden and Shropshire forgemen surnamed Symons has been established. However, it appears that this family was present in North Yorkshire at a rather earlier date. The parish register of Helmsley called Peter Symons 'Master of the furnysh at Rivalx' in January 1578, when he acted as godfather to Peter the son of Lambert and Elizabeth Semer of Rievaulx. Peter acted as sponsor at another baptism in May of that year, but did not appear thereafter. It seems probable that he left Rievaulx very shortly after this, because his prominent position at the blast furnace, which had been installed only two years earlier, would have ensured his future participation at baptisms.

Purford

It seems probable that both the English-born John Rychebell and George Laby, who each employed one alien at Newdigate in 1563, were engaged in the iron industry. However, Rychebell's servant, Nicholas Purford, is not otherwise known in the Weald.

The surname Purford or Burford does not seem to recur in England in connection with iron.

513. ESRO, PBT 1/1/13/79 (will of Thomas Wright).

514. ESRO, QR 35, mm. 93, 105; I am indebted to Brian Phillips for these references.

Blackheath and Wotton hundred

Cranleigh

Huysson

All three of the aliens who paid the poll tax at Cranleigh in 1551, Charles, Crystyan and Adrian Huysson, perhaps came from the Spanish Netherlands as was certainly the case with 'Christian Hewgynson, gonmaker', born subject to the Emperor, who received denization in 1561.[515] It looks as though at least shot-casting must have been carried at Vachery Furnace in its earliest days.

Bearing in mind the Flemish aspirated 'G', an earlier bearer of this surname may have been Colin Guyson, who in 1418 supplied 7,200 rounds of iron ammunition from Maubeuge to Ghent.[516]

Descendants are more probably to be sought in the secondary metal trades than in those involved with the primary production of iron.

Miles

There is no sixteenth-century parish register for Cranleigh available to throw further light on John Myles, the alien who paid the poll tax there in 1557. He presumably worked at the Vachery Furnace or Forge.

The French original of this name may have been *Dumoulin* or *Desmoullins*. Both surnames were well-represented at Neufchâtel-en-Bray in the sixteenth century, but there is nothing to connect either name with metalworking or with emigration to the Weald. In the 1520s the surname Miles or Mylys was well represented in West Sussex; Milles occurred at Hartfield and Mill at Battle, and a'Myll was found in all parts of the county.

Richard a'Mill who was assessed for £15-worth of goods at East Grinstead in 1524 may well have been the 1574 ironmaster at Mill Place Furnace, who died shortly after that survey. There is no reason to suppose he was of other than indigenous stock.

A Brightling labourer named William Myles, who made his will in 1607, may have had links with ironmaking and could have been of immigrant descent. He appointed the immigrant ironfounder Laurence Harrowe of Mountfield the main overseer of his will, which was witnessed by both Laurence and his son Nicholas. Although his goods were assessed at only £8 2s 1d, in addition to tools Myles left iron pots of 3 gallons and 6 quarts, a posnet of 3 pints, an iron dripping pan, a spit, a pair of cob-irons, a mortar and pestle and an iron pot-lid to his only child Richard.[517]

Further indications of ironworking connections of members of these families and of their possible immigrant origin are not forthcoming.

Abinger hundred

Massey

The French original of this name was probably *Masset* or *Massé*. Stephen Macie married another member of the immigrant community, Katherine Tollatt, at Abinger early in 1568. He paid the poll tax as an alien there in 1571.

The name recurred at Rogate in 1626 when Francis Massey married a widow named Susan Bray. Their children, Peter, Francis and Anne, were baptised between 1627 and 1632, but Francis did not survive. The elder Francis himself was buried at Rogate early in 1641. Peter Massey married a Midhurst widow, Katherine Rowe, at Rogate in 1654.

In South Yorkshire an isolated entry in the Sheffield parish register, for the baptism of Hellen

515. *Calendar of Patent rolls, Elizabeth I*, **2**, p. 2.
516. Gaier, *L'industrie et le commerce des armes*, p. 146.
517. ESRO, PBT 1/1/12/220, 1/3/3/100.

daughter of Thomas Massey in March 1587, perhaps relates to this family.

In the Stour valley Thomas Massie, whose son Solomon was baptised at Stourport in 1832, was described as a foundry moulder of Mitton. In 1851 at Lower Bar in Newport in Shropshire the census recorded three householders of the Massey family who were described as millwrights. The father was presumably the 66-year-old John Massey whose place of birth had been Stoke on Trent. His sons William and George were both 'millwright engineers': William, who had been born in Newport 40 years earlier, was the employer of 25 men; George Massey had been born at Chetwynd 30 years earlier.

Shalford hundred

Lambourne

Nicholas Lamboren paid the poll tax in 1572 at Shalford in the Surrey hundred of Blackheath and Wotton. He was probably 'Old father Lambourne, collier', buried at Chiddingfold in 1613. Another Chiddingfold collier, Giles Lambourne, who was buried there in 1612, was probably one of his sons. Giles' son Thomas had been baptised at Chiddingfold in 1611.

Alice Lamporne and Richard Lambourne, buried at Thursley in 1627 and 1633 respectively, will also have been members of this family.

Another son will have been Nicholas Lamborne, whose children, Mary, Joan, and Nicholas, were baptised at Fernhurst from 1616 to 1618, although only Nicholas survived infancy. Thereafter, Nicholas's further children appear to have been Elizabeth Lamber baptised in 1621, but buried as Lambard in 1624, Joan Lambon baptised in 1623 and James Lamboll baptised in 1626.

The last entry probably results from assimilation to a family recorded as Lamball in the subsidy rolls for West Sussex in the 1520s. Edward Lambole, whose son Robert was baptised at Petworth in 1625, a month after his father's death, Thomas Lambole, buried at Petworth in 1612, and Widow Lamboll, perhaps Edward's widow, buried at Petworth in 1634, were possibly all of indigenous stock.

The same perhaps applies to the blacksmith Barnaby Lamboll, buried at Dunsfold in 1671. His wife Amy Lamboll had been buried at Dunsfold in 1658.

But more equivocal is Francis Lamby, whose son Thomas was baptised at Fernhurst in 1610. Francis had been married, as Francis Lambole, to Joan Copper in 1609, and when his daughter Mary was baptised in 1620 he became Francis Lamboll.

STAFFORDSHIRE

Cuttleston hundred

Regett

Nicholas Regell, whose name appeared under 'Ridgeley' in Cutteslowe hundred in May 1563, was almost certainly Nicholas Regyn who appeared in 1572, but not in 1571, as a Frenchman employed in Cleobury Foreign. Bearing in mind the confusion between terminal 'tt' and 'll' in scripts of the period, the true surname was perhaps Regett.

Where this surname appeared in the Weald, it is difficult to distinguish it from a local surname derived from the Surrey town of Reigate. However, since this Midlands Nicholas was an alien, the surname in this case perhaps originated with Pierre Raghet, the Namur ironworker from Jausse-les-Ferons, who in 1371 took over the lead furnace below Sclaigneaux and converted it into an ironworks.

In England the name has not otherwise been connected with iron. Richard Raggett, a member of a Battle family of this surname, was stated to be a surgeon in High court proceedings of 21 October 1578, and the family had been present in thre town since at least 1500.[518]

518. HEH, BA Vol. 54/1314, 96 ff 36-7.

SHROPSHIRE

Stottesden hundred

Done

John Done was assessed for £3 in goods in both 1571 and 1572 at Cleobury Mortimer, on which he paid firstly 10 shillings and then 6 shillings.[519] He has not been identified in the Weald.

The French surname Donne is uncommon, but persists at Neufchâtel-en-Bray and at Nesle-Hodeng. In Britain it would assimilate to Dunne, but is not otherwise found in connection with ironworking.

Hewgate

'Hewgate Fownder', who paid £1 13s 4d in 1571 and £1 in 1572 to the subsidies in Cleobury Foreign on £10-worth of goods, has already been discussed in relation to the Hugget family, of which Wealden branches were of both indigenous and immigrant stock.

Although the lack of a sixteenth-century parish register for Cleobury Mortimer, and lack of Hewgate's baptismal name, make it impossible to know whether Hewgate ended his days there or moved on, an entry for the baptism of Edward Hewgate early in 1595 at Leintwardine, a parish adjacent to Bringewood Forge, makes it appear possible that he or his family moved on to the ironworks in the Chase of Bringewood. Unfortunately, at Leintwardine the baptismal name of the father also remains unknown, because parents' names were seldom included in that parish register before 1600.

Tronchin

Glowde Trunchyn paid 4 pence to each of the subsidies of April 1571 and September 1572 at Cleobury Foreign in Shropshire, although in 1571 his name was mistakenly entered as *Stronchin*.[520] The original French surname was probably *Trenchepain*, the name of a prominent Beaussault family which by 1540 was represented in Dieppe by Louis Trenchepain, burgher and merchant of that town. Vincent Trenchepain was another burgher of Dieppe in 1561. At Beaussault the family was represented by Colin (*c.* 1500), Pierres (*fl.* 1494-1537) and Pierre (d. 1566), an intervening generation represented by Guyon, who died around 1540, having fallen by the wayside.[521]

Glode Tronshion went on to Rievaulx in North Yorkshire, where his son Paul was buried in 1587. His daughter Rebecca was baptised in December 1588, but died before the month was out.

Meanwhile other representatives of the family had appeared elsewhere in England. Peter Trunchin was at Norton-in-Hales in north Staffordshire, where his daughter Katherine was baptised in 1596. Perhaps Peter was the father of Christopher Trunchean, whose daughter Mary was baptised at Castle Donington in 1609, but who had moved on by 1611 to Wem in Shropshire, where his son Edward was baptised.

In the Weald Richard Tronchin was baptised at Fletching in 1589. Richard Tronchin was presumably the eldest child of Richard Trunchyn, whose other children, Thomas who survived less than two years, Philip, Gane (i.e. Jane), Nicholas, Thomas, and Magdalen who died in 1610, were baptised at Maresfield between 1590 and 1606. William a son of Richard Truncheon was buried at Maresfield in May 1618 and his father followed him to the grave only six days later. Widow Trunchion, whose name is unknown, was buried there in 1623.

Thomas Truncheon, who apparently did not marry, was buried at Crawley in 1636, the bishop's transcript disclosing that he was 'a tapster at the George in Ifield'. He died intestate and administration of his effects, valued at £14 12s 2d, was assigned to his brother Nicholas Truncheon of Maresfield, finer.[522]

The marriage of Nicholas Trunchion has not been found, but his children, John, Mary, twins

519. TNA, E 179/167/44 and 50.
520. TNA, E 179/167/44 and 50.
521. See Ch. 4 pp. 101-2.
522. ESRO, PBT 1/3/6/240.

named Nicholas and Elizabeth, Mary, Anne and William, were baptised at Maresfield between 1627 and 1640. Of them, only Nicholas and Anne survived childhood.

In 1647 Nicholas Trunchen of Maresfield, forgeman, was presented at quarter sessions charged with the theft of an iron bar belonging to Christopher and Richard Fowle, gentlemen. The proceedings disclosed that Trunchen was keeper of an unlicensed alehouse and that he was illiterate. Under examination he stated that the iron bar, which had been made from Mr William Fowle's iron, and was to have been used for bearing-wheels, had been found by his son Nicholas and the maid of Thomas Norman, the forgeman at Park Forge. They sold the bar, which weighed between 40 and 50 pounds and was worth 7 or 8 shillings, to Thomas Norman, a Maresfield blacksmith.[523]

POSSIBLE IMMIGRANT WORKERS MENTIONED IN PARISH REGISTERS AFTER 1550

Burgess

Denys Burgess of Buxted was among the Protestants martyred at Lewes alongside the forgemaster Richard Woodman in 1557. This family had been in the ironworking area from at least 1500, when on 16 June property in High Hurstwood Ward was surrendered to the use of Henry Burgeis.[524] The same, or another Henry Burgess, was taxed on goods worth £14 in Loxfield hundred in 1524 and was still at Buxted at the time of the 1543 subsidy. The same two baptismal names occurred in 1554 at Rotherfield, where Denys son of Henry Bourgoys was then baptised.

In the Pays de Bray Anthoine Bourgoise had been verderer of the Forest of Eawy in 1536.[525] The name was widespread in Sussex in the 1520s so distinguishing immigrant families from those of indigenous stock is a difficult task and the name is not easily linked with ironworking outside the Weald.

The proof that the family was, or had become linked with ironworking did not come until February 1595, when the Abinger hammerman, Henry Burges, took administration of the goods of his father, Nicholas Burges of Rotherfield, valued at around £20. Nicholas Burgys had been left land by his father-in-law, the forgemaster William Fowle of Rotherfield, in 1560.[526] Evidence that this Rotherfield branch of the family continued its link with ironworking came in a burial entry of 1646 for the wife of the collier John Burges. He had married Margaret Smith in 1644.

Maybury

This surname went unrecorded in the Sussex subsidy rolls of the 1520s and first appeared in the Weald at Brightling in 1565 when John Maberie married Margaret Bourder on 23 December. Margaret's death was recorded at Mayfield in February 1576 and in June of that year Maberye married a widow, Alice Fuller. This second marriage allows the identification of the Mayfield and former Brightling man with the hammerman John Maberye, whose wife Alice was buried at Ellastone in north Staffordshire in May 1603. Members of the family worked at numerous forges in Wales and the west Midlands, and also appeared in Cumbria and Ireland, over a period of three centuries, a descendant still serving as a melter at Llanwern in the 1980s.

Nicholas Merbury had commanded the English artillery at Agincourt in 1415,[527] and since John Mabery did not appear as an alien in the subsidy rolls of the 1570s for Mayfield it might be supposed that he was English born. However, since the surname did not occur in the subsidy rolls of the 1520s either, Maybury may have been of French parentage. The name could derive from *Mabire* or *Maubire*, found anciently in the Beaubec-la-Ville area, or from *Dumabrier* or *Dumarbrier*, found anciently at Neufchâtel.

At Beaubec-la-Ville were firstly Jehan Maubire (1486) and Godin Mabire (d. 1505), followed

523. ESRO, QR 77, mm. 33, 50-1; I am indebted to Brian Phillips for this reference.
524. TNA, SC 2/206/33, f. 29.
525. ADSM, 2 E 14/1174 (4 Nov 1536).
526. ESRO, PBT 1/3/2/204 (1595); 1/1/4/494 (1560).
527. O. F. G. Hogg, *English artillery, 1326-1716*, p. 97.

by Godin's brother Nicolas Mabire.[528] In 1504 Guillaume Maubire of Beaubec-la-Ville bought from the curé of Louvicamp a rent of a livre on Pierre Mallerbe of Beaubec, whose surname, most uncommon in the Pays de Bray, was that of the Le Becquet hammerman Henry Malherbe. Later came Jehan Mabire of the parish of La Bellière (1537) and Joachim (1544) and Colin Maubire (1545) of Beaubec.[529]

At Neufchâtel, Pierres Dumabrier, styled either *Noble homme* or *escuier*, was *grenetier* of the town from 1482 to 1512. He was followed by Jehan Dumarbrier, *escuier* (1513), and Franchoys Dumarbrier of Arques, who was imprisoned in 1528 at the instance of Guyon Guerard of Les Hayons in Esclavelles, a collier.[530] The family did not apparently continue at Neufchâtel, but a French cleric named John de Marbrier, who migrated to England, became a Norwich surgeon, and was made denizen in January 1541.[531]

Margaret Bourder bore John Maybury at least seven children, Joan, Nicholas, Elizabeth, Richard, Christopher, Mary and Clement,[532] of whom Richard was buried at Mayfield in 1572. The baptisms of Joan and Nicholas have not been found, but the baptisms of Elizabeth and Richard show that the family was at Etchingham in 1569 and 1570, and those of the remaining children took place at Mayfield from 1573 to 1575. In addition, two illegitimate children were born to Maybury, John baptised at Etchingham in 1570, and a daughter named Awdryan, who was baptised at Mayfield in 1573, but survived only two months.

Alice Fuller, whom Maybury married in 1576, bore him two more children, John and Agnes, who were baptised at Mayfield in 1577 and 1578, after which he moved to Lyhode borough in Hartfield where he paid fines of 2 pence in May and November of 1581 for default from views of frankpledge.[533] He may have resided in Hartfield for a year or two longer, but had apparently left the Weald by 1587, when he was no longer recorded at Lyhode.

As we saw, the burial of John Maybury's wife Alice was recorded at Ellastone in north Staffordshire in 1603. John Mayberye of Makeney, whose son John was baptised at Duffield in 1600, was perhaps their eldest son, but John Mowbray of Duffield, whose children were baptised at Duffield from early in 1607 up to 1620, may have been a different person.

The John Mayberie who was buried at Bexhill in 1593 could be the hammerman's illegitimate son, baptised at Etchingham in 1570. However, if this was the case the two John Mayburys of the year 1606 are difficult to account for. First came John Maybury at Cleobury Mortimer, whose children, Francis, Thomas, Richard and William, were baptised between 1604 and 1613, of whom Thomas was baptised in November 1606. He may have been the Makeney John Mayberie of 1600, but was clearly distinct from John Mayberie, whose son William was baptised at Monmouth in July 1606.

A double finery forge had been built under a sixteen-year lease of Monmouth fulling mill made in November 1603 by Moore Waters of Monmouth to Robert Chantrell of London, gentleman, and Thomas Mathew, gentleman, who acted in trust for Edmund Mathew of Radyr in Glamorgan. The house in which Robert Chantrell, John Mayberie and others dwelt at the forge was mentioned in a Chancery case brought in 1606 by Chantrell against Moore Waters, who had been encouraged by the forge's success to take a share in it.[534]

Chantrell, who in 1607 obtained a 21-year patent 'to make and forge iron and steel with slow coal, sea coal, pit coal and peat coal',[535] had already become involved together with Mayberie in a scheme to smelt iron with 'peate and sea coale, without or with very little mixture of charcoale' at Whitfield Forge in Hampshire, which John Astell of Gray's Inn, esquire, held on an 18-year lease from Sir Walter and Dame Katherine Long. This project led to two chancery suits, one initiated by Astell and the other by Dame Katherine's second husband, Sir Edward Fox, in which Chantrell was alleged to have claimed

528. ADSM, 2 E 14/1140 (15 Dec 1486); 2 E 14/1150 (12 Nov 1505).

529. ADSM, 2 E 14/1147 (11 Nov 1504); 2 E 14/1177 (7 Sep 1537); 2 E 14/1188 (30 May 1544); 2 E 14/1189 (18 Apr 1545).

530. ADSM, 2 E 14/1139 (3 Mar 1482); 2 E 14/1154 (3 Aug 1512); 2 E 14/1156 (14 Jun 1513), 2 E 14/11 (1 Apr 1528).

531. *Letters and Papers, Henry VIII*, **16**, 580 (59).

532. All these children except Richard were mentioned in 1578 in the will of their uncle John Border of Etchingham, who left £24 to be divided amongst them (ESRO, PBT 1/1/7/249).

533. ESRO, ACC 3587/8, ff 193, 211.

534. TNA, C 2 Jas I, C22/69.

535. *Calendar of State Papers Domestic, James I, 1603-1610*, p. 346.

that Mayberie, who had worked for him some 20 years earlier, 'was the perfectest man under God for the bringinge therof to perfection'. Mayberie was brought from Monmouth to work at Whitfield in April 1606 but although he was paid 10 shillings a week until Whitsuntide 1608, he made many costly trials without success.[536]

The sexual licence of the former Mayfield hammerman makes it entirely credible that he was this man, who had apparently now embarked on a third marriage, and whose son William had been baptised at Monmouth, though it is not clear where Maybury could have formerly worked for Chantrell.

Meanwhile, other sons of the former Mayfield man were at work elsewhere in the Midlands. Clement Maybury was first encountered as a hammerman in Staffordshire in 1603, when Gilbert Robertes of Brewood Park, hammerman, was bound in £10 to keep the peace towards him.[537] Later Clement was at Wednesbury, where his daughter Isabel and son Edward were baptised in 1608 and 1609. He moved on to Parkend Forge in the Forest of Dean, where his daughter Joan was baptised in 1617. By 1621 he had returned to the Midlands: his son Thomas was baptised at Wednesbury in 1621 and his daughter Anne at Kinver in 1624. He was probably followed to Kinver by a nephew, John Mayberry and his wife Elizabeth, whose son Thomas was baptised at Wednesbury in 1625, and who were probably parents of a child baptised at Kinver in March 1628.[538]

Clement's elder brother was probably the hammerman, Nicholas Mebrye of Fernhill Forge near Oswestry, who was buried at Whittington early in 1634. The hammerman Martin Mobrye, who married Abigail Ussall at Whittington in 1637, was perhaps Nicholas's grandson, though no intervening generation is recorded. In 1651 Martin Maybery was transferred to the East Denbighshire works,[539] whose forge was at Pont-y-Blew.

It seems possible that Roger Mowberi (Maybery or Mowbery), who married Joan Lightwood at Aston-next-Birmingham in 1599, was a son of John and Alice Mabery, baptised around 1579 after their move to Hartfield. Roger's daughters Mary and Margery were baptised at Aston in 1600 and 1601. He was buried as Roger Mobury at Aston in 1624.

Returning to the Cleobury Mortimer family, Clement's and Nicholas's half-brother John Maybery was probably the man of that name buried there early in 1618, and his widow probably the Eleanor Maybery buried in 1620. His eldest son John was probably the forgeman John Mabery whose eldest surviving son was John Maybery, baptised at Cleobury Mortimer in 1624, the mother being named as Elizabeth. As we have seen their second son Thomas was baptised at Wednesbury in 1625 and another child was apparently baptised at Kinver in 1628, the mother's name unusually being the only one legible throughout the three entries. This John Maybury was probably John Maybury 'of the Forge' who was buried at Cleobury Mortimer early in 1651.

Their eldest son will have been the 56-year-old John Mowbray, hammerman at Wentbridge Forge in Yorkshire, who gave evidence in a Chester Exchequer court case of 1680 relating to the South Yorkshire ironworks.[540] It is impossible to know whether John Maybery of Colnbridge, whose children, William, Mary, Elizabeth and Hannah, were baptised at Huddersfield from 1679 to 1685, was on temporary secondment at Wentbridge in 1680, or whether this Wentbridge man was the father of the Colnbridge man. The Colnbridge man was presumably the John Mabury whose son John had been baptised at Rotherham in 1675 and whose first son named William was buried at Huddersfield in 1678.

Francis Mabury, baptised at Cleobury Mortimer in 1604, married Joyce Potter at Neene Savage in 1627 and was the hammerman whose daughters, Mary, Katherine and Elizabeth, were baptised at Cleobury Mortimer from 1628 to 1632. His younger brother the forgeman Richard Maybery married Elizabeth Newey at Cleobury Mortimer in 1630 and their children, William and Richard, were baptised there in 1631 and 1632. After 1634, a ten-year gap ensued in the parish register during which both Francis and Richard probably left the parish.

Richard and Elizabeth Mayberye's later children, Elizabeth, Humfrey, Thomas, Francis and John, were baptised at Longnor from 1639 to 1650, John being a posthumous child. Their second son

536. TNA, C 2 Jas I, A11/20 and F2/44.

537. Burne, *Staffordshire Quarter Sessions Rolls*, **5**, p. 33.

538. No further Maybury entries occurred at Wednesbury after 1625. Only the mother's name (Elizabeth Mebry) is legible at Kinver on 5 Mar 1628.

539. I. Edwards, 'The early ironworks of north-west Shropshire', pp. 190, 201.

540. TNA, CHE 15/88 (Spencer v. Alsopp, 28 Mar 1680).

Richard stayed at Longnor and he and his wife Sara's children, Robert, Thomas, Sara and Ann, were baptised there from 1659 to 1673.

The youngest brother of Francis and Richard may have been William Maybury 'of the Forge' whose wife Margaret was buried at Cleobury Mortimer in 1648. The name of his second wife was Susanna and their children, Sarah, Susanna, Rowland who did not survive infancy, and Richard, were baptised there from 1653 to 1665. Another William Maybury whose twins were baptised at Cleobury Mortimer early in 1679, but were buried the following day, was apparently described as an 'artisan' in the burial entry.[541]

The last member of the Maybury family mentioned in connection with the forge at Cleobury Mortimer was Thomas Maybury. Thomas and Alice Maybury's son Thomas was baptised there in 1669.

Later we shall see that by the 1620s elements of indirect-method technology, including the drome-beam hammer, had been introduced into the bloomery forges of Furness. Instrumental in this transfer of technology may have been another Richard Maybury. The hammerman John Maybury's son Richard had died in 1572, so this forgeman may have been a son of John's second wife Alice, born at Hartfield in the 1580s. By early 1627 he was well enough established in Furness to marry Anne, daughter of the Cumbrian forgemaster William Wright. They were described as being of Churchtown in Cartmel, both at their marriage and when their children, John, Mary, Nicholas, Martin, James, Godfrey and Clement, were baptised between 1628 and 1642. However in the entries for the baptism of two sons, both named Richard, in 1637 and 1638, their father was named Richard Maybury 'of the forge'. Of these children, James, the first Richard, and Godfrey did not survive infancy.

Both Richard Maybury and his wife died in 1642, when their eldest son John was aged only 14, and it was Robert Skyring who from 1641 to 1654 was described in the parish register as 'of the forge'. Later it seems that Peter Russell, who had been at Hornby Forge from 1635 to 1640 and who succeeded Richard Russell as hammerman at Force Forge in 1647, moved on to Cartmel Forge in 1658, leaving Force Forge in the care of his son James. Peter Russell 'of the forge' was buried at Cartmel in 1673.

The reason for John Maybury's failure to play a leading role at Cartmel or elsewhere was disclosed in 1708 by 'Richard Maybury of Lisnayrell, county Londonderry, forgeman, son of John Maybury of Cartmel, forgeman'. His father had been 'a wasteful man and had to retire from business in 1657 to Ireland, where he died in 1677'. John Maybury was almost 29 years of age when he moved to Ireland, which was where the younger Richard Maybury had been born.[542]

In the Midlands the Maybury family was meanwhile represented at Coalbrookdale, where Thomas Maybury was hammerman in 1668.[543] Edward Maybury who was buried at Madeley in 1665 may have been Clement Maybury's son. Thomas perhaps appeared in the Madeley parish register in 1672, when John son of Thomas and Margery Maybury of Coalbrookdale was baptised there. It seems possible that this Thomas Maybury was Richard Maybury's son baptised at Longnor early in 1643, because Richard's other sons, William and Humphrey also appeared in the Madeley parish register in 1662 and 1665 respectively. Whilst Thomas Maybury was not mentioned after 1672 at Madeley, William and his son Silvanus, baptised in 1662, continued in the parish. William Maybury the elder was buried at Madeley in 1703 and Silvanus was still at Madeley when his wife Elizabeth was buried there in 1718.

By his first wife Sarah, Silvanus Maybury had sons named Edward and Silvanus baptised at Madeley in 1686 and 1688, of whom Silvanus did not survive. By his second wife Sarah Forshea, he had two more sons named Silvanus baptised in 1692 and 1697, of whom the latter apparently survived. Richard and Mary Maybury's children, Margaret who died aged 10, William, Mary, Jane, Margaret, Elizabeth, Silvanus and Anne, were baptised from 1690 to 1708. Either these families left the area, or they became nonconformist, because the surname is not found in the parish register after 1718.

On the other hand the family became prominent in Wales, at the Stour forges, and at Powick Forge and Bewdley in Worcestershire, where they may also have been nonconformist in sympathy. John Maidbury of Llanelly, forgeman, was mentioned in 1727 in the will of his father-in-law, Thomas Watkins of Abergavenny, and was probably the forgeman William Maybury of Machen whose will was

541. It is suggested that the transcriber of the printed register, the original of which no longer survives, wrongly expanded an abbreviated form of this word into 'artist'.

542. TNA, C 10/527/77.

543. B. S. Trinder, 'A description of Coalbrookdale in 1801', *Transactions of the Shropshire Archaeological Society*, **58** (1967-8), p. 251.

proived at Llandaff in 1740; Maybury's wife Elizabeth was a certainly a widow in 1777.[544]

At Hartlebury on the lower Stour, William and Mary Maybury's son Thomas was baptised in 1692. No further entries for this man appear in local parish registers, but he was probably William Maybury of Mitton, forgeman, whose will was dated 5 June 1753 and was proved in April 1754. William Maybury was survived by his wife Mary, three daughters, and a son and grandson both named William Maybury, though not by his son Thomas.[545]

The elder of the two William Mayburys could havc been William Maybury of Bewdley; he and his wife Elizabeth had their daughter Margaret baptised at Wolverley in 1747. The younger was perhaps William Maybury of Mitton who married Elizabeth Hutton of Hartlebury at Stourport in 1777, and whose children, Isabella, William, Thomas and Hanna, were baptised at Hartlebury from 1778 to 1789.

In addition to giving rise to a Maybury family which entered the iron industry at entrepreneurial level in South Wales, the Powick branch of the Mayburys produced a forgeman William Mabury, who was born at Powick around 1777 and married Margaret Bishop at Hartlebury in 1804. Their children included the hammerman Henry Mabury, baptised at Stourbridge in 1814, another forgeman William Mabury, who was born at Stourbridge and was aged 26 at the time of the 1851 census, and probably also the spade-plate forger, John Maybury, also born at Stourbridge, who was aged 31 in 1851.

The Wolverley parish register shows that at least two forgemen from this family, Francis and William Maybury, worked at Cookley Forge in 1813 and 1814 respectively. Francis Maybury had perhaps married Mary Harrison at Hartlebury in 1790; if so he must have remarried, perhaps more than once; his wife was stated to be Elizabeth in 1813 and Sarah in 1815. William Maybury of Cookley's wife was named Ruth.

Santo

John Sancto was first mentioned in the Weald at Frant in March 1572, when the birth of his son Edmund was recorded. Sadly, this son and Santo's wife both died in April 1573. Santo then established himself at Hawkhurst, where the marriage of Thomas Robins to Alice Santo had been recorded in 1561. John Sancto married Alice Springett at Hawkhurst in April 1574 and the baptisms of their children, Mary and William, were recorded at Hawkhurst in 1579 and 1581. 'Santo a Frenchman' was buried there in 1587.

The family was next found at Ticehurst, where John Saynto married Elizabeth Smythe in 1601. Elizabeth bore John Santo one child, Catheryn, in 1603, but died the following year. Santo next married Joan Broddin at Whatlington in 1606 and their children, Mary, John, Alexander and Grace, were baptised at Ticehurst between 1607 and 1615, though John and Grace did not survive childhood. The family then moved to Goudhurst, where their children John and Joan were baptised in 1618 and 1622. John Santo appears then to have married yet again, because, following his own burial at Goudhurst in 1630, a widow named Mary was buried there early in 1633.

John's sons John and Alexander were married in 1641 and 1645 respectively, John at Ticehurst to Dorothy Fuller and Alexander at Goudhurst to Anne Gouldringe. Dorothy bore John Santo one still-born child who was buried at Ticehurst within a month of their marriage and a daughter Mary who was baptised at Goudhurst early in 1642. Unfortunately Dorothy was buried at Ticehurst one week later.

Is it then credible that John Santoe, who married Elizabeth Gerrat at Hawkhurst only eight days later could have been this widowed John Santo of Goudhurst? Certainly he married again quite soon because his son John was baptised at Goudhurst in 1645 and Alexander's children, Joan and Alexander, were baptised at Goudhurst in 1646 and 1654.

It seems more likely that the John Santo who married Elizabeth Gerrat was a son of William Santo. William had been born at Hawkhurst in 1581 and had married Elizabeth Patchinge in 1604. They reappeared at Hawkhurst in 1614, for the burial of their son Robert, who had apparently been baptised elsewhere, so Elizabeth Gerrat's husband may also have been born during this sojourn elsewhere than Hawkhurst. William and Elizabeth's children baptised at Hawkhurst after their return to the parish around 1614 were Joan and Elizabeth, baptised in 1615 and 1619, but their mother died as a result of

544. National Library of Wales, LL/1740/128; Canning, L.H. ed., 'Catholic registers of Abergavenny, Mon., 1740-1838'*Catholic Record Society*, **27** (1927), pp. 113n, 127.

545. Worcestershire Archive and Archaeology Service, 008.7 BA3585/515.

childbirth and was buried only ten days after Elizabeth's baptism. It must be presumed that William soon married again because his son William was baptised at Hawkhurst in 1622. This younger William Santo was probably the man buried at Hawkhurst in 1679, whilst William Santo, whose two wives named Anne were buried at Hawkhurst in 1685 and 1690, will have been the third generation of Santos with this baptismal name.

Only its persistence in ironworking parishes on the Kent-Sussex border, and the 1642 marriage of William Santo to Elizabeth Gerrat, can be adduced as evidence for a connection of this family with the manufacture of iron.

9

EXPANSION THROUGHOUT BRITAIN AND TO AMERICA, 1575-1650

During this period the spread of Walloon ironworking was as spectacular within Britain and overseas as was its growth around much the same time in the Rhineland and beyond. The north of England was penetrated during the late 1570s, north Wales and southern Ireland during the 1590s, and the extreme north of Scotland by around 1610. It seems that attempts were made to exploit the mineral resources of Virginia almost from the colony's inception and only the complete destruction of the works and the massacre by Indians of all the forgemen but one at Falling Creek in March 1622 prevented these plans being carried through. During the 1640s a plant embodying a blast furnace and finery forge was set up in New England at Braintree near Boston, followed by a complete ironworks called Hammersmith, with double finery and slitting mill, at Lynn near Salem, which was completed by around 1650.

It is hoped to demonstrate that in the expansion of the indirect process throughout the British Isles and to New England, ironworkers from the Weald, and more especially those of immigrant stock, whether of Walloon, Brayon or more broadly French descent, played the dominant role. There is no means of quantifying this exactly, and indeed the proportions of immigrant to native personnel may have varied from one ironworks to another. Also, the singularity of many of the foreign surnames known from the denization and subsidy rolls makes the immigrant presence more immediately perceptible than that of native ironworkers. Nevertheless, it seems probable that up to around 1650 the role of the descendants of immigrants was preponderant as far as the very specialized work at the forge was concerned. It can be argued that among furnacemen the immigrant proportion may have been diluted, but even there, in the specific case of New England, both the first ironfounders, Roger Tyler and Robert Post, were of Brayon descent.

Bloomery forges in Cumbria

Paradoxically, the supremacy of the indirect process in Britain was demonstrated in the bloomery forges of Cumbria, where firstly drome-beam hammers and later plated forge-hearths, were installed. The forgemaster William Wright's contract for building Muncaster Head Forge in 1636 mentioned the 'hirst' and 'boits' of the hammer assembly. The use of the drome-beam hammer at Force Forge around 1660 is confirmed, not only by the 'hurst', and by the 'bolts' in which the hurst pivoted, but by the protective collar, or 'bray', strapped onto the helve at the point where the 'arms' of the 'hammer beam' struck it from below to lift it. The 'legs' between which the hurst pivoted were also mentioned at Force.

Iron was still smelted direct from the ore in the traditional manner in these Cumbrian works and the smelter remained a 'bloomer', but his hearth was now called a 'finery'. The former 'string' hearth of the bloomery was now called a 'chafery' and the man who operated it was a 'hammerman' rather than a 'stringer'. Although Force Forge had only a single finery, the agreement for Wright to build Muncaster Head Forge in 1636 envisaged three hearths, two of which will have been so-called fineries, of which Cunsey Forge, built in 1618, had two in 1639.[1]

At Force Forge the 'water post', which supported the end of the drome beam adjacent to the water wheel, and the 'prick post', which supported the drome beam's other end beyond the hammerman, were both mentioned. At Milnthorpe in 1655 a 'tree for the blast poule for the bellis' equates with 'a pole to the phurnis to lift up the bellows' mentioned at Panningridge in 1549 and suggests that at both places the bellows were linked by a harness, which at Force involved a 'swingletree'; this lifted the top bellows-boards alternately to reinflate them, after the action of the cams on the hammer beam had depressed them to produce the blast. At Force Forge the hammer-beam was even strapped with 13 wrought-iron

1. Awty and Phillips, 'The Cumbrian bloomery-forge of the seventeenth century and forge equipment in the charcoal iron industry', pp. 29, 31.

hoops, exactly the number inventoried at Park End and Lydbrook Forges of the indirect process in the Forest of Dean.[2]

The imported technology in use in Cumbria can be taken back to at least 1628 by the mention in depositions taken then at Ulverston of the 'hoops' of the hammer beam, of the 'makett' (Fr. *maquette* - a partly formed piece of iron) and 'loop' (Fr. *loupe*) in place of bloom at Burnbarrow Forge. Plates, probably those of a plated hearth were referred to at Milnthorpe in the 1650s, and for Force Forge six plates (possibly the four side plates, a bottom plate and a work plate) were shipped from Bristol to Grange in 1675 to be installed at the forge.[3]

William Wright, who initiated many of the Cumbrian forges, obtained the lease of Burnbarrow Forge in 1614, but had been in the Cartmel area from at least 1608. The surname Wright was common in Cumbria, and the names of other forgemen particularly associated with the indirect process cannot be shown to have arrived in the area before 1627, so it seems possible that Wright brought in these innovations.

No member of the Maybury or Russell families, each formerly associated with the indirect system in the Weald, deposed to the Ulverston inquiry of 1628, but Force Forge had been built in 1621 and Burnbarrow Forge even earlier. Richard Maybury married at Cartmel in 1627 and was buried there in 1643, and Richard Russell was married at Colton in 1629 and was mentioned in that parish register in connection with Force from 1630 to 1647. In the 1630s three 'foreners' from the Russell family working at Hornby Forge were mentioned in Melling parish register,[4] Peter in 1635, Charles in 1637 and George in 1640. Peter Russell left Hornby to follow Richard Russell as hammerman at Force Forge, and remained there up to June 1658, but then moved to Cartmel, where he remained until his burial in 1673. His son James Russell, the next hammerman, stayed at Force until February 1660, and was later mentioned at Cartmel in 1680 and 1683. The hammerman Charles Russell moved from Hornby to Cunsey Forge, where he was succeeded by his eldest son Charles in 1669. His younger son Robert was hammerman at Force Forge in the 1670s, but when Robert died in 1681 his will showed him then to be hammerman at Hacket Forge.

TECHNOLOGY IN THE WIDER INDUSTRY

The slitting mill

The addition, during the second half of the sixteenth century, of the slitting mill to the workshops deployed by the indirect process was the final stage in the development of the charcoal iron industry. Two hundred years later the iron industry described in the *Encyclopédie* embodied no further improvement. Substantial changes did not come until the eighteenth and nineteenth centuries, when the discovery firstly of a way to employ mineral fuel in the furnace and secondly the introduction of hot blast, allowed phenomenal increases in furnace size and pig iron production, accompanied by even more revolutionary changes in the forging process.

The blast furnaces of the charcoal era produced a variety of cast iron depending on the quality of the ores used. The best quality of 'tough' pig iron was readily produced from haematite ores found in areas such as the Forest of Dean and Furness; in other areas only a minority of the ores available gave 'tough' pig iron, and much of the cast iron produced was to a greater or lesser degree 'cold short', that is to say it was subject to fracture when cold. Skilful blending at the forge enabled acceptable qualities of bar iron to be produced from these different kinds of pig iron.

Whilst 'best merchant' bar was suitable for use in a wide variety of trades, the greater proportion of 'cold short bar' went into the nail trade. But much manual labour was expended in reducing bar iron to sizes suitable for making nails. A great advance came with the introduction of 'rod mills' for rolling and slitting iron. Heated bar iron was firstly flattened into a thinner plate by passing it between rollers set on parallel axles one above the other; this plate of iron was then split into rods by passing it between

2. Ibid., pp. 31, 33.
3. Ibid., pp. 29, 35.
4. 'Foreners' in the colloquial sense of strangers to the area, in contrast to 'stranger', still used throughout the sixteenth century in place of 'foreigner'.

steel discs similarly set on parallel axles; some descriptions suggest that both rollers and discs were set on the same axles, but the principle remained the same. Again 'best mill rod' had wide suitability, but 'cold-short rod' went almost exclusively to the nail trade.

The fact that the Beaussault forgemasters had supplied large quantities of iron in rods (*verges*), quite distinct from iron in bars, but sold at the same price, to a Rouen merchant in 1512 has already been commented on, with the caveat that these cannot have been the kind of rods which were later produced at slitting mills. Nevertheless, it must be conceded that the earliest mention of a slitting machine (*instrument a coupper feire*), which came in 1579, occurred in France, when the duke of Guise leased Linchamps Forge, adjacent to the upper Meuse, to Jean David of Mézières. Furthermore, the first illustration of such a slitting machine was published at Nancy in 1584.[5]

In the Netherlands three slitting mills were set up in 1583 on the Vesdre in Franchimont by David and Remacle Kock, who were probably descended from the Namur family of that name.[6] Another mill, whose site is unknown, belonged to the Liégeois forgemaster Laurent Budbach, and this could have been slightly older, because by 1587 its rollers and other instruments were said to be much decayed.[7]

In England Bevis Bulmer obtained a 12-year patent in 1588 for the exclusive right to operate a water-powered engine for cutting iron into small bars or rods. By tradition the first such mill was erected in 1590 at Dartford in Kent by Godfrey Box, who claimed to be a native of Maastricht,[8] but whether Bulmer was involved in this is not known. Bulmer's patent was not renewed in 1600 and Box died in 1604.[9]

In December 1618 Clement Daubeney was granted a 21-year patent for 'engines to be driven by water for cutting of iron into small bars', and already in January 1617 Sir Francis Bacon had averred that the nailers and blacksmiths of London were 'now supplied' by Daubeney, although it was they who had been most vociferous in opposing his patent when he first applied for it in 1613.

In Ireland at the East India Company's ironworks and dockyard near the castle of Dondaniel in county Cork, the master carpenter William Burrell of Deptford had already erected a slitting mill by 1613. Another was erected in Ireland at Tallowbridge in county Waterford in 1624 by Richard Blacknall and Henry Wright, tenants of Richard Boyle's ironworks there.

Much around the same time the first slitting mill in the Midlands was set up, as we shall shortly see, in the Whorwood manor of Stourton around 1614. The second known mill in the Midlands was that on the Paget estate at Rugeley, which was held by Thomas Chetwynd together with Bromley Forge in 1623. Inevitably, the great forgemaster Richard Foley of Stourbridge set up his own slitting mill at the Hyde, Kinver, around 1625 and in 1633 he agreed to supply bar iron to another slitting mill, Bustleholme mill near West Bromwich.[10]

The blast furnace

The spread of larger blast-furnace hearths, which had evolved from the need to run greater quantities of cast iron in one tapping for the casting of large cannon, can probably be seen at Rievaulx in North Yorkshire in 1587, where 'a new furnace hearth of a new facion' was installed, although the existing furnace was only about ten years old. It was accompanied by the new practice of weighing the sows produced at the blast furnace. The consequent detailed output figures for the campaign of 1591-2 show that the furnace did not attain its optimum output of one ton of iron per tapping until over eight weeks into the campaign. At Rievaulx, contrary to received opinion, output did not rise towards the end of the campaign as wear and tear increased the size of the casting hearth; the figures show that a sow of one ton was the highest amount cast at one tapping throughout the whole of the 30-week campaign.[11]

5. André and others, *La métallurgie du fer dans les Ardennes (XVIe- XIXe)*, p. 14, and n. 26.
6. Hansotte, 'La métallurgie wallonne', p. 140.
7. Yernaux, *La métallurgic liégeoise*, p. 28.
8. Kirk and Kirk, eds. *Aliens dwelling in London,* **1**, p. 417. Godfrey Box the younger first appeared in London in 1565 and Godfrey Box the elder in 1567.
9. For this and the following paragraphs see Schubert, *British iron and steel industry*, pp. 304-5.
10. *Victoria County History of Shropshire*, **2**, pp. 111, 114.
11. Schubert, *British iron and steel industry, p. 200,* Appendix X.

INDIRECT-PROCESS IRONWORKS IN ENGLAND AND WALES

The Weald

At the extreme west of the Wealden area, Rogate Forge and Coombe Furnace are thought to date from 1589, and from Rogate, parish-register evidence, including the burial of a finer named Stephen Hunt, who could have been of English descent, as early as 4 February in that year, suggests that building might have commenced during the previous year.

Later in 1589, children of the finer Abraham Bluett, of Anthony Farnes, of John Gringoe, all men of immigrant descent, were baptised at Rogate. Henry Pascue, who married Elizabeth Sudgwicke in January 1589, bore a name not found in the Sussex subsidy rolls of the 1520s and was presumably an intruder whose surname could be a French patronymic. Henry Sone, who was in the parish from 1590 to 1593, and the collier William Kenchyard, who was buried at Rogate in 1599, were probably of English descent, but Charles Unckles, George Chiverill, Laurence and Martin Pynnion, Nicholas Lenie, Elizabeth Gagge, Dominic and Clemens Busse, Peter de Vale, Thomas Rowe 'a straunger', Richard Marian and Peter White, whose names all appeared in the parish register during the 1590s, seem to be persons brought to the parish in connection with the forge, and all of probable immigrant descent.

Bramshott Forge was started much about the same time as Rogate, and Thomas Bettsworth supplied Henry Champion with pig iron for it, probably from Milland Furnace. Bramshott parish registers mentioned Adrian Dogyn of Frensham in 1570 and Thomas Bilbowe in 1582, but it was from 1589 that names of immigrant ironworkers began to appear with frequency. Jarman Larby had children baptised there in 1589 and 1592, Gilbert Perigo in 1593 and 1597, Thomas Barden in 1595 and 1596, and Robert Turke from 1598 to 1605; he was probably Robert Turke 'of the hammer' buried at Bramshott in 1642.

Men from immigrant families married at Bramshott were William Jarlet in 1591, John Thousand in 1592, Edward Jelly in 1599 and Samuel Briday in 1600, and the baptisms of Briday's children followed from 1601 to 1618. Anthony and Charles Oubery (alias Larby) were married at Bramshott in 1604 and 1609 and Charles Oubery's children were baptised there between 1613 and 1621. John Barden's daughter Magdalen was baptised there in 1605. Thomas Turke married at Bramshott in 1607 and may have been married there again as Thomas Tompling alias Turke in 1628. Roubery, whose sons Edward and Henry were baptised at Bramshott in 1623 and 1625, was perhaps John Rowberie who had further children baptised at Bramshott between 1637 and 1640. Richard White's son Marian was baptised and buried at Bramshott in 1634 and Roger White married Mathew Rowbery there in 1646.

Although Knepp Furnace was reputed to have been worked by the Carylls from 1568 to 1604, nothing in the subsidy rolls of the 1570s confirms this. The furnace will have worked in conjunction with Shipley Forge. No sixteenth-century parish register exists and before the series of bishop's transcripts commencing in 1593, only that for 1584 survives. The marriage of Philip Frances to Agnes Thousand early in 1594 was almost certainly between two people of French descent. The furnace was probably in blast by then or 1595, when Charles son of the ironfounder Roger Quentens (alias Tyler) was baptised at Shipley.

At the other extremity of the Weald where Westfield Forge and Brede Furnace dated from the late 1570s, the fragmentary state of Westfield parish register prevents the identification of immigrant families until the baptisms of Elizabeth Spray and Peter Honyset in 1586, and of Susanna the daughter of the finer Nicholas Messans in 1589. John Almon alias Laby, who was a finer at Westfield in 1596,[12] seems not to have made any impact on the parish register, either then or earlier.

Westfield Forge ran in conjunction with Brede Furnace and Brede parish register showed the presence there of the founder William Jarrat by early in 1582. His children, Anthony, Thomas and Anne, were baptised there in 1582, 1584 and 1586. The collier Nicholas Fever's son James was baptised there in 1588, whilst Charles Lambert appeared there in 1594 and Charles Pulleyn in 1596.

For Beckley information is more sparse because the parish register started only in 1597, around

12. Cockburn, *Sussex Assize records, Elizabeth 1*, no. 1646; Hunnisett, *Sussex Coroners' inquests 1558-1603*, no.492.

ten years after the building of Beckley Forge.[13]

South-west England

The earliest ironworks operated on the indirect method in south-west England so far identified is a furnace on the river Dart in Ausewell Wood in Ashburton parish, some 15km upstream from Totnes. It was referred to in 1598 as 'certayne yron Milles nere Ashpurton of Mr Adryan Gilbertes', which produced good steel and iron from iron ore carried to it from Brent Hill, which lay about 10km to the north.[14]

The works was depicted on a map of the manor of Ashburton dated 1605;[15] this indicated that two mills were powered from a leat some 600m long which ran parallel to the river on its eastern bank. Water was diverted into the leat by a weir across the Dart, and the long strip of land formed between the leat and the river was divided into three sections by two channels of discharge which allowed water to return to the Dart. The northernmost of these channels was a spill-way for surplus water. On the southernmost and largest island, south of the second of the channels, were depicted two buildings; the largest of these, perhaps incorporating a finery and a hammer mill, was situated on the south side of the second channel, and the smaller building, probably the furnace, was driven off the main leat, shortly above its end, where the remaining water returned to the Dart.

Near the furnace site glassy slag, varying from green to black, has been found; the more northerly site yields slag, which could be from a bloomery perhaps operated before the building of the blast furnace, or from a finery.[16]

Adrian Gilbert has been identified as commander of the Chagford and Ashburton stannary militia in 1586-7 and as the representative of Ashburton stannary at the Tinners' parliament at Crockerntor in 1600.[17]

It seems possible that Thomas and Edmund Mocumber, from the immigrant family of that surname, may have moved from the Weald to Devon in the context of the setting up of Ausewell Furnace; their respective sons Thomas Mocumber, the future Exeter ironmonger, and his cousin and servant Samuel, were baptised at Exeter in 1606 and at Totnes in 1622 respectively.

In north Somerset an 'iron mill commonlie called Horner Mill situate in the parish of Luccombe' was set up at much the same time by George, William and Robert Hensley of Selworthy, but its exact site has not been identified. After George Hensley's death in 1606, his widow married John Edbroke of Selworthy. Edbroke and she brought a chancery suit against her brothers-in-law for her late husband's share in the profits of the mill.[18]

The case shows that 'tonnes of iron' were acquired from Jeremey Waters, perhaps a relative of the Waters family which had been involved in setting up Monmouth Forge. If this suggestion is correct it looks as though Horner mill was not itself a finery forge, but perhaps worked up wrought iron shipped across the Bristol Channel from Wales. Nevertheless, John Edbroke's surname is unusual in the area and is reminiscent of the Wealden hammerman, Thomas Edborough of Frant, who in 1586 was allowed benefit of clergy when found guilty of the theft of three bushels of barley-malt from Edward Chapman.[19]

The surnames of Alexander, John and Peter Jurden (1594-1607), Robert Ewens (1596-1603), in the form of Yowins, Henry Tyler (1595-97), Henry Valentine (1599), Hugh Pray (1603), Philip Rowland and Joan Kemp (both 1608), and Hugh Skinner (1621), which occur in bishop's transcripts for Luccombe, were Wealden and do not seem to be local ones. The same may be said of the surnames of Robert Huesh of Luccombe who married Agnes Lawrence at Selworthy in 1616, perhaps of those of

13. Not identified until after Brian Awty's death, Hothfield Forge, north-east of Ashford in Kent, came into being as late as the 1650s, but at least some of the ironworkers mentioned in the Hothfield registers, such as Francis, Fuller, Harvy, Jerman or Jarmyn, Lambert, Missing and Russell, may have had immigrant forebears.
14. Devon Record Office, Exeter, 123M/E33.
15. TNA, MPB 7.
16. C. R. Blick (ed.), 'Early blast furnace news', *Historical Metallurgy*, **18**, *1* (1984), p. 47.
17. The Devon Centre for Further Education, *Historical Metallurgy Society visits Devon, September 19th - 21st 1986*, p. 9.
18. TNA, C 2/Jas I, E3/31.
19. Cockburn, *Sussex Assize records, Elizabeth I*, no. 2135.

Thomas Chepman, who married Agnes Valentine, probably Henry Valentine's widow, in 1605, and of George Chepman who married Joan Kemp in 1609. Henry Tyler's widow was probably Tamson Tyler, who married John Hurley in 1605. Richard Rayment, who was buried at Luccombe in 1595 also looks like an intruder in the parish. The other 'foreign' name to occur was that of the supplier of iron, Jeremy Waters, whose son Richard was baptised at Luccombe in 1605.

Lastly, the move of the finer Thomas Leonard from Cleobury Mortimer to Pensford on the Chew in Somerset around 1630 should be noted. In this case it seems very unlikely that pig iron worked at the forge would have been brought so far inland from South Wales; a local source of pig iron in Mendip would indicate that the iron industry noted there by Leland almost a century earlier had continued, or had been revived.[20]

The other ironworks of this period in the south-west were Funtley Forge near Fareham and its furnace on Sowley Pond south of the New Forest, which belonged to the earl of Southampton and are thought to date from 1605. The forge could be thought of as a westward extension of the Wealden works and indeed many of the surnames in the Fareham parish register before 1605 are similar to those encountered in the Weald. However, the closely related families of Ellis and Laby or Lavy, which appeared in that register between 1605 and 1610 were clearly immigrant ones, as was the Greengo family, which moved from the western Weald to Funtley rather later, but eventually acquired a proprietorial interest in both works.

At Sowley the surnames Gerrat or Jarrett, Greengo, Hussey, Kervil, Lambert, Le June, Post and Voashall, which appeared in the Beaulieu parish register between 1653 and 1694 are clearly those of immigrant ironworkers; the names Dussell [more probably Duffell], German, Jurdenne, Laussell and Wassell are probably from the immigrant community too, whilst Thomas Trafiche [more probably Traficke], who was buried at Beaulieu in 1687, may also have originated in the Weald.

Wales

Two out of three furnaces built in Monmouthshire in 1576 had Wealden connections: Pontymoel was built by the ironfounder John Truve [or True], presumably related to the ironfounder of that name who had worked at Robertsbridge in the early 1540s, and in this case the forgemaster was perhaps the Wealden Thomas Fermor, who certainly possessed the furnace during the 1580s; Abercarn was established by Edmund Roberts of Hawkhurst, and there guns were cast before Roberts died in 1579, after which it came into the hands of the Worcestershire forgemaster Richard Hanbury, who may have held it until his death in 1608.[21] But Trosnant Furnace in Monmouthshire, also built in 1576, was Hanbury's own foundation.[22]

Coity Anglia Furnace and Forge in Glamorgan were built on land north-east of Bridgend, demised in 1589 by Sir Robert Sidney and his wife Barbara (née Gamage), whose inheritance it was, to John Thornton of Neen Savage and John Crosse of Cleobury Mortimer. By 1600 the Coity works were in the hands of Willard and Bullen, two Wealden forgemasters.[23]

The furnace at Bedwellty in Monmouthshire in the Sirhouwy valley was operated in 1597 by a London haberdasher named John Challoner and by Thomas Moore of Bristol, ironmonger.[24] Of these Challoner was perhaps connected with the Sussex family of that name.

The Midlands

The concentration of ironworking around Cannock Chase and Abbots Bromley had led by 1595 to that area being badly disforested. Around 1570 Sir Francis Willoughby had considered setting up ironworks on his estate at Middleton near Tamworth. He was dissuaded from the enterprise by the shortage of wood and especially a report that 'there is not any leafte in the cowntrey to be bowght, except it be in Drayton

20. H. Scrivenor, *History of the iron trade*, p. 35.
21. Schubert, *British iron and steel industry*, pp. 366, 384.
22. Ibid., p. 177.
23. Ibid., p. 372.
24. Ibid., p. 367.

(Basset) lordshyppe'.[25] Instead, a bloomery forge was set up at Hints. Nicholas Lycette, forgemaster at Horsmonden in 1564, who had held the lease of the earl of Shrewsbury's forge at Oakamoor in north Staffordshire from 1572 to 1577, was put in charge at Hints.

On the other hand, the Harcourt family of Ellenhall, which had held the manor of Godstone in Surrey in the 1560s when Woodcock Forge and Warren Furnace were built, set up a furnace near Stone and a forge at Norton in Chebsey parish, which Schubert thought might go back to 1574.[26]

Upstream from Market Drayton two forges were established around 1590 on the river Tern. A third was probably started at much the same time near Wrinehill on the Checkley Brook which flows into Cheshire. The entrepreneur at Norton Forge was William Grosvenor of Bellaport; the pond there was said to date from 10 October 1589 and in November 1590 the forge was leased to George Leicester.[27] The second forge, that of Sir Thomas (later Lord) Gerrard, was at Winnington in Mucklestone parish, and since Sir Thomas's hammerman, George Growte, is shown by the respective parish registers to have moved from Betley to Mucklestone, and therefore from Tib Green Forge near Wrinehill to Winnington, between 1593 and 1596, it must be presumed that Winnington Forge was set up around 1595 and that Tib Green Forge preceded it.

Near Norton Forge, the Tern is bordered by Norton parish on the north and by Mucklestone on the south, so workers there appeared in both parish registers. At Winnington, Woore parish lay to the north and Mucklestone to the south, but no ancient parish register for Woore survives, so Mucklestone's register is the only source of information about forgemen there.

The source of sow iron for these forges is a problem not easily solved. The suggestion that it may have been Madeley in Staffordshire is prompted by the baptism at Norton in 1596 of William son of Quinten Tayler (*recte* Tyler, the ironfounder), whose other children were baptised at Madeley, and who was buried at Betley in 1622. But if Tib Green Forge, a mile downstream from Madeley Furnace, was in action by 1593, a second furnace for these three forges probably has to be sought. A possibility might be Heighley Furnace, which Walter Chetwynd is thought to have closed down after he secured possession of Madeley furnace in 1649.[28]

The Norton parish register recorded the burial of Katherine, the wife of a finer named Jonson in September 1591. If the finer Joseph, whose son Gilbert was baptised and buried at Norton in May and June 1592, was the same man he must have rapidly remarried, but in any case neither man was referred to again. Edward Richardson, whose son Thomas was baptised at Mucklestone early in 1600, was hammerman at Norton, and the same register shows that this family was still represented at Norton Forge up to 1728. Norton register also recorded the brief presence in 1596 of Peter Trunchin, when his daughter Katherine was baptised there.

Richardson was probably, and Trunchin certainly of immigrant descent, but the native Hansen family, associated by 1652 with Norton Woodseats Forge near Sheffield, first appeared in the Mucklestone register in 1605 when John Hansen married Ann Gibbens [*Gittens*?].

John Lee married Elizabeth Addams at Mucklestone in 1601; that both their families were still associated with Norton Forge in 1727 was shown by the Mucklestone register, which then recorded the baptism of Edward son of Thomas and Rachel Lea, and by the Norton register, which recorded the baptism of Ralph son of Ralph Adams. John and Katheryn Barnett first appeared in the Mucklestone register in 1608, but it was with Norton Forge that the same register associated Humphrey and Elizabeth Barnet in 1670. Though presumably descended from the Winnington hammerman George Groote, Abraham Grout, who married Jane Whitmore at Mucklestone in 1653, worked at Norton Forge.

Almost all parish register entries relating to Winnington Forge were recorded at Mucklestone. In addition to Growte, Sir Thomas Gerrard probably employed a worker named Bilbowe, because 'Widow Bilboo' from Sir Thomas's works in Winnington was buried there in 1599. Perhaps her husband had

25. R. A. Pelham, 'The growth of settlement and industry, 1100-1700' in *Birmingham and its regional setting*, 1950, p. 148.

26. Schubert, *British iron and steel industry*, p. 388.

27. Burne, *The Staffordshire Quarter Sessions Rolls, II: 1590-1593*, p. 4; National Register of Archives, Crewe MSS. Thomas Leicester, one of George Leicester's brothers had married Susanna Lodge, daughter of Sir Thomas Lodge, who in 1563 had held five forges, presumably bloomery forges, in north Staffordshire, and another brother William was at one time mayor of Chester, a market, and port of export, for iron.

28. Awty, 'Charcoal ironmasters of Cheshire and Lancashire', p. 73.

been John Bilbowe who, together with his wife and son, had been at Shipley Hirst Forge in Yorkshire in 1593.[29] Gerrard also employed a hammerman named John Githinges, whose son Gilbert was baptised at Mucklestone in 1601, but this family, perhaps of Welsh origin, also later worked at Norton Forge, from where another John Gittins was buried in 1694.

The presence of the Brisburne family of forgemen at Winnington was first noted with the marriage of Thomas Brisburne to Alice Jelly of Gnosall in 1602. He will have been Thomas Brisbourne the elder, of Winnington Forge, buried early in 1652. His son Thomas Blisburne (*sic*), baptised in 1605, was the Winnington forgeman whose first wife Eleanor was buried in 1655 and who married Anne Wilkinson early in 1656. The younger Thomas Brisborne, described in his will as a 'forge finer',[30] was buried in 1661. Another member of the family mentioned at Mucklestone was Gilbert Brisburne who married Ann Partington there in 1610 and whose daughters, Susan and Eleanor, were baptised there in 1611 and 1613. The baptism of John, son of William and Catherine Brisburne, was recorded at Norton in 1643 and although William's later children, Alice, Peter and Joseph, were baptised at Mucklestone from 1649 to 1654; the last entry confirmed that he worked at Norton Forge.

Another family probably of French descent was that of Mathew; Thomas and Edward, sons of Edward and Elizabeth Mathew, were baptised at Mucklestone in 1600 and 1606. Both sons went on to Fernhill Forge near Oswestry, where the Whittington parish register showed that they pursued the ancestral trade of the Mathew alias Bewser family, that of fining, but their parents perhaps ended their days at Wortley Forge in Yorkshire.

The Mucklestone register shows the appearance of new surnames at both forges after the Civil War. These were John Dutton of Winnington Forge, who was buried in 1664, Benjamin and Katherine Bluit of Winnington Forge who first appeared in 1669, and John Moral, or Murrall, who married Katherine Tharpe in 1671. Morrall was stated to be of Winnington in 1673, but in 1678 was of 'the new forge', probably Bearstone. Humphrey and Mary Tomkison also appeared at Bearstone Forge in 1683, and John and Mary Heiley at Norton Forge in 1686.

Bearstone Forge had first been mentioned in the parish register in 1675, when Benjamin Bluit was there. He and his son Simon stayed at Bearstone Forge until their respective deaths in 1693 and 1699. The Murralls however were back at Winnington Forge by 1688. A younger Benjamin Blewit and his wife Mary were described as of Oakley from 1690 to 1695, of Norton Forge in 1698 and 1700, but had moved to Knighton by 1704. The same Benjamin Blewit will have been the man of that name who was at Bearstone in 1706, but who was described as a 'servant forgeman' of Winnington Forge at his burial in 1726.

Other new surnames continued to appear; William Plant of Bearstone Forge in 1693, Hugh Keay of Dorrington, forgeman, in 1699, William Ellet of Norton Forge in 1718, William and Margaret Dawes and William and Magaret Grove both of Winnington Forge and Paul White of Norton Forge, all in 1720. Thomas Errington of Winnington Forge appeared in 1722, Philip Mathers (more probably Mathews, who had been at Makeney in the 1670s, or his son Philip baptised at Duffield in 1674) of Winnington Forge in 1725, Joseph Emberton, forgeman, in 1726, Thomas Lennard of Norton Forge in 1730, Thomas Bromhall of Norton Forge in 1738 and Richard and Hannah Timmis of Winnington Forge in 1743.

A collier named Berrie had children baptised and buried at Mucklestone in March 1597, but the parish register failed to reveal his baptismal name; the child baptised was Edward Berrie. William Mynion, a Market Drayton collier, had children baptised at Mucklestone in 1599 and 1602 and at Market Drayton in 1604. His daughter Mary was buried at Drayton in 1606 and he himself was buried there in 1607. The Norton register named another collier, Thomas Serjante, whose daughter Alice was baptised in 1602. The entry of 1604 at Mucklestone for the baptism of John son of Thomas and Joan Sargant showed that the couple then lived further up the valley at Aston (*Asheton*). Thomas, together with John Sarjant, who worked as collier at Oakamoor around the same time, remind us of *petit* Jehan Le Sergent alias Platebourse, and Guillaume Sergent, his brother, of Auvillier, from whom the Beaussault forgemasters bought charcoal in 1541, and suggest a further immigrant family from France.

The detailed findings from Mucklestone register have been recounted at length because no other parish register in the country recorded the workplaces of forgemen so consistently over so long

29. TNA, E 134/35/6 Elizabeth 1, Michaelmas 34.
30. LRO, Wills proved at Lichfield, Thomas Brisbume, 1661/2.

a period.[31] But it must be suspected that several persons mentioned in Mucklestone and Norton parish registers who were not named in association with any forge were nevertheless involved in ironworking. At Mucklestone, the 'stranger' William Minshowe who was buried in 1591 may have been a forgeman. This could be a Cheshire name Minshull, but its occurrence in other ironworking parishes opens the possibility that the original surname might have been Mishawe, assimilated to Minshawe.

Peter Spencer, whose children, William, John and Anne, were baptised at Norton from 1588 to 1594, disappeared from the area, but was probably Peter Spencer 'of the Iron Mylls' mentioned in the Condover parish register in 1609. People from Woore and Knighton mentioned in the Mucklestone parish register, especially members of the Hussey family, and Thomas Trevett, who married Elizabeth Serjeant of Wybunbury in 1724, may also have been involved at the forges, but no parish register entry confirms this.

It will be seen that in the early period surnames belonging to immigrant families predominated, and that even after the Civil Wars, half of those newly engaged were possibly of immigrant descent. The proportion became significantly less only after 1690.

	Immigrant	Possibly immigrant	British immigrant
1590-1640	G. Growte	Jonson	J. Hansen
	P. Truncin	E. Richardson	J. Lee
	J. Bilboo	Berrie	H. Adhams
	W. Minyon	T. Seriante	J. Githinges
	T. Brisburne	J. Barnett	J. Dutton
1640-1690	B. Bluit	H. Barnett	H. Tomkison
	J. Murrall	J. Heiley	
1690-1740	P. White	W. Ellet	W. Plant
	T. Lennard	W. Dawes	H. Keay
	P. Mathers		W. Grove
			T. Errington
			J. Emberton
			T. Bromhall
			R. Timmis

Table 11: Forgemen on the River Tern

It should be noted that the names Adams and Grove were Wealden ones and that Gittins probably came to the Midlands from South Wales.

The furnace at Madeley in Staffordshire was probably in being by 1595. It perhaps worked in conjunction with Tib Green Forge, further down the valley near Wrinehill, first mentioned in the Betley parish register in 1619, but probably in being in 1593, when George Growte was first noted at Betley. Growte perhaps came from the Rugeley area where Peter Growte has been encountered earlier and where Lawrence Growte had been finer at Bromley Forge in the 1580s.

Around 1590 Sir Francis Willoughby at last went ahead with his plan of rebuilding the bloomery forge at Hints as a finery forge to convert sow iron produced at his new Warwickshire furnace at Middleton into bar iron. Being heavily indebted by having built Woollaton Hall in Nottinghamshire in 1588, he somewhat later set about converting the bloomery forge on the earl of Shrewsbury's estates at Oakamoor in the Churnet valley into a blast furnace. Spasmodic financial accounts are available for both enterprises.

No contemporary parish register survives for Middleton, so the only names of furnacemen known are the few mentioned in the accounts. In 1592 the founder appears to have been Addams,

31. The period 1650 to 1743, apart from 1703 to 1709, is particularly helpful in this regard.

assisted by Quintin Tyler, the keeper, and by Kyrby. A filler named Gyll or Gyllam was also mentioned. In 1593 Quintin was founder, assisted apparently by Jo[hn] Gyll[am]. A singularity of the 1593 accounts is that they disclose that Quintin Tyler was married on 12 June, because from the day of his marriage John Morishurst took over accounting for the carriage of wood. The colliers were Jenson and Mynion, perhaps the William Mynion who later appeared at Norton, as did Quintin Tyler.

Accounts for Hints Forge in 1595-6 name the principal workers, who had livery coats, as Gregory [Haddock] and [Thomas] Drewett; the others were Gunn, Asheforde, Nicholas, Holier and Whitbe.[32] The parish register described Thomas Druett as the finer and Gregory [Haddock] as the hammerman.

But names connected with the indirect process in the Weald can be found in the Hints parish register from its commencement in 1559, suggesting that the bloomery forge had already been established by that date.

A daughter of Thomas Devell was baptised early in 1560. Thomas Devell was buried early in 1573 and a widow named Margery Devell early in 1577, but Hugh Devell married in 1582 and baptisms of his children, Jane, Agnes, Margery, Edward, Dorothy, John, Thomas, Joan, Elizabeth, Hugh, Margaret and Raphe, followed from 1583 to 1608.

Roger Buttry was buried at Hints early in 1564 and William Buttry in 1569, whilst baptisms of Henry Buttrey's children commenced with Edward early in 1572, and continued with Jane, John and James, up to 1582.

Hugh Garratt was buried at Hints in 1566, and a widow named Isabel Garrat in 1570. Henry Garrat married Amy Beck there early in 1575, and baptisms of their children, Edward, Jane, James and John neither of whom survived, Anne, John and Walter, followed from 1575 to 1594. The burial of Henry's 17-year-old son John at Middleton (furnace?) was noted in the Hints register.

Nicholas Gardyner was married at Hints in 1568 and the baptism of his son Edward followed in 1569; Richard Gardener's daughter Jane was baptised in 1574, but neither man appears to have stayed at Hints.

The 1590s and the changeover to the indirect system saw the appearance of surnames belonging to English families engaged in the iron industry. These were Gregory Harrock or Haddock (1594), William Brookshaw (1598), John Hiley (1599), and Roger Wynfield (1605). In 1603 Nicholas Brookshaw married Helen Haddock. The name Wynfield is reminiscent of the payment recorded in the Robertsbridge Forge accounts in 1551 of 8 pence 'to George Coke for a drynke for boy Wynfyld and for helyng of hys backe when he cam owt of France'.[33]

A *filius terre* or illegitimate child was baptised with the French name Pascall in 1580. Thomas Drewytt, the finer, whose children, Ralph who did not survive, and Katheryn, were baptised at Hints in 1594 and 1596, was almost certainly of French descent. Other definitely French surnames did not appear until Humfrey Morall's son Humfrey was baptised at Hints in 1609 and John Jellie's daughter Elizabeth was baptised there early in 1622. Morall had previously been at Burrington in Herefordshire in 1599, and he later returned to Goodrich in that county, before perhaps ending his days in Derbyshire. This branch of the Jellie family stayed at Hints until at least the 1670s.

At Oakamoor the new works was laid out lavishly with a double-finery, as shown by a reference to 'the nether fynery'. At the furnace Welsh names predominated. The founder was Humphrey Bedall or Beddowe, recruited from Stourbridge. The first campaign ran for 13 weeks from September 1593 to January 1594 and Beddowe left at the end of it; he perhaps went on to Cleobury Mortimer, where a man of that name was buried in 1608. It is not clear who succeeded him; a keeper named Myell Watkyne was mentioned and the founder was helped by Mathew and Haskye, or Hastye. In 1596 the founder was possibly William Pryce and in 1598 perhaps John Beaven,[34] but from then until 1608 no founder was named. Of these only Mathew is likely to have had French ancestry.

However, at the forge the finer was Maurice Lawrence, probably of French descent, and recruited from Attercliffe forges near Sheffield; hammerman was the English Richard Widdowson. Lawrence left in May 1594 and was followed as finer by Hopkins, an English name which had occurred, again without baptismal name, as helping to set in the hammer block at Robertsbridge in October 1551, along with

32. UNMASC, Middleton Papers, 5/165/49, 51 and 57.
33. KHLC, U1475 B8/4.
34. UNMASC, Middleton Papers, 5/165/53, 59 and 63.

the immigrant finers Peter Gelly, Hugh Marchant and John Lenard.[35] The Oakamoor man was perhaps Thomas Hopkins, who by 1599 was finer at the 'New forge' in West Bromwich.

Others named at Oakamoor were Peter 'the finer', and Barlo 'the fyner', but whether the former was Peter Venton, of immigrant stock, who was paid 1s 4d for two days work at the dam, and whether the latter was the Lewes Barlow (probably English) is not certain. Other workers at the forge in 1593-4 were Armyshaw and Vallo. In 1596 the labourers at the forge were Barton, George Jolye and his brother Richard, Robyn 'the finer's man' and Gregory [Haddock]. In 1599 Drewett and old Drewett were mentioned, but again it is not clear which one of these was Drewett 'the Fyner'.[36]

The miners in 1593-4 were Thomas Allyn, Francis Morris and Thomas Wardle. In 1599 they were Thomas Mylles and 'young' Mylls, in 1600 Roger, Glover, Mylles and Cotterill, in 1605 Benett, Lyssett, Dayken, Gregorie and Mylles, in 1607 Gregorie, Mylles and Johnson, and in 1608 Mylles and Whithurst.

Initially John Harvye corded wood and John Sarjant, related presumably to the Mucklestone collier Thomas Serjante, was the collier. In 1593-4 the colliers were John Sargent, John Morres, John Harvye and Thomas Watkyne. In 1594 they were John Harvye and Blake (i.e. Black) [Thomas] Foster. In 1596 they were John Sargent and John Harvye. In 1598 they were John Harvye and Tingell. In 1599 they were John Harvye and Thomas Tyngell, who had been at Rievaulx in Yorkshire from 1588 to 1595. In 1599 they were Harvye, Ball, [Thomas?] Tyngell and Roggers. In 1600 they were John Harvye, [Thomas?] Tyngell, Ball and Foster.[37]

From 1605 onwards the colliers at the forge were distinguished from those at the furnace. John Harvye continued as collier at the forge. At the furnace there were [Thomas?] Foster and [Thomas?] Sarggente in 1605, [Thomas?] Foster and Thursfeld in 1607 and [*blank*] Harvye and [Thomas?] Foster in 1608.[38]

Woodcutters in 1593-4 included Lawrence and Thomas Harvye, Randall Jackson, Jolye, Richard Fawlkner and John Hees, in 1596 John and Lawrence Harvye, William Bardye [Barden?] and Bagnall, in 1598 John and Richard Barton, Maryan, Anthony Clarke, William Lawrence, Francis, John Harvye and Hugh Hull, in 1599 they included Hugh Harvye and Mabberlye, in 1600 they included James Clarke, Timothy Rallinge, Thomas and John Barton, Edward Vastell [Vashall?], William Vynton and John Holme, in 1605 Thomas Barton and Leonard and William Clarke, in 1607 Gregorie, Awberie, Harvye and Botte and in 1608 Robert Bothe [Booth or Botte?], Thomas Barton, Hopkyns, and Ralfe 'the Collyer'.[39]

A hint that John Harvye may have come from the Weald along with Nicholas Lycette, who had been forgemaster at Horsmonden in 1564, was given by John's marriage to Joan Lycette at Rugeley in 1585. That the Lycette family continued at Oakamoor is shown by the participation of one member in mining for the ironworks there in 1605. Their surnames suggest that this work-force was evenly divided between those of immigrant and those of native descent.

A casual worker at Oakamoor in 1607 and 1608 was 'Old Brysborne', who will have been related to the families of that surname at Mucklestone. He was paid 4 shillings for eight days work in 1607.[40] His name provides a link with 1637, when Richard son of John Brisbie was baptised at Cheadle.

Also at Oakamoor around 1630 were Thomas Bartholomew and John Pountin, who may both have been descended from Bartholomew Ponting. Thomas Bartholomew had earlier been at Ellastone, where his sons Richard and William had been baptised in 1626 and 1629. The same man was presumably indicated when a wife of Thomas Bartholomew 'of Oakamore' was buried at Cheadle in November 1636 and also when Dorothy wife of Thomas Pountin was buried there in August 1638. Thomas Pountin married a third wife, Anne Aspie, in October 1639. Five daughters of John and Anne Pounton were baptised at Cheadle from 1640 to 1648, but John Pountin himself was buried there early in 1652.

Abraham Pountin who was buried at Cheadle in 1649 will also have been from this family and it continued at Cheadle in the persons of John and Sarah Bartholomew, whose children John and

35. KHLC, U1475 B8/4.
36. UNMASC, Middleton Papers, 5/165/52, 54, 59 and 64.
37. Op. cit., 5/165/52, 53, 55, 59, 63, 64 and 66.
38. Op. cit., 5/165/68, 71 and 72
39. Op. cit.., 5/165/54, 59, 63, 64, 66, 68, 71 and 72.
40. Op. cit., 5/165/71 and 72.

Thomas were baptised there in 1668 and 1670, William and Sara Bartholomew whose daughter Sarah was baptised there in 1671, and John Bartholomew whose daughter Elizabeth was baptised there in 1694.

Loscoe Furnace in the Derbyshire parish of Heanor was established by Sir John Zouche of Codnor in 1582. The ironfounder at Loscoe was Charles Tyler, who had married Margaret Valliance at Ashburnham in 1562, and who was buried at Heanor in 1610. Judging from their surnames it seems probable that all four of the sons-in-law mentioned in his will,[41] George Berry, Thomas Hooke, Richard Snape and Henry Dale, had accompanied him from the Weald, although it was at Heanor that Richard Snape married Tyler's daughter Mildred in 1598.

In the Middleton papers survive accounts for Makeney Forge on the Derwent for the years 1590 to 1592, because the younger John Zouche, who succeeded his father around 1588, leased it, together with Loscoe Furnace and another forge at Hartshey to Sir Francis Willoughby, in order to pay his debts. Robert Darby, who came to Makeney on 20 May 1592 was paid £3 9s 0d to run the forge until 31 July. The accounts show that Gregory and Barden were finers there;[42] there was no mention of Jordan Russell II who had been hammerman in 1583, when he instituted his Chancery case concerning the ironworks in south Wales. Barden was probably James Bardyn of Makeney, whose wife Dorothy was buried and whose infant son James, who did not survive, was baptised at Duffield in September 1605.

Other Makeney workers mentioned in the Duffield parish register were probably Ralph Johnson (1599), Thomas Johnson (1600), John Mayberye (1600), who may have been the John Mobery of Milnhey buried at Heanor in 1616, and Peter Pavye, who had been at Danby in North Yorkshire in 1586, and whose wife Elizabeth was buried at Duffield in 1602. John Morrell who was at Makeney in 1604, went on to another works at New Mill later that same year. Francis Lassells was at Makeney in 1606, followed by William Johnson in 1607, Simon Lees in 1608 and Thomas Dakyn in 1613, though Dakyn was of New Mill by the time he died in 1644. Other workers mentioned at New Mill were Henry Scott and Robert James (1600), Jeremy Myngoes (1601), though he was styled 'of Duffield' in 1602, Robert Morrell (1602), John and Thomas Bab (1636), John Jolly (1637-40), and Thomas Russell, who was Valentine's son and Jordan II's grandson, and had been baptised at Helmsley in 1610; he married Ann Hill at Duffield in 1639.

Other workers of immigrant descent were mentioned in the Duffield register: Richard Vinton of Rotherham, who married Alice Crosse of New Mill in 1645; William Perigo of New Mill, the Attercliffe finer who had married at Sheffield in 1657, and whose children Sarah and Gilbert were baptised at Duffield in 1660 and 1665; Edward Lambard of New Mill who was buried early in 1666; from 1674 to 1677 three children of Philip Mathews, who was variously described as 'of New Mill', 'of the Forge', and 'of Makeney Forge', Philip, James and John, were baptised at Duffield.

John Mathew, from the Mathew alias Bewser family, whose sons William and Joseph were baptised at Duffield in 1626 and 1634, was at Hopping Mill in 1626 and at New Mill in 1634. He went on with Oliver Mathew from Pleasley, to become a finer at Wadsley Forge near Sheffield before February 1641, when his daughter Ellen was baptised at Ecclesfield. He was dead by 1647, when his son Joseph was apprenticed to Hugh Hobson, a Wadsley cutler.[43] It seems probable that Samuel Mathew who married Elizabeth Bardin, perhaps the daughter of the finer James Barden, at Duffield in 1623, and was 'of Hopping mill' in 1624 and 1625, was also from this family.

John Whiston 'de Makeney, finer at the forge', who was buried at Duffield in 1697, was however probably of English descent. He was presumably related to William Whistons, 'finer at the forge', buried at Wednesbury early in 1680.

The Heanor parish register had mentioned other furnaces than Loscoe, all of which were possibly quite short lived. Anthony Shorter of the furnace in Codnor Park had been buried in 1599, but Thomas Shorter of the same furnace was married in the same year. Charles Tyler's son-in-law, Richard Snape, who had worked at Loscoe Furnace in 1611 was stated to be of Denby Furnace when he was buried early in 1625. Early in 1626 Ann the daughter of John Mason of Shiple[y] Furnace was baptised.

Another man who may have been from the Weald was John Emerie of Loscoe Furnace who was buried at Heanor early in 1620. It also seems certain that both John Spurre of the parish of Denby, who

41. LRO, Will of Charles Tyler of Heanor, 1609.
42. UNMASC, Middleton Papers, 5/165/48.
43. Leader, *Company of Cutlers in Hallamshire*, **2**, p. 290.

married Helen Walker of Langley at Heanor in 1600, and whose daughter Helen was baptised at Heanor in 1602, and also Marian Spurr, whose daughter Margaret was baptised there in 1603, were children of Marian Deproan who had married at Kirdford in 1565 and three of whose children, Charles, Mary and John, had been baptised at Worth from 1572 to 1578.

Marian Deproan was in Yorkshire by the late 1580s, where he worked as a collier for the forgemaster Thomas Dyke at Dacre and at Warsill, near Ripon.[44] Later, as 'Marian Spur' he was among the workmen engaged by Thomas Proctor to set up a furnace near Shipley Hirst on the river Aire, intended to smelt local ores using a mixture of coal and peat as fuel.[45]

After 1603 John Spurr presumably moved on to join his elder brother Charles, from Castle Donington, and their father Marian who by 1660 had moved further down the Aire valley to Calverley. Both Marian's sons, Charles and John Spurr, had children baptised at Calverley in 1604 and 1606.

Richard Spurr of Shipley Park, where Heanor parish register had showed that there was a furnace in 1625, and who had his daughter Ellen baptised at Heanor in 1624, and John Spurr whose son John was baptised at Heanor in 1645, were possibly sons of the younger Marion Spurr, who had stayed on in the Heanor area.

Another Derbyshire forge which extensively employed forgemen of immigrant descent was Pleasley, thought to have been set up in 1611.[46] Early in 1615 Valentine Russell II, son of the finer Valentine Russell I, Jordan Russell II's son, who up to 1610 had been at Rievaulx in North Yorkshire, was baptised at Pleasley, whilst John son of Richard Russell, finer, was baptised there only a few weeks later. Valentine Russell I was buried at Pleasley in 1647, but both Valentine Russell II, and Richard Russell, the finer, appear to have moved on to Colnbridge Forge near Huddersfield in Yorkshire. Towards the end of 1615 a third finer of French descent named Gilbert Hosey [Hussey] married Jane Swinscoe, but she died in June 1619.

Elizabeth, the daughter of a fourth finer of immigrant descent, Oliver Mathew, was baptised at Pleasley in 1639. Oliver moved on, with John Mathew from New Mill, firstly to Wadsley Forge, from where his daughter Isabella was buried at Ecclesfield in September 1641. Another daughter Katherine was buried at Sheffield in 1645, by when he was presumably employed at the Nether Hammer (Attercliffe Forge). His son Oliver was baptised at Sheffield in 1648, and in 1649 his son John was apprenticed to Richard Shirtcliffe of Bridgehouses, cutler.[47]

Another possibly immigrant family at Pleasley during the seventeenth century was that of Spray, most of whose members were either husbandmen or labourers, though Thomas Spray of Sherbrooke, who was buried in 1619, was a cooper. In 1641 Anne Spray married Abraham Minion, who may have been from the family of colliers formerly noted at Market Drayton.

Meanwhile, furnaces and forges had proliferated in what was to become called the Black Country, some of them on the sites of former bloomsmithies. The Sedgeley parish register mentioned several hammermen between 1578 and 1585, and a finer in 1610. At Ettingsall there was a furnace whose founder James Tyler was buried in 1603; he was probably the founder who had been at Sheffield in South Yorkshire in 1577.

To the east in Shenstone parish lay Little Aston Forge, the forge, chafery and hammer mill of which had already fallen into decay by 1600, when Roger Fowke leased it to the Wednesbury yeoman and former nailer, Thomas Parkes. Parkes was already a considerable forgemaster by 1597, when he owned a furnace at Perry Barr and a forge in Handsworth and held the lease of a forge in West Bromwich.

A rival forgemaster of higher social standing was William Whorwood of Sandwell, esquire, who owned the moiety of a forge at Perry Barr and held moieties of leases of a second furnace at Perry Barr and of a forge at Wednesbury.

Each of these works was cited in quarter sessions proceedings because of an act of violence committed on 8 July 1597 and the subsequent reactions; on that day Whorwood's leasehold furnace at Perry Bar was broken into by Thomas and Richard Parkes and their Perry Bar employees, Ralph and Thomas Wyllys and Edward Ashmore. Six days later all three of Parkes' works were subjected to similar

44. TNA, C 183/7/1055.

45. TNA, E 134,/35/6 Elizabeth I, Michaelmas 34.

46. P. Riden, 'The charcoal iron industry in the East Midlands, 1580-1780', *Derbyshire Archaeological Journal*, **111** (1991), p. 68.

47. Leader, *Company of Cutlers in Hallamshire*, **2**, p. 290.

treatment at the hands of Whorwood and his employees: the house of Robert Tomplyns at Perry Bar was broken into and Parkes' servant Edward Ashmore was assaulted there; twelve persons assembled by Whorwood's friends at Handsworth carried off 1000 pounds of bar iron, 37 pieces of bar iron weighing 1500 pounds, 'one paire of Chaferie bellowes ... two paire of fynerie bellowes', four pairs of tongs, three chisels, a great forge hammer, four little hammers, thirteen great iron plates, 'two Twyornes of Iron', one iron sledge, two 'hammer Eies of Iron', seven iron pins, 'Two pattens of Iron for the fynerie bellowes', 'sixe greate Iron Clammes', 'fower Ringers of Iron', 'A furgen of Iron', 'A Stocker', 'a hurste', 'a Brey', 'divers iron wedges', two anvils, two iron 'Cosses', three weights for weighing iron, and six iron hooks.

The final outrages took place on 18 July, when William Cumberford's smithy at Wednesbury, which was in lease to Whorwood, was broken into by Thomas and Richard Parkes, Ralph and Thomas Willies and Edward Ashmore, and on 19 July, when William Whorwood's iron mill at Perry Bar was broken into by Ralph and Thomas Willis.[48] At the date of the inquisition Whorwood's moieties of the furnace at Perry Barr, and of the forge at Wednesbury, and Parkes' Forge at West Bromwich, were still being held by the opposing parties and Whorwood was still being disturbed in his use of his forge at Perry Barr.

If the terms finery and chafery were not enough to testify to the employment of the indirect process here, the hurst and the bray for a drome-beam belly helve, and the terms of French origin for ironworking tools, such as 'ringers', 'furgen', and 'stocker', make it clear enough.

The reference in the Handsworth parish register of 1602 to Richard Haddock of 'le old forge iuxta handsworth, hamberman', is apparently to the hammerman of Witton Forge which lay just across the Warwickshire border in Aston-next-Birmingham. One of the godparents at the baptism of David Haddock on this occasion was Edward Bomer, the finer of the Old forge.

Two earlier hammermen at Witton, George Lea, or Ley, and Thomas Dutton alias Tomlynson had been referred to in the Aston parish register in 1580 and 1581 respectively. Together with Richard Pennesall of Perry Barr, founder, and others they were presented for riotous assembly and assault at Perry Barr in September 1590. They and the others involved were subsequently outlawed.[49] The Aston parish register shows that already in 1583 Laurence Marrian (alias Dipperey) was at Witton, when it recorded the baptism of his son William there. He may be the man who from 1573 to 1580 had been in Sheffield.

It seems likely that Thomas Parkes was the entrepreneur at this earliest known forge in the Birmingham area, because the hammerman George Lea and the finer Francis Best from Witton were among Thomas Parkes' accomplices and witnesses cited in the quarter sessions presentments of 1597, whilst Katherine Deppery and Thomas Hopkins, the finer of the 'New forge' in West Bromwich according to the Handsworth parish register (1599), were witnesses for Parkes concerning the break-in at Robert Tomlyns house and the assault on Edward Ashmore.

Another of William Whorwood's forgemen was presumably the finer, Blaise Vyntam of Wednesbury, who had been presented at quarter sessions for assaults on William Awton of Wednesbury in April 1596 and on Beatrice wife of John Markes of Wednesbury in September.[50] However, in 1597 two finers named Blaise Vintam were summoned to answer trespasses and misdemeanours. From 1598 both featured in the Handsworth parish register; it was presumably the younger man who married Eleanor Knolles in May 1598, and in November 1601 this Eleanor was godparent for Isabella daughter of Thomas Watkyns 'de purye Forge, hamberman'. In March 1599 William son of one of the Blaise Vyntams was baptised and buried at Handsworth, his father now being styled 'de purye alias pyrry forge homberman'. In January Alice daughter of Blasius Vyntam of Perry Forge, finer, was baptised. The last mention of Blase Vintome at Aston came in 1605 when his son, a third Blase, was baptised. It seems likely that Blaise Vyntam I was the son of James Vintam baptised at Worth in Sussex in 1561. We shall see that the family of Blaise Vintam II moved on to Donington Forge on the Trent, later to one of the forges on the Smestow Brook north of Stourbridge, and finally to New England.

Bromford, a new forge in the area, was first mentioned in the Aston parish register in 1606,[51] when Dorothy, the daughter of its clerk Thomas Crosse was baptised. Witton Forge apparently still

48. Burne, *The Staffordshire Quarter Sessions Rolls, III: 1594-1597*, pp. 297-309.
49. Burne, *The Staffordshire Quarter Sessions Rolls, II: 1590-1593*, pp. 73, 279.
50. Burne, *The Staffordshire Quarter Sessions Rolls, III: 1594-1597*, pp. 204, 297.
51. Legh, the miller at Bromford mill had been referred to as recently as 1 March 1592.

continued, because Robert Gotier (Gosher and Cocher in the parish register), a finer who had previously worked on the Smestow Brook, appeared at Witton in the 1630s. His son Francis, who had been baptised at Wombourne in 1629, was buried at Aston in 1633 and his son Robert was baptised there in 1635. He and his wife Elizabeth soon went on to Morville near Wenlock, where their son Henry was baptised in 1639.

The building of Bromford Forge may have prompted the arrival of two new names in the area. Roger Maybery (*Mowberi*) was married at Aston in 1599 and stayed there until his burial in 1624; the name Lambard occurred from 1601 onwards; Emote daughter of William Lambard was baptised there in 1601. The name Lambard was connected unequivocally with ironworking when Peter Lambard 'of Bromford forge' had his daughters Margery and Ann baptised at Aston in 1613 and 1617. In 1623 the name Brisburne first occurred; a child of John Bresborne 'of the forge' was buried in February 1623 and in the following month Allan son of Robert Bresbur 'of the forge' was baptised. No further references to John Bresborne followed, but entries for Robert Bresburne continued until the burial of his wife Elizabeth in 1639, though in the entries for 1638 and 1639 he was of 'Erdington' and no longer 'of the forge'. John Heeley of the forge was mentioned in 1605 and 1607, Francis Bradshaw of the forge was buried at Aston in 1608 and Thomas son of Richard Carter of the forge was baptised there in 1615. John Heeley (*Hiley*) had previously been at Hints, where his children Gabriel and Mary had been baptised early in 1599 and in 1601. At a later period Sarah and Anne, daughters of Richard and Mary Douler of the forge were baptised at Aston in 1676 and in 1678.

Of these surnames Maybury, Lambard and Bresburne originated in the Weald, the latter two of undoubted immigrant origin. Robert Brisburne came direct from the Forest of Dean, where his sons Peter, Stephen and Roger, had been baptised at English Bicknor from 1615 to 1620, though Peter did not survive.

Some of these Aston men probably moved on to the Staffordshire forge of Little Aston. William Lombard and Thomas Watkins were Shenstone hammermen by 1604 when another, John Atherton was bound in £10 to appear at quarter sessions and meanwhile to keep the peace towards them.[52] Children of Roger Brisbone were baptised at Shenstone or Aldridge from 1654 to 1663, and children of William Brisbone, Roger's younger brother who had been baptised at Aston early in 1629, were baptised at Shenstone from 1669 to 1683 and the family continued in the area until around 1750.

In 1537 an earlier William Whorwood, Henry VIII's solicitor-general, had purchased the reversions of the manors of Kinver and Stourton, and possession was due to revert to him in 1564.[53] By a happy chance it was just around this time that ironworking started at Cleobury Mortimer, from where bar and sow iron probably soon started to be ferried across the Severn at Bewdley and went onwards via Kidderminster to the markets of the Birmingham area. This trade was augmented by the establishment of another works operating on the indirect system in the more distant Bringewood Chase, an event which probably occurred soon after 1584, when Burrington Forge had been leased by Lord Craven to Francis Walker.[54]

Nailmaking had been a long-established occupation in the Midlands and before the end of the century the trade in sow iron across the Severn led to the building of forges on the Smestow Brook, a tributary of the Stour. Edward Jorden of Dunsley had bought the manor of Wombourne and Swindon, with a mill in Swindon, in 1592. Heath Forge and Swindon Forge were presumably the forges alluded to in the Wombourne parish register. When it was sold to Hugh Wrothesley in 1601, Heath Forge was newly converted from a corn mill; Swindon Forge was probably intended when 'Barnet of the neither Hamber' was mentioned in the Wombourne register in 1610, but Barnet entries in the parish register went back to 1600, as did probably the forge. John Jeffries was the first hammerman cited at Wombourne in 1604, and in 1605 a collier named Foulke Browne and Lambert 'an hammerman' were mentioned. Further down the brook in Kingswinford, Greens Forge was a newly built hammer mill in 1602; by around 1650 all three forges were in the hands of Thomas Foley, firstly as leaseholder but later as proprietor.[55]

52. Burne, *The Staffordshire Quarter Sessions Rolls, V: 1603-1606*, p. 179.
53. *Letters and Papers, Henry VIII*, **12** (2), no. 1008 (4).
54. L. Ince, *The Knight family and the British iron industry,* Merton Priory Press, 1991, p. 7.
55. *Victoria County History of the county of Stafford, vol. 20* (ed. M. W. Greenslade), Oxford University Press, 1994, *pp. 212-13.*

At Kingswinford, Roger and Mary Barden, whose son Davie was baptised there in 1611, sound like a forgeman's family. In the 1620s the Kinver parish register mentioned two couples from the Maybury family, Clement and Mary Mebrye and [name illegible, but probably John) and Elisabeth Mebry, whose children were baptised there in 1624 and 1627 respectively. At Wombourne the 'hamber manne' John Mebry's son Francis was baptised in August 1628.

On the Stour itself, Hales Furnace was built on a bloomery site at Halesowen before 1605 and was operated by Humphrey Lowe, who by 1610 also had a lease of Lord Dudley's furnace and forge at Cradley. At Kinver a slitting mill, where bar iron for the use of nailers was cut into rods mechanically, rather than by hand as formerly, was set up at Stourton. It was the subject of interrogatories on 17 April 1634. A local man, Richard Garrett of Stourton, stated that the site was that of a fulling mill built around 40 years earlier (1594), 20 years before it became a slitting-mill (1614), a date which made it the oldest slitting mill in the Midlands; another deponent, Richard Foley of Stourbridge, stated that he had known the mill for seven years.[56]

Locally the impact was such that by 1616 a third of the children baptised at Kingswinford were recorded as being born to nailers.[57] Whittington mill, further down the Stour in Kinver was converted into a forge in 1619 and during the late 1620s Foley converted another fulling mill at the Hyde into a slitting mill.[58]

The marriage of Roger Mowberi at Aston in 1599 had been the earliest mention of this family in the Midlands and it is almost certain that both the Kinver men had previously worked for William Whorwood at Wednesbury. Clement Mawbery, 'hammerman', had first been mentioned in Staffordshire in 1603, when Gilbert Roberts of Brewood Park, 'hammerman', entered a bond to appear at the next sessions and meanwhile to keep the peace towards him.[59] In 1608 and 1609 and again in 1621, Clement Maybery had children, Isabel, Edward and Thomas, baptised at Wednesbury. John and Elizabeth Mayberry's son Thomas was baptised at Wednesbury in April 1625.[60] It seems likely that both men worked at Whorwood's Wednesbury Forge, before Clement moved to Kinver between 1621 and 1624, followed by John between 1625 and 1627.

In the north Midlands ironworking continued to spread in both Staffordshire and Shropshire. At Ellastone, the parish register mentioned three hammermen before 1608, John Maberye, whose wife Alice was buried in 1603, Richard Jolley whose daughter Frances was baptised in 1605 and Anthony Guyes, whose son German was baptised in 1608. Mabury had married Alice Fuller at Mayfield in the Weald in 1576, Anthony Guyes had married Dorothy Young at Cranbrook in 1594, and Richard Jolley was certainly a Wealden descendant of immigrants from northern France. Only the founder, Thomas Turneley, mentioned from 1607 to 1610, was of English descent. Later forgemen of French descent at Ellastone were the hammerman Hermon Brusboye, who had three children baptised there between 1611 and 1615, before he moved on to Rievaulx in North Yorkshire, Peter Tullot, who came from Ardingly, and whose son Henry was baptised at Ellastone in 1621, and Gilbert Pinion whose son Bartholomew was baptised there in 1628.

A finery forge near Wem, which is shown by the parish register to have flourished from 1610 to 1622, may have been situated at Soulton mill. Sir Thomas Lodge, who had bloomeries in north Staffordshire around 1550, had formerly had an interest in the mill and later George Lewis became lessee. By Lewis's will the lease passed to his sons Andrew and Anthony Lewis; the ironworking interest may have arisen from the fact that Roger Kynaston of Ruyton was one of the executors.[61] It should be noted that this site was fairly remote from any known blast furnace of the period, but was in the area near Weston-under-Redcastle where Roger Morall had paid a shilling on £2-worth of goods to the lay subsidy of 1525 and not far from Kenstone where he had paid 2s 5d on £5-worth of goods.[62]

The various workmen mentioned in the parish register were the collier Robert Gotier (1610-

56. TNA, C 21/W5318.
57. In 1616, 13 fathers out of 40 were nailers, in 1618 the figure was 19 out of 48, a proportion which remained little changed in 1686 when 23 fathers out of 66 were nailers.
58. *Victoria County History of the county of Stafford, vol. 20*, pp. 146-7.
59. Burne, *The Staffordshire Quarter Sessions Rolls, V: 1603-1606*, p. 33.
60. I am most grateful to Peter Tyler for these Wednesbury references.
61. TNA, C 3/212/64.
62. M. A. Faraday, ed., *The lay subsidy, for Shropshire 1524-7*, nos. 370, 395, 152, 455.

1620), the forgeman Francis Simons (1612), the hammermen Edward Russell (1610-1612), John Myell (1613), Nicholas White (1614-1617), Roger Davice (1617), Thomas Parker (1622) and Richard Symmons (1622), the finers Edward Powell (1618), Peter Senior (1619) and Robert Jeffrey (1619) and the shinglers John Hughes (1618-1621), Roger Gorstelo (1615-1621) and Robert Wilkason (1623). Other probable forgemen were Christo[pher] Trunchin (1611), William Pridden, whose wife Margaret was buried at Wem in 1612, William Haddock, who married Joan Butcher in 1616, and the labourers Mathew Brisko (1612) and Humphrey Gregory (1616). The fact that in the space of 13 years at least six hammerman and three finers worked at the forge makes it absolutely certain that it converted sow iron into bars.

Also present were certain yeomen who may have been connected with the forge. Most obvious and perhaps most important was Nicholas Blewett, whose children, Jane and Richard, were baptised in 1612 and 1614, but who was already dead when the latter was baptised on 30 October; John Massie, whose first wife Sara was buried in 1616, who married Mary Downes of Weston in 1617, and whose children Thomas (who did not survive), Thomas and Mary were baptised from 1616 to 1620; and William Nevett, who married Margaret Shoone in 1621, but who was probably related to Amy Neevett who had married Robert Gotier in 1617. Quite surprisingly John Amyes from Wolverley was at Wem in 1617, where his daughter Anne was then baptised. Wolverley Forge on the Stour is thought to have been built in the 1650s; Amyes was perhaps from the family to which the forgeman William Ames, mentioned in the Kingswinford parish register in 1689, belonged.

Lastly William Gardner, gentleman, of Albury in Surrey should be mentioned. He left a will in which he asked to be buried in the parish of Wem in Shropshire,[63] and the parish register for Wem duly recorded his burial in the chancel there on 13 March 1644. He was himself probably the youngest son of John Lambert alias Gardener, the Cranleigh forgemaster who had died in 1593, and therefore of French descent. The large number of employees of immigrant descent at this forge, Blewett, Russell, Gotier, Trunchin, Simons, Myell, White and Senior, perhaps owed something to Gardner. It seems certain that he had been connected with the forge in some capacity, but since he apparently died unmarried, the Wem parish register failed to furnish additional information about him.

The lease for the building of Fernhill Forge near Oswestry was granted to Arthur Kynaston on 1 March 1623, much about the time that the forge in Wem parish closed. Originally Kynaston had been in partnership with Walter Coleman of Cannock, but Coleman left the partnership before 1627 and Kynaston's later partners were William Boycott, who is shown by the Whittington parish register to have been resident at Fernhill in 1634, and William Fownes.[64]

It seems quite surprising that from among the forgemen at Wem only the shingler John Hughes appeared in the Whittington parish register in 1624. In its published version his occupation was transcribed as 'fingler' (1624) and then as 'singler of Babbies woodde' (1626). An immigrant name was that of John Hussey 'of the Cabin in Babyes Woodde', which appeared in 1623 and 1624. From Winnington Forge came Edward Mathew, who married Alice verch Edward in 1625. Also from Winnington came Edward's brother, Thomas Mathewes, finer, who married Mary Edwardes in 1629. In 1630 Elizabeth daughter of William Blockley 'of the forge in Fernhill.' was baptised. Another finer was George Mathew of Fernhill, first mentioned in 1634, but by 1637 his name too had become Mathewes. Perhaps Peter Mathewes, a man of Herefordshire who died at the 'Iron Mille' in 1633 was really of Welsh ancestry.

More familiar names soon followed; Nicholas Mobrye of Fernhill, hammerman, was buried in March 1634, an entry preceded early in 1633 by the burial of his wife. Martin Mobrye married Abigail Ussall [Vassall or Hussey?) in 1637. Thomas Richardsonne of Fernhill, mentioned early in 1640, was probably the son of the Norton hammerman Edward Richardson, who had been baptised at Mucklestone early in 1600. Members of the Russell and Tyler families who may have played a part in the works were Benjamin Russell of Fernhill, whose daughter was born in July 1653, and George Tyler, who was buried at Whittington early in the following year.

The furnace and forge at Longnor were erected by Richard Holbeck under a lease dated 1605.[65] These works were first mentioned in a parish register in 1609 when a daughter of Peter Spencer of the 'Iron Mylls', who had formerly been at Norton Forge, was buried at Condover. Recruited from a

63. TNA, PROB 11/194/347.
64. I. Edwards, 'The early ironworks of north-west Shropshire', pp. 187-8.
65. *Victoria County History of Shropshire*, **8**, p, 112.

considerable distance was William Cranage, whose son Francis was baptised at Condover in 1619. He was the Rievaulx man who had married Elizabeth Rodhouse at Helmsley in 1605, and whose children, Thomas, Robert, Anne, were baptised at Helmsley from 1606 to 1612. Henry and Sara Turneley 'from the Forge', two of whose children were baptised at Condover in 1630 and 1633, had come from the adjacent parish of Acton Burnell, where their children, John, Rachael and Mary, had been baptised from 1620 to 1627.

From the Weald came Nicholas Douse, a Frenchman who had paid the poll tax at Wartling in Sussex in 1576, and who then appeared in the Wartling parish register too. He was buried at Condover in 1617, his widow Mary following him to the grave in 1624. The widow Anne Harding 'from the Forge', who was buried at Condover in 1627, may also have belonged to the Harding family who were colliers in the Weald. The Symons family too came from the Weald, but apparently indirectly. Richard and Alexander, sons of the hammerman Hugh Symons who was buried at Worth early in 1612, had been baptised at Worth in 1594 and 1601 respectively. Eleanor, the daughter of Richard Symmons, hammerman, had been baptised and buried at Wem in 1622. His brother, Alexander Simons 'from the Forge', was buried at Condover early in 1627 and Anne daughter of Richard and Jane Simons, 'from the Forge', was baptised there in 1628.

The provenance of John Cooper and Magdalen Doe of the 'Iron Mylls', who were married at Condover in 1610 and whose children, John, Thomas and William, were baptised at Condover from 1616 to 1621, is less easy to establish. William and Anne Smith 'from the Yron Mylles', whose daughter Jane was baptised in 1618, also bear a name difficult for family historians to trace elsewhere. However, John Brooke 'from the Forge', who was buried at Condover in 1629 may also have come from the Weald.

Turning now to the Longnor parish register, two ironworking families which came from the Weald appeared during the 1630s. Richard Maybury and his wife Elizabeth Newey had married at Cleobury Mortimer in 1630 and it was their later children, Elizabeth, Humfrey, Thomas, Francis and John, who were baptised at Longnor from 1639 to 1650. The last child was posthumous, but Richard Mayberye was followed at Longnor by his eldest son and namesake Richard. Robert, Thomas, Sara and Anne, children of Richard and Sara Mayburie were baptised at Longnor from 1659 to 1673. John and Elisabeth Bluitt were also at Longnor from 1632 to 1635, when their children Elizabeth and Simon were baptised. After the Civil War two further members of the immigrant community can be identified at Longnor; Gregory Bardon, whose unnamed son was baptised there in 1660, and William Gerrard 'from Longnor Forge', who was buried at Condover in 1675.

Later forgemen identified in the two parish registers were Stephen Morgan and his wife Sarah (1728), Thomas Harrison and his wife Mary (1747), John Lloyd and his wife Jane (1748), John Jones and his wife Martha (1754) and William Jones and his wife Martha (1755), all mentioned in the Longnor register; in the Condover register were mentioned, John Harrison 'of the Forge', a Churchwarden in 1728 and buried in 1756, and Thomas Harrison 'of the Forge', whose wife Mary was buried in 1778. John Lloyd, and John and William Jones will certainly have been of Welsh descent, and Stephen Morgan was probably Welsh, despite the forgemen named Morgan traced in the Weald. John Harrison was probably the son of Thomas and Mary Harrison, baptised in 1686. He had a younger brother, Thomas Harrison baptised in 1688, and Thomas's son Thomas, baptised in 1719 was probably the forgeman whose wife was buried in 1778. The surname Harrison went back at Longnor to 1675, when an earlier John Harrison and his wife Margaret first arrived in the area. Again the surname was so common as to make its provenance uncertain, but the family could have been descended from the immigrant Reynold Harrison.

More certainly descended from former immigrants may have been Richard France, whose son Michael was baptised at Condover in 1709, and William Lambeth who was buried there in 1716. Samuel Bamford or Banford, who was buried there in 1722, was perhaps from the native family first traced as ironworkers at Attercliffe Forge almost a century and a half earlier.

Forgemasters from the Weald played a part in further Midlands ironworks established on the Derbyshire-Leicestershire border south of the Trent by the early seventeenth century. Most information about this was recorded in the will of Arthur Middleton of Ticknell, dated May 1610. He left 10 shillings apiece to his hammermen and finers at Donington and Melbourne. The location of other works is perhaps indicated by his bequest of £2 to the poor in each of the parishes of Hartshorne, Melbourne,

Calke (in which parish Staunton Harold Furnace was situated)[66] and Castle Donington, and of £5 to the poor of Ticknell. Arthur's brother, the forgemaster David Middleton of Chailey in Sussex, took administration of the will.[67]

Donington Forge was built under a royal licence granted in 1593 to the tenant of the royal corn mills, Christopher Crofts; it was to be sited on the river Trent above the corn mills. The annual rent of £1 10s 0d was payable in 1618 to the earl of Huntingdon, who held from the Crown the park of Castle Donington, with its corn mills, fulling mills, horse mill and forge.[68] Melbourne Forge was perhaps near the site of the later Melbourne Furnace.

Staunton Harold Furnace had been leased in April 1606 by Sir George Sherley to an ironfounder named Richard Marchant for three years in trust for himself, and for various other parties, an arrangement which, together with a dispute about Bringewood ironworks in which all the parties were involved, resulted in 1614 in a Chancery suit between two of them, Robert Steward and William Angrome, both of Bringewood.[69]

By 1614 Marchant was of Toadhole Furnace in Derbyshire, which had been set up since 1609.[70] The surname Marchant was both indigenous to the Weald and an immigrant one; the ironfounder could have been descended from Sir William Sidney's former finer, Hugh Marchant. He was more probably Richard Marchaunte who had married Joyce Kirkam at Rugeley in 1583, than the son of George Marchant, baptised at Mayfield in 1577. Was he perhaps also the man of that name who married Petronella Dudley at Duffield early in 1601? Probable probate material for him at Lichfield dated 1629 no longer survives.

Whether Staunton Harold Furnace was the subject of a further lease to Middleton in 1609 is not mentioned in the Chancery case. The likelihood that such was the case is increased by the fact that this furnace was the subject of a further lease to John Wenham of Battle in 1624.[71]

The possibility of discovering the surnames of men employed at Middleton's ironworks is much reduced by the failure of all but the parish registers of Castle Donington to extend back before the Civil War. Castle Donington's register showed that Thomas Drewett, probably the finer formerly employed at Hints and Oakamoor, was at Donington from September 1601 until May 1606. Blaze Vynton, whose son George was baptised at Donington early in 1608, was probably the younger of the two Wednesbury finers of 1597, but by 1614 he had moved on to the Stourbridge area. The hammermen Henry Mathewe, who was buried at Donington in 1603, and Peter White, whose son Arthur was baptised there in 1609, but followed his master Middleton to the grave in July 1610, were both probably of immigrant descent, White having married Angell Tullett at Worth so lately as 1608.

Another immigrant name mentioned at Castle Donington was that of Charles Spurre, whose children Francis and Mary were baptised there early in 1601 and in 1602. By 1604 he had joined his father Marian at Calverley in the Aire valley in Yorkshire. Other immigrant names were perhaps those of Lawrence Boyer, who had been drowned in 1598, Christopher Trunchean, who was at Castle Donington in 1609, but by 1611 had moved on to Wem in Shropshire, and possibly George Lamley (Lambley in 1617), who married Isabel Ryley in 1608, and whose children, Mary and Dorothy, were baptised in 1609 and 1617. He was still at Castle Donington in 1634, when his wife Isabel was buried there.

At a later period Jerome Blewitt (1623), Steven Blewit (1629-1631), Thomas Gonet, who, together with his wife Elizabeth, was buried in 1623, and probably John Taberer (1629), were other ironworkers of immigrant descent mentioned in the Castle Donington parish register. Lewis Morrell, 'at the Mills', whose daughter Joan was baptised in 1621, was probably from the immigrant community, but because there were two fulling mills and two corn mills on the Trent at Castle Donington, his precise

66. P. Riden, *A gazetteer of charcoal-fired blast furnaces in Great Britain*, p. 24.

67. TNA, PROB 11/117/358. Arthur and David Middleton were the sons of William Middleton of Westerham in Kent, a family distinct from that of Horsham, to which Arthur Middleton, former forgemaster at Huggetts and Maynards Gate furnaces, belonged. Their involvement in iron could have arisen through their mother Jane, the daughter of Richard Lewknor.

68. TNA, DL 42/98; DL 43/6/5.

69. TNA, C 2 James I, A3/31.

70. P. Riden, 'The charcoal iron industry in the East Midlands', p. 67.

71. P. Riden, *A gazetteer of charcoal-fired blast furnaces in Great Britain*, p. 24.

occupation remains undetermined.

Forgemen from English families at Donington Forge could have been John Dutton, whose wife was buried in 1598, William Sands (1601-1622), Robert Simmes (1615-1621), Henry Dutton (1625-1627), Jeremy Scott (1624-29), James Scott (1631) and John Egleton (1632), though Sands, Simmes and Egleton could have originated in the Weald.

Forgemen of French ancestry were well represented in the forges set up on the Nottinghamshire-Derbyshire border during the seventeenth century. Bulwell Forge had first been mentioned in 1615,[72] but it was first noted in the parish register when John the son of 'William Crosse of Bulwell forge' was baptised in 1653. Personnel from the Weald were shown to have been involved by the burial of Jeffrey Dawes 'of Bulwell forge' in 1657. Families of immigrant descent will have been those of Nicholas and Margery Turke (early 1636) alias Tomplin (1640), who had been at Rotherham in 1631 and whose children Robert and William were baptised at Bulwell, Christopher and Dorothy Lambert whose daughter Bridget was baptised in 1640 and was buried in 1642, William Morrell whose wife Anne was buried at Bulwell in 1641, as was he himself in 1647, and Gregory Morrell, 'householder', whose burial in 1651 had been preceded by that of his wife less than two months earlier. Later men of immigrant descent were Thomas Druett, an iron finer of Bulwell Forge, who married Ann Daye of Papplewell in 1663, Thomas Vallans, a Bulwell forgeman, who married Barbara Drewett in 1684,[73] and probably John France 'of Bulwell forge' who was buried in 1709, whilst Frederick France whose daughter Alice was baptised at Bulwell early in 1712 may also have been connected with the forge.

Cuckney Forge was set up around 1617 to fine iron from Whaley Furnace.[74] No parish register survived until 1633, but Anne and Elizabeth, the daughters of Thomas Tullet, were baptised at Cuckney in 1636 and 1639, followed in 1643 by the baptism of George son of William Tullitt of Cuckney. William Tullitt later went on to Clipstone Forge and Thomas Tullet to Attercliffe in Yorkshire. William and Francis Johnson, and Robert Johnson alias Rawlin, all mentioned in the register of the 1630s were perhaps other forgemen from an immigrant, or partly immigrant family. Humphrey Brooks, a forgeman who married Susanna Tullitt in 1645 may also have been of immigrant stock. After the Civil Wars, the Cuckney hammermen, John Braddow, a widower who married Martha Turner in 1688, and John Braddy, who married Margaret Norman in 1691, were perhaps descended from the immigrant finer Blaise Briday.[75] On the other hand George Turneley, mentioned in the 1630s and 1640s, was clearly indigenous.

John Goacher (Gotier) of Langwith, which was upstream towards Whaley Furnace, had three children, John, Henry and Richard, baptised at Cuckney between 1655 and 1661, but was himself buried early in 1664. Goacher entries continued in the Cuckney parish register until at least 1721, but little information was given about them, except that William Goacher, whose son Henry was buried at Cuckney early in 1694 was 'of London'. Forgemen from indigenous families named in the register were probably John Simms, whose son John was buried at Cuckney in 1718, and Thomas and Francis Burgain, who were both buried in 1723.

Carburton Forge was first mentioned in Cuckney parish register in 1656 in connection with Nicholas Vallance, who was perhaps Nicholas Valiance the elder buried early in 1672. Another Nicholas Valiance buried in August of that year was 'of Cuckney'. John Valiaunce was buried early in 1675, and Robert Valliance in 1698, although he had married only the year before. His infant son Robert survived to raise a family of his own at Cuckney in the 1720s.

Two other forgemen from immigrant families were connected by the register specifically with Carburton Forge: Samuel Powell, who had been at Kilnhurst Forge early in 1724, but who was mentioned at Norton Cuckney from 1728 onwards, where his wife Mary was buried early in 1733, and where he married Mary Wilson early in 1735, and Richard Jelley, whose son Richard was buried at Cuckney in 1732.

Like Carburton, Clipstone Forge dated from the middle of the seventeenth century.[76] Here, the

72. Riden, 'The charcoal iron industry of the East Midlands', p. 70.

73. Blagg and Wadsworth, *Abstracts of Nottinghamshire Marriage Licences*, volume I, pp, 215, 372.

74. Riden, 'The charcoal iron industry of the East Midlands', p. 68.

75. Blagg and Wadsworth, *Abstracts of Nottinghamshire Marriage Licences*, volume I, pp. 417, 439. The two had earlier appeared as Bradwall at Staveley Forge, where the younger man was baptised in 1668, the variation in orthography of the recorded surnames perhaps confirming their alien origin.

76. Riden, 'The charcoal iron industry of the East Midlands', p. 70.

first mention of ironworking in Edwinstowe parish register occurred in 1653, when a widow, Eleanor Kirbie, 'from the forge house in Clipston Park' was buried. Early in the following year Mary Bartlemew from 'Clipston forge' was buried. Other immigrant names connected with the industry soon appeared: John, son of William Tullitt who had previously been at Cuckney Forge, was baptised at Edwinstowe early in 1656, but Tullitt's still-born daughter and Hannah Tullett his wife were buried on 22 and 26 December; the forgeman Thomas Tullett, who married Elizabeth Leichfield in 1662;[77] Katherine Mathew, a widow and mother of a family, who was buried at Edwinstowe in 1655, and William, son of John and Anne Mathew from the 'Forge house in Clipston park', who had been baptised in 1654 and was presumably her grandson. This Katherine Mathew may also have been the mother of Edward Mathew who married Sarah Tullett in 1656, and whose children, Rebecca, David, Frances, Thomas and Arthur, were baptised over the next ten years, the latter just less than eight months after his father's burial.

William Grout was at Clipstone Forge in 1661, and John James, who was buried at Edwinstowe in 1663, was from the 'slitting milne, being first inventor of it there'. 'Fisher' of the slitting mill was buried at Edwinstowe in 1669, and Thomas James and William Hayes were described as being of Clipstone mill and 'at Slitting Mill' respectively in 1670. The final mentions of the slitting mill ran from 1688 to 1694, when Richard Grant,[78] Edward Grout, William Grout and Mary Grout from it were all buried.

John and Jane Perigoe and their descendants were mentioned in the Edwinstowe parish register from 1671 until 1728, Richard Vintin of Clipstone Forge was buried there in 1671, and the widower Humphrey Brookes, who had formerly been at Cuckney Forge, was now a Clipstone forgeman and was remarried to Mary Challand in 1678.[79] William Son of Richard Wintin (*sic*) was baptised at Carburton in 1718, and entries concerning the forgeman Jeremiah Bartholomew III, who had earlier been at Stone Forge in Laughton-en-le-Morthen, are found at Carburton from 1726 to 1732, after which he returned to Sheffield.

Later, in the 1720s, entries for the baptism of children of John Goacher of Carburton were made in the Edwinstowe parish register, and the marriage of John Goacher and Mary Taylor of Carburton, recorded there in 1732, was perhaps a second marriage of the same man.

In north Derbyshire a furnace and forge were built on the earl of Shrewsbury's estate at Barlow around 1605. Related entries in the parish register are hard to identify, but Arthur Heath (1610), Gervaise Bawdon or Baughden (1614-1623), John Heath (1626-1637), and Christopher Lillye (1638) bear surnames which may have a Wealden origin. George Hambleton (1637) and Nicholas Bamford (1646) were probably also connected with ironworking. Immigrant surnames could be those of John Robinett, who married Grace Calton at Barlow in 1648, and Robert Morrill, whose daughter Helen was baptised there in 1658.

A name quite firmly connected with ironfounding was that of Edward Legas, whose forebears had come from Liège to Ireland in the 1630s; he paid the tax on three hearths at Barlow in the 1670s. Legas went on to cast ironware at Rockley Furnace, one of the duke of Norfolk's works in South Yorkshire, in 1691/2, including 31 tons of bullets made by him and his man for which they were paid 9 shillings a ton. In 1696/7 he cast pots at Vale Royal Furnace in Cheshire, which were marketed in Wrexham, Nantwich and Chester.[80]

Staveley Furnace and Forge were in being by 1639 and probably earlier; the related slitting mill at Renishaw was added in 1653.[81] Entries in the pre-Commonwealth parish register for Staveley are not readily discernible on the microfilm available in the County Record Office. However, Roger Tyler, whose name figured in the Staveley Protestation returns and who married at Eckington in 1640, will certainly have been in ironfounder there. Possible immigrant surnames mentioned in 1654 were those of Robert and Helen Arthur, Nicholas and Mary Valence, and Samuel Vileince, who was buried

77. Blagg and Wadsworth, *Abstracts of Nottinghamshire Marriage Licences*, volume I, p. 214.

78. Were it not that Brice Grant is known to have worked Bidston slitting mill on Wallasey Pool in 1781, Grant might be construed as a misreading of Grout (Awty, 'Charcoal ironmasters of Cheshire and Lancashire', p. 108).

79. Blagg and Wadsworth, *Abstracts of Nottinghamshire Marriage Licences*, volume I, p. 321.

80. SA, SIR/1/2/1, p. 244; Foley MSS. (per courtesy of B. L. C. Johnson's notes). Unless Edward Legas of Vale Royal was the Madeley man who had married Anne Tench of Brocton at Much Wenlock in January 1686.

81. Riden, *A gazetteer of charcoal fired blast furnaces*, p. 24; Schubert, *British iron and steel industry*, p. 311, n. 2.

at Staveley in 1657.

Bishop's transcripts for the period after 1660 suggest, as was the case with the forges above Market Drayton on the river Tern, that indigenous ironworkers began to predominate in the Restoration period. John Brailsford and Thomas Inggs (both 1663), Thomas Brailsford (1665), Peter Parker (1666), George Babb (1667), and William Bruckshaw (1670), were all mentioned in connection with the forge, the only immigrant names being those of William Perigoe (1667), and possibly Richard and John Bradwall (1668),[82] and Margaret Billington (1669). In the 1670s were found John Roger (1671), Ottiwell Babb and Edward Bruckshaw (1672), John Barker (1673), Edward Brandon (1676), Richard Babb (1677), with one possible immigrant name, that of John Collins (1675).

In the 1680s probable immigrant surnames were those of Thomas Matthews 'de Forge', who was buried in 1681, and Thomas Valence, whose daughter Mary was baptised at Staveley early in 1687. These surnames were matched by the indigenous ones of John Lea, first mentioned in 1685, and Richard Lea mentioned early in 1686, John Adly (or Adby) in 1687, and Francis Clay early in 1688. In the 1690s indigenous surnames mentioned were those of Godfrey Brailsford and John Babb.

Indigenous names mentioned in connection with the forge in the later parish registers were those of Michael Babb (1718-29), Thomas Hatfield (1720), George Hayfield (1725), Nicholas Halifax (1727), Alexander Stevenson (1729), John Wade (1732-39), John Dyson (1733-41) and George Holt (1738). But immigrant names still connected with the forge in the eighteenth century were those of Thomas Pountin alias Bartholomew (1718-1723), Richard Vintin (1729), John Vintin (1734), and probable immigrant names so connected were Jonathan Johnson (1732-42) and Samuel Powell (1737).

Yorkshire

The indirect process spread widely in North Yorkshire during the last quarter of the sixteenth century. Firstly, in 1577 the bloomery forge at Rievaulx was modernised, with a blast furnace built adjacent to the abbey site and a finery forge less than 1km downstream. Both works were mentioned in January 1578 when Peter Symons, 'Master of the furnysh at Rivalx', and Peter Semer, 'master of the fordge there', were two of the godparents for Peter, son of Lambert and Elizabeth Semer of 'Rivalx', baptised at Helmsley on the 26th of that month. The furnace was probably enlarged in 1587, when 'a new furnace harth of a new facion' was installed.[83] It was perhaps at this point that the practice of weighing the sows of iron produced at the furnace was introduced.

A finer who was brought from Staffordshire in 1578 cannot readily be identified, but the changes of this period were followed by the disappearance of the Semer family from the parish register. Firstly, Peter Semer the iron finer, whose son John had been baptised in May 1578, was buried in December 1580. His relative Lambert Semer had married Elizabeth, daughter of John Sympson of Harome in September 1576; their son Peter was baptised, as mentioned, in January 1577, followed by a son John in November 1579 and a daughter Jane in December 1581. But the sole Semer entry which followed in the parish register was the burial in July 1584 of Agnes Seamer 'of Rivalx, poore woman'.

It seems possible that Thomas Browne arrived at Rievaulx in connection with the enlarged hearth installed in 1587. He first featured in the Helmsley parish register when acting as a sponsor for a baptism in December 1588. In June 1589 he married Jordan Russell II's daughter Rebecca, who had been baptised at Frant in the Weald in 1569. Their children, William, Elizabeth and Anne, were baptised from 1590 to 1597. But further Browne entries connected with Rievaulx do not occur at Helmsley after 1597. Thomas Browne perhaps moved to the Sheffield area, where in 1609 Thomas Browne, 'founder att your Lordships Iron Workes' petitioned the earl of Shrewsbury for his arrears of wages.[84]

On the other hand, several workmen who moved in the other direction from Sheffield to Rievaulx can be identified. George Bowmer, who had been baptised at Sheffield in July 1562, married Mabel Minto at Helmsley in 1584. In 1606 Michael Allen, who had been baptised at Sheffield in 1579, married Jordan Russell's daughter Isabel, who had herself been baptised at Sheffield in 1582. Hugh

82. The possibility that Richard Bradwall, who was buried in 1668, and John Bradwall, whose son John was baptised in 1668, were descended from the immigrant finer John Briday has earlier been argued for.

83. Schubert, *British iron and steel industry*, p. 200.

84. SA, BFM/2/228.

Bamforth, buried at Helmsley in June 1615, was probably the son of the Attercliffe hammerman of the same name.

From Shropshire came the Frenchman Glode Trunshion, who had been at Cleobury Mortimer in the early 1570s. His son Paul was buried at Helmsley in 1587, and his daughter Rebecca was baptised there in 1588.

Numerous other ironworkers probably came from the Weald, either directly or indirectly; Thomas Rowe of Rievaulx, who was buried at Helmsley in 1580, Francis Rawe, who married Grace Brand at Helmsley in 1585, Francis Johnson of Rievaulx, whose son George was baptised in 1585, John Buttrye of Rievaulx, whose 80-year-old wife Isabel was buried in 1587, Francis Paul of Rievaulx, whose daughter Ann was baptised in 1589, Jordan Russell II's son Valentine, who married Ann Skott at Helmsley early in 1590 and stayed at Rievaulx until 1610, before moving on to Pleasley Forge in Derbyshire by 1615, and Edward Sage of Rievaulx, whose wife Elizabeth was buried at Helmsley in 1592.

William Russell of Rievaulx was presumably among the covenant servants there, because Peter Vynton, buried at Helmsley in 1597, was described as his servant. William Russell was at Rievaulx from 1594 until 1610, and may have stayed there longer, because his eldest daughter Rebecca married George Boulbie at Helmsley as late as 1618. Another member of this family at Rievaulx was Richard Russell, whose children were baptised at Helmsley from 1621 to 1631. The marriages of neither William nor Richard Russell were recorded, so both may have married before arrival in North Yorkshire. William could be a younger son of Jordan Russell II whose baptism has not been traced, but no baptism of Richard Russell is recorded at Helmsley, and the second marriage of Valentine Russell, whose first wife Ann died in 1602, cannot be found at Helmsley either.

Recruited from elsewhere in North Yorkshire was Simon Lavender, whose daughter Rebecca was baptised at Helmsley in 1592; he had married in the Weald at Worth, but the baptism of his son Marian at Pateley Bridge in 1589 indicated he was then employed at Summerbridge Forge in Nidderdale. Roger Brusbie, who was buried at Helmsley in 1630, and his son Nicholas Brusbie, who was married there to Anne Sanderson in 1625, had been at Danby in Eskdale in 1594 and at Summerbridge Forge in 1597.

The hammerman recruited from Staffordshire in 1615 was Harmon Brusboye, whose children, William, Mathew and Dorothy had been baptised at Ellastone from 1611 to 1615. Two of these Staffordshire-born children were mentioned at Rievaulx, Dorothy who was buried at Helmsley in 1618, and William who married Elizabeth Sheeles there in 1635. Harmon's younger children, John, Ellen, Anne and Richard, were baptised at Helmsley from 1618 to 1631. It is impossible to tell whether John Brusbie, who was buried at Helmsley in 1627 and whose children, Anne, Kathren, Barbara, Elizabeth and Isabel, were baptised there between 1616 and 1626, came along with Harmon Brusboye out of Staffordshire, or was related to Roger and Nicholas who came to Rievaulx by way of Danby and Summerbridge.

Outside Rievaulx the introduction of the indirect process to North Yorkshire was largely the work of the Pembury and Frant forgemaster Thomas Dyke. In the 1580s he took over works belonging to Thomas Proctor of Warsill near Ripon, which were stated to be in the manor of Brimham. William Brokebank, a citizen and grocer of London, had bought the Brimham Hall estate in 1585, and in 1586 Thomas Proctor, who wished to finance his plan of obtaining a patent for smelting iron with coal fuel, mortgaged the ironworks at Brimham and also his Warsill estate to Brokebank. However, Brokebank agreed to sell the Brimham estate, which included 'a close called Hallgarth and two other messuages or granges in Kirkby Malzeard and Ripley, Ripon and Hampsthwaite' and 'a certain ironworks and stock of iron, coals and iron mines and water courses' to William Grene of Egham for £2,600. In this agreement, 'not having knowledge of ironworks', Grene associated himself with the forgemaster Thomas Dyke, who soon found means to divert the whole to himself.[85]

The works Dyke operated included a finery forge at Summerbridge on the river Nidd, which may have been at the site of the original bloomery belonging to the Brimham estate. Glode Gellot, a Frenchman who was married at Pateley Bridge in August 1586, was the first man of immigrant stock known to have worked there. The blast furnace which supplied sow iron to this forge has not been identified, but obtained its charcoal from woodlands adjacent to Warsill. Dyke did not himself move to Yorkshire, but his younger son Robert Dyke, who lived firstly at Brimham and later at Westwick near

85. TNA, STAC 5/Gl4/27.

Boroughbridge,[86] perhaps had the oversight of these works.

Another blast furnace was built in the North Yorkshire moors, probably following an inquisition held at Malton in April 1583 which reported that there were mines of coal and stone quarries in the wood called Cropton Spiers, the northern part of which yielded a seam of coal nine inches thick and stone 'like unto iron stone'.[87] The site of this furnace has been identified at Spiers Bank and in the late 1580s it was worked by Robert Taverner and John Brockman. A reference to the hammerman 'Mabrey' in connection with the felling of trees near Spiers Bank suggests that the furnace had its own forge not far away.

In 1590 a complaint was investigated that indiscriminate felling of oak, beech and ash trees had been made by Thomas Dyke and his officers in several areas, and by Sir John Danvers in the Forest of Danby. Smelting in Danby Forest may have been done near Furnace farm, with its forge adjacent, or possibly further down the river Esk near Egton Bridge.

Between 1 April 1587 and 21 March 1589 Dyke had felled 125 oak trees of 18 in 'over the stub', 64 of 24 inches and 14 of 32 inches, all within Cockshott, Intack and Somerwood in the parish of Kirkby Malzeard, 10 miles distant from the Ure at Boroughbridge. Within Dacre Pasture he had felled 183 oaks of 18 inches, 367 of 24 inches and 30 of 32 inches; in the Northfields, which was adjacent, 122 oaks of 18 inches and 61 of 24 inches; in Heyshaw 37 of 18 inches and 17 of 24 inches, all 12 miles distant from the Ure. Near Warsill he had felled within the Horse Close 115 oaks of 18 inches and 27 of 24 inches; in Calfe Pulle 52 of 18 inches and 34 of 24 inches; in Little Wood Spring 24 of 18 inches, 18 of 24 inches and 12 of 32 inches; in Byllyngton Spring, Tuppe Close and the Knockes 100 of 18 inches and 43 of 24 inches, 'but not any of beech or ash'; these were all within 9 miles of the Ure and although all the trees felled were said to have been used for smelting and making iron it was those felled near Warsill that were specifically noted as having been used at Dyke's furnace, which was not otherwise mentioned.

All this information was the testimony of Francis Mawtus, a Warsill yeoman, who had himself measured the stubs. But for Spiers and Spaunton, Mawtus was dependent on information given him by 'one Sympson and one Lambert Semar', who sound like the Rievaulx ironworkers, but were now according to Mawtus 'workmen in the said grounds', where they worked for Taverner and Brockman. Within Spiers and Spaunton 1140 oaks of 18 inches and 100 of 24 inches had been felled and within the Queen's woods in Spaunton 185 of 18 inches and 28 of 24 inches, but not any beech or ash. The site was 12 miles from Runswick and the 'Stayres' [Staithes?].

In the Forest of Danby, 140 oaks of 18 inches but no beech or ash had been felled in Lealholme Park and Crunkley Gill by Danvers' clerk, Thomas Turner, gentleman, and 'one Lawrence Angell alias Russell being a collyer'; it had been coaled and used for making iron at the direction of Sir John Danvers and his officer Robert Hytche. These woods were 5 miles from Runswick and Staithes.

In response to the 24th interrogatory Mawtus revealed that 'one Maryon [Deproane alias Spurr] went to the growndes called Speyers and Spawyngton and gave notyce and warnynge to one Mr Hamond who was clerke to the worker there and to one Mabrey who was hammer man there to make yron, that this examinate and others were comynge to take a viewe of the said growndes, to thintent that they that kept the grounds should resyst the viewers', which explained why in this instance Mawtus had been unable to make his own measurement of the stubs.

Two colliers of French descent corroborated these statements as far as their own knowledge would allow. The 70-year-old Lawrence Angell alias Russell gave evidence to the effect that he was Dyke's collier at Warsill, that Morgan and Maryon were Dyke's colliers at Dacre, and that his brother-in-law Richard Evered was collier at Spiers and Spaunton. The 27-year-old Davy Frauncis of Warsill, collier, confirmed the evidence about the felling at Dacre because he 'wrought neare to the said groundes', and also that he himself was employed at Warsill and that the charcoal from Warsill had gone to the furnace 'where Dykes made his yron'.[88]

The references to wood-felling in Kirkby Malzeard are somewhat misleading; Summer Wood House, and perhaps also Cockshott and Intack, is located in a quite remote and detached part of the parish only 3km north-west of Summerbridge on the river Nidd, where Dyke's finery forge was situated.

86. C. Collinson, 'Enterprise and experiment in the Elizabethan iron industry: the career of Thomas Proctor', *Yorkshire Archaeological Journal*, **68** (1996), p. 195n.

87. TNA, E 178/2654.

88. TNA, E 133/7/1055.

Pateley Bridge parish register recorded the baptism of a son of 'James Kirring hammer man at Sommer Brigges' in February 1588 and the burial of a 'child of on[e] James a woorkman at the forge' in August 1590. James Kirring will have been of French descent, and in the case of Glode Gellot, who married Dorothy Ellis in August 1586, the parish register confirmed his French nationality.

Ellis, Pullen and Lambert were surnames indigenous to North Yorkshire, so it is not always easy to distinguish newcomers. However, Giles Garrit, who married Margaret Kirrin in December 1589, and only a short time earlier had been at Battle, was clearly of French descent, and was named under his alias Gyles Warnett when his daughter Joan was baptised at Pateley Bridge in January 1590. Also of French descent were Simon Lavender, whose son Marian was baptised at Pateley Bridge in 1589, and Roger Brisborne, whose daughter Jane was baptised there in 1597, and who had earlier been at Danby.

Other intrusive surnames were borne by Edward Ramme, whose son Lambert was baptised in 1587, Thomas Grubar whose son Sampson was baptised in 1596, Anthony Runder or Rundall, who had children buried in 1597, and whose daughter Agnes was baptised in 1598, and possibly Lambert Smith, whose children Thomas and Susan were baptised in 1588 and 1592, and who was remarried in 1595 to Dorothy Emerson. John True, whose wife was buried in 1598, but who remarried in time to have a daughter Anne baptised in June 1600, had perhaps been at Pontymoel in Wales in 1576, and an earlier man of that name had been ironfounder at Robertsbridge in the early 1540s.

The use of timber from the Warsill area for charcoal at Dyke's furnace suggests that its site was near Sawley or Fountains Abbey, but further parish register references to Simon Lavender at Ripley in 1601 and Hampsthwaite in 1604, where the register started only in 1603, suggest other possible locations, either further down the Nidd, or above Ripley on the Thornton Beck.

At Danby, Katherine daughter of Peter Pavye had been baptised and Pawkhewe [*Paco*] Spurre had been buried in 1586. Further definite intruders from the Weald were Francis Paul, who had been at Rievaulx in 1589, who had a daughter baptised at Danby in 1591, and who later went on to Thomas Proctor's works at Shipley Hirst, and Roger Prisball, whose son Nicholas was baptised at Danby in 1594, and who went on to Summerbridge Forge and later to Rievaulx. Possible arrivals from the Weald were Christopher Foard, whose daughter Jane was baptised at Danby in June 1593, and who may have been the man married at Kirdford in Sussex early in 1592, and from the mid-1590s, Bartholomew Holland, whose daughter Anne was baptised at Danby, and Richard Holland who was buried there. Prudome entries occurred in the parish register from 1587, very shortly after its inception, and the will of Robert Prudome of Glaidsdale, is that of a well-established local yeoman and betrays no connection with iron.[89] Just possibly in the case of Jane Prudome, because in 1604 she married William Osborne, whose surname though English was intrusive in the register, is there room for suspicion that she might have been an intruder.

The hammerman mentioned in the interrogatories about Spiers and Spaunton was perhaps Francis Mowbray who married Elizabeth Wood at Danby in October 1599. Mowbray was still in the area in 1607, when his daughter Helen was baptised at Danby. A later hammerman was probably Humphrey Bamforth, who married Elizabeth Stringer at Danby in 1609. Their children were baptised there between 1610 and 1622. He was a son of the Attercliffe hammerman Hugh Bamforth, baptised at Sheffield in 1588, and both he and his younger brother Hugh, baptised at Sheffield in 1588, evidently moved on to North Yorkshire, where Hugh was buried at Helmsley in 1615.[90] The Stringer connection suggests that Richard Stringer, whose daughter Anne was baptised at Danby early in 1592, may have been an ironworker.

Steven Lafargo who was buried at Danby in May 1603 was more probably surnamed Lafarge, a variation of this ironworking name which suggests an origin in southern France or the Pyreneean region. Another intrusive surname at Danby was that of Thomas Ferrye, who was buried there in 1594, whilst John Ferrye married Bridget Foard in 1632. Despite the caveat that Lambert was a North Yorkshire name, a last French name from the Danby parish register may have been that of Simon Lambert, whose

89. Borthwick Institute, Wills proved at York 26/369. The Prudome family must, like Lambert and Pullen, be considered of local origin, especially as Maryan Predome had arrived in England only in 1539. The Beawshaw family of Brompton in Ryedale might more cogently be thought of immigrant origin, because Mathew Beawshaw had arrived in England as long ago as 1520, but positive evidence is lacking.

90. The will of their brother Ralph Baumeforth, hammerman at Kirkstall, shows that their father Hugh was still alive in 1635 (Borthwick Institute, Wills proved at York, 42/484).

infant child was buried there in 1621.

Meanwhile Thomas Proctor, whose works near Brimham had been taken over by Dyke in 1586, had thrown his resources into procuring a patent for smelting iron, steel and lead using coal, peat and charcoal as fuel. He and William Peterson obtained a seven-year patent to this effect in 1589, and under it Proctor granted smelting rights to Sir Edward Fitton of Gawsworth in Cheshire. In partnership with Edward Cage, citizen and grocer of London, Proctor built his own ironworks, a forge at Shipley Hirst (now Hirst Wood) below Bingley on the river Aire, and a furnace at a nearby site called Brucrofts.

The first furnace was apparently too small, lacked an adequate water supply and the carpenter who worked at the forge was unable to fashion the water wheels properly. Around Christmas 1592 sows were taken to Summerbridge Forge for conversion into bars but the results were so bad that the forgemaster declared that if he could have 1000 tons of it delivered free, he would not work it. Numerous lawsuits ensued, firstly between Sir Edward Fitton and Thomas's son, Stephen Proctor, who had advanced money on Fitton's behalf tohis own father in payment for Fitton's licence. There was also litigation between Thomas's sons, Stephen and Elias Proctor, and a Hull merchant, Gregory Pormort, who may himself have been of French extraction, on the one side, and Edward Cage on the other.[91]

Depositions of June 1593 show that Proctor then had three men of French descent employed at Shipley: Marian Spur, his wife, his wife's mother and five or six children; John [Bilbowe?], his wife and a boy; Francis Johnson, his wife and two children, one of them perhaps his son George baptised at Helmsley in 1585. All had been hired at Cage's expense, but were quite without work.[92] A later worker in the area of French descent was Francis Paul, who had come from Rievaulx, and whose son Walter was baptised at Bingley in May 1598, However, Paul's wife was buried at Bradford less than three weeks after the birth and his unnamed child, buried at Bradford in September, was perhaps the motherless Walter. Whether Widow Kirkby of Shipley Smithies who was buried at Bradford in 1603 was from the aborted ironworks, or from Gawcliffe smithies, opposite Shipley on the Bradford Beck, it is impossible to tell, but the family Kirkby, possibly of French descent, we have earlier found at Strudgate Furnace and Worth in the Weald.

Two further North Yorkshire furnaces are known from the fact that both supplied hammers and anvils to Rievaulx Forge: the furnace near Follifoot on the Crimple Beck, south-west of Harrogate, supplied hammers, anvils and 'other rough iron' via Spofforth in 1605; Tanfield Furnace was situated in lower Wensleydale and its founder supplied three hammers and an anvil to Rievaulx in 1615-17.[93]

The Follifoot enterprise was that of George Clifford, third earl of Cumberland. However it was his wife, Margaret, younger daughter of the William Whorwood who had acquired the manor of Kinver and Stourton for his family, who first became involved in mineral affairs. From 1589 she was involved in lead-mining, and she also invested in iron in the 1590s, perhaps with Cage, Proctor and Pormort. Proctor's lobbying for his patent had certainly brought him contact with Sir Francis Walsingham, but apparently also with the head of Elizabeth's government, Lord Burleigh. Burleigh had been kept informed about the progress of the experiments to smelt iron using coal or peat fuel. When the question of a renewed patent for Proctor was raised in March 1595 Burleigh's son, Sir Robert Cecil, and Cumberland were both involved, but Margaret, though she asked that she and her other partners be included, was left out.

It was envisaged that as many as two new ironworks using the new process could be built each year over a period of 31 years. The works would be built and stocked by Cecil and Cumberland and leased back for Proctor to run, but Proctor was to involve no other person in the deal and Cecil and Cumberland reserved a right of veto on the sites chosen, set strict limits to their own financial involvement, and defined their profits as a proportion of their investment. A grandiose scheme indeed.

In the event Proctor's patent was not renewed. In May 1595 Cumberland's agents obtained a 16-year lease of the Spofforth woods from the earl of Northumberland, but a delay of two years ensued, perhaps because iron ore had to be obtained out of the Forest of Knaresborough which belonged to the Queen's Duchy of Lancaster. Cumberland was actually steward of the forest, but on account of

91. Collinson, 'Enterprise and experiment in the Elizabethan iron industry', pp. 197-202. Pormort, the unusual surname of the Hull merchant, was perhaps derived from Portmort in the parish of Graval, 4km north of Beaussault.

92. TNA, E 135/35/6 Elizabeth 1, Michaelmas 34.

93. Schubert, *British iron and steel industry*, pp. 379, 389.

his privateering activities he was temporarily out of favour with the Queen, so it was only after Cecil was made Chancellor of the Duchy of Lancaster in October 1597 that Cumberland went ahead with the erection of a forge. He then petitioned the Queen to allow him to mine in the forest and to erect a furnace higher up the Crimple Beck. This request was acceded to in February 1598, after a Commission of Inquiry had considered the matter, with a 21-year lease at a rent of £6 per annum instead of the £3 6s 8d recommended by the Commission.[94]

The parish registers for Pannal and Spofforth, the latter commencing only in 1604, afford little information. The intrusive Francis Tyler, whose son George was baptised at Pannal in 1603, was almost certainly the son of Charles Tyler, the Loscoe ironfounder, because Francis's marriage to Anne Hey of Loscoe at Heanor in July 1598 was followed by no other reference to him there. Possibly Michael Russell, who married Phillis Pickering at Pannal in 1609 was a forgeman; his sons, William and Ralph, were baptised in 1610 and 1612 respectively. However, there is no proof that Cumberland's works still continued in 1655 and 1658, or had been revived at that time, when Martin Barden and Thomas Morrell had children baptised at Pannal.

The venture at Tanfield in Wensleydale was perhaps Cecil's own, because the manors of West and East Tanfield, Waith and Carethorpe, with the office of feodary of Tanfield had been granted to his father in April 1572.[95] No information about personnel involved there is available due to the lack of an early parish register.

At Leeds, a more permanent forge was established on lands which had belonged to the former Cistercian abbey of Kirkstall. After the Dissolution, the abbey had passed through several hands, ending up with the former Archbishop Cranmer, and reverting to the Crown upon his attainder. After the Crown had disposed of the abbey lands again, they came in 1584 into the possession of Sir Robert Savile, whose son John, baron Savile of Pontefract, became Comptroller of James I's household.

Until March 1617, no forge was mentioned in the Leeds parish register. However, the register showed that several men, who later worked at the forge, were on the abbey site over ten years earlier, which suggests that they could have produced iron there by the direct method before a finery forge was built. The men mentioned at the forge were Francis Crosse, Christopher Mitchell (both 1617), Peter Russell (1618), William Bowmer or Bowman and Thomas Barley (both 1620), John Haukshey or Hawksley (1621), William Waid (1623), Thomas Wood and Richard Oldershay (both 1624), James Russell (1627), John Russell (1629), William Mitchell and Ralph Baumforth (both 1635) and Brian Poe (1637). Additionally, Isabel Sowden 'of the Forge' was buried in 1620.

Of these men, three, Christopher Mitchell, Francis Crosse (in the misreading *Crawe*), and Peter Russell, had previously been 'of the Abbey' all from 1614 onwards. But at the abbey site they had been preceded by Roger Russell, who was there from 1605 until 1611, and Gilbert Bowmer, who was there from 1607 until 1617. That Roger Russell was, like Peter, James and John Russell, engaged in the production of iron is suggested by his marriage in 1604 to Margaret Bawmforth, Ralph Baumforth's sister. Both Margaret and Ralph were the children of Hugh Bamforth, the Attercliffe Forge hammerman, and had been baptised at Sheffield in 1582 and 1586 respectively. Gilbert Bowmer too had been baptised at Sheffield early in 1564; his wife Mary was buried at Leeds in 1617.

It is obviously unlikely that everyone at the extensive abbey site was employed at the bloomery, but Lionel Bradforth (1615-1621), William Crosse, buried at Leeds in 1617, Laurence Casson, who was at the abbey in 1621, but by 1624 went on to Weetwood, where there was also a bloomery, and both Nicholas Morrill, buried at Leeds in 1616, and William Morill (1618), may all have been employed there. Whilst Bamforth and Bowmer came from Sheffield, Waid may have been a local man, because colliers named Wayed or Wayde had worked at Esholt bloomery, further up the Aire valley, in 1568.[96] The Russells were almost certainly, and the Morrells possibly, of French descent, though their immediate point of origin is not known.

The involvement of John Crosse of Cleobury Mortimer at Coity Anglia Furnace in Glamorgan in 1589, and the fact that in 1606 Thomas Crosse was clerk of Bromford Forge near Birmingham, has already been commented on. Forgemen surnamed Crosse later became widespread in the South

94. R. T. Spence, 'Mining and smelting in Yorkshire by the Cliffords, earls of Cumberland, in the Tudor and early Stuart period', *Yorkshire Archaeological Journal*, **64** (1992), pp. 162-67.

95. *Calendar of Patent rolls, Elizabeth 1*, **5**, 3326.

96. B. G. Awty, 'Sir Richard Shireburn's Esholt ironworks', *Bradford Antiquary*, new series, **40** (1960), p. 3.

Yorkshire, Derbyshire and Nottinghamshire areas. However, the strange spelling of Francis Crosse's name as 'Crawe' in 1614 might be explained if he were of French origin, with a surname such as *Croix*, or *Descroix*, the latter an uncommon surname, but actually well-represented at Bouelles in the sixteenth century.

The forge seems to have been built with the intention of attracting a leaseholder, because the term 'forge' was used in the parish register a whole year before the first lease of it, which was made in May 1618. The principal party to the lease was Sir Francis Fane, who was the son and heir of the Wealden forgemaster, Sir Thomas Fane of Badsell, and was soon created earl of Westmorland. His associates in the lease were Sir Edward Barrett, Robert Leigh and George Hemsworth. That Fane was intent on firmly establishing himself as a Yorkshire forgemaster is evident from the fact that in April 1621 he took from Sir Francis Wortley of Wortley a 21-year lease of all his 'Iron Smythees' with their 'houses, strange hearthes, bloom hearthes, dames, streames, goats (goyts) and water courses ... formerly in the tenure of Matthew Stafford and Ambrose Wood deceased, and of John Turneley ... with all the bellowes, tools and implements now at the said smythees, or any of them or used to the Iron Works there'. At Wortley, Fane's associates were Sir Richard Beaumont of Whitley, Francis Burdet esquire of Birthwaite, and the local clergyman, Edmund Cundy of Wortley.[97]

These two forges were to form the nucleus of the Spencer, Cotton and Heyford partnerships, the second most important group in Yorkshire after the Shrewsbury works around Sheffield, which after the extinction of the Talbot line passed to the Howard family and became known as the Duke of Norfolk's Works. But the 1621 lease made it abundantly clear that Wortley was still a bloomery forge and the Leeds parish register, though it mentioned a dozen forgemen, never once referred to finers or hammermen, so it was, like the contemporary Cumbrian forges, possibly still operated on the bloomery system, but perhaps like them with a drome-beam hammer and plated hearths. Fane's accession to the Westmorland peerage, in right of his mother Mary Nevile in 1624, and his premature death in 1628 may have impeded the fulfilment of his schemes.

The earliest known partners in these Yorkshire works were William Fownes of Kenley in Shropshire, his brother Gilbert, and a London merchant, John Spencer I, whose family came from Criggion, near the Welsh border with Shropshire. Spencer was engaged in the Shrewsbury drapery trade and his interest in iron probably arose through the marriage of William Fownes to his sister Elizabeth, which took place at Shrewsbury in 1625. But the marriage of major Walter Spencer, John Spencer I's brother, to Frances daughter of Thomas Barnby had taken place in 1605,[98] so a Spencer connection with the Barnsley area preceded by many years that of the Fownes brothers and this link presumably paved the way for the establishment of the partnership's main furnace on Sir Charles Barnby's land at Barnby.

Neither Mott nor Andrews found convincing evidence that the indirect system was used in this part of Yorkshire before around 1650.[99] Barnby Furnace was apparently in being then because in that year the head of the Spencer family, Randolph Spencer, eldest brother of Walter and John, sent his son, John Spencer II to act as ironworks clerk there. John Spencer I's will showed that the partnership was formed around Wortley forges and Colnbridge Forge near Huddersfield, together with Barnby Furnace and Bank Furnace in Farnhill., the lease of the forge at Kirkstall being obtained only shortly before Spencer's death in 1658. The furnace built in 1654 by William Cotton at Bank could in fact have been the second furnace erected for the partnership at this site.

It looks as though Colnbridge Forge, and therefore possibly the first Bank Furnace,[100] were operating the indirect method of iron production considerably before 1650. The Huddersfield parish register shows that Valentine Russell II, Francis Spurr and Thomas Bardin were all at Colnbridge in

97. R. A. Mott, 'Kirkstall Forge and monkish ironmaking', *Publications of the Thoresby Society*, **53** (1973), pp. 161-2; C. R. Andrews, *The story of Wortley ironworks: a record of its history and traditions, and eight centuries of Yorkshire ironmaking,* 3rd ed., Nottingham, Milward, 1975, p. 22.

98. Two hundred pounds, due to Walter Spencer by the marriage agreement of 29 August 1605, was paid late and resulted in a financial dispute between the parties (TNA, C 2 Jas I B6/68).

99. Mott, 'Kirkstall Forge and monkish ironmaking', pp. 162-4; Andrews, *The story of Wortley ironworks*, pp. 22-3.

100. Bank Furnace built in 1654 was perhaps Upper Bank Furnace which had an average production of over 400 tons a year, whereas the Nether Furnace which produced only around 150 tons will have been the older one (A. Raistrick and E. Allen, 'The south Yorkshire ironmasters (1690-1750)', *Economic History Review*, **9** (1939), p. 172).

the 1650s and Russell's presence had already been noted there when his son George was baptised at Huddersfield early in 1645. But Valentine had come to Colnbridge from Pleasley, a move which suggests that Richard Russell of Colnbridge, noted in the Huddersfield parish register from 1625 to 1638, could have been the man who had been finer at Pleasley in 1615, the year of Valentine's birth. His move to Colnbridge by 1626 suggests that the forge there, and the first Bank Furnace, may have been built in the mid 1620s

A Russell presence at Colnbridge was maintained after Valentine Russell II died in 1653, at least until the burial of his son George's wife there in 1679, George's son Valentine Russell III had apparently moved on by 1700 to Wortley forges, where he stayed until at least 1728.

Other immigrant names at Colnbridge which appeared in the Huddersfield parish register after Thomas Bardin's death in 1659, were Daniel Barden, who was there in 1690 and 1692, and a presumably later Daniel Barden, who married Rebecca Haigh at Kirkburton in 1740, Henry Tyler alias Pick, whose family worked at Wadsley Forge, but who was at Colnbridge in 1660 and 1663, and William Vintin who was there from 1666 to 1668. For John Maybery, whose family may not have been immigrant, but which certainly came from the Weald, Huddersfield parish register entries ran from 1678 to 1685. Perhaps, however, he was not at Colnbridge for the whole of this time, but was identical with John Mowbray of Wentbridge, hammerman, aged 58, who on 28 March 1680 served as a deponent in a Chester Exchequer case brought by Edward Spencer against Russell Alsopp, after the first partnership in the South Yorkshire forges had ended in discord and acrimony.[101]

At Wortley forges deficiencies in the parish register enforce recourse to bishop's transcripts. Anthony France, who married Helen Bingley in 1636, and whose daughter Ellin was baptised there in 1638, may have been of immigrant descent, and Edward Matthe, probably from the Mathew alias Bewser family, and his wife Elizabeth who was buried there in 1639, were perhaps the couple encountered earlier at Winnington forge. Much later, William Vintin had children, John, William and Samuel, baptised at Wortley from 1717 to 1729. Thomas Bartholomew, who was buried there in 1717, and Peter Bartholomew, whose wife Margaret was buried there in 1730, were almost certainly descendants of Bartholomew Pouting.

However, the hammerman John Haugh or Hough (1737-1747), the finer Samuel Simpson, who was buried at Wortley in 1737, Joshua Bamforth (1742), John and Samuel Wainwright (1742 and 1748), William Rollins, who was buried at Wortley in 1745, and Thomas Simpson (1750), were all perhaps forgemen of local stock.

Whilst the Spencer ironworks were evolving in West Yorkshire, perhaps during the 1620s, the Duke of Norfolk's works in South Yorkshire were let to Lionel Copley in 1639.[102] At Wadsley, where a forge was erected below the site of the former blast furnace, the effect was striking. Immigrant names appeared in the Ecclesfield parish register starting with John Mathie, Oliver Mathies, Thomas Morrell and Thomas Gellie all in 1641, John Gellie in 1641, Andrew Russell, buried at Ecclesfield in 1642, William and John Powell in 1643,[103] and Thomas Russell in 1644. The hammerman Anthony Tyler was probably the man whose child was buried at Ecclesfield in 1659, but the first Tyler family entry was that for the marriage in 1655 of John Morrell and Jane Tyler.

From their use of the baptismal name 'Dud' it looks as though the Gelly family had formerly worked in the Midlands for Dud Dudley, but it was in Derbyshire at New Mill that John Jolly had been recorded in the Duffield parish register from 1637 until early in 1640. Thomas Morrell was probably the son of John Morrell of New Mill Forge, who had been baptised at Duffield in 1603. John and Oliver Mathew were finers, probably belonging to the Mathew alias Bewser family, who had also come from Derbyshire, where John was shown by the Duffield register to have been at Hopping Mill from 1626 to 1633, and at New Mill in 1634, whilst Oliver appeared in the Pleasley parish register in 1639. Thomas Russell, the son of Valentine Russell I, had been baptised at Helmsley, had married Anne Hill at Duffield in 1639, and had still been at New Mill in July 1640; he was perhaps the Thomas Russell buried at

101. TNA, CHES 15/88.

102. He had apparently already taken over the Attercliffe forges in 1618 (Crossley, ed. *Waterpower on the Sheffield rivers*, pp. 19-20).

103. The Powells probably descended from the immigrant Paul Hedowell or Eudes, and were not of Welsh ancestry. The names of John Crippin and William Artur who also first appeared in 1643 should perhaps be added to this list.

Rotherham in 1661. The occupations of the finers John and Oliver Mathew were shown, as we have seen, when their sons Joseph and John were apprenticed to Sheffield cutlers in 1649 and 1647 respectively, by which dates the elder John was dead and Oliver had moved on to the Nether Hammer at Attercliffe.

Near Rotherham, Kimberworth Forge, perhaps built on the former furnace site, was mentioned in September 1613, when Quintine Pountinge, the finer there, made his will.[104] John Pitt, whose children, John and Margaret were baptised at Rotherham in 1626 and 1628, and who married his second wife Joan Morrell at Rotherham in 1631, was shown to be the forge finer at Kimberworth in 1638, when his son George was apprenticed to a Wincobank scissorsmith.[105]

At Rotherham itself Masbrough Forge was in existence by 1655, when its Welsh finer Hawell Johnes married a Masborough widow Anne Beale, whose surname was a Wealden one. This forge, like Wadsley may go back to around 1640, because apprenticeship records show that John Bab, who had been at New Mill in Derbyshire in 1636, was a forge finer at Rotherham by 1645, when his son John was apprenticed to a Wadsley cutler.[106] Though not of immigrant descent, it seems possible that John Bab was the son of William Bab, baptised at Harting in West Sussex in May 1617. Masbrough Forge became a slitting mill in 1666-7.[107]

Thomas Tullet was among the forgemen who came to Sheffield from Norton Cuckney in Nottinghamshire around 1640. The family continued in Sheffield in the person of John Tullett, who married Hanna Bramall in 1688. He was the son of William Tullett baptised at Sheffield in 1643, but his father had died the following year. The family's connection with the Attercliffe forges was revealed in the parish register on the occasion of Anne Tullitt's marriage to the forge carpenter Peter Vintin in 1659, but neither Thomas nor John Tullitt was listed with the other forgemen in the hearth tax of 1672. Forgemen of immigrant descent who were listed then at Attercliffe were Jeremiah Bartholomew, Henry Pick [alias Tyler], and Gyles Gilliam.[108]

The Vinton family was first noticed in South Yorkshire when William Vinton married Ann Holmes at Rotherham in 1611. His son Samuel was baptised at Sheffield in 1615. Richard Vinton's son Richard was baptised at Rotherham in 1617. The connection of the family with ironworking was demonstrated in 1659 when Peter Vintin, an Attercliffe carpenter, married Anne Tullet, and William Vintin, an Attercliffe hammerman, married Martha Mathew.

Peter Vintine the younger 'de Forge', buried at Sheffield in 1699, was probably the carpenter's youngest son, baptised at Sheffield in 1676. The hammerman's eldest son William, baptised in 1660, was probably the forgeman William Vintin, buried at Sheffield in 1725. His father went on to work firstly at Colnbridge Forge, near Huddersfield, and later at Norton Woodseats Forge, just south of Sheffield, where he was buried in 1684. John Vinton, who worked alongside him at Norton seems to have been his brother. He and his wife Margaret were not mentioned at Norton after the 1670s and were perhaps the forebears of the branch of the Vinton family which later worked in the steel mills of the Tyne valley, John and Margaret were first mentioned in county Durham in the Medomsley parish register in 1685.

The carpenter Peter Vinton and his son Samuel, baptised at Sheffield in 1660, worked as forge carpenters in both the Duke of Norfolk's works and for the Spencer partnerships in the area around Sheffield, where they shared most of the carpentry work in the ironworks with the bellows-makers from the indigenous Osborne family.

A second branch of the Bartholomew alias Pountin family arrived in the Sheffield area around 1660. The prevalence of the baptismal name Jeremiah in this family suggests a link with Thomas and Jane Bartholomew, whose son Jeremiah was baptised at Chetwynd in Shropshire in 1637. Jeremiah Bartholomew I married Jane Chadwick at Rotherham in 1664 and although further parish register entries failed to appear, he was among the Attercliffe forgemen included in the hearth tax returns of 1672. His father was perhaps the Thomas Bartholomew buried at Sheffield early in 1669.

Thomas Bartholomew II, the forgeman who married Mary Crosse at Sheffield in 1666, was perhaps Jeremiah's brother. He was probably the forgeman buried at Sheffield in 1727, and it was through his son Jeremiah Bartholomew II (1667-1729) that several generations of Attercliffe forgemen

104. Borthwick Institute, Wills proved at York, 32/666.
105. Leader, *Company of Cutlers in Hallamshire*, **2**, p. 318.
106. Ibid., p. 116.
107. Schubert, *British iron and steel industry*, p. 311, n. 2.
108. D. Hey, ed. *The hearth tax returns for south Yorkshire, Lady day, 1672*, p. 10.

were descended, whilst his younger sons Peter and Thomas, baptised in 1669 and 1672, were perhaps Peter Bartholomew who married at Penistone in 1703 and later appeared at Wortley, and Thomas Pountin alias Bartholomew, whose children were baptised at Staveley in Derbyshire from 1718 to 1723. Parish register entries suggest that Jeremiah Bartholomew II's son Jeremiah III was forgeman at Stone or Roche Abbey Forge, from 1718 to 1725, at Carburton from 1726 to 1732, but that he was back in Sheffield in 1735 and 1736.

The Perigo family was represented at Attercliffe Forge by the finer William Perigoe who married Anne Ferborough at Sheffield in 1657. The Duffield parish register shows him to have been at New Mill Forge in Derbyshire from 1660 to 1665, but by 1667 he had moved to Staveley, where he and his daughter Susanna were buried in December of that year. William Perigoe 'of the Hammer', who married Anne Barton at Norton Woodseats in 1685 was probably his eldest son. Both William and Anne Perigo were buried at Norton in the 1730s, but their son William, baptised at Norton in 1686, married Hannah Trickett at Chesterfield in 1714 and by 1717 had established himself at Kirkstall Forge, where he remained up to his burial in 1747. At Kirkstall the last Perigo forgeman died in 1800.

Other forgemen of immigrant descent at Norton Woodseats were connected with William Russell of Norton Forge, who married Alice Sandford there in 1627. He may have been the son of Nicholas Russell, who was buried at Norton in 1625, and the grandson of Peter Russell who held the mill at Brightside in the late 1580s. His sons, Godfrey (1627-1679) and William (1637-1673), were both hammermen at the forge according to apprenticeships registered by the Company of Cutlers in Hallamshire.[109] Godfrey's only surviving son John Russell became a Freeman in 1685 and William's two younger sons, Samuel and Joshua, became Freemen in 1683. William's eldest son William Russell, when married at Norton in 1685 was 'of Forge', but later parish register entries, including his burial in 1695, say solely 'of Woodseats'.

Ireland

Attempts were made before 1600 to set up ironworks on Sir Walter Raleigh's estates in County Waterford. The estates included localities such as Kilmackoe, Lisfinny, and the town of Tallow. The pioneers were Robert Robins and William Carter from Kent who had undertaken to erect an ironworks in the county under a lease from the bishop of Lismore before June 1591, by when Carter was reported to be dead.[110] They were followed by George Goringe and Herbert Pelham, the Sussex forgemaster, but although these men sent over workmen and servants their efforts had come to nothing by 1596, partly on account of the obstinacy and 'forward dealings' of Raleigh's other tenants.[111] The next evidence is from 1593, at which date Thomas Norreys of Moyallo, also on Sir Walter's estate, obtained the right to cut wood and dig ore for his 'iron mylles' for 21 years. Norreys was apparently Sir Thomas Norris, vice-president of Munster, to whom the castle and town of Tallow were granted in 1588. The earliest works were at Mogeely, west of Tallow.

Because these works had been overrun by the Irish in 1598 and the town of Tallow had been burned to the ground, Richard Boyle, a young lawyer from Kent and future earl of Cork, was able to acquire Raleigh's estates cheaply after his attainder in 1603. A London merchant named Thomas Ball, together with two partners, erected works at Kilmackoe, not far from Mogeely, to which iron ore was shipped from England in 1606. This works, in which he already had an interest, was taken over by Boyle in 1619. It was around this time that he was alleged to have begun gunfounding in Ireland.

Under the auspices of the East India Company an ironworks was erected around 1611 near Dondaniel on the river Bandon in Cork. The works were built by the company's master carpenter, William Burrell of Deptford, who held the lease until 1619, and one of his partners was Andrew Burrell. William Burrell held a licence to import iron ore from England in 1611.

In addition to the works at Kilmackoe, Boyle erected a furnace at Cappoquin on the river Blackwater in 1615, and two furnaces at Araglyn, north-west of Lismore, in 1625 and 1626. He bought the castle of Skariff and together with Sir Charles Coote took over an ironworks at Tomgraney in county

109. Leader, *Company of Cutlers in Hallamshire*, **2**, p. 335.
110. *Calendar of Acts of the Privy Council*, **21**, pp. 213-14.
111. Ibid., **25**, p. 453.

Clare in 1634. This had been set up around 1632 by Richard Rowley and six other partners. Sixteen Walloons from the principality of Liège were engaged to work at Tomgraney in 1633.

These immigrants seem to have formed the first large-scale infusion of foreign personnel into the British iron industry for more than a century, and were perhaps the last for many years. They were recruited by Richard Rowley and Jaquisse Lagasse (*Lagace*) and included Lambote and Bastile Lagasse and Bastile Lagasse the younger. The family can be traced back to Jean de Lagache, one of the proprietors of the *usine des Aguesses* in Liège, who in 1566 complained successfully against the alteration, to the detriment of their works, of the watercourses adjoining the lower Ourthe by the forgemaster Wauthier Godefroid.[112]

Jaquisse Lagasse and his relatives were the earliest members of a family destined to play an important role in English ironfounding. The burial of one of them at Madeley in Shropshire was recorded at some length – 'Lambert Leagas was borne in the Citty of Leech in Lukeland and was buried' on 18 September 1668. Few English industrial regions were without a representative of this family for a century and a half. Edward Legas, as we have seen, was at Barlow in Derbyshire in the 1670s, and went on to cast ironware and shot at Rockley Furnace in South Yorkshire in 1691/2, and pots in 1696/7 at Vale Royal Furnace in Cheshire. James Legas not only bought pot-iron from Bishopswood and Blakeney furnaces in the Forest of Dean in the period from 1692 to 1711, but also cast pots for the Forest of Dean partnership itself at 20 shillings the ton.[113]John Legas (1690-1752) became heavily involved in gunfounding in the Weald in the early 1720s, taking, together with Thomas Hussey, a lease of Gloucester Furnace in Lamberhurst from Samuel Gott and acquiring Hawksden Forge in Mayfield in 1727. From 1741 Legas was partner with William Harrison in these works and in Westfield Forge and Waldron and Beckley furnaces, where guns were cast in the 1740s. After Harrison's death in 1745 Legas and Samuel Remnant administered the Harrison estate too.[114]

Other names included were Jan de Benn [Beyne], Jan de Deven, Jan de Butson [Bodson], Wishawe Gyllman, Gyllowe de Hotsowe, Matheo and Jan de Martyn, Matheo de Rumsey [Romsée], William and Gyles de Jesper, Jan de Sueker [Succa?], Jacquisse de Ney and Michaell de Bumall.[115] Of these the de Beyne family were proprietors of the important, Grivegnée furnaces at Liège from around 1560 to 1661.[116] Mathy de Romsée had been tenant of the furnace of Neuve Forge at Pouhons-lez-Harzé in the Lienne valley from 1628 to 1633. In Wishawe Gyllman, can perhaps be seen the forebear of the family of English forgemen named Wishaw.[117]

Sir Charles Coote had a furnace at Mountrath on the river Nore in county Leix. In partnership with Boyle he erected a double furnace and two forges near Lough Allen in county Leitrim in 1630. It was Coote from whom John Winthrop the younger, son of the Massachusetts governor, John Winthrop, apparently took advice when contemplating setting up ironworks in New England in the 1640s.[118]

Many of these ironworks were destroyed in the Irish rebellion of 1641, and the reconquest of the country by Cromwell and Ireton between 1649 and 1652 only exacerbated division and dissension. However, after the Restoration 'many English workpeople' were employed at a new ironworks erected at Enniscorthy in County Wexford in 1661. In Ulster new ironworks were erected and older ones were revived and in the south the furnaces at Araglyn and Tomgraney were again active.

112. R. Evrard and A. Descy, *Histoire de l'usine des Vennes*, p. 39.

113. B. L. C. Johnson, 'The charcoal iron trade in the Midlands, 1690-1720', M.A thesis, University of Birmingham, p. 51.

114. J. S. Hodgkinson, 'The iron industry in the Weald in the period of the Seven Years' War, 1750-1770', MA thesis, University of Brighton, 1993, pp. 22, 107; Cleere and Crossley, *The iron industry of the Weald*, pp. 193, 200, 204-207.

115. Bodleian Library, Oxford, MS Rawlinson, D 918, f. 133. I am grateful to Michael Webb of the Bodleian Library for kindly transcribing these names.

116. Evrard and Descy, *Histoire de l'usine des Vennes*, pp. 325-6; Yernaux, *La métallurgie liègeoise et son expansion*, p. 54.

117. Otherwise the possibility that this ironworking family originated from Wishaw in Scotland should be considered.

118. Hartley, *Ironworks on the Saugus*, p. 51.

Scotland

The most northerly blast furnaces in the British Isles date from the first quarter of the seventeenth century and were built in Wester Ross. It seems possible that a bloomery forge at Fasagh on Loch Maree, similar to those established around the same time in Cumbria, may have given a Scottish nobleman, Sir George Hay, the idea of bringing the indirect process to the Highlands.

In October 1607 equal shares in the barony of Lewis and other lands in the north west had been granted to James Spens of Wormiston, Sir George Hay of Netherliff and James Elphinstone, lord Balmerino, with the idea that they encourage the settlement of more tractable Lowlanders in that unruly area. However, they relinquished the grant in favour of Kenneth Mackenzie, lord Kintail, in exchange, according to a late seventeenth-century account, for a sum of money and the woods of Inverewe in Gairloch. The only certain date relating to this exchange was the approval of Kintail's Lewis grant under the great seal in July 1610.[119]

Macadam, the first historian to deal with the subject, gave a date of 1607 for the establishment of Sir George Hay's ironworks, and among the supporting evidence he cited was the recruitment for the area in 1608 of a clergyman capable of ministering to immigrant Englishmen at Letterewe, 'engaged in making iron and casting cannon'. However, this may have been an aspiration rather than accomplished fact and evidence for the casting of cannon is not forthcoming before the 1620s. Further evidence cited by Macadam for the participation of Englishmen was the fact that a graveyard called the Englishmen's burial ground (*Cladh nan Sasunnach*) lay near the works at Fasagh, in a very remote area at the head of the loch.[120]

In December 1610 Hay was granted a commission to manufacture iron and glass in Scotland for 31 years, a grant which was ratified in October 1612 at the time when Archibold Primrose received a commission to make iron in the sheriffdom of Perth. In March 1612 a commission of justiciary was granted to Hay over both his native workmen and the many skilled workers he had imported, with permission for the 'strangers' to bear arms the better to protect themselves from the neighbouring Highlanders. This grant suggests that the project was by then up and running and that its inception could have been around 1610.[121]

By 1617 Hay was back on a regular basis in Edinburgh, where he became Lord Chancellor in 1622, but died in 1634. Up to 1617, however, he had resided at Letterewe on Loch Maree and he still continued a management role in some ironworks in 1620; as late as 1621 he was granted a licence to sell iron.[122]

In June 1626 Charles I reported to the Scottish privy council the grant of a patent for the manufacture of iron ordnance in Scotland and of £2,000 sterling to James Galloway and Nathaniel Udward. In fact it was in June 1628 that a grant was made to them of the sole right to make ordnance and ammunition in Scotland for 21 years. Meanwhile in August 1627 they had complained that as a consequence of the nonpayment of their grant they had been obliged to take the earl of Seaforth into partnership. A letter of the king in March 1628 stated that 'the said Erle is to have a care that the course intendit for the yrne workes and casting of ordinance in these northerne parts (whither he is with all haist to repaire) should take affect'. That this venture was a continuation of the earlier one is suggested by a late reference to 'Letter iu, where the English had a forge and ironworks under Seaforth' about 1634.[123]

No contemporary record survives which names the English personnel involved. A Wealden gentleman who lost more than £500 in Sir George Hay's project was John Wilson of Searles in Fletching. From a family which originated at Tockwith in Yorkshire, Wilson had earlier had the management of the property of the Wealden forgemaster Richard Leech, which accounted for his residence in the Fletching area. He married Mary, the daughter of Thomas Gardener, Master of the Fine Office, and

119. J. M. Lindsay, 'The iron industry of the Highlands: charcoal blast furnaces', *Scottish Historical Review*, **56** (1977), pp. 49-50.

120. W. I. Macadam, 'Notes on the ancient iron industry of Scotland', *Proceedings of the Society of Antiquaries of Scotland,* new series, **9** (1887), 89, 111.

121. J. M. Lindsay, 'The iron industry of the Highlands', p. 50.

122. Ibid., p. 51.

123. Ibid.

moved on to live at Holmesdale, and later to Sheffield House, a former property of Richard Leech, which had devolved on the earl of Nottingham through his marriage to Leech's widow.[124]

The acts of the English privy council include a list dated 31 July 1628 of six founders and fillers, who had been persuaded by Nathaniel Edwards (*sic*) to go into Scotland: they were Thomas Gunter, Robert Fryer, Richard Hook, William Shoobridge and his son, and John Jarret, all workers employed by the king's gunfounder, John Browne of Brenchley. These men, and a further 30 named employees of Browne, were forbidden to go abroad as long as Browne had work for them. Of course, by the time Browne's list reached the privy council some of these men may have been in Scotland. It also seems unlikely that Browne would have been able to offer all of the men constant employment, so both lists contain men who potentially went to Wester Ross.[125]

Macadam suggested that two English surnames found in the area, Kemp and Crosse, might have been implanted two and a half centuries earlier.[126] In both cases Macadam may have been correct. In the Weald an Englishman named Simon Kemp was already a covenant servant at Robertsbridge Forge in 1546.[127] Around Wadhurst this family was particularly associated with iron: in 1640 a pot-founder, Lawrence Kemp, was cited in a marriage bond;[128] in the churchyard is a cast-iron headstone of obscure date in memory of John son of Henry Kemp; in the early eighteenth century the Kemps of Great Pell were founders at the Gloucester Furnace in Lamberhurst.[129] As regards the Crosse family we saw that John Crosse of Cleobury Mortimer was involved in 1589 at Coity Anglia Furnace in Glamorgan, that by 1606 Thomas Crosse was clerk of Bromford Forge near Birmingham, and that the first citation of Francis Crosse of Kirkstall Forge as Francis 'Crewe' in 1614 could suggest that this branch of the family was of French origin, with an original surname such as *Croix*, or *Descroix*.

Another name, Bethune or Beaton, was included by Dixon with Kemp and Cross, as among those 'still known in Gairloch parish as belonging to descendants of the ironworkers'.[130] We have seen that over half the Frenchmen employed in the Wealden ironworks came from the Béthune valley, whilst Béthune in Artois was the market in which Brayon cattle were sold in 1540 by the Vassagne family of Dieppe and Neufchâtel. But some caution should be exercised in drawing firm inferences from this, because, as a surname Bethune is of extreme rarity in Normandy. It was never used for the river of Neufchâtel or Dieppe in notarial acts of the first half of the sixteenth century, and was first encountered for the river in a printed source in 1604 and so had perhaps come to be adopted late in the sixteenth century. Properly the name was first applied to the river's headwaters above Beaussault and was, according to a source of 1784, derived from a meadow named Béthune, between Gaillefontaine and Les Noyers, in which it found its source.[131]

Nathaniel Udward was described by Lindsay as 'an unconventional entrepreneur resident in Leith' and he had earlier (as Nathaniel Edwards) been engaged, to the annoyance of the Muscovy Company, in whaling and the Greenland trade. Galloway, later lord Dunkeld, was Master of Requests and in 1641 became Master of the Royal Mines. In 1634 he and Richard Ferrar were given a 31-year monopoly of steel production in Scotland.[132]

Apart from the then plentiful timber which attracted charcoal ironworks to the area, the small sheltered natural harbour at Poolewe, where the 3km-long river Ewe from Loch Maree flows into the ocean inlet Loch Ewe, must have been very attractive to the newcomers. Here, iron ore could safely be

124. R. W. Blencowe, 'Paxhill and its neighbourhood; with extracts from the manuscripts of the Wilson family', *Sussex Arch.Colls.* **11** (1859), pp. 8-10; I am very grateful to Tom Evans for drawing my attention to this source.

125. *Acts of the Privy Council, 1628-9*, pp. 71-2'; I am grateful to David Crossley for kindly sending me a copy of this list (TNA, PC 2/38/237).

126. Macadam, 'Notes on the ancient iron industry of Scotland', p. 116.

127. KHLC, U1475 B8/4.

128. Dunkin, *Sussex Marriage Licences, Lewes 1670-1729*, p. 285.

129. R. M. Willatts, 'Pre-Industrial revolution cast-iron grave slabs', *Wealden Iron*, Bulletin of the Wealden Iron Research Group, 2nd series, 8 (1988), p. 42; Lower, 'Historical and archaeological notices of the iron works of the county of Sussex', p. 213, n. 59.

130. J. H. Dixon, *Gairloch in north-west Ross-shire*, Edinburgh, 1886, p. 84.

131. G. Gaudefroy, 'Les noms de nos tours d'eau ont aussi leur histoire' in M. Coffin, *Promenade géographique, historique, touristique en Pays de Bray*, Office du Tourisme, Forges-Les-Eaux, **4** (1998), pp. 110-12.

132. Lindsay, 'The iron industry of the Highlands', pp. 51, n. 4, 52.

unloaded and finished goods dispatched. On Loch Maree charcoal could be boated without the risk of its being fragmented into dust, which prevented its transport over longer distances on land. It is suggested that pasturing of sheep in the Loch Maree area has prevented the regeneration of the former trees.[133]

Three sites where ironworkers from England probably worked were located at Red Smiddy, around 1km upstream from Poolewe towards Loch Maree, at Furnace, on the north shore of Loch Maree 1km beyond Letterewe, and at Fasagh, near the head of the loch. On the first two sites Macadam found both iron ores from central Scotland and imported haematites; at Fasagh he identified only bog ores.[134] Macadam thought that Fasagh might have been the earliest site in the area, but that it was a bloomery forge only. He thought that when Sir George Hay passed by it on the road to Lewis he conceived the idea of introducing the indirect system, which he did further down the loch near Letterewe.

However, the English graveyard at Fasagh suggests that workers from England were also employed there and it must be assumed that ironworking was carried on contemporaneously with the other sites. The haematite ores similar to those of Furness found by Macadam at Letterewe and Red Smiddy indicate that, as was the case at the furnaces of the eighteenth century in Argyll, imported ores were among those smelted on Loch Maree in the seventeenth century.

In 1957 the only remains still standing were those at Red Smiddy, east of Poolewe. The site was excavated in 1980 and though its use as a blast furnace was confirmed, only clayband iron ores could then be found. Cannon are supposed to have been cast at Red Smiddy as late as 1668, after which there are no further references to ironworking. The last forgemaster at Red Smiddy, John Hay, was buried at Gairloch in 1670.[135]

Tylecote thought that Fasagh might have been a primitive blast furnace,[136] and certain elements in Macadam's plan of the site support such a conclusion. However, when the site was examined in 1982 only bloomery slag was found. Two tree trunks, forming the bases for anvils, which had been noticed by Macadam, were again located; they measured 900 and 950 mm in diameter and were set in level platforms of slag and small stones. However, in 1982 the adjoining hearths or 'furnaces' reported by Macadam were obscured by rubble and vegetation. The Letterewe site was subjected to only a brief visit in 1980.[137]

Of Nathaniel Udwards' men, Thomas Gunter was baptised at Burwash early in 1593. The son of the ironfounder Henry Gunter, he married firstly Frances Guylford at Mayfield in 1613 and secondly Susanna Ellis at Wadhurst in 1621. His daughters Elizabeth and Joan were baptised at Mayfield and Maresfield respectively in 1614 and 1618. The baptism of his son Thomas has not been found in the Weald and could have occurred in Scotland, where Gunter could have been between 1621 and 1637. By 1637 he was back in the Weald as ironfounder at Northiam[138] and by 1639, when he signed the marriage bond for his daughter Elizabeth's marriage to Thomas Marten of Battle, at Mountfield.[139] The younger Thomas Gunter was also married in 1639 to Frances Nepekar at Battle. By 1646 when he made his will the elder Gunter was ironfounder at Crowhurst; there he evidently worked in the Farnden interest, because in his will he appointed Tobias Farnden's son Peter one of his overseers.[140]

The Hook family was well represented in Mayfield, the borough of Greenhurst (Buxted) and Laughton in the subsidy rolls of the 1520s. The Greenhurst entries in particular are compatible with early involvement in the iron industry and John Hoke, recorded as one of Thomas May's servants in the Kent hundred of West Barnfield in 1543, may have been the unmarried John Hooke of Balcombe who in 1558 instructed his executor John Senoke of Balcombe to deliver 'a tonne of iron that lieth at Harry Anemes in Word (Worth)' to his sister Alice. He was to gather in £7 14s 2d owed to him by Austin Mychell, gentleman, and John Gaynesford of Lingfield, gentleman, and £4 11s 7d owed to him by eight

133. Gairloch Heritage Museum, *The local 17th century ironworks: a brief history and description of the iron works around Loch Maree which include the earliest blast furnace in Scotland*, Gairloch, n.d.

134. Lindsay, 'The iron industry of the Highlands', p. 52.

135. J. H. Lewis, 'The charcoal-fired blast-furnaces of Scotland; a review', *Proceedings of the Society of Antiquaries of Scotland*, **114** (1984), pp. 433-79.

136. R F. Tylecote, *Metallurgy in archaeology*, London, Arnold, 1962, p. 292.

137. J. H. Lewis, 'The charcoal-fired blast-furnaces of Scotland', pp. 444-5.

138. ESRO, QR 38, m. 105. I am grateful to Brian Phillips for this reference.

139. Dunkin, *Sussex Marriage Licences, Lewes 1586-1643*, p. 259.

140. TNA, PROB 11/217/523.

other persons; part of his goods was to go to his sister Jone's children at his executor's discretion.[141]

Richard, the son of Nicholas Hoock, ironfounder at Strudgate Furnace, was baptised at Ardingly in 1584. Nicholas and Margaret, earlier children of Nicholas and Joan Hook, had been baptised at Worth in 1580 and 1582, and the family probably went on to Kirdford, where further children, Mary, Joan, William and John, were baptised from 1587 to 1596. The Kirdford parish register laconically recorded the burial of 'Whook's wife' in May 1597, after which entries at Ardingly, such as the burial there early in 1604 of 'Whook', and the marriage of the 19-year-old Joan early in 1609 to William Linfield, an Ardingly husbandman, are consistent with a return of the family to that parish.

Peter Hook married Friswith Johnson, daughter of the immigrant gunfounder John Johnson, at Rotherfield in 1592. She had been baptised at Rotherfield in 1575. There is no proof that Peter Hook was an ironworker, but this marriage made him brother-in-law to the queen's gunfounder, Thomas Johnson. Peter and Friswith's children, Peter, Mary and John, were baptised at Rotherfield, Frant and Maresfield, in 1593, 1594 and 1600 respectively, but Friswith was buried at Maresfield in August 1601, just over a fortnight after John's baptism, and the infant John Hooke survived only around two months. The following year Peter Hooke married Sislye Olde, perhaps the daughter of the immigrant Maryan Old and sister of the hammermen Steven and Walter Old.

There seem to be no further entries concerning this branch of the Hooke family in the parish registers of the Weald. However, the relationship with Thomas Johnson, Thomas Browne's predecessor as the queen's gunfounder at Horsmonden Furnace, may have had something to do with Charles Hooke's appearance in the 1628 list of John Browne's furnacemen bound for Scotland. Charles Hooke of Tonbridge, ironfounder, died in 1635 leaving all his goods by a nuncupative will to his wife Mary, apart from 7 shillings each to his three unnamed children.[142] One of Charles's children will have been Thomas who was baptised at Ticehurst in 1627. Another child was

presumably Charles Hooke, who accompanied his stepfather, the ironfounder Richard Post of Rotherfield, whom his mother Mary Hooke had married in 1636, to New England, where both worked as miners and furnacemen in the 1650s. The younger Charles Hooke appears to have returned to England, was ironfounder at Hamsell Furnace in 1680,[143] and was buried at Rotherfield in 1690.

The elder Charles Hooke's children would scarcely have been old enough to have included Richard Hooke, whom Nathaniel Edwards sought to recruit for Scotland in 1628. Richard could have been Nicholas Hooke's son, baptised at Ardingly in 1584. Nicholas Hooke's eldest son baptised at Worth in 1580 may have been the Nicholas Hooke whose son John was baptised and buried at Cowden in 1606, but then he too disappeared from record in the Weald.

In 1604 William Shobridge of Cowden, gunfounder, had been bound in £12 to keep the peace towards a shoemaker named Simon Holmden.[144] He was buried at Cowden in 1632.

INDIRECT PROCESS IRONWORKS IN CONTINENTAL EUROPE

The superiority of iron guns cast in the Weald led to attempts by foreign forgemasters to learn the secret of producing them 'after the English fashion'. A double furnace was built at Asslar in the duchy of Solms in 1604. Henri de Harscamp and Guillaume de Moniot of Namur also built a double furnace at Sossoye, which was referred to in 1630.[145] Efforts were also made to secure the emigration of gunfounders from the Weald to continental Europe.

A gunfounder mentioned in this connection was Thomas Weken of Maresfield, who was recruited by Michael Donnevide and his assistant Anthoine Le Brun on behalf of the duke de Bouillon in 1627.[146] The Weken or Wicking family came from the Cowden and Hartfield area of the Weald. John Weken had taken a 21-year lease of Parrock Furnace and Forge in 1570, but the works were soon in Lord Buckhurst's hands. Another member of the family, Andrew Wykinge of Hartfield, husbandman,

141. ESRO, PBT 1/1/4/87.
142. KHLC, DRb/PW29.
143. ESRO, SAS/CO 1/631, f. 17.
144. KHLC, QM/SRc/1604-5.
145. Schubert, *British iron and steel industry*, pp. 253-4.
146. *Calendar of State Papers Domestic, Charles 1*, **2**, pp. 196, 254.

made the Cowden ironfounder Drew Tyler the elder, the overseer of his will in 1609,[147] and Drew's sons Anthony and Francis Tyler both married members of the Wicking family at Cowden in 1615 and 1623. Thomas Wicking could have been the youngest son mentioned in Andrew Wycking's will.

Thomas Wickinge was among the founders and fillers of the king's gunfounder John Browne forbidden in July 1628 to leave his service so long as he had work for them.[148] This does not prove that he had by then returned from France, still less that he had never been there; it may have been thought necessary to include his name in the list for punitive sanctions in any case.

In 1636 Weken also had the misfortune to be accused of being in possession of a ringer, believed to be one of two ringers 'called furgons'; which together with a pair of iron tongs and other iron instruments had been stolen from William Fowle's forge. It was alleged that Thomas Weekins had taken this furgon to Richard Snashall's shop and asked him to make from it a 'toole to take up mine', offering him a cold chisel in payment, because he had no money to pay him. Weekins claimed to have owned the ringer for about 20 years and the chisel, which he had obtained from Thomas Andrews, for the same length of time.[149]

The possibility that this man was Thomas Wiggins who was mentioned in documents concerning the Hammersmith works in New England in the 1650s should not be ruled out.

INDIRECT PROCESS IRONWORKS IN NORTH AMERICA

Virginia

The Jamestown settlement of 1607 in Virginia was the earliest successful English colony in the New World and it was the first in which attempts to smelt iron were carried out, though none achieved success. Somewhat surprisingly the first concerted move resulted from a bequest made in 1619 of £550 for 'the bringinge up of Infidells children in true religion and christianity'. The shrewd colonists decided to use this money, together with 'a farr greater some, toward the furnishinge out of Captaine Bluett and his companie being 80 verie able and sufficient workmen with all manner of provisions for the setting up of an iron worke in Virginia, whereof the profitte accruinge' was to be for the education of 30 infidel children in the Christian religion and otherwise. From the employment of 80 men it can be seen that the undertaking was planned on the grandest scale; unfortunately the head ironworker, Bluett, became ill and died shortly after his arrival in the colony.[150]

However, Bluett was not the only person in the field, and Virginia Company records of 1619 mentioned 150 men sent 'to set up three Iron workes' in the colony, of whom about 110 were from Warwickshire and Staffordshire and about 40 from Sussex 'all framed to Iron-workes'. Three of the 'master workmen' died, but by 1620 they had been replaced. In March 1620 the Treasurer of the Company reported that 'one Mr King' was to go with 50 persons to Virginia 'to sett on foote Iron Workes', but it is thought this party never set sail.[151]

By May 1621 £4,000 had been spent without much result, some of the workmen having preferred to set up in the lucrative trade of tobacco planting. But it was now reported that 'a fourth gent (named mr John Berkly ...) did now offer himsellf to goe upon the said service and carry over with him 20 principall workemen well experienced in those kind of workes'. Of the workmen eight were to be for the furnace, two each to be founders, keepers, fillers and carpenters, and twelve were to be forgemen, four finers with two assistants, two chafery men, two hammermen and their two assistants.[152]

Early in 1622 Berkeley reported that he had found a fit place 'for wood, water, myne and stone' and was confident of making iron by Whitsuntide. However, on 22 March 1622 the works were attacked by Indians, 27 persons were killed, including Berkeley himself, the ironworks were ruined and the workmen's tools were thrown into the river. The site of the tragedy is known to have been at Falling

147. ESRO, PBT 1/1/12/355.
148. *Acts of the Privy Council, 1628-9*, pp. 71-2.
149. ESRO, QR 35, m. 93.
150. Hartley, *Ironworks on the Saugus*, pp. 32-3.
151. Ibid., pp. 33-5.
152. Ibid., pp. 35-6.

Creek, but although efforts made in 1951 to discover its exact location did not prove successful.[153] The speed with which Berkeley set up his works suggests that he may have taken over a site used previously in one of the three earlier aborted attempts. Only Berkeley's son Maurice, who was away from the works at the time of the massacre, survived.[154]

The fact that Berkeley undertook to assemble his party at the Isle of Wight in time to sail by July 1621 suggests that this fourth party of ironworkers was largely drawn from the Weald. However, apart from Captain Bluett, Berkeley himself and his son, the names of none of the participants in the four attempts to set up ironworks in Virginia is known. It is perhaps worth noting that Berkeley himself came from Beverstone in Gloucestershire, not far from where William Bluit and other members of that immigrant ironworking family are known to have lived during the first two decades of the seventeenth century.

New England

The first successful attempt to transplant the indirect method of ironworking to the New World was planned and set on foot by the son and namesake of the governor of Massachusetts, John Winthrop the younger. He had no practical experience in ironworking, but his library was reckoned 'the best collection of scientific materials available in one place in America'. Among his papers was 'Sir Charles Coote's Account of His Ironworks', which of course had been set up in Ireland. The ironworks was only one among young Winthrop's designs for initiating industrial projects in New England. In later years he became governor of Connecticut, and in the scientific sphere he was a member of the Royal Society of London; his correspondents numbered some of the most intelligent minds in England, whilst further afield they included Comenius.[155]

In June 1641 the General Court of Massachusetts passed a measure entitled 'Encouragement to discovery of mines etc.', and although this was imprecise in content, the fact that Winthrop set sail shortly afterwards for England, where he arrived in Bristol towards the end of September, suggests that either he or his father was its inspiration.[156] The Long Parliament had convened the previous year, causing the conduct of public affairs in England to slip into Puritan hands. The Parliament was firmly in control in London, a situation which did not change after Charles I raised his standard at Nottingham in August 1642, or at any time during the ensuing Civil War. It was against this background, and among religious sympathisers and the merchants of London that Winthrop found a ready ear for his proposals to establish an ironworks in the colony.

Nevertheless the 'Company of Undertakers of the Iron Works in New England', of whom the names of 24 are known, took some time to assemble. The leading member was John Becx, a Dutchman resident in London, who already had a saw-mill in New England, who traded with the West Indies, and who by the 1650s had ironworking interests in the Forest of Dean and Ireland, as well as in New England. The company included two practising ironmasters, Thomas Foley, the second son of the Worcestershire ironmaster Richard Foley, and Lionel Copley, whose ironworking interests were centred on South Yorkshire, but who played a more prominent part in the affairs of the company than Foley. Another member connected with the iron trade was Joshua Foote of the London Company of Ironmongers, who was among a group of merchants who had set up the ironworks at Tomgraney in County Clare in Ireland in 1632, for which workers had been recruited from Wallonia. The Tomgraney works was bought by Richard Boyle and Sir Charles Coote, and Hartley suggested it might have been the prototype for the Massachusetts works.[157]

Whilst he was in England, in the autumn of 1642 Winthrop took the opportunity of visiting Hamburg, The Hague and also Brussels, from where the ironworks of Wallonia would have been easy

153. In 1999 a geophysical survey revealed the possible site of the furnace contiguous with the site of Archibald Cary's Chesterfield Forge; L. E. Browning, 'Falling Creek Ironworks: Past, Geophysics, and Future', *Quarterly Bulletin of the Archeological Society of Virginia*, **60**, 1 (2005), pp. 43-55.

154. Ibid., pp. 36-7, 40n.

155. Ibid., pp. 50-1.

156. Ibid., pp. 53-4.

157. Ibid., pp. 61-8; Bodleian Library, Rawlinson MSS, D 918 f. 133; Schubert, *British iron and steel industry*, p. 190.

to reach. It was towards the end of May 1643 that he finally embarked in the *An Cleeve* of London on the return voyage to New England. He had with him three workmen found for him by Foote, including an ironfounder and his son, but three other workmen absconded, and neither the total number of those who eventually sailed, nor their trades, apart from the founder, are known. Due to unfavourable winds the voyage lasted 20 weeks and during it, all of Winthrop's party were ill with ship's fever. Time for recuperation and the onset of winter meant that nothing practical could be done in New England before 1644.

During the interval Winthrop made a survey of possible sites, and work finally commenced in the early spring at a site favoured by him, at Braintree south of Boston. A blast furnace was certainly at work in May 1645, by when Winthrop had acquired a miner, a founder, a finer, a smith and a clerk. The latter was presumably William Osborne, who drew up an account of receipts and expenditures up to December 1644, which amounted to £390, in addition to sums due on notes drawn by Winthrop himself.[158]

It does not seem that any forge was built at this time, so the works can have produced only small castings and sow iron. Another disappointment for Winthrop seems to have been the lack of interest in the project displayed by New England residents, only five of whom contributed just over £170 to add to the £1,000 advanced by the Company of Undertakers. At all events, by the end of 1644 Winthrop was already very disillusioned, and other projects had started to interest his inquiring mind. Fortunately for all concerned, Winthrop's waning enthusiasm coincided with the decision of the company to appoint as manager someone with more experience in iron.

It is evident that Hartley's deduction was correct, that of several closely related men of identical name, the new manager Richard Leader was the son of David Leader of Speldhurst in Kent. The involvement of the Leader family with ironworking went back to at least November 1544, when William Ledder I was paid for the 'sawyng of 900 planks and bordes and other necessary tymber for the reparacions of the forge and fornace' at Robertsbridge.[159] It seems that the family could have arrived in Robertsbridge immediately after the establishment of the ironworks there because, although the name Leader, Ledder, or Latter, did not occur at Robertsbridge in the 1524 subsidy roll, Richard Ledder I, who was among the Robertsbridge woodcutters in 1542, acquired a copyhold tenement named Haightons in Robertsbridge in November 1541.[160]

Richard I was perhaps the son of William Ledder I and is probably also identifiable as Richard Leader the elder of Robertsbridge, who died in the 1590s possessed of 83 acres of land in Salehurst parish, and of other lands in Westfield and Battle. To his son William Leader II he left 60 acres of land in Salehurst, some of which he had recently purchased from the bankrupt forgemaster John Ashburnham, all his land in Westfield, four silver spoons and a chest marked with a rose, a half-moon and a star. Of his other sons, Martin was to have the land in Battle, and Edmond the chest marked with carved faces. His married daughters Joan and Elizabeth were to have £10 and £5 respectively. His son Richard Leader II was to have over 23 acres in Salehurst, a silver gilt goblet, four silver spoons, the two greatest chairs in the bedchamber, the French chair, together with all his wares, implements and furniture in both his shops, and was to be residuary legatee. The poor of Salehurst were to have £2 and the poor of Battle, Westfield and Brightling were to share 10 shillings between them. Richard's sons Martin and Anthony (who was presumably already provided for) were to be his executors.[161]

If Richard Leader I was the son of the man who had supplied planking to Sir William Sidney in 1544, by occupation he was perhaps therefore a carpenter. If so his son Richard Leader II, who inherited the two shops, may have followed the same trade. He died in 1614, and was survived by a widow Dorothy. It was their son John Leader who first established a link with Ireland. Born in 1579, he was evidently a scapegrace. His father left him only his best black cloak, and it is the will of his mother Dorothy which shows that in 1626 he was living in Ireland. She left John an annuity of £8, with £80 to come in 1632 provided 'he show amendment of life', of which amendment the details were suggested in

158. Hartley, *Ironworks on the Saugus*, p. 102-3.

159. KHLC, U1475 B7/3.

160. KHLC, U1475 B7/2; D'Elboux, *Surveys of the manors of Robertsbridge*, no. 33.

161. TNA, PROB 11/85/106. Richard Leader I died between 1 May 1592, the date of his will, and 7 Feb 1595 when the will was proved, but his burial was not recorded at Salehurst, though that was where he wished to be buried.

the will.[162]

It seems likely that Richard Leader of Salehurst, gentleman, whom Hartley described as having trading links with Limerick,[163] was not Richard Leader IV, David's son, but John's younger brother Richard Leader III, the youngest son of Richard Leader II; he had been baptised at Salehurst in 1598.

Some evidence suggests that the elder son of Richard Leader I, William Leader II, may have had rather closer links than his brothers with the iron trade. Firstly, the Sidney family's Survey of Robertsbridge, made in 1567, shows that the *Bull* in Robertsbridge, residence of William Blackenall, clerk of the ironworks, together with other properties which were Blackenall's from 1550 onwards for the term of his own and his wife's lives, were afterwards to devolve on William Leader.[164] The second piece of evidence is the peripatetic nature of William Leader's life. He was apparently in Robertsbridge from 1576 to 1579, years when his daughters Mary and Dorothy were baptised at Salehurst and his son David was buried there. The baptism of a second son named David seems to have occurred elsewhere in the early 1580s. William reappeared in the Salehurst register only after Blackenall's burial, which took place at Salehurst in February 1585. His children, Daniel, Constance and John were then baptised, and his son Richard buried, at Salehurst, between 1585 and 1591.

The Salehurst parish register continued to record entries concerning the family of Richard Leader II, but William's family was next recorded in October 1608 at Hawkhurst, where his sons Daniel and David were married on successive days. Whilst these Hawkhurst entries were closely followed by baptisms of Daniel's children at Salehurst from 1611 onwards, William and his son David were soon found in another ironworking parish of the Weald, Mayfield, where the register recorded between 1609 and 1615 the baptisms of four of David's children, Richard Leader IV, David, Deborah and Elizabeth. The register also recorded the burial of 'William Ledder of Salehurst' himself in August 1611.

David Leader displayed the same mobility as his father. He had returned to Robertsbridge by 1617, and four more of his children were baptised at Salehurst between then and 1623. However, his four youngest children were baptised at Mountfield from 1624 to 1631. It was only after David's next move, to Speldhurst in Kent, that his connection with the iron trade became explicit; in 1640 Sussex quarter sessions required him to make good the highways damaged by the carriage of pig iron from Snape Furnace in Wadhurst, via Ticehurst, to Collin's forge in Burwash.[165]

Richard Leader IV will have been the London merchant who in 1643 invested 25 marks in Irish land and later bought more land there in conjunction with his father David. In 1644 he was engaged with Robert Petley in the coal trade between Leith and London. This was the 'Perfect Accountant', whom the Company of Undertakers appointed in March 1645 to succeed Winthrop in New England at a salary of £100 a year. He probably set sail in June and was established in the colony by September of the same year.[166]

It is to Leader that Hartley ascribed the building of the forge at Braintree. From later comments it is clear that Winthrop's furnace at Braintree was not ideally situated from the point of view of water supply.[167] Since Winthrop's furnace was all that Leader had to work with on arrival, he built the complementary forge to it at a more suitable site some two miles distant on the Monatiquot River. To retrieve the situation thoroughly Leader determined to erect a furnace at Lynn on the Saugus River, north of Boston, at a site which came to be called Hammersmith, and here the first successful ironworks plant in America, including a furnace, two fineries, a chafery, and even a slitting mill, had been built by 1650, when Leader relinquished control. The name 'Hammersmith' was first applied to the plant in Essex county records in June 1650.[168] Winthrop's furnace was by then no longer in use and Braintree Forge had become a subsidiary of the main Hammersmith plant, whence it received its pig iron.[169]

Due to documents resulting from litigation which arose during the tenure of the next manager,

162. ESRO, PBT 1/1/1 4/218, 1/1/20/160.
163. Hartley, *Ironworks on the Saugus*, p. 117.
164. D'Elboux, *Surveys of Robertsbridge*, 25.
165. ESRO, QR 50, m. 10; I am very grateful to Brian Phillips for this reference.
166. Hartley, *Ironworks on the Saugus*, pp. 117-20.
167. Ibid., p. 109.
168. Dow, *Records and files of the quarterly courts of Essex county, Massachusetts, 1636-1656, vol. 1*, p. 192.
169. Inventories of the furnace, forge and slitting mill at Lynn and of the forge at Braintree were taken on 20 and 24 Dec 1650 respectively on Gifford's taking over (*Essex records and files*, **1**, pp. 294-5).

John Gifford, a great deal is known about the ironworks and its workers in the early 1650s, but insight into progress made during Leader's period as manager is almost entirely inferential. For instance 'the iron works in Lin' were first referred to in the quarterly court of Salem in December 1647, when John Turner who lived at the works, and who from later records can be identified as a finer, was presented for stabbing his daughter-in-law and other transgressions.[170]

Hartley deduced that Braintree Forge, for which land was purchased at the end of September 1645, could have been in production in the spring of 1646, whilst at Lynn, where an initial purchase was made in December 1645, but the final agreement handing over all the deeds and instruments relating to the site was not concluded until May 1647, he deduced that construction began in 1646, but carried over into 1647.[171] This corresponds well with the first mention of the ironworks in December 1647 cited above, though whether the second finery and the slitting mill at Lynn were necessarily completed by then is quite uncertain.

Of the workers, very many of their surnames are traceable in the Weald. Most seem to have been recruited direct from there, but the founder Roger Tyler was last traced in England in Derbyshire, and could have been recruited through the agency of Lionel Copley, whilst the finer John Vinton came from a forge near Stourbridge and could have been recommended by Thomas Foley.

By tradition it was Roger Tyler who 'layed the first stone of the foundation of the furnace at Hammersmith'.[172] This seems to be borne out by a bequest of £10 made in May 1646 by George Pollard of Marblehead to 'Goodman Tiler of linne', at a time when the furnace may still have been in the course of building. There seems little doubt that the New England founder was Roger Tyler, grandson of the French immigrant Quintin Tyler. Before emigrating he evidently worked at Staveley Furnace in Derbyshire, where his name was included in the Protestation return of the early 1640s.[173] His marriage to Anne Padley at Eckington in Derbyshire in 1640, and the mention of both Roger and his wife Anne in depositions relating to an altercation which they had with Sarah, wife of Lawrence Turner, at Lynn in the summer of 1650, substantiate the identification.[174]

The next person associated with the ironworks at Lynn in the Essex county papers was John Turner, the finer, who could also have been of French descent. Unfortunately his name can be replicated many times over in almost every English county, so the only circumstance helpful towards his identification is that he emigrated with his already adult son Lawrence. No baptism for Lawrence has so far been identified.

John Turner first appeared in Massachusetts in December 1647 when he was presented for the stabbing already alluded to, also for swearing 'by the eternal God that he would kill John Gorum', another ironworker, and for being 'overtaken in drink'. For the three offences he was sentenced to be severely whipped at Salem, to be sent to Boston prison 'until he be whole', and later to be whipped at the ironworks. However, this sentence was revoked, in conformity with customary lenity towards ironworkers, against whom no earlier prosecutions had been brought, though later informations laid against them in the court are sufficient to suggest that the whole ironworking project might have juddered to a halt had its workers been treated with the severity accorded the general run of inhabitants of the colony.

Among such miscreants at Lynn in July 1647 Nicholas Pinyon, the forge carpenter and occasional hammerman, was presented for having beaten his wife and for common swearing. In February 1648 he was again in trouble, both for swearing and for having absented himself from meeting on four successive Lord's days, but instead spending his time in drink and profanely. One of these days was spent in the company of Nicholas Russell at the house of another worker, Joseph Armitage, who had provided them both with 'strong water'. Nicholas Russell was also fined for remaining in Nicholas Pinyon's house, despite having been ordered to keep away, upon which Pinyon's wife had threatened to leave home with him. She too was presented for swearing, and because she had broken her bond of good behaviour, was

170. Dow, *Records and files of the quarterly courts of Essex county, Massachusetts, 1636-1656, vol. 1*, p. 130.
171. Hartley, *Ironworks on the Saugus*, pp. 122, 125.
172. Ibid., p. 188.
173. I am grateful to Peter Tyler of Birkenhead for this information.
174. Dow, *Records and files of the quarterly courts of Essex county, Massachusetts, 1636-1656, vol. 1*, pp. 106, 199.

ordered to pay a fine or be severely whipped.[175]

In this Puritan society oaths which involved the name of the deity were uniformly punished with the substantial fine of 10 shillings, whilst crimes of violence appear to have been regarded as less heinous. In March 1648 Pinyon was again presented on a charge, supported by his wife, of killing five of his children, one of them being a year old. The following day she was presented for fighting three times with her husband during the night after having been bound to keep the peace, whilst he was presented for beating her and causing a miscarriage. In July 1649 Pinyon was fined £1 10s 0d for swearing three oaths and was admonished for striking Charles Hooke.

The evidence that Pinyon had sworn these oaths was deposed to by Quinton and Richard Pray, who were probably his distant relatives, but at the same time Quinton Pray was fined for breaking Pinyon's head with a staff with an iron two feet long on the end of it, for striking Thomas Billington, and also for swearing. Further misdemeanours of Nicholas Pinyon were mentioned, without being specified, in court proceedings of June 1652.[176]

When Nicholas Pynion testified against the loyalty of a neighbour in April 1661, he gave his age as 53.[177] This evidence makes it almost certain that he was the son born in 1608 to Nicholas Spraye alias Pinyon of Warbleton in Sussex. The father had perhaps first been married to Elizabeth Billin at Burwash in 1600, but she was buried at Burwash in 1602, after bearing him just one child. Nicholas Pinyon then married Mary Jeslbe at Warbleton in 1604, and the future forge carpenter at Hammersmith was the second child of that union.

Unfortunately it is impossible to trace this family further back with certainty. The New England man's grandfather could have been the immigrant John Pynyan, who, along with Adrian Pynyan, paid the poll tax in Netherfield hundred in 1572 and 1576. He may have been the John Spray who was buried at Mountfield in 1579 and could perhaps, under the name John Pynnyon, have married Alice Marten at Warbleton in 1571. It is the marriages of both John and Nicholas at Warbleton, in 1571 and 1604 respectively, which lend colour to this suggestion.

The position is rendered more obscure by the fact that two Nicholas Pinions were baptised at Mountfield, in July 1577 and January 1578 respectively, without their parentage being recorded in the parish register. John Pynion is likely to have been the father of one of them, and one of them is likely to have been the man who married at Warbleton in 1604 and to have been father of the Hammersmith Nicholas Pennion, but it appears unlikely that certainty about this will ever be established.

Court records of 1650 gave the name of Nicholas Pynion's wife as Elizabeth,[178] presumably Elizabeth Starr whom he had married at Burwash in 1639. Their two children, Ruth and John, were baptised at Burwash in 1640 and 1642, after which the family disappeared from the record in the Weald, apparently to a life of marital discord in the New World. After managerial legal disputes had led to interruption of working at Hammersmith, Pynion moved on to the ironworks set up in the early 1660s at New Haven, Connecticut.

We saw that Nicholas Pynion's distant relative from the Pray family, Quintin Pray, was fined for breaking Pynion's head. Quintin and his son Richard were first mentioned in Essex court records in February 1648, when both were fined for swearing. The following month Quintin was one of the witnesses when Nicholas Pynion was accused of killing five of his children, In March 1648 Richard Pray was fined 10 shillings for swearing, 10 shillings for cursing, £1 for beating his wife and £2 for contempt of court, failing payment of which he was to be whipped at the Lynn Iron Works.

This spectacular catalogue of fines was caused by his declaring that he would not desist from beating his wife, that 'he did not care for the court and if the court hanged him for it he would do it'. When told 'that the court would make him care, for they had tamed as stout hearts as his', he 'answered that if ever he had trouble about abusing his wife, he would cripple her and make her sit on a stool, and there he would keep her'.[179] The fine had still not been paid by February 1649 and Captain Bridges was then ordered to issue a warrant for the marshal to go to the iron works at Lynn and demand payment,

175. Ibid., pp. 133-4.
176. Ibid., pp. 137-8, 173-4, 254.
177. Pope, *The pioneers of Massachusetts*, p. 362.
178. Dow, *Records and files of the quarterly courts of Essex county, Massachusetts, 1636-1656, vol. 1*, p. 198.
179. Ibid., pp. 134-6.

failure to comply with which was to be followed by whipping 'upon a lecture day'.[180]

That appears to have been the end of this matter, but earlier in the same month Quintin Pray and his wife had been fined £2 10s 0d for five oaths. In February 1650 Richard Pray's wife was admonished and ordered to pay 2s 6d costs for calling her mother-in-law an 'old hogge' and throwing stones at her; she had also thrown a trencher and a bone at her husband, when he took from her a letter to England which had been written for her.[181]

Quintin Pray is known to have been a finer of iron, whilst Richard worked as a collier. Quintin was certainly at Lynn until July 1649 and Richard until February 1650, but at some time around 1650 Quintin Pray left Lynn. His oaths and swearing did not preclude administrative abilities and these gave him the opportunity to take charge of operations at Braintree Forge.[182]

When Quintin Pray deposed in the legal proceedings of the Gifford era in October 1653 he gave his age as around 58,[183] which enables him to be identified as one of the twin sons born to Robert Pray alias Pynion in 1595 and baptised in November of that year at Chiddingstone in Kent. Quintin died at Braintree in 1667 and administration of his effects was granted to his widow Joan.

Joan Pray will have been Joan Valliance, a woman of French descent whom Quintin married at Mayfield in June 1621. Their first child, Elizabeth, was baptised at Mayfield in 1622, after which there is a gap in the Wealden parish records for the family until their reappearance at Frant in 1628. It seems possible that during this time Quintin was in the Forest of Dean, where his sons Richard and Quintin, the latter of whom was buried at Frant in 1630, may have been born. Other children named Dorothy, John and Anna [Hannah], who together with Richard came to New England, were baptised at Frant in 1634, 1637 and 1638 respectively and the last mention of the couple in the Weald came in May 1643 when their infant child Thomas was buried.

The other finer at Hammersmith in the 1650s was John Vinton. He was first noticed in Salem court records in September 1649, when his own and Henry Leonard's wives were fined for 'scolding and uttering opprobrious words towards their neighbours'. He himself was fined in July 1653 for striking William Emorie.[184] Children born to Vinton and his wife Anna were baptised in Massachusetts between 1648 and 1662.[185] The eldest of their sons was named Blaise, and John himself was descended from James Vinton, whose family had come from Neuville-Ferrières in the Pays de Bray around 1515; James's children Blaise and Constance had been baptised in the Weald in 1561 and 1571, at Worth and Mayfield respectively.

There were no further entries after 1571 in Wealden parishes for the family of James Vinton. He presumably took part in the transfer of the indirect method of iron manufacture to the Midlands of England. Blaise Vyntam, late of Wednesbury, finer, who was arraigned before Staffordshire quarter sessions for assault and battery upon William Awton on 4 April 1596 and upon Beatrice, wife of John Marckes, on 5 September 1596, may have been his son. But it is evident that there were two men of that name; in January 1597, two Wednesbury finers named Blaise Vintam, together with others, were ordered to appear before quarter sessions, to which order the sheriff Thomas Whorwood, returned that 'Blaise Vintam and the rest have not been found in my bailiwick'.[186] The two men were presumably the child baptised at Worth in 1561, and his similarly named son.

Less than eighteen months later, the two Vintams were working at the neighbouring forge of Perry Bar, which was run by the sheriff's cousin William Whorwood, and the marriage of the younger man to Eleanor Knolles was recorded in the parish register of St Mary Handsworth on 8 May 1598. A son William, who did not survive infancy, was baptised there in March 1599 and a daughter Alice in February 1600, whilst another child baptised in 1605 was a third Blase Vintom. Blaise Vinton II went on to work at Donington Forge on the Trent, where his son George was baptised early in 1608, and then back to a forge on the Smestow Brook north-west of Stourbridge, from where his son John was baptised at Womborne in 1614. In the late 1630s Blase Vinton III was at Goodrich Forge on the Wye, but his

180. Ibid., p. 159.
181. Ibid., pp. 156, 184.
182. Hartley, *Ironworks on the Saugus*, p. 189.
183. Pope, *The pioneers of Massachusetts*, p. 371.
184. Dow, *Records and files of the quarterly courts of Essex county, Massachusetts, 1636-1656, vol. 1*, pp. 174, 287.
185. Pope *The pioneers of Massachusetts*, p. 472.
186. Burne, *The Staffordshire Quarter Sessions Rolls, III: 1594-1597*, pp. 292, 345.

younger brother George stayed at Wombourne. The fact that John Vinton of Hammersmith named his first child Blaise suggests that he was the younger brother of Blaise and George baptised at Wombourne in 1614, and that he named his own son after his father and grandfather.

In New England, John Vinton had by the 1660s moved on to the New Haven ironworks in Connecticut. During the late 1670s, after the Leonard family had been discharged from Bromingum Forge at Rowley in Massachusetts, John Vinton the younger became one of the chief workmen there. His elder brother Blaise also worked at Bromingum, which was a three-hearthed bloomery forge.[187]

Ralph Russell, a forgeworker at Lynn, was first mentioned in Essex county records in February 1648, together with Nicholas Pinyon's drinking companion Nicholas Russell. Nicholas Russell was fined for swearing, whilst Ralph twice acted as the witness in cases brought against Nicholas Pinyon and his wife.[188]

It looks as though Ralph Russell had been born in 1607, the eldest son of Anthony Russell alias Mynion and Elizabeth Kidd who had married at Buxted the previous year. Anthony Mynion had been baptised at Buxted in 1583, the son of Peter Russell alias Mynion, who had in the immediately previous years lived at East Grinstead and Chiddingstone. Peter and Alice Russell, who were among the godparents at a Turke family baptism at Maresfield early in 1583, were presumably Anthony's parents. Views of frankpledge for Danehill Sheffield hundred show Peter Russell to have been a defaulter in Hendall borough from April 1588 to April 1591, apart from 1589 when he was headborough; in September 1588 he was recorded there as Peter Mynion.[189] Hendall borough was at the northern extremity of Buxted parish and there Russell will probably have worked at Nicholas Pope's Hendall Forge. The burials of Peter Russell and of his unnamed wife were recorded at Buxted in 1613.

Baptismal entries show that Anthony Russell stayed in Buxted until his father's death; afterwards he was in Hartfield in 1616 and East Grinstead in 1619, but he and his wife Elizabeth were both buried at Maresfield in April 1634. Ralph Russell, baptised at Buxted in 1607, married Anne Humphrey at Maresfield in 1633 and their first child was baptised there later in the same year. They were at Withyham in 1636 and 1638, but by 1641 had moved to East Grinstead, where they remained until the baptism of their daughter Sarah early in September 1647. In order to be in New England by February 1648 it seems possible that Ralph may have preceded his wife in taking passage across the Atlantic. There is no further trace of Ralph's family in East Grinstead, though his brother Charles Russell's family continued to reside there.

Richard Post, Tyler's assistant at the furnace, was first mentioned in New England as being fined for drunkenness at the county court held at Salem in February 1649.[190] He was the son of the founder Daniel Post, and was baptised at Rotherfield in 1607. He appears to have been several times married; firstly to Elizabeth Palmer at Rotherfield in 1632, but this marriage cannot have continued long because 'Richard Post of Rotherfield, founder', was granted a licence in July 1636 to marry Mary Hooke of Rotherfield, a widow, at the church of Lewes St John.[191]

Mary Hooke was the widow of the ironfounder Charles Hooke, who had been buried at Tonbridge in October 1635. Charles left three young children, unnamed in their father's nuncupative will,[192] of whom we can suppose Thomas Hooke, baptised at Ticehurst in 1627, to have been one, and the future ironfounder Charles Hooke, whose baptism has not been traced, to have been another. As well as a wife, Richard Post had therefore acquired by his marriage three young stepchildren.

Their recruitment by Richard Leader, or perhaps by his father, will not have been difficult because Rotherfield lies less than 12km south of Speldhurst. Accounts for Hammersmith ironworks show that Richard Post and his stepson Charles Hooke dug 248 loads of bog ore at 1s 8d the load, for which they were owed £20 13s 4d in 1653.[193] Hook had been a witness, along with Quintin Pray, to one of the Pynion marital misdemeanours in March 1648, so it seems probable that Richard Post too was

187. Hartley, *Ironworks on the Saugus*, p. 298.
188. Dow, *Records and files of the quarterly courts of Essex county, Massachusetts, 1636-1656, vol. 1*, pp. 134, 138.
189. ESRO, ACC 3957/1, ff 27, 33v., 67v., 78, 107, 119, 143v.
190. Dow, *Records and files of the quarterly courts of Essex county, Massachusetts, 1636-1656, vol. 1*, p. 157.
191. Dunkin, *Sussex Marriage Licences, Lewes 1586-1643*, p. 231.
192. KHLC, DRb/PW29.
193. Dow, *Records and files of the quarterly courts of Essex county, Massachusetts, 1636-1656, vol. 1*, p. 292.

at Lynn by that date. It will also be recalled that it had been Charles Hooke whom Nicholas Pynion attacked in September 1649.

Charles Hooke appears to have returned to the Weald by 1664, when Edward son of Charles and Elizabeth Hooke was baptised at Rotherfield. By a second wife, Hester, Hooke was father to two more sons, Thomas and Richard, baptised in 1674 and 1677 respectively, though Thomas did not survive to adulthood. In 1680 Charles Hooke served as ironfounder at Hamsell Furnace.[194] He was buried at Rotherfield in 1690.

Richard Post seems to have succeeded Roger Tyler as ironfounder at Hammersmith, where he was doing the 'blowing' in 1657.[195] He was married twice more in New England, firstly to Susanna Sutton in February 1650 and again in November 1662 to Mary Tyler, perhaps a daughter of Roger Tyler.[196]

Henry and James Leonard, thought to have been born around 1618 and 1620 respectively, had by tradition learned their trade at Pontypool in Monmouthshire.[197] They were the sons of Thomas Leonard, thought to have been born within ten years of 1585, and the grandsons of Henry Leonard, thought to have been born within 20 years of 1555. Henry Quinton alias Leonard, who was baptised at Etchingham in Sussex in 1562 and cannot be traced in the Weald after the early 1590s, would fulfil these conditions.

Henry Quinton was the son of Martin Quinton alias Leonard, a finer whose elder son, John Lenard, had been baptised at Frant in 1548. Martin's father was presumably a Frenchman named Quintin Leonard whose death had occurred before the numerous denization rolls and subsidy rolls of the 1540s and who had somehow escaped being recorded in the subsidy rolls of 1524 and 1525. Martin Leonard was buried at Burwash in 1592 and we should expect his son to appear in Wealden records during the 1580s.

Henry Leonard actually appeared in the Danehill Sheffield hundred views of frankpledge as a defaulter in Sheffield borough from April 1588 to April 1591.[198] He may have arrived at Sheffield some years before 1588 because views of frankpledge for the hundred do not survive for the period 1582 to 1587. Nor can it be proved that he left Sheffield during 1591 because the court book came to an end with the entry for April 1591.

Sheffield lay within Fletching parish and it was there that one of Henry Leonard's sons was baptised in 1591. Unfortunately the baptismal name of the child was not recorded. The baptism fell within the required parameters of ten years before or after 1585 for the birth of Thomas Leonard, but all certainty on this point is precluded. Nor has any entry for Henry Leonard's marriage been found, so both the marriage and any earlier baptisms could have occurred in parishes adjacent to Fletching, such as Horsted Keynes and West Hoathly, for which no sixteenth-century parish registers survive.

It seems probable that Henry Leonard left the Weald shortly after 1591 and a move to Monmouthshire, where the indirect process was being established at this time, would be unsurprising. If the child born in 1591 was Thomas, children fathered in Pontypool in 1618 and 1620 could well have been his.

The Leonard family was first noted in New England when the wives of Henry Leonard and John Vinton were cited by the court held at Salem in September 1649 as having been fined for 'scolding and uttering opprobrious words towards their neighbours'. In September 1650 Lawrence Turner, son of the finer John Turner, accused Henry Leonard and his wife Mary of defamation, whilst Leonard accused Turner and his wife Sarah of battery. John and Lawrence Turner were ordered to bring Sarah before the court and she was sentenced to be whipped, 'for her many offences'. The court seems to have taken the view that she was at the root of these troubles between the two families.[199]

It was actually away from Hammersmith that the Leonard brothers came into their own.

194. ESRO, DYK 614.

195. Hartley, *Ironworks on the Saugus*, p. 188.

196. Pope *The pioneers of Massachusetts*, p. 369.

197. A. A. Everett, 'Leonards of Monmouthshire and Somersetshire, England', *The American Genealogist*, **53** (1977), pp. 101-4.

198. ESRO, ACC 3597/1, ff 26, 33v., 68,79v., 107v., 119,143v.

199. Dow, *Records and files of the quarterly courts of Essex county, Massachusetts, 1636-1656, vol. 1*, pp. 174, 198-200.

Firstly, after local merchants had taken over the Hammersmith works, it was to James Leonard that they divested themselves of the forge at Braintree by lease in 1659, though Hartley doubted whether this enterprise absorbed much of his attention.[200]

In 1652 the inhabitants of Taunton in Massachusetts had determined to run their own works, which the Leonards were invited to set up in conjunction with Ralph Russell. This was the beginning of Raynham Forge and it was here that James Leonard primarily established himself and his family, though when manufacture first began in 1656 John Turner, perhaps a son of the Lynn finer, worked the forge. Turner left in 1659 and it was under the new regime established then that James Leonard became principal workman. Raynham Forge was a two-hearthed bloomery and as in the contemporary forges in the English Lake District, the two hearths in it were named, or misnamed, the smelting hearth as 'finery', and the hearth where the iron was shingled and hammered into bars as 'chafery'. By 1683 Leonard's son Thomas Leonard had become manager.[201]

James Leonard had meanwhile set up Whittenton Forge, a one-hearthed bloomery on Mill River to which two further hearths were eventually added. It remained in Leonard hands until 1807. Another Leonard forge near Taunton, Chartley Forge at Norton, was established in the late 1690s by Thomas Leonard and his brother James Leonard II. This ran for most of the eighteenth century. Thomas's son Elkanah Leonard had a share in King's furnace, set up in 1724 in East Taunton. James Leonard II's son, James Leonard III, built Brummagem Forge at Easton in 1720, where his son Eliphalet Leonard was put in charge. There Eliphalet's son, Eliphalet Leonard II is thought to have made steel prior to 1771, and further steel furnaces were built there by his son Jonathan Leonard in 1787 and 1808, whilst Jonathan's brother, Eliphalet Leonard III built a further small forge there in 1790.[202]

It was the number and longevity of these enterprises set up and operated by James Leonard's descendants that gave rise to the saying, 'Where you can find iron works there you will find a Leonard'.[203] However, as we have seen, the persistence of members of the Leonard family in the trade of finer in the English Midlands was almost equally impressive.

Meanwhile Henry Leonard, who had stayed on at Lynn during the Gifford era at Hammersmith and into the period when the Company of Undertakers had given way to local merchants, had become a freeman of Massachusetts Bay in 1668. Outside the area, as 'Mr Leonard', though still illiterate, he became manager of the three-hearthed bloomery forge known as Bromingum Forge in Rowley village. With such auspicious beginnings it might have been supposed that Henry Leonard's descendants would prove equally successful. But such was not to the case; by 1673 he was leasing the plant at an astonishing rent of almost £190 a year and rapidly ran into debt. Later in that year he absconded to New Jersey to escape his creditors, and although his sons Samuel, Nathaniel and Thomas Leonard continued to work there, their wild and unruly behaviour caused them to run into trouble with the new partnership which was running the works, and they were soon dismissed.[204]

In New Jersey Henry Leonard and his three sons built a new forge at Tinton Falls for James Grover and his partners. The works had two fineries, a chafery and a power-driven hammer, though whether these were genuine fineries and chafery, which operated in conjunction with a blast furnace as Hartley supposed, or were actually the similarly named hearths of an elaborate bloomery forge, similar to the one built at Raynham seems uncertain. But the Leonard involvement at Tinton Falls proved quite ephemeral and by 1679 Henry Leonard and his sons were back at Rowley, though to what extent they participated in the ironworks there is unknown.[205]

John Francis, who worked as both collier and hammerman at Hammersmith during the 1650s, probably also came from the Weald. He was presumably a member of the Obell alias Francis family of forgemen, descended from Francis Obell who lived first at Ardingly and was at Worth from 1568 to 1578. At Hammersmith John Francis was in charge of the chafery and the hammer. In September 1653 he was owed £48 8s 0d by the Company of Undertakers for having 'coaled' 176 loads of wood for the Hammersmith works at 5s 6d the load; in 1655 he asserted that £26 was still owed to him. When he

200. Hartley, *Ironworks on the Saugus*, pp. 256; 266.
201. Ibid., pp. 272-4.
202. Ibid., pp. 275-6.
203. P. Fobes, *Topographical description of the town of Raynham*, (1793).
204. Hartley, *Ironworks on the Saugus*, pp. 294-7.
205. Ibid., p. 299-301.

died in 1668 his goods were inventoried at only £18 10s 0d, whilst the debts owing to him – £25 4s 0d – suggests that he recovered little of the amount owed to him by the company in 1655.[206]

About John Dimon and John Gorum, both of whom bore surnames attributable to the eastern Weald, little is known. Hartley classed them among those who barely met the criteria for full-time ironworks employees. Their baptismal names are no help in eliciting their origins.

John Dimond was in New England by February 1649. The surname was that of an immigrant family who cast guns at most of the Kent gunfoundries such as Cowden, Brenchley, Bedgebury and Hawkhurst. The extreme difficulty of ascertaining the descent of those John Diamonds who remained in the Weald is such as to make the task of tracing the origins of the Hammersmith man appear unrealistic.

John Gorum was more probably connected with William Goram, a 'founderer', who was buried at Stowe-by-Chartley in Staffordshire in 1617, than with the Gorhams of the eastern Weald.[207] He was the man whom the finer John Turner swore 'by the eternal God' he would kill in December 1647. Two years later he was a witness of the attack by Nicholas Pynion on Charles Hooke.[208] In 1650 the widow of Thomas Cooke of Ipswich, who himself had been noted for drinking offences, sought to recover £5 8s 0d, a 'debt of John Gorames at the Iron Works'. Gorum was fined in June 1651 for being drunk and abusing the constable of Lynn, in November 1652 for wearing silver lace in defiance of the sumptuary laws, and again in July 1653 for once more being drunk.[209]

William Osborne already acted as clerk for the ironworks in Winthrop's time and drew up the account of moneys expended up to December 1644. It appears just possible that he was already resident in New England before Winthrop's return from England in 1643, because a man of that name was empanelled on a trial jury at Salem in December 1642.[210]

However, this is rendered less likely because Osborne appears to have been technically more competent than either Winthrop or Leader. Incredibly, when in 1655 Winthrop asked Leader to give him working dimensions and other data needed for the furnace he then wished to build at New Haven in Connecticut, Leader replied that the book containing the data was packed away and unavailable and that Winthrop should turn to Osborne for advice.[211]

In the hiatus of around six months between Leader's departure and Gifford's arrival in 1650, Osborne effectively ran the ironworks. Retrospectively, Gifford stated that when he arrived in December 1650 the ironworks had been in 'ruinated condition'. John Becx, on the contrary, wrote in 1652 that 'in osbornes time theare was good store of barr Iron, sow Iron, Potts, Coale, wood and myne leaft and the works in good repair'. Indeed, when a special court, set up in Massachusetts in 1653 to unravel the triangular dispute between the Company of Undertakers, their manager John Gifford, and the local creditors, awarded the ironworks to the creditors towards the end of the year, they in turn offered its management to Osborne, but he declined on account of the confusion and debts. And when the creditors made revised proposals to the Company of Undertakers in September 1654, John Becx countered with another proposal which would have seen Osborne reinstated as 'uper Clarcke' with a salary of £20 or £30 a year.[212]

Ultimately, William Osborne ended his days as clerk of the new ironworks set up under Winthrop's inspiration at New Haven in Connecticut, which, like Hammersmith, was intended to work by the indirect method. Other former Hammersmith employees there included Nicholas Pynion, Ralph Russell, Roger Tyler and John Vinton. Osborne clearly knew his way around in more ways than one, because after his death in August 1662 his estate was valued at £836 7s 5d.[213]

The surname Osborne was a common one in most parts of the Weald, and without further

206. Dow, *Records and files of the quarterly courts of Essex county, Massachusetts, 1636-1656, vol. 1*, p. 292, 400; Hartley, *Ironworks on the Saugus*, pp. 189, 211.

207. Jonas Gorham of Salehurst was a clothier (ESRO, PBT 1/1/19/59 (1625)), his sons Jabez a husbandman (PBT 1/1/23/80 (1633)) and Jonas a yeoman (TNA, PROB 11/193/504 (1645)); George Gorram of Tudeley in Kent was a broadweaver (KHLC, DRb/PW27 (1628)).

208. Dow, *Records and files of the quarterly courts of Essex county, Massachusetts, 1636-1656, vol. 1*, pp. 130, 174.

209. Ibid., pp. 196, 228, 271, 287.

210. Ibid., p. 44.

211. Hartley, *Ironworks on the Saugus*, p, 119.

212. Ibid., pp. 144-5, 247-8.

213. Ibid., pp. 211, 284-6.

evidence it is impossible to suggest which of the many William Osbornes alive in the first half of the seventeenth century emigrated to New England. The name has strong associations with trades closely related to ironworking such as charcoal-burning, tanning, and bellows-making.

Richard Leader of New England's cousin Martha, daughter of Richard Leader II of Salehurst, had married a Heathfield tanner named Walter Osborne at Salehurst in 1607. Walter Osborne was probably the only son of Thomas Osborne, who was buried at Heathfield in 1584 and his grandfather was perhaps 'Master Water Oseborne, tanner' who had witnessed the will of John a'Courte of Mayfield in 1567.[214] However, Walter and Martha Osborne's only son was Richard, baptised at Heathfield in 1610.

A tanner named John Osborne was buried at Mayfield in 1604, but his only son was named Thomas.[215] Another man related to the Sussex Osbornes may have been Walter Osborne, citizen and leatherseller of London, who died in 1633, but he mentioned no relative named William in his will.[216]

George Osborne, a Kirdford collier, who was whipped for a theft in 1623,[217] was perhaps baptised at Worth in 1590, the son of John and Elizabeth Osborne. He married Dorothy Norton at Kirdford in 1617, where three of their children were baptised between 1618 and 1625, but none was named William.

The father of Thomas Osborne, a Hartley husbandman who was buried at Cranbrook in 1659, was a Hawkhurst bellows-maker named William Osborne. The bellows-maker cannot have been William Osborne, who married Ellyn Sheff at Hawkhurst in 1589 and who died in 1611, because that parish register recorded the baptism of nine of their children, none of whom was named Thomas. It looks as though the Hawkhurst bellows-maker must have moved to that parish only after the baptism of his son Thomas. Perhaps William Osburn, whose seven children baptised at Goudhurst between 1605 and 1620 included Thomas baptised in 1615, later moved on to become this Hawkhurst bellows-maker. This possible bellows-maker had another son named William, who was baptised at Goudhurst in 1607; could he have been the fixture clerk of the Hammersmith ironworks?

But there were dynasties of bellows-makers named Osborne in other English ironworking areas. Roger Osborne, whose daughter Mary was baptised at Birmingham in 1635, was perhaps the bellows-maker of that name who was buried at West Bromwich in 1657. In South Yorkshire, another Roger Osburn of Attercliffe who died in 1684, Joshua Osborne of Ecclesall who died in 1699, and William Osborne also of Ecclesall who died in 1705, were all bellows-makers. From among these, the man baptised at Goudhurst in 1607 seems the only possibility.

Other Wealden names paralleled among Hammersmith men were a worker and boatman named Bayley – a collier John Bayliefe (1587) or Baylye (1588) of Nutley in Maresfield;[218] Thomas Beale, the filler, had as namesake Thomas Beel of Burwash, one of the carpenters who in 1556 had repaired the hammer beam at Robertsbridge Forge; John Hardman, the collier, had as namesake a Frant collier, who was a quarter sessions witness in 1648; John Lambert, the boatman, in whose case the Lambert forgemen in various regions of England are too numerous to mention; Henry Tucker, the collier, who was paralleled in the Weald by Thomas Tucker, a Maresfield and Buxted pot-founder (1594-1604); Thomas Wiggins, the miner, paralleled in the Weald by John Wickens, a Heathfield collier (1648), was possibly even the same man as Thomas Weeken or Wickings, the Maresfield founder who in 1627 had been recruited by the French.[219] Additionally, the surnames Checkswell and Tingle occurred in the Weald and Tingle was found in the ironworks at Rievaulx in North Yorkshire, at Oakamoor in north Staffordshire, and elsewhere in the Midlands. Thomas Billington may have sprung from the immigrant family of Boysard alias Billing.

Needless to say, the ironworkers employed at Hammersmith were only the first of a steady stream to cross the Atlantic to seek success as ironworkers overseas. It seems almost certain that a

214. WSRO, STA1/4/18.
215. ESRO, PBT 2/2/2/114.
216. TNA, PROB 11/164/156.
217. ESRO, Q1 1, f. 1.
218. ESRO, ACC 3597/1, ff 15, 63v., 88v., 109, 128.
219. KHLC, U1475 B8/8 (Beel). ESRO, QR 4, m, 1 (Tucker), QR 80, m. 57 (Hardman), QR 81, m. 32 (Wickens); I am indebted to Brian Phillips for all these quarter-sessions references. *Calendar of State Papers, Domestic, Charles 1*, **2**, p. 196 (Weeken). Entries for Tucker run from 1590 (marriage), through 1592 and 1599 (baptisms) to 1604 (burial) in the Buxted parish register,ESRO, PAR 284/1/1/1.

Udimore farm labourer William Urian Doust, who in 1855 settled in Syracuse in New York state, and was later employed there by the steel firm Sanderson Brothers, had reverted to the trade of his ancestor Robert Dowst, who in 1515 had come from Auneuil in Picardy to work in the ironworks of the Weald. In contrast Thomas Tyler, who in 1899 also emigrated with his family to work at Syracuse for Sandersons, was descended from Brayons who had been continuously employed for almost four centuries in iron and for two and a half centuries in the forges of South Yorkshire.

EPILOGUE

By 1650 it is evident that what had formerly been a country whose main industries had been agriculture and the clothing trade had now taken its first, but decisive steps to becoming the world's first major industrial power. We saw in the Pays de Bray that the presence of local furnaces and forges encouraged the establishment in the area not only of blacksmiths, nailers and lock-smiths, who could make use of the locally produced iron, but the trades of blade-smithing, sword-smithing and cutlery whose workers, in addition to locally produced iron, probably depended on imported Spanish iron for the cutting edges of their instruments, and who probably made use of imported copper and bronze too.

In England the rapid expansion of the iron industry, the establishment in 1568 of the Company of Mines Royal and of the Mineral and Battery Society which now added copper and zinc to the metals already produced indigenously, and perhaps above all the continued development of the coal industry, which was of course stimulated by the perceived shortage of wood, all contributed to what Nef called the 'First Industrial Revolution'. This terminology was perhaps unfortunate and has been criticised and even derided in comparison with developments which occurred after 1750.

But it was also once thought that the Civil Wars were followed in Britain by a period of relative decline in the iron industry, from which it was rescued only by the discovery at Coalbrookdale of a method of smelting iron with coke fuel. It is now realized that the period of the Foley, Lloyd, Spencer, Cotton and Hall, and Crowley partnerships was one of consolidation, during which the use of blast furnaces of much larger size became widespread, even if their total number showed little growth.[220]

By 1700 much of the infrastructure for the industrial revolution was in fact in place. Watch and clock-making was a growing and widespread trade, with the Company of Clockmakers in London incorporated in 1631; the manufacture of cutlery expanded in many centres, especially around Sheffield, where the Company of Cutlers in Hallamshire was established in 1624. By 1637 the Birmingham area was described as being 'full of inhabitants and resounding with hammers and anvils for most of them are smiths';[221] the extent to which the locksmiths of the Black Country seized the international market is demonstrated by the magnificent display of their artefacts in the Musée le Secq de Tournelles at Rouen. Meanwhile the expanding English merchant marine needed, not just nails in its construction and guns for its defence, but navigational instruments too; and all these newly established industries themselves needed tools.

The extent to which such necessities began to be supplied during the seventeenth rather than the eighteenth century has been underestimated. In specialist trades for instance, John Hussey of Nantwich, who died in 1660, described himself as an 'instrument maker';[222] he may even have been of immigrant descent. Mathematical instrument-makers became numerous in London during the Restoration period, but because no guild for them was established, it was to the Grocers' Company, to the Stationers, to the Weavers and, because many early measuring instruments were made of wood, to the Joiners' Company that early instrument makers belonged. Trades more closely allied to the making of mathematical and optical instruments, such as the Spectaclemakers and Clockmakers, were incorporated as early as 1629 and 1631 respectively.

Augustine Ryther, a maker of theodolites and engraver of maps, belonged to the Grocers' Company. Another engraver and instrument maker, Charles Whitwell (d. 1611), was apprenticed to

220. M. W. Flinn, 'The growth of the English iron industry, 1660-1760', *Economic History Review,* 2nd series, 11 (1958), pp. 151-2.

221. C. Wilson, *England's apprenticeship, 1603-1763*, p. 86.

222. J. P. Earwaker (ed.), *An index to the wills and inventories now preserved in the Court of Probate at Chester 1660-1680*, Manchester, Record Society of Lancashire and Cheshire, **15**, 1887, p. 147.

Ryther in 1582, and he in turn took Elias Allen as his apprentice around 1602. Elias Allen, who was made free of the Grocers' Company in 1611 and who worked in brass, was one of the earliest members of the Clockmakers' Company, being its Master in 1637, and by around 1650 described himself as a 'mathematician'.[223] During the second half of the century some thirty Clockmakers' apprentices were apprenticed, or re-apprenticed to mathematical instrument makers.[224] Frenchmen had been apprenticed in the Clockmakers' Company in the 1650s,[225] and far from the influx of Huguenot refugees from the 1680s onwards having led to London supplanting Paris as the chief centre of instrument making, it looks as though London may have taken the lead in this respect during the seventeenth rather than the eighteenth century. Only eight mathematical instrument-makers are known to have traded in London in 1601, but that number had expanded to 30 by 1651 and 123 by 1701.[226]

Only against this rapidly maturing mathematico-industrial background could the skills needed in precision engineering be nurtured. The first steam engine, the Newcomen engine, used mainly for pumping in the mines, could thus be marketed even before the great Coalbrookdale ironworks actually became involved in the project, with the first mention of Stanier Parrot in the company's books not coming until 1718.[227] Each had evolved independently; their coming together helped to ensure the success of both. It was through the exploitation of similar coincidences that the industrial revolution was born.

The manufacture of crucible steel was indeed an eighteenth-century invention, but high grade cementation steel was produced successfully in the Midlands by Ambrose Crowley at Stourbridge in 1682, at Abbots Bromley by 1686, and in the north-east by Dennys Hayford at Blackhall Mill by around 1690. Both at Stourbridge and at Blackhall Mill, imported Swedish iron was used for the best quality of steel.

So far from being a symptom of industrial decline, increased imports of iron from abroad in the century up to 1750 were the result of the spectacular growth in secondary metal trades, and of the consequent demand for more specialized raw materials which the British iron industry found it difficult, and in some cases impossible to supply.

In turn, when coke-fired smelting allowed the dramatic increase in production of iron and steel which during the Industrial Revolution made Britain the 'workshop of the world', additional smelters of iron and steel, and forgemen for the new trades of puddling and rolling did not have to be found within the industry itself, or be recruited from abroad, but could easily be trained from the vast reservoir of skilled workers already available from the secondary metal trades of Britain's burgeoning industrial areas.

AN IRONWORKING PROFILE

Employment

Ironworkers were hired as 'covenant servants' for varying periods, as was the case at Robertsbridge in 1546 when Perrigo and Simon Kempe were hired for one year, but 'Gowtre' and Hugh Marchant were hired for four years.[228] Earnest money was paid to the worker at the signing of a new covenant, a shilling to Perrigo and Kempe, but 4 shillings in the case of the four-year covenants. Sir William Sidney's 'Book of covenants' was referred to in 155 1,[229] but, unlike muniments of title to land, such documents were in the long term of small legal importance and it is unsurprising that none has survived.

223. C. E. Atkins (ed.), *Register of apprentices of the worshipful Company of clockmakers of the city of London,* London, Clockmakers' Company, 1931, p. 122.
224. Ibid., pp, 1, 19 (2), 21, 23, 24, 26, 37, 38, 56, 62, 66, 77, 97, 102, 105, 122, 145, 160, 224, 234, 251, 252, 257, 265, 283, 304, 305, 323.
225. Ibid., pp. 240, 247.
226. G. Clifton (ed.), *Directory of British scientific instrument makers 1550-1851,* London, Zwemmer, 1995, p. xiv.
227. Raistrick, *Dynasty of ironfounders*, pp. 126-9.
228. ESRO, SHE 6//1/11/1.
229. KHLC, U1475 B8/4.

Legal proceedings were instituted if an ironworker broke his covenant. In 1546 Harry Westall paid 5 shillings for 'warraunts upon the statute' had from Master Darrell in 1546 'for ij of my masters frenchemen that wold not kepe in his worke', and a particular problem arose that year, when peace with France made the Channel crossing easier; Westall rode to London 'to aske councell what ordre shuld be taken for to reteyne my masters Frenchemen after the peace was proclamyd'.[230] On the other hand, when in July 1549 the furnace, and apparently the forge too, had been temporarily put out of action by rioters from Kent pulling them down, Westall himself went to Rye to 'speke for passage for Hugh Marchant', the finer.[231]

At Panningridge Sidney's furnacemen were paid by the six-day founday, the founder receiving 8 shillings and the filler 6 shillings per founday up to 1556. Later the filler was paid 6s 8d, and, because the combined total in 1562 came to 15s 8d, it seems that the founder was now paid 9 shillings.[232]

In view of higher rates paid to founders at gun-casting furnaces and at Sir Henry Sidney's Tongwynlais Furnace in Glamorgan, attempted comparisons with a later period have questionable validity. However, as the yield of a founday was around five tons of sow iron, the sum of 15s 8d a founday paid at Panningridge seems comparable with the 16s 8d paid to Charles Clay, ironfounder in the south Yorkshire partnerships at the end of the seventeenth century, for five tons of iron at 3s 4d a ton.[233] It would bear out David Crossley's conclusion that as a result of the early scarcity of their skills specialist ironworkers started at relatively high rates, but that their rates of pay remained static relative to general prices and to the cost of raw materials such as charcoal,[234] which rose fourfold in price by around the end of the sixteenth century.

Annual sums paid to Panningridge founders (rounded up)[235]

1547	1548	1549	1550	1551	1553	1554	1555	1556	1558
£41	£24	£21	£33	£34	£21	£21	£18*	£17	£33

* An additional sum of £28 17s 6d was paid at Panningridge this year, mysteriously recorded as being 'for the castyng of 770 great lodes of myne at divers prices', in addition to the normal 22 foundays and five days worked.

Accounts for Ralph Hogge's ironworks show that rates of pay at gunfounding furnaces were rather higher. At Marshalls Furnace in 1577, Ralph Hogge's founder Thomas Cade received 14 shillings the founday for both sows and guns. For casting shot however, in which the metal could not be poured from the hearth but had to be laboriously ladled out, the rate increased to 19 shillings the founday. At the same furnace the filler was John Dyne and his pay also varied, not according to what was cast, but to whether the furnace was charged with wood chips or coals (*charcoal*); if wood he received 11 shillings, if charcoal 10 shillings the founday.[236]

But if these rates were high, for the gun-casting moulds Cade was paid at the inexplicably low rate of 7 shillings a dozen, which was less than the 8 pence each paid by Sir William Sidney for charcoal baskets. Opening the moulds, for which John Pope was paid £1 3s 4d in 1577, was a charge reckoned against what had been paid to the founder. As at Panningridge, hearth-mending was paid at 5 shilliongs and breaking an old hearth at a shilling.[237] Another task which must normally have been one of the gunfounder's 'extras' was cutting away the gun-head from the muzzle of the finished cannon. Hogge's surviving accounts do not mention this, but at Hamsell Furnace in December 1679 Message was paid £2 for cutting the muzzle of a demi-cannon and 5 shillings for cutting the muzzle of a saker.[238]

In 1568 at Sir Henry Sidney's more remote works at Tongwynlais near Cardiff, wages at the furnace were already paid by the week rather than the founday. The Master founder was paid 9s

230. ESRO, SHE 6/1/11/1.
231. KHLC, U1475 B8/3.
232. Crossley, *Sidney ironworks accounts*, p. 23.
233. Raistrick and Allen, 'The south Yorkshire ironmasters (1690-1750)', p. 174.
234. Crossley, *Sidney ironworks accounts*, p. 24.
235. Ibid., passim.
236. Crossley, 'Ralph Hogge's ironworks accounts, 1576-81', pp. 68-70.
237. Ibid., pp. 69.
238. ESRO, SAS/CO 1/631. I am grateful to Roger Davey for drawing my attention to these accounts.

6d a week, 'his fellow' (the associate founder) was paid 8 shillings a week, whilst 'their man' had 6 shillings. The filler, who was still paid rather curiously by the founday, had 6 shillings, the same pay as at Panningridge.[239] This was a weekly rate of 7 shillings, thus marginally exceeding what was received by the founder's 'man'. Total weekly furnace payments were £1 10s 6d, or around £1 6s 0d the founday. The payments to the founder and his two assistants totalled £1 3s 6d a week, equal to around £1 0s 2d a founday, This seems excessive when compared with the rates of 8 shillings and 9 shillings paid to the founder at Panningridge, but less surprising when compared with the payments of 14 shillings and 19 shillings paid by Hogge at his gunfoundry.

At Robertsbridge Forge the finers and hammermen were paid quarterly 'wages', which in the case of the finer Peter Gellie amounted to annual sums of £1 8s 4d in 1562 and £1 6s 8d in each of the next three years, the lesser sum probably paid quarterly at 6s 8d, the larger sum amounting to the curious amount of 7s 1d a quarter. Peter Bartholomew, who was perhaps the second finer, was paid £1 6s 8d in 1563 and 1564, but had been paid 18s 4d in 1562, perhaps because he did not work the full financial year. Philip Hills, who appears to have succeeded Bartholomew, was paid 13s 4d in 1565, perhaps because he worked for only half the year. James Barden, the hammerman, was paid 16s 8d in 1562, perhaps at 4s 2d a quarter, £1 in 1563 and 1564, presumably at 5 shillings the quarter, and finally £1 6s 8d in 1565.[240]

However, much the greater part of the income of the forgemen came from piecework, which was reckoned at 13s 4d per ton of iron produced, divided equally between the two operations, 6s 8d going to the hammerman and 6s 8d to the finers. Since there were two finers, each presumably received 3s 4d a ton, but out of these sums they, as was the case also with the hammerman, were expected to pay their assistants, which they probably did by customary arrangements, which we have no means of knowing but which may have differed little from forge to forge. Here again rates of pay remained relatively static in the long term.

Annual sums paid at Robertsbridge to forgemen (rounded up)

1547	1548	1549	1551	1553	1554	1555	1556	1558	1563	1568	1572
£114	£96	£6	£103	£84	£86	£112	£85	£86	£66	£83	£102

Later, finers tended to be paid more than hammermen, because fining was a difficult art, whilst the hammerman's task was more dependent on bodily strength. This change had already taken place at Robertsbridge by 1563, when the finers were paid £40 6s 4d, but the hammerman only £25 8s 8d for producing T 76 4 cwt 3 qr of iron. In Glamorgan in 1568 Sir Henry Sidney's finers and hammermen were paid £1 per ton of iron produced, half as much again as at Robertsbridge, but the breakdown between the two trades was not revealed.[241] In 1640 in the Pelham family forges, the finer at Bivelham was paid 8s 6d per ton of iron and the hammerman 7 shillings, whilst at Glaziers Forge the corresponding amounts were 9 shillings and 7s 6d, giving totals of 15s 6d and 16s 6d. In 1677-8, at the end of the period covered by the Pelham accounts, the higher rate was being paid at both forges.[242]

Ralphe Hogge's surviving accounts yield no comparable figures. Peter Bartholomew, probably a finer, was in receipt of annual wages of £8, but was also paid 6s 8d a ton, or £3 15s 0d for T 11 5 cwt of iron made. He was also paid 13s 4d a ton for making 2.5 tons of 'heads' (*hedes*), and then 4 pence the hundredweight for 11 cwt of 'heads', rates which appear irreconcilable, but relate to the fining of cast-iron gun-heads. He was also paid 2 shillings for dressing bellows, 4 pence for bearing 14 loads of coal, and £1 4s 0d 'due to him for cotton cloth', perhaps in lieu of a livery coat; his 'boys' were paid 1s 8d for beating shot. The hammerman Roger Shermne was paid a total of £3 5s 0d, but his work was not defined. [Thomas?] Sprey, or Praye, another hammerman, was paid 3s for beating shot, but none of his

239. Crossley, *Sidney ironworks accounts*, p. 245-6.

240. KHLC, U1475 B3/10. What role was played at Robertsbridge by Thomas Glid, presumably the later forgemaster, who was paid wages of £1 in 1562 and £2 in each of the three following years, is unclear. Perhaps he was a clerical assistant, as Richard Martin had been earlier.

241. Crossley, *Sidney ironworks accounts*, p. 184, 248.

242. BL, Add. Mss 33,155 (ff. 4v, 10, 89v, 159, 159v).

other work was defined.[243] It looks as though the main payments to Shermne and Sprey must have been recorded in the books kept by Hogge's other clerks, Sampson Coulstock and George Kenyon, of which none survives.

The Sidney colliers were also covenant servants; at Panningridge in 1549 they were Peter Uncle and George Meriall, each paid wages of 6s 8d a quarter, an arrangement which still continued in 1551.[244] However, by 1556, when the colliers were Lawrence Henold and (Lewis) Ransell, the wages had been halved to 13s 4d for the whole year.[245] This probably did not matter too much because the chief source of income for the colliers was again piecework, a rate of 1s 3d for each load of wood coaled, which during 1555 in the case of Thomas Duggan amounted to the substantial sum of £28 is 3 pence for coaling 449 loads of wood. In the same year Adrian Doggen was paid £29 10s 0d for coaling 472 loads of wood.[246]

These rates of pay to colliers may seem high but it is probable that they too had to pay a proportion of these earnings to assistants. Moreover, the employment by Sidney of colliers on covenant, in most years from the immigrant community, reflects the absolute necessity of having charcoal of the best quality if the blast furnace was to function well. Charcoal burning had been a trade with a long history, but some generations seem to have elapsed before indigenous colliers were able to produce charcoal suitable for the indirect process. Once this problem had been overcome covenants for colliers may have become obsolete. But colliers always remained worth their pay and in contrast to the minimal increases paid to furnacemen and forgemen, the Pelham accounts for Glaziers and Bivelham forges show that by 1640 the rate paid for coaling wood had doubled to 2s 6d the cord.[247]

Mining too was done at Panningridge by covenant servants. In 1550 these were Philpot [Mittell] and John Margo [alias Longley] and they were paid at the rate of 10 pence a load for the mine or ore which they dug. However, some of the ore dug in that year came from the woodland of John Cressie of Mountfield, and the ore dug there, both by Cressie's sons and by Philpot and Margo, was paid for at 8 pence the load. Philpot earned £21 15s 10d and Margo £29 0s 6d during the year.[248] Ralph Hogge's payments were perhaps roughly comparable, because he paid 1s 2d a load delivered at the furnace.[249]

Mining was a trade which complemented ironfounding and the same names occurred in both; Simon Tyler worked as a miner at Panningridge, but most members of his family were known as ironfounders; Jarman Mittell also mined at Panningridge before he and his descendants went on to work as ironfounders in the Pelham interest.

Charles Gerard, who was the master founder of William Levett and not a covenant servant of Sidney, was called in to lay the hearth at Panningridge at the start of each new campaign, and for this and for dressing the bellows he was paid 5 shillings, a task which in 1548 he carried out in both May and December.[250] Over and above this, in 1551, he was paid a penny for each of the six cams for the bellows-tree from plates of iron sent from Robertsbridge, and for making a new stirrup for the bellows harness he received 6 pence; further items he made later in the same year were another stirrup for which he was paid 8 pence and two new vental boards for the bellows, for each of which he was paid 2 pence.[251] In 1553 he was paid 14 shillings for five days work in mending the 'forefront of the fornes mouth', the differential in skill being reflected in the 8 pence a day paid to the filler [Simon] Spray, who assisted him. Peter 'the Founder' and Spray and his son dug (building) stone, probably for these repairs, whilst Denis 'Frenchman' dug (casting) sand.[252] In 1554 Gerard cast seven new hammers for the forge for which he received 1s 4d each; the following year he was paid at the same rate for casting six hammers, and he also cast three anvils at 8 pence each and two new *shamowes* (shammel plates) for the bellows at 6 pence each.[253]

Covenant servants supplemented their incomes by helping with wood-cutting, but the bulk of

243. Crossley, 'Ralph Hogge's ironworks accounts, 1576-81', pp. 67, 71, 77.
244. KHLC, U1475 B10/4 and 5.
245. KHLC, U1475 B10/9.
246. Crossley, *Sidney ironworks accounts*, pp. 137-9.
247. BL, Add. Mss 33,155, f. 4.
248. Crossley, *Sidney ironworks accounts*, p. 91.
249. Crossley, 'Ralph Hogge's ironworks accounts, 1576-81', p. 60.
250. KHLC, U1475 B2/1.
251. KHLC, U1475 B10/5.
252. KHLC, U1475 B10/6.
253. KHLC, U1475 B10/7 and 8.

this was done by casual labour. Covenant servants also did more specialized tasks around the works. Some of these tasks could yield them an income even at times when severe frost or drought brought bellows and hammer to a halt, as happened at Robertsbridge in January 1551 when 'because of the froste the[y] cold not worke' or in September 1554 when 'no yeren made thys reconyng for lacke of water'.[254]

As we have seen in the case of Charles Gerard, the founder was paid extra when producing castings rather than sow iron; in 1546, Vincent, the founder at Robertsbridge, was paid 6 shillings for casting plates, hammers and anvils for the forge;[255] in 1549 Nicholas Gerard was paid 13s 4d for casting a ton of brandirons at Panningridge; in 1554 Simon Pray was paid 2s 8d for scouring the 'fornes whych' (more properly the wooden 'hutch', which carried the waste water away from the water-wheel) and he and his son also received 1s 6d for a day and a half s work scouring the furnace-wheel ditch. The additional annual 'wage'of 12 shillings which Spray received in 1555 'for beryng of colles for on hole yeer' was perhaps stipulated in his covenant.[256]

The forgemen received extra payments for all kinds of extra work around the forge; in 1548 the regular forgemen, Gyllain [Hatto], [John] Collyan, [Thomas] Callish and Peter Gellie, received payment for setting new hoops on the hammer beam and fixing the beam itself in position, whilst Hugh Marchant was paid for 'the new dawbyng of the finery chimney'.[257] In 1551 the forgemen John Collyan, Peter Gelly, Hugh Marchant and Hopkins were each paid a shilling for three days labour in helping to set in a new 'hammer block' (more probably the anvil block), with meat and drink, whilst John Lenard who worked only two days at this had 8 pence. Here the receipt of meat and drink accounted for their pay being 4 pence a day rather than the 8 pence a day paid to Simon Spray when helping Gerard. In 1552-3 extra pay was received by John Collyan, Hugh Marchant, Peter Gelly and Robert Turke for dressing bellows and by Collyan, Marchant, Turke and Myghell Lassall for heaping coals.[258]

Making baskets for carrying coals and mine was another source of income; in 1549 the miner John Margo (alias Langley) was paid 2 shillings for three coal baskets and in 1552-3 the finer Goddard [Vackett] received 8 pence for one new coal basket; in 1551 the finer John Lenard had been paid 5s 4d for eight coal baskets which he had made, even though he was apparently not among Sidney's covenant servants.[259]

To a greater extent than other ironworkers, colliers perhaps supplemented their income by cutting wood. However, in 1553 the collier Adrian Dogen carried two old ringers from the furnace to the forge and two new ringers from the forge to the furnace.[260]

As servants of a noble master, Sidney's workers were entitled to annual livery coats, but these liveries were mentioned in the accounts only when money was paid in lieu, as was the case with 10 shillings given in 1544 to Guyllam, perhaps the hammerman.[261] The Panningridge colliers Peter Uncle and George Morrall each received 8 shillings for their liveries in 1550.[262] The 1553 accounts for Panningridge show the receipt by Simon Pray of 3s 4d for five yards of frieze to make livery coats due to him and his son under his covenant for 'blowing', and 6 shillings for three yards of russet to make his wife a petticoat. The following year's accounts show that he was paid 6s for each founday worked, with 12 shillings to pay for his own livery coat and those of his wife and son.[263]

To a limited extent the wives of ironworkers were involved around the works. Seven colliers mentioned at Robertsbridge in 1546 included Gillet's wife, and in 1548 Harvy's wife heaped 'coles' at Panningridge.[264] The Valliant family supplied grease for the furnace bellows at Panningridge; George supplied a gallon for 18d in 1549, John the same quantity for 2s 4d in 1551, and John Valliant's wife a shillings-worth in 1553 and 2 gallons for 2s 1d in 1555.[265]

254. KHLC, U1475 B8/4 and 6.
255. ESRO, SHE 6/1/11/1.
256. KHLC, U1475 B11/3, B10/8.
257. KHLC, U1475 B8/1.
258. KHLC, U1475 B8/4 and 5.
259. KHLC, U1475 B8/3 (1548), 4 (1551) and 5 (1552-3).
260. KHLC, U1475 B10/6.
261. KHLC, U1475 B1/1.
262. Crossley, *Sidney ironworks accounts*, p. 94.
263. KHLC, U1475 B10/6 and 7.
264. ESRO, SHE 6/1/11/1 (1546); KHLC, U 1475 B2/1 (1548).
265. KHLC, U 1475 B10/4, 5, 6 and 8.

The provision of livery coats for the sons of covenant servants, noted in the case of Simon Spray shows that older children often worked alongside their parents. During the building of Panningridge Furnace Come Langley and his son dug building stone and cleared wood out of the pond, each being paid 6 pence a day.[266] At Robertsbridge in 1543 Brisboy's boys were paid for 'heaping coles' and in 1549 Gwillam [Hatto?] and his boys were similarly employed.[267] The 6 shillings a founday paid to Simon Pray under his covenant apparently envisaged that his son [Adrian?], for whom a livery coat was written into the covenant, would work alongside him at no extra cost; however, each received payment when they worked on the additional tasks such as scouring the wheel pit.

Apprenticeship

It was undoubtedly in the semi-formal way just described that the next generation of ironworkers learnt the skills of their trade. By 1546 Brisboy's boys, Nicholas and James, were mentioned separately in the Sidney accounts; 'Old Brisboys bellows' and 'Young Brisboys bellows' were both referred to, and 'Young Brisboy' was in fact probably the finer Nicholas Brisboy, whose covenant was transferred during that year to the forgemaster Richard Woodman for 10s 8d.[268] In the following century at Glaziers Forge, John Messenge became finer in 1652 in place of Stephen Leanie, but John (or 'Young') Leany worked alongside Messenge up to 1656, in this way presumably completing his initiation, though he was not subsequently employed at the forge.[269] At Glaziers Forge where carpenter's work was paid at 2 shillings a day in the 1670s, John Hushyer was paid 1s 4d a day in 1675-6 for helping, whereas two years earlier, when a new hammer beam was installed there, 'young' Hushyer had received only a shilling a day.[270] At Bivelham Forge, where in the 1670s George Ongly was finer, he and his boy [Nicholas Ongly?] were paid 4s 4d in 1677-8 for clearing the river.[271]

Formal apprenticeship appears to have been resorted to when a father died young, leaving his children unprovided for. The immigrant Francis Obell probably died shortly after the baptism of his daughter Mary at Worth in 1578 and one of his orphan sons will have been Thomas Francis, probably born about 1566 or 1567, before the arrival of the family at Worth; in 1583 when the Nuthurst hammerman John Perigo made bequests to his apprentices, these were of £1 'over and above wages afore bargained' to Thomas Francis and 10 shillings to Peter, whose surname is unknown.[272]

In 1616 Worth parish apprentices included Bridget Roberts 'one of the poor frendless children' and William Roberts, perhaps her brother, who was apprenticed to John Bartholomew alias Pounteine of Tinsley, ironworker, and his wife Mary. Even the illegitimate could be provided for if they had viable relatives around, as was the case in 1617 when the 14-year-old Peter Harvy, illegitimate son of the widow Tamson Harvey and Peter Lockier, was bound apprentice to his legitimate half-brother Reynold Harvy, a Beeding finer.[273] Nevertheless, apprenticeship was quite rare and in Wealden probate records, apart from John Perigo's apprentices, only the hammerman Walter Old's apprentice Charles Growt was referred to; he was to have 5 shillings at the end of his term.[274]

Apprenticeship was perhaps also resorted to when a craftsman was childless. A citation from a later period illustrates this when in 1710-11 at Vale Royal Furnace in Cheshire 'Mr Thomas Hall, taking into consideration the use and necessity of preserving the art of a founder and the present and future advantage of our own works ... bound Timothy Copland to himself as a Covenant Servant for term of five years to be taught and instructed by Thomas Phillips our founder'.[275]

266. Crossley, *Sidney ironworks accounts*, pp. 44-5.
267. KHLC, U1475 8/2.
268. ESRO, SHE 6/1/11/1.
269. BL, Add. Mss 33,155, ff 71-81.
270. BL, Add. Mss 33,155, ff 145v, 155.
271. BL, Add. Mss 33,155, f. 159.
272. WSRO, STC 1/13, 107b.
273. WSRO, Par 516/33, 3, 4 and 6.
274. ESRO, PBT 1/1/26/28.
275. Foley Mss (by courtesy of B. L. C. Johnson's notes).

Housing

What proportion of employees was provided with housing is unclear. At Panningridge the 'felling, framing and setting up of a new house for George Meryall my master's collier' cost 13s 4d in October 1548, and carriage of the wood and thatching and daubing it cost a further£1 2s 6d; this was clearly a half-timbered house. In November 1548, Warnet, the founder, was paid 3s 4d 'in recompence for making his house'.[276] In 1556, 13s 8d was paid 'for the makyng of Peter Founders howse' with an additional 1s 4d for the carriage of timber and broome for it.[277]

At Robertsbridge a loft was made in [Gwillam] Brisboy's house in 1544. Thomas Mascall was paid 8 pence in 1556 'for pollyng downe of Audryan Dogens howse' after Dogen had left the forge, and the thatching of Peter Gellie's house was referred to in the same year.[278] These and other houses were clearly half-timbered, but the 1567 survey of the manor of Robertsbridge showed that James Lamye alias Barden, the hammerman, was housed in 'an howse made of lyme and stone, annexed to' the East Gate of the former abbey, with 'a lowe rome underneath nowe beinge the Storehowse for Iron'. This survey also included the 'Fyners Howse', lying between the principal mansion of the Manor and Courthills Meade; it consisted of 'one Messuage, one kytchen and one garden' of which Peter Jellye was tenant 'at the lords will' rent-free. Additionally, Barden, Jellye, and the other finer Peter Gonett held at will Great Pyebroke (6 acres), a mead in Ewhurst parish adjoining the stream running from the forge. Next to Great Pyebroke was Frenchmens Wood (42 acres), of which almost half was pasture ground and this too was rent-free on account of the Frenchmen's service.[279]

The Catsfield forgeman John Creasey testified in 1616 that he was a covenant servant of Mr Richard Alfrey, that he worked at Alfrey's forge and lived in his house, which would mean a house provided by the forgemaster.

At Glaziers Forge the Pelham accounts for 1640 record that £1 4s 6d was paid to Simpson the mason 'for makeing the Chafery chimney and other worke done about [Stephen] Lenies house and [Henry] Germains chimney' and 10 shillings 'for 2 loads of straw to thetch Lenyes house at 5 shillings per load'.[280] Pelham's workmen at Bivelham Forge also appear to have had houses provided; the mason Thomas Ellyot was paid no less than £5 10s 0d in 1656 'for building of Chymney att [Thomas] Francises [the hammerman's] house, he finding bricks and workmanship'. [281]

Tools

Because most of an ironworker's tools belonged to and were inventoried with the furnaces and forges at which they worked, tools appear sparsely in probate records. Exceptions were mining tools and the mortar and pestle with which the ironfounder ground specimens of ore to prove their content.

A reason for supposing that Thomas Bodell of Waldron, who made his will in December 1545, was an ironfounder is the fact that he bequeathed his iron mortar and iron pestle to his brother John Bodell.[282]

The immigrant ironfounding family of Tyler handed on its mortars. Even in the case of the second earliest member of the family to leave a will, Simon Tyler, a miner who worked at Panningridge in the 1550s, a mortar may have been subsumed under the heading 'all implements'. His will was dated 1561, named him Simon Tulye of Ashburnham, and by it he left to his son John a quilt, a mantle, 'all my rayment and all implements therto belonging to the fornys, and all implements belonging to mine and all manner of edge tools that is my fathers and all manner of things that he hath to ride withal'.[283] Simon's father was Robert Tyler who had worked for Sir William Barrentyne and who had perhaps retired to France by the time that Simon made his will, leaving his professional gear with his son.

276. KHLC, U1475 B2/1.
277. KHLC, U1475 B10/9.
278. KHLC, U1475 B7/3, B8/8.
279. D'Elboux, *Surveys of the manors of Robertsbridge*, pp. 126, 140.
280. BL, Add. Mss 33,155, f. 6v.
281. Op. cit., f. 90v.
282. ESRO, PBT 1/1/1/71.
283. ESRO, PBT 1/1/5/13.

The ironfounder Roger Tyler of Shipley in Sussex, who died in 1617, bequeathed two mortar moulds, 'my best' to his son Richard, the other to his son Roger Tyler,[284] the man who was destined to become in the 1640s the first ironfounder at Hammersmith in New England. Inventoried among the iron goods of the founder Charles Tyler of Heanor in Derbyshire in 1610 were two mortars and one pestle. A mortar was the last item among 30s-worth of iron goods belonging to the founder Quintin Tyler of Madeley in Staffordshire

inventoried in 1625.[285]

In 1586 John Bottinge of Hartfield left all his mining tools, with money due to him on bills, bonds and scores, or any other reckonings, to his wife Anne Vintam, whom he had married at Mayfield in 1573. In 1614 in Staffordshire the Winnington hammerman George Growte's inventory included a 'morter of iron and pestell' valued at 3 shillings.[286]

SECONDARY OCCUPATIONS

Husbandry

As in the Pays de Bray, ironworkers in England carried on small-scale husbandry to supplement their incomes and to sustain them in times when ironworks, for one reason or another, were not in production.

This was recognised by the forgemasters themselves. In 1552-3 the Robertsbridge Forge accounts were charged with 10 pence for the expense of driving back to Penshurst in Kent milch cows which Sir William Sidney had lent to each of his finers, Hugh Marchant and Peter Jelly.[287] In 1551 the forgemaster Thomas Mychell of Worth left in his will £6 13s 4d and three cows to 'poor Browne that worketh at the furnace', which would have been his Chittingly Manor Furnace in West Hoathly. That same year another forgemaster, Nicholas Eversfield, bequeathed a cow to Lawrence Lambert 'so he contynue at the forge'.[288] In August 1541 a bequest between forgemasters of equal standing was evidently envisaged by the immigrant Stephen Colyn of Withyham who, in addition to the bequest of £10 for the repair of a highway, left one cow each to the wife, and John and Robert, the two sons of the forgemaster, John Baker of Withyham.[289]

Immigrant ironworkers also bequeathed their cattle. In March 1559 Richard Weekes' forgeman, James Templeir of Mountfield, left a cow, 'the best that she will choose' to his second wife, Anne; his younger children Robert and Joan were each to have a cow, whilst his eldest son received a 12-monthing. The finer James Henesye [Hunnisset], who was buried at Nuthurst in 1560, left a cow and a featherbed to each of his daughters Agnes and Elizabeth.[290] Simon Tyler, who worked as a miner at Panningridge in the 1550s, made his will as 'Simon Tulye of Ashburnham' in 1561 and appointed 'a red gored cow, a gray mare, a peck of hay, a sow and a hanging over a bed' to be sold to pay his debts. He probably had more livestock than this, but that formed part of the residuary estate left to his widow Joan. The Salehurst hammerman, John Ellis, who died in 1567, left a cow and a calf to each of his four children, John, Anthony, Joan and Dorothy.[291] The finer Bartholomew Pounten of Rotherfield, who died in 1571, left all his household stuff, two cows and £6 to his third wife Joan. The former finer at Robertsbridge, Peter Jolly, who died in 1594, left a cow and a hog, to his second wife, Katherine; each of his sons, was also to have a cow and a hog, with £10 each to Charles and Henry and £6 to John.[292]

In 1560 the Robertsbridge hammerman John Templer, from the first generation of English-born ironworkers, whose two sons were minors, left to Henry a cow which he was to have at the age of 20, and to William two cows which were to be leased out until he was 20. In 1579 William Rowland alias Mocumber, the Fletching miner, left two steers, two cows and a black heifer with a white back, to his

284. WSRO, STC 1/9/S. Dean 1617, p. 28.
285. LRO, Inventories of Charles Tyler (1610), and Quintin Tyler (1625).
286. LRO, Inventory of George Growte (1614).
287. KHLC, U1475 B8/5 (1552-3).
288. TNA, PROB 11/34/438 and 35/238.
289. ESRO, PBT 1/1/1/37.
290. ESRO, PBT 3/1/1/56; WSRO, STC 1/10/51.
291. ESRO, PBT 1/1/5/13 and 455.
292. ESRO, PBT 1/1/6/37; 1/1/9/257.

daughter Parnell, and three steers, a branded cow and a two-yearling heifer to his son-in-law, Thomas Furner; Annis Mocumble, perhaps his niece, was to have a two-yearling red heifer.[293]

In 1593 the hammerman, Peter Honisett of Westfield, made bequests of a colt and four sheep to his eldest son John, and to his second son Clement of a cow, a 12-monthing and four sheep, beasts which were already in their keeping. In 1604, Mary Tollet of the parish of Petworth, widow of the immigrant Richard Tollet, left a 2-yearling bull to her eldest son Peter, a cow to her other son Marian, and a heifer to her daughter Alice.[294]

In 1605 Stephen Blewet, the Catsfield collier, left to his third wife Elizabeth three cows, a 12-monthing bullock and 'all manner of household stuff', and to his son, Nicholas Blewet the hammerman, a 12-monthing bullock, already in his keeping. In 1610, the Mountfield hammerman, Anthony Pullen, left his mare and a steer to his son Stephen, a cow each to his second son Edmund and to his daughter Alice, a one-yearling bullock to his daughter Margery's son Nicholas Angerfield, and a two-yearling heifer bullock (*sic*) to Edmund's son Nicholas.[295]

The East Grinstead pot-founder Anthony Durrant bequeathed two red cows in 1613, one 'with some white upon her' and the other 'with a white star' on its forehead. In 1614 Lambert Fashall, the Cranbrook collier, left to his wife Margaret a red cow with a white face and a red heifer with a white back, and to Lambert the son of Anthony Guise a lamb.[296] Peter Snashall of Rotherfield died in 1618 and left his best black cow to his daughter Mary, a white or red pied cow to his son Simon Snashall, the collier, a brown pied cow, a ewe and its lamb to his son Thomas, and another ewe and lamb to Thomas's son John.[297]

Later forgemen who bequeathed livestock included Walter Old, the Fletching hammerman who died in 1639; he left three cows called Shell, Whiteface, and Brown Cow, 10 tegs, a sow with farrow, and some skeats. In 1641 the hammerman Jordan de Verray of Mayfield left two cows, with a third of the wheat in the barn and of the victuals in the house, to his second wife Denise. In 1665 the children of the ironfounder Thomas Jaret of Mountfield were to share between them four cows, a young heifer, two weaning calves, and two hogs.[298]

Further afield, the ironfounder Charles Tyler of Heanor in Derbyshire died early in 1610 and although his inventory included a sheep-brand no farm animals were recorded; but these apparently belonged to his son-in-law Henry Dale, who at his death in 1631 owned 71 sheep worth £3 8s 0d.[299]

In Staffordshire, George Growte, the Winnington hammerman, who died in 1614, left seven sheep valued at £1, and a cow, somewhat surprisingly inventoried together with a malt mill at £3 16s 8d. In April 1617 the goods of John Dipprie alias Marian of Lizard hammers included a variety of livestock; six 'beasts' and a yearling calf valued at £14, two mares and a yearling colt worth £3 6s 8d, 73 sheep, hogs and wethers worth £18, swine, geese, ducks, hens and other poultry worth £1 10s 0d. The goods of the ironfounder, Quintin Tyler of Madeley, yeoman, were inventoried in 1625 and included three cows and a stirk or bullock valued at £8, eleven sheep valued at £2 10s 0d and a pig valued at 6 shillings.[300]

These quantities of livestock presupposed land on which to nourish them, whilst arable land was also needed. We have seen that the Sidney family made considerable provision at Robertsbridge for this. In 1614 Quintin Buley of Pembury, who described himself as a husbandman, bequeathed a swarm of bees and an acre of wheat to his eldest son Rowland Buley, and Lambert Fashall, the Cranbrook collier, bequeathed to his wife an acre of wheat in the Upper field in the time of harvest, with 10 bushels of oats and one bushel of wheat.[301]

In 1621 Stephen Dowst, the Crowhurst hammerman, left his widow a seam of wheat and a seam of oats, and she was to hold the house and lands until their son Gilbert came of age. In 1629 the ironfounder Charles Tiler of Hawkhurst left to his eldest son Elias the house and lands called Tubbs

293. ESRO, PBT 1/1/5/12; 1/1/7/159.
294. ESRO, PBT 1/1/9/134; WSRO, STC 1/15/58.
295. ESRO, PBT 1/1/12/135 and 412.
296. TNA, PROB 11/121/222; KHLC, PRC/17/57/336.
297. TNA, PROB 11/132/146.
298. ESRO, PBT 1/1/26/28; PBT 2/2/6/75; PBT 1/6/2/94.
299. LRO, Inventories of Charles Tyler (1610) and Henry Dale (1631).
300. LRO, Inventories of George Growte (1614), John Dipprie alias Marian (1617), Quintin Tyler (1625).
301. KHLC, DRb/PW23; PRC/17/57/336.

Lake, 'late purchased of Alexander Weller'. In 1639 the wife of Walter Old, the Fletching hammerman, was to have 'so much wheat now on the ground as will keep her house during ... one year and likewise so much malt'.[302]

In Staffordshire the Winnington hammerman George Growte's hoops of onions and garlic were worth 10 shillings in 1614, and these bring to mind the garlic often found on Wealden furnace sites. In 1617 the Lizard finer John Dipprie alias Marian had corn upon the ground and in the barn, which together with the hay was valued at £5, with bacon, beef and malt worth £1 10s 0d. In 1625 the Madeley founder Quintin Tyler held a second house and a barn at Betley, at which husbandry was also carried on.[303]

Textiles

To what extent women members of ironworking households were involved in spinning or weaving is difficult to assess. It seems very probable that whilst their menfolk worked in the ironworks it was the agricultural and stock-management tasks that devolved on the women. However, in the clothing areas of Kent, Elias Bluatt, the Biddenden hammerman, left all his tussome and linen yarn to his wife Margaret.[304]

Such references are difficult to find in Sussex, though in 1556 Anthony Ellis of Etchingham left his slays, used in beating up the weft in weaving, to his younger son Richard. It is not certain that John Starr of Waldron, who in 1567 left 12 pounds of linen yarn to his wife Joan, was of immigrant stock or even an ironworker.[305] The clearest reference in probate records to spinning was made in 1607 by Bartholomew Buley alias Jordan of Chiddingly, who mentioned in his will both yarn and (spinning) wheels, but this was years after he had been referred to as a miller.[306]

Further afield in the north Midlands rather more evidence for spinning and weaving is forthcoming. The probate inventory of John Dipprie alias Marian of Lizard hammers referred in 1617 to yarn worth 5 shillings and to looms, bowks and spinning wheels; in 1625 Quintin Tyler of Madeley's inventory included yarn, tow, spinning wheels, and five yards of woollen cloth.[307]

Status

The question of the status of the ironworker in society is not easy to resolve. For reasons unknown the leader of one of the first groups of ironworkers to arrive in Virginia in 1619 was styled 'Captain' Bluet. Did he own the boat in which he and his eighty men made the voyage? Perhaps he was Abraham Bluet who in 1581 in the Linchmere parish register had been referred to as 'Goodman Bluett'. But unlike the immigrant masters of glasshouses, even an ironworker as important as William Levett's founder Charles Gerard is nowhere referred to as 'Master Gerard', even after he had gone into partnership with Christopher Draper and Harry Westall. The same applies to John Harvo, gunstonemaker to the king, and John Lambert alias Gardener, who were every bit as much forgemasters as any others in the sixteenth-century Weald. Indeed, a good argument for supposing that Henry Gardener, who was forgemaster of the Tyrwhitt ironworks around 1560, was of native stock is the fact that he was referred to as 'Master Gardener'.

In South Yorkshire pretensions to grandeur were firmly repressed in 1578 when John Valyance and his wife appeared in the earl of Shrewsbury's manor court for a breach of the sumptuary laws: instead of the cap appropriate to the lower orders, they attended the parish church wearing hats.[308] However, the broad-brimmed hats and long flowing garments of furnacemen and forgemen depicted in Diderot's *Encyclopédie* were paralleled by those worn by the forgemen shown in Angerstein's sketch of Bromford

302. ESRO, PBT 1/1/18/30; KHLC, WC PRC/17/67/297; ESRO, PBT 1/1/26/28.
303. As note 81 above.
304. KHLC, PRC/17/63/307.
305. ESRO, PBT 1/1/13/200; 1/1/5/427.
306. ESRO, PBT 1/1/12/205.
307. LRO, Inventories of John Dipprie alias Marian (1617), Charles Tyler (1624).
308. Awty, 'French immigrants and the iron industry in Sheffield', p. 60.

Forge near Birmingham.[309] Earlier evidence seems contradictory; broad-brimmed hats were notably absent in the paintings of Patenier and Blès; whilst some of the furnacemen in Patenier's painting wear knee-length garments, others do not. There is a similar ambiguity in many of Blès' paintings; only when we look at the two furnacemen and the finer in his *Paysage et forge* at Prague, each dressed in flowing ankle-length garments, do we find assurance that the long dress, which formed an essential item of an eighteenth-century forgeman's equipment, went back to the period when the indirect process was brought to England.

In any case their horses, swords, firearms and possibly hats were items that ironworkers obviously clung to. Horseback was the ironworker's usual mode of transport over longer distances. When in the 1570s Jordan Russell II hoped to set up ironworks in the Cynon valley in Glamorgan we can be sure that it was on horseback that he made his preliminary survey, because the lameness of his horse was the reason he advanced for being unable to accompany William Darrell on a further visit there.[310]

In 1561 the will of Simon Tulye of Ashburnham, the Panningridge miner, mentioned his grey mare and his father's riding gear. The Salehurst hammerman John Ellis, who died in 1567, had two sons, John and Anthony; each son was bequeathed a hat and sword, but Anthony also received a dagger; each received a featherbed, John had his father's leather jerkin and the body of a doublet of taffeta, whilst Anthony had his best coat and cloak. Another coat went to Ellis's ward, the younger Anthony Ellis.[311]

In 1579 the Fletching miner William Rowland alias Mocumber's eldest son John Mocumber, who had perhaps moved before his father's death to Wadhurst, was bequeathed, in addition to a grey mare and other livestock, his father's sorrel horse, his saddle and bridle, his best sword, his best boots, spurs and boot-hose, his best shirt and 13s 4d in ready money. However, that other mark of gentility, his best hat, went out of the family, along with an old canvas jacket and a pair of hose, to a servant, Thomas Webbe.[312]

The hammerman John Perygoe, who was buried at Nuthurst in January 1584, left a gun and a sword to his brother [Perigo?] and his bow and arrows to his brother Henry [Bull?]. Among goods stolen from the Nutley collier Anthony Post in 1588 was a sword valued at 10 shillings.[313] The Mountfield hammerman Anthony Pullen died in 1610 and left his mare and a steer to his 45-year-old son Stephen, and the Fletching hammerman Walter Old who died in 1639, left to his wife Elizabeth his best horse with a side saddle and bridle .[314]

Further afield in the north Midlands, the Heanor ironfounder Charles Tyler, who made his will in 1609 and died early in the following year, bequeathed to his daughter Thomasyn his best cloak, a gold ring, and a piece of gold worth £1 and to her husband George Berry his gun and bay mare, valued at £4; to his daughter Mildred, wife of Richard Snape who received his tools, he left £2, a flock bed and his cloak with a silver lace; to his son Francis's wife Agnes he gave a silver-gilt ring. To the poor he left 5 shillings, to the ringers at his funeral 2 shillings, and £1to be distributed on the same occasion.[315]

George Growte of Winnington Forge who died in 1614 no doubt cut the dashing figure expected of Lord Gerrard's hammerman when wearing his apparel, sword, boots and silver buttons valued at £2 10s 0d; his mare was thought to be worth £3 13s 4d; it had two saddles and apparel (items of harness) worth 7 shillings. Even John Dipprie alias Marian of Lizard hammers, whose apparel was praised at a modest £1 10s 0d in 1617, had two mares and a yearling colt valued at £3 6s 8d. A shooting piece and three saddles were among the goods left by the ironfounder Quintin Tyler of Madeley in 1625, but horses failed to be mentioned in the inventory.[316]

In the colonial situation of New England, the Hammersmith worker John Gorum was fined in November 1652 for wearing silver lace in defiance of the sumptuary laws. The more egalitarian society set up in the colony did however encourage a rather wider employment of the approbatory title awarded

309. Angerstein, *Illustrated travel diary, 1753-1755*, p. 36.
310. TNA, C 3/216/15.
311. ESRO, PBT 1/1/5/13 and 455.
312. ESRO, PBT 1/1/7/159.
313. WSRO, STC 1/13/107b; Cockburn, *Sussex Assize records, Elizabeth I*, nos. 1069, 1091.
314. ESRO, PBT 1/1/12/412, 1/1/26/28.
315. LRO, will of Charles Tyler (1609/10).
316. LRO Inventories of George Growte (1614), John Dipprie alias Marian (1617), Quintin Tyler (1625).

in 1646 to the later ironfounder at Hammersmith, 'Goodman Tiler of linne'.[317]

In 1624 Quintin Tyler of Madeley in Staffordshire described himself as 'yeoman' in his will and was apparently literate. And in August 1677, his son John Tyler of Leighton in Shropshire claimed for himself the title 'gentleman' in his will. The inventory totalled an impressive £406 2s 11d, but the item, 'Remains in stocke att the Furnace and Forge in Cheshire that is to say Duddington Furnace and Lea Forge accordinge to the Accompt given in by Mr Richard Pencill the 1° May 77', was deleted and no valuation was attached to it. The signatories included Francis Boycott and Thomas Newton,[318] both of them partners in Leighton Furnace, who were evidently, along with the deceased and Richard Pensell, prospective partners in the new Cheshire works.

These men were clearly determined to prevent Tyler's eldest son Charles, described as 'a very necessitous and fraudulent person' in the testamentary proceedings of his brother Elias Tyler of Leighton, yeoman, in 1687,[319] from obtaining any interest in the new partnership. In this way was the passage of the Tyler family of Shropshire into the ranks of ironmasters and gentry blocked.

Indeed in relatively few cases the threshold between yeoman and gentry status was successfully crossed. The Collyn family of Brightling made the transition unobtrusively. True, the founder of the family, John Collyn of Burwash, described himself as 'yeoman' in his will, as did his son Alexander (1550) and grandson Stephen (1612) of Lamberhurst, who disposed of the ironworking interest in 1584. But his other grandson Alexander (1566) and great-grandson Thomas (1612) of Brightling, who continued as landlords of Socknersh Furnace, made no claim to status in their wills. And where John Tyler of Leighton's heirs did not aspire to be gentlemen, the Gringo family of Fareham succeeded in making that transition, the last of his line claiming the title 'esquire'. But perhaps theirs was a special cases arising out of the espousal by at least one generation of the family of the Quaker faith, where status was not inherited but was regarded as innate and differed only according to the individual's suitability, or unsuitability, to perform duties and functions within the religious community.

Another apparently upwardly mobile member of the immigrant community was John Bluett of Cuckfield, who from 1611 until his burial in 1623 was styled 'gentleman' in the parish register. He was probably the John Bluat 'lawyer', whose first wife had been buried at Cuckfield in 1604. Members of the family had resided in Cuckfield from around 1580, when Abraham Blewett was there, but John was perhaps the eldest son of Abraham's brother, Nicholas Blewett the hammerman, who had been baptised at Bexhill in 1570.

Exceptionally, a steelmaker presumably employed at the earl of Southampton's Funtley Forge was the 'Monser de Roche' buried at Titchfield in 1624. George Valiance, left fatherless in 1597 at the age of two near Sheffield, became one of the earliest members of the Company of Cutlers in Hallamshire and its Master in 1633, perhaps through the agency of one of his sister Mary's husbands, John Parker, whom she married in 1604, or John Allen. But Valiance achieved his ambition after a decisive break with his ironworking forebaears, and not aat all as a result of his origins.

Wealth

Relative wealth among different ironworkers is difficult to measure. In France notarial acts by which aging people divested themselves of much of their estate in return for the promise by their heirs to maintain them in old age were not uncommon and indeed occurred in the case of the parents-in-law of the forgeman Jehan Denquiere alias Louvel, of Hodeng and of the Forge of the Isles. Can this have happened in 1620 in the case of the finer William Morrell of Catsfield, who left goods inventoried at only £3 16s 4d and made bequests of only 5 shillings each to his son John and to three daughters? Finers are generally thought to have been the best paid workers in the charcoal iron industry and Morrell did in fact leave 10 shillings to the poor.[320] In contrast, the goods of William's relative Richard Morrell of Westfield, who perhaps had no connection with iron and died in 1631, were inventoried at £560 18s 0d,

317. Dow, *Records and files of the quarterly courts of Essex county, Massachusetts, 1636-1656, vol. 1*, p. 271.
318. LRO, B/C/11, will and inventory of John Tyler, 1677/8.
319. LRO, B/C/11, will of Elias Tyler (1686/7).
320. ESRO, PBT 1/1/17/92, 1/3/5/51.

whilst he also made bequests to his children which totalled £320.[321]

A more typical insight into the rising wealth of one particular ironworking family is that obtained from the inventoried goods of the hammermen Peter and Clement Hunisett of Westfield; Peter died in 1593 with goods worth £34, but in 1617 the goods of his son Clement were valued at £153.[322]

The following tables extracted from the probate act books of Lewes archdeaconry for the period up to the civil war suggest that the most prosperous group of ironworkers were the founders with around £80-worth of inventoried goods each. There was surprisingly little difference between finers and hammermen who averaged goods of around £52 each. Colliers came next with around £41 each and miners last with £33. The perhaps uncharacteristic case of the miner William Rowland alias Mocumble is counterbalanced by the fact that few miners from the more prosperous seventeenth century are recorded. Several colliers were recorded in their wills as husbandmen or even yeomen, but their trade can be identified from other sources. Anthony Ellis, a Cuckfield yeoman at his death, had earlier followed his father Anthony Ellis (1595) as a Fletching hammerman.

Italicised amounts are calculated at half the probate bond
(all refs. are ESRO, PBT)

1561 Simon Tulye	Ashburnham	£12 14s 2d	1/1/5/13
1580 William Rowland/Mocumble	Fletching	£115 16s 7d	1/3/1/80
1586 John Bottinge	Hartfield	£5 0s 0d	1/3/2/13
1589 Andrew Rowland	Fletching	£19 8s 6d	1/3/2/77
1627 Thomas Creasy	Brede	£11 10s 10d	1/3/5/310

Table 12: Wealth of Wealden miners

1592 John Johnson	Rotherfield	£30 0s 0d	1/3/2/136

Table 13: Wealth of Wealden gunfounders

1553 John Trwe	Brightling	£112 13s 4d	1/1/3/95
1557 Nicholas Tyler	Fletching	£27 2s 4d	1/1/3/225
1581 Reynold Harvie	West Hoathly	£14 0s 4d	1/3/1/141
1585 Jarman Myttell	Waldron	£136 19s 0d	1/3/1/142
1592 Nicholas Jarrett	Dallington	£39 1s 6d	1/3/2/139
1595 Thomas Catte	Maresfield	£33 3s 6d	1/3/2/210*
1606 Lawrence Leonard	Brede	£147 12s 4d	1/3/3/62
1607 William Jarret	Brede	£43 17s 8d	1/3/3/106
1608 Henry Gunter	Mountfield	£73 7s 9s	1/3/3/122
1615 Jeremy Philpot/A'Broke	Burwash	£66 6s 0d	1/3/4/72
1620 Thomas Aynat	Dallington	£54 17s 4s	1/3/5/62
1625 Jarman Mittell	Waldron	£104 10s 0d	1/3/5/206
1634 Thomas Jarrett	Brightling	£30 18s 0d	1/3/6/190
1635 Lewis Dueprey	Waldron	£89 12s 10d	1/3/6/219
1638 Henry Gunter	Crowhurst	£102 19s 0d	1/3/7/125

Table 14: Wealth of Wealden ironfounders

1580 Thomas Wheeler	Rotherfield	£72 10s 2d	1/3/1/80
1591 Valentine Diproane	Etchingham	£25 2s 0d	1/3/2/127

321. ESRO, PBT 1/1/22/68, 1/3/6/138.
322. ESRO, PBT 1/3/2/166, 1/3/4/148.

1594 Peter Jelley	Salehurst	£42 7s 0d	1/3/2/199
1606 Adrian Messant	Westfield	£125 17s 6d	1/3/3/87
1607 John Symons	Worth	£35 0s 0d	1/3/3/107
1612 John Allen	Mountfield	£72 11s 6d	1/3/3/271
1616 John Gardner	Catsfield	£36 12s 6d	1/3/4/108
1620 William Morrell	Catsfield	£3 16s 4d	1/3/5/51

Table 15: Wealth of Wealden finers

1553 Denys Labye	Wartling	£4 8s 8d	1/1/3/60
1554 Bartholomew Collen	Burwash	£96 5s 10d	1/1/3/108
1561 John Templer	Robertsbridge	£11 6s 0d	1/1/5/1
1567 John Ellis	Salehurst	£27 2s 0d-	1/1/5/455
1592 Roger Lambert	Hartfield	£44 6s 8d	1/3/2/138
1593 Peter Honisett	Westfield	£34 0s 0d	1/3/2/166
1595 Anthony Ellys	Fletching	£64 0s 8d	1/3/2/207
1596 John Deproane	Etchingham	£55 12s 10d	1/3/2/212*
1606 Stephen Blewet	Catsfield	£37 13s 8d	1/3/3/70
1610 Anthony Pullen	Mountfield	£27 6s 6d	1/3/3/192
1612 Hugh Symons	Worth	£57 18s 1d	1/3/3/260
1617 Clement Hunisett	Westfield	£153 0s 0d	1/3/4/148
1621 Peter Mynage	Westfield	£36 0s 10d	1/3/5/84
1621 Stephen Dowst	Crowhurst	£23 11s 2d	1/3/5/101
1638 Nicholas Pounting	Rotherfield	£38 5s 3d	1/3/7/94
1638 Anthony Milham	Ardingly	£38 1s 4d	1/3/7/117
1638 John Billings	Horsted Keynes	£50 17s 8d	1/3/7/119
1639 Walter Old	Fletching	£81 1s 0d	1/3/7/158
1639 Anthony Ellis	Cuckfield	£118 3s 6d	1/3/7/182

Table 16: Wealth of Wealden hammermen

1589 Lawrence Lambert	Horsted Keynes	£20 0s 0d	1/3/2/88
1597 John Bartholomew	Maresfield	£29 1s 8d	1/3/2/243
1626 Nicholas Dowst	Crowhurst	£61 6s 0d	1/3/5/254
1641 James Sneade	Warbleton	£36 18s 0d	1/3/7/240
1560 John Varnysh	Ardingly	£7 18s 11d	1/1/4/337
1560 John Valyants	Dallington	£10 11s 2d	1/1/41420
1565 Thomas Dodgyn	Ashburnham	£16 0s 8d	1/1/5/243
1576 Nicholas Seddes	Herstmonceux	£15 15s 6d	1/3/1/47
1581 Stephen Freminge	Hartfield	£9 0s 0d	1/3/1/102
1582 Thomas Deprone	Etchingham	£15 6s 8d	1/3/1/118
1587 Adrian Dogen	Worth	£8 13s 4d	1/3/2/40
1591 Philip Hewashe	Hartfield	£52 13s 4d	1/3/2/132
1598 Stephen Blewett	Ashburnham	£58 1s 8d	1/3/2/255
1602 Edward Raunser	Westfield	£119 11s 0d	1/3/3/14
1605 John Bowyer	Mountfield	£35 2s 10d	1/3/3/40
1607 Peter White	Worth	£33 16s 0d	1/3/3/99
1612 John French	Barcombe	£96 10s 0d	1/3/3/262
1614 William Mepam	Crawley	£23 5s 10d	1/3/4/43
1614 Anthony Standen	Catsfield	£57 9s 8d	1/3/4/52
1616 John Farnes	Horsted Keynes	£64 9s 4d	1/3/4/116
1619 Andrew Snashall	Crawley	£110 7s 0d	1/3/5/9
1620 Solomon Fuller	Waldron	£56 2s 4d	1/3/5/34

1620 Edward Bassett	Fletching	£61 15s 4d	1/3/5/66
1626 Isaac Vintin	Hartfield	£10 0s 0d	1/3/5/235
1632 Walter Good	Balcombe	£14 19s 10d	1/3/6/123
1636 William Freeman	Brightling	£5 11s 0d	1/3/7/11
1638 Nicholas Millington	Rotherfield	£74 2s 4d	1/3/7/113
1638 Mathew Humfry	Maresfield	£25 0s 0d	1/3/7/126
1642 John Holmes	Balcombe	£23 11s 0d	1/3/7/292

Table 17: Wealth of Wealden forgemen

1541 Stephen Colyn	Withyham	£24 16s 0d	1/1/ 1/37
1557 John Ellys	Etchingham	£16 9s 9d	1/1/4/12b
1558 John Hooke	Balcombe	£23 9s 4d	1/1/4/87
1560 Thomas Kerey	Burwash	£11 5s 6d	1/1/4/442
1564 Jordan Russell	Salehurst	£17 3s 8d	1/1/5/155
1574 William Burdytt	Ewhurst	£20 0s 0d	1/3/1/3
1577 Nicholas Levett/Catlin	Etchingham	£14 6s 9d	1/3/1/55
1579 John Harve	Penhurst	£3 14s 0d	1/3/1/72
1582 Richard Gilham	Ardingly	£5 6s 4d	1/3/1/106
1584 Nicholas Lambert	Fletching	£12 11s 4d	1/3/1/127
1588 William Dudgwine	Worth	£46 6s 4d	1/3/2/69
1588 Roger Turke	Dallington	£10 15s 0d	1/3/2/68
1589 Daniel Kerine	Ashburnham	£7 18s 0d	1/3/2/82
1590 John Angerfylde	Frant	£33 13s 6d	1/3/2/107
1594 Humphrey Barre/Brysboll	East Grinstead	£18 19s 4d	1/3/2/197
1596 Charles Growte	Beeding	£15 10s 0d	1/3/2/213
1596 John Tomplen/Turke	Bexhill	£32 15s 4d	1/3/2/220
1596 Lawrence Busse	Maresfield	£4 3s 3d	1/3/2/222
1596 John Pynion/Barden	Hartfield	£7 3s 2d	1/3/2/223
1597 Stephen Harvye	Crowhurst	£12 3s 4d	1/3/2/235
1597 John Nevell	Hartfield	£33 15s 5d	1/3/2/237
1605 Gilbert Pynion	Ashburnham	£18 0s 2d	1/3/3/58
1606 Simon Perrigoe	Ewhurst	£46 19s 0d	1/3/3/74
1607 Robert Gottie	Fletching	£52 6s 6d	1/3/3/110
1608 James Goddard/Kinge	Mountfield	£49 19s 1d	1/3/3/113
1616 John Alowe	Etchingham	£29 10s 1d	1/3/4/118
1618 Paul Waters	Heathfield	£31 2s 5d	1/3/4/167
1618 Robert Spray/Pynion	East Grinstead	£10 5s 10d	1/3/4/167
1627 Quintin Husher	Burwash	£7 10s 6d	1/3/5/316
1627 John Pummy	Peasemarsh	£46 14s 2d	1/3/5/324
1634 Anthony Russell	Maresfield	£36 18s 8d	1/3/6/136
1634 Bartholomew Vashall	Crawley	£3 3s 10d	1/3/6/194
1637 Roger Gownut	Burwash	£3 15s 0d	1/3/7/66
1637 John Messidge	Peasemarsh	£46 1s 0d	1/3/7/70

Table 18: Wealth of others connected with the Wealden iron industry

Violence

The possession of swords and daggers reflected the level of violence that prevailed in society. In the Weald there is more evidence for violence between members of the immigrant community and between rival ironworkers or groups of ironworkers, than for friction between immigrants and the indigenous community. And generally speaking it must be suspected that ironworkers were well able to take care of themselves, whether immigrants or not.

The first known act of violence involving ironworkers occurred at Ticehurst between two immigrant Frenchmen from Etchingham in July 1521, when Peter Ferrour attacked the hammerman John Ongerfield with a dagger in the house of a tailor, Thomas Lambard. Ferrour chased Ongerfield with a dagger from Lambard's house to that of John Fowell, where he cornered him against a wall, and seeing that he could not escape, Ongerfield turned on his assailant with a knife and struck him a blow to the chest, as a result of which he at once died. Despite the verdict of the inquest jury that Ongerfield had killed Ferrour in self-defence, the word 'murder' was used and the case went to King's Bench; Ongerfield was eventually outlawed in September 1523.[323] In this case the antagonists were both French and the surname Ferrour suggests that the assailant was an ironworker too.

In 1529 the Dallington view of frankpledge dealt with several cases of assault; the Frenchmen John Barden and Thomas Vouchell were each fined 2 pence for a fight between them involving daggers and malicious language; an unknown Frenchman was fined 6 pence for attacking John Ganmot, who may also have been French, with a staff and giving him a bloody head; finally the Frenchmen John Garret and George Vouche were each fined 2 pence for a fight in which Vouche inflicted a bloody wound on Garret's face.[324]

In October 1530 it was presented to the Hawksborough hundred court that at Burwash Gewe Frenchman had attacked [John?] Rowland Frenchman with a staff and a dagger and that Rowland had attacked Gewe with a dagger worth 8 pence. Gewe was fined 8 pence and Rowland 4 pence. A sequel to this came in October 1531 when it was presented that Gewe had attacked another Frenchman with a dagger worth 2 pence. On this occasion Gewe's dagger was confiscated.[325]

Another murder occurred at the house of John Foster alias Blake John in 'the Wastes' (lez *Wast*) of Buxted in February 1531. John Milward alias Frengman of Buxted, labourer, came to Foster's house late at night and Foster gave him a wound in the stomach two inches long with a knife worth 2 pence which he held in his right hand. Milward immediately died and Foster, who had no goods or chattels at the time, fled. He was outlawed the following year.[326] Black John could well have been a collier and both he and the Frenchman Milward may have been employed at an ironworks in Buxted in lease to John Levett at the time.

A coroner's inquest of April 1535 found that in February Simon Frengman had murdered John Holgatt, *Frengman*, at Buxted with a dagger by giving him a big wound to the heart, from which he immediately died. Simon Frengman was outlawed in December 1537.[327]

In 1537 further assaults were recorded at Burwash; between the Frenchman Barden with a staff on another Frenchman named Thomas, who himself was guilty of shedding Barden's blood with a knife; another Frenchman Adrian attacked a Frenchman named Gellett Baster with a sword, and Gellet Bastard in his turn had drawn Adrian's blood.[328]

An Uckfield inquest of October 1543 found that on 28 July, in an encounter between three Wadhurst Frenchmen in Frankham Park Mayfield, Adrian Annessett [Hunnisett], aided and abetted by John Annessett, had inflicted a two-inch wound in the side of Jordan Tassen with a Flemish prag or spike, which he held in his right hand. Tassen immediately died and both his assailants fled. For this Adrian Annessett was outlawed as late as 1550, but was subsequently pardoned.[329] As we have seen, the Hunnisett family originated in the southern Netherlands, but these immigrants to the Weald came immediately from France and are likely to have been based in the Beauvaisis. They would therefore rank as Picards, whilst Tassen was probably a Norman from the vicinity of Forges-en-Bray.

Another assault took place at Penhurst in September 1548, when a Mountfield collier, Martin Denewe, Frenchman, attacked Corney Charlowe and his wife Mariette, both of French nationality, with a meat-knife. Denewe gave Mariette a wound in her right arm from which she died about an hour later. Although the word 'murder' was used in this instance, Denewe was later rather surprisingly pardoned;

323. Hunnisett, *Sussex Coroners' inquests, 1485-1558*, no. 13.
324. ESRO, ASH 290. I am grateful to Christopher Whittick for a photocopy of this court roll.
325. BL, Add. Roll 31,818.
326. Hunnisett, *Sussex Coroners' inquests, 1485-1558*, no. 79.
327. Ibid., 100.
328. BL, Add. Roll 31,322.
329. Hunnisett, *Sussex Coroners' inquests, 1485-1558*, no. 126.

he was stated to have had no goods, lands or tenements.[330]

The Frenchman George Mahouude, a Frant collier, killed another Frenchman named John Edmundes alias Marian in November 1574. The murder was noted in the Frant parish register at Marian's burial and Mahouude was eventually outlawed.[331]

The most spectacular affray in which Wealden ironworkers took part occurred at Plaistow on 2 March 1580. It arose when Richard Cowlstock of Kirdford, yeoman, was riding on a horse, with Roger Noras or Norris, a Northchapel miner, mounted behind him. As they rode along Nicholas Unyon, a Dunsfold, hammerman, pulled Norris from the horse 'in order that they should wrestle'. In the struggle between them 'Noras by misadventure tore Unyon's breeches. Thereupon Unyon struck Noras on the left ear with his right fist and so they fought together'. Nine additional ironworkers who then arrived on the scene 'set upon Unyon and Noras and they all fought together'.

During the course of this affray one alien, Charles Pavye, a Northchapel finer, had his head broken to the length of one inch, but who did it and with what weapon the inquest jurors were unable to say. Although Pavve's wound healed within three weeks 'except for a length of an eighth of an inch', he became sick with 'le styche' on 26 March and on 4 April he died. The other ironworkers involved were a hammerman John Coppyn, a miner John Chaundler, and a finer William Foster, all of Northchapel, Charles Foxe a finer from Dunsfold, and four Kirdford men, James Bewsar and Adrian Pavye alias Foye, both finers, Peter Madbow ('Madlow alias Dubes' in the inquisition), a collier, and 'a certain Alexander' servant of John Smyth.

By 4 April Roger Norris had evidently escaped custody because two Petworth yeomen and Nicholas Elliott of Lurgashall, gentleman, entered recognizances at Chichester sessions to appear in connection with his escape.

The inquest held at Northchapel on 6 April found that Pavye had died 'by the Visitation of God and not otherwise'. The case, which went to the Lewes assizes in July, was therefore not one of murder but of affray. At the inquest two Kirdford tailors, Thomas Smarte and Robert Penfold, had entered recognizances to give evidence against Roger Norris, Adrian Pavye and others, and Bewsar, together with a Kirdford hammerman, Nicholas Tyler, had also entered recognizances to give evidence against Noras.

On 15 April Nicholas Elliott, now described as a Lurgashall clothier, and Edward Naldrett, a Northchapel husbandman, entered recognizances for the appearance of Norris before Henry Percy, the earl of Northumberland, JP.[332]

It is difficult to suggest what lay behind most of these fights and disturbances, because legal proceedings limited themselves to matters of fact and did not impute motives which were matters of opinion. However, in an assize case concerning Sir Henry Sidney's German steelworkers it was thought relevant to mention that before a quarrel in November 1566 between two German (*Dutch*) labourers in which Pantellus Hacker (or Acor) stabbed Harman Skryver, inflicting a wound from which Skryver died six days later, both men had joined a party of Germans who were drinking at a Salehurst 'colehouse' and had drunk together.[333] Such details were seldom cited.

Factional affrays between the workers of rival forgemasters were not uncommon. Straker related in vivid terms the prolonged encounter between the ironworkers of Denise Bowyer, tenant of Parrock ironworks, and the servants of William Saunders, after the latter had bought the manor of Parrock from William Warner in 1547.[334] And the forgemaster Thomas Hay believed that a gang of men who assaulted him on his way from Ashburnham to Dallington and left him in despair of his life were acting on the instructions of the rival forgemaster George May. When the dam of Socknersh Furnace was breached and drained in December 1593, only a few days after the furnace had been put in blast, Thomas Collins alleged that men assembled by the widow and son of the late George May, with whom he had had a long-running dispute, were responsible.[335]

330. Ibid., 144.
331. Hunnisett, *Sussex Coroners' inquests, 1558-1603*, no. 135.
332. Cockburn, *Sussex Assize records, Elizabeth 1*, no. 801. Hunnisett, *Sussex Coroners' inquests, 1558-1603*, no. 243.
333. Ibid., no. 227; I am grateful to Anne Dalton for pointing out this circumstance to me.
334. Straker, *Wealden iron*, pp. 242-4.
335. J. J. Goring, 'Wealden ironmasters in the age of Elizabeth', in E. W. Ives and others, eds. *Wealth and power*

In November 1568, when the servants of Lord Bergavenny tried to enforce his right to work five foundays 'by separate agreement' at Cowford Furnace, the lessees, Bartholomew Jeffrey and William Relfe resisted, and pointed out that the lease gave the proprietor no such right. Their workers, who opposed Bergavenny's servants in 'warlike and riotous manner', some with 'bows bent and arrows ready' and others 'having great shovels filled with hot burning cole and cinder', were described as 'lewd and evil disposed persons', and were named as Stephen Dennett, Thomas Wesson, John Capell, Hanno Gewe, John Ryckford, Gillam Bygnoll [Bigo?] alias Founder, William and John Usher, John Jewell and Richard Stevenson.

Further trouble occurred in January 1569 when Bergavenny's servants tried to prevent tree-cutting. They were opposed by Stephen Dennett, Thomas Weston, John Homesby, William Bygnoll alias Founder and another Frenchman, who was perhaps Hanno Gewe.[336]

In the Plaistow case however, the two Northchapel miners, Chaundler and Norris, had appeared at the assizes in 1577, when Chaundler had successfully defended himself against an accusation brought by Norris of grand larceny for breaking into his close and stealing goods worth 7s 6d.[337] The 'not guilty' verdict perhaps left lingering bad blood between the two men. The ironworkers involved at Plaistow were five from Kirdford, four from Northchapel and two from Dunsfold; Plaistow lay mid-way between Dunsfold and Kirdford. Beyond the mention that 'Alexander' was a servant of Thomas Smyth of Kirdford, there is no suggestion that any forgemasters' interests were involved.

When violence was used by a body of rioters from Kent against the Sidney ironworks, it was probably occasioned more by the impact of the iron industry on fuel supplies and fuel prices than by any animosity towards the ironworkers themselves. This body of 'Kentysh men' came to Robertsbridge in 1549 to 'putt downe the Forge'. The ironworks clerk, Harry Westall, spent a shilling in their company on 27 June, apparently to no avail. They went on to Panningridge and on 4 July Westall had to pay [Thomas] Hogens 8 pence 'for hys expenses in rydyng to London to certify my Master of the pullyng downe of hys fornes'. After Panningridge, the rioters proceeded to Mayfield, with what intent is unknown, but Hogens had followed them and was paid 4 pence on 3 July for his expenses in doing so.[338]

Not only had the forge to be repaired, for which carpenters and sawyers were paid £12 16s 11½d, but repairs to houses at Robertsbridge called for timber to be sawed at a cost of £1 3s 1½d. At Panningridge £14 19s 8d was paid to labourers 'for the reparyng of the fornys wall and the fornysshe and for neccessaries bought for the same' and carpenters were paid £9 2s 6d 'for hewyng of tymber and makyng of laths'. In detail, at the furnace Charles Gerard superintended repair of the furnace wall, bellows and hearth, John Alye made the furnace wheel, a new penstock, and 'pieced' the floodgate, the repair of the furnace wall itself involving 23 man-days, using clay and cinder.[339]

Resentment over the amount of timber consumed in charcoal manufacture could have accounted for this 1549 incursion by men from parishes which had their own secondary metal trades, and where clothiers needed wood to heat the vats for washing and dyeing wool. But ironworking spread into Tonbridge and Hawkhurst parishes in the early 1550s and by the 1560s Horsmonden Furnace was in being, developments which confronted later generations of Kentish men with this problem much closer home. However, the incursion may have also been part of the nation-wide unrest of 1549 against the conversion of agricultural land into sheep-pasture, a process probably speeded up by the transfer of monastic lands into secular ownership. The unrest hastened the end of the earl of Somerset's protectorate and culminated in his execution.

In south Staffordshire the dispute between the former nailer, and now yeoman forgemaster, Thomas Parkes, and the forgemaster William Whorwood of Sandwell, esquire, reached epic proportions. A full-scale war between adherents of both parties began on 8 July 1597 when Parkes and his men seized a furnace in lease to Whorwood at Perry Bar. On 14 July 16 persons assembled at Handsworth to attack both a furnace at Perry Bar belonging to Parkes and a forge belonging to him, probably the 'Old

in Tudor England (1978), p. 216.

336. TNA, STAC 5/A2125.

337. Cockburn, *Sussex Assize records, Elizabeth I*, no. 636. I am grateful to Anne Dalton for drawing my attention to this earlier case.

338. KHLC, U1475 B8/3; these riots can be associated with the activities of the 'Commonwealth Men', anti-enclosure protestors who were certainly active in Netherfield, for which see ESRO, ASH 590.

339. Crossley, *Sidney ironworks accounts*, pp. 76 and n. 3, 78 and n. 13.

forge' at Witton in Aston-next-Birmingham, carrying off both finery and chafery bellows and the great hammer, together with ironworking tools and a considerable quantity of iron, all cited at considerable length in the presentments. On 16 July a forge at West Bromwich in lease to Parkes, probably the 'New forge', was taken over by adherents of Whorwood. On 18 July Parkes and his men took possession of a smithy at Wednesbury in lease to Whorwood and finally on 19 July Parkes' men broke into the moiety of Whorwood's furnace at Perry Bar, 'disturbing' his use of it until the time of the inquisition. All the relevant presentments were endorsed 'true bill' at quarter sessions.[340]

Again, the causes of this fierce rivalry went unexplained, but the presence of rival works in close proximity at Perry Bar and Witton provided the opportunity for disputes over watercourses, and the competition for charcoal supplies could have exacerbated the situation.

In violence between immigrants and Englishmen, in April 1534 the hundred court of Hawksborough presented 'Peter [*blank*] a Frencheman' along with John Vynton for their part in a bloody sword-fight at Bivelham with Richard Muddyll (perhaps hammerman at Robertsbridge in 1542) and others unknown. Both John Venton and Muddyll were fined 8 pence for this breach of the peace.[341]

In May 1596 when the Westfield finer, John Almon alias Laby, was on the road between Westfield Down and Westfield Forge his passage was blocked by an Ashburnham husbandman, John Fuller, with a little staff. Almon returned to his house at Westfield, took his own staff, and when he returned killed Fuller. Richard Dowle, Thomas Almon and John Burr of Westfield, labourers, were the witnesses against John Almon. A Brede butcher, Richard Younge, and the Westfield hammerman, Clement Honisett, were sureties for John Almon's appearance at the assizes, where he was found guilty, but pleaded benefit of clergy, was branded and released.[342]

In 1613 Edward Pynyon alias Praye late of Cuckfield, labourer, murdered Joan wife of 'old' Richard Norman, late of Cuckfield, hammerman, at Cuckfield with a penny knife. Pynyon was charged with manslaughter, but pleaded benefit of clergy and escaped with being branded. In 1624 Robert Androwes late of Slaugham, collier, who was possibly from an immigrant family, feloniously killed John Higgins of Slaugham with a staff. Androwes' goods were valued at £3, but he managed to evade arrest.[343]

Certain crimes were committed against local officials, often in circumstances which resulted in the escape from justice of felons. At Burwash in 1536 two out of three offences were of this nature; Thomas Donett resisted the headborough, Richard Bennett, and allowed Barden Frenchman to escape; two Frenchmen, Warnett and Thomas, who attacked William Gate with a sword, drew blood; Donett, Warnett and Thomas were each fined a shilling; finally, Jasper a Frenchman attacked and resisted Alexander Chamberlayn, the deputy constable[344] At Waldron in 1562 John and Marian (*Marionus*) Johnson were accused of an affray in which John Johnson attacked the headborough John Harper with a dagger, intending to impede him in the execution of his office. They were fined 3s 4d.[345]

Other forms of violence prevalent at the time were domestic squabbles and verbal abuse, but English records do not throw much light on these subjects. Ironworks were set in rural or even forest areas where violence which did not attract the attention of the outside world could be ignored, so long as forgemen worked satisfactorily; petty thefts and violence resulting in bloodshed were dealt with in manor or hundred courts; deaths in suspicious circumstances and murder came before coroners' courts and could go on to the assizes, which also dealt with larger thefts and serious affrays. As for verbal transgressions, blasphemy was not dealt with in the civil courts, but sedition incurred severe punishment at times when the civil power felt insecure.

Forgemasters drawn from within the immigrant community such as Woodman and the Collyn family espoused the Protestant cause; John Collyn II and his brother Alexander were witnesses against William Inold of Rye who in August 1537, during the earliest phase of the Reformation, urged the people of Burwash 'to remain as of old time they had done';[346] it was later remembered that Alexander's widow

340. Burne, *The Staffordshire Quarter Sessions Rolls, III: 1594-1597*, pp. 297-301.

341. BL, Add. Roll 31,819.

342. Hunnisett, *Sussex Coroners' inquests, 1558-1603*, no. 492; Cockburn, *Sussex Assize records. Elizabeth*, no. 1646.

343. Hunnisett, *Sussex Coroners' inquests, 1603-1688*, nos 129, 296.

344. BL, Add. Roll 31,322.

345. BL, Add. Roll 32,526.

346. *Letters and Papers, Henry VIII*, **12** (2), no. 505.

Julian Collyn 'was narrowly sought after for religion' during Mary I's reign, whilst Richard Woodman, after earlier having been driven to take refuge abroad for his Protestantism, paid the supreme price in that cause during the same reign. But immigrants lower down the social scale stuck to their tasks and appear not to have made forays into national or religious politics.

It seems strange then that the treasonable utterance of Joan, wife of the Chiddingstone collier Stephen Botting, at a time in February 1599 when the government of Elizabeth I was entitled to feel reasonably secure, should have resulted in Joan being sentenced to be hanged.[347] It seems unlikely that the words of a collier's wife could have involved allusion to the succession to the throne, the only subject on which Elizabeth I had reason to feel uneasy at this time. Her troubles with the earl of Essex arose later in the year. Perhaps the utterance was against the queen as head of the English church.

That domestic violence did quite often occur within ironworkers' families seems likely from the experience in New England. Although set up by royal charter granted to the Governor and Company of Massachusetts Bay, the community in which the ironworkers found themselves there had crossed the Atlantic in order to set up a Puritan Commonwealth intended to conform to God's law rather than to that of the king, or even parliament.

A catalogue of misdemeanours can be drawn up from the various charges brought against ironworkers over the years, and it seems possible that if the Massachusetts courts had proceeded against them with the severity meted out to the generality of inhabitants the consequences for the ironworking project might have been serious.

The sentence of whipping both at Salem and then, after he had recovered, again at the ironworks, imposed in 1647 on the finer John Turner for stabbing his daughter-in-law Sarah, for swearing 'by the eternal God that he would kill John Gorum', a colleague, and for being drunk, was in fact revoked.[348] Two years later Turner and his son Lawrence were ordered to produce Sarah in court, after she and her husband had been accused of battery by Henry Leonard. She was held primarily responsible for the quarrel and was sentenced to be whipped 'for her many offences'.

Serious marital problems were evident in the households of Nicholas Pinyon and Richard Pray, probably themselves distant relatives. In July 1647 Pinyon was presented for beating his wife and for swearing. He was presented again in February 1648 for swearing and for absenting himself from public worship in order to spend time drinking with his colleagues. When one of these, Nicholas Russell, was forbidden his house, Pinyon's wife threatened to leave home with him. For breaking her bond of good behaviour she was sentenced to pay a fine, or be severely whipped. However, these appear to have been only the symptoms of a more serious problem because in March 1648 Pinyon's wife supported an accusation that her husband had killed five of their children, one of them being only one year old.[349] The following day she was presented for fighting three times with her husband during the night after having been bound to keep the peace, whilst he was presented for beating her and causing a miscarriage.

Quintin Pray had been one of the witnesses against Pynion on the murder charge. In March 1648 his own son Richard Pray was fined 10 shillings for swearing, 10 shillings for cursing, £1 for beating his wife and £2 for contempt of court, failing payment of which he was to be whipped at the Lynn Iron Works. These fines were imposed after he had declared that 'he did not care for the court and if the court hanged him for it he would do it' and had promised to cripple his wife if the court interfered further.[350] The fine had still not been paid by February 1649 and Pray was threatened with whipping 'upon a lecture day'.[351] The sequel is not recorded.

However, the women too were far from blameless. In February 1650 Richard Pray's wife was admonished and ordered to pay 2s 6d costs for calling her mother-in-law an 'old hogge' and throwing stones at her; she had also thrown a trencher and a bone at her husband, when he took from her a letter to England which had been written for her.[352]

347. Cockburn, *Sussex Assize records, Elizabeth 1*, no. 2664.
348. Dow, *Records and files of the quarterly courts of Essex county, Massachusetts, 1636-1656, vol. 1*, p. 130.
349. Ibid., pp. 133-4.
350. Ibid., pp. 134-6.
351. Ibid., p. 159.
352. Ibid., pp. 156, 184.

Mobility

The peripatetic and adventurous lives of many ironworkers are evident enough from their family histories. Over this whole period economic advantages induced them to relinquish their homes and to migrate to areas where their skills were as yet unknown and where their services could secure an income not available at home. It was often political and military situations which opened up these attractive employment opportunities. Such factors can be readily deduced from the contexts in which the moves occurred, and indeed were explicit in the 1490s in the move to the Weald. Even more explicit was the religious persecution in parts of western Europe which, particularly after 1560, impelled emigration on ironworkers. In this second wave of Walloon migration described by Yernaux, religious persecution in the Netherlands was coupled with the desire of Protestant states, especially Sweden, to improve their industrial and military potential; both set in motion particularly spectacular moves to the north and east.

But the availability of huge quantities of unexploited and hitherto unmarketable timber, rather than military or religious factors, played the main role in inducing the spread of ironworks and ironworkers to distant and even remote parts of the British Isles. Sir Henry Sidney had brought the indirect process to Glamorgan in the early 1560s, but it was not until after 1575 that shot was cast at Dyffryn and cannon at Abercarn. In Ireland furnaces were first set up in the 1590s, but it was not until 1619 that the production of ordnance was undertaken by Robert Boyle. In Wester Ross the first ironworks were established around 1610, but evidence that gunfounders were lured to that area comes only after the royal licence of 1626 for the casting of ordnance and ammunition in Scotland.

Markets undoubtedly played the primary role in encouraging the establishment of forges in the Birmingham and Sheffield areas, with the blast furnaces which furnished the sow iron quite close by. But other areas in which ironworks were set up, such as South Wales, North Yorkshire, Ireland and the Highlands of Scotland were remote from substantial markets. Sir Henry Sidney's furnace at Tongwynlais sent much of its product in the form of plates to the Weald where it was converted into steel. Jordan Russell II's chancery statement of 1583 said nothing about markets but exulted in a 21-year lease of all the woodlands in the Cynon Valley area, thought sufficient over the period of the term for a double furnace and forges rather than the one originally projected. In remote North Yorkshire Laurence Russell alias Angell and his companions cut down hundreds of oaks at the behest of Thomas Dyke and others, with apparent disregard of the beech and ash also available.

The family history sketches included in these volumes give some idea of the frequency of movement which often makes it difficult to track ironworking families down. Just occasionally, as with the Ardingly finer, Abraham Bluet, a deposition made by him facilitates the quest. In 1584 he stated that he had been born in Battle around 1555, and his working and wandering life had begun in 1572 at Worth, where he married Jane Rofe and had spent three years. Since then he had spent two years at Linchmere, two at Dunsfold, one at St Leonards, three at Cuckfield and one at Ardingly.[353]

However, baptismal entries for Abraham's children continued at Linchmere from 1576 to 1583, which suggests that Jane did not follow all her husband's wanderings. The baptism in 1585 of their daughter Rachel took place at Ashburnham, perhaps because it was there that Abraham's elder brother Nicholas Bluet the hammerman, who had been with him at Worth, was now established; and their father, Stephen Blewett the collier, lived not far away at Catsfield. But the baptism at Rogate of Abraham's daughter Mary suggests that Jane was back with her husband in 1589, for the building of this new forge. After that Abraham was lost to sight in the Weald. Did he move to another ironworking area in the British Isles; or could he have been Captain Bluett who ended his days in 1619 in Virginia?

A statement made by the founder Laurence Harrowe of Battle in 1583 shows that he had then lived at Battle since 1577, before which he had been two years at Mountfield, six months at Mayfield, and three years during the early 1570s also at Battle, and that he had been born in France forty years earlier. A further statement made some 30 years later narrowed his place of birth down to Rainville (*Rangville*) in the Perche.[354]

James or Jacob Whit, an Ashburnham miner, testified in 1586 that he had been born in Tonbridge about 30 years earlier. He had lived in Hadlow, Cuckfield and Slaugham, in each case for

353. WSRO, Ep II/5/2, f. 226.
354. WSRO, Ep II/5/3, f. 45 and 9, f 46.

periods of one year and had been in Ashburnham since around 1580[355]

Harrowe had been born in France and both the other deponents cited were of French descent; probably only Abraham Bluett's father had been born in the Weald. Depositions made at a later period appear usually to record only the last place of such itinerant workers' abode. The only deposition made by an ironworker of English descent at this period was one made in 1581 by the Rotherfield founder Thomas Catt, who had been born in Rotherfield around 1535 and had lived there all his life.[356] This rather confirms what one would anyway suspect, that ironworkers of English descent tended to be itinerant to a lesser degree than their French-descended counterparts.

Something of the story of Jordan Russell II's life can be gleaned from parish registers and from his chancery statement of 1584. He was married at Maresfield in 1562 to Margery May of Frant, and it was at Frant that two of his children were baptised in 1566 and 1569. He worked for 'one Paler', about whose treatment of him he remained unhappy in 1584; this was John Paler of Rotherfield who held Howbourne Forge in Buxted, and the period was no doubt around 1571 when Russell's daughter Elizabeth was baptised in that parish. By 1572 or 1573 he was engaged on his abortive Welsh project, but by 1577 he was shown by the Sheffield parish register to have been in South Yorkshire. He was last mentioned at Sheffield in October 1582 and at the time of the Chancery case in 1584 he was hammerman in Duffield parish, and therefore probably at Makeney Forge on the Derwent.

Such a life-style was adventurous to the extent that the individual was prepared to bear and accept it, but must have required self-sufficiency, independence and resourcefulness of a high degree. Some fell by the wayside, as exemplified by the forgeman John Maybury of Cartmel and the ironfounder Charles Tyler of Leighton, as well as others of whom no record survives.

The industrial revolution changed techniques, massively increased the output of the iron industry and greatly expanded the workforce. But it also increased workloads and downgraded the importance of the individual workman. The family ties which enabled a forgeman who moved between different industrial regions to rely on finding in his new place of work kith and kin, or at least people of whom he had heard tell, were now much less significance. This very ancient style of cohesiveness was lost and the evolution of the trade union movement during the nineteenth century went only part way to replace it.

The very success of the iron industry in encouraging the growth of secondary metal trades had built up a cadre of metallurgical expertise which constituted the base from which further industrialisation recruited its labour. This can be seen within the iron industry itself, where the new tasks of puddling and rolling were to a great extent accomplished by the recruitment of local labour, something which would have been unthinkable during the sixteenth and early seventeenth centuries.

Puddlers and rollers were likely to be local men, hammermen were made extinct, and finers were confined to isolated corners of the industry where highly specialized work still required special qualities of iron. The rapidly changing scene is demonstrated in the census returns for Wellington in Shropshire. Of 15 puddlers recorded in the 1841 census only two were born outside the county. By 1851 the number of puddlers had expanded to over 50, not one of whom had been born outside Shropshire.

The keenness of ironmasters to embrace these changes of technique was sharpened by the expectation that it would serve to break down the old cohesiveness of the workforce, where it was the master finers and master hammermen who decreed who should be taken into apprenticeship, and what proportion of piecework money should be paid to an apprentice and what to a journeyman, who in any case might be their own sons, or the sons of a near relative.[357]

These efforts by ironmasters were not entirely successful. In 1883 the expression 'gentleman puddler' was now evoked to describe a Dowlais ironworker 'who "filled the whole chapel with his presence, and alone and unaided he made a greater flutter as he swaggered down the aisle than did the minister and his family". At work he wore on his head a duck or checked turban, he stood before his furnace in his shirt and sleeves with *a clwtyn chwys* (sweat wiper) slung carelessly around his neck'.[358]

However, it was a different world, and from the period when these changes first started to

355. WSRO, Ep II/5/3, f 56.
356. WSRO, Ep II/5/2, f. 3.
357. C. Evans, 'A skilled workforce during the transition to industrial society', pp. 149-51.
358. J. A. Owen, *The history of the Dowlais iron works 1759-1970,* Risca, Newport, Starling Press, 1977, pp. 82-3.

take effect the evidence of his settlement certificate shows that James Lavender, born around 1763 at Hartlebury worked firstly at Wilden Forge where his father was hammerman. In the late the 1780s he was at Bradley, where John Wilkinson had his works, but by 1790 he was in South Wales where he worked at a forge in the Usk Valley for three years and then for five years at the Kendalls' Beaufort ironworks above Ebbw Vale. After working for some time at Machen Forge in Monmouthshire he was by 1811 at Pentyrch in Glamorgan, where he worked with his three sons.[359]

During the 34 years following 1784 the hammerman William Russell worked at no fewer than 15 different sites, mostly in the Black Country, but also stretching to Benthall in Shropshire, and into the Forest of Dean, Warwickshire and Monmouthshire. In the case of the forgeman William Lambert, the Kirkstall Forge wages book shows that after leaving there he worked between 1797 and 1802 at Cleator in Cumbria, at Newland in Furness and at Wilsontown in Lanarkshire.[360]

None of these forgemen was unemployable; on the contrary, their life-histories indicate that they were very employable indeed. Nevertheless, none of them ever did find a place where their skills would enable them to settle down in a permanent home. Each was clearly from a family whose experiences have formed the basis of this volume, but they were born into a period when resourcefulness in the face of challenging situations was not enough and seems to have been replaced by near desperation. The kind of world which had existed for their predecessors had vanished forever, at least for this time and for these men.

IMMIGRANTS MENTIONED IN SUBSIDY ROLLS AFTER 1575

SUSSEX

Foxearle hundred

Fuller

Because the Foullon family of Hodeng had apparently become involved in the Brayon iron industry by 1509, when a house conveyed along with the corn mill and forge of Hodeng was described as being inhabited by Jehan Foullon, it is surprising that no alien named Foullon or Fuller was recorded in Wealden subsidy rolls until 1595. In that year James Fuller paid the poll tax in Foxearle hundred.

In 1596 it became possible to locate him more precisely, when the baptism of John son of 'Jakes Fuller, frenchman' was recorded in the Wartling parish register. Further baptisms followed in 1597 and 1599, when firstly Thomas son of 'Colier Fuller' was baptised, followed by a second John son of 'Jakes Fuller, forgeman'. The last parish register entry for this immigrant came in 1615 when 'James Fuller alias Jakes Collier, householder' was buried at Wartling, and this entry was followed early in 1625, when 'Widow Fuller alias Joxe, very poor', was buried there.

There seem to be no probate entries relating to these two deaths, but two generations of descendants are quite easily detectable. In the first generation Remy Fuller's son James was baptised at Herstmonceux early in 1617, but Remy's wife Benet, who was buried on the same day, evidently died in childbirth. Further entries concerning Remy Fuller have not been found and the possibility that he returned to France seems strong.

However, Nicholas Joakes alias Fuller, who in 1640 married Margaret Longly at Herstmonceux, was presumably the immigrant's grandson, even though the intervening connections seem not to be traceable in parish registers. Nicholas Fuller held the copyhold tenement Stoneacre in Herstmonceux. He was buried at Herstmonceux in September 1659, his wife having predeceased him during the previous month. Their children, Mary and Joseph, were baptised in 1641 and 1645. Joseph succeeded his father at Stoneacre, but in 1671 he surrendered it to the use of Thomas Byne.[361]

It also seems possible that Raynold Fuller, whose son James was buried at Wartling early in 1618, might have been connected with this family. Reynold Fuller had previously married Elizabeth

359. C. Evans, 'A skilled workforce', p.145-6.
360. Ibid., p.146.
361. ESRO, HBR 9/23 - Herstmonceux Tenement analysis.

Shadwell of Hellingly at Ashburnham early in 1595, and in 1618 he was remarried at Brede to Anne Billins, the widow of the former Westfield hammerman Adrian Billings.

The subsidy rolls of the 1520s show the surname Fuller to have already been widespread in parishes of the eastern Weald, but by the second half of the century the name is found so often in the context of the metalworking trades that immigrant input at an earlier period must be considered a probability. Even the Fuller family of Tanners, who were among the most prominent of Wealden cannon-founders in the eighteenth century, seem to have had early connections with the industry. Samuel Fuller married Joan French, daughter of the forgemaster Stephen French in 1615, and his own connection with the trade seems indicated by the charge of perjury laid in 1640 against a Dallington collier John Wilkins, who gave evidence that 'Mr Petter' had paid for coaling wood, that had in reality been paid for by Samuel Fuller.[362]

Mark Lower described as 'foolish', the tradition current in the vicinity, that the founder of the Waldron family of Fullers gained his wealth by hawking nails about the county of Sussex on the backs of donkeys, but one pedigree of the Fuller family suggests that Adam Fuller, a Waldron smith who died in 1561, was the brother of Samuel Fuller's grandfather. Lower also mentioned that the late John Fuller esquire of Rose Hill adopted *Carbone et forcipibus* (by charcoal and tongs) as his motto.[363]

A connection with James Geryng, one of Davy Willard's workers in the South Borough of Tunbridge in 1572, seems to have been established when Matthew Fuller of Waldron married Margery Gerynge at Rotherfield in 1566. Their second son, born at Waldron in 1571, was given the baptismal name Jarman, commonly used by French immigrants, and specifically that of Jarman Mittell, the immigrant ironfounder whose son Thomas was baptised at Waldron early in 1568. The ironfounder could have been godfather to this child.

Few branches of the family escaped contact with iron. The Ticehurst blacksmith William Fuller, a deponent in an ecclesiastical case of 1601,[364] was the son of Austin Fuller who in 1568 at Ticehurst had married Katheryn Lourker, probably from the English ironworking family of that name. William Fuller was baptised at Etchingham in 1575. His elder brother James, who had been baptised at Ticehurst in 1569, was father of Dorothy Fuller, baptised in 1616, who in 1641 married John Santo, another man of French descent. Thomas Fuller, who married another person of French descent, Elizabeth Husher, at Ticehurst in 1640, was either Thomas, son of James Fuller, baptised at Ticehurst in 1605, or Thomas, son of the blacksmith William Fuller, baptised at Ticehurst in 1609.

The yeoman John Fuller of Cade Street in Heathfield had formerly lived at Cross-in-Hand in Waldron. In a deposition of 1601, he claimed to have been born around 1537 and to have lived in Heathfield for 60 years.[365] In 1567 lie styled himself smith, when together with the forgemaster Thomas Stollyan, who was probably his cousin, he was a testamentary bondsman for Francis Byfflet of Heathfield, shearman.[366] He died in 1603, leaving all the tools in his forge at Cade Street to his son John. He was well landed, perhaps in right of his second wife Elizabeth, to whom he left Seggers, Digges Heath, Pylland and Paynters, though the timber trees on these lands were reserved to his heir Thomas. After Elizabeth's death these lands were to go to their son Nathaniel, but Skorhall he left to Richard, and Braylsham and Stot Rede to John, his younger sons by his first wife. When a new administration was granted in November 1613 to his son Thomas, by now a Hellingly yeoman, John Fuller's goods were still valued at £80 15s 10d.[367]

John Fuller died unmarried in 1614, with goods valued at only £3 8s 4d, mostly perhaps the tools of the forge which, together with £20, he bequeathed to his eldest brother Thomas Fuller of Hellingly. He bequeathed £10 to Thomas's son John, £5 to his kinsman Thomas Boorder, £1 each to Joan and Dorothy daughters of John Collin of Heathfield and £2 to the poor of the parishes of Heathfield and Hellingly. All his lands he left to his brother Richard, but out of them an annuity of £6 was to go to

362. ESRO, QR 49, m. 38; I am indebted to Brian Phillips for this reference.
363. M. A. Lower, 'The ironworks of the county of Sussex', p. 219; J. F. Fuller, 'Pedigree of the Family of Fuller of Waldron and East Hoathly etc.', *Miscellanea Genealogica et Heraldica, 4th series*, **3** (1910), p. 166; ESRO, PBT 1/1/4/355 (Adam Fuller).
364. WSRO, Ep II/5/6, f. 271.
365. WSRO, Ep II/5/6, f. 277.
366. ESRO, PBT 1/1/5/448.
367. TNA, PROB 11/104/559; ESRO, PBT 1/1/14/148, PBT 1/3/4/23.

his sister Margaret Payne for life, and her sons were each to receive £20 out of these lands at her death, or on reaching their majorities. He made his kinsmen Thomas Fuller of Hastings and Jonas Fuller of Heathfield overseers of his will and his brother-in-law Jeremy Tomkin executor.[368]

Thomas Fuller of Heathfield, smith, had appeared as a probate bondsman in 1595, 1601 and 1606. A deposition of 1607 shows him to have then been resident in Hailsham for around a year,[369] but by 1613 he was, as we have seen, living in Hellingly.

His surviving brother Richard Fuller, who in 1615 took as his second wife Denise Standen of Hellingly, widow, is shown by the marriage licence also to have been by then resident in Hellingly.[370] Richard Fuller of Hellingly, smith, died in 1616, and by his will left £20 to Denise, in addition to the cow and household stuff she had brought with her. His daughter Mary was also to have £20 at the age of 18, whilst his son John was to be schooled until 14 and then apprenticed until 21. Legacies to the two children of his sister Margaret Payne were to be paid out of the sale of underwood on the Heathfield properties, and the overplus from this sale was to go to his son John, whom he appointed his executor and residuary legatee. Since John was still a minor, probate was however granted to Richard's elder brother Thomas Fuller and to their brother-in-law Jeremy Tomkin.[371]

It will be recalled that in 1614 John Fuller of Heathfield had appointed his kinsman Thomas Fuller of Hastings as his overseer. The marriage licence issued to this Thomas Fuller for his second marriage, to Alice Iden of Heathfield, widow, in 1625 shows him to have been a Hastings gunsmith.[372] Thomas was the eldest son of another yeoman smith of Heathfield, Richard Fuller. Thomas's son Do-good had predeceased him, so when he died in 1637 he left Coxes and Coxland in Heathfield to his grandson John, his lands, tenements and shops in Hastings to his grandson Jonas, and Highlands and Brewers in Heathfield, and Northheath and Southheath in Hailsham to Thomas, a third grandson. He had presumably recently been married for a third time, because to his wife Elizabeth he left only a silver cup. He appointed his son Jonas his executor, but probate was granted to his brother, Richard Fuller of Brede, who was one of the overseers, along with a cousin, Richard Fuller of Heathfield.[373]

Richard Fuller of Heathfield, smith, had been witness and executor to Heathfield wills made in 1580 and 1588,[374] and was perhaps the brother of John Fuller, progenitor of the family previously under discussion. The names given by Richard to his remaining children, Caleb, Zealous, Obedient, Patience, Amity and Do-well, suggest that he was of a pronounced Puritan faith. His will was proved in February 1590 and his goods inventoried at the time were valued at £104 5s 8d. He left £40 each to his sons Caleb and Zealous, to be paid at their ages of 24, and £20 each to his daughters Patience, Amity and Do-well, to be paid at marriage or their ages of 21. His wife Alice, who was appointed executrix and residuary legatee, was given liberty to sell all his freehold land in Burwash and Heathfield in order to perform bargains he had made with Adam a'Wood, John Willerd and Edward Bonneeke, but the lands he had bought from Lord Buckhurst, lord of the manor of Heathfield, were to remain to Alice's profit during her life, and then to devolve on their eldest son Thomas and his heirs. Richard Fuller made his cousin, the forgemaster Thomas Stolyan, overseer of his will.[375] Not mentioned in the will were his two other sons, Obedient and Richard.

None of Richard Fuller's descendants appears to have remained in Heathfield. In addition to the gunsmith Thomas Fuller, Zealous Fuller moved to Hastings, where by early 1607 he was established as a shoemaker; he left goods valued as little as £11 5s 4d when he died in 1622.[376]

When he married at Hailsham early in 1607, Obedient Fuller was a husbandman; parish register entries suggest that by 1609 he was at Wartling and by 1615 at Crowhurst, where he was buried in April 1616. However, in his will he described himself as being of Catsfield; his goods were inventoried at £183.[377]

368. ESRO, PBT 1/1/14/208, 1/3/4/41.
369. ESRO, PBT 1/3/2/218, 1/3/3/1 and 74; WSRO, Ep II/5/8, f. 41.
370. Dunkin, *Sussex Marriage Licences, Lewes 1586-1643*, p. 96.
371. TNA, PROB 11/127/410.
372. Dunkin, *Sussex Marriage Licences, Lewes 1586-1643*, p146.
373. TNA, PROB 11/174/262.
374. ESRO, PBT 1/1/7/185, 1/1/8/222.
375. ESRO, 1/1/8/341, 1/3/2/89.
376. ESRO, 1/1/18/91, 1/3/5/235.
377. Dunkin, *Sussex Marriage Licences, Lewes 1586-1643*, p. 57; ESRO, PBT 1/1/15/143, 1/3/4/115.

Richard Fuller established himself as a Brede yeoman; he made his will in 1645 and it was proved the following year.[378]

The brother most likely to have had further links with the iron industry was Caleb Fuller, who moved to Cuckfield. He married at Balcombe in 1596 and it was there that he was buried in 1604, but his son Henry Fuller, who had been baptised at Cowfold in 1600, was probably the man of that name who married Alice Richards at Lindfield in 1621. Their son Thomas Fuller, baptised at Lindfield in 1622 was probably the blacksmith of that name, whose four daughters were named in a probate record of 1652.[379]

The smith, Robert Fuller of Mountfield, who was bondsman for a probate administration in 1566,[380] was perhaps the Mountfield man of that name buried at Heathfield early in 1597. He had made his will some three years earlier. He left 3s 4d to the poor of each of the parishes of Mountfield and Heathfield. To his eldest son Richard he left furniture, to his brother Abraham his apparel, and the remainder of the household stuff was to be divided between his wife Alice and his three children, Richard, Marie and David. His wife was to have the house at Mountfield, but was 'not to meddle with the shop, nor the rooms in the shop, nor with the mill nor colehouse', which together with all the lands in Mountfield were to go to his eldest son Richard. Of the freehold in Heathfield, Whatlington, Withyham and Pevensey, that at Heathfield was in the tenure of Humphrey Sommer, and out of it an annuity of 6s 8d was to go to Robert's sister Margaret Poile. He made his son David executor, but because David was a minor probate was granted to two of the overseers, his brother Richard Fuller of Mayfield and Humphrey Sommer. The other overseer was his brother-in-law Thomas Downton.[381]

Robert's widow Alice married Thomas Dawe, who predeceased her. When she died in 1615 her will showed that Richard Fuller was by then living in Goudhurst. David Fuller had moved to Lewes, but died in 1613 and administration of his estate, valued at £278 4s 4d, was taken by his brother Richard Fuller of Goudhurst, gentleman, whilst John Fuller of Goudhurst, gentleman, possibly their cousin, acted as bondsman.[382] As we shall presently see, this John Fuller was a forgemaster.

Robert Fuller's connection with the Heathfield area is clear enough. In a deposition of 1609, his brother Richard's son John Fuller, claimed to have been born in Heathfield around 1574 and styled himself 'gentleman'. He said that he had moved, presumably along with his father Richard, to Mayfield about 20 years earlier,[383] and this is confirmed by views of frankpledge for Isenhurst, in which Richard Fuller first appeared as a defaulter in April 1588. He was however excused his fine because he was a cooper in the queen's service (*in servicio regine*). Thereafter, his name failed to appear in April 1589, and he was subsequently excused (*essoined*) on three occasions, and only in April 1590 did he pay a fine of 2 pence.[384]

Richard Fuller of Mayfield, yeoman, died in October 1602 and was buried at Mayfield. In his will he left £2 to the poor of Mayfield and 10 shillings to the poor of Heathfield. He left 5 shillings to each child of his brother Robert and, like his brother, he left clothing to his brother Abraham Fuller, as well as an annuity of 13s 4d. To his wife Margaret he left an annuity of £12 out of land in Heathfield, with the use of two loft chambers over the new kitchen in his house at Cade Street, and with a fourth part of the household goods in the house at Old Mill in Mayfield. The house at Old Mill itself was to go to his son John. Should John die without heirs the houses and lands at Heathfield and Hellingly were to go to his daughter's son, Richard Downton. He left £4 to his servant Joan Chapman and a shilling each to his servants Henry, Daniel and William. He made his son John his residuary legatee and executor.[385]

It seems possible that this son was the Goudhurst gentleman John Fuller who acted as bondsman when his cousin Richard Fuller of Goudhurst took administration of the effects of David Fuller of Lewes. He was undoubtedly the gentleman who, along with Richard Maynard deceased and others, had been one of the 'farmers and occupiers' of Old Mill Furnace and 'used to goe with Oxen horses, courtes,

378. TNA, PROB 11/196/367.
379. TNA, PROB 11/220/438 (Thomas Faulconer of East Grinstead).
380. ESRO, PBT 1/1/5/356 (Richard Pooke of Westfield).
381. TNA, PROB 11/89/145.
382. ESRO, PBT 1/1/15/25, 1/3/4/6.
383. WSRO, Ep II/5/1, ff 26-7.
384. ESRO, ACC 3597/1, ff 22, 66, 122, 139v.
385. TNA, PROB 11/100/290.

waynes and other cariyages both for coles myne and other things to and from the said furnace' through lands of Thomas Aynescombe of Mayfield esquire, which John Baker of Mayfield acknowledged in 1618 was only by Aynescombe's leave and goodwill, and not as of right.[386] In partnership with Richard Maynard, Richard Fuller the Old Mill yeoman was probably the first forgemaster from the Fuller family, and may well have had Old Mill Furnace before his son.

It remains to say something about the extraordinarily large numbers of colliers from the Fuller family, who number no fewer than six, excluding the immigrant Jakes Fuller of Wartling.

Firstly comes William Fuller of Laughton, who in 1627 was a surety for the appearance at quarter sessions of the Chiddingly labourer Edward Page.[387] He was probably the same as William Fuller of Waldron, collier, whose 20-year-old wife Sylvester deposed in 1605 that she had been born in Mayfield around 1585, but by 1605 had been resident in Waldron for around one year.[388] William Fuller was probably the youngest son of Raphe Fuller, baptised at Waldron early in 1584. Raphe Fuller, who could also have been the father of the Hartfield collier Francis Fuller, died in 1593. No children from the marriage of William and Silvester Fuller are recorded at either Waldron or Laughton.

Nor do entries for Raphe Fuller's son Francis appear in the Waldron parish register. He perhaps first moved to East Grinstead, where a Francis Fuller appeared among Shovelstrode defaulters from the view of frankpledge in April 1589.[389] However, the baptisms which the East Grinstead parish register records of Tabitha Fuller in 1585, Frauncis Fuller in 1589 and Dorothy Fuller in 1592 do not disclose the names of the parents, and some of these children could be those of an otherwise unknown Lawrence Fuller, who is shown by views of frankpledge to have followed Francis at Shovelstrode in October 1589 and to have left there around May 1590.[390]

Views of frankpledge for Hartfield indicate that neither Francis nor Lawrence Fuller moved there immediately after leaving Shovelstrode. Nevertheless, the East Grinstead Francis Fuller of April 1589 was almost certainly the Hartfield collier, whose children William and Thomas were baptised at Cowden in 1605 and 1608, and whose first wife Rebecca was buried at Cowden in 1621. After Rebecca's death Francis Fuller married Frances, the widow of Isaac Vinton, at Hartfield in April 1622. In January 1626 administration of around £10 of Isaac Vinton's goods was granted to Francis Fuller, as husband of Vinton's widow, with John Alfrey of Hartfield, yeoman, signing the bond.[391]

Francis Fuller was buried at Hartfield in 1638 and his widow Frances was buried there early in the following year. Other children of Francis Fuller by his first wife could have been baptised at Hartfield, where the pre-Civil War parish register is lost and where apart from an isolated example in 1594, bishop's transcripts commence in 1604 but lack the years 1605, 1607, 1619, 1623 and 1625. Among such children may have been the Hartfield colliers Henry and Edward Fuller.

Like Francis Fuller, the collier Henry Fuller, , married a widow from an immigrant family, Margery Pavie, in 1628. Henry's occupation was given in the bond he signed when in 1636 his wife took administration of the goods of her sister, the widow Agnes Perryman of Hartfield.[392] He could very easily have been baptised during the registration gap of 1594 to 1604 at Hartfield.

Similar remarks apply to the collier Edward Fuller of Hartfield, for whose children Joan, Katherine, Nicholas, Margery, Mary and John, baptismal records commence at Cowden in 1624 and continue until beyond 1640. Two of his children, an earlier John (who was probably buried at Cowden in 1631) and Jane, were baptised at Hartfield in 1630 and early in 1636 respectively. Edward's occupation was recorded when he was examined at quarter sessions in 1651 about the theft of a ewe belonging to one of the magistrates; he was absolved of this crime and discharged.[393]

Another Waldron collier was Solomon Fuller. No baptismal record for him appears to survive. He married Mary Martin, possibly a widow, at Waldron in 1613. Of the two children she bore him

386. Straker, *Wealden iron*, p. 285,

387. ESRO, QR 26, m. 29; I am indebted to Brian Phillips for this reference.

388. WSRO, Ep II/5/1, f. 4.

389. John and Francis Fuller, who in May 1578 (ESRO, ACC 3597/8, f. 77) were ordered by the Dill hundred court to cut their hedges overhanging the queen's highway from Tanner's Brook to Wood Place, are likely to have been father and uncle of Samuel Fuller, esq.

390. ESRO, ACC 3597/1, f. 92v., 114v.- went away (*abiit*).

391. ESRO, PBT 1/3/5/235. The bond was in £20.

392. ESRO, PBT 1/3/6/193.

393. ESRO, QR 90, m. 59 and 98.

before he died in 1619, the baptism in 1618 of the second, Joan, was recorded at both Waldron and East Hoathly. Solomon was educated enough to sign the will which he left, and its witnesses were William Osborne and Nicholas Fowle. His goods were inventoried at £56 2s 4d and he provided for his son John to receive £10 at the age of 10 and his daughter Joan to receive £6 at the same age. He made Henry Parson and his father-in-law Thomas Bassett his overseers, each to receive 10 shillings for their pains, in addition to expenses. He made his wife Mary his residuary legatee and executrix.[394]

A Ewhurst collier was John Fuller, who at the assizes in 1622 was indicted for rape, but was stated to be 'at large'. He was possibly the John Fuller whose children were mentioned in the Ewhurst parish register between October 1620 and June 1633. However, because of the long gap in the Ewhurst register before 1604 it impossible to be sure whether the collier's father was John Fuller of Brede, who remarried the widow Joan Damper of Ewhurst in February 1620, or Bartholomew Fuller of Ewhurst who in 1615 mentioned a son named John in his will.[395] If Bartholomew's son had been born around 1603 he could easily be the John Fuller who married Bridget Holman in 1638, and this would not preclude him from having been the offender of 1622.

It is difficult to link the Warbleton forgeman Thomas Fuller, who was excused the payment of hearth tax on one hearth on account of poverty in 1665,[396] with other members of this family. The Warbleton parish register recorded the baptism of Thomas son of Thomas Fuller in 1645 and of Samuel son of Thomas Fuller in November 1660. The register recorded the mother of neither child and though one would suspect that the father of the second child to have been the forgeman, the same cannot be said of the father of 1645.

Another Thomas Fuller was a collier, who together with his wife Susan, was returned in 1680 by the overseers of Salehurst parish to his place of settlement, Etchingham.[397]

Andrew Fuller, the Brede pot-founder who died in February 1693, had previously lived at Tonbridge in Kent, where it will be remembered there was a tradition of pot-founding, carried on earlier in the century by members of the Jarrett and Despar families. Andrew had married Peircy Hoffer at Tonbridge in September 1671 and their children Mary, Anne, Henry and John had been baptised between 1672 and 1678. Peircy's death was not recorded at Tonbridge, but in June 1679 Andrew was remarried to Mary Dalton. She bore him twins, Frances and Elizabeth, in April 1680, but was buried four days after their baptism. The daughter Elizabeth was buried at Tonbridge in October 1682. No record has been found of Andrew Fuller's third marriage, but his third wife bore him another daughter named Ann in May 1681.

In his will, made on 10th February 1693, Andrew Fuller made his third wife Elizabeth his residuary legatee and executrix, provided she would bring up his children, Frances and Anne. He left a shilling to each of his daughters Mary and Jane, but must have guessed that his son Henry would not survive, because no provision was made for him.[398] In the event, father and son were both buried at Brede on 14th February.

It is difficult to suggest an origin for the first element of the surname Orbell alias Fuller. In 1584 Robert Orbell alias Fuller took a lease for lives of Strudgate Furnace from Raphe Valley, who held the furnace from Lord Bergavenny.[399] William, the son of a later Robert Orbell was baptised at Cranleigh in September 1635.

Shoyswell hundred

Deboyse

The 1576 appearance of John Deboyse as a poll-tax payer in Shoyswell hundred seems to find no corresponding entries in parish registers. A related name is that of Debew, but Anthony Debew's appearance in the Goudhurst parish register in 1579 and 1580, followed a move from East Grinstead well

394. ESRO, PBT 1/1/17/56, 1/3/4/45.
395. Will of Bartholomew Fuller of Ewhurst, husbandman, 1 Dec 1615 (ESRO, PBT 1/1/15/72).
396. TNA, E 179/258/20.
397. M. J. Burchall, *Eastern Sussex settlement certificates, 1670-1832*, p. 41.
398. ESRO, PBT 1/1/41/83.
399. Straker, *Wealden iron*, p. 407.

after 1576. He had a child baptised at East Grinstead in March 1577 and his wife Joan was buried there in the following May. Anthony's son John Debew was aged seven in 1576. The Debews are considered later among the aliens of Rushmonden hundred.

Netherfield hundred

Bowyer

John Bowyer, who paid the poll tax in Netherfield hundred in 1595, was a Mountfield collier, who died in 1604, having made his will on 24 November of that year. He had married Joan Predam at Horsmonden in 1576 and their children, John, Richard, Nicholas, Alexander and Thomas were baptised at Mountfield between 1577 and 1588. Joan must have died shortly after Thomas's birth, because in 1591 Bowyer married his second wife, Jacqueline Ruffold, at Mountfield. This was also Jacqueline's second marriage, for she was Jacqueline Lambert by birth and in 1583 had taken as her first husband Peter Ruffolde.

John Bowyer bequeathed 10 shillings each to his stepdaughter Joan Predham and to Mary Harvie, He left a quarter of his household stuff to his wife Jacqueline and three quarters to be divided between his five sons, those under 21 to take their shares on attaining their majorities. Bowyer left the lease of his house and land to his second son Richard, provided he pay an annuity of £1 to Jacqueline during her life. The residue of his goods and stock, his corn, cattle and hay were to be appraised and sold, and what remained after the payment of the legacies was to be held by his executor Richard Brabon, a man of immigrant descent, who was to pay out of it an annuity of £2 to Jacqueline. After Jacqueline's death the proceeds of this sum were to be divided between Bowyer's sons. His goods were appraised at £35 2s 6d.[400]

John Bowyer's son Richard married Elizabeth Iden at Mountfield in 1605. They had three daughters, Elizabeth, Joan and Denise, who were baptised between 1607 and 1611, though Denise died in infancy. Richard's stepmother Jacqueline died in 1610 and he himself died intestate in 1611. His goods were valued at £32 13s 10d.[401] Elizabeth Bowyer, who married the miller Simon Crownage at Mountfield in 1612, was his widow.

No reason had been given in John Bowyer's will for the bequest of his house to his second son Richard. Could his eldest son have been the blacksmith, John Bowyer of Leeds, who was indicted at Kent assizes for a theft from William Howtinge at Hollingborne in 1601?[402] There is no certain evidence for John's return to the Weald, nor for the continuance there of the three younger brothers, Nicholas, Alexander and Thomas.

It is not absolutely certain that John Bowyer of Mountfield was the first Wealden immigrant of that surname. The Hartfield yeoman John Bowyer, who supplied shot to Henry VIII in 1513, was presumably the man who made his will in 1536[403] but who, before his death at an unknown date, had taken a lease of the Parrock ironworks, a lease which was still held by his wife Denise during the 1540s. He did not appear in the Sussex subsidy rolls of the 1520s.

The only two Pevensey rape Bowyers noted in the subsidy of 1524, Valentine and Nicholas, paid tax on land at Hartfield, worth £3 and £2 respectively, and were not classed as aliens. However, John Bowyer could easily have been the son of an immigrant of the early 1490s, whilst his wife Denise bore a name which was much used among French immigrants. Valentine and Nicholas were both names favoured in the immigrant community, and when he made his will in 1558 Valentine used the form Wryght alias Boyer. Wright was the surname of a Pulborough miner, William Wrighte, who in 1595 was required to give evidence at the assizes.[404]

Valentine Bowyer's goods were inventoried at £69 9s 2d. He made bequests of cattle and small amounts of money to his sons, Thomas and Roger, and to his daughters, Joan, Agnes and Isabel. To his

400. ESRO, PBT 1/1/12/45, 1/3/3/40.
401. ESRO, PBT 1/3/3/260.
402. Cockburn, *Kent Assize records, Elizabeth 1*, no. 2879.
403. TNA, PROB 11/33/222. The will was proved by John's son William in 1550, after his mother Denise's death.
404. Cockburn, *Sussex Assize records, Elizabeth 1*, no. 1579.

son Thomas 'the carpenter', he left a cow called Coppe and a two-yearling heifer. He made his son John his residuary legatee and executor and John was required to keep his youngest daughters Elizabeth and Mary until they were 14, and to pay them £3 and £2 respectively at their marriages.[405]

Like his brother Thomas, Valentine's son Roger Bowyer alias Wryte of Hartfield was a carpenter. When he died in 1592 he left five young children and his goods were valued at £76 19s 11d.[406]

Valentine's daughter Isabel married William Longlie at Rotherfield in 1563. Their children Mary, William and Eleanor were baptised at Mayfield between 1570 and 1575, whilst Nicholas was baptised at Rotherfield in 1581. Isabel made her will as a Wadhurst widow in 1591, perhaps moving there after 1581 with her husband, who was probably buried at Wadhurst, the sixteenth-century parish register for which is lost. Isabel's daughter Mary married John Hugget of Wadhurst as her first husband and after his early death was remarried to Lawrence Clarke of Frant. Valentine's younger daughter Mary married John Levit at Framfield in 1580.

The surname Bowyer seems not to occur among ironworkers outside the Weald.

Harrowe

In a deposition made in 1583, the Battle ironfounder Laurence Harrowe claimed to have been born in France some 40 years earlier. In a further deposition of 1613, when he was described as a Mountfield labourer, he identified his place of birth more closely as Rainville (*Rangville*).[407] It was at Mountfield that he was eventually buried in 1623 at the age of around 80.

Apart from those recorded in the Westminster denization roll of 1544, Harrowe's is the only precise place of birth known of any French immigrant ironworker. Rainville Furnace lay in the Perche, west of the Seine, in the parish of Longny, where ironworks on the indirect system were established during the 1470s. Laurence may have been related to the Harou family, who later established themselves as forgemasters in the Pays d'Ouche at the ironworks of Trisay and Bourth.[408]

It appears from Laurence Harrowe's statement made in 1583 that he had arrived in England around 1571. He had firstly lived in Battle for three years, in Mayfield for about six months, in Mountfield for two years, and had then returned to Battle, where by 1583 he had lived for a further six years. His payment of the poll tax in Netherfield hundred in 1576 would coincide with his residence in Mountfield. In July 1575 he married Constance Weston at Burwash, but their subsequent residence in Battle, a parish for which the sixteenth-century register has not survived, would explain the fact that the record of the baptism of their eldest son Nicholas has not been found. It is evident from the baptisms of other children, William, Mary who died in infancy, and Thomas, between 1587 and 1594, that by 1587 the family had returned to Mountfield.

It seems probable that Joan and Elizabeth Harrow, who were married at Mountfield, to Thomas Cresse in 1599 and John Lambert in 1600 respectively, were two more of Laurence Harrow's children baptised at Battle. Joan's son Thomas Cressey subsequently became a Brede miner, but her first husband soon died and in 1608 she married the Mountfield ironfounder Richard Gunter, who was later established at Salehurst.

Laurence's sons continued at Mountfield, where Nicholas married Tomsine Pellet in 1602, William married Alice Stempe in 1609 and Thomas married Joan Lambard in 1614. Laurence's wife Constance was buried at Mountfield in 1613, and he himself was buried there ten years later. In 1607 Laurence Harrowe acted as overseer to the will of William Miles of Brightling, and Laurence and his son Nicholas both witnessed this will.[409]

In 1620 Nicholas Harrow was one of the churchwardens at Mountfield. His son Laurence, who had been baptised in 1603, was still at Mountfield in 1630, when his son John was baptised there. However, by 1634 he and his wife Alice had moved on to Hawkhurst, where their son Nicholas was baptised under the surname Harold. Of Nicholas's other children, Constance, William, John and Mary, baptised between 1605 and 1612, only Mary appears to have survived infancy.

405. ESRO, PBT 1/1/4/208.
406. ESRO, PBT 1/1/9/31, 1/3/2/140.
407. WSRO, Ep II/5/3, f. 45 and Ep II/519, f. 46.
408. Belhoste and others, *La métallurgie normande*, pp. 151, 209.
409. ESRO, PBT 1/1/12/220.

Hawksborough hundred

Noell alias Christmas

The surname Christmas did not occur in East Sussex in the subsidy rolls of the 1520s. No example of the name being used as an alias for Noell has so far been found, but there seems no doubt that Daniel Nuell, baptised at Lamberhurst in 1604, was the future Bexhill ironfounder Daniel Christmas, who married Deborah Stevens, daughter of the Crowhurst yeoman Robert Stevens, at Battle in 1631 and whose eldest surviving son Thomas was baptised at Northiam in 1639.

The name first occurred in East Sussex at Rotherfield in 1553, when Anne daughter of William Chrysmas was baptised. But the alien surnamed Christmas, who paid the poll tax in Tottingworth borough as a servant of Henry Collen of Burwash in 1576, will have been Anthony Christmas. His son John was baptised at Fletching early in 1567, but cannot have survived long because in September 1568 another son of Anthony and Jane Christmas named John was baptised at Worth.

The Brightling parish register, which recorded the baptism of Anthony Christmas's daughter Thomasine in December 1570, showed that he was then living at Flemings in Burwash and was presumably already working for Henry Collen at Burwash Forge. However, he stayed there less than a decade because he was buried at Mayfield in 1580, where his daughter Jane had been baptised in 1579. His family continued at Burwash, where his daughter Thomasine married Jordan Leonard in 1591 and his son John married Elizabeth Verye in 1593. His youngest daughter Jane moved to Ticehurst in 1597.[410] His widow 'Mother Christmas' was buried at Burwash in 1610.

The Lamberhurst parish register fails to mention the parentage of Daniel Nuell who was baptised there in 1604. However, he was almost certainly the son of Robert and Mary Nuell or Newell, whose other children, Mary, James and another Mary, were baptised at Lamberhurst between 1606 and 1611. Robert Newell's first wife died later in 1611, but early in 1614 he married Susan Colyer at Biddenden. Their children, Elizabeth and Anne, were baptised at Biddenden in 1614 and 1616, but Elizabeth did not survive infancy. Robert's second wife Susan Christmas was buried at Cranbrook in 1637.

Daniel Christmas married Deborah Stevens at Battle in March 1631 and their son Daniel was baptised there in 1632. There had been earlier persons named Christmas in Battle, where views of frankpledge had recorded James Cristmas as a Sandlake defaulter in October 1581 and October 1583, and Thomas Cristmas as a Sandlake defaulter in April 1583 and April 1584. However, because John Christmas, who married Mary Smith at Battle in June 1631, had his daughter baptised as Deborah in 1635, it seems possible that he was closely related to Daniel Christmas. The parish register does not disclose which of the two men was father of Lawrence, William and Dorothy Christmas, baptised at Battle in 1634, 1637 and 1638, but it looks as though Lawrence and William were the persons of that name buried within days of their baptisms.

A child who did survive was Thomas the son of Daniel and Deborah Christmas, but he was baptised at Northiam early in 1639. Another child of Daniel Christmas was Sarah, baptised at Biddenden in June 1654. She had been born five days earlier, perhaps at the home of her grandfather, after whom Daniel's second son was named, though Robert's baptism has not been found.

When Daniel Christmas of Bexhill, ironfounder, made his will in 1666 he left £7 to his eldest son Thomas, £5 to his son Robert, and three pieces of land (9 acres) to his third son John. He left a shilling to his daughter Mercy, his tenement and two pieces of land (3 acres) named Kingsmill Woods to his second daughter Elizabeth and more land to his third daughter Mary. He had evidently married again because his wife was named Mercy.[411]

Another member of this family was perhaps Andrew Christmas, whose son Martin was baptised at Biddenden in 1600. Martin did not survive infancy and another of Andrew's sons, Thomas Christmas, was buried at Biddenden in 1613. He himself was buried there in 1615. Other members of the family were William Christmas, whose son Richard was baptised at Fletching in 1581, and Richard Christmas who married Catherine Dine at Waldron in 1586.

In the west of the Weald Balthazar Christmas married Margaret Rapley at Chiddingfold in 1580. Their children, Thomas, William, Edward and Joan, were baptised at Lurgashall between 1581

410. WSRO, EpII/5/6 pp. 201-2.
411. ESRO, PBT 1/1/30/303.

and 1594, though Joan did not survive infancy. Thomas married Anne Freeman at Lurgashall in 1604 and their children, Richard and Thomas, were baptised at Chiddingfold in 1606 and 1611. Other sons of Thomas were John, who was baptised at West Chiltington in 1615, and Nicholas, whose baptism has not been traced. The latter was perhaps Nicholas Christmas of Lurgashall, whose son Thomas was a beneficiary under the will of William Christmas,

Edward Christmas, a Lurgashall husbandman, made his will in 1630 and William Christmas, a Northchapel yeoman, made his will in 1638. Though the family lived in ironworking parishes its surprising affluence makes it unlikely that it had close ironworking connections. Edward Christmas hoped to be buried in the chancel of Lurgashall church and William Christmas, who also asked to be buried at Lurgashall, left no less than £500 to his daughter Agnes.[412] In their wills both Edward and William referred to the children of another brother named John.

Henhurst hundred

Rootes

John Rootes paid the poll tax in Henhurst hundred in 1576. He seems not to have been noticed in the parish registers of Etchingham or Ticehurst. There is no evidence that he was connected in any way with Abraham Rootes, the Lewes cutler, the only person of the surname to be employed in a metal trade, who in 1605 witnessed a marriage bond.[413]

It is quite uncertain whether he could be 'John Rootes a stranger' who was buried at Frant in February 1623, because by 1623 the word 'stranger' was less often used with the ancient meaning of 'foreigner'.

The surname does not appear to be linked with the primary production of iron anywhere in Britain.

Staple hundred

The 1576 list of aliens for this hundred starts with the ironworker Peter de Goye, but continues with two glass workers, Godfrye de la Haye and Ogniben Lutere. It seems probable, however, that the remaining names were concerned with iron rather than with glass. Stephen de Voye has already been dealt with.

Fycot

The name of John Fycot, who paid the poll tax in Staple hundred in 1576 does not seem to appear in parish registers of the area. The name Vigot has earlier been equated with Bigo or Bigot. Perhaps Fycot should be equated with the name Feegod, later found at Buxted.

Richard Fegod of Buxted's will was proved in 1598 by his son Richard Fegod alias Godleye. However, there was nothing in this will to relate the family with ironworking.[414] The younger Richard Feegod's wife Jane was buried at Buxted early in 1631.

King

Peter Kinge, who paid 3s 4d to the subsidy as an alien in Staple hundred in 1595 was undoubtedly the man who had married Susan, the widow of John Messans, at East Grinstead in February 1571. The finers Nicholas and Adrian Messant were therefore his stepsons, which explains why both commenced their careers in the south-east of the Weald.

Nicholas Messant of Cranbrook, finer, was indicted in 1595 along with Peter King of Sedlescombe, collier, and others for the theft at Ewhurst of some stockings.[415] Adrian Messant's first

412. TNA PROB 11/157/545 and 184/446.
413. Dunkin, *Sussex Marriage Licences, Lewes 1586-1643*, p. 50.
414. ESRO, PBT 2/2/2/45.
415. ESRO, QR 6, m. 13.

child was baptised at Salehurst and buried at Bodiam in 1585, the latter the parish where both his mother and Peter King were buried in the autumn of 1608.

The name is almost certainly a translation of Le Roy and was dealt with when considering the family Goddard alias King which, because Peter King never used the alias Goddard, looks as though it may not have been closely related to him.

Battle hundred

Welles

A gentry family lived at this time in Battle, to which Robert and Edward Welles, gentlemen, mentioned in the Battle view of frankpledge for October 1583, clearly belonged.[416]

The alien William Welles, who paid the poll tax in Battle hundred in 1576, was probably the man fined 1s 8d at the Battle view of frankpledge of April 1577 for an attack on Giles Harvye.[417] Harvye was presumably from the ironworking family of that name, which supports the idea that Welles may also have been engaged in ironworking.

A Cardiff man of the same name had bought iron from the Glamorgan undertaking of Sir Henry Sidney in the 1560s,[418] but it is not clear how the Battle alien could be connected with him. No later connections of a Welles family with ironworking in the Weald are known.

Loxfield hundred

Pinson

The name occurred as *Pinson* or *Pinchon* in Normandy, though *Planchon* was and is more commonly met with in the Béthune valley. Guillaume Planchon of Gratenoix and Henry Planchon of Sausseuzemare, with his sons Cardin and Pierre Planchon, were referred to in Neufchâtel notarial acts of 1512.[419]

None of these names occurred in the Sussex subsidy rolls of the 1520s. Robert Pynson was mentioned in the Uckfield parish register in 1532 and the parish registers of Wartling and Herstmonceux show that the name Pinson or Pinchon was already well-established in Foxearle hundred by 1545. Although an administration bond of 1564 showed that Leonard Pynchyn of Wartling was a husbandman,[420] his fourth and last wife whom he married in 1572 was Richardine Lake, who bore a Goudhurst scythe-smithing surname. After her burial at Herstmonceux in 1577, Leonard moved to Salehurst, where he was buried in 1590. John Pinson, who married Alice Lame alias Barden at Salehurst in 1600, was conceivably his son.

Rather more certainly involved in the iron industry was John Pynson, who married Elizabeth Turner at Pembury in 1561. John's son Hugh was baptised at Pembury in 1565 and buried there in 1574. John's twins, Richard and Mathew, were baptised in 1575 with Nicholas Turner and Joan Gyllett among the sponsors, and his son John in 1582. Two Goudhurst parish register entries are probably linked with them, the burial of Hugh Pynson's wife, who may have been John's mother, in 1567 and the baptism of William Pinson in 1568, whose parents were undisclosed but who may have been John's son.

Of this family only William Pinson appears to have remained in the Teise Valley. His daughter Anne was baptised at Lamberhurst in 1605 and more twins, Richard and Elizabeth, of whom the latter did not survive, in 1608. Nicholas, Ellen and Francis Pinson who were baptised at Lamberhurst between 1597 and 1602 were probably also children of William Pinson and his wife Mary. Francis Pinson settled in Wadhurst where he married Anne Seisley in 1620. His younger brother Richard Pinson stayed in Lamberhurst where he married Margaret Bates in 1631.

The first mentions of Mathew Pynson the miller, probably the man baptised at Pembury in

416. HEH, BA Vol. 97 f. 31.
417. HEH, BA Vol. 96 f. 34.
418. Crossley, *Sidney ironworks accounts*, p. 241.
419. Guillaume (ADSM, 2 E 14/1154 (29 May 1512)); Henry (2 E 14/1156 (11 Nov 1512)).
420. ESRO, PBT 1/1/5/198.

1575, occurred in the Herstmonceux parish register in 1598, 1600 and 1604, and between 1608 and 1616 he was a bondsman for four probate administrations.[421] He died in 1635 leaving goods valued at £88 15s 6d, having been predeceased in 1631 by his son John Pinson, another miller, who left goods valued at £38 12s 0d.[422]

A second Mathew Pynson who was a sawyer was mentioned in the Herstmonceux parish register in 1603 and was buried there in 1612. He was probably the man whose daughter Abigail had been baptised at Wartling in 1587, but whose later children were baptised at Herstmonceux. Since the miller was repeatedly stated to be of Herstmonceux it looks as though Mathew Pinson of Wartling referred to in the Herstmonceux parish register in 1592 was the sawyer; could he also have been 'Father Pynson the Joyner' whose wife was buried at Herstmonceux in 1600?

John Pincen of Cowbeech was referred to in 1574 in the Wartling parish register, without any indication of whether he was involved in the ironworks there. However, the baptism of Abraham son of 'John Pynchin of Watlynge' at Warbleton in 1581 might indicate that he was, although the son Abraham probably became Abraham Pinson of Herstmonceux, glover, who in 1625 was bondsman for a probate administration.[423]

Although a great deal is known about this interesting family, all the evidence for its probable French origin and possible connections with the iron industry is purely circumstantial.

In the case of Gabriel Penson the subsidy roll showed quite clearly that he paid the poll tax as an alien at Mayfield in 1576. He was first mentioned in 1572, when his son William was baptised at Mayfield, an entry followed by the baptisms of two daughters, Jane and Eleanor, in 1575 and 1579, and the burial of a son named Robert in 1579. Because the parish register styled him 'Goodman Gabryell' in 1575 it seems probable that he had been resident in Mayfield for some time.

There seems to be no evidence for Gabriel Penson's presence at Mayfield or in the Weald after 1579, nor is there any evidence that he was engaged in the iron industry.

Rotherfield hundred

Good

The name seems almost certain to have been a simple translation of *Le Bon.* At Neufchâtel-en-Bray, Jehan Le Bon had been a locksmith during the 1530s and early 1540s.[424]

Nicholas Good paid the poll tax as a servant of John Saunders at a forge in Frant in the subsidy of 1576. This suggests that Saunders, who is known to have taken a lease of Brooklands and Verredge forges in 1610, was perhaps involved there much earlier.

It seems certain that in the 1570s there were two immigrants named Nicholas Good. The poll-tax payer was presumably the man who married Julian Dobet at Tonbridge in August 1573. Their son Peter was baptised at Frant in December 1574. It is not certain that there are other entries concerning this Nicholas Good until the burial of Gillian Good 'an old widow' at Horsham in March 1614 proves that both he and his wife had died.

The other man named Nicholas Good had a son Nicholas baptised at Fletching in 1572. He probably went on to be the St Leonards Forest forgeman who in 1585 testified to Exchequer commissioners that he was aged around 40.[425] Nicholas Good and his wife Mercy were stated to be of the parish of Beeding when the baptism of their son Abraham was recorded at Horsham early in 1580. Abraham failed to survive the year, but other children of Nicholas and Mercy Good baptised at Horsham in 1581 and 1584 were Mary and Elizabeth. Since the other Nicholas Good had died at least ten years earlier, this man was perhaps the person buried at Shipley in March 1624.

It is quite evident that some entries concerning this family were recorded in the Nuthurst parish register. Two of these were the marriages of Peter Goode and Parnell Growte in 1599 and of Nicholas

421. ESRO, PBT 1/3/3/140 and 229; 1/3/4/64 and 113.
422. ESRO, PBT 1/1/21/143, 1/3/6/98, 1/1/24/27, 1/3/6/228.
423. ESRO, PBT 1/3/4/199.
424. ADSM, 2 E 14/1168 (28 Nov 1533); 2 E 14/1182 (29 Jan 1540), 2 E 14/1186 (9 Mar 1542).
425. TNA, E 134/27 Elizabeth I Easter 16.

Good and Agnes Loret in 1614, both of them obviously marriages within the French community. Nicholas and Agnes Good's children may have been Mercy, Anne and Marie Goode, baptised at Nuthurst in 1617, 1619 and 1623 respectively, though without indication of parentage.

An earlier marriage at Nuthurst was that between Peter Gorde and Agnes [a'Deane?] in January 1585, which was followed by the baptisms at Horsham of Richard, son of Peter and Anne Goode (*sic*), later in 1585, and of Peter, son of Peter and Agnes Goodge, in 1589. It must be quite uncertain whether this family is related to the immigrant one. The family of Gorde had been represented in Hartfield hundred in the subsidy roll of 1524 and was apparently indigenous. In view of this should not the surname of the Frenchman Thomas Goord buried at Rotherfield in 1570 rather have been written 'Good'?

The family of Walter Good, a collier, for which entries occur in the Balcombe parish register from 1604 onwards, must undoubtedly have been immigrant, though the link back to either of the Nicholas Goods cannot be traced. Walter Good of Balcombe, collier, was a bondsman when a licence was issued in 1613 for the marriage of Bridget Dudgeon of Balcombe, maiden, to John Shirlock, a Balcombe husbandman.[426] Children of Walter Good were baptised at Balcombe from 1604 to 1623, but his wife Margaret was buried there early in 1626. He must have married again because a further child named Margaret was baptised in 1627. However, Walter Good himself was buried at Balcombe in 1628 and in 1632 administration of his goods, valued at £14 19s 10d, was assigned to his son Antony Good, the child who had been baptised in 1604, also a Balcombe collier. However, in a quarter sessions recognizance of 1632 Anthony Good was described as a Horsted Keynes collier.[427]

Another branch of the Good family was found at Haslemere from 1598 onwards in the person of William Good. His son Robert, baptised at Haslemere in 1602, was buried there in 1639, but his second surviving son William moved on to Frensham. The burial of one of William's daughters was recorded at Haslemere in 1638, whilst his son Charles was baptised there in 1639.

Further afield, in South Yorkshire Thomas Good married Margaret Byrley at Sheffield early in 1576. It looks as though no children arose from this marriage, but just over 20 years later probably the same Thomas Good married Denise Robertes. No children from this marriage were baptised at Sheffield either.

Danehill Sheffield hundred

Carman

Dennis Carnellum and Robert Carmarynge, who in 1576 paid the poll tax as aliens in Danehill Sheffield and in Buttinghill hundreds respectively, were perhaps father and son.

The Buttinghill man will have been Robert Carman, whose daughter Lettice was baptised at Maresfield in 1581, with Peter Pontinge, Margaret Perygoe and Collas Sherron, all of immigrant descent, as godparents.

The immigrant was clearly not Denis Cardman, the Fletching collier, who in 1598 claimed to have lived in Fletching for 20 years and to have been born in Sussex around 40 years earlier.[428] The younger Denis Carman may have been an English-born brother of Robert and was probably the father of Richard and Thomas who were baptised at Fletching in 1586 and 1592, and of Eleanor who was buried at Newick in 1595. Stephen Carman of Fletching who married Mary Rickward at Newick in 1622 was presumably another of the younger man's sons. A daughter may have been Mary Carman, who married Henry Turner at Fletching in 1609.

However, the surnames Carnell, and Carnell alias Carlton also occur. At Fletching Joan (*Jonne*) Carnell was buried early in 1554. The alias occurred twice in 1606, when Dorothy Carnell alias Carlton was buried early in the year at Worth and when John Carlton alias Carnell married Joan Homan at Hartfield in September. At East Grinstead George Carnell's son Edward was baptised in 1602 and at Worth Annis Carnall was buried in 1638.

426. Dunkin, *Sussex Marriage Licences, Lewes 1586-1643*, p. 88.
427. ESRO, PBT 1/3/6/123; QR 32, m. 53; I am grateful to Brian Phillips for this reference.
428. WSRO, EpII/5/6 p. 204.

This version of the surname went back to the 1550s at Tonbridge, where Katherine Cardnell and a child named Elizabeth Carnell were buried in May 1551 and June 1552 respectively. The second burial was followed in July by that of Elizabeth wife of Roger Carnell and Roger Cardnall himself was buried at Tonbridge in April 1559.

Later, Richard Carnell married Joan Dorrante at Horsmonden in 1596 and their daughter Joan was baptised in that parish early in the following year. Joan Dorrante was the youngest daughter of the pot-founder Remy Durrant, who was buried at Horsmonden in 1591 and who left £10 to her in his will.[429] Evidence is so far lacking that later members of this family were involved in ironworking, or that they participated in the spread of the iron industry beyond the Weald.

Barcombe hundred

Cavenche

John Cavenche paid the poll tax in 1576 in Barcombe hundred as second in a list of six aliens who could have worked at Fletching Forge. The only supporting parish register entry occurred at Maresfield in May 1568 when Agnes Caffynch was sponsor to a baptism. There appears to have been an indigenous family of this name in West Sussex, because Edward and Simon Cafynche were recorded at Apsley in the subsidy rolls of 1524.

It seems possible that Cavenche rapidly moved to the east of the Weald, because apart from the marriage of John Cafnich (*sic*) to Sarah Snatt at East Hoathly as late as 1635, parish register entries in that part of Sussex did not follow. At Northiam, on the other hand, the baptism and burial of Elizabeth daughter of John Caffinch were recorded in June and September 1584. Later entries for the family occurred in registers of parishes near the Kent and East Sussex border.

At Cranbrook a later John Caffinche had children baptised from 1615 to 1628. At Salehurst George Caffinche married Ann Page in 1619 and their children were subsequently baptised at Cranbrook from 1622 to 1635, except for William at Salehurst in 162.6. George Caffinche was buried at Cranbrook in 1635. Samuel Caffinch married Mary Fryland at Cranbrook in 1637.

Children of Richard Caffinche were baptised at Salehurst in 1629 and 1630, and at Cranbrook in 1633. Children of Jeremiah Cafinche were baptised and buried at Biddenden from 1630 to 1639, and Thomas Caffinch married Mary Phillips at Biddenden early in 1645.

Direct evidence that this family participated in the iron industry has not so far been forthcoming.

Buttinghill hundred

Tuck

No Robert Tuck, who together with his two sons paid the poll tax as aliens in Buttinghill hundred in 1576, has been traced in parish registers or other sources. It is difficult to read this entry as 'Turk' and in any case the children of the forgeman Robert Turk alias Tomplier, who had last appeared in subsidy rolls in 1560 in Foxearle hundred, were apparently all English-born.

Perhaps one of Tuck's sons was Thomas Tucker, who married Anne Russell at Buxted in 1590. A quarter sessions recognizance of 1594 bound Christopher Cressey of Maresfield, labourer, to keep the peace towards Thomas Tucker of Maresfield, pot-founder, and to prefer a writ of indictment and testify against the founder John Carpe alias Devale.[430]

Thomas Tucker's children were Mary and Charles, baptised at Buxted in 1592 and 1599, and Anne Tucker, baptised at Maresfield in 1596. He was buried at Buxted in 1604. Some 18 months later Tucker's widow Anne married Simon Coleman, probably the son of Simon Coleman, a Dallington tailor, baptised at Brightling in 1577. In a deposition of 1613 Anne Coleman described her husband as an Uckfield potter. She had been born at Hartfield around 1569 and had lived at Uckfield around two

429. TNA, PROB 11/79/295.

430. ESRO, QR 4, m. 51; I am grateful to Brian Phillips for drawing my attention to this recognizance.

months;[431] she was buried at Buxted in 1624. Simon Coleman was probably the Brede pot-founder who signed marriage bonds in 1634 and 1635.[432] Again it is difficult to know whether his marriage brought Coleman into the pot-founding milieu, or whether it resulted from his already being employed in it.

Charles Tucker married Margaret Furbie at Buxted in 1622, but after the baptism of two children, Margaret and Richard, at Buxted in 1623 and 1625, he moved to Rotherham in South Yorkshire, where his daughter Sicilye was baptised in 1629.

Thomas Tucker's daughter Anne married Nathan Neves at Buxted in 1622. John Tucker, whose children were baptised at Biddenden from 1620 onwards, was perhaps from this family too.

Poulter

This ironworking family was first noted in the Weald when the forgeman John Poltar's son John was baptised at Frant in 1571. It must be supposed that John Poltar from Frant was one of the aliens, father and son, named Polter who paid the poll tax in Buttinghill hundred in 1576. It seems probable that he moved on to Dunsfold in Surrey; although no sixteenth-century parish register is extant for Dunsfold, the Surrey muster rolls for 1583-4 show that among the gunners at Dunsfold, who included men identifiable as ironworkers, was John Poulter.[433]

Another member of this family may have been Robert Powlter of Beeding, a mine digger who gave evidence to Exchequer commissioners in 1588.[434] He gave his age as around 40 and was possibly the man whose son John had been baptised at Balcombe in 1578.

A third man of this name involved in the manufacture of iron was Henry Poulter, an East Grinstead husbandman, who had been involved as clerk at Richard Infield's Mill Place Furnace. He made a deposition in 1612 in which he claimed to have been born in West Hoathly about 40 years earlier and to have lived there all his life apart from the last three years, when he had lived at East Grinstead. He had been clerk at Mill Place for the last five years.[435]

Henry Powlter was the eldest son and executor of the West Hoathly yeoman Henry Powlter who made his will early in 1606. One of the father's overseers was Jerrard Powlter, a Balcombe yeoman, who was possibly his brother. Both may have been sons of Walter Powlter, whose children were baptised at Balcombe from 1543 onwards. It is quite uncertain whether this family was of immigrant stock, or otherwise involved in any way in ironworking. It could also have included the Beeding 'mine digger' Robert Powlter, especially as he was first encountered at Balcombe.

Members of these families are not known to have been involved in ironworking outside the Weald.

Dallanton

The alien John Dallanton paid the poll tax in Buttinghill hundred in 1576. The Worth parish register showed his continued presence there when it recorded the baptism of Joan daughter of John and Audrey Dalinton in August 1580.

Other references to this family in connection with ironworking are not known either in the Weald or elsewhere.

Burbeech hundred

Agamo

Neither Peter Agamo, nor his two sons and his servant, who each paid the poll tax in Burbeech hundred in 1576, can be traced in other Wealden sources. The surname is not known in connection with iron either in the Weald or further afield in Britain.

431. WSRO, Ep II/5/1, f . 32.
432. Dunkin, *Sussex Marriage Licences, Lewes 1586-1643*, pp. 211, 219.
433. Craib, *Surrey musters*, p. 17.
434. TNA, E 134/30 Elizabeth 1, Easter 17.
435. ESRO, Ep 11/5/9, f. 50.

Taber

The occupation of John Taber as an iron miner was disclosed in 1598 when he entered a recognizance, under the name John Tabarett of Rudgwick, to appear at the assize court.[436] He had earlier appeared in Burbeech hundred in the subsidy of 1576 as John Taber, an alien who together with his mother paid the poll tax.

It was in East Sussex that he next appeared as John Taberer at Etchingham in 1588, when his daughter Joan was baptised. Back at Worth, Richard, the son of John and Joan Tabret was baptised early in 1596, whilst Nicholas Tabret, who had been buried at Worth in 1595, was presumably from his family. His assize recognizance of 1598 brought him firmly back to West Sussex.

It seems probable that John Taverner, a Witley furnaceman, who in 1616 also entered a recognizance to make an assize appearance, was either the former miner who had graduated to extra responsibility at the furnace, or was his son, especially as one of the bondsmen was a Rudgwick ironfounder, John Haylor.[437]

KENT

Brenchley hundred

Burlett

William Burlett, who paid the poll tax in Brenchley hundred in 1598, 1599 and 1600, had arrived in the Weald at least 20 years earlier. He married a widow named Margaret Dan at Brenchley in 1575. Their children, William, Ellen, Ralph, Richard, John and Bartholomew, of whom Ellen and John died aged 14 and 4 respectively and Richard died aged a few weeks, were baptised between 1576 and 1587. William's first wife died in February 1589 and in 1590 he married another widow named Sara Taylor. She bore him twins, Robert and Elizabeth, in 1591.

Burlett may have arrived in the Weald as a collier, but when he made his will in 1603 he was a tanner.[438] He left £1 to the poor, 5 shillings to each of his elder sons, William and Ralph, and £2 each to his younger sons, Bartholomew and Robert. He made his wife Sara his executrix and residuary legatee. Burlett was buried at Brenchley in March 1603, but his will was proved only after the deaths of his sons William and Ralph, in July 1604 and May 1605 respectively. By a nuncupative will, proved later in May, Ralph Burlett bequeathed £2 to his brother Bartholomew and made his half-brother Robert Danne his residuary legatee and executor.[439] William Burlett's widow Sara was buried at Brenchley in September 1605.

Bartholomew Burlett and Elizabeth Briant, both stated to be of Speldhurst, were married at Pembury early in 1625, but their children, Margaret, John, Elizabeth, Marie and Anne were baptised at Brenchley between 1626 and 1636. Bartholomew Burlett, described as a 'housekeeper' as distinct from 'poor', was buried at Brenchley in March 1638. His widow Elizabeth married Robert Austen of Brenchley at Horsmonden in June 1638.

Bartholomew's will shows that he too was a tanner, though more prosperous than his father. He bequeathed to his four daughters £40 apiece, to be paid them at their marriages or at the age of 21. He left 30 acres of land, called Cafinche or Beckets Grove, to his son John who was also a minor. His wife was to be executrix, but should she marry again, which she rapidly did, the executorship was to pass to Bartholomew's brother John Hartridge of Pembury and his son.[440]

436. Cockburn, *Sussex Assize records, Elizabeth I*, no. 1753.
437. Cockburn, *Surrey Assize records, James I*, no. 814.
438. KHLC, DRb/PW20.
439. KHLC, DRb/PW20.
440. KHLC, DRb/PW30.

SURREY

Reigate hundred

Elliot

Like the related surname Ellis, the name Elliot probably had an initial 'H' in French, and appeared as *Heliot*, though Helion was more common. At Ticehurst between 1571 and 1580 Hellyote was used on six occasions, but in 1568 Ellyet was used and in 1589 Eliat. Related names were Ellet and Ellyard, and some parish registers exchanged these names somewhat haphazardly.

In 1576 the alien John Ellyot paid the poll tax in Leigh and Newdigate. He was perhaps the John Elliott whose children, Katherine and Nicholas, were baptised at Newdigate in 1577 and 1580. He could earlier have been at Worth, where Jane and Charles, children of John and Eleanor Elliott, were baptised in 1570 and 1571.

If this link is correct, the family moved to Maresfield around 1602. Charles's first child Richard was baptised at Worth in 1601, but subsequent children, Sisseley, Charles and Elizabeth, were baptised at Maresfield from 1604 to 1611. This family was still at Maresfield up to 1617, the children Sisseley and Charles being buried there in 1616 and 1617.

The link with immigrant ironworking families is confirmed by the marriage of John Ellyat to Tomsen Vinten at Maresfield in 1603. That this was a second marriage of the alien father is suggested by the rapid demise of both parties, John early in 1606 and Thomasine in December 1608, both being buried at Fletching. But rather than the father, the John Ellyat involved could have been John Elliotte baptised at Newdigate in 1567, whose parentage was not stated in the parish register, but who could have been the first child of the immigrant.

The hanaper roll shows that John Ellyard was a 1541 denizen;[441] his name is not enrolled on the surviving two membranes of the denization roll for that year.

Robert Elyard, a Withyham smith who died in 1565, was perhaps John's son. He held Partridges in Withyham, the profits of which were to go to his wife Joan for bringing up their four children, all minors. Partridges was to pass to their eldest son Robert when he attained 21. Smith could also mean blacksmith and the main reason for supposing that Robert Elyard was more closely involved in the ironworks was that the ironmaster John Palar was the third witness to his will.[442]

Roger Ellyard of Warbleton was a tailor and was first noticed there in 1569 when his eldest son Thomas was baptised. The family's earlier connection with the iron industry is perhaps reflected in 1603, when Roger bequeathed his two great iron pots to his daughters Sara and Confidence. Roger made his 'two young masters', Thomas Stollian the younger and Richard Stollian, overseers of his will. They will have been appointed as the sons of Thomas Stollian in his capacity of lord of the manor, rather than as ironmaster. Roger Ellyard's goods were inventoried at £183 10s 8d.[443]

Rather than Elliot, it is the surname Ellet or Ellit which occurs in connection with the iron industry in the Midlands. At Makeney in Derbyshire Margery Ellet was buried early in 1683. The hammerman of Lea Forge, Harman Ellit, was mentioned in the Wibunbury parish register from 1714 to 1718. Around the same time Margaret the daughter of William Ellet of Norton Forge was baptised at Mucklestone in 1718. Was this William Ellet the forgeman buried at Tong in 1762? The use of the baptismal name Harman by the hammerman, and also as the name of his child baptised in 1714, suggests that he could have been of foreign descent.

However, the surname Ellet was perhaps brought direct to the Midlands because its occurrence in the Weald is very ptchy. Alexander son of John Elat was baptised at Burwash early in 1585 and early in 1606 a 'child of Elates' was buried there, but otherwise Eliot or Elliott was more usual at Burwash, though no John Eliot appeared. In 1591 administration of the goods of Richard Ellett of Bexhill was granted to his widow Agnes.[444] Entries between 1608 and 1617 at Rotherfield for Herbert and William Ellatt used that surname only, but the name of Mary Elliott who married Richard Marchant there early

441. TNA, E 101/223/10.
442. ESRO, PBT 1/1/5/279.
443. ESRO, PBT 1/1/11/223, 1/3/3/25.
444. ESRO, PBT 1/3/2/109.

in 1616 was also spelled Ellatt, so, although Herbert Ellatt did not otherwise appear at Rotherfield, that spelling appears to have been the practice of the current incumbent or parish clerk.

IMMIGRANTS MENTIONED IN PARISH REGISTERS

Gybrig

John Gybrig, supposedly a French collier, was buried in 1561 at Fletching. It seems legitimate to question whether this was not the confession by the parish clerk that the French name was 'gibberish' to him, rather than a genuine surname.

Potter

The occupational surnames *Potier, Poterie* and *de La Poterie* were ubiquitous in the Pays de Bray, and the last two were particularly well represented in the parish of Bouelles. In East Sussex the name occurred only at Lewes and Danehill Sheffield in the 1520s.

Back in 1493 Henry Potier had been a wheelwright (*caron*) at des Mares in the parish of Mauquenchy. At Merimont in the parish of Esclavelles in 1528 the alias of Colin Bertin *dit* Potier was occupational and Merimont long remained a centre of earthenware pot-making.

However, Thomas de La Poterie was one of the many Neufchâtel cutlers of the 1560s,[445] and a smith from Normandy named Thomas Potter, who had been born around 1508, had come to England around 1526, and was made denizen in 1544; proof that he came to the Weald is lacking.

But Frenchmen named Potter were working in the Weald by the 1560s. Robert Potter's first child was perhaps Francis Potter, baptised at Frant in 1565, without note of the parents' names, and buried at Ardingly in 1573. The name was first noted as French at Rotherfield, where in March 1566, Robert child of a Frenchman, was buried. In May 1566 'a young child of Potter Frenchman' was buried there. The baptismal names Robert, the occurrence of Francis Potter at both Frant and Ardingly, and the relative scarcity of the name in the Weald allow the link to be made with Robert Potter, 'fyner of the hammer' whose unnamed child was baptised at Ardingly early in 1572. Another child of Robert's, Edmund Potter, was baptised in the same parish in 1573, whilst earlier that year his children Mary and Francis had been buried there. By early 1584 he reappeared at Frant, where Joan daughter of 'Robert Potter forgeman' was buried. He was perhaps the Robert Potter who was buried at Buxted in 1586.

That first Frant baptism of 1565 had been closely followed in 1568 by the burial at Brenchley of Mary, wife of John Potter Frenchman, 'who died at Old Hag'.

The surname is not used later in the Weald in connection with iron manufacture, nor is it sufficiently widely used elsewhere in the iron industry to support the idea of descendants of these immigrants being involved.

Caffe or Taffte

The surname of Markes Caffe, a Frenchman whose daughter Dorothy was baptised at Ardingly in 1566, seems totally unlike any French name.

Bearing in mind that upper case 'C'and 'T' can be almost indistinguishable in some hands, the similarity to the name of Lawrence Tarffe, Tafte or Toffte, whose children, Nicholas, Clement, William and Joan, of whom Nicholas and William did not survive, were baptised at Pembury from 1573 to 1578, is striking. However, although the baptismal names Laurence, Nicholas and Clement seem French enough, the surname is again difficult to relate to any French surname.

Although both Ardingly and Pembury were important ironworking parishes, concrete evidence that either Markes Caffe or Lawrence Tarffe was involved in the iron industry is not forthcoming. The surnames are not known to be linked with iron in other areas.

445. ADSM, 2 E 83/411 (7 Jan 1493); 2 E 14/1167 (6 Oct 1528); 2 E 14/1209 (5 Jul 1566).

Blunden

The surname *Blondel* is far more common than *Blondeau* or *Blondin* in Normandy. In the Béthune valley the occurrence of the surname *Le Blond* far exceeded them all. In the Sussex subsidy rolls of the 1520s Blunden did not occur at all, whilst Blundell occurred only in West Sussex. In the second half of the sixteenth century the name Blundell was common in Tonbridge and Lingfield, from where it seems to have spread into East Grinstead and adjoining parishes such as Worth and Cuckfield. However, in many other parishes the names Blundell and Blunden were often interchanged.

Peter Blunden, a Frenchman, was buried at Lamberhurst in 1567. This was an isolated entry in Lamberhurst parish register and it was at Burwash that the name occurred more regularly. Having married Joan Clinker at Salehurst in 1575, Nicholas Blunden moved to Maresfield, where his daughter Joan was baptised in 1578, back to Salehurst, where his children Agnes and Peter were baptised in 1579 and 1581, and finally established himself in Burwash, where his sons, Stephen, Adrian and John, were baptised between 1584 and 1591. Nicholas Blunden was buried at Salehurst in 1607.

Nicholas Blunden's son Peter married Anne Jewell at Warbleton in 1612, but there appear to have been no children, and she was buried there in 1617. In 1618 Peter married a widow named Alice Crappe at Mountfield. Their son Thomas was baptised at Mountfield in 1619, but Alice was buried there in 1624. Peter next married Sara Reeve at Burwash in 1626 and moved on to Catsfield where he joined his brother Adrian. Adrian's sons, Richard and Peter, had been baptised at Catsfield in 1622 and 1625 and Peter's daughter Elizabeth was baptised there too in 1627. Both then moved on to Ashburnham, where Peter's daughter Ellen was baptised in 1629, and where Adrian was buried in the same year, followed by his sons Peter and Richard, who were buried in 1635 and 1640 respectively.

Nicholas's son Stephen married Mary Tomplin at Burwash in 1609 and their children, Constance, John, Stephen, Richard, Henry, Nicholas and Mary, were baptised at Burwash between 1610 and 1626, though Stephen did not survive childhood. Stephen's son Henry married Ann Mills in 1641, but his wife died in childbirth in February 1642, she and the infant Agnes both being buried the day following the child's baptism. Stephen's son Nicholas Blunden married Mary Rack at Heathfield in 1644 and their son John was baptised at Burwash in 1645. Stephen's daughter Constance married Lewis Stephens at Ashburnham in 1642.

Nicholas's son John married Parnell Perin at Brede in 1620, but of the six children born to them only the first-born, Moses, survived. Moses married Frances Rayner at Peasmarsh in 1645.

There are no indications of the occupations of this numerous family, but the baptismal names are characteristic of French immigrants and the changes of residence experienced by many of them suggest that charcoal burning for the ironworks may have played a large role in their lives.

Several Blundell families lived close to the Sussex border with Kent and Surrey, but there is no reason to think that they were other than of native descent. Michael Blondyll was the son of a Tonbridge cutler named William Blondyll and in 1570 inherited from his father all the implements of the shop, and from his mother Joan in 1592 'the mill with all its implements'.[446] His mother also bequeathed £1 to the cutler Richard Heath, probably her son-in-law.[447]

John Blundell of East Grinstead, who died in 1596, was a smith whose goods were inventoried at £16 3s 2d.[448] The Worth sheath-maker, William Blundell, who died in 1608, possessed houses and land in both Worth and Horne, whilst his brother Roger, who then lived in William's house at Horne, had formerly lived in or near East Grinstead, where his children, Dorothy, Ursula, Margery and John, had been baptised between 1587 and 1598, However it seems possible that both men had come from Lingfield where Roger's daughter Thomasine had been baptised in 1584. William's goods were inventoried at £50 5s 0d and because he had only one surviving child, a four-year-old daughter Elizabeth, he made provision for both his houses to go to Roger's sons George and John, in the event of his daughter's dying without issue.[449]

Another Worth craftsman in a metalworking-related trade was the bellows-maker Edward Blundell. He had married Katherine Aburley at Worth in 1588. Edward Blundell died in 1634 and in his

446. KHLC, DRb/PW9 and PW15.
447. He had married Dorothy Blundell in 1561.
448. ESRO, PBT 1/1/9/41 1, 1/3/2/228.
449. ESRO, PBT 1/1/12/253, 1/3/3/115.

will he made his son John his residuary legatee and executor, but all his tools belonging to the trade of bellows-making he left to his son Joseph. His goods were inventoried at £25 5s 8d.[450] Joseph had been baptised in 1591, but outlived his father by only slightly more than twelve months.

These families seem not to have been involved in ironworking elsewhere in Britain.

Phillips

Margaret daughter of a Frenchman named John Philip was baptised at Frant in 1569. Despite the fact that the baptismal name John makes it hazardous to seek this immigrant elsewhere it seems possible that he was the John Phillippe whose son Robert was baptised in the adjoining parish of Speldhurst in 1579.

An earlier entry had occurred at Frant for this family in December 1559, when Mercy Philip acted as godparent at the baptism of Peter Turner's daughter Ann. Mercy wife of Robert Phillipp was buried at Worth in 1568. They could have been the parents of the Frant Frenchman John Philip. Henry Phillip who married Joan Bolen at Worth in 1570 could have been another of their sons.

A collier named 'Pyllape Mr Bowyer's collier at Duddleswell' supplied three loads of coals to Ralph Hogge's works in 1577,[451] and another, or the same collier 'Philip', whose son James was baptised at Ardingly in 1591, dwelt at Westhill in Thomas Newnam's wood.

Another man of this surname connected with the iron industry was Edward Phyllapes or Pyllaps, who worked for Ralph Hogge in 1577 and 1578, carrying wood from High Hurstwood to Langleys Furnace, mine out of Etchingwood and High Hurst, and shot to and from Lewes.[452] As Edward Phyllyppe he was a baptismal sponsor at Maresfield in 1572 and again, as Edward Phillippes, in 1585. His own son William was baptised at Buxted in 1582. However, an earlier Edward Philipp had appeared in Danehill Sheffield hundred in the 1524 subsidy roll without any indication that he was a foreigner.

The surname Phillips occurred later in the context of the iron industry over a wide area of the Midlands, where the name was so common as to render attempts to relate ironworkers to forebears in the Weald seem hazardous. In particular Thomas Phillips, who was ironfounder at Vale Royal Furnace in Cheshire in 1710-11, his brother John, who was also an ironfounder,[453] and George Phillips of Bromford Forge near Birmingham, who was first cited in the Aston parish register in 1704 and again at his burial in 1725, may be mentioned.

Diamond

No person of this surname appeared in the Sussex subsidy rolls of the 1520s, nor did any person of the surname pay the alien tax in subsidy rolls of the sixteenth century.

In parish registers the family first appeared at Mountfield in the 1570s. Peter Demon was baptised there in 1574 and John Dymon in 1576, and also in 1576 Nicholas Demon was buried there. The parish register of the period gave no parents' names, listed no marriages of the family and gave no indication whether the burial was that of a man or a child, so these entries provide little more than a bare indication of the presence of the Diamond family at Mountfield. One later burial occurred there, that of Mercy Diamond in 1588.

The family next appeared in Parrock borough of Hartfield hundred, where John Dyamond was noted as a defaulter from the view of frankpledge in May 1577, but was essoined. In October 1577 he was present and in May 1578 he was recorded among the jurors. In October 1579 he was fined 2 pence for failure to appear and in May 1580 he was sick. In May 1581 he appeared again,[454] but in July 1585 probate of John Deaman's will was granted to his son Thomas, the other executor being his wife Joan.[455] No copy of this will survives.

450. ESRO, PBT 1/1/23/88, 1/3/6/178.

451. Crossley, 'Ralph Hogge's ironworks accounts', p. 71.

452. Ibid., pp. 62, 75.

453. John died around 1725 and Thomas around 1730, both being unmarried; Thomas was wealthy enough to acquire Doddlespool House, which he bequeathed to Thomas Coape, the son of an ironworker (R. Parrott, 'An account of Audley', p. 35).

454. ESRO, ACC 3597/8, ff 34v., 52, 78v., 128v., 151, 192.

455. ESRO, PBT 1/3/1/145.

The records of views of frankpledge for Hartfield hundred recommence in October 1587, when John Dyamonde of Parrock, presumably the other son of the deceased, was reported to be sick. In April 1588 he failed to appear, but like his father was essoined, and in April and October 1589 he appeared as headborough for Parrock. In both May 1590 and in April 1591, the end of this record series, he was essoined.[456]

Thomas Diyamonde was buried at Hartfield in September 1593. In his will, made in August, he was described as a husbandman. He was apparently unmarried and made his brother John his residuary legatee and executor. He left £2 to his cousin Richard Palarde. To his brother Roger he left his bed and bedding. He left £3 to Joan Colier, to be paid to her at the age of 14, and £1 to be paid at the age of ten to Robert Haynes, son of his deceased sister Joan, who had married Samuel Haynes at Frant in 1590, and had left only the one child. Thomas's overseer was Roger Hartefeld, who was to have 5 shillings, and who was a witness along with Dennys Johnson, presumably a member of the gunfounding Johnson family, then centred at Falkenhurst in Hartfield. Thomas Diamond's goods were valued at £5 0s 11d.[457]

Thomas's brother Roger Diamond was buried in 1612at Horsham, where the burial entry noted him as a householder. In 1614 an otherwise unknown Edmund Dimon, a tailor, was buried at Horsham. Edmund could have been Roger's son. Widow Dimond was buried at Horsham in 1618.

Thomas's brother John Diamond had married Katherin Taler [Tyler?] at Mayfield in 1589. She was buried at Hartfield in 1610, in which year John Diamond himself served as churchwarden. John was buried in August 1617, described as a yeoman in his will. The will amply demonstrated his yeoman status: he left £30 to his daughter Margaret and £40 to each of his younger daughters, Elizabeth and Mary, the latter of whom had been baptised in 1609. To his son John he left a messuage and 8 acres of land in Steyning. To his son Bartholomew he left Mathews Croft and 10 acres of land, once part of Pyttlands in Hartfield, and all the timber and boards lying upon these lands. He made his son John and his daughter Margaret residuary legatees and executors. It was Margaret Diamond who took probate in September 1617, power being reserved to John Diamond.[458]

Both of the sons took wives from the immigrant community:[459] John was married to Mercy Valentine at West Hoathly in 1626 and Bartholomew to Anne Bar at East Grinstead in 1627. Bartholomew's son John was baptised at East Grinstead in December 1628, but survived only just over one month. John was the father of Susan, baptised at Lindfield in 1633, but then moved on to Bersted in Kent, well beyond the ironworking area, where Susan was buried in 1637 and where further children named Ann, Mercy and Elizabeth were baptised between 1635 and 1640.

Later centred on Brenchley, the Diamonds became one of the most important families to be involved in English gunfounding. But astonishingly, the list of around 30 furnacemen at John Browne's gunfoundries from as late as 1628, preserved in the acts of the Privy Council, includes not a single member of this family.[460] Nonetheless, the parish register for the gunfounding parish of Brenchley recorded the burial of 'John Dimond Frenchman' in November 1638 and reflected his significance by adding that he was the man 'from whom all the Diamonds came'.

It would have been thought that the Diamond family's involvement in gunfounding originated during their period at Parrock, when gunfounding was carried on at Cowden by the queen's gunfounder Thomas Johnson, who from 1587 to 1591 lived in the adjoining borough of Falkenhurst.[461] Early in the 1590s Johnson acquired Horsmonden Furnace and at this period a move to Brenchley could have taken place. However, none of the sons of the first Parrock John Diamond seems to have been involved; Thomas styled himself 'husbandman', Roger was perhaps father of a Horsham tailor, and though the term 'yeoman' by no means excluded participation in the iron industry, the timber and boards lying on the second John Diamond's lands at Mathew's Croft suggest otherwise.

The 1628 list of Browne furnacemen, which mentions no one named Diamond, and the 1638

456. ESRO, ACC 3597/1, ff 8v., 28, 60, 89v., 110v., 146.

457. ESRO, PBT 1/1/9/204, 1/3/2/182.

458. TNA, PROB 11/130/294.

459. This factor appears to speak for the coherence of the story outlined so far, but whence came John Deman of Hartfield, butcher, whose licence to marry Catherine Nevill (another immigrant surname) of Hartfield, maiden, was granted in February 1624? (Dunkin, *Sussex Marriage Licences, Lewes 1586-1643*, p. 140).

460. *Acts of the Privy Council, 1628-9*, pp. 71-2; I am grateful to David Crossley for a copy of this list.

461. ESRO, ACC 3597/1, f. 8 (16 Oct 1587) to f. 146 (29 Apr 1591).

entry for the burial of John Diamond at Brenchley, which suggests that the family was celebrated in the area, indicate their arrival at Brenchley during the 1630s. The burial there in 1638 of the Frenchman John Diamond 'from whom all the Diamonds came' suggests that a different branch of the Diamonds was involved.

The baptism of John Diamond's son William at Warbleton in 1633 occurred before any connection with Brenchley can be shown. In the Brenchley area the first indication of a Diamond presence came in June 1634, when Mathew Diamond married Catherine Hunt at Horsmonden. Meanwhile John Diamond appears to have moved to Brenchley between 1635, when his daughter Elizabeth was baptised at Warbleton, and early 1638, when his daughter Anne was baptised at Brenchley. Late in 1639 his son John was baptised at Speldhurst, but by the mid-1640s he was back at Brenchley, where his son Jasper and daughter Elizabeth were baptised in 1645 and 1647. He could be the John Demonte buried at Brenchley in 1651.

However, about this time another John Dimond was among Richard Leader's employees at the Hammersmith ironworks in New England. He appears to have been employed intermittently without definable occupation. He was still in New England in December 1661, when he was fined for excessive drinking by the Salem County court.[462]

Mathew and Catherine Diamond had seven children baptised at Brenchley from 1636 to 1648, but Catherine was buried at Brenchley in 1657. Mathew Diamond alias Demont of Brenchley, gunfounder, was married secondly to the Lamberhurst widow Elizabeth Gibbons at Lamberhurst in 1658, but she was buried at Brenchley in 1660. Mathew's third wife was another widow, Anne Laffam of Mayfield, whom he married at Brenchley in 1661. He was buried at Brenchley in 1670.

Jasper Diamond married Catherine Fissenden at Tonbridge in 1638 and their children, Catherine, Jasper, Paul and Esther were baptised at Brenchley between 1639 and 1647, after which he moved on to Cowden, where his children Mary, Elizabeth and another Mary, were baptised in 1648, 1651 and 1654. His wife Katherine was buried at Cowden in 1657. Their daughter Catherine had married Robert Johnson of Cowden at Penshurst earlier in that year. No record of Jasper Diamond's burial has as yet been found.

Another John Diamond appeared on the scene at Cranbrook in 1656. His wife was named as Joan Jariot in the Cranbrook parish register, but in reality she will have been a member of the Jarrett family of ironfounders. Their children, Mathew, Anne and Peter, were baptised at Cranbrook between 1656 and 1660. All three baptismal entries confirm that John Diamond worked at Bedgebury Furnace, but whilst the 1656 entry styled him 'gunfounder', in 1658 and 1660 he was a 'fordgman'. Later probate material makes it clear that this John Diamond was a gunfounder by profession, so the term 'forgeman' was probably used in an unspecific sense as an equivalent for ironworker. Later entries for children of John and Joan Diamond occurred at Goudhurst. Two Henrys, baptised in 1662 and 1665, died in infancy, but Robert and Jasper, baptised in 1671 and 1673 appear to have survived. John Diamond was buried at Goudhurst in 1690 and was styled John Diamond the elder of Goudhurst, gunfounder, in the probate inventory dated 1691.[463]

The younger John Diamond or Demont had married Elizabeth Thorp at Goudhurst in 1675. Their children John, Richard, Elizabeth, Peter, Thankful, Mercy, Edward, who probably died in infancy, and Thorp were baptised between 1676 and 1694. 'Mistress' Elizabeth Diamond was buried at Goudhurst in 1703.

Several children of John and Elizabeth Diamond moved to Sussex. The Heathfield John Diamond, who married Hannah Hugget, also of Heathfield, in that parish in 1708, was probably their eldest son. The youngest son Thorp Diamond and his wife Sarah had four children baptised at Mountfield between 1722 and 1729. Thorp left a will in 1751 which described him as a Mountfield founder and grinder. Neither of Thorp's sons named John appears to have survived and he made his youngest son Thorp Diamond his residuary legatee and executor and also left him a messuage and garden in Brede, in lease in 1751 to Thomas and William Jarrett. To his daughter Anne, wife of the Mountfield farmer Edward Fuller, he left £50. The elder Thorp Diamond was involved in the casting of a new bell for Wadhurst in 1754, when he sent his sone to account for the waste and surplus metal, explaining that he had been ill

462. G. F. Dow (ed.), *Records and files of the quarterly courts of Essex county, Massachusetts, 1656-1662, vol. 2*, Salem, Essex Institute, 1912, p. 335.
463. TNA, PROB 4/1060.

for some time. He did not die until June 1762 and his son proved the will in 1763.[464]

Another John Diamond married Margaret Paulle at Goudhurst in 1668. They had just one child, Joseph, baptised at Hawkhurst in 1679. John Diamont alias Diamond of Hawkhurst, gunfounder, made his will in 1687.[465] He made his wife Margaret his executrix and sole legatee. A Cranbrook John Diamond married Anne Moor of Cranbrook at Mountfield early in 1724. Among other members of the family were Ashburnham moulders, who were asked to advise at other furnaces, and were highly thought of by the ironmaster John Fuller.[466]

Two of the sons of the gunfounder, John Diamond the elder of Goudhurst, had been baptised Henry, but neither survived. About 1690 another Henry Diamond was born who was destined to become keeper at the Duddon Furnace in Cumbria. The furnace had been built less than two years, and Henry Diamond was working as a collier at Harthwaite Bank, when his twin children John and Mary were baptised in 1738 at the nearby parish church of Broughton-in-Furness. An entry in the furnace book shows that by 1757 he had advanced to the position of keeper at the furnace.[467] He was buried at Broughton aged 88 in 1779.

Edmond alias Marian

This alias occurred only in the case of John Edmond alias Marian, the Frenchman who was murdered at Frant in November 1574. He was doubtless Edmond, 'a collier', whose son Giles had been baptised at Frant in 1572. A coroner's inquest found another alien collier, George Mahouude, guilty of his murder, an offence for which he was outlawed.[468]

There were various reasons for the use of an alias, so it cannot automatically be assumed that one of Marian's forebears had been named Edmond Marian. It seems likely that he was related to other immigrants of the Maryan family, but no other references to this John Marian are known. The man of that name whose children Clemence and John had been buried at Mayfield in 1574 was presumably the carpenter John Maryan, who himself was buried at Mayfield in 1585.

Moolett

German Moollett and Joan Molet were buried at Mountfield early in 1576. Early in 1558 Peter Molet had been buried there too. It seems possible that Edmund Mullet who had been baptised at Penhurst in 1563 was from the same or a related family. Further afield Joan Molet had married Michael Vyllaine at Chailey in 1563.

However, an isolated Malett baptism at Mountfield in 1568, taken together with the payment of the poll tax by the alien Collen Mallet, a servant of Goddard Walsh, in Henhurst hundred in 1552, raises the possibility that Mallet was the correct reading of the immigrant name. This has been discussed earlier in relation to Clement Malet, who paid the poll tax in Danehill Sheffield in 1552. However, the other form of the surname appears to have persisted in the Mountfield area as shown by the marriage of John Mollet and Jane Hamon at Dallington in 1650.

The possibility also arises that the surname Muglett, unknown in Sussex in the 1520s, but used firstly in Rotherfield and later in Maresfield, was a related one. Four children of Thomas Muglett, who was buried at Rotherfield in 1583, were baptised at Rotherfield from 1568 to 1578. Among these was another Thomas Muglett, who in 1621 married Anne Tickredg at Maresfield and raised a family there. Muglett's wife was buried at Maresfield in 1639 and Thomas Muglett himself was buried there early in the following year.

From Collen Malet's employment by Goddard Walsh, and from Clement Mallet's occupational surname of 'Collyer', it seems clear that the Mallet family was employed in ironworking. The concentration of Moollet family entries in the Mountfield area also suggests their employment in the iron industry but in their case, and even more in the case of the Muglett family, there is no proof of this. There is nothing

464. ESRO, PBT 1/1/60/713; PAR 498/10/1/7.
465. TNA, PROB 11/388/412.
466. J. S. Hodgkinson, 'The iron industry in the Weald in the period of the Seven Years' War, 1750-1770', p. 83.
467. LA, DDX192/2 (12 Jul 1757).
468. Hunnisett, *Sussex Coroners' inquests, 1558-1603*, 135.

to show that this family was involved in the spread of the industry outside the Weald.

Trafford

Because the surname Trafford appeared also in the forms Traffet, Trafficke and even Traffique, it might be thought French in origin. However, no member of the family appears to have paid the alien tax and John Trayford who appeared in West Street, Chichester in the subsidy rolls of the 1520s, was apparently English.

Well before the appearance of the name in connection with iron in the Weald, it had occurred at Rugeley in Staffordshire, where Richard Traford held 'a blame harthe and a burne harthe yron myll' for the space of eight weeks during the lifetime of John Weston of Rugeley. He had obtained it by the 'sufferance and demise of one [*blank*] Marten of Walsall', to whom he had returned it in good 'plyte' and well repaired and tenantable. Richard Weston, John Weston's son, claimed that his father had let the walk (fulling) mill at Rugeley to Richard Wood of Colton in Staffordshire and that it had come through several assignments into the hands of Trayford, who had allowed great decay, spoil and waste in and upon the mill and houses belonging to it, so that through lack of sufficient covering, walling and necessary reparations the said houses and timber had utterly decayed and fallen down. Trayford disclaimed ever having to do with the walk mill, but claimed that Richard Weston entered upon the 'blome harthe and burntharthe myll' immediately after the death of his father, 'being then well builded and in good reparations and pulled the same down and bestowed the same about his own necessary business'.[469] Trayford claimed to have a wife and nine small children to support. The time scale was such that the two ironworkers of this name first to appear in the Weald could have been among them.

In 1583 David Trayford, a 35-year-old finer from Kirdford, was a deponent in the Court of Requests case concerning Dunsfold hammer.[470] He was not otherwise known in the Weald.

Richard Trafford was a defaulter from East Grinstead views of frankpledge for Brambletye from October 1587 to April 1591. He paid his fine of 2 pence for these defaults, except on two occasions when he was described as a pauper, so he was probably an occasional worker at Brambletye Forge. Only twice towards the end of the series did the name vary from Trafford, into the forms Traffet or Traffote.[471]

However Richard appeared, usually as Traffet, in the East Grinstead parish register from 1580 until 1595. In 1580 he was married to Joan W[. ..]. Their son Anthony was buried at East Grinstead in 1585 and their children John, Jane who died in infancy, Richard, Anne and Thomas, were baptised there from 1586 to 1595, though the parentage was in fact confirmed only in the cases of the two children buried. This family later moved to Chiddingstone where Elizabeth and Margaret, daughters of Richard Traffique, were baptised in 1596 and 1599. Finally, Richard Traffick moved to Hartfield where the burial register recorded the interments of his first wife Joan in 1624, of a second wife Katherine in 1627, and finally his own burial in 1631.

Richard's son John Trafferd married Dorothy Tiler at Hartfield in 1610. Ann daughter of John Traffick was baptised at Mayfield in 1611, his children Philip and Dorothy at Frant in 1612 and 1614, and his son John was buried at Frant in 1613. In 1616 John's wife gave birth to twins, John and Elizabeth, who were baptised at Wadhurst in 1616, and their children Joan and William were baptised at Frant in 1619 and 1621. Later baptisms, all of which took place at Wadhurst, were of twins, Richard and Katherine, in 1623 and twins, Francis and Mary, in 1625. Finally came the baptisms of single children, Edward, Thomas and Joan, from 1627 to 1631.

The occupation of this branch of the family was confirmed only in 1625 when John Travett of Wadhurst forgeman was one of the sureties for a quarter sessions recognizance by which another forgeman, Hugh Pray of Frant, undertook to keep the peace.[472]

The forgeman John Traffick who paid the tax on two hearths at Brede in 1665 was probably the son born to the earlier John Traffick at Wadhurst in 1616.[473] His children, Dinah and John had been baptised at Burwash in 1649 and 1651, whilst his son Thomas had been baptised at Brede in 1660.

469. TNA, C 3/187/69 (undated but probably from the early 1560s).
470. TNA, REQ 2/125/14.
471. ESRO, ACC 3597/1, ff 12, 31, 50, 74v., 93, 114, 131v., 147.
472. ESRO, QR 21, m. 82; I am indebted to Brian Phillips for this reference.
473. TNA, E 179/258/20 (1665).

Daughters of the earlier John Traffick whose marriages have been traced were Dorothy, who married Alexander Winder at Wadhurst in May 1638, Elizabeth who married John Morgan at Cranbrook in April 1638, and Katherine who married James Standen at Biddenden in 1650. Another marriage which took place at Biddenden in 1650 was that of Anne Traffick to John Greengow, though if this was John Traffick of Wadhurst's daughter she would at that date have been aged 39.

Richard Trafford's two younger sons, Richard and Thomas, both moved to Fletching. Richard married the widow of Richard Morrell, born Mary Ellice. She had three children by Morrell, but by Trafford only one, Denise, who was baptised at Fletching in 1618. Richard Trafford's marriage has not been traced. He was buried at Fletching in 1621, but his widow lived on until 1637. She left a will by which she bequeathed two pieces of pewter and an iron 'merment' to her son Richard Morrill, a cupboard and an iron pot to her son John Morrill, her gown and hat to her daughter Mary and a shilling to Mary's husband Andrew Jarratt. Mary's goods were inventoried at £14 7s 4d and she made Denise Trafoot her residuary legatee and executrix.[474]

Thomas Traford married Mary Muttrell, from a family of obvious French descent who may have been weavers, at Fletching in 1617. His further moves have not been traced in the Weald.

Outside the Weald it seems possible that Thomas Trafiche, who was buried at Beaulieu in 1687, could have been a worker at the ironworks on Sowley Pond, who was descended from the Wealden family.

Back in the Midlands, William Trafford of Bloxwich was buried in 1616 at Aston near Birmingham, where his son Samson had been buried the previous year. Margaret Treffor of Ward End was buried at Aston in 1632, and Mary daughter of John and Joan Trafford of Erdington was buried there in 1638. Finally, an entry in the West Bromwich parish register for the baptism in 1659 of Samuel son of William Traford 'of the forge' made the continuing connection of this family with iron clear. These Midlands ironworkers were presumably in direct descent from Richard Trayford of Rugeley.

Cousin

The name occurred in the Sussex subsidy rolls of the 1520s only in the person of an alien named Gerlond Cosyn who paid tax on wages of £1 10s 0d in Litlington. The presence in England of Pierre Cousin, the son and heir of Thomassin Cousin and perhaps originally from Sommery, had been indicated in 1551 in a notarial act of Beaubec-La-Rosière, by which he sold his two mares to Jehan Ruffault of Beaubec-La-Ville for 15 crowns of the sun.[475]

No reference to Pierre Cousin has been found in the Weald. However, John Cosenet, apparently a diminutive of this surname, had paid the poll tax in 1543 as a servant of the forgemaster Nicholas Eversfield in Hoathly and Waldron, and the entry for the burial of Lawrence Cossens, Frenchman, at Heathfield in 1589 confirmed the presence of French persons of this surname in the Weald.

The surname first occurred in Wealden parish registers at Rotherfield in 1558, when Harry Cozyn married Elizabeth Hylles. The bequest of 6s 8d to Harry's daughter Bridget by the forgeman Leonard Callis of Rotherfield in 1582 does not necessarily make their French ancestry more certain because Callis made a large number of bequests, many to persons from indigenous families.[476]

At Rotherfield John, Nicholas and Margery, the children of Henry Cosen were baptised between 1562 and 1569. In the next generation John's children, Elizabeth, Joan, William, Annis, Mary, Henry, Hellen and John, were baptised between 1597 and 1618.

Nicholas Cossen had meanwhile moved to Maresfield, where he was buried in 1607. He was succeeded there by his son George, who had been baptised at Maresfield in 1604, and was married to Ann Gryffith in 1629. Their children Alice, George and Thomasine were baptised at Maresfield between 1633 and 1640.

It is not easy to demonstrate a connection with iron. However Roger Baker of Guestling, blacksmith, referred to his son-in-law, a Hastings blacksmith named Richard Cozens, in his will of 1638. Cozens owed £9 to the forgemaster Peter Farnden of Sedlescombe for half a ton of iron and Baker

474. ESRO, PBT 1/1/25/20, 1/3/7/47; *marmite* is a French word for a stew-pot, widely re-adapted in ironworking areas.

475. ADSM, 2 E 83/412 (16 Jul 1551).

476. ESRO, PBT 1/1/7/3.

authorised the deduction of that sum from the £10 legacy made to Richard's daughter Mary Cozens by Zealous Fuller, the Hastings shoemaker, should Cozens not make payment on the due date.[477]

Other early references are from Horsham, where a young man named Edward Cozin was buried in 1563, and Edward, son of another Edward Cosyne, was buried in 1580. Henry Coussen of Horsham was buried at Warnham in 1565.

In Kent the wife of Robert Cossen was buried at Cranbrook in 1562, and Francis Cossin married Margery Browne in 1568. Robert had been married twice more by 1568. Francis, who was widowed early in 1594, married a widow, Mary Kingswood, in June of that year. 'Old Robert Cossin' was buried in 1592. The children of Francis Cossin by his second wife were evidently, Robert, Elizabeth, another Robert, Mary and Catherine, baptised between 1595 and 1601. The children attributed to Francis Cossen, Bridget, Joan, Margery and Elizabeth, baptised between 1610 and 1615, were evidently those of Francis Cossin who was baptised in 1583, but whose parentage was not disclosed, and who married Bridget Jenkynges in 1609.

At Penshurst John Cosin's children, William, Thomas, Elizabeth, Mary and John, baptised between 1581 and 1588, were followed by those of his son Thomas, baptised in 1582, and married to Margaret Baker at Brenchley in 1612.

Kirby

A French subject named Anthony Kyrby received letters of denization in March 1567.[478] No archival mention of this man has so far been discovered in Wealden sources. The link with iron was established by the Ardingly parish register which recorded the burial of Thomas Kerbee of Strudgate Furnace in 1591.

The earliest mention of the surname in Wealden sources appears to be the marriage of Ann Kyrbe to William Lawmporthe at Tonbridge in 1558. John Kyrbye was buried at Tonbridge in 1574. The surname also occurred at East Grinstead, where two Joan Kerbys were baptised, in 1584 and in 1587. One of these Joan Kirbys was presumably the woman of that name buried at East Grinstead in 1628. However, she and John Kirby, who was buried at East Grinstead in 1625 could have been their parents.

The Kyrbye family of Strudgate Furnace continued the link with iron because Christopher Kyrbye, who married Alice Baker at Ardingly early in 1599, moved on to the ironworking parish of Worth, where his son John was baptised in 1600.

In the Midlands Kyrby worked alongside Quintin Tyler as keeper of Middleton Furnace in Warwickshire in 1592. He appeared, again without benefit of baptismal name, as Cyrby in the accounts for Oakamoor Forge in 1594.[479] No further mentions of Kyrby occurred in the Middleton Papers. John Kyrbee, who married Margaret Smyth at Hints in 1607, might be a different member of this family.

In Yorkshire it is unclear whether 'Widow Kirkby of Shipley Smithies' who was buried at Bradford in 1603 was from the aborted blast furnace at Brucroft near Shipley Hirst, or from Shipley or Gawcliffe smithies on the Bradford Beck. Another man from this family who may have been involved in iron was Francis Kirkbee, a 'householder' who was buried at Bulwell in Nottinghamshire in 1638, around the date when Bulwell Forge was first set up.

Despar

The Despars were a family of pot-founders, first mentioned in the parish register of Goudhurst in 1623 when William Dispar married Elizabeth Hewes. Their son Edward was baptised at Cranbrook in 1625 and the baptisms of two further children, both named Joan were recorded in Tonbridge parish register in 1633 and 1637, though the 1637 baptism had taken place at Penshurst. Mercy daughter of Richard Desperwas baptised at Penshurst early in 1631, but was also recorded at Tonbridge.

The occupation of the family was disclosed early in 1640, when the burial at Tonbridge of 'Desper the pot-founder' was recorded. The man in question could have been either William or Richard Despar, because neither of these men was mentioned again in parish registers.

477. ESRO, PBT 1/1/25/199.

478. *Calendar of Letters Patent, Elizabeth 1*, **4**, p. 32.

479. UNMASC, Middleton Papers, 5/165/49 and 55.

A further member of the family was mentioned in 1643, when Henry Desparre married Hellen Jarret at Horsmonden. There is nothing to show whether he was the son of Richard, or whether he was the youngest of three brothers. The baptisms of Henry Desparre's children, Joan, Edward, Christopher and William, were recorded at Horsmonden in 1646, 1650, 1655 and 1657. In 1655 and early in 1660 respectively, an earlier child named William, whose baptism has not been found, was buried at Horsmonden together wiuth an unnamed child. A final entry relating to this family occurred at Horsmonden in August 1672, when the baptism of Joan Desper was recorded, though her parents' names were not disclosed.

The family emigrated to New England, where in August 1673 the proprietors of a new ironworks at Lynn, among their number the former Hammersmith agent, John Gifford, engaged Henry Dispaw and his similarly named son to serve them for six years as 'master workmen for pot making'. The Dispaws were to be paid £35 a year, have housing, a garden plot, and passage, which included Henry Dispaw the younger's wife and child, who may have been the Joan Desper baptised at Horsmonden the previous year. Unfortunately, the works had not yet been completed and disputes arose in the partnership, even whilst the work was being hurried on, and after 400 loads of charcoal were on hand. A suit brought against the proprietors in January 1675 by the destitute Dispaws, which resulted in the award to their attorney of £500, did not help and it seems doubtful whether the furnace was ever set in blast.[480]

IRONWORKERS MENTIONED IN OTHER SOURCES IN THE WEALD

Mahoude

A coroner's inquest of November 1574 found that the collier George Mahouude of Frant had murdered a Frenchman named John Edmunds alias Marian,[481] an offence for which Mahouude was outlawed. As noticed earlier, the name Mahoude seems to have had earlier continental links with the iron industry because in 1473 the Burgundian forgemaster Samson Mahourde took a nine-year lease of the forge at Diénay, north-west of Dijon.[482]

Coupled with Phlyppyng Fardell and Gyllam Borgonyon, who had both worked in Foxearle hundred for Richard Woodman around 1550, Mahoude provides further evidence for an input of immigrants from Burgundy into the Weald.

Shortly after the outlawry of George Mahouude, court rolls provide evidence for the presence at Battle of two members of the family. At the view of frankpledge of April 1578 John Mauwood was fined 2 pence as a defaulter in the borough of Sandlake, and James Mauwood was fined apenny for being at Battle without being a tenant or native of the town. In the view of frankpledge of October 1578 James's name appeared as Mahoulde; in that of October 1580 John Mauhode was presented for not clearing his ditches and thereby fouling the Queen's highway leading from Battle to Hastings. In a High court of October 1580 John was fund 3 pence for failing to appear to pursue his action for debt against Richard Sheryffe, and in that of 6 December when he appeared as a surety for James Mauwoode in a court action brought by Richard Reade, John's occupation was revealed to be that of tailor. On 27 December he did jury service under the name John Mauwoode alias Hamonde, whilst on 17 January 1581 Thomas Myller was fined for failing to pursue a case he had brought against James Mauwood alias Hamond.[483]

From these references a valid inference might be that the forebear who first arrived in England was named Hamon Mahoude.

The Manor court of April 1581 reported that John Mauwoode and his wife Joan had surrendered a messuage and garden in Sandlake to the use of Richard Staple. The view of frankpledge for October 1583 shows that James Mauwoode was then headborough of Sandlake. The Manor court of October 1585 reported the death of John Mauwood and summoned his son John to do homage at the next court

480. Hartley, *Ironworks on the Saugus*, p. 291-3.
481. Hunnisett, *Sussex Coroners' inquests, 1558-1603*,no. 135.
482. Belhoste and others, *La métallurgie comtoise*, p. 42.
483. HEH, BA Vol. 96 ff 34-35, 74 79-84; in many of these Battle entries the name appears to be written Manwood, but a distinction between 'u' and 'n' in the contemporary script can hardly be made.

for a freehold tenement in Sandlake.[484]

Although evidence for the participation of the family in the spread of the indirect method of iron manufacture to other parts of England has not been found, there is evidence for its continuance in metallurgy. John Parkinson Mawhood registered his trade mark with the Company of Cutlers in Hallamshire in November 1871.[485]

IRONWORKERS FIRST MENTIONED IN OTHER PARTS OF BRITAIN

Drewett

Because the surname Drouet or Drewett was associated with ironworking both in the Pays de Bray and in the English Midlands, it seems reasonable to assume that there was a connection between the Drewetts and ironworking in the Weald, though direct evidence of this has not so far been traced.

In the Pays de Bray, Gerosme Drouet witnessed four notarial acts: two of November 1553 by which Guillaume Lambert, forgemaster at Neuville-Ferrières, purchased wood; and two for the sale of iron from the forge, in September 1554 to Jehan Vincent of Eu, and in February 1555 to François de Clery of Aumale.[486]

Geoffrey Drowet, a native of Normandy who came to England around 1520, paid the poll tax at Wrotham in 1572, and a clear descendant, William Jeffery alias Druet, appeared in the Tonbridge parish register early in 1604. The Westminster denization roll recorded Geoffrey twice, in one instance as Geoffrey Drwett, who had been 26 years in England and had an English wife, and in the other as Jeffrey Droyett, who had been 20 years in England and had four children by his English wife.[487]

Richard Drewet first appeared in parish registers at Horsham, which was just to the east of an area where English persons surnamed Druett had been located in the subsidy rolls of the 1520s. The possibility that he was an immigrant ironworker arises from hs itinerant lifestyle, appearing in the registers of two other ironworking parishes of the Weald. His daughters Ann and Joan had been baptised and buried respectively at Horsham in 1554; Elizabeth Druet was baptised at Cowfold in 1560; Richard's wife Joan, and Agnes, perhaps his daughter, were buried at Newick in June 1565. And in addition to the Tonbridge William Jeffery alias Druet of 1604 already cited, another Druet in the ironworking area, Robert Druet, was buried at Burwash in August 1619.

In the Midlands in May 1594, Joan wife of Richard Druyte of Town End, finer, was among the godparents of John the son of the hammerman Sylvester Leger (or Leiger) at Handsworth near Birmingham. The possibility that this Richard Druyte was the man who had been in the Weald from 1554 to 1565, now happily remarried, can by no means be excluded.

Thomas Drewett, another Midlands finer, was at Hints early in 1594, when his son Ralph, who did not survive childhood, was baptised. The accounts for Hints Forge in 1595-6 show that Drewett was among the principal workers at the forge and mention his livery coat,[488] and his daughter Katheryn was baptised at Hints in 1596. However, by 1599 Drewett and 'old Drewett' [Richard?] were mentioned in the accounts of the forge at Oakamoor, although it is not clear which one of them was Drewett, 'the Fyner'.[489] By 1601 Thomas Drewett was at Castle Donington Forge on the Trent, where the baptism of his daughter Joan and the burial of his first wife Margaret were recorded in the parish register in September 1601. In November 1602 he married Ann Burgen at Castle Donington and their unnamed son was baptised there six days later. The register also recorded the baptism of their daughter Eleanor there in May 1606, after which Thomas Drewett perhaps moved on.

From the next generations of this family came William Druett of Crich in Derbyshire, fyner, who in 1639 married Margaret Dawes, formerly of Papplewick, but then of Nottingham. They probably

484. HEH, BA Vol. 96 ff 77-78, 97 ff 31, 47-48.
485. J. Unwin 'The marks of Sheffield cutlers 1614-1878', *Historical Metallurgy,* **33** (1999), p. 99.
486. ADSM, 2 E 14/1194 (13 and 18 Nov 1553); 2 E 14/1195 (30 Sep 1554, 1 Feb 1555).
487. The Chancery roll for 1544 gave his name as 'Drowet'. Perhaps two men of this name really were involved.
488. UNMASC, Middleton Papers, 5/165/49, 51 and 57.
489. Op. cit., 5/165/52, 54, 59 and 64.

moved on to Bulwell Forge, where both were buried, William in May 1672 and Margaret in the following March. A son named William had been buried at Bulwell in 1657, but another son may have been Thomas Druett of Bulwell, iron fyner, who in 1663 married Anne Day of Papplewick, an orphan girl aged 22. Later still, Mary Druit (aged 23) married Thomas Ablett of Bulwell Forge, blacksmith, at St Peter's, Nottingham in 1683, and Barbara Drewett (aged 30) of Bulwell, spinster, married the Bulwell forgeman, Thomas Vallans, also probably of immigrant descent, at Papplewick in 1684.[490]

Martin

There is no particular reason to suppose that ironworkers bearing this surname were of French descent. The surname was widespread in Sussex in the 1520s and not until the mid-seventeenth century did three colliers of the surname appear in the Lindfield parish register. However, the number of ironworkers who took spouses surnamed Martin is quite impressive, so it seems possible that one of the earliest immigrant families involved in ironworking could have been named Martin.

In the Pays de Bray the surname was not uncommon. Neufchâtel notarial acts relating to Richard Martin, variously described as rector and curé of Til-en-Bray, just to the north of Forges, stretch from 1504 to 1540.[491] Another Richard Martin, who resided at Neuville-Ferrières, leased several pieces of land near Brémontier from Pierre Liston, the curé of Neuville, in June 1500, and himself leased other land to Nicole Tison of Neuville, probably himself an ironworker, early in 1501.[492] Anthoine Martin, who was miller at Neuville-Ferrières, was mentioned in notarial acts stretching from 1529 to 1544.[493]

In 1509 Richard Martin of Til-en-Bray sold three *vergees* of land there to Jehan and Colin Mesnage of Plix in Serqueux, who may have been ironworkers. In 1509 and 1510 he raised 90 l.t. by the sale of rent charges to Pierre Dugardin of Neufchâtel, the second of which was witnessed by Merigon and Colin Lambert, both probable ironworkers. He witnessed several notarial acts including one by which Jehan Machens the younger of Dencourt, who was subsequently involved in wood purchase for the ironworks, bought a rent charge in 1520.[494] In 1563 Valentin Martin of Neufchâtel witnessed the act by which the Beaussault forgemasters undertook to restore the Neuville ironworks to good repair.[495]

In the Weald a part was played from 1546 to at least 1558 in the management of the Sidney ironworks by another Richard Martin, who acted as an assistant, firstly to Harry Westall and then to William Blackenall, without his role ever being clearly defined. He was paid his keep, or 'board wages' of 2s 4d a week, originally at Robertsbridge, but from 1549 at Panningridge, together with a largish quarterly wage of 13s 4d, and although there were no payments for piece-work such as boosted the regular ironworkers' quarterly wages into a living wage, he must have received almost £10 a year from these other payments. If he was the Ashburnham man who died around 1566 his death could have occasioned the change of handwriting between 1563 and 1568 noticed by David Crossley in the Sidney accounts.[496]

Richard Martin was particularly used in visits to other forgemasters concerning the employment of Frenchmen. On 21 September 1546 Westall wrote, 'Paid for my expens with my Felow Martyn in rydyng to Buckstede to speke with master parson Lyvett to requyre hys goodwyll for a Fyner who shuld worke in my masters workes 9d'.[497] In 1547 Martin was paid 8 pence 'for his expence in goyng with ii warrantes for to attache ii of my masters Frenchmen' and a shilling 'for his expence in goyng to receve money of master Archdeacon of Lewis for old Brysbye denyson', which would be the balance of what Sir William had advanced for William Brisboye's letters of denization.[498] In 1548 he was paid 1s 7d for 'goyng to Fletchyng to speke with master Archdeacon for mones that Adryan Hatto and Gwyllam Bellet owe to my master for there letters patentes'; the same year he and Peter the Founder were sent

490. Blagg and Wadsworth, *Abstracts of Nottinghamshire Marriage Licences, vol. 1*, pp, 175, 215, 367, 372.
491. ADSM, 2 E 14/1146 (9 Mar 1504); 2 E 14/1183 (5 Jun 1540).
492. ADSM, 2 E 14/1143 (19 Jun 1500, 9 Jan 1501).
493. ADSM, 2 E 14/1164 (16 and 25 Apr 1529); 2 E 14/1188 (25 Jun 1544).
494. ADSM, 2 E 14/1152 (19 Feb 1509, 14 Jul 1509); 2 E 14/1153 (23 Mar 1510); 2 E 14/1158 (2 Oct 1520).
495. ADSM, 2 E 14/1202 (13 Feb 1563).
496. Crossley, *Sidney ironworks accounts*, p. 190n.
497. ESRO, SHE 6/1/11/1.
498. KHLC, U1475 B10/1.

to Birchden 'to attach Gwillam Bellet'.[499] Occasionally he was cited as having witnessed particular payments; in 1555 he bought five quires of paper at Battle to make a forge book; in 1556 he went to London 'divers' times to know Sir Henry's pleasure.[500] In 1558 the making by Charles Gerard of a new pillar (*botteres*) for Panningridge Furnace for 18 shiullings was 'bargenyd be Marten' and reference was also made to 'Martens harth'.[501]

Richard Martin was clearly English born, but was he of French descent and employed as intermediary on account of the large number of Frenchmen employed by Sidney? Richard Martyn of Ashburnham's will was proved in 1566 and he left goods valued at £299 7s 0d.[502] Apart from his two daughters, Richard's surviving relatives were his brother Christopher, and Richard Martin, son of his deceased brother Thomas.

Other members of the Martin family clearly knew what they were doing in relation to forge technology. From Sir Henry's iron, John Marten of Ewhurst made '11 great panyd hopes of yeren for the hammer beme' at Robertsbridge in 1556.[503] A Beckley whitesmith named Henry Marten (1587) and a Pembury sickle-maker named Roger Martyn (1636) were other metalworkers with this surname.[504]

Around the middle of the seventeenth century, three colliers named John, Richard and William Marten were all mentioned in the Lindfield parish register in 1654.

Earlier than any of these came the mention in the Midlands of a finer named Roger Martyn who worked at one of the forges on the Smestow Brook north of Stourbridge; he and his wife True had sons named Roger and [Humphrey?], and two daughters the second of whom was named Margaret, baptised at Wombourne from 1627 to 1635. Further south on the Stour, Thomas Martin of Cookley Forge was buried at Wolverley in 1685.

In the following century, Nathaniel and Mary Martin of the Forge were mentioned in 1739 in the Cheddleton parish register, which carried entries for employees at the north Staffordshire forge of Consall on the Churnet. Nathaniel had been baptised at Cheddleton in 1703, when his parents were named as Thomas and Sarah Martin. It seems possible that Thomas Martin was the son of William and Magdalen Martin, baptised at Tiptoe in 1666 and married there to Sara Fisher in 1689.

499. KHLC, U1475 B2/1.
500. Crossley, *Sidney ironworks accounts*, pp. 70n, 151, 171.
501. KHLC, U1475 B10/10.
502. ESRO, PBT 1/1/5/329.
503. KHLC, U1475 B8/8.
504. ESRO, PBT 1/1/8/95. KHLC, DRa/PW1.

APPENDIX I

IRONWORKERS LISTED IN THE DENIZATION ROLLS OF 1541 AND 1544

Although numerous letters of denization or naturalization were issued throughout the Tudor period, it was the time of diplomatic isolation commencing in 1539, and the renewed wars of the 1540s, that first made the build-up of a foreign population in the south-east of England seem threatening to Henry VIII. The danger of war in 1541, and its reality in 1544, made it desirable to ensure the loyalty of these foreigners, by ordering those who had not already become denizens to quit the realm, or to apply for letters of denization.

The denization roll of April 1541 (TNA, C67/72) regularly recorded the denizens' countries of origin, and the length of their residence in England; it very occasionally stated their ages. The roll of July 1544 survived in two forms; the Chancery copy (TNA, C67/73) recorded merely the names of the new denizens and the amounts they had paid for denization; the Westminster roll, which survived in the archives of the Dean and Chapter of the abbey (WAM 12261), recorded not only the denizens' countries of origin and the length of their stay in England, but often recorded their ages too, and sometimes their towns or cities of birth.

William Page produced an alphabetical list of all recorded denizens for the period 1509 to 1603.[1] The 1541 denization roll consisted of only two membranes of parchment, and Page calculated that, among the 395 names it recorded, 119 were Frenchmen. The Westminster roll of 1544 was made up of more than 30 membranes and recorded a total of around 1900 immigrants. Numerous sections of both rolls appear to be copied from original lists, which at least in some cases had been submitted by their employers; this is more evident in the case of the Westminster roll, because 15 lists of ironworkers in it were headed by such words as 'Frenchmen to be made denyzens by John Baker', or 'With my lorde of Norfolk in Sheffeld'; no similar headings survive in the 1541 roll, but it is clear that some groups of its denizens were either ironworkers, or were immigrants domiciled in the Weald.

Of the French names recorded in 1541 around one fifth were perhaps ironworkers; in the Westminster roll, where ironworkers are more certainly identifiable, they amount to about one tenth of the Frenchmen made denizen.

It is also apparent that some immigrant ironworkers figured in neither roll; among these was the ironfounder Charles Jerett; he appeared in three lay subsidy rolls for Sussex, on the last occasion contributing in 1552 as an alien and denizen to the relief levied in the hundred of Battle. Although he failed to appear in the denization roll of 1541, the Exchequer hanaper roll shows that he had paid for letters of denization in that year; his name appeared as 'Charles Jerart' in 862nd place among over 1270 aliens who paid for denization then.[2]

Unfortunately, beyond their names and the amounts they paid for letters of denization, the hanaper roll contained no further information about these immigrants, so there is no certain way of identifying the Frenchmen among them. If the proportion of ironworkers in it was similar to that among the 119 Frenchmen recorded in the 1541 denization roll, perhaps as many as 50 of the hanaper-roll denizens could have been ironworkers. It is difficult to identify quite so many, but the extracts from the two denization rolls reproduced here are followed by further lists of probable and possible ironworkers, of other aliens domiciled in the Weald, and of workers in the Royal Ordnance, extracted from the hanaper roll.

A. The denization roll of April 1541

It is clear that the two surviving membranes of the 1541 denization roll are but a small part of the original document; close examination of its two membranes show that they are consecutive membranes of the original roll, but that they are now sewn head to tail in reverse order. The break occurred between the entry for Gillet Russell and that for Adrian Hanysite, so that Hanysite now heads the roll and Gillet Russell concludes it. This roll must

1. W. Page, 'Letters of denization and Acts of naturalization for aliens in England 1509 to 1603', *Publications of the Huguenot Society of London*, **8** (1893).
2. TNA, E 101/223/10. I am indebted to Christopher Whittick for the suggestion that payments for denization would be found there.

originally have contained many more names; surprisingly, the aliens listed in the hanaper roll include only about 230 of the 395 names found in the denization roll. It looks as though almost 1000 more names may have been included on the missing membranes of this roll.

The following so-called 'Lists' include all the immigrants of French nationality who immediately preceded or followed persons it is possible to identify as ironworkers. Immigrants identified with some certainty as ironworkers are indicated by capitals.

Page's variant readings are indicated by round brackets. Interesting variants from the hanaper roll are between square brackets. An alias is indicated by / between the two surnames.

Name	Years of age	Years in England	Wife's nationality
List 1			
1) Robert Valley*		17	English
2) Peter RUSSELL		22	English
3) Peter de Lyle*		30	English
4) William Teale (Teoile)		40	English
5) Peter HARBY		20	English
List 2			
6) John ANGERFELD (Augerfeld)	50	20	English
7) William MESANS [Gillam MESAUNT]		18	English
8) David de MOONSELL [MOUNSELL]	50	20	alien
9) John GODARD		18	alien
10) John Dure		14	alien
List 3			
11) John VALION [VALLION]		17	alien
12) Francis Dolard		20	alien
13) Dennis LE BE [LE BEES]		18	alien
14) John BYLLARD [BELLARDE]		17	alien
15) John HATTO [Hatche?]		20	alien
16) Bartholomew D(-----?) [Darraigne]		18	alien
17) Overus RUSSELL [not in HR]		17	English
18) Giletus (William) RUSSELL [twice in HR]		22	English
19) Adrian HANYSITE [ANYSETT twice in HR]		18	English
20) Jakes HANYSITE [HANYSETT]		24	alien
21) Peter RUSSELL [only once in HR]		19	alien
22) James Parmenty [not in HR]		27	English
List 4			
23) William ELLIS [ELYS]		60	English
24) John ELLIS [not in HR]		30	English
List 5			
25) Lawrence BLEWETO [BLEWETT]		12	alien
26) Jakes RACREFFO [Jaques RECREFF]		18	English
27) William HATTOWE [Gilam HATT']		20	alien
28) Anthony HELYS [ELYS]		20	alien
29) John Bekebote [Bytebote]		18	alien
30) Vincent DEWPRONE [DUPROUNDE]		17	alien
31) John CARBONAT		23	alien
32) William Bennardus [Baynarde]		28	English

Isolated entries in this roll

33) John STIELE [STELE]	50	English
34) John BODYING	28	English

Other Wealden residents in this roll
LABYE, John [Battle, 1540] [not in HR] POLLYNG,
Stephen [Southover, 1550-1563]

* Names found at Wrotham in the subsidy roll of 1545, indicating that this suggested list consisted of Wealden residents rather than of ironworkers.

B. Westminster denization roll of July 1544

List 1
Frenchmen to be made denyzens for Iron Workes by William Levett, clerke

36) Nicholas Gerarde	For personal details see		157
37) Abre Russell	"	"	158
38) John Pynyon	"	"	149
39) John Perago	"	"	160
40) Gilbert Averell	"	"	152
41) Anthony Morrys	"	"	150
42) James Morrell	"	"	156

Frenchmen to be made denyzens by John Baker

43) Mathew Beawshaw	For personal details see		192
44) Cardo Kydvilde	"	"	191
45) Peter Whight	"	"	195
46) John Bottinge	"	"	196
47) John Robynett	No personal details		

Frenchmen to be made denyzens by Eystred [Isted] widow

48) John Shermun	For personal details see		174
49) Marian Deprey	"	"	175
50) William Ogyer	No personal details		
51) Peter Baynowe	"		
52) William Freman	"		

Frenchmen to be made denyzens by Nicholas Eversfield

53) George Moryow	For personal details see		168
54) Peter Vynten	"	"	165
55) Peter Vyllan	"	"	164
56) William Fremens	No personal details		
57) Roger Tankerye	For personal details see		167
58) Quintin Pyllar [*recte* Tyllar]	For personal details see		166

Frenchmen to be made denyzens by Richard Wekes

59) Peter Lambert	No personal details
60) James Tamplier	"
61) Philip Toulett	"
62) Warnett Geratt	"
63) Nicholas Kynnery	"
64) John Vigott	"

List 2

With my lorde of Norfolk in Sheffeld

65) Peter Almande	France		33	French, Michell
66) Nicholas Lawhen	France		30	English
67) Jelett Mocomble	France		50	French, Marian
68) John Carye	France		30	English
69) John Myschewe	France		30	French, Johan
70) John Gavell	France		30	French, Bonie
71) Lewys Botery	France		22	French, Mylsent
72) Peter Bulie	France		25	French, Michell
73) Jelett Bartyne	France		15	French, Marian
74) Morys Larbye	France		20	French, Katheryn
75) Remy Tyller			22	
76) Remy Morell			22	
77) Mawdyn Lucas			20	
78) John Bartyne			16	

In the Kynges forge att Newbridge

79) Thomas Layne	Picardy	34	20	Burgundian
80) Peter Fremyng	Normandy	36	22	French
81) Nicholas Tyler	Normandy	30	18	single
82) James Lenarde	Picardy	26	19	single
83) Charles Mottynge	Normandy	30	20	

In the forge at Parrockes

84) Nicholas Growte	Normandy	52	22	French
85) John Lambert	Normandy	56	34	English
86) Peter Denwall	Picardy	40	37	French
87) John Turke	Picardy	60	38	French
88) John Jonnett	France	31	19	French

List 3

In Sir Robert Tyrwights Iron Worke

89) Thomas Dewprown	Normandy Beuvisaut		20	English
90) John Carbonett	France Ownell		30+	English
91) Nicholas Bartyn	Normandy Elbuseyt	40	23	
92) Charles Poleyn	Normandy	29	12	
93) John Margoo	Normandy		16	

List 4

In Master Pelhams Iron Worke

94) Isambert Bilet	Bewesyn	45	30	French
95) Simond Tyler	Normandy	40	20	French
96) Nicholas Uddys	Bewasyn Saucye	60	16	French
97) John Vynton	Normandy	50	25	English
98) Lewes Raunser	Normandy	25	10	

In Master Lunsfords Iron Worke

99) John Deford	Normandy	60	35	French
100) Gilham Nuffyld	Normandy	30	14	
101) Everode Pynyon	Bewuasyn Aunell	50	34	French

In Master Wybarns Iron Worke

102) Gilham Bennett, priest	Normandy	40	12	
103) Gilham Holmes	Normandy	30	16	English

104) Frauncys Tollett	Normandy	28	15	French

In Master Mays Iron Worke

105) William Harchaunt	Normandy	21	7	
106) Jerman Tollett	Normandy	30	14	French
107) Valentyne Deprowne	Normandy	16	15	

In John Barhams Iron Worke

108) Marian Lamberd	Bewasyn Bewverse	50	28	French
109) Gilham Soberis	Normandy	18	7	
110) John Gardambas	Normandy	33	14	English

List 5

Sir William Sidney for six [in margin]

111) Jeffery Totayn	Normandy	8	English
112) Laurence Graunte	Beauface Canney	6	
113) Peter Cachery	Beauface Canwey	20	
114) Gilham Velett	Normandy	7	
115) John Marie/Margotes	Beauface	11	
116) Robert Lygon	Normandy	5	

List 6

With Sir William Barrentyne

117) Anthony Burder	Normandy Beaufote	20
118) Robert Tyler	Normandy Boell	20
119) Anthony Tyler	Normandy Newville	10

Only the first three were ironworkers in this list of 16 aliens, which also included four priests, a labourer, a joiner and a barber.

List 7

Servant to Sir William Sidney knight

120) Gilham Torshey France collier

List 8

[No heading]

121) Cardo Boyle	Normandy Newcastell	25	English
122) Gwillam Brisboye	Normandy Grisoldes	27	French
123) John Langleys/Margo	Normandy Haucort	18	French
124) Thomas Dogyn	Normandy Compenfelde	20	French
125) Philpott Mettell	Normandy Beaufold	30	
126) Giles Gillett/Duforde	Normandy Gile Fountenayes	37	English
127) Robert Dows	Beauface Hownwell	29	French
128) Jamys Cacherie/de Mergeyes	Bewface Canvey	20	French
129) Joachim Clachoo	Normandy Harbfilde	8	
130) Adrian Dogyn	Normandy Compenfeld	14	

All except 121 were mentioned in Robertsbridge forgebook, 1546

List 9

[No heading]

131) Jurdain Bullie	Normandy Beaufote	26	Dutch, Johanne
132) Barton Pullen	Normandy Newvill	22	single
133) Charles Pullen	Normandy Newvyll	2	single
134) Rowland Mocumble	Normandy Newvill	44	English, Johanne

135) Henry Meryall	Normandy Collo		12	
136) James Vernys	Normandy Boell	22	English, Elizabeth	
137) Peter Gayne	Normandy Rone		10	English, Agnes
138) John Vernys	Normandy Boell		4	single
139) Nicholas Delyche	Depe		10	English, Margaret
140) Martyn Tournewys	Beauvasse Caynne		3	English

All are known to have worked for Sir William Barrentyne except 135 (who did however live at Fletching), 139 and 140.

List 10

Servants of My lorde of Norfolk

143) Adrian Attour	Normandy Rone	ireworker	14	
144) John Gumrie	France	fyner	10	English, Johanne
145) Francis Lambert	France	moyner	8	English
146) Maryan Predome	France	fyner	5	
147) John Roberie	France			
148) Reynolde Harrison	France			

These names came in three sections; 143 was the earliest in the roll; 144 to 146 came much later, closely followed by 147 and 148. Closely following 148 came a second entry for 'Adryan Hatto', who was from Normandy, but had been 17 years in England.

List 11

[No heading]

149) John Pynion	Awnell	Picardy	40	24	English
150) Anthony Morys	Bewbecke	Normandy	20	30	English
151) John de Vere	Bewsaut	Normandy	47	21	English
152) Gilbert Averell	Bewcaut	Normandy	54	36	French
153) John Morrell	Nevill	Normandy	30	12	English
154) William Provott	Borge	France	40	24	English
155) Charles Motton	Crofecure	Picardy	30	22	English
156) Jamys Morrell	Bewell	Normandy	60	19	married
157) Nicholas Jerard	Newell	Normandy	22	14	English
158) Abre Russell	Newell	Normandy	52	26	English
159) George Ravenell	Nackfilde	Normandy	70	30	priest
160) John Perago		Picardy	53	30	married
161) Fraunces Turrell	Nevill	Normandy	33	15	English
162) Nichas Mighell		Normandy	60	40	priest
163) John Ganard	Bewsaut	France	40	30	married
164) Petre Fellyn	Bewbecke	Normandy	35	25	married
165) Petre Fynto	Nevell	Normandy	44	30	English
166) Quynten Tyler	Nevill	Normandy	30	13	English
167) Roger Tancre	Nevell	Normandy	47	30	English
168) George Moreway	Bewsaut	France	28	15	English
169) William Dechyn	Nevill	Normandy	28	15	
170) Woden Vasell	Varowe	France	44	36	English
171) Petre Gaege	Canny	Normandy	25	16	
172) Nichas Michell		Normandy	52	30	priest
173) Jermayn Mitell		France	30	14	English
174) John Sherowe	Pesuys	Normandy	52	32	English
175) Maryon Dupre	Halautier	Normandy	33	15	English
176) Symon Rawe	Bafronats	Normandy	36	15	married
177) Richard Marian	Depe	France	42	41	English

178) Giles Laurence	Croofelde	Normandy	43	34	English
179) Peter Cotting	Bewsawe	Normandy	66	52	married
180) Giles Glodde	Newfeilde	Normandy	38	23	married

This list came at a relatively early point in the roll; it included personal details for seven of William Levett's Frenchmen, for two of Widow Isted's Frenchmen and for five of Nicholas Eversfield's Frenchmen. Both Charles Motton and the Newbridge forgeman, Charles Mottynge, were aged 30, and their years in England were not very different, but Mottynge was stated to be from Normandy; the two must surely be identical. John Morrell, Dechyn, Vasell, Gaege, Mitell and Lawrence were ironworkers known from subsidy-roll and/or parish register entries, and de Vere from the Mayfield parish register. No evidence has so far been found to link Provott, Ravenell, Mighell, Michell or Marian with ironworking, but Turrell, Ganard, Rawe, Cotting and Glodde were probable ironworkers. There was a will for Richard Marian (ESRO, Battle 1/51).

List 12
[No heading]

181) John Harve	Normandy	Roise	18	Norman
182) Remye Harve	Normandy	Roise	18	
183) John Roboye	Beawface	Owney	8	
184) Isambarde Lamme	Normandy	Newcastell	26	Wife from Treport

List 13
[No heading]

185) Onyan Russell	France	hammermaker [*recte* hammerman]	22
186) Philippe Bakaell	France	hammermaker [*recte* hammerman?]	12
187) Nicholas Richard	Normandy	collyer	35
188) John Lyonarde	France	fyner	30
189) Thomas Borde	Normandy	laborer	15
190) Robert Blanke	France	fyner	17

List 14
[No heading]

191) Charde Kyrdebyll	Newcastell	Normandy	41	26	French
192) Mathewe Bewsawe	Catilion	Normandy	48	24	married
193) John Daboundcorde	Catilion	Normandy	37	22	English
194) Robert Pylas	Bewface	Picardy	36	12	married
195) Peter Whyte		Normandy	40	23	English
196) John Butting	Henno	France	36	25	English

The first two and last two entries give personal details for four of John Baker's ironworkers. John Daboundcourt was probably the father of the finer Bartholomew de Boncorte, baptised at Rotherfield in 1539, and could also have worked for Baker. John Dabacourt, a hanaper-roll denizen of 1541, could have been from an earlier generation of this family.

List 15
[No heading]

197) Hollowyn Belhache Roon			16	
198) Simon Tyler		Normandy	20	French
199) John Bynton		Normandy	29	married
200) Isambert Bylett	Bewevers		30	French
201) Nicholas Oddes	Bewevers		15	French

The last four entries duplicate entries for Master Pelham's Frenchmen (Bynton being Vynton), with slight

(Oddes) and larger (Vynton) discrepancies in years of arrival in England. Holand Belhatch paid tax as an alien in St. Katherines near the Tower in 1545 and 1549 (Kirk and Kirk, *Aliens in London*, vol.1, pp. 109, 154).

List 16
[Individual denizens known, or thought to be ironworkers]

202) Lambert Symer 'With my Ladye of Rutlande' iron maker 50 English
203) Robert Caron Depe 40
204) John de Bellevelle France collyer 40 married
205) John Makecowmbull France Colyar 34
Z06) Anthony Myttzell Normandy Nevyll 22 22
207) Mighell Bellatt Normandy 40 20
208) Rowland Clarke France 33 17
209) Jenyns [James in Chancery roll?] Tyler France miner 14
210) William Burdett Normandy 14
211) Tarsell Crysson collyer 7
212) Philippe Deffere France collyer 3

Was 209 one of the two alien Janyn Tylers taxed among the 'Hospicia tenentes' in Aldersgate Ward in London on 21 April 1549 (Kirk and Kirk, *Aliens in London, vol.1*, p. 137), or was he the alien James Tyller taxed at Horsted Keynes in the Weald on 2 May 1549 (See Appendix 2)? Quite bafflingly, not one of these men reappeared in earlier or later lay subsidy rolls for the two areas. 211 has not been traced in the Weald, but his occupation makes a Wealden location quite likely.

List 17
Salt peter makers, servants to John Bowyer

213) Richard Bennett Normandy
214) John Dewvan
Normandy 215) Nicholas Gowghtier
Normandy
216) William Pynson Normandy

List 18
[Possible ironworkers and persons connected with the trade]

217) Michael Lambert Picardy 55
218) Piers Garvis Normandy 45
219) Robert Turnysh Normandy 60 40
220) Nicholas Allarde Picardy 40
221) Gloude Fresard Picardy 33 28 English
222) Robert Rowe Normandy 27
223) John Snatchall France 26 English
224) John Ellyott France 26
225) Vincent Buckett Flanders 26
226) Geffery Drwett Normandy 26 English
227) Clement Russell Rhone Boelles 24
228) Nicholas Almonde Normandy 20
229) Richard Labye Normandy labourer 40 20
230) Nicholas Heth Normandy 23 20
231) William Bynnet France Roon 20
232) John Benne France 20 English
233) Peter Barton Rhone Royvele 20
234) Francis Gillett Brittany joyner 20 English
235) Thomas Potter Normandy smith 36 18 English
236) Reynolde Shoell Picardy 24 17
237) John Androwe Rone gunner with Peter Baude 17

238) John Lavender	France		22	15	
239) Nicholas Douggen	Normandy	Congville	34	14	
240) Francis Shivaller	France		18	13	
241) Peter Deboye	France	smith		13	
242) Michaell Oyddes	Bovessyn		21	12	English
243) Benett Nicoll	France	smith		11	
244) Nicholas Beuser	Rone		13	10+	
245) Nicholas Collier	France			4	
246) John Philpot	Brittany				

Rhone and Rone perhaps mean the diocese of Rouen.

List 19
[No heading]
247) Hugh Marchaunt
248) John Jouly [Jolys]
249) Nicholas Showen
250) John Weyo [Welleyn]
251) John Vylean [Vyall]
252) John Gottere [Guntier]
253) George Potte(r?) [Colyer]
254) Aubrey Russell
255) James Walys [Manton]
256) John a Paryse [Aparys]
257) Nowell Darby [Derby]
258) William Roys
259) Clement Colyer
260) John Sampson [Collyer]
261) Lawrence Poutsse
262) Nicholas Gotter
263) Marten Loye
264) John Howell
265) Myntan Russell

There were originally two lists of miners engaged under royal commission by William Pexwell (*recte* Pepwell), a Bristol merchant who perhaps originated from Rowley Regis. One list contained 14, the other 19 immigrants. Numbers 261 to 265 did not occur in the shorter list, but for the remainder the order of listing suggests the identifications given within square brackets. In the shorter list a period of 40 years was alluded to, but in the longer list the men were stated to 'have contynued here in England by a great space' and to have been born 'in Croys and other cytyes and townes in Fraunce'. The two lists have here been conflated.

Hugh Marchant was the name of a finer at Robertsbridge forge. Numbers 252 and 262 have names similar to two colliers employed by Hugh Collins around 1550. It will be noticed that three of these workers bear the name Collyer, or a variant. Number 254 may be identical with 17 and possibly with 37 and 158.

C. The hanaper roll of 1541

Probable ironworkers, with Wealden subsidy-roll, court- roll and parish-register references.
Fawtrell, John [Fettery (alias Hatto), Hartfield, 1524]
Servile alias Cheverell, Francis [Hartfield, 1524]
Garrett, John [Garret, Dallington hundred and court roll, 1529]
Colyns, John [Colyn, Netherfield, 1540]
Jerart, Charles [Charlys, Loxfield, 1543]
Angell, John [Loxfield, 1543?]

Reder, Adrian [Hartfield, 1543]
Rychardson, Barnard [Rycharson, Rushmonden, 1543]
Archer [Archer?], John [Arter, Hawksborough, 1552; Artor, Danehill Sheffield, 1560, etc.]
Pullen, John [Pullyng, buried Maresfield, 1558]
Damery, Nicholas [Demerowe, Street North, 1560]

Possible ironworkers
Barbye, James
Carpenter, John
Coppyn, James
Dabacourt, John
Devild alias Deviell, Nicholas
Duffett, John
Ellys, Robert
Growte, Peter
Mawcombe, John
Morell, John
Myskyn, Henry
Whilmaker, Peter [Peter Whelebarowmaker, Burbeech, 1576?]

Other Wealden residents
Frawndbeff, John [Battle, 1524-40]
Ellyard, John [Family at Withyham (1565) and Warbleton (1569)]
Beckys, Leonard [Dill, 1572]

Ordnance workers at the Tower
Johnson, Henry [this name occurs in the roll several times]
Reynolds, Warnard [1540-49, Kirk and Kirk, *Aliens in London,vol 1*, pp. 19-196]

APPENDIX II

ALIENS IN LAY SUBSIDY ROLLS OF THE WEALD, 1524-1595

According to Giuseppi's *Guide to the Public Records* the subsidy was 'a tax which from the reign of Richard II was imposed on persons according to the reputed value (on a very moderate estimate) of their estates, at the rate of 4s in the pound for lands and 2s 8d for goods, those of aliens being valued at a double rate'.[1] In practice things were not always so simple. In the mid-1520s, the subsidy was combined with a kind of poll tax, resulting in the most comprehensive assessment of the century for Sussex. It gave rise to the sort of complexities and anomalies described by J. Cornwall in the introduction to his Sussex Record Society volume on that subsidy.[2]

Later, during the financial crisis of Edward VI's reign we are looking at what were in fact 'reliefs' rather than subsidies. In some cases the rolls recorded only the amounts contributed, so that the actual assessment can only be arrived at by calculation. Because of this and because only just more than ten per cent of aliens were affluent enough to pay tax on goods, it seems simpler to reverse Cornwall's procedure by stating the tax paid, rather than the value assessed. The proportion of aliens qualifying to pay on land was minute - Nicholas Jarrett is the only one who springs to mind.

It is evident from the four consecutive rolls of 1549-52 in Sussex that the turnover of ironworkers was large. Some two-thirds of those listed failed to appear in at least one of these rolls. Some aliens known, from the evidence of parish registers and other sources, to have been in the Weald at the time failed to be taxed at all. This under-recording is so great as to suggest that only those aliens at the time working under contract were liable to tax.[3] A comparison of the names of Frenchmen listed in the subsidy rolls as being in the employ of Sir William Sidney with the names of those mentioned in the Sidney accounts serves to confirm this; Sidney's founder, finers, hammerman, colliers and many of the miners appeared in both, but Frenchmen mentioned solely for woodcutting, carrying, or day labour, such as repairing and scouring water-courses and the dam, were not recorded in the subsidy rolls. From 1542 onwards members of the Pray or Spray family were mentioned in the accounts,[4] but it was only after 1553 that they became covenant servants; accordingly, no Spray was mentioned in any of the reliefs of 1549-52, but Simon and Adrian Spray both paid the poll tax as servants of Sir Henry Sidney in 1560.

The circumstances in which women were liable for tax are obscure. Widows were occasionally taxed, but if this was during the remainder of a year for which their husbands had been under contract, why was Jane Bine taxed in three successive years at Robertsbridge from 1549 to 1551? Occasionally, unmarried women were also taxed; in Shoyswell in 1560, both Joan (Johan) and Roulande Leonard paid the poll tax; both were married the following year, Joan at Pembury to Michael Piccat and Rowland at Goudhurst to Peter Degoye! In later rolls for the rapes of Lewes and Bramber, and very occasionally in other parts of the Weald, wives and children of aliens paid the poll tax.

Because some ironworks were situated on streams which served as boundaries between rapes, hundreds, boroughs and parishes, it is difficult to identify the ironworks at which some aliens in particular hundreds worked. Workers at Robertsbridge forge appeared in both Robertsbridge and Staple hundreds, and those from Panningridge furnace appeared in both Foxearle and Netherfield. Anthony Pelham had workers in both Foxearle and Netherfield hundreds too; were these employed at one ironworks or two?

Where workers were designated as hammermen and finers there must have been a forge; where founders and miners are mentioned a furnace must be suspected. But does John Baker's miner in Hawksborough hundred (1549) indicate a separate furnace (Bungehurst perhaps), or was this miner attached to Baker's Old Mill furnace in the Isenhurst part of Mayfield parish, returned as the northern

1. M.S. Giuseppi, *Guide to the Public Records* (rev. ed. 1963), vol. 1, p.66. 2.
2. J. Cornwall, ed., *The Lay Subsidy Rolls, 1524-5* (Lewes, 1956).
3. Except the rolls for 1524, which is probably an almost complete list of landowners, wage earners and heads of households.
4. Kent History and Library Centre, Maidstone. I am grateful to the Rt. Hon. the Viscount De L 'Isle for permission to consult these papers.

part of Dill hundred in the rape of Pevensey?

Further problems arise from the difficulty of knowing what the precise boundaries of hundreds and boroughs were. Throughout the second half of the sixteenth century the boroughs of West Hoathly and Ardingly, which later formed part of the hundred of Butting Hill, were returned separately as the hundred of Streat North, though they were not even contiguous with the remainder of Streat hundred. This fact is evident from the subsidy rolls themselves. Another problem is that the boundaries of boroughs or tithings very often failed to coincide with those of parishes.

My comments on the subsidies have relied heavily in this respect on Budgen's map of Sussex (1724) and on the maps included in Hasted's *History of Kent* (1797-98). Mayfield was returned as part of Loxfield hundred, but Budgen's map showed that the boroughs of Isenhurst and Bivelham in the south of Mayfield parish were parts of the hundreds of Dill (Pevensey rape) and Hawksborough (Hastings rape) respectively. It showed that Bivelham forge itself lay outside Bivelham borough and belonged to Shoyswell hundred. This was Anthony Pelham's forge and its location in Shoyswell explained the excessive number of forgemen returned in that hundred. Budgen's map also appears to show that Warbleton Priory lay on the boundary between Foxearle and Hawksborough hundreds, which allows Warbleton Priory works to be located in Foxearle hundred, and not in Hawksborough hundred, in which Warbleton borough itself lay. Budgen was less helpful in defining the complicated boundaries between Netherfield and Foxearle hundreds in the vicinity of Ashburnham furnace (formerly Dallington), which was in a detached portion of Dallington parish, but in the manor of Penhurst.[5] In January 1549 the jurors of Rye, Winchelsea and Hastings referred to the iron mill at Penhurst, which might mean either Ashburnham or Penhurst furnace. The subsidy rolls suggest that both were in existence by that date.

The schedules reproduced here relate mainly, but not exclusively, to areas in which ironworking is known or suspected to have been carried on during the sixteenth century. For instance, in Hastings rape the hundreds of Gostrow, Guestling and Goldspur, and the Cinque ports have been omitted; in Pevensey rape only the hundreds of Dill, Shiplake, Loxfield, Rushmonden and those further north have been included; in Lewes rape only Barcombe, Butting Hill and Streat North. Similarly in respect of date, the rolls for 1524/5 and 1543 and those between have been included only for Pevensey and Hastings rapes and the adjacent parts of Kent. Excluded are the rolls dated 1544-48, which failed to tax aliens, perhaps in recognition of the amounts lately mulcted from them in payment for letters of denization.[6] Rolls for 1563 exist only for the central areas of Lewes and Bramber rapes, the hundreds of Tandridge and Reigate and the lathe of Sutton-at-Hone. In the 1590s Surrey and parts of Kent have several rolls surviving, but that of 1595 for Hastings rape is one of the few for Sussex.

In Surrey in 1557 the levy on goods worth up to one and two pounds was 8d per pound. Otherwise the rates levied on goods per pound were 1s (1540, 1541, 1549, 1550, 1551 and 1552), 2s (1524, 1560, 1563 and 1572) and 3s 4d (1576 and 1595). Rates of poll tax were 4d (1540, 1541, 1557, 1560, 1563, 1572, 1576, 1589 and 1595) and 8d (1549, 1550, 1551, 1552, 1594, 1598-1600). On land valued at one pound Nicholas Jarrett paid 2s 8d in 1560 and 1572 and 3s 4d in 1576, the first assessment being in Battle and the later ones in Netherfield.

Abbreviations

A = alien	F = Frenchman	L = land
D = denizen	P = poll tax	

5. Straker, *Wealden iron*, pp. 364-6.
6. In Kent in 1544 the rates levied were reduced to 1d for poll tax and 2d on goods worth one pound.

The rape of Hastings

The hundred of Foxearle

6 April 1524
(E179/189/128)

Holand Frenshman 8d
- - - -
Gyllam Frensshman 2s
- - - -
John Armeran A 8d
- - - -
Gylys Duffourd A 8d

10 November 1539
(E179/190/187)

Olyver Taylor A 1s
John Colyer A 2s

3 May 1549
(E179/190/233)

Frenchmen in Mr Pelhams worke
John Valeant 2s
Guillam Clerke P
John Bourdell P
Phyllypp Chapleyn P
Sampson Frenchman P

Frenchmen in Sir Willyam Sydneys worke
John Longley P
Phyllypp Mettett P
Petre Ungell P
Jamys Morrell P
George Morrys P
John Marygon P
Stephyn la Mell P
Clementt Grewe P

Frenchmen in Mr Ashburnhams worke
Thomas Dyggyn P
John Furrye P

Frenchemen in Richard Wodmans worke
Phlyppyng Fardell P
Sambert Lamen P
John Stampylyon P

12 April 1550
(E179/190/239)

Servauntes to Mr John Assheborneham
Thomas Dyggen P
Antony Hoysc P
Barden P
servaunte to Richard Wodman

Alyens servauntes to Mr Antonye Pelham
John Valeant 2s
Stephen Lamell P
Nicolas Mary P
George Morryes P
John Maryon P
John Langlas P

Aliens servantes to Sir William Sidney
Peter Ungell P
Phillyppe Motet P

26 March 1551
(E179/190/244)

Frenchmen servauntes to Mr Antonye Pelham
John Valyaunte A 1s
Simon White A P

Servauntes to Sir Willm Sidnet knight
George Morryes P
John Langles A P
Peter Unkyll A P
Peter the servaunte
of Peter Unkyll P
Phlippe Metett A P

Servauntes to Robert Woodman
William Brousbull A P
Gyllam Burgonyon A P

John Dygon servaunt
to Mr Ashburnham P

4 March 1552
(E179/190/247)

Aliens servauntes to Antonye Pelham esquire
John Valeaunt P
Clement Griaunt P
Simon White P

Aliens servauntes to Sir William Sidnet knight
George Morreys P
John Russell P
John Langlesse P
Peter Unckell P
Phillippe Metet P

Alien servaunte to John Ashburnham esquier
Thomas Digon P

Aliens servauntes to Thomas Woodman
Peter Rowland P
John Neve P

1 February 1560
(E179/190/266)

Aliens
Thomas Dugyn D 2s
Symon Tiler D 2s
Lewes Rawnser D 2s

Servauntes to Sir Henry Sydney
Simon Spraye P
Audryan Spraye P
- - - -
Richard Valyante D 4s
Robart Tompler D 2s
John Rowlande D 4s
John Levee P
Maryan Leve P
Zamberte Barden P

10 October 1572
(E179/190/283)

Aliens
John Lemotte 2s
Mychaell Sede P
John Sellem P
James Lyvarde P
Gilbert Pynyan P

27 July 1576
(E179/190/298)

Alyens
John Le Motte P
Adam Tottoe P
John Selen P
Frauncysce Dowste P
Nicholas Dowlse P

10 October 1595
(E179/190/332)

Aliens
John Sellen P
Peter Lemote P
James Fuller P
John Ades P
Adrian Ades P

In 1551 an otherwise unknown John Dygon appeared as servant to Mr Ashburnham. This is almost certainly an error, because the name appeared consistently as Thomas in the other four returns of 1549 to 1560. On the other hand, Izambard Lamye was at Dunsfold in Surrey in 1551 and 1552, exactly when he did not appear here between 1549 and 1560. The ironmasters shown in place of Richard Woodman in 1551 and 1552 were presumably his brother Robert, and either his father Thomas, or his other brother Thomas, who is reputed to have subsequently betrayed him.

The hundred of Bexhill

6 April 1524
(E179/189/128)

(nil)

10 November 1539
(E179/190/187)

Olyver Debyll A P
Phylyp Mary A P
Nycholas Lawrens A P
Nycholas Arysman A P
Gyles Duffen A P
Dyryk Corver A P
Peter Johnson A P

3 May 1549
(E179/190/233)

John Rowland F D 1s

12 April 1550
(E179/190/239)

John Rowland D 1s

26 March 1551
(E179/190/244)

(lacks Bexhill)

4 March 1552
(E179/190/247)

(nil)

1 February 1560
(E179/190/266)

(nil)

10 October 1572
(E179/190/283)

Alyens
Growshe P
and his wife P

27 July 1576
(E179/190/298)

Alyen
William Waters man P

10 October 1595
(E179/190/332)

(nil)

The seven aliens of 1540 require explanation. The names Arysman, Corver and Johnson could be Flemish, rather than French. Gyles Duffen, on the other hand, was presumably 126 in the lists of denizens.

The hundred of Ninfield

6 April 1524
(E179/189/128)

Morys Frensheman 8d

10 November 1539
(E179/190/187)

(nil)

3 May 1549
(E179/190/233)

(nil)

12 April 1550
(E179/190/239)

(nil)

26 March 1551
(E179/190/244)

(nil)

4 March 1552
(E179/190/247)

(nil)

1 February 1560
(E179/190/266)

Alien
John Mocko P

10 October 1572
(E179/190/283)

(nil)

27 July 1576
(E179/190/298)

Alyens
John Harvye P
Christmas Russell P

10 October 1595
(E179/190/332)

(nil)

The hundred of Shoyswell

6 April 1524
(E179/189/128)

The borow of Pashely

Gelote [- -]	8d
Nicholas [- -]	8d
John [- -]	8d
John P[er]yg[o] F	8d
Roger Elys F	8d
Gyllam Furneys F	8d
Gyllam Tassen F	8d
Garrard Colyar F	8d
Rowlande Maknyle F	8d
Gyllam Taylboy F	8d
Philpott Wodetaller F	8d

10 November 1539
(E179/190/187)

(lacks Shoyswell)

3 May 1549
(E179/190/233)

Vyncent Deproune F D	P
servauntt to Thomas Shoyswell	
Jakes Recrewe F D	2s
servauntt to Thomas Maye	
Thomas Deproune colyer F D	P
Valentyne Deproune fyner A	P
Richard Roche F D	P
Gladd fyner F	P
Labys wydowe	P
John Derrye	P
in the workes of Ambras Comportt	
Antonye Ellys A D	6s
John Antonye his servauntt A	P
Nycholas Colyar A	P
servauntt to Jakes	
Charles Pullyn A	P
servauntt to Ambras	
John Bee A	P
servauntt to John Dory	
- - - -	
Nycholas Hedowell A D	1s
Paule Hedowell his son	P
Nycholas Lamberd	P
servauntt to thesame Nicholas	
- - - -	
Petre Weldern A D	P

12 April 1550
(E179/190/239)

Alyens in the works of Mr Maye	
James Tomple	P
Jack Recrewe	P
Nicolas hys man	P
Vincent Deproyne	P
Thomas Deproyne	P
Rychard Roche	P
Valentyne Deproyne	P
Nicolas Skellerye	P
Robert Tomple	P
Herbe wydowe	P
Labye wydowe	P
Antonye Ellys	3s
Alyens in the works of Mr Pelham	
John Barden	2s
Poull Hedoll	P
Michaell Hedoll	P

26 March 1551
(E179/190/244)

Peter Labye taylor A	P
Servauntes to John Wybarne	
Jakes Recrowe A	P
Nicolas his servaunt A	P
Servauntes to Ambrose Comporte	
Antonye Ellys A	[-]
Nicolas his servaunt	P
Nicolas Labye A	P
John [- -] A	P
Servauntes to Thomas Maye	
Vincent Deprowne	P
Thomas Deprowne	P
Valentyne Deprowne	P
Richard [- -] A	P
Jamys Tomplen	P
Richard [Roche?]	P
Nicholas H [- -]	P
Thomas	P

4 March 1552
(E179/190/247)

Aliens servauntes to Thomas Maye, gent.	
Vincent Deproine	P
Thomas Deproine	P
Valentine Deproine	P
Marten Quinto	P

John Capper	P
Allo	P
Gillam	P

Aliens servauntes to Ambrose Comporte

Antonye Ellys	2s
Nicolas	P
Nicolas Labie	P

Aliens servauntes to Thomas Shoswel, gent.

Hector P Lunto	P

1 February 1560
(E179/190/266)

Aliens

Vincente Deprove	P
Thomas Deprove	P
Valantyne Deprove	P
Petar Degoye	P
Myshawe	P
Johan Leonarde	P
Allo Fyllet	P
Stephyn Untill	P
John Prevaute	P
Nycholas Mynnage	P
Poule Judde	P
Roulande Leonarde	P
Nicholas Frencheman	P
and his too sonnes	PP

10 October 1572
(E179/190/283)

Alyens

Marten Le Mowle	P
Lucyan	P
John Humfrye	P
John Cracye	P

27 July 1576
(E179//90/298)

Alyens

Folentyne Deprone	P
John Cressye	P
John Deboyse	P
Leonard	P
Robert Dooall	P
Peter Calober	P
Stephen	P
Peter Deforre	P
Peter Lavender	P
Stephen	P
Peter Deforre	P
Peter Lavender	P

10 October 1595
(E179/190/332)

Leonard Garden	P

Although Bevilham borough was part of Hawksborough hundred, Budgen's map (1724) shows Bevilham forge to have been within Shoyswell hundred, and this probably accounts for the forgemen attributed to Mr Pelham. In the north, Chingley furnace would be on the Kent border.

The hundred of Netherfield

6 April 1524
(E179/189/128)
(Obscure, c. 1525)
(E179/189/161)

John Jonner A	8d
Robert Jhonson Scott	8d
Petar Marten A	8d
- - - -	
John Rever F	8d
John Bygo A (1525)	8d
- - - -	
Brother Frenshman	8d
Shyvall A F	8d
Sampson Frensshman	8d

10 November 1539
(E179/190/187)

John Colyn A	4s
George Boy A	1s
Luce Tyler A	P
Frauncys Hynche A	P
Jamys Turke A	P
Hewe Turke A	P
Jamys de Merket A	P
Nycholas Capell A	P
Flyx A	P
old Tullet A	P
D[- -] Capell A	P
Peter Borne A	P
Bormeyne Bredes A	P
Nycholas Bertyn A	P
Thomas o Prowne A	P
Valentyne de Prowne A	P
Wenys[ent]de Prowne A	P
Graund John Colyer A	P

3 May 1549
(E179/190/233)

Frenchemen denizens

Warner Gerrard	P
Laurence Blewett	1s
Guillam Sobrys	P
Nycholas Jerard	2s
John Carbonett	P
Jamys Templyer	P
Robert Dowse	1s
Jamys Secherye	P
Petre Secherye	P
John Rybonar	3s
Jarman Myttyll	P
Antonye Myttyll	P
Symon Tyler	2s
Roger Tynker	1s
Lewys Renser	P
George Bogge	1s
Guillam Bordett	2s

Frenchemen not denizens in Sir William Sidneys workes

Peter Tourner	P

in Mr Antonye Pelhams workes

Phyllypp Grewe	P
John Lemett	P

in Richard a Wykes workes

Berrye Bordett	P
Antonye Keller	P

in Nynyon Burrells workes

Peter Sebrys	P
Clementt Gryans	P
Robert Templyer	P
John Benett	P

in Richard a Wekes workes

Nycholas Werett	P
Robert Morreys	P
Michaell Bellett	P
Flyppyng Tollett	P
John Dewewe	P
Lewys Sampson	P

12 April 1550
(E179/190/239)

Aliens

Simon Tylar	1s
Robard Dowse	1s
Nicolas Gerard	2s
Lawrens Blouet	1s
Gyllam Sobrys	1s
Jarmyn Mitell	P
John Ryboner	3s
Rodger Tenkerye	1s
Lewes Renser	P
George Bogge	1s
John Farne	1s
Peter Gayne	1s
John Carbonet	1s
Warnet Gerard	1s
James Kescherell	1s

Alyens servauntes to Richard Wyke

Lewes Sampson	P
John Brye	P
Antony Kyllere	P
John Pyballyar	P
Phlyppyng Toilet	P

Aliens servauntes to Sir William Sidney

Peter Turner	P
John Lamot	P

Aliens servauntes to Mr Antony Pelham

Clement Grians	P
John Benet	P

26 March 1551
(E179/190/244)

Servauntes to Richard a Wyke

Antonye Kellarye A	P
John Grate A	P
Lewys Sampson A	P
John Pyballary A	P
John Bossell A	P
Lawrens He[us?] A	P
Davy Hatto A	P

Servauntes to Sir Willm Sidney knight

Phlypinge Tollet A	P
Peter Turner A	P

Antony Toullet servaunt to Wy[kes]	P

Servauntes to Charles Warner

John Russell A	P
Nicolas Fewer A	P

Aliens

Lawrens Blewet	1s
Nicolas Gerard	2s
Jarmen Mitell	[?]
Warnet Jerard	1s
James Morell	1s
Obrye Larber	1s
Gyllam Burdet	1s
Symon Tyler	1s
Robert Dosse	1s
Lewes Rawncer A	P
Rodger Tynkary	1s

John Polvo	1s
John Ryboner	3s
George Bogge	1s

Servauntes to Charles Warnet

Nicolas Hoschett A	P
Willm Pawyer A	P
Peter Petyre A	P
Peter Lamere A	P
Stephyn Melle A	P
Petar Latornys A	P

4 March 1552
(E179/190/247)

Aliens servauntes to Sir William Sidney knyght

Robert Dowse	1s
Simon Tiler	2s
Peter Turner	P
Phlyppyng Tollet	P

Aliens servauntes to Antony Pelham esquire

Roger Tankerye	1s

Aliens servauntes to Richard Wikes

James Tamplier	P
John Quen	P
Glode Tomplyar	P
Nicolas Jerett	2s
Peter Lamar	P
Lawrens Blewet	1s
John Grate	P
Warnet Jeret	P
James Morell	P
John Jerott	P

Aliens servauntes to Harry Westall and Charles Jerat

Jarmen Mitel	P
John Tyler	P
William Pavye	P
Obrye Larber	P
John Jelet	P
his servaunt	
Peter Lamar	P

Aliens householders

George Bogge	1s
John Robover	3s

1 February 1560
(E179/190/266)

Robart Dosse	2s
Jarmen Myttell	2s
Marryan Bennet	2s
John Nevell	2s
Guylham Cardo	P
too Frenchemen	P
dwellinge with Stephyn Blewet	P
Nicholas Pete	P
and his manne	P
Lawrens Dupre	P
Phillip Grotte	P
Simon Kennet	P

10 October 1572
(E179/190/283)

Alyens

Nycholas Jerrarde L	2s 8d
Nycholas Furre	P
Adryan Pynyan	P
John Pynyan	P
John Jellye	P

27 July 1576
(E179/190/298)

Nicholas Jarrett L	3s 4d
Nicholas Pettit	P
Awdrean Pynean	P
John Pynyan	P
Laurence	P
John Valyance	P
Bastyan Lambert	P
his two men	PP
Nicholas Furry	P

10 October 1595
(E179/190/332)

Aliens

John Cressie	P
John Bowyer	P
Lawrence Hawrowe	P
John Defect	P
Peter Weaver	P

The hundred of Hawksborough

6 April 1524
(E170/189/128)

Gyllam F	8d
Jorden Frencheman	8d
Tanit Harby F	8d
John Grant F	8d
John Russell F	8d
Alyn Russell F	8d
Voden Voystell F	8d
John Tompkyn F	8d

Thomas Sage F	8d
- - - -	
(servants of John Collen)	
John Turkes F	8d
Barden Frencheman	8d
Cropper Frencheman	8d
John Darvie* F	8d
Jenken Frencheman	8d
John Jellot F	8d
Adrean Frencheman	8d

[Bivelham]

John Merteyley F	8d

[Tottingworth]

Venten Frencheman	8d

10 November 1539
(E179/190/187)

Charles Motye A	1s
John Vynter A	2s
John Jespere A	(1s?)
Clement Quyer preste A	P
John Carry A	P
William Taylor A	P
Nycholas Hyndall A	P
Rychard A	P
John Gawyn	P
Peter Makkowe A	P
Thomas Sampton A	P
John Nonno A	P
John Gyllat	P
Robert A	P
Peter Ferlekett A	P
John Garrard A	P
John A	P

3 May 1549
(E179/190/233)

Aliens in the works of Nycholas Pelham esquyer

Guyllam Fawke fynar	1s
Mychell Hedhall colyar	P
Garman the hamerman	P

Aliens in the works of John Collyn

John Mynyon colyar	P
Audryan Hatto hamerman	P

Alien servauntt to Bartylmewe Geffrey

Peter Hese fownder	P

Aliens servaunttes to Antonye Pelham esquyer

John Vynton fynor	2s
John Leonard fynor	P

Aliens in the works of Joane Istedd

Robert Blank fynor	P
Petre Borayne fynor	P
Gyles Laurence fownder	P
John Maryon mynor	P

Aliens in the works of John Bakar

David Demoyschell miner	P

Alien in the works of John Saxpes

Robert Carone colyer	P

Aliens in the works of Richard Wodman

Nycolas Gottye colyar	P
Denys Lebbys hamerman	P

Alien in the works of Antonye Pelham esquyer

Barden hamerman	2s

12 April 1550
(E179/190/239)

[Warbleton]

Aliens servauntes to Richard Wodman

Denys Lobbys hamerman	P
Nicolas Gottye colyer	P
John Gottye colyer	P

[Tottingworth]

Alyens servauntes to John Collyn

John Gue thelder colyar	P
John Gue the yonger colyar	P

[Bevilham]

Aliens servauntes to Mr Antonye Pelham

John Vinton fynor	1s
John Leonarde fyner	P
Hedall colyer	P

Arter colier	P
servaunte to John Baker	

Aliens servauntes to Joane Isted

Robert Banke fynor	P
Gyles Lawrens fownder	P
John Maryan filler	P

26 March 1551
(E179/190/244)

[Warbleton]

Alyen

Dennys Lybbys	P

* An alternative reading to 'Darme', that of J. Cornwall. Capital 'D's and 'h's are also very alike in this MS. so that one could perhaps read 'Harvie'. John Harvie came to England in 1522 and later worked for Hugh Collyn at Socknersh.

servaunt to Richard Wodman
hammerman

[Bevilham]

(nil)

[Tottyngworth]

Servauntes to Mr Antony Pelham

John Vinton fyner A	1s
Hedall colyar A	P
Simon his man A	P

Servauntes to Joane Isted

Giles Lawrens fownder A	P
John Curleggo A	P
Robert fyner A	P
Peter Lawrens A	P

[Burwash]

(nil)

4 March 1552
(E179/190/247)

Aliens servauntes to Richarde Woodman

Denys Lebys	P
Gelum Fasshatt	P

Aliens servauntes to Joane Isted

Gyles the Fownder	1s
Maryan	P
John Haunyng	P

Aliens servauntes to Thomas Morley, gent.

Glode Aufrey	P
John Vinton	P

Alien servaunt to John Baker

John Botton	P

Aliens servauntes to Bartilmew Jefferye

Everet	P
Michaell	P

1 February 1560
(E179/190/266)

Aliens

Bardyn	P
John Gryndegore	P
Glode Averye	P
Peter Lamberte	P
John Everet	P

10 October 1572
(E179/190/283)

Alyens

Jerman Myttell	2s
Drushe	P
servante to John Glasyer	

servantes to Thomas Greene

Powle Edolfe	P
John Nono	P
- - - -	
Roger Tanckerell	P

27 July 1576
(E179/190/298)

[Warbleton]

(nil)

[Byshoprich]

Jacob A	3s 4d

[Tottingford!]

Christmas A	P
servaunt to Henry Collen	

[Bivelham]

Alyens

Bosewaye	P
Dynnys Bosard	P

[Burwash]

Drowsh A	P

10 October 1595
(E179/190/332)

(nil)

This hundred included the south-eastern part of Mayfield, the borough of Bevilham. However, as explained earlier, Bevilham forge lay in Shoyswell hundred and outside the borough of Bevilham proper.

There is an error in the return for 1551; the clerk went straight on from Bevilham without recording the aliens working in that borough for Joan Isted and Anthony Pelham; he entered them at the end of the Tottingworth return.

The errors in recording foreign names are put in perspective by the 1576 return, which named that borough Tottingford.

The hundred of Henhurst

6 April 1524
(E179/189/127)

Laurence Docheman	2s
John Lambard F	8d
John Frenchman	2s
Jellat Collyn	8d
Robynet Colyer	8d

13 Feb 1525
(E179/189/133)

William Alyn F	8d
- - - -	
John Alyn F	8d
William Brown F	8d

10 November 1539
(E179/190/187)

Marten Braband A	1s
Wyllm A	P
Wyllm A	P
John Morrant A	1s
Husbote A	P
Remy A	3s 4d
Garred Essewe A	P
Antony Essewe A	P
Thomas Essewe A	P
John Derrett A	P
Marten Derrett A	P
Thomas Desyen A	P
John A	P

3 May 1549
(E179/190/233)

John [- -]go brewer	P
servauntt to Joane Welsche	
[- -]daig[- -] colyar	P
servauntt to Godard Welsche	
Maryon Benett	P
serv[auntt to] Willyam Haye	

12 April 1550
(E179/190/239)

Aliauntes servauntes to Joane Walshe and to Godard her sonne

John Turke	P
Guyllam Dygon	P
Obery Russell	P
John Margo	P

Alyauntes servauntes to John Haye

James Frencheman	P
Maryan Bonnat	P

26 March 1551
(E179/190/244)

(nil)

4 March 1552
(E179/190/247)

Aliens servauntes to Godarde Walshe, gent.

Aufrye Russell	P
Collen Mallet	P

Aliens servauntes to Hugh Collyn

Simon Cleriewe	P
Lewes Burden	P
John Cherterye	P
John Harvye	P
Remy Harvye	P
Gyllam Detrove	P

1 February 1560
(E179/190/266)

Aliens

John Harvie	P
John Morgo	P
Anthonye	P

10 October 1572
(E179/190/283)

Alyens

John Tassell	P
John Harvye	P
Charles Levyvache	P

27 July 1576
(E179/190/298)

Alyens

John Rootes	P
Nicholas	P
John Jellye	P
Alloe	P

10 October 1595
(E179/190/332)

(nil)

The hundred of Robertsbridge

6 April 1524
(E179/189/127)
13 Feb 1525
(E179/189/133)

Quinto F	2s
Fayther Daye F	2s
A Docheman (1525)	8d
Jaket Frenchman (1525)	8d

10 November 1539
(E179/190/187)

Vyncent Bokett A	P
Peter A P Garrett A	P

3 May 1549
(E179/190/233)

Aliens in workes of Willyam Sidney knight

Willyam Fawtrell alias Fatter	P
Laurence Fawtrell	P
Richard Byne	P
Jane Byne	P
Hugh Marchaunt	P
Jamys Growte	P
Willyam Duggyn	P
Vyncentt Bokett nayle maker	P
Aleyn Jerre his man	P

Aliens in the works of John Philpott

Lewes Bayarde	P
Laurence Lokear	P
John Nayler	P
Maryon Mayskyn wydowe	2s

12 April 1550
(E179/190/239)

Aliens in the workes of Sir William Sidney

William Fawterell alias Hatto	P
Jane Byne vidua	P
William Vacket	P
Richard Falyant	P
Charles Pullen	P

Aliens in the works of Philpot

Lewes Bayard	P
Lawrens Lokkyar	P
John Clowcher	P
Vincent Bookett nayle maker	P

26 March 1551
(E179/190/244)

Aliens servauntes to Sir Willm Sidney knight

William Fawterell	P
Jane Bine widowe	P
Hugh Marchaunt	P

Aliens servauntes to John Philpott

Lewes Bayerde	P
Lawrens Lokyar	P
John Cloucher	P

4 March 1552
(E179/190/247)

Aliens servauntes to Sir William Sidney knight

Hewe Marchaunte	P
Peter Jollye	P

Aliens servauntes to John Philpott smythe

Lawrens Loyeker	P
Lewes Berarde	P
John Clocher	P
Vincet Boket	P

1 February 1560
(E179/190/266)

Aliens

Peter Joly	2s
Jarman Dallamot	P
Pe John Clotear	P

10 October 1572
(E179/190/283)

Peter Jellye A	2s

27 July 1576
(E179/190/298)

Alyens

Peter Jellye	3s 4d
Thomas Powle	P
Charles Fever	P

10 October 1595
(E179/190/332)

(nil)

The hundred of Staple

6 April 1524
(E179/189/127)
13 Feb 1525
(E179/189/133)

(nil)

10 November 1539
(E179/190/187)

(lacks Staple)

3 May 1549
(E179/190/233)

Frenchment in the works of Willyam Sydney knight

Petre Jollye	P
Nicholas Marye	P
Roger de Prewe	P
Adryan Duggyn	P

12 April 1550
(E179/190/239)

(incomplete)

26 March 1551
(E179/190/244)

(lacks Staple)

4 March 1552
(E179/190/247)

Adryan Doggyn D	1s
Frauncis his servaunte	P
Damarons alias Kessle	1s
Peter Damarons his son	1s

1 February 1560
(E179/190/266)

Fraunces A	P

10 October 1572
(E179/190/283)

Alyens

William the Frenchman	2s
Edward Ransome	P
Bastyan F	P

27 July 1576
(E179/190/298)

Alyens

Peter de Guye	P
Godfrye de la Haye	P
Ognilen Lutere*	P
John Mary	P
Stephen de Voye	P
John Fycot	P
Rowland Meadowe	P

10 October 1595
(E179/190/332)

Peter Kinge A	3s 4d

* Should read 'Ogniben Lutere', the name of a well-known Italian glassmaker.

Both de la Haye and Lutere were glassmakers. The payment of Peter Kinge was listed as 4s 4d, but the roman iiijs has arabic 3s entered above, which would be correct.

The hundred of Battle

6 April 1524
(E179/189/127)
13 Feb 1525
(E179/189/133)

Symon Merser F	2s
- - - -	
Corneles Androwis Docheman	8d
- - - -	
Anyonye Denaybone F	2s 6d
Gorge Joyce Docheman	8d
John Frambofe A	1s
- - - -	
Corneles Capper Docheman	8d
- - - -	
Peter Byshopp F	8d

- - - -
John Petygrewe Scotte 8d
- - - -
Wlliam Nele F (1525) 8d

10 November 1539
(E179/190/187)

John Frondebeyff A 2s
John Laby A 6s
Wyllm Velo A 1s
George Johonson A P

3 May 1549
(E179/190/233)

Alyens
Harman Stempe D 25s 4d
George Johnson Flemyng P
Petre Byneham F P
Antonye Gyles A P
servauntt to
Robert Harrys

12 April 1550
(E179/190/239)

(return incomplete)

26 March 1551
(E179/190/244)

(lacks Battle)

4 March 1552
(E179/190/247)

Alyens
Charles Jerett D 8s

Harmer Stempe D 25s
Fryso Harmer
Docheman P
his servaunte
William a Woode
Docheman P
Symon F P
Peter Byman F P
Antonye Gyles F P

1 February 1560
(E179/190/266)

Aliens
Harman Stempe 14s
Nicholas Jarret L 2s 8d

10 October 1572
(E179/190/283)

Alyens
Herman Stempe 2s
Lamberte Fleete P
John Platten P

27 July 1576
(E179/190/298)

Alyens
James Minidge 3s 4d
Christofer Burdett P
Lambert Flitt P
John Platten P
William Welles P

10 October 1595
(E179/190/332)

(nil)

The rape of Pevensey

The hundred of Loxfield

6 April 1524
(E179/198/117)

[Wadhurst]
John Bodewyn F 2s
Laurence Streter F 2s
Peter Herby F 2s
Reme le Bages F 2s

[Mayfield]

(nil)

[Buxted?]
Gylbert Verall F 8d
William Lovet F 8d
Peter Russell F 8d
Colen Lambert F 8d

Uncertain, c. 1525
(E179/189/165)

[Greenhurst]
John the Brewer F 8d
- - - -
Bartylmewe Docheman 8d

29 November 1543
(E179/190/191)

[Wadhurst]

Alyens

Lawrens Bluytt 8d
Peter Russell 16d
Wylliam Obery P
Peter Turner P
Maryon Gardyner P
John Nayler P
John Gardymbas P

[Mayfield]

Alyens

Peter Stoberne P
Nycholas Relf P
Glade the colyer P

[Uckfield]

Alyens

Hubberd Skrett P
servant to Robert Vaut
Lawrens Peterson 4s

[(Green)Herst]

Alyens

Charlys 3s 4d
Perygo 8d
John Penyon 4d
Gylbert 8d
John Morrell 4d
Angell 4d

2 May 1549
(E179/190/237)

[Wadhurst]

Alyens

Marian Lambert P
Nicholas Lambert P
Stephan Collet P
John Rowbye P
[Jo]hn [Har]ve P
[Reme H]arv[e?] P

[Mayfield]

Peter Stoburne A P

(lacks remainder of Loxfield)

21 April 1550
(E179/190/239)

[Wadhurst]

Alyens

Gellet Russell F 2s
Barthelmewe Polyne P
John Rowebowe P
John Harrewe P
Maryen Gardiner P
Gilbert Frenshe P
William the parishe P
prest of Maughefeld

[Mayfield]

Aliens

Peter Stoneborne P
Rowe the collier P

[Framfield]

Alyens

Menten Tyller P
Symon Clerygo P
Reme Tyller P

[Buxted]

Alyens

Charles Garrete 20s
John Penyon 1s
Marye Shelley P
wydowe
Peter Lambert P
Hambrey P
John de Mounle P
Hambonye Fraunces P
Hambonye Bordye P

26 March 1551
(E179/190/237)

[Wadhurst]

Alyens

John Trantham P
Steven Collete P
John Harvey P
John Robey P
Worrell Robeys man P
[Tosain?] his man also P
Barton Powllen P
William Duchin P
Thomas Ramset P
Symon Heyward P
Remy Harvye P
Peter Bigod P
Olde Gilberd P
Marryan Gardiner P

[Mayfield]

Peter Stoborne A P

[Framfield]

Quinten Tyller A P
servant to Nicholas Eversfelde

[Greenhurst]

Alyens

John Rynion	P
Marten Sampson	P
James Sampson	P
Gyllyam the collier	P

28 April 1552
(E179/190/247)

[Wadhurst]

Alienes	
Old Gylbert	P
Marian Gardiner	P
Marians servant	P
Stephen Collet	P
John Pynnen	1s
Mihell Hedell	P
John Roboye	P
Roboyes servant	P

[Mayfield]

Peter Stoporne A	P

[Framfield]

Peter Quintun A	1s

7 February 1560
(E179/190/265)

[Wadhurst]

Aliens	
John Royboy	P
Richard Benet	P

[Framfield]

Widowe of Thomas Smythe	P

30 September 1572
(E179/190/283)

[Lamberhurst]

John Gunson A	P

10 July 1576
(E179/190/298)

[Wadhurst]

John Johnson A	P

[Mayfield]

Gabrell Penson A	P

As it stands roll 237 (1549) contains some anomalies. Both Wadhurst and East Grinstead occur twice, so that in the case of Wadhurst, John Roboye and Stephen Collet appear twice. Bartholomew Polen appears in both Wadhurst and Danehill Horsted. It is evident that the first membrane of the roll as it is now constituted belongs to a different subsidy. I have transferred its entries to 1551, the roll for which (242) otherwise lacks Loxfield hundred. As a result Bartholomew Polen is found at Danehill Horsted in 1549, moves to Wadhurst in 1550 and is still there in 1551. This rearrangement seems to work satisfactorily in other respects too. The second membrane, which is for East Grinstead, contains no aliens, but is dated to the reign of Henry VIII and is also an intruder in this roll.

The hundred of Hartfield

6 April 1524
(E179/189/117)

Garfysh F	8d
- - - -	
John Blank F	2s
- - - -	
John Myskyn F	8d
Raynald Robyn A	8d
Jakes Asces A	8d
Maryon A	8d
Jakatt A	8d
Fraunces Hankes A	8d
Nicholas Robard A	8d
Antony Capell A	8d
John Garner A	8d
Laussnet A	8d
Petter A	8d
Jelye A	8d
John Fettery A	8d
Kennad A	8d
Peter A	8d
Nicholas Groute A	8d
- - - -	
Filpott Lambert A	8d
Lambert Lyllat A	8d
Robert Temple A	8d
William Brisball A	8d
John Dessat A	8d
John Corse A	8d
Colne Capyll A	8d
Allyn Moris A	8d
John Gossatt A	8d
Nouell May A	8d
William Russell A	8d
Perese Botell A	8d

(E179/189/164)

Effryt Pennyon A	8d
Jacobe Caserall A	8d
Colles Robyn A	8d
William Milkylbyll A	8d
- - - -	
Nicholas Jenkes A	2s
John Temple A	2s
Fraunssis Cheverell A	8d

[Wethyham]

Michell Shosmyth F	8d
Alyn colyar F	8d

29 November 1543
(E179/190/191)

Alyens servants to Mrs Bower	
More	P
Fremyng	P
Thomas Collyar	P
Nycolas Growt	P
John Gardener	P
Antony Fownder	P
John Turke	P
Peter Collyar	P
William Bordyn	P
Peter Flemyng	P
- - - -	
Gyllam Thomas	P
Gavylls prisoner	
- - - -	
servants to parson Levett	
Gylberd the collyar	P
Charlis	P
Scrace	P
- - - -	
Adryan Reder	P
servants to Adrian Reder	
Bartelmewe Pountye	P
John Godfrye	P
Frauncis Jayms	P
- - - -	
servants to Leonard Callis	
Cardo Kervyle	P

2 May 1549
(E179/190/237)

(lacks Hartfield)

21 April 1550
(E179/190/239)

Alyens	
Barthelmew Fyner	P
Frymynge Collier	P
Fetter Colyer	P
Mores Fyner	P
Myclowe Colyer	P

26 March 1551
(E179/190/242)

Barthelmew Pownting A	P
Leonarde Curlyffe A	P
Davye A	P
- - - -	
Alyens	
Peter Collyer	P
Nycholas Rychard	P
Fremiyng the fyner	P
Mowery the fyner	P

28 April 1552
(E179/190/247)

Alenes	
Peter Collyar	P
Jurden	P
Fremyng	P
Marian	P
Jhon his man	P
Bartyllmewe fyner	P
Mathewe Bewser	P
Kyrwyn Carde	P

7 February 1560
(E179/190/265)

aliens	
Peter Collyer de Newbrege	P
Dawne hamerman de Paroke	2s
Gyfferd the collier	P
Frimyng Stephen colloer	P

[Withyham]

Bartholomew Powntyngs	P
Fynche	P

30 September 1572
(E179/190/283)

Alyens	
Gyllam Pykes	P
Phillipp	P

10 July 1576
(E179/190/298)

[Hartfield]

Alyens	
John Arthur	10s
Gyllam Fortell	P
Anthonye Lavyntor	P
Freming	P
Peter Marygold	P

[Withyham]

James the Smyth	P

The hundred of Rotherfield

6 April 1524
(E179/189/117)

John Colyen F	8d
- - - -	
John F	8d

29 November 1543
(E179/190/191)

alyons

Gyllet Russell	4s
Jakes Hanizett	1s
Godderd alias Kyng	1s
William Home alias Shynny prisoner to Jamis Oxley*	2d

2 May 1549
(E179/190/237)

Alyens

John Goderd	2s
Jakes Hamyng	2s
Jakes Hanyng junr	P

21 April 1550
(E179/190/239)

Jakes Hanynges	(amounts)
John Goderd	wanting)

26 March 1551
(E179/190/242)

Alyens

Jakes Honynges	P
John Goderd	2s
Peter Rowland	P
Gloves Jonney	P

28 April 1552
(E179/190/247)

Alienes

Jakes Hanyng	2s
John Godderd	16d
John Masens	P
Audrian Lauris	P
John Lucian	P
Antony Lucian	P

7 February 1560
(E179/190/265)

[South Borough]

Aliens

Hugo	P
Guilam Pygot	P

30 September 1572
(E179/190/283)

Alyens

Gyllam Pycott	P
Renny Durrant	P
Furr' servaunt to Alexander Farmer	P
Peter Lambert servaunt to John Carpenter	P
Pullen servaunt to John Barham	P
Anthonye Pavye servaunt to John Porter	P

10 July 1576
(E179/190/298)

[Rotherfield]

Remy Durraunt A	P

[Frant]

Alyens

Nicholas Good servaunt to John Saundre	P
Pollen	P

* The fact that William Home paid 2d on goods seems to preclude his being an alien. In 1543 2d was the poll tax paid by an alien; the minimum aliens paid on goods was 4d. Otherwise identification with John Wybarn's ironworker Gilham Holmes would have seemed likely.

The hundred of Danehill Horsted

6 April 1524
(E179/189/164)

(nil)

29 November 1543
(E179/190/191)

Servants to Sir Wylliam Barrentyne

Jordayne Bowelly	P
Jamis Jenne	P
Bartyne Pullyne	P
Davyd Hawtont	P
Antony Fownder	P
Robert Tylar	P
Nycolas	P
Antony Tylar	P
Jamis Collyar	P
Peter Gayn	P
Obury Morrys	P
John Colyar	P
John Pycarte	P
Rowland Mocumlye	P

2 May 1549
(E179/190/237)

Alyens

James Farnes	1s
Robert Tyler	P
Anthonye Tyller	1s
James Tyller	P
Jorden de Lawnse	1s
Barthelmew Polen	P
Charles Polen	P
John Vernes	1s
Richard Monyon	1s
Barthelmew Jorden	P
Denys Jorden	P
Thomas Picard	P
Umfrey Polen	P
Thomas Monyon	P

21 April 1550
(E179/190/239)

Robert Tyller A	P

26 March 1551
(E179/190/242)

Alyens

John Fernes	1s
Peter Gayne	P
Mychell Alyne	P
Robert Tyller	P
Peter Belly	P
Anthonye Tyller	P
Onyon Russell	P
John Pollerd	P

28 April 1552
(E179/190/242)

Alyenes

James Farnyse	1s
John Pekerde	P
Robert Tylor	P
Henry Marian	P
Antony Tylor	P
Peter Bely	P
Owen Russell	P
Moris Lerby	P
Marian Dawe	P
Charrelles Lerby	P
Antony Lerby	P

7 February 1560
(E179/190/265)

Aliens

Anthony Tylor	P
William Pavy	P
uxor at fill'	PP

30 September 1572
(E179/190/283)

Alyens

John Pyckard	P
John Gyllam	P
Gyllam Hatto	P

10 July 1576
(E179/190/298)

(nil)

The hundred of Danehill Sheffield

6 April 1524
(E179/189/164)

John May Doucheman	2s 6d
Edward Groyne Doucheman	8d
Lose Doucheman	8d

29 November 1543
(E179/190/191)

alynes servants to the duke of Norfolke	
Coly	4d
Tantas	4d
Peter Laby	4d
Maryon	P
Jellett	4d
Blake John	4d
Jamis Fyllar	P
Lewis Collyar	P
Jelett Colyar	P
Jorden Moyner	P
John Myschaue	P
Jakes Collyar	P
Jelett the younger	P
Nawde	P
Tantas	P
servant to John Vere	
Stevyn Almon	P

2 May 1549
(E179/190/237)

Alyens	
Peter Gage	1s
James Swage*	1s
Jellet Barten	2s
John Barten	P
Gylgys Neve	P
John Gomer	1s
Peter Gomer	P
Mores Larkes	P
John Showse	1s
Marian Predome	P
Peter Carler	1s
Reme Kelet	P
John Morrell	1s

21 April 1550
(E170/190/239)

Aliens	
Peter Carler	1s
Peter Gagge	1s
Peter Lorman	1s

26 March 1551
(E179/190/242)

Alyens	
Maryan Mocombell wydowe	1s
Jellete Rewy	P
Comes wydowe	P
John Rewy	1s
Gylles Neve	P
Martyne Peter	P
John and Gylles	PP
servants to John Rowye	
Clemente Collyer	P
Thomas Borde	1s
Anthony Border	P
Gyllam the Fyner	P
Marryan Perdone	P
John Rewy	P
Peter Carler	1s
Remy Ayelar	P

28 April 1552
(E179/190/247)

Alyenes	
Clement Malet	P
Marten	P
John Bordet	P
Antony Bordet	P
John Barten	P
Gyllet Barten	P
Gylles Newewe	P
Peter	P
Mother Combe	P

7 February 1560
(E179/190/265)

Aliens	
John Barton	2s

* The eight names from James Swage to John Showse have been superimposed on erasures. 'Mores Larkes' should obviously read 'Mores Larbe', the 's' perhaps showing through from the erased entry. But other entries are unsatisfactory, both here and elsewhere. 'Reme (Kelet?) (1549) and 'Remy Ayelar' (1551) should probably read 'Remy Tyler'. In 1550 he was correctly entered at Framfield, but the Westminster denization roll had included him among the duke of Norfolk's ironworkers.

Gyllam Hato 2s
John Artor P
Clement Collyer P

30 September 1572
(E179/190/283)

Carden Tostet A P

10 July 1576
(E179/190/298)

Alyens
Myshawe P
Dynnys Carnellum P

The hundred of Rushmonden

6 April 1524
(E179/189/164)

[Rottingham]
John Ducheman 8d

29 November 1543
(E179/190/191)

Barnard Rycharson A 4d

2 May 1549
(E179/190/237)

Barnard Richardson A 1s
Lawrans Hamson A P

21 April 1550
(E179/190/239)

(nil)

26 March 1551
(E179/190/242)
Alyens
Peter Alman 1s
Anthony Lucas P
Jarman Tulloke 1s
John Gomer 1s
Anthony P
servant to the said Gomer
Barden 1s
Peter Gage 1s
Barnard Rychardson P

28 April 1552
(E179/190/247)

[Rottingham]
Barnarde Richardson A 1s
- - - -
Alienes
Peter Alman 18d
Antony Lucas P
Peter Gostocke P
Peter Gayge P
John Gummer P
Charrelles Pullyn P
Nicolas Laby P
Barden P
Gyllet P
Roger Gaunet P
Lenarde P

7 February 1560
(E179/190/265)

[Maresfield]
Aliens
Peter Almon 10s
Peter Gage D P
Charles Pollyn D P
David Hato D P
John Myshar alias Rovero D P

30 September 1572
(E179/190/283)

Alyens
Nycholas Gotyer 6s
Peter Debewe P
Peter servaunt to Gotyer P
Robert Blowe P
Maryan Olde P

10 July 1576
(E179/190/298)

Alyens
Maryan Olde P
Myshawe P

The hundred of East Grinstead

6 April 1524
(E179/189/117)

[Borough]

Guye Deryk stranger 8d

29 November 1543
(E179/190/191)

(nil)

2 May 1549
(E179/190/237)

(nil)

21 April 1550
(E179/190/239)

(nil)

26 March 1551
(E179/190/242)

Henry Thomas A P

28 April 1552
(E179/190/247)

Harri Thomas A P

7 February 1560
(E179/190/265)

Anthony Burdewe P

30 September 1572
(E179/190/283)

Alyens
George Gyles P
Peter Busse P

[Borough]

Harry Thomas A P

10 July 1576
(E179/190/298)

[Borough]

Henry Thomas A P

The hundred of Lindfield Arch

6 April 1524
(E179/189/119)
16 April 1524
(E179/189/126)

Peter Arnold A (1524) 2s

Francis Flote A labourer (1525) 8d

29 November 1543
(E179/190/191)

Alyens
John Johnson P
servant
to Harry Lucas
Harry Lucas 5s
Cornelius P
servant to
the said Harry
Cornelys Harmon P

2 May 1549
(E179/190/237)

(lacks Lindfield Arch)*

21 April 1550
(E179/190/239)

Alyens
Harry Lucas 2s
Nycholas Fownder P
John Johnson P
James Gascon P

26 March 1551
(E179/190/237)

Alyens
Henry Lucas 2s
John Johnson P
James Gascon P
Nycholas Founder 1s

28 April 1552
(E179/190/247)

Alienes
Henry Lucas 2s
John Johnson P
The Founder P

7 February 1560
(E179/190/265)

Aliens
John Pycard P

Guillam Daglon P

30 September 1572
(E179/190/283)

(nil)

10 July 1576
(E179/190/298)

(nil)

* As explained under Loxfield, the first membrane of 190/237 (which contains an entry for Lindfield Arch) properly belongs to 1551 and has been transferred here.

The hundred of Dill

6 April 1524
(E179/189/123)

[Hellingly]
Peter Frenshman 8d

29 November 1543
(E179/190/191)

[Isenhurst]
Alyens not worth 20s
Gyles Myner A servant to John Baker P
Peter Wete A servant to the said John P
Petter Botten A servant to the said John P
Robert Caron A servant to William Woddy P

2 May 1549
(E179/190/237)

[Isenhurst]
Peter Whitt A 2s
- - - -
(Gawnt A P
(John Bottinge A P
(servants to John Baker)

21 April 1550
(E179/190/239)

[Isenhurst]
Peter Whit A 2s
John Bottinge A P

26 March 1551
(E179/190/242)

[Isenhurst]
Peter Whit A 4s

Frenshmen
(Gow A P
(Gow A P
(Nycolas A P
(Harye A P
(Servantes to Mr Goddard Walsh)

28 April 1552
(E179/190/247)

[Isenhurst]
Peter Whit A 4s

7 February 1560
(E179/190/265)

[Isenhurst]
Alyenes
Roger Tankerell 2s
Anthony Pottell 2s
Nycholas Forrell 2s

30 September 1572
(E179/190/283)

Alyens
Arnolde Duchmen P
William Hambleton P
Leonard Beck P

10 July 1576
(E179/190/298)

[Hellingly]

Anthony Frenchman	P
Nicholas Frenchman	P
Leonard Bekes	P
Wylliam Hambleton	P
John Peters	P

The hundred of Shiplake

12 Dec 1524
(E179/189/146)

[Laughton?]

Henry Potte A	6s

[Rype]

John Sand [A?]	[?]

29 November 1543
(E179/190/191)

[Hoathly and Waldron]

Alyens

John Rowland A	P
George Morrys A servant to Nicholas Eversfield	P
John Trowley A servant to the said Nicholas	P
John Cosenet A to the said Nicholas	P
- - - -	
Marten A servant to Nicholas Pelham esquire	P

2 May 1549
(E179/190/237)

(lacks Shiplake)

21 April 1550
(E179/190/239)

[Chiddingly]

John Sherwood*	P

26 March 1551
(E179/190/242)

[Chiddingly]

John Scherin A servant to John Frenche	P
William A servant to the said John	P

[Hoathly]

Nicholas A	1s

28 April 1552
(E179/190/247)

[Hoathly]

Nicholas Varyet A	P

[Chiddingly]

Robert Blant A	P
Peter Barham A	P

7 February 1560
(E179/190/265)

(nil)

30 September 1572
(E179/190/283)

Laurence A servant to John French	P
German Frenchman A	P

* Not stated to be an alien, but taxed as such.

The hundred of Barcombe

23 November 1543
(E179/190/193)

[Barcombe]

Lewes Reignold A servant to John Webbe	P
- - - -	

[Newick]

John West A	4d

4 May 1549
(E179/190/235)

John West A	1s
- - - -	
William Car A	3s
- - - -	
John Cole A	P

4 March 1550
(E179/190/239)

William the Scotte	18d
John Weston A	P
John Polle A	P

12 April 1551
(E179/190/246)

William the Scotte	1s
- - - -	
John West A	P
(John Coler?)*	

1 April 1552
(E179/190/247)

John West A	12d
William Michell A	P

5 February 1560
(E179/190/267)

Peter Unkle A	P

16 May 1563
(E179/190/274)

[Barcombe]

(nil)

[Newick]

Peter Willen A	P

30 September 1572
(E179/190/283)

(nil)

12 July 1576
(E179/190/299)

John Harvye	P
John Cavenche	P
Gillam Hussher	P
Gillam Bygood	P
Peter A	P
Gillam A	P

* This blurred entry is incomplete and is perhaps intended to be deleted.

The hundred of Streat: north borough

23 November 1543
(E179/190/193)

(nil)*

4 **May 154**
(E179/190/235)*

Cornell A	P
- - - -	
Harman Tulli A	P

4 March 1550
(E179/190/239)

Cornell A	P
- - - -	
Herman Tully A	P

12 April 1551
(E179/190/246)

Cornell A	P
- - - -	

Harman Tully A P

1 April 1552
(E179/190/247)

Nicholas the Founder A P
- - - -
Herman Tull' A P
- - - -
Cornell A P
Jeffrey A P

5 February 1560
(E179/190/267)

George Tullye A P
Peter Gayne A P
John Meshowe A P
- - - -
John Cary A 2s
James Fernis A P
Nycholas Homan P
Nycholas Demerowe P
- - - -
Morres Larbye A P
Glowe A P

16 May 1563
(E179/190/274)

[Hoathly]

Peter Gayne A P
George Tullie A P
and his wyffe A P

[Ardingly]
Aliens
Anthonye Hewashe P
and his wyffe P
Fraunces Obbell P
and his wyffe P
Charles Growte P
and his wyffe P

[Balcombe]

(nil)

30 September 1572
(E179/190/283)

George Tollye A
and Jone his wyfe A PP
Crystofer Rossoll servant A P

12 July 1576
(E179/190/299)

Joane Tollye A P

* Cornelys Breten, who paid the poll tax in 1543, and Cornelis Burton, Goffe (deleted) Shomaker, and Richard Marion, who all paid the poll tax in 1549, probably belonged to Streat South.

The hundred of Buttinghill

23 November 1543
(E179/190/193)

[Cuckfield]
Jerard Ducheman A P
his* servant
- - - -
William Ducheman A P
- - - -
Thomas Nicholas D L 16d

4 **May 1549**
(E179/190/235)

Davy A 1s
and his ij sisters PP
Marian A P
Jerman A P
Thomas Brosball A 1s
John Cari A 1s
Nicholas Tiller A 1s
Antoin Beg A P
Roveri A P
Renni A P
Loyes Botri A P
Loye A P
Thomas Bordell A P
Antoin Bordell A P
Pebealet A P
Mihell A P
- - - -
William Johnson A P

4 March 1550
(E179/190/239)

Holland Seller A	P
- - - -	
William Johnson A	P
Adrian Ridleygh A	P
- - - -	
John Robery A	P
Marien A	P
John Care A	1s
Nicholas Tiler A	1s
Remy A	P
Loye A	P
Gellet Low A	1s
Clement A	P
Lowes A	P
Jeloys A	P
Thomas Burdel A	P
John Misse A	P

12 April 1551
(E179/190/246)

Holland Celler A	P
- - - -	
William Johnson A	P
Adrian A	P

[Crawley and Worth]

John Hauneng A	1s
Jordyn A	1s
John Cary A	1s
Henri his man	P
Nycolas Tiller A	1s
Lewes A	P
John his man	P
Baringtons man A	P
John Messon A	1s
The potter A	P

1 April 1552
(E179/190/247)

William Johnson A	P
George Tull' A	P
Holland Seller A	P

[Crawley and Worth]

John Messowe A	1s
John Cary A	1s
John forger	1s
Peter Bylwarn A	P
Jemis finer A	P
Dawse the hammerman A	P
Jemis Colbor A	P
John Hans A	P
Cristofer Hans A	P

5 February 1560
(E179/190/267)

Blasse Bryda A	P
Peter Starre A	P
Peter Devall A	P

16 May 1563
(E179/190/274)

[Crawley]

Gabriell A	P

[Worth]

Aliens	
George Tyler	P
Blase Bryda	P
Rychard Whit	P
Gillome Rafe	P
John Jonsone	P
Gillome Dermetond	P
Danyell Collier	P

[Cuckfield]

John Carye A	P
Peter Lurye A	P

[Slaugham]

John Artor A	P
his wife A	P

[Balcombe]

Nicholas Lurie A	P
and his wyffe A	P
Nicholas Hune A	P

30 September 1572
(E179/190/283)

Pawco A	P
Morrys A	P
Quynale A	P
Charles Pullyn A	P
Bluetts ij frenchemen	PP

12 July 1576
(E179/190/299)

Anthonye Huashe A	P
John Rossett A	P
Robert Buse A	P
his ij sonnes A	PP
Glade A	P
his ij sonnes	PP
Nicholas Furrye A	P
Robert Tuck A	P
his ij sonnes	PP
Polter A	P
his sonne A	P

John Braye A	P
Fraunces Howbeth A	P
and his wyffe A	P
Robert Carmarynge A	P
Charles Pullen A	P
John Dallanton A	P

The rape of Bramber

The hundred of Burbeech

15 February 1560
(E179/190/268)

The forest of Saynt Lenards

Marigold A	P
servant to Roger Grateweke	
Jocab A	P
servant to the same Roger	

[Sedgwick]

Jamys Hennesey A	8s
Martyn Heath A	P
howsholder	

15 May 1563
(E179/190/344)

William Panny A	P
servant to Swayne and Ilman	
John Parrys A	P
servant with Swayne and Ilman	
Adrian A	P
with Roger Gratwike	
Jacob A	P
being with the same Roger	

22 October 1572
(E179/190/283)

[Ifield]

Audryan Duddinge A	6s
John Thowsandman A	6s

[--] **July 1576**
(E179/190/297)

[Ifield]

Adrian Dogen A	10s
his wife A	P
his son A	P
and ij daughters A	PP
John Towsand A	10s
his wife A	P
and two servauntes AA	PP
Peter Agamo A	P
his ij sonnes A	PP
and j servaunte A	P
Peter whelebarow maker A	P
and his wife A	P
John Taber A	P
and his mother A	P

The rape of Arundel

The hundred of Rotherbridge

22 October 1572
(E179/190/283)

[Petworth]

(nil)

[North Chapel]

Charles Payve	P
Nycholas Mores	P

[Loxwood]

Allyans

Hawns Tenrad	4s
Audryan Bussher	P
Mary Bussher his wife	P
Honybyn Lutery	P
Lucy his wife	P
John Manaforton	P
John Hussy	P
Julian Carye	P
Susanna Rammye	P
John Rickeawe	P

Jacob Conkell	P
George Kowsett	P

[Diddlesfold]

William Carden	P
and his wife	P

20 October 1595
(E179/190/334)

[Loxwood?]

Peter Madlier A	P
Robert Cocklie A	P

[North Chapel]

Ananias Hensey A	6s 8d

[Petworth]

Steven Hollier A	P

Many, or perhaps all, the aliens listed under Loxwood, including Honybyn Lutery, who moved on to Staple hundred by 1576, and Ananias Hensey (1595), were glassworkers. The other large group of glassworkers, including Peter Campe and three members of the Bongard family, were enrolled at Ashfold in Bury hundred in 1572.

The rape of Chichester

The hundred of Easebourne

18 September 1572
(E179/190/283)

[Linchmere]

Blase A	P

KENT

The lathe of Scray

The hundred of Cranbrook

(Wanting, c. **1524**)
(E179/125/324)

[John?] Savage A	8d
- - - -	
John Deryk A	8d
- - - -	
Felip Frare A	8d
- - - -	
Gye Spall A	8d

6 November 1541
(E179/124/240)

Alyens	
Laurence Frelyng a doucheman	10s
Lewys the Joyner of Gowethurst	10s
Symon Fork the glasier	P
Peter Whir D	P
John Sprynger	P
Gosvyn Brynger	P
Powles Walter	P
John Dale	P
Nicholas the Tynker	P
Sc[t?]one	P
John Crane	P

10 November 1543
(E179/124/259)

Askell de Wordon A	16d
- - - -	
Genkyn Crane A	4d
- - - -	
Gaskyn A	2d
Peter Whyte A	4d

John Spryngett A	2d
Edmund Saddler A	2d
John Frerend A	2d
Peter Husshe A	2d
Burkley Weston A	2d
Powllys Walter A	2d
- - - -	
Laurence Frelynge D	3s 4d
- - - -	
Lewys Valet A	4d

10 November 1544
(E179/125/273)

John Selyes A	2d
- - - -	
Lawrence Frelyng A	6s 8d
Jasper the ioyner A	20d
- - - -	
Joskyn A	4d
Peter Whyte A	20d
John Sprynget A	4d
- - - -	
Edmond Sadler A	4d
John Fremde A	4d
Peter Hushe A	4d

Burkeley Weston A	4d
Pawles Walter A	4d
- - - -	
Lewes Valette A	4d

12 April 1550
(E179/126/333)

Peter Whyte A	6s
John Sprynget A	P
William a Castell A	P
Jasper the Joyner	6s
Olyver Buke A	P
Mathewe Busse A	P

12 September 1572
(E179/126/423)

Peter White A	2s
Phillip Hellen A	P
John Peerson A	P
Easter Light A	P

(Obscure, c. **1600)**
(E179/127/533)

(nil)

The last return is indexed as 42 Elizabeth I, but is labelled 39 Elizabeth I on the wrapper.

The hundred of Berkeley

(Wanting, c. **1524**)
(E179/125/324)

Symon Petegrew A	8d

10 November 1543
(E179/124/259)

John Selys A	4d

Only these aliens were returned in Berkeley hundred during the sixteenth century. An Englishman, 'Borden the hamarman', who paid 3s on goods in 1572 (E179/126/423), was presumably a member of the Barden family of hammermen, and will have worked at Biddenden hammer.

The hundred of Barnfield

(Wanting, c. **1524**)
(E179/125/324)

Garard Jonson A	2s

6 November 1541
(E179/124/240)

(nil)

10 November 1543
(E179/124/259)

(nil)

10 November 1544
(E179/125/273)

(nil)

12 April 1550
(E179/126/333)

John Bousellowe A P
John Cornelys A P

12 September 1572
(E179/126/423)

Thomas Vynsenall A P

(Obscure, c. **1600**)
(E179/127/533)

(nil)

The lathe of Aylesford

The hundred of West Barnfield

20 April 1525
(E179/124/186)

(illegible)

31 October 1541
(E179/124/249)

Arnold Johnsone A P
Peter Taylor A P
John Lasye A P

Wanting, c. **1543**
(E179/125/268)

*Mayes servauntes**
(ends:)
John Loye A P
- - - -
Arnold Johnson A 4d
- - - -
Peter Wyldorne A 4d
Maryan Rawe A P
- - - -
James Sherlowe A P
John Fowndrynge A 4d

12 April 1550
(E179/126/333)

George Rosell A P

12 September 1572
(E179/126/423)

John Michell A 2s
John Myllam A P
Peter Nonkell A P
John Ponynges A P
Peter Degoy A P

25 September 1600
(E179/127/527)

(nil)

* Thomas May was the employer of five servants, of whom the first four were English. These all paid on goods, viz.: the later ironmaster Bartylmewe Jeffrey (8d), Adams Cossam (6d), Richard Knell (2d) and John Hoke (2d).

This hundred was returned with Aylesford lathe as West Barnfield until 1543, but from 1550 onwards as Little Barnfield in Scray lathe.

The hundred of Brenchley

20 April 1525
(E179/124/186)

(illegible)

31 October 1541
(E179/124/249)

Gilbert Andersone A P
George Browne A 1s

Wanting, c. **1543**
(E179/125/268)

[Brenchley]

Rowland Clerke A P
- - - -
Henry Dove his* servaunt A P
John Ang[erfield] A 1s

[Horsmonden]

(nil)

[Lamberhurst]

George Browne A 4d

[--] **April 1550**
(E179/126/336)

[Brenchley]

Henry Blanke A P

* servant to Edmond Cougherst.

- - - -
John Ingerfyld D 2s
Nicholas Colleyn A P

[Horsmonden]

Gilbert Anderson P
Peter Fannor P

[--] **September 1572**
(E179/126/424)

(nil)

22 September 1599
(E179/127/522)

[Brenchley]

William Burlet A P
James Pome A P

The hundred of Washlingstone

20 April 1525
(E179/124/186)

[Barden]

Peter Stace Doucheman 2s

[Sunningleigh]*

John Kyng F 3s
Peter Frensheman 3s

4 November 1541
(E179/124/249)

(nil)

Wanting, c. **1543**
(E179/125/268)

[Speldhurst and Rustall]

Philyppe Davor A P

[Tudeley?]

Mr Vanes servauntes
(ends:)
Mathew Delamerr A P

[--] **April 1550**
(E179/126/336)

(nil)

[--] **September 1572**
(E179/126/424)

(nil)

22 September 1599
(E179/127/522)

(nil)

* Thomas May and John Barham each employed one English servant in this borough, Thomas Catcher and John Lorkyn respectively. As wages these men received one pound each as against the three pounds in wages at which each of the Frenchmen was assessed. May and Barham paid tax on goods worth eight and three pounds respectively.

The lowey of Tonbridge

1525

(no return survives)

20 October 1541
(E179/124/223)

John Johnsone A	P
John Marten A	P
John Flemmyng A	P
John Warde A	P

[Hadlow?]

Budden Bricke A	1s

[--] **November 1543**
(E179/124/262)

(nil)

Wanting, c. **1544**
(E179/125/275)

Leucas Jonsone A	2d
John Warde A	2d

[Hadlow]

Boden Dericke A	5s

Wanting, c. 1546
(E179/125/307)

[Wrotham]

Peter de Lilo D	4s
Robert Valye D	6s

[--] **April 1550**
(E179/126/336)

The Towne

Lowkas Jonson	P
Nicholas Danyell A	P
John Martyn A	P
Nicholas Wyngget A	P
Nicholas Powell A	P

[Hadlow]

Anthony A	P

[--] **September 1572**
(E179/126/424)

[Tonbridge]

Nicholas Wingat A	2s
Edward Garette A	2s
Arthure Shulder A	P
Peter Wynget A	P
servaunt to Henry Parker	

[Southborough]

John Broke A	2s
Laurence Duffyll A	2s
Maryan Dabat A	P
servaunt to David Willard	
Mighell Pycot A	P
servaunt to the said David	
Roberte Turner A	P
servaunt to Laurence Duffyll	
William Furrie A	P
servaunt to the said David	
Nicholas Furrie A	P
servaunt to the said David	
James Geryng A	P
servaunt to the said David	
John Berehowse A	P
servaunt to the said David	

[Hildenborough]

Fraunces Gyllyt A	P

[Wrotham]

Jefferay Drowant A	P

20 September 1598
(E179/127/515)

[Tonbridge]

Barnarde Cornelius A	P

[Hadlow]

Peter Wyngate A	P

[Southborough]

Robert Turner A	P

The hundred of Somerden

1525

(no return survives)

20 October 1541
(E179/124/223)

[Penshurst]

Lucas Johnsone A	2s
John Symon A P	
servaunte to John Pelsort	
Michael Peryon A	P
servaunte to John Pelsort	P
Tyse Shulle A	1s

[--] **November 1543**
(E179/124/262)

[Penshurst]

Lucas Jonsone A	4d
Titio Shull A	4d
John Svmon A	2d
John Frenchman A	P
Arnold Garrett A	P
Francis Gillot A	P

Wanting, c. **1544**
(E179/125/275)

[Penshurst]

Francis Gillote A	P
Egidius A	P
serviens Edwardo Lucas	
Barnardus A	P
serviens eidem Edwardo	

18 February 1560
(E179/126/391)

[Cowden]

William Brisboll A	P
servaunt to Andrew Firmynger	
Jeffrey Tootyng A	P
servaunt to the seid Andrew	

28 December 1563
(E179/126/393)

[Cowden]

Peter Russell A	P
Charles Mores A	P
Myshoe A	P
Bonford A	P

17 October 1572
(E179/126/422)

(nil)

Wanting, c. **1600**
(E179/127/530)

(nil)

The hundred of Westerham

1525
(no return survives)

20 October 1541
(E179/124/223)

[Westerham]

Richard Johnson a Skote	P
William Sely a Flemmyng	P

[Brasted]

Isaac Silibrigg ducheman	16d
John Ducheman A	P
servaunte to William Crowne	

[--] **November 1543**
(E179/124/262)

[Westerham]

John Engleche A	P
Peter Jonesone A	P

[Brasted]

Thomas Cobham A	P

Wanting, c. **1544**
(E179/125/275)

[Edenbridge]

Reginald Reyer A	P

[Brasted]

James Leynarde A P

18 February 1560
(E179/126/391)

[Edenbridge]

Reynold Rey A 2s
John Quinton A 2s
John A P
servaunt to Quynton
Gillam A P
servaunt to Mr Thatcher
Crippyn A P
and his servaunt P
Goldshoe A P

28 December 1563
(E179/126/393)

[Westerham]

William Sely A P

[Edenbridge]

Quynton Tyler A 2s
Stephen Cryppyn A P
Reynold Ray P

[Brasted]

Nicholas Holybrand A P

14 October 1572
(E179/126/422)

[Edenbridge]

Quynton Tyler A 6s
Reignold Ray A P
Mathew Washer A P

SURREY

The hundred of Tandridge

12 March 1551
(E179/185/258)

[Crowhurst]

John Johnson A P

[Godstone]

Mathew Vanwey A P

7 February 1552
(E179/185/265)

[Crowhurst]

John Joly A P
Charles A P

3 May 1557
(E179/185/275)

(nil)

27 July 1559
(E179/185/282)

[Lingfield]

Anthony A P
serviens Mri Spylman
Nycholas A P
serviens Mri Johannis Gresham

[Godstone]

Mathew Fanwaye A P
Gwyllyam Fraunces A P
serviens Roberti Rede

(Obscure, c. **1563**)
(E179/185/281)

[Lingfield]

Aliens
(John Bontinge P
(William Bontinge P
servauntes to Edward Askew of London

[Godstone]

Guyllam Fraunces A P
servaunte to Robert Reed

2 July 1576
(E179/185/308)

[Crowhurst]

Nicholas Gelke A P

[Tandridge]

Hugh Merchant A 6s 8d

20 October 1593
(E179/186/352)

(nil)

[--] October 1599
(E179/186/373)

[Godstone]

William Crill A	P
William Simons A	P
John Cukin A	P
Arott Boven A	P
Jacob Reddishe A	P
John Gylpin A	P
William Bruler A	P
Henrye Bruler A	P

The known ironworks in this hundred was Woodcock forge. This lay in the south of the hundred, within the parish of Lingfield, but in an enclave which was a detached part of Godstone parish. I have omitted aliens listed in northern parts of the hundred (Oxted, Bletchingley), but have included Godstone aliens. I have included the sole alien returned for Tandridge itself, Hugh Merchant (1576), since he was a former finer at Robertsbridge and Abinger forges. [Since this was written the forge at Crowhurst has been identified; see p. 390, n. 633].

The hundred of Reigate

12 March 1551
(E179/185/258)

(nil)

7 February 1552
(E179/185/265)

[Newdigate]

Richard Tyll A	P
Peter Ganny A	P

3 May 1557
(E179/185/275)

[Leigh]

Maryan Predron A	P
John Jolye A	P

[Newdigate]

Obre A	P
Roberte le Jean A	P
Symons A	P
Roybie A	P

27 July 1559
(E179/185/282)

[Leigh]

Maryan Predon A	P
serviens Mri Christoferi Dorrell	

[Newdigate]

serientes Mri Dorrell

Obraye A	P
Adryan A	P
Robert Younge A	P

(Obscure, c. **1563**)
(E179/185/281)

Parte of Nudgate

John Gomber A	P
servaunte with Mr Christofer Dorrell	
Peter Ubbris A	P
servaunte with Mr Christofer Dorrell	
Nicholas Collen A	P
servaunte with Mr Christofer Dorrell	
Nicholas Purford A	P
servaunte with John Rychebell	
Hollan Ussher A	P
servaunte with George Laby	

2 July 1576
(E179/18/308)

Lye and parte of Nudgate

Pownsley Prudam A	P
Guyllam Pickarde A	P
John Ellyot A	P

[Charlwood]

Nicholas Downe A	P

20 October 1593
(E179/186/352)

(nil)

[--] October 1599
(E179/186/373)

(nil)

The hundreds of Blackheath and Wotton

12 March 1551
(E179/185/262)

[Cranleigh]

aliens	
Charles Huysson	P
Crystyan Huysson	P
Adryan Huysson	P

[Dunsfold]

Bardyn A	P

[Abingworth]

Harman Thornton A	P

7 February 1552
(E179/185/265)

[Dunsfold]

Alyens	
Izamberd Lamye alias Bardyne	P
Roger	P

[Cranleigh]

John Mocomber A	P

[Abinger]

Harman Thorne A	P

3 May 1557
(E179/185/275)

[Abinger]

Harmon Thorne A	P

[Cranleigh]

aliens	
James Haward	P
John Myles	P

[Shalford]

aliens	
George Brewer	16d
William [Somersoe?]	P

27 July 1559
(E179/185/285)

[Dunsfold]

Alliens	
John Garrett	P
John Rewe	P

[Shalford]

Cornelyous Deryckson	3s 4d

[Cranleigh]

James Wayner	P

30 September 1571
(E179/185/301)

[Cranleigh]

Mariam Predam A	P

[Abingworth]

Hugh Marchaunt A	P
Steme Masse A	P
Oberie Larbie A	P

[Shalford]

John Cowper A	3s 4d
Thosaine John+	P
Nicholas Lamboren A	P

(Obscure, c. **1589**)
(E179/185/336)*

[Cranleigh]

James Wheler A	P
his wif A	P

28 October 1595
(E1791186/357)

(nil)

+ Entry crossed through. This looks like an attempt to make the alien finer, John Thousandman, who contributed to the subsidy at Ifield in Surrey 1572 and 1576, to pay in Surrey too.

* This subsidy, and those for the following years (186/351 (1593), 361 (1594), and 357 (1595), also recorded alien glassworkers in the boroughs of Ewhurst and Alfold, including Alverton Hensey and James Appel (at Ewhurst in 1589), Francis Doohoo (at Alfold in 1589), Peter Comley (at Alfold from 1589 to 1595) and Rafael the Italian (at Alfold 1594). It looks as though Francis Misshoo (Alfold, 1589), John Misher, Misshion or Myshowe (Alfold, 1593 to 1595), and Christmas (Ewhurst, 1589 and 1593) were also glassworkers, despite the similarity of their surnames to those of two ironworking families.

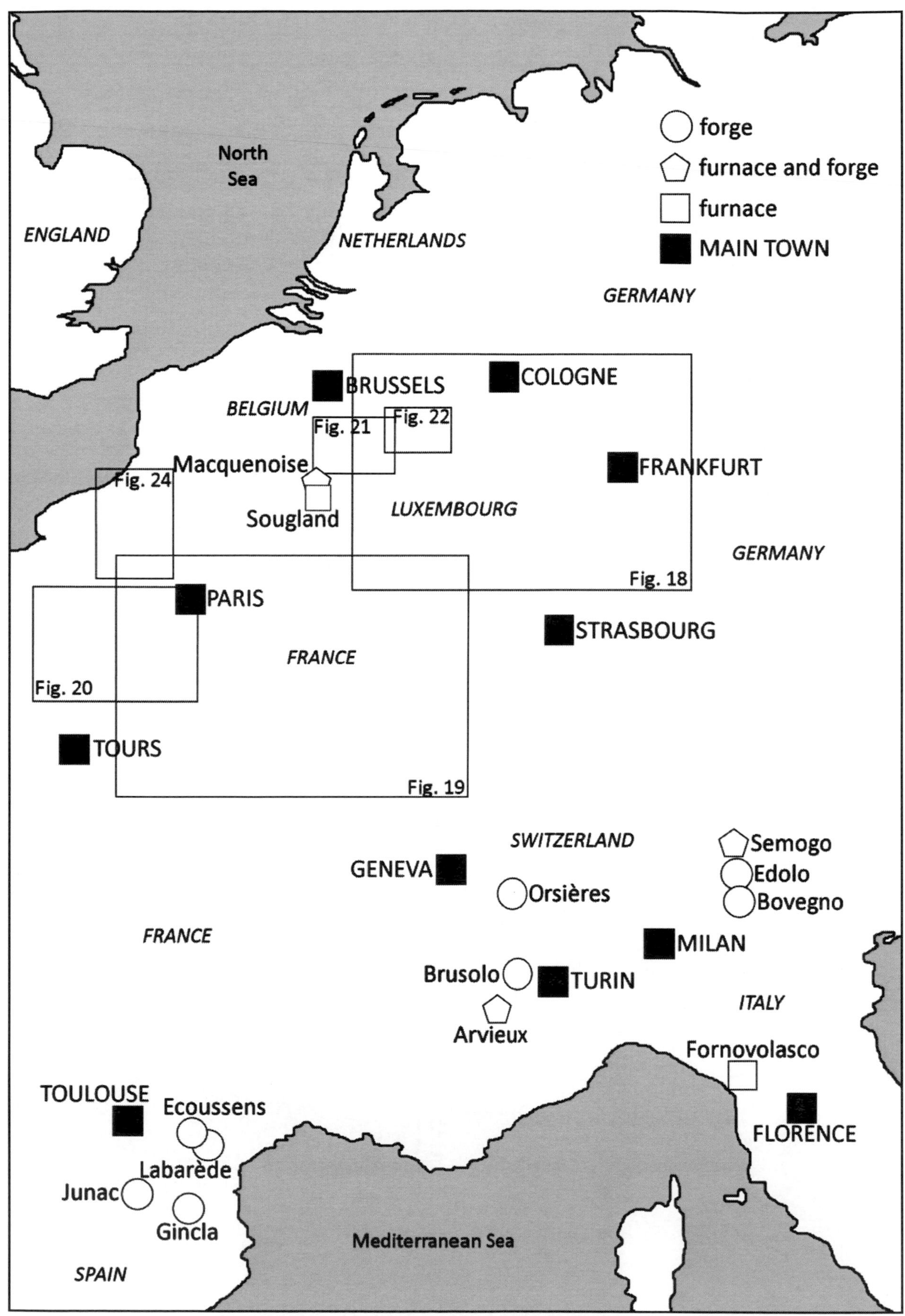

Figure 17: Map of Western Europe showing detailed area maps, and other sites mentioned in the text not included therein.

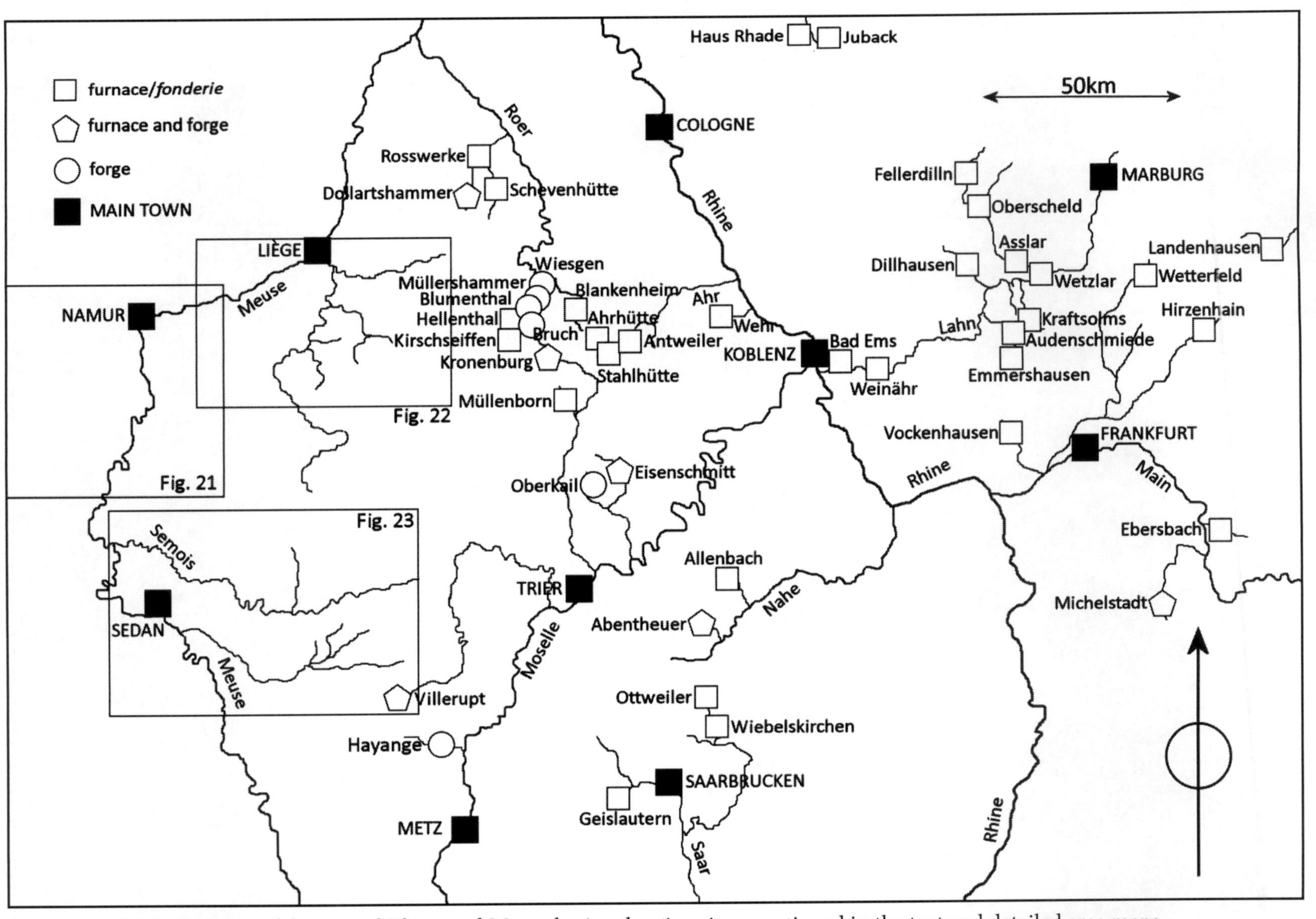

Figure 18: Map of the central Rhine and Meuse basins showing sites mentioned in the text and detailed area maps.

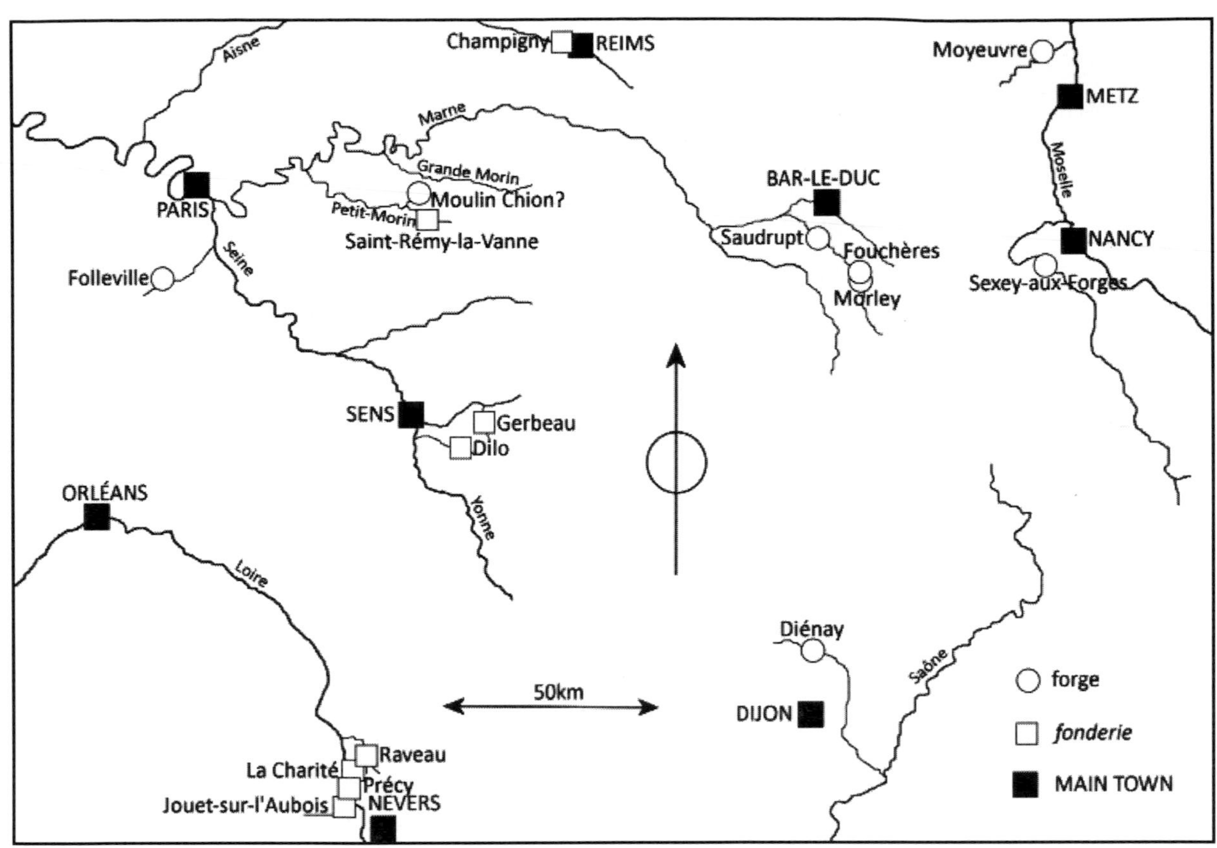

Figure 19: Map of Burgundy showing sites mentioned in the text.

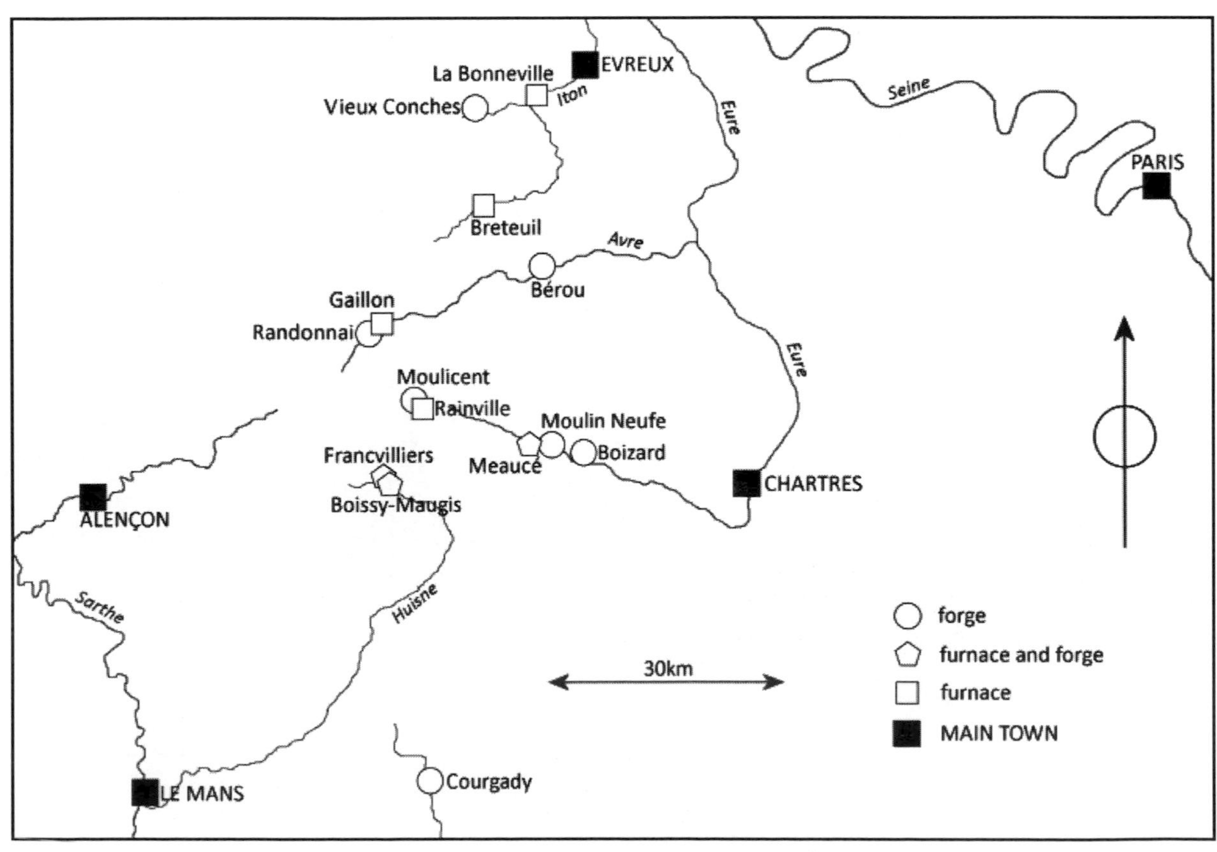

Figure 20: Map of the area west of Paris showing sites mentioned in the text.

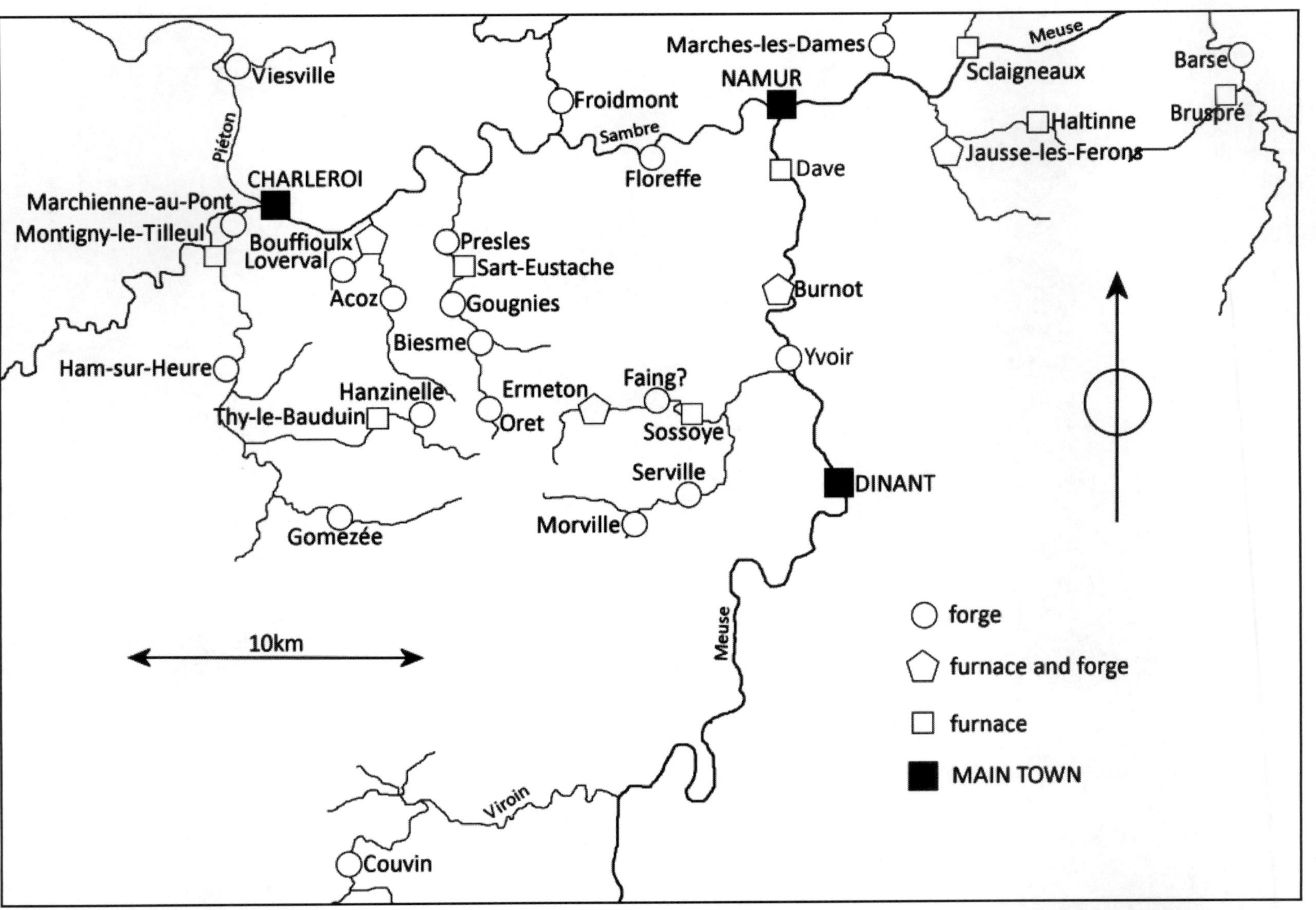

Figure 21: Map of the Entre-Sambre-et-Meuse and adjoining areas showing sites mentioned in the text

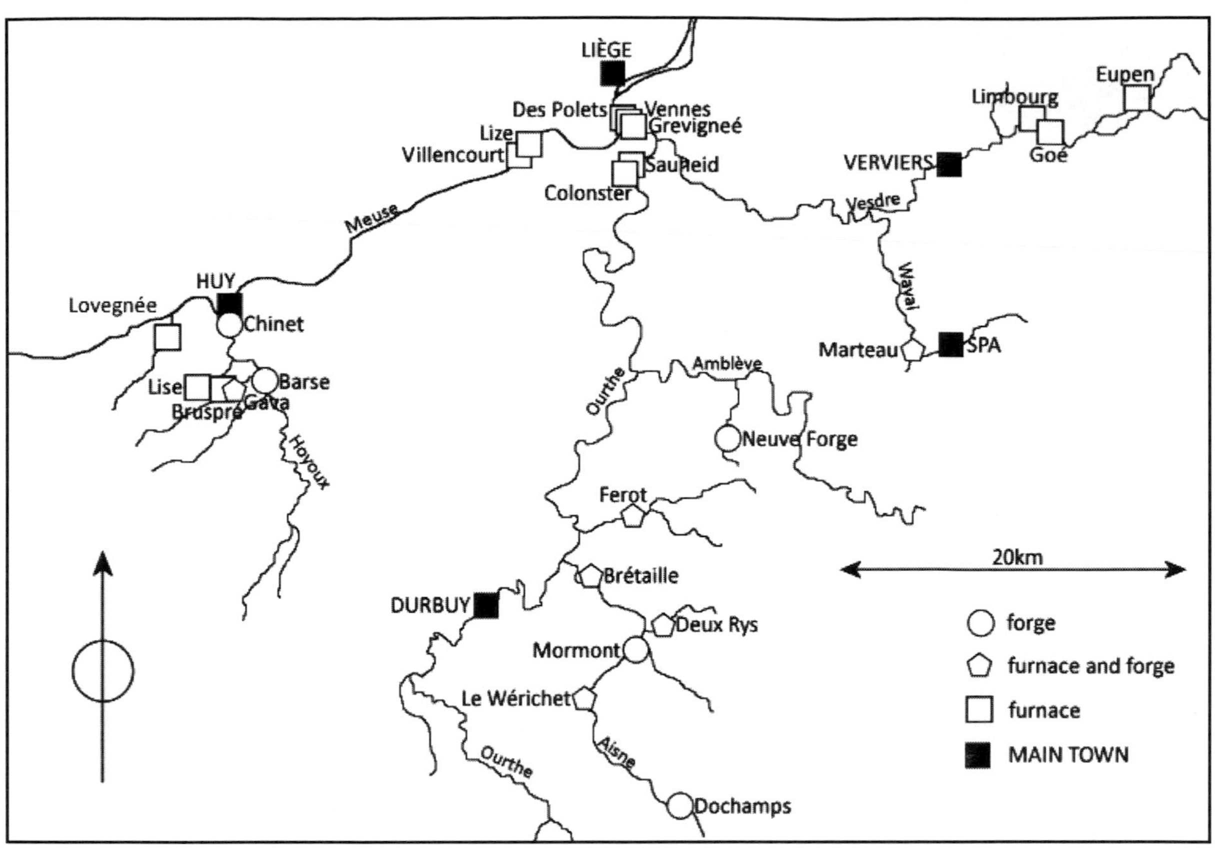

Figure 22: Map of sites in the Hoyoux, Ourthe and Vesdre basins of Belgium mentioned in the text.

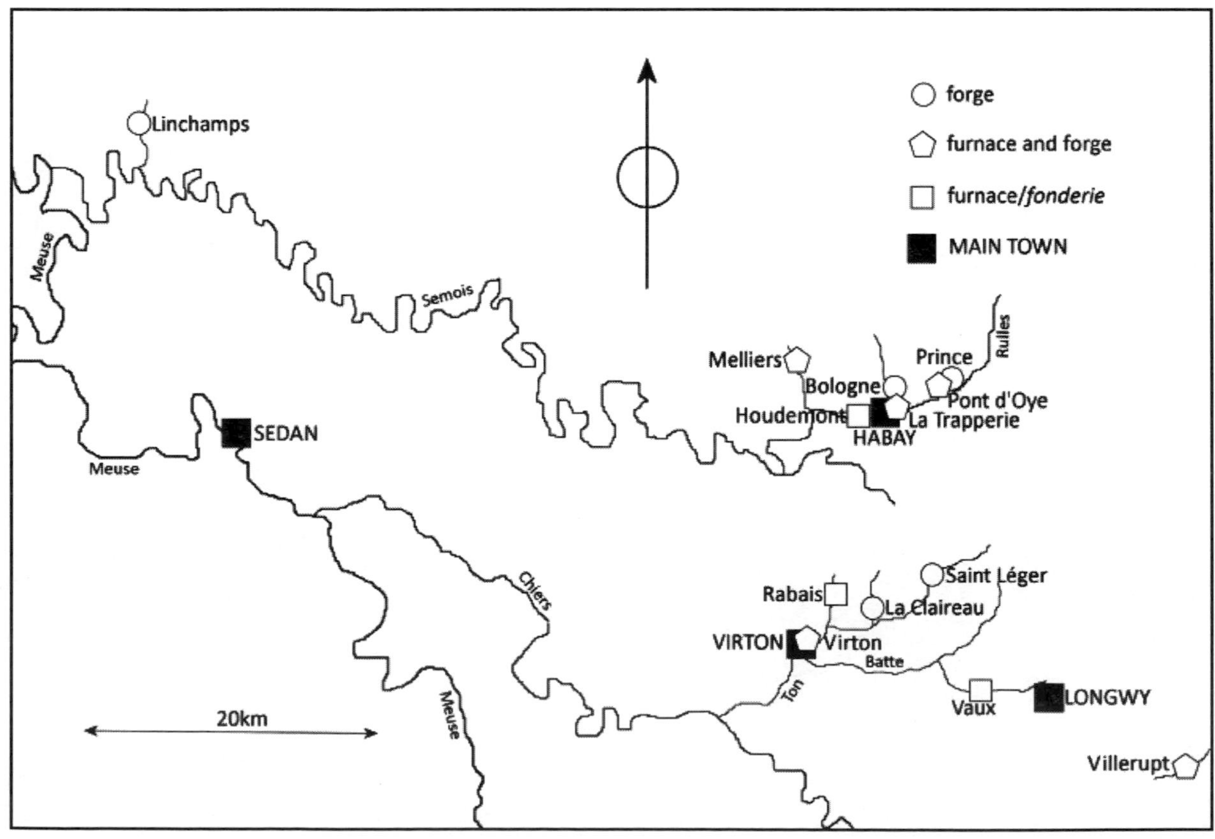

Figure 23: Map of southern Wallonia showing sites mentioned in the text.

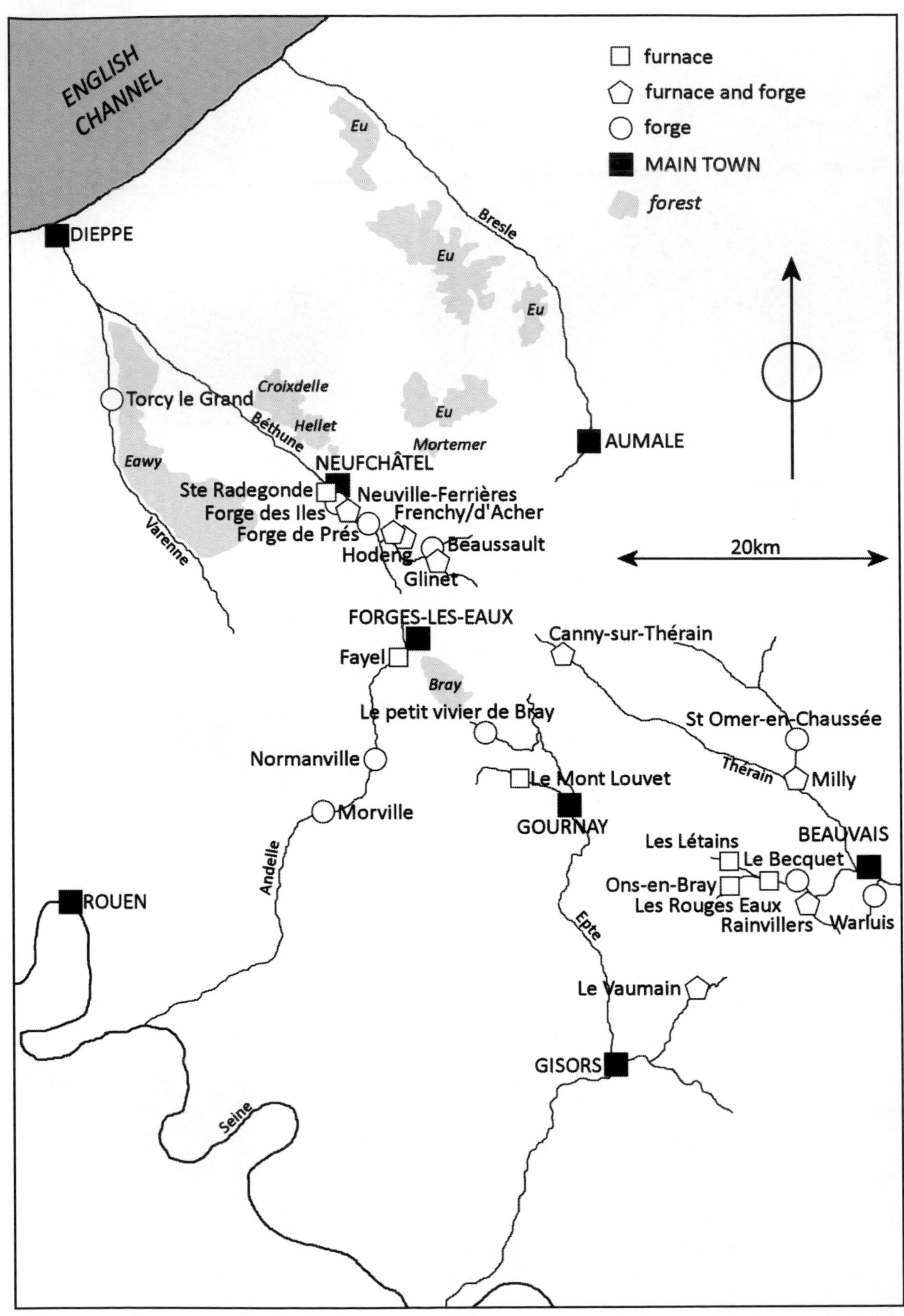

Figure 24: Map of the Pays de Bray showing sites mentioned in the text.

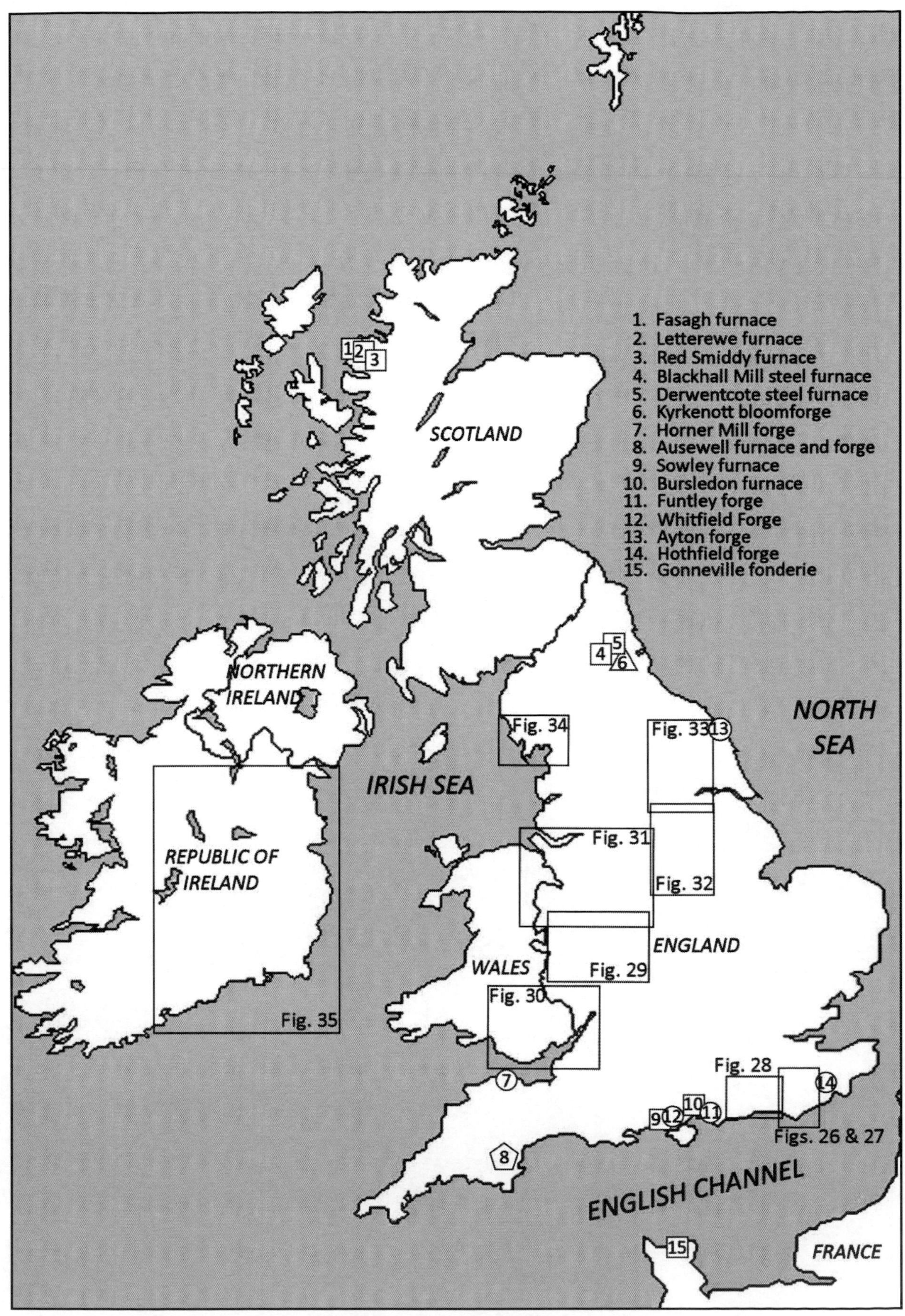

Figure 25: Map of the British Isles showing detailed area maps, and other sites mentioned in the text not included therein.

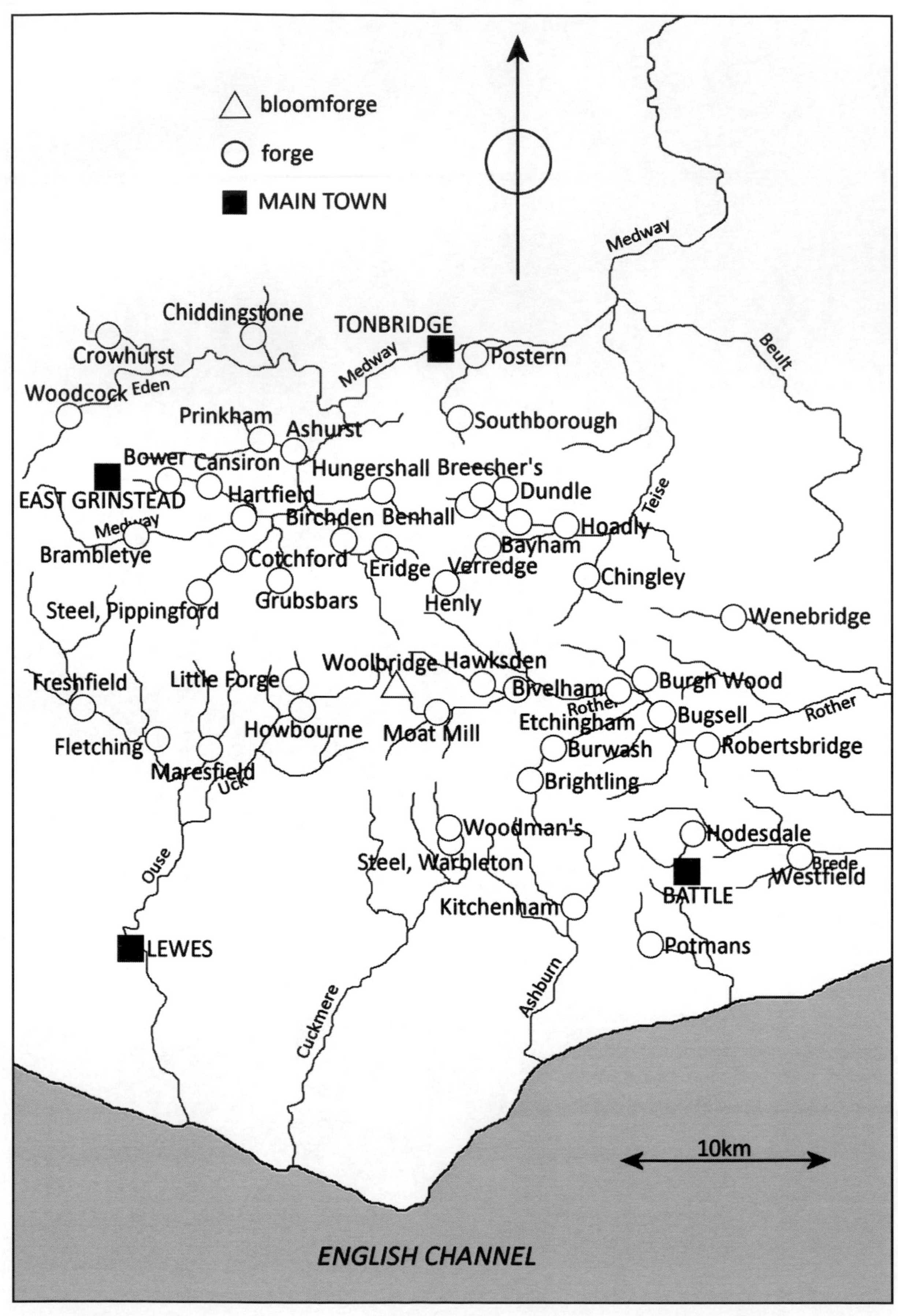

Figure 26: Map of the eastern Weald in south-east England showing forges mentioned in the text.

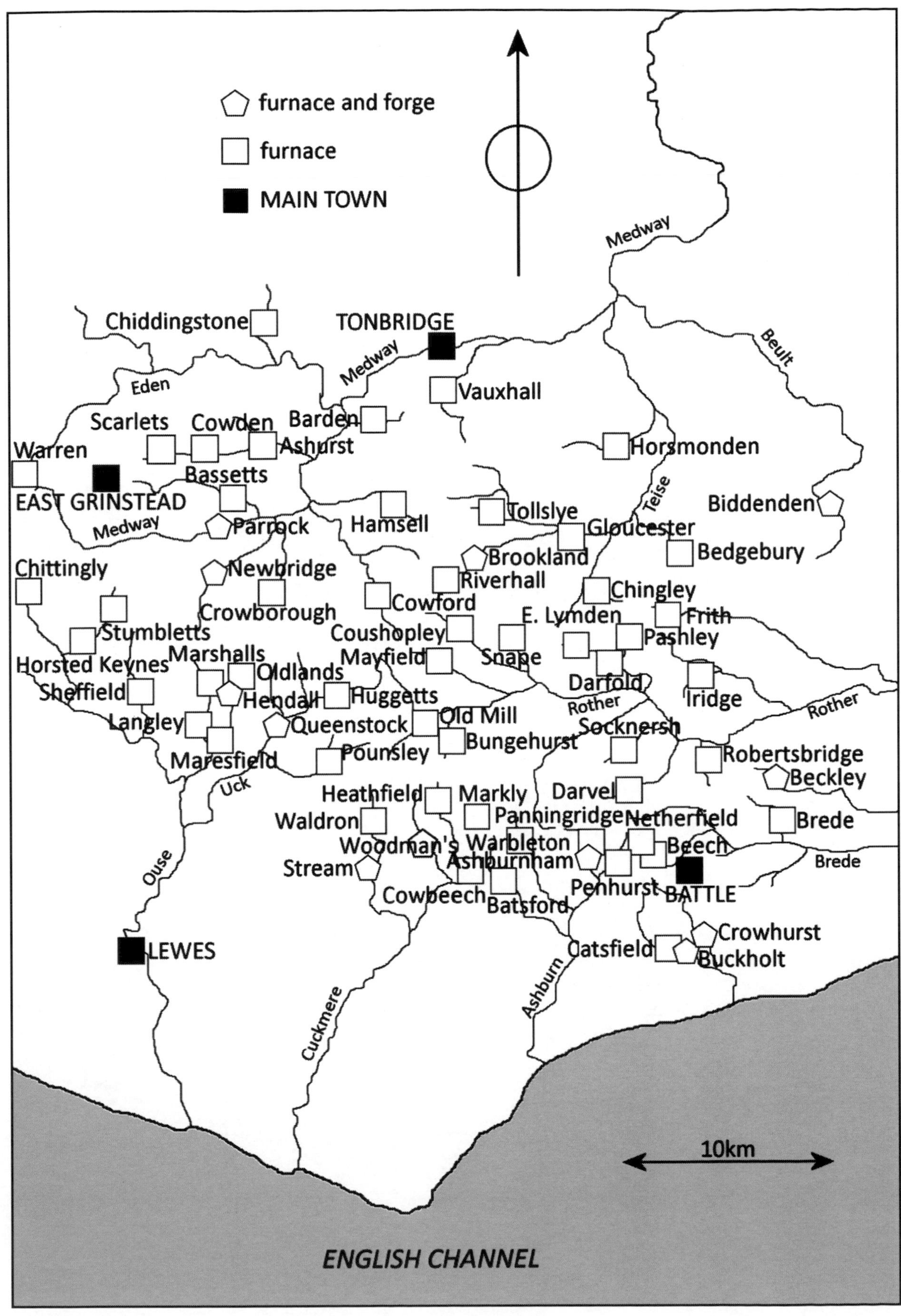

Figure: 27: Map of the eastern Weald in south-east England showing furnaces and combined sites mentioned in the text.

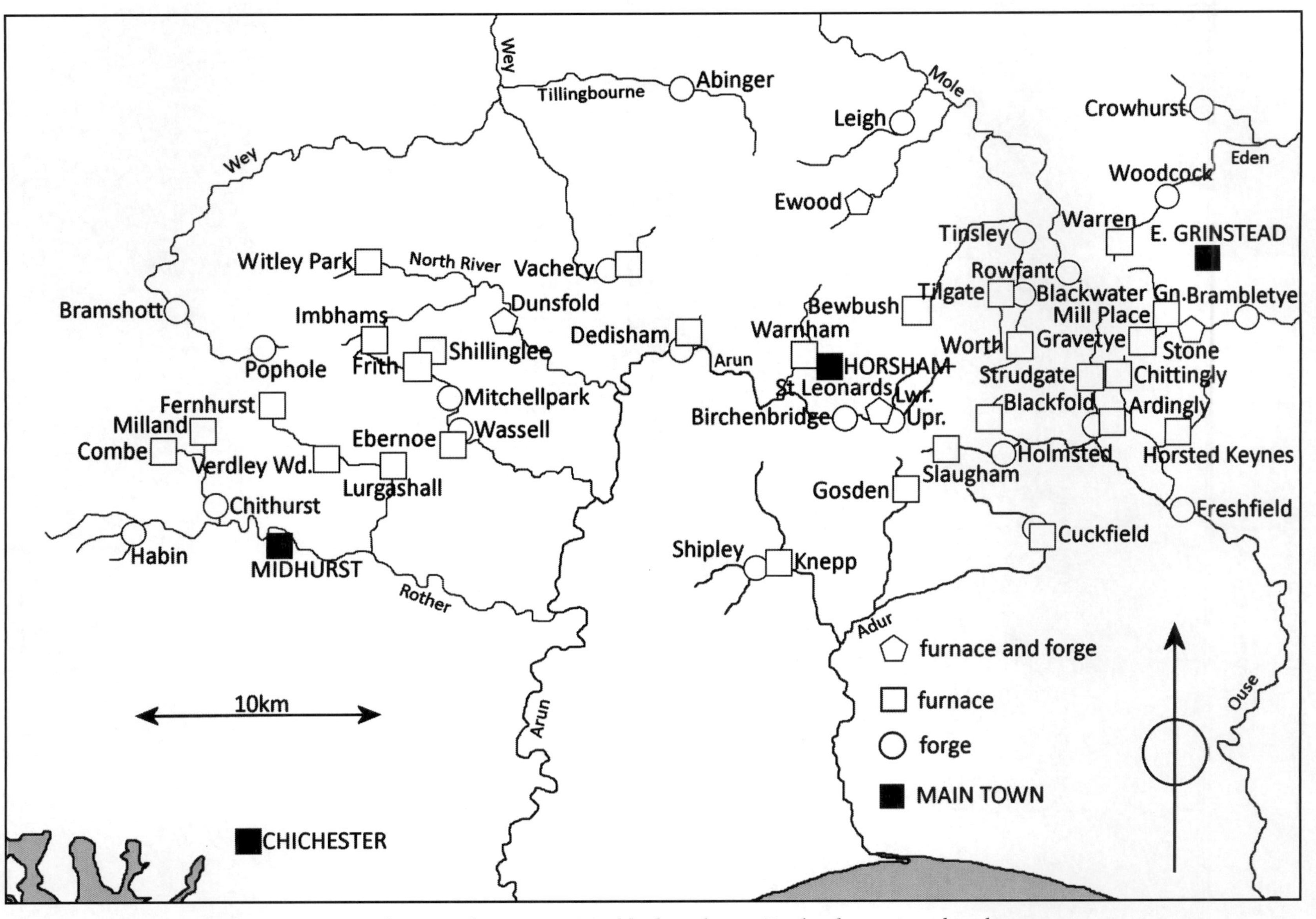

Figure 28: Map of sites in the western Weald of south-east England mentioned in the text.

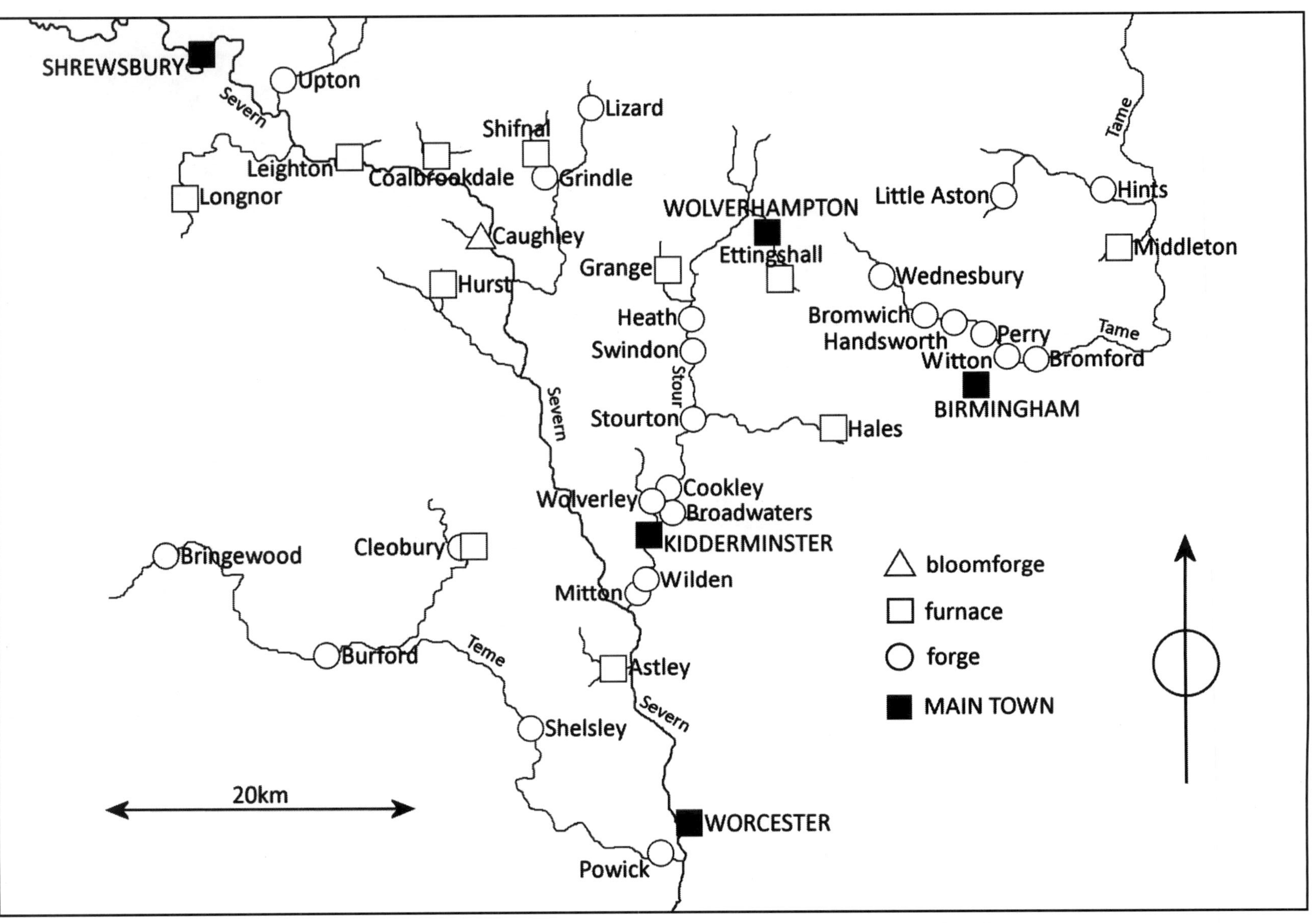

Figure 29: Map of the English south-west Midlands showing saites mentioned in the text.

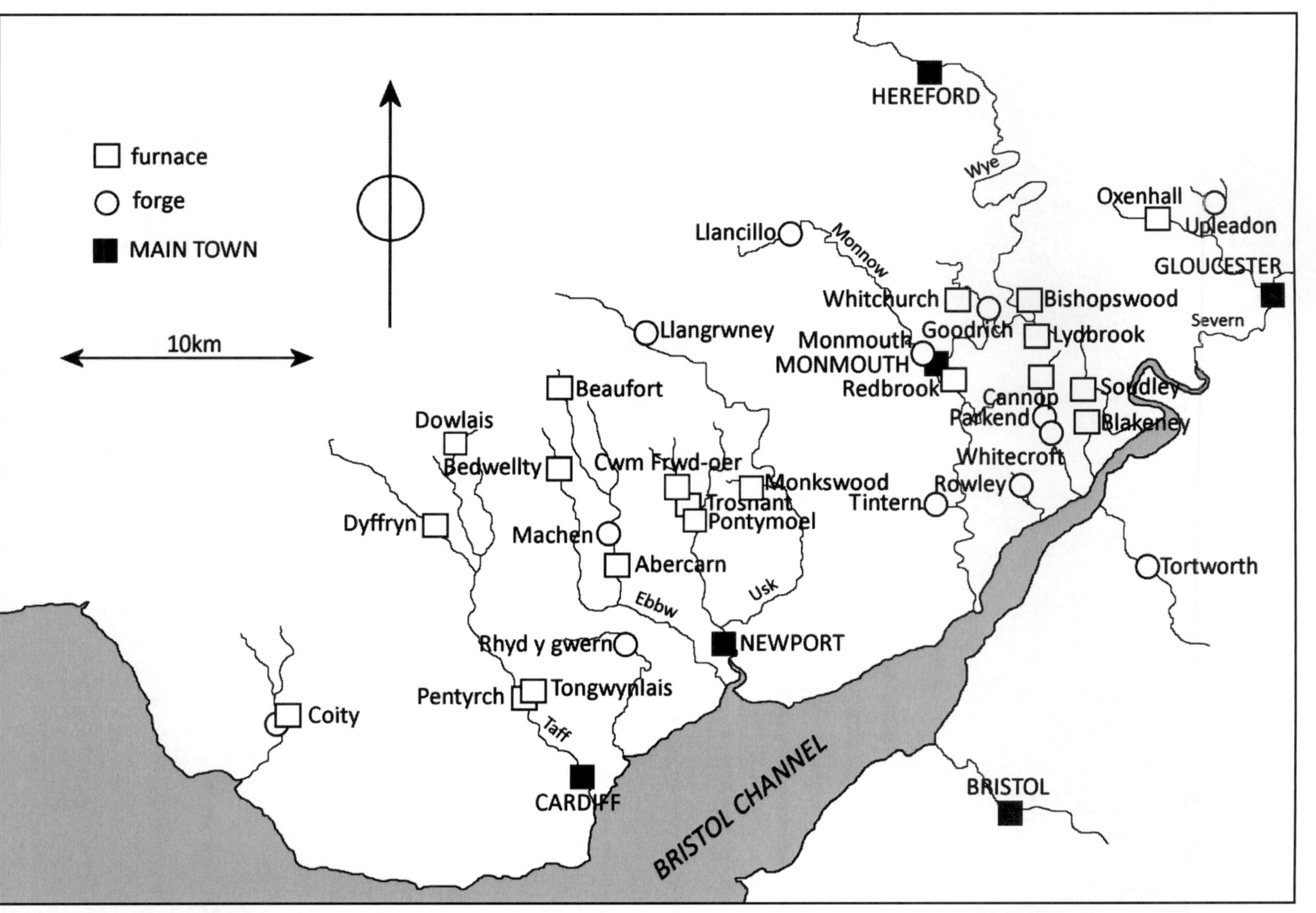

Figure 30: Map of South Wales and the Forest of Dean showing sites mentioned in the text.

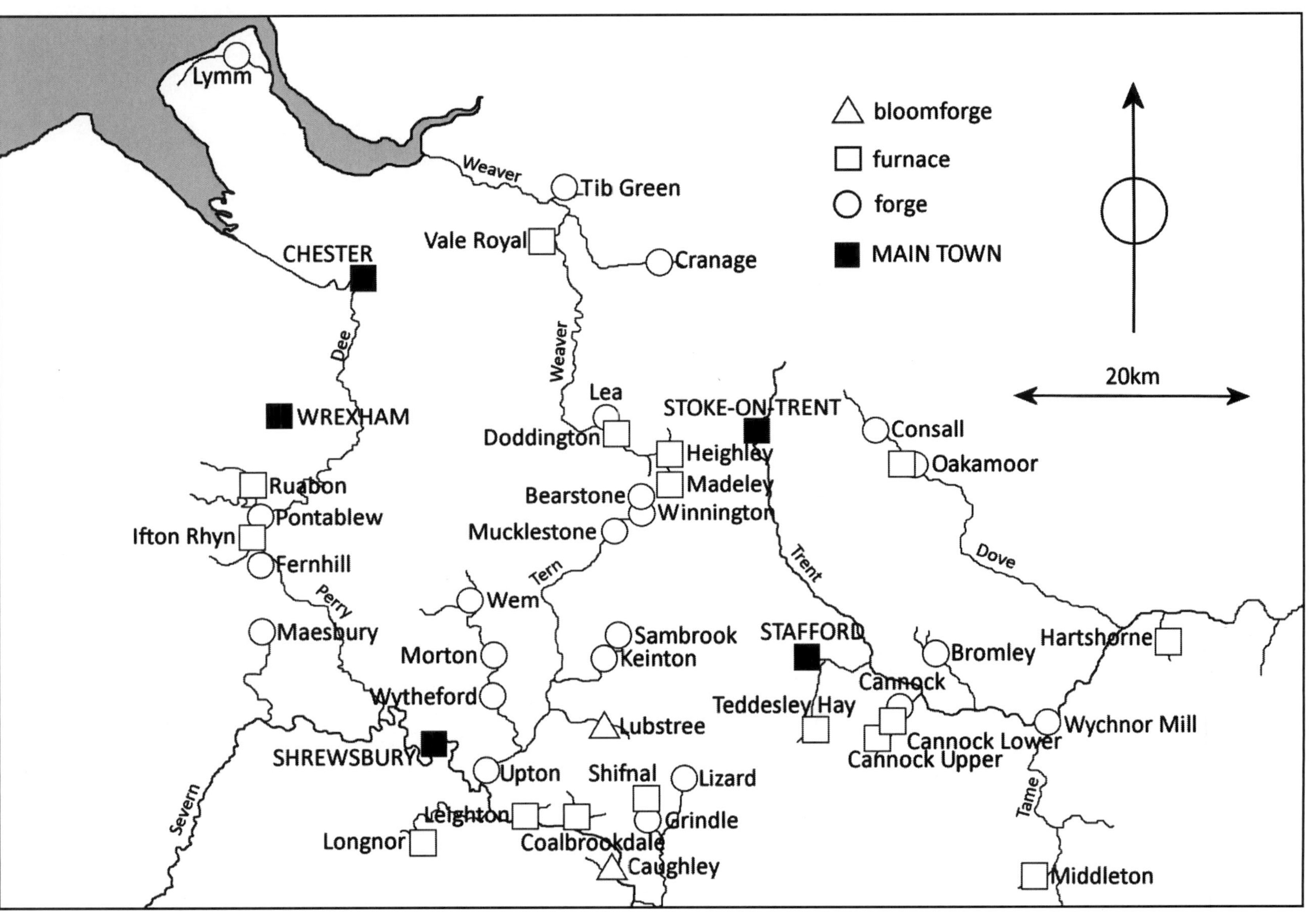

Figure 31: Map of the English north-west Midlands showing saites mentioned in the text.

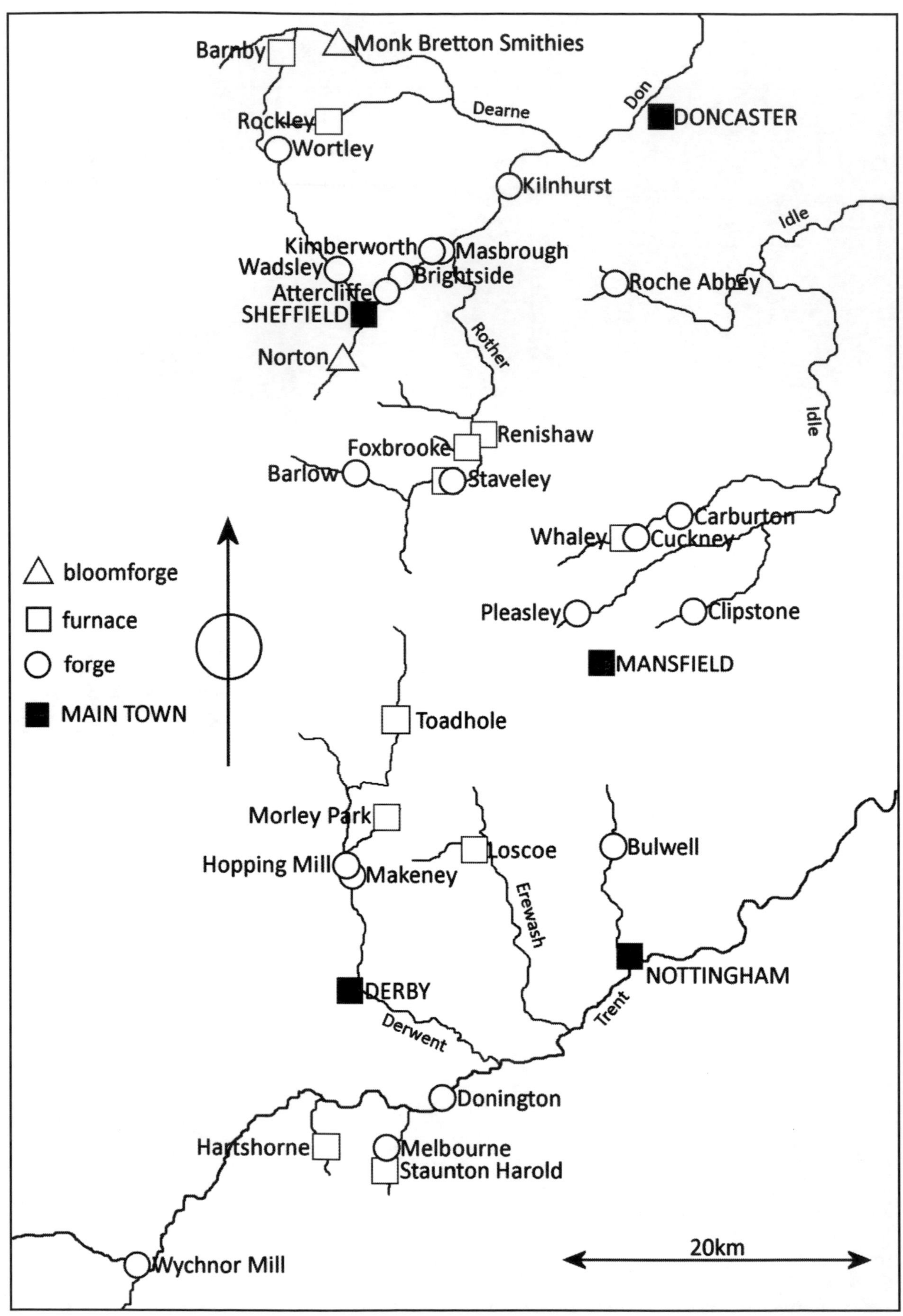

Figure 32: Map of the English north-east Midlands showing sites mentioned in the text.

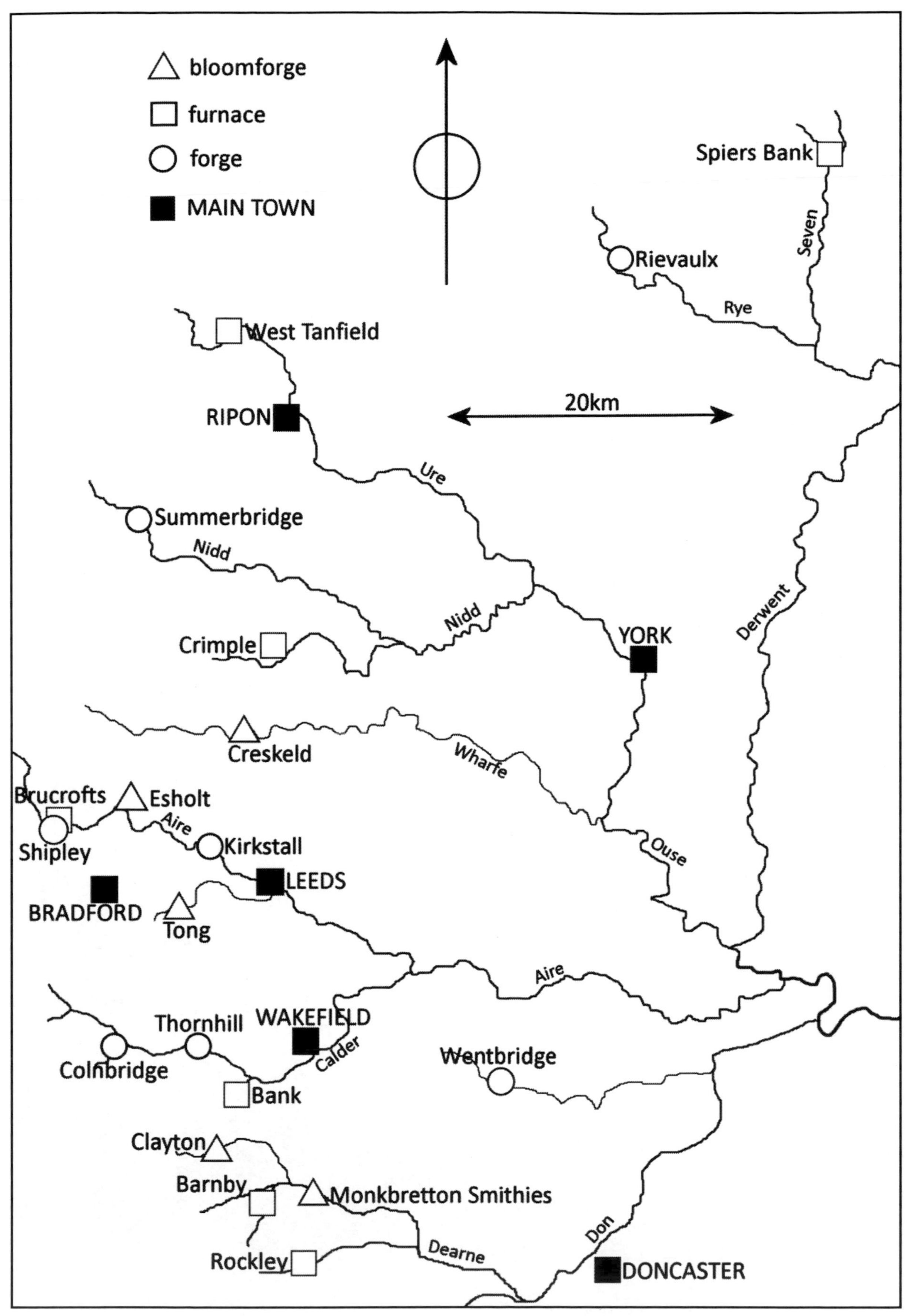

Figure 33: Map of the English county of Yorkshire showing sites mentioned in the text.

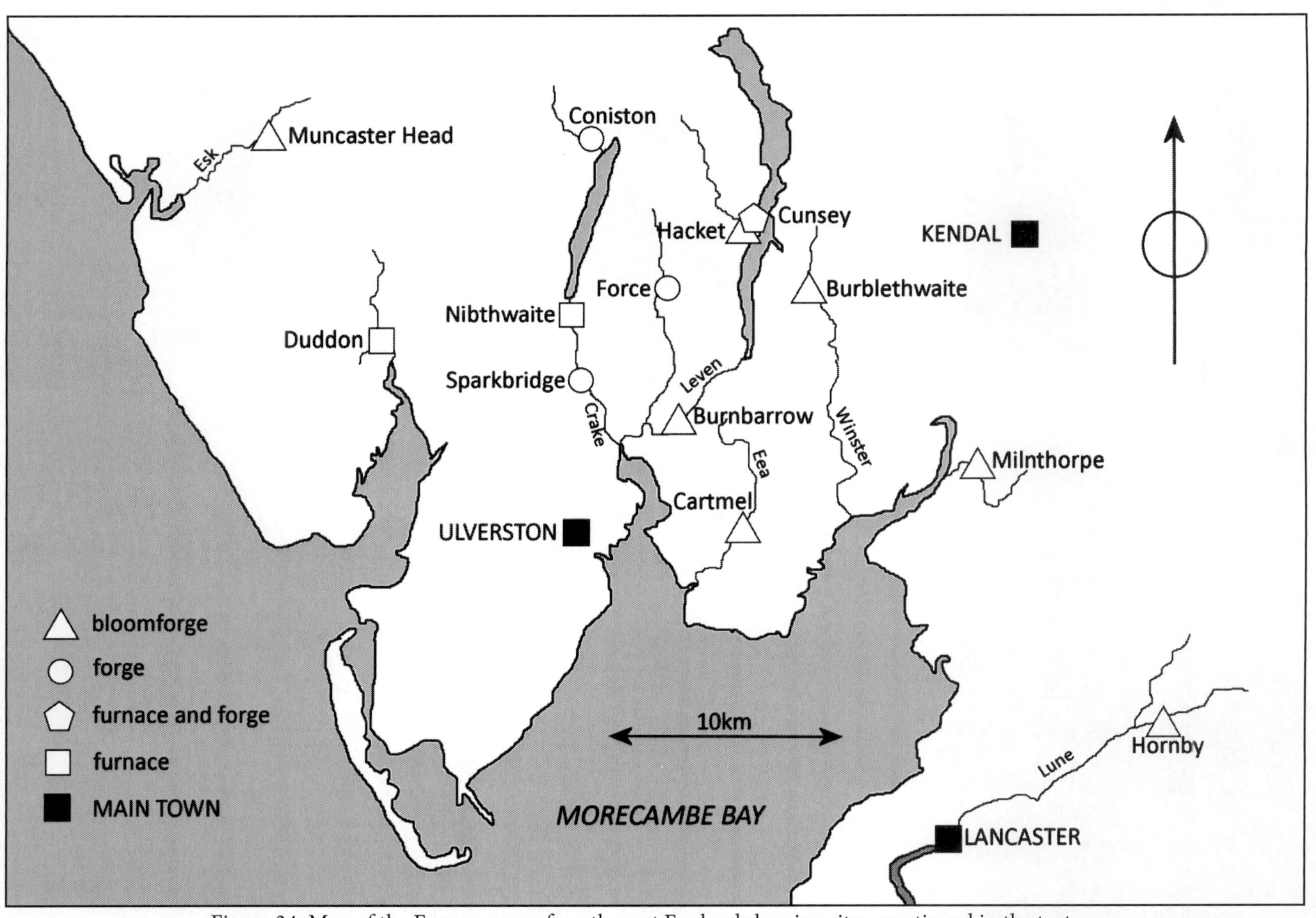

Figure 34: Map of the Furness area of north-west England showing sites mentioned in the text

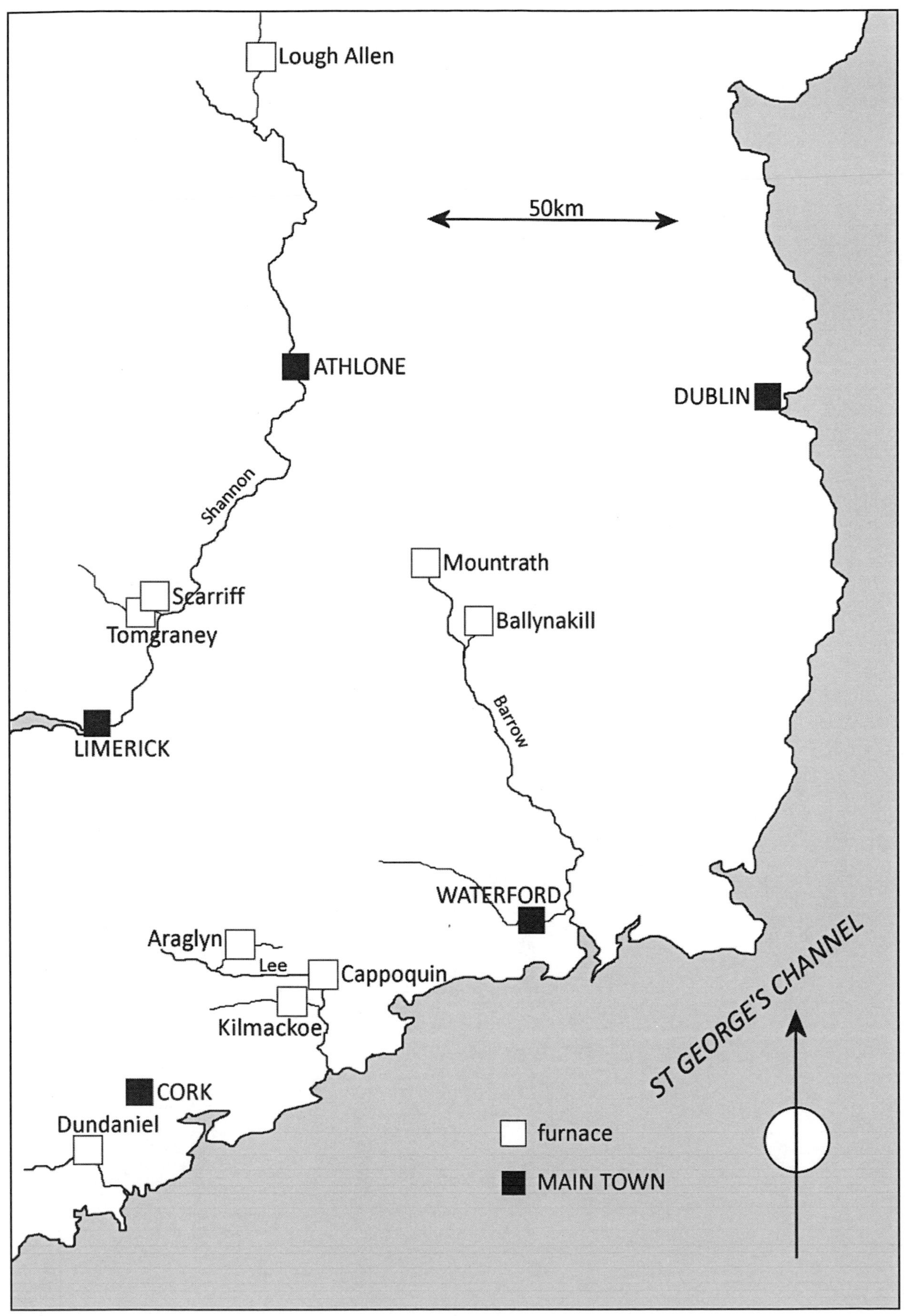

Figure 35: Map of south-east Ireland showing sites mentioned in the text.

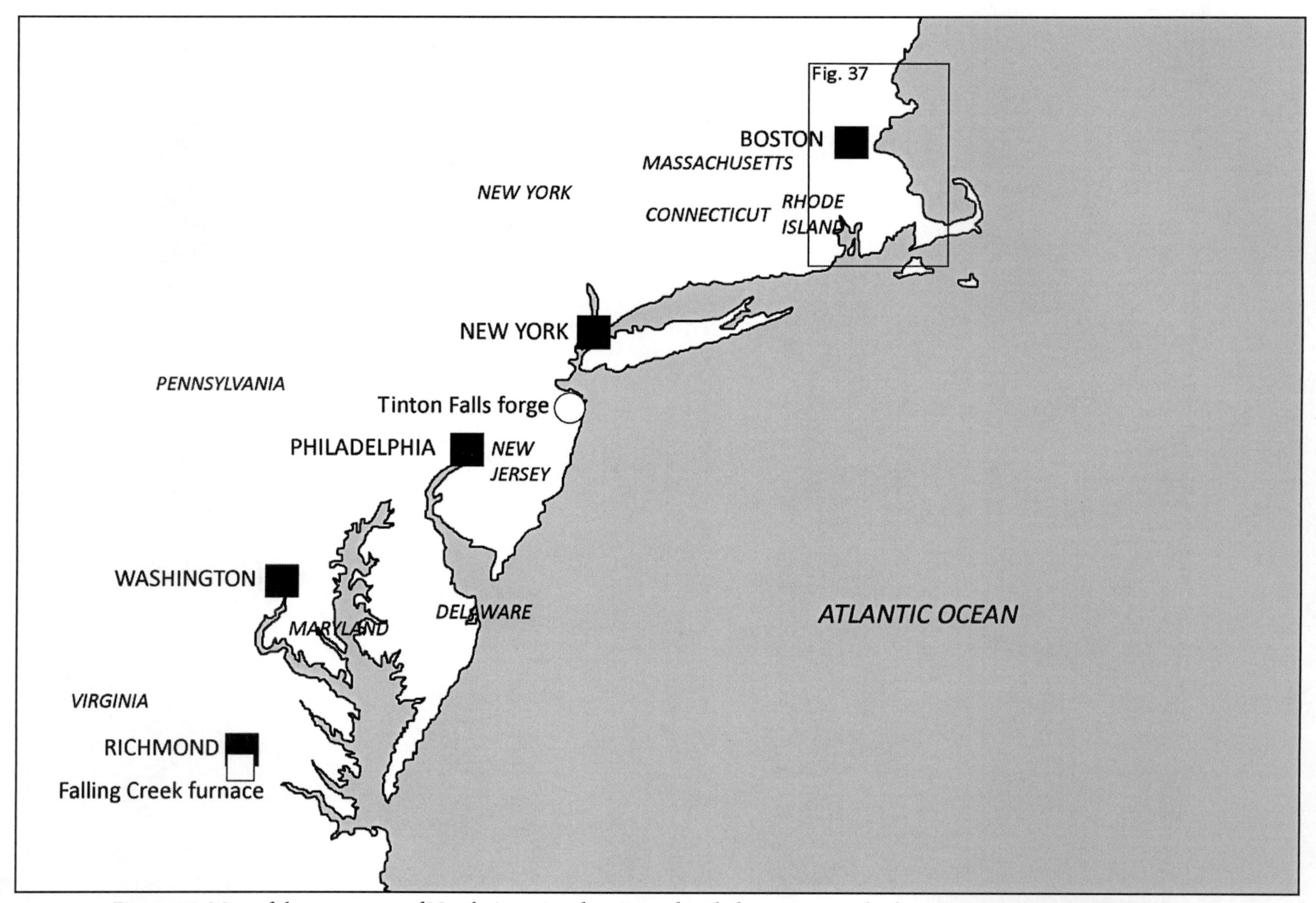

Figure 36: Map of the east coast of North America showing a detailed area map and other sites mentioned in the text.

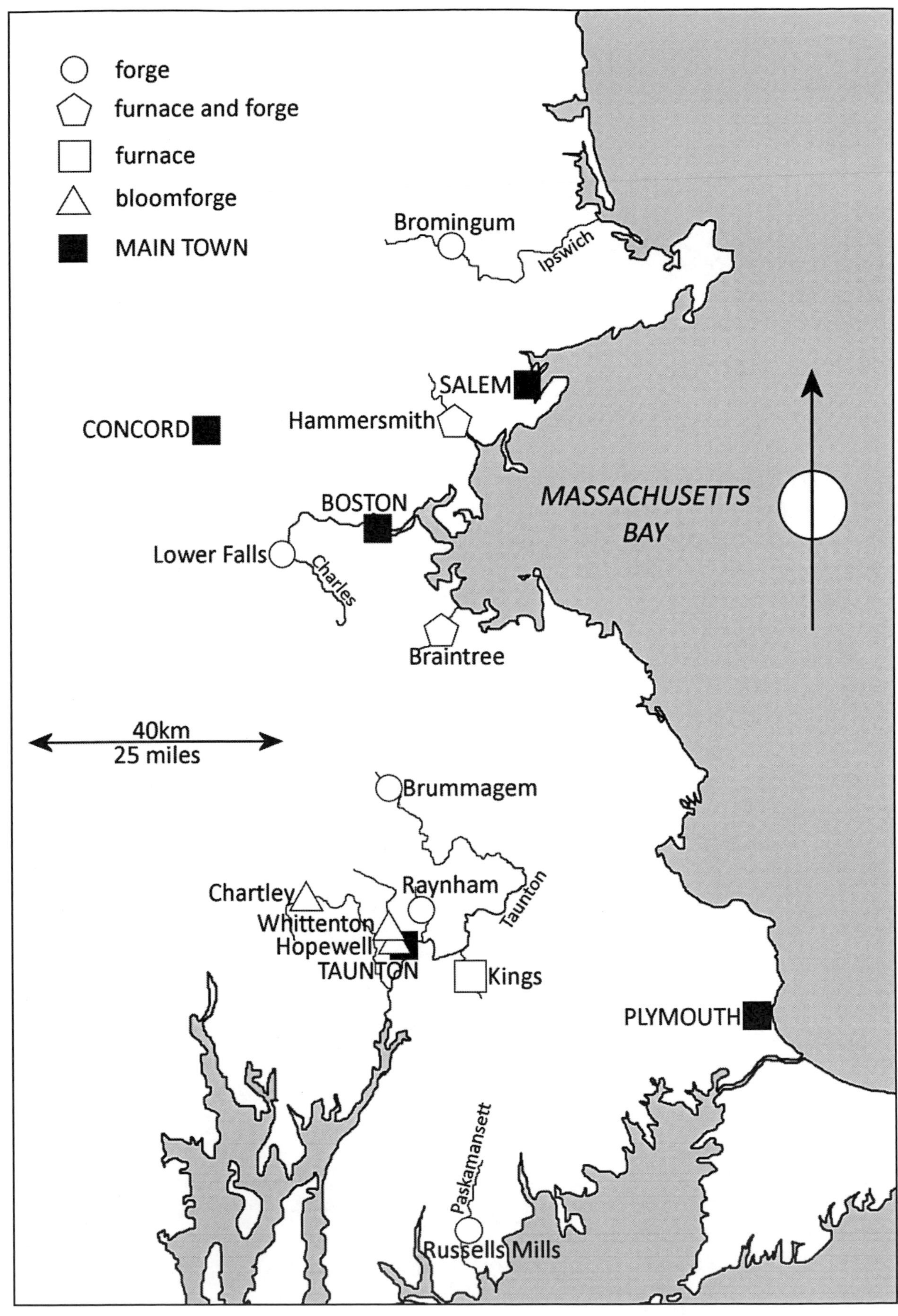

Figure 37: Map of eastern Massachusetts, North America, showing sites mentioned in the text.

BIBLIOGRAPHY

PUBLISHED PRIMARY SOURCES

Acts of the Privy Council of England : new series. Vol. 21 1591 (ed. J. R. Dasent), London, HMSO, 1900.

Acts of the Privy Council of England : new series. Vol. 44 June 1628-April 1629 (ed. R. F. Monger), London, HMSO, 1958.

Letters and Papers foreign and domestic of the reign of Henry VIII, vol. 1: 1509-14 (ed. J. S. Brewer), London, HMSO, 1920.

Letters and Papers, Foreign and Domestic, Henry VIII, Volume 2 1515-1518 (ed. J. S. Brewer), London, HMSO, 1864.

Letters and Papers, Foreign and Domestic, Henry VIII, Volume 3 1519-1523 (ed. J. S. Brewer), London, HMSO, 1867.

Letters and Papers, Foreign and Domestic, Henry VIII, Volume 4 1524-1530 (ed. J. S. Brewer), London, HMSO, 1875.

Letters and Papers, Foreign and Domestic, Henry VIII, Volume 5 1531-1532 (ed. J. Gairdner), London, HMSO, 1880).

Letters and Papers, Foreign and Domestic, Henry VIII, Volume 6 1533 (ed. J. Gairdner), London, HMSO, 1882.

Letters and Papers, Foreign and Domestic, Henry VIII, Volume 8 January-July 1535 (ed. J. Gairdner), London, HMSO, 1885.

Letters and Papers, Foreign and Domestic, Henry VIII, Volume 9 August-December 1535 (ed. J. Gairdner), London, HMSO, 1886.

Letters and Papers, Foreign and Domestic, Henry VIII, Volume 11 July-December 1536 (ed. J. Gairdner), London, HMSO, 1888.

Letters and Papers, Foreign and Domestic, Henry VIII, Volume 12 Part 2 June-December 1537 (ed. J. Gairdner), London, HMSO, 1891.

Letters and Papers, Foreign and Domestic, Henry VIII, Volume 13 Part 1 January-July 1538 (ed. J. Gairdner), London, HMSO, 1892.

Letters and Papers, Foreign and Domestic, Henry VIII, Volume 13 Part 2August-December 1538 (ed.J. Gairdner), London, HMSO, 1893.

Letters and Papers, Foreign and Domestic, Henry VIII, Volume 14 Part 1 January-July 1539 (ed. J. Gairdner and R. H. Brodie), London, HMSO, 1894.

Letters and Papers, Foreign and Domestic, Henry VIII, Volume 14 Part 2 August-December 1539 (ed. J. Gairdner and R. H. Brodie), London, HMSO, 1895.

Letters and Papers, Foreign and Domestic, Henry VIII, Volume 16 1540-1541 (ed. J. Gairdner and R. H. Brodie), London, HMSO, 1898.

Letters and Papers, Foreign and Domestic, Henry VIII, Volume 17 1542 (ed. J. Gairdner and R. H. Brodie), London, HMSO, 1900.

Letters and Papers, Foreign and Domestic, Henry VIII, Volume 19 Part 1 January-July 1544 (ed. J. Gairdner and R. H. Brodie), London, HMSO, 1903.

Letters and Papers, Foreign and Domestic, Henry VIII, Volume 20 Part 1 January-July 1545 (ed. J. Gairdner and R. H. Brodie), London, HMSO, 1905).

Letters and Papers, Foreign and Domestic, Henry VIII, Volume 21 Part 2 September 1546-January 1547 (ed. J. Gairdner and R. H. Brodie), London, HMSO, 1910.

Calendar of State Papers, Domestic, Charles 1, vol. 2, 1627-9 (ed. J. Bruce), London, Longman, 1858.

Calendar of the patent rolls preserved in the Public Record Office: Edward IV, Henry VI. 1467-1477 (ed.

R. C. Fowler), London, HMSO, 1900.

Calendar of the patent rolls preserved in the Public Record Office: Edward IV, Edward V, Richard III. Vol. 3 1477-1485 (ed. R. C. Fowler), London, HMSO, 1901.

Calendar of the patent rolls preserved in the Public Record Office: Henry VII. Vol. 1 1485-1594 (ed. J. G. Black), London, HMSO, 1914.

Calendar of the patent rolls preserved in the Public Record Office: Edward VI. Vol. 1 1547-1548 (ed. R. H. Brodie), London, HMSO, 1924.

Calendar of the patent rolls preserved in the Public Record Office: Edward VI. Vol. 3 1549-1551 (ed. R. H. Brodie), London, HMSO, 1926.

Calendar of the patent rolls preserved in the Public Record Office: Philip and Mary. Vol. 1 1553-1554 (ed. M. S. Giuseppi), London, HMSO, 1937.

Calendar of the patent rolls preserved in the Public Record Office: Philip and Mary. Vol. 3 1555-1557 (ed. M. S. Giuseppi), London, HMSO, 1938.

Calendar of the patent rolls preserved in the Public Record Office: Philip and Mary. Vol. 4 1557-1558 (ed. M. S. Giuseppi), London, HMSO, 1939.

Calendar of the patent rolls preserved in the Public Record Office: Elizabeth I. Vol. 3 1563-1566 (ed. J. H. Collingridge and R. B. Wernham), London, HMSO, 1960.

Calendar of the patent rolls preserved in the Public Record Office: Elizabeth I. Vol. 7 1575-1578 (ed. J. H. Collingridge), Kew, HMSO, 1982.

Calendar of the patent rolls preserved in the Public Record Office: Elizabeth I. Vol. 8 1578-1580 (ed. M. Post), Kew, HMSO, 1986.

F. W. T. Attree, *Post mortem inquisitions taken in Sussex 1 Henry VII to1649 and after*, Lewes, Sussex Record Society, **14**, 1912.

C. E. Atkins, *Register of apprentices of the Worshipful Company of Clockmakers of the city of London*, London, Clockmakers' Company, 1931.

A. R. Bax, 'The Lay subsidy assessments for the county of Surrey in 1593 or 1594', *Surrey Archaeological Collections,* **19** (1906), pp. 39-101.

T. M. Blagg and F. A. Wadsworth (eds), *Abstracts of Nottinghamshire Marriage Licences*, volume I, The British Record Society, 1930.

M. J. Burchall, *Eastern Sussex settlement certificates, 1670-1832*, Brighton, Sussex Genealogical Centre, 1979.

M. J. Burchall, *East Sussex contributors to the relief of Irish Protestants*, Brighton, Sussex Genealogical Centre, 1984.

S. A. H. Burne (ed.), *The Staffordshire Quarter Sessions Rolls, II: 1590-1593*, Kendal, William Salt Archaeological Society, Third series, 1930.

S. A. H. Burne (ed.), *The Staffordshire Quarter Sessions Rolls, III: 1594-1597*, Kendal, William Salt Archaeological Society, Third series, 1932.

S. A. H. Burne (ed.), *The Staffordshire Quarter Sessions Rolls, V: 1603-1606*, Kendal, Staffordshire Record Society, Third series, 1940.

L. H. Canning (ed.), 'Catholic registers of Abergavenny, Mon., 1740-1838', *Miscellanea, 14*, Catholic Record Society Record Series, **27** (1927), pp. 98-235.

G. Clifton (ed.), *Directory of British scientific instrument makers 1550-1851*, London, Zwemmer, 1995.

J. S. Cockburn (ed.), *Calendar of assize records: Sussex indictments, Elizabeth I*, London, HMSO, 1975.

J. S. Cockburn (ed.), *Calendar of assize records: Kent indictments, Elizabeth I*, London, HMSO, 1979.

J. S. Cockburn (ed.), *Calendar of assize records: Surrey indictments, Elizabeth I*, London, HMSO, 1980.

J. S. Cockburn (ed.), *Calendar of assize records: Surrey indictments, James I*, London, HMSO, 1982.

J. Cornwall (ed.), *The Lay subsidy rolls for the county of Sussex 1524-25*, Lewes, Sussex Record Society, **56**, 1956.

T. Craib (ed.), *Surrey Musters (taken from the Loseley mss.)*, Guildford, Surrey Record Society, **3**, 1918.

G. F. Dow (ed.), *Records and files of the quarterly courts of Essex county, Massachusetts, 1636-1656, vol. 1*, Salem, Massachusetts, Essex Institute, 1911.

G. F. Dow (ed.), *Records and files of the quarterly courts of Essex county, Massachusetts, 1656-1662, vol. 2*, Salem, Massachusetts, Essex Institute, 1912.

E. H. W. Dunkin, (ed.), *Calendar of Sussex marriage licences recorded in the consistory court of the bishop of Chichester for the archdeaconry of Lewes, August 1586 to March 1642/3 etc.*, Lewes, Sussex Record Society, **1**, 1901.

E. H. W. Dunkin, (ed.), *Calendar of Sussex marriage licences recorded in the consistory court of the bishop of Chichester for the archdeaconry of Lewes, August 1670 to March 1728-9 etc.*, Lewes, Sussex Record Society, **6**, 1906.

J. P. Earwaker (ed.), *An index to the wills and inventories now preserved in the Court of Probate at Chester 1660-1680*, Manchester, Record Society of Lancashire and Cheshire, **15**, 1887.

R. H. D'Elboux (ed.), *Surveys of the manor of Robertsbridge*, Lewes, Sussex Record Society, **47** 1944.

M. A. Faraday (ed.), *The lay subsidy for Shropshire*, Shropshire Record Series, **3**, University of Keele, 1999.

M. Gachard (ed.), *Correspondence de Philippe II sur les affaires des Pays-Bas, Tome 3*, Brussels, Mucquardt, 1858.

M. Gardiner and C. Whittick, *Accounts and Records of the Manor of Mote in Iden, 1442-1551, 1673*, Lewes, Sussex Record Office, **92**, 2011.

W. H. Hall (ed.), *Calendar of Wills and Administrations in the Archdeaconry Court of Lewes* [etc.], London, British Record Society, **24**, 1901.

D. Hey (ed.), *The hearth tax returns for south Yorkshire, Lady day, 1672*, University of Sheffield, 1991.

J. J. Howard and J. L. Chester (eds.), *The Visitation of London A.D. 1633, 1634 and 1635*, vol. 2, London Harleian Society, **17**, 1883.

R. F. Hunnisett (ed.), *Sussex Coroners' inquests, 1485-1558*, Lewes, Sussex Record Society, **74**, 1985.

R. F. Hunnisett (ed.), *Sussex Coroners' inquests, 1558-1603*, Kew, PRO Publications, 1996.

R. F. Hunnisett (ed.), *Sussex Coroners' inquests, 1603-1688*, Kew, PRO Publications, 1998.

R. E. G. and E. F. Kirk (eds.), *Returns of aliens dwelling in the city and suburbs of London from the reign of Henry VIII to that of James I, vol. 1, 1525-1571*, Huguenot Society, 10, Aberdeen University Press, 1900.

P. D. Mundy (ed.), *Abstracts of Star Chamber proceedings in Sussex Henry VII to Philip and Mary*, Lewes, Sussex Record Society, **16**, 1913.

W. Page (ed.), *Letters of denization and Acts of naturalization for aliens in England 1509-1603*, Publications of the Huguenot Society of London, **8** (1893).

E. Ralph and N. M. Hardwick (eds.), *Calendar of the Bristol apprenticeship book 1532-1565*, pt. 2, 1542-1552, Bristol Record Society, **33**, 1980.

R. G. Rice (ed.), *West Sussex Protestation Returns, 1641-2*, Lewes, Sussex Record Society, **5**, 1905.

E. Straker (ed.), *The Buckhurst Terrier*, Lewes, Sussex Record Society, **39**, 1933.

S. P. Vivian (ed.), *The Manor of Etchingham cum Salehurst*, Lewes, Sussex Record Society, **53**, 1953

SECONDARY SOURCES

S. Adams, ' "Because I am of that countrye & mynde to plant myself there": Robert Dudley, Earl of Leicester and the West Midlands', *Midland History*, **20** (1995), 21-74.

G. Agricola, *De re metallica* (ed. H. C. and L. H. Hoover), New York, Dover, 1950.

L. André and others, *La métallurgie du fer dans les Ardennes (XVIe- XIXe)*, Paris, Inventaire Générale, 1987.

C. R. Andrews, *The story of Wortley ironworks*, 3rd ed., Nottingham, Milward, 1975.

A. Angelucci, *Documenti inediti per la storia delle armi da fuoco italiane*, Torino, Cassone, 1869.

R. R. Angerstein, *Illustrated travel diary, 1753-1755*, London, Science Museum, 2001.

M. Arnoux, *Mineurs, férons et maîtres de forges; étude sur la production du fer dans la Normandie du Moyen Age. XIe-XVe siècles*. Paris, Comité des travaux historiques et scientifiques (CTHS), 1993.

D. Arribet, 'La sidérurgie indirecte dans le pays de Bray normand (vallée de la Béthune) de 1485 à 1565', Paris, Mémoire de maîtrise, 1985-6.

D. Arribet, 'Les sites de la sidérurgie indirecte du pays de Bray', Memoire de D.E.A. Paris, 1986/7.

D. Arribet-Deroin, *Rapport de la fouille programmée du site de Glinet à Compainville (Seine-Maritime)*, 1994.

D. Arribet-Deroin, *Rapport de la fouille programmée du site de Glinet à Compainville (Seine-Maritime)*, 1996.

G. G. Astill *A medieval industrial complex and its landscape: the metalworking watermills and workshops of Bordesley Abbey*, Council for British Archaeology Research Reports **92**, York, 1993.

B. G. Awty, 'Sir Richard Shireburn's Esholt ironworks', *Bradford Antiquary*, new series, **40** (1960), pp. 243-54.

B. G. Awty, 'The continental origins of Wealden ironworkers, 1451-1544', *Economic History Review*, 2nd series, **34** (1981), pp. 524-39.

B. G. Awty, 'French immigrants and the iron industry in Sheffield', *Yorkshire Archaeological Journal*, **53** (1981), pp. 57-62.

B. G. Awty, 'The Arcana family of Cesena as gunfounders and military engineers', *Transactions of the Newcomen Society*, **59** (1987/8), pp. 61-80.

B. G. Awty, 'Parson Levett and English cannon founding', *Sussex Archaeological Collections*, **127** (1989), p. 133-45.

B. G. Awty, 'The blast furnace in the Renaissance period: *haut fourneau* or *fonderie*?', *Transactions of the Newcomen Society*, **61** (1989/90), pp. 65-78.

B. G. Awty, 'Were there medieval ironworking contacts between Sweden and Namur?', *Historical Metallurgy*, **28**, *1* (1994), pp. 7-10.

B. G. Awty, 'Crookford furnace, not Cotchford but Worth', *Wealden Iron*, Bulletin of the Wealden Iron Research Group, 2nd series, **3** (2003), pp. 21-3.

B. G. Awty, 'The Development and Dissemination of the Walloon Method of Ironworking', *Technology and Culture*, **48**, *4* (2007), pp. 783-803.

B. G. Awty and C. B. Phillips, 'The Cumbrian bloomery forge in the seventeenth century and forge equipment in the charcoal iron industry', *Transactions of the Newcomen Society*, **51** (1979-80), pp. 25-40

B. G. Awty and C. H. C. Whittick, 'The Lordship of Canterbury, iron-founding at Buxted, and the Continental antecedents of cannon-founding in the Weald', *Sussex Archaeological Collections*, **140** (2002), pp. 71-81.

J. P. Bacon Phillips, 'Maresfield Place-names', *Sussex Notes and Queries*, **1** (1927), p.126.

S. Bagshaw, *History, gazetteer and directory of Derbyshire*, Sheffield, The author, 1846.

E. Baraldi, 'Per un'archeologia dei forni alla bresciana', *Quaderni storici*, **70** (April 1989), pp. 101-22.

C. Barnes, 'Iron-working sites in the Haslemere area', *Wealden Iron*, Bulletin of the Wealden Iron Research Group, 2nd series, **11** (1991), pp. 19-28.

S. Barter Bailey, 'Information relating to the operation of the early cast-iron gun industry, from a manuscript account book in the collection of the Royal Armouries', *Journal of the Ordnance Society*, **3** (1991), pp. 11-23.

J. A. Beaden, 'The trials and tribulations of Robert Perigoe', *Sussex Family Historian*, 11, *1* (March 1994), pp. 21-23.

A. Beaucousin (ed.), *Registre des fiefs et arrière-fiefs du bailliage de Caux en 1503*, Rouen, Lestringant, 1891.

L. Beck, *Geschichte des Eisens in technischer und kulturgeschichtlicher Beziehung*, **1**, Braunschweig, Vieweg, 1884.

L. Beck, *Geschichte des Eisens in technischer und kulturgeschichtlicher Beziehung*, **2**, Braunschweig, Vieweg, 1893-5.

O. Bedwin, 'The excavation of a late sixteenth-century blast furnace at Batsford, Herstmonceux, East Sussex, 1978', *Post Medieval Archaeology*, **14** (1980), pp. 89-112.

J. -F. Belhoste, "The origins of direct reduction water-powered ironworks: reflections based on the evolution of terminology", in E. Tomàs i Morera (ed.), *La farga catalana en el marc de l'arqueologia siderúrgica : aquest libre conté les comunicacions presentades al Simposi Internacional sobre la Farga Catalana, celebrat a Ripoll del 13 al 17 de setembre de 1993*, Andorra la Vella, Govern d'Andorra, Ministeri d'Afers Socials i Cultura, 1995, pp. 385-398.

J.-F. Belhoste and others, *La métallurgie normande xii*[e]*-xvii*[e] *siècles: la révolution du haut fourneau*, Caen, Association Histoire et Patrimoine Industriels de Basse Normandie, 1991

J.-F. Belhoste and others, *La métallurgie comtoise XV*[e]*-XIX*[e] *siècles; étude du Val de Saône*, Besançon, ASPRODIC, L'Inventaire général, 1994.

S. Benoît, 'La sidérurgie du Châtillonnais après l'avènement du procédé indirect (c.1480-c.1570); matériaux et hypothèses' in P. Benoît and P. Braunstein (eds.), *Mines, carrières et métallurgie dans la France médiévale : actes du Colloque de Paris, 19, 20, 21 juin 1980*, Paris : Centre national de la recherche scientifique, 1983, pp. 77-116.

P. Benoît and P. Braunstein (eds.), *Mines, carrières et métallurgie dans la France médiévale, Actes du Colloque de Paris (19, 20 & 21 June 1980)*, Paris, CNRS éditions, 1983.

P. Benoît and D. Cailleaux (eds.), *Hommes et travail du métal dans les villes médiévales*, Paris, AEDEH, 1988.

P. Benoît and others, 'Iron, cast iron and bronze: new approaches of the artillery history' in G. Magnusson (ed.), *The importance of ironmaking: technical innovation and social change; papers presented at the Norberg Conference on May 8-13, 1995*, **2**, Stockholm, Jernkontorets, 1996., pp. 241-57.

R. Bird, 'Drew Barentyn', *Wealden Iron*, Bulletin of the Wealden Iron Research Group, 2nd series, **7** (1987), pp. 20-1.

L. Bittner, 'Das Eisenwesen in Innerberg-Eisenerz', *Archiv für österreichische Geschichte*, **89** (1901), pp. 451-641.

R. W. Blencowe, 'Paxhill and its neighbourhood; with extracts from the manuscripts of the Wilson family', *Sussex Archaeological Collections*, **11** (1859), pp. 1-49.

C. R. Blick (ed.), 'Early blast furnace news', *Historical Metallurgy*, **18**, *1* (1984), p. 44-50.

H. W. Böcking, *Abentheuer; Beiträge zur Geschichte des Ortes und seiner Eisenhütte*, Neuwied, Birkenfeld, 1961.

G. Bois, *Crise du féodalisme: économie rurale et démographie en Normandie orientale du début du XIV*[e] *siècle au milieu du XVI*[e] *siècle*, Paris, Editions de l'Ecole des haute études en sciences sociales (EHESS),

1976.

M. Bourguignon, 'Les usines du bassin de la Rulles', **1**, *Annales de l'Insitiut archéologique du Luxembourg*, **57** (1926), pp. 1-84.

M. Bourguignon, 'Les usines du bassin de la Rulles', **2**, *Annales de l'Insitiut archéologique du Luxembourg*, **58** (1927), pp. 41-172.

M. Bourguignon, 'Les anciennes forges de La Claireau', *Le Pays gaumais*, **26** (1965), 106-28.

H. Brackenbury, 'Ancient cannon in Europe, part II', *Minutes of proceedings of the Royal Artillery Institution*, **5** (1867), pp. 1-37.

H.-J. Braun, *Das Eisenhüttenwesen des Hunsrücks; 15. bis Ende 18. Jahrhundert*, Trier, Verlag Trierer Historische Forschungen, 1991.

P. Braunstein and O. Chapelot, 'Mine et métallurgie en Bourgogne à la fin du moyen âge: première esquisse' in P. Benoît and P. Braunstein (eds.), *Mines, carrières et métallurgie dans la France médiévale : actes du Colloque de Paris, 19, 20, 21 juin 1980*, Paris : Centre national de la recherche scientifique, 1983, pp. 31-66.

J. Brent, 'A dispute over iron ore between two county grandees', *Wealden Iron*, Bulletin of the Wealden Iron Research Group, **11** (1977), pp. 20-6.

R. R. Brown, 'Notes from the Office of Ordnance: the 1650s', *Wealden Iron*, Bulletin of the Wealden Iron Research Group, 2nd series, **20** (2000), pp. 39-55.

J. Bunel and A. Tougard, *Géographie du département de la Seine-Inférieure; arrondissement de Neufchâtel*, Rouen, Cagniard, 1875.

M. J. Burchall, 'The Mowcumbers, a French family in Sussex', *The Sussex Genealogist and Local Historian*, **1**, *1* (1979), pp. 18-20.

M. J. Burchall, 'The Snashall family, Quakers and blacksmiths', *The Sussex Genealogist and Local Historian*, **2**, *1* (1980-81), pp. 11-14.

J. W. Burgon, *The Life and times of Sir Thomas Gresham, vol. 2,* London (1839).

S. A. H. Burne (ed.), *An Account Who Have Enjoyed the Several Estates in the Parish of Audley and Hamlet of Talk in the County of Stafford For the Past 200 Years by Richard Parrott, 1733*, Kendal, Staffordshire Record Society, Third series, 1944, pp. 1-74.

M. Calegari, 'Forni alla bresciana nell'Italia del XVI secolo', *Quaderni storici*, **70** (April 1989), pp. 77-99.

A. Callow, 'A blast furnace at Netherfield, Battle, East Sussex: a new water-powered site identified', *Wealden Iron*, Bulletin of the Wealden Iron Research Group, 2nd series, **23** (2003), pp. 3-4.

C. S. Cattell, 'The 1574 lists of Wealden ironworks', *Sussex Archaeological Collections,* **117** (1979), 161-71.

W. R. Childs, 'England's iron trade in the fifteenth century', *Economic History Review,* 2nd series, **34** (1981), pp. 25-43.

C. M. Cipolla (ed.), *The Fontana Economic History of Europe,* **1**, *The Middle Ages*, London, Collins, 1972.

P. Ciszéville, *Statistique de Forges-les-Eaux, Rouen, an XIII*, Rouen, Mari, 1804.

H. Cleere and D. Crossley, *The iron industry of the Weald*, Cardiff, Merton Priory Press (2nd ed., 1995).

E. Cobby, *The Lewknors of Sussex*, Cranleigh, 1991.

J. P. D. Cochet, *Répertoire archéologique du département de la Seine-Inférieure,* Paris, Imprimerie nationale, 1871

M. Coffin, *Promenade géographique, historique, touristique au coeur du Pays de Bray*, Forges-Les-Eaux, Le Syndicat d'Initiative, 1977.

W. G. Collingwood, *Elizabethan Keswick*, Kendal, Wilson, 1912.

C. Collinson, 'Enterprise and experiment in the Elizabethan iron industry: the career of Thomas Proctor', *Yorkshire Archaeological Journal*, **68** (1996), p. 191-208.

G. Le Compasseur de Crequi-Montfort, Marquis de Courtivron, and E.-J. Bouchu, *Art des forges et des fourneaux à fer*, Paris, 1762.

P. Combes and C. Whittick, 'Iron Plat, Queenstock hammer-pond and a 15th-century ironworking site at Buxted', *Wealden Iron*, Bulletin of the Wealden Iron Research Group, 2nd series, **22** (2002), pp. 10-18.

D. C. Cox (ed.), *Shropshire historical documents; a miscellany*, Shropshire Record Series, **4**, Keele, Centre for Local History, 2000.

E. Coyecque (ed.), *Recueil d'actes notariés relatifs à l'histoire de Paris et de ses environs au XVIe siècle*, **2**, Paris, Imprimerie nationale, 1923.

D. W. Crossley, 'A sixteenth-century Wealden blast furnace; a report on excavations at Panningridge, Sussex, 1964-1970', *Post-medieval archaeology*, **6** (1972), pp. 42-68.

D. W. Crossley, 'Ralph Hogge's ironworks accounts, 1576-1581', *Sussex Archaeological Collections*, **112** (1974), pp. 48-79.

D. W. Crossley, *Sidney ironworks accounts*, London, Royal Historical Society, 1975.

D. W. Crossley, *The Bewl valley ironworks*, London, Royal Archaeological Institute, 1975.

D. Crossley and others (eds.), *Water power on the Sheffield rivers*, Sheffield Trades Historical Society, 1989.

D. Crossley and R. Saville (eds.), *The Fuller letters: Guns, Slaves and Finance 1728-1755*, Lewes, Sussex Record Society, **76**, 1991.

S. Crowley, 'Mallow Iron Mines', *Mallow Field Club Journal*, **22** (2004), pp. 21-32.

W. B. Crump, 'Early iron workings at Creskelde, near Otley', *Thoresby Society Miscellany XII*, **41** (1954), pp. 300-8.

A. Dalton, 'Burgh Wood forge, Etchingham', *Wealden Iron*, Bulletin of the Wealden Iron Research Group, 2nd series, **17** (1997), p. 40-6.

W. R. Deane, 'Genealogical memoir of the Leonard family', *New England Historic-Genealogical Register*, **4** (October 1851). pp. 404-25.

S. Deck, 'Le temporel de l'abbaye de Beaubec; II. Dans la deuxième moitié du XVe siècle', *Annales de Normandie*, **24** (1974), pp. 221-46.

P. de Grousset, *Recueil de la vertu de la fontaine médicinale de Saint Eloi*, Paris, 1607

E. W. Dahlgren (ed.), *Louis de Geers brev och affarhandlingar* , Stockholm, Norstedt, 1934.

L.-R. Delsalle, *Entre Robec et Aubette*, Bois Guillaume, TAG, 1994.

A. den Ouden, 'The introduction and early spread of the blast furnace in Europe', *Wealden Iron*, Bulletin of the Wealden Iron Research Group, 2nd series, **5** (1985), pp. 21-35.

D. Diderot and J. D'Alembert, *Encyclopédie, ou dictionnaire raisonné des sciences, des arts et des métiers*, **7**, Paris, 1757.

J. H. Dixon, *Gairloch in north-west Ross-shire*, Edinburgh, 1886.

M. B. Donald, *Elizabethan copper: the history of the Company of Mines Royal, 1568-1605*, London, Pergamon Press, 1955.

M. B. Donald, *Elizabethan monopolies*, Edinburgh, Oliver and Boyd, 1961.

P. den Dooven, *La métallurgie au pays de Franchimont; géneralités; 1, Les forges de Spa*, Stavelot, the author, 1979

K. De Vries, *Medieval military technology*, Ontario, Broadview, 1992

W. Dugdale, *Monasticon Anglicanum*, London, 1693.

I. Edwards, 'The early ironworks of north-west Shropshire', *Trans. Shropshire Archaeological Society*, **56** (1957-60), pp. 185-202.

J. English, 'Vachery forge and furnace, Cranleigh, Surrey', *Wealden Iron*, Bulletin of the Wealden Iron Research Group, 2nd series, **19** (1999), pp. 19-29.

C. Evans, 'A skilled workforce during the transition to industrial society: forgemen in the British iron trade, 1500-1850', *Labour History Review*, **63** (1998), pp. 143-59.

A. A. Everett, 'Leonards of Monmouthshire and Somersetshire, England', *The American Genealogist*, **53** (1977), pp. 101-4.

R. Evrard, *Forges anciennes*, Liège, Solédi, 1956.

R. Evrard and A. Descy, *Histoire de l'usine des Vennes*, Liège, Solédi, 1948.

R. W. Eyton, *Antiquities of Shropshire, Vol. VI*, London, John Russell Smith, 1858.

R. Fawtier, 'Documents inédits sur l'organisation de l'artillerie royale au temps de Louis XI', in A. G. Little and F. M. Powicke (eds.), *Essays in medieval history presented to Thomas Frederick Tout*, Manchester, 1925, pp. 367-77.

A. Fell, *The early iron industry of Furness*, London, Frank Cass, 1908.

M. W. Flinn, 'The growth of the English iron industry, 1660-1760', *Economic History Review*, 2nd series, **11** (1958), pp. 144-53.

P. Fobes, 'Topographical description of the town of Raynham', *Collections of the Massachusetts Historical Society*, **3** (1794), pp.166-75.

J. Foster (ed.),. *The Visitation of Middlesex began in the year 1663*, London, The author, 1887.

J. Fraikin, *L'industrie armurière liégeoise et le Banc d'Épreuves des armes à feu de Liège*, Liège, Vaillant-Carmanne, 1940.

M. François, 'Note sur l'industrie sidérurgique et les privilèges des maîtres de forges au XVIe siècle', *Mémoires de la Société nationale des antiquaires de France*, **81** (1945), pp. 117-26.

C. M. Fraser, ed. *The accounts of the Chamberlains of Newcastle upon Tyne 1508-1511*, Society of Antiquaries of Newcastle upon Tyne Record Series, **3**, 1987.

J. F. Fuller, 'Pedigree of the Family of Fuller of Waldron and East Hoathly etc.', *Miscellanea Genealogica et Heraldica*, 4th series, **3** (1910), pp. 166-73.

C. Gaier, 'The origin of Mons Meg', *Journal of the Arms and Armour Society*, **5**, *12* (1967), pp. 425-31.

C. Gaier, *L'industrie et le commerce des armes dans les anciennes principautés belges du XIIIme à la fin du XVme siècle*, Bibliothèque de la Faculté de philosophie et lettres de l'Université de Liège, **202,** Paris, Les Belles Lettres, 1973.

Gairloch Heritage Museum, *The local 17th century ironworks: a brief history and description of the iron works around Loch Maree which include the earliest blast furnace in Scotland*, Gairloch, 2000.

R. Gandilhon, *Politique économique de Louis XI*, Paris, Presses Universitaires de France, 1941

J. Garnier, *L'artillerie des ducs de Bourgogne*, Paris, Champion, 1895

G. Gaudefroy, 'Les noms de nos cours d'eau ont aussi leur histoire' in M. Coffin, *Promenade géographique, historique, touristique en Pays de Bray*, Office du Tourisme, Forges-Les-Eaux, **4** (1998), pp. 110-12.

F. Geisthardt, 'Fruhes Eisengewerbe an Sieg, Dill und Lahn' in H. Kellenbenz (ed.), *Schwerpunkte der Eisengewinnung und Eisenverarbeitung in Europa, 1500-1650*, Köln, Böhlau, 1974, pp. 188-203.

A. Gillard, *L'industrie du fer dans les localités du Comté de Namur et de l'Entre-Sambre-et- Meuse de 1345 à 1600*, Bruxelles, Pro Civitate Collection histoire, **29**, 1971.

B. Gille, *La grande industrie métallurgique*, Paris, Domat-Mont-Chrestien, 1948.

B. Gille, 'L'évolution de la technique sidérurgique', *Revue d'histoire des mines et de la métallurgie*, **2**, *2* (1970), pp. 121-266.

J. W. Gilles, 'Der Stammbaum des Hochofens', *Archiv für das Eisenhüttenwesen*, **23**, Düsseldorf, 1952, pp.407-15.

J. Gimpel, *The medieval machine: the industrial revolution of the middle ages*, 2nd ed., London, Pimlico, 1992.

A. Girardot, 'Fondeurs d'artillerie et sidérurgistes, une direction de recherche?' in P. Benoît and P. Braunstein (eds.), *Mines, carrières et métallurgie dans la France médiévale : actes du Colloque de Paris, 19, 20, 21 juin 1980*, Paris : Centre national de la recherche scientifique, 1983, pp. 67-76.

J.-B. Giraud, *Documents pour servir à l'histoire de l'armement au moyen âge et à la renaissance*, **2** *(1) Notes pour servir à l'histoire de la sidérurgie en Lorraine: Arsenal de Nancy, mines, forges, armes, etc.*, Lyon, The author, 1899.

M. S. Giuseppi, 'The accounts of the iron-works at Sheffield and Worth in Sussex, 1546-1549', *Archaeological Journal*, **69** (1912), p. 276-311.

A. Goodman, *The Wars of the Roses: military activity and English society, 1452-97*, London, Routledge, 1981.

J. J. Goring, 'Wealden ironmasters in the age of Elizabeth', in E. W. Ives and others, eds. *Wealth and power in Tudor England*, London, Athlone, 1978, pp. 204-27.

P. Goubert, 'Commerce et prix du fer en Picardie (XVI-XVIIe siècles)' in *Le fer à travers les âges; hommes et techniques: actes du colloque international, Nancy, 3-6 octobre, 1955*, Nancy, Annales de l'Est de la Faculté des lettres de l'Université, 1956, pp. 175-86.

L. Graves, 'Précis statistique sur le canton d'Auneuil' in *Annuaire de l'Oise*, Beauvais, Achille Desjardins, 1831.

G. Hansotte, 'L'industrie sidérurgique dans la vallée de l'Ourthe liégeoise aux temps modernes', *La vie wallonne*, **29** (1955), pp. 116-220.

G. Hansotte, 'L'industrie métallurgique dans le bassin de la Hoègne aux temps modernes', *Bulletin de l'Institut archéologique liègeois*, **76** (1963), pp. 5-44.

G. Hansotte, 'Contributions à l'histoire de la métallurgie dans le bassin du Hoyoux aux temps modernes', *Bulletin de l'Institut archéologique liégeois*, **80** (1967), pp. 59-90.

G. Hansotte, 'La métallurgie wallonne au XVIe et dans la première moitié du XVIIe siècle; un état de la quéstion' in H. Kellenbenz, ed. *Schwerpunkte der Eisengewinnung und Eisenverarbeitung in Europa, 1500-1650*, Köln, Böhlau, 1974, pp. 126-46.

G. Hansotte, 'Les fourneaux à fer dans la vallée de la Meuse liégeoise aux XVIe et XVIIe siècles', *Bulletin de la Société Royale Le Vieux-Liège*, **9** (1978), pp. 228-31.

E. N. Hartley, *Ironworks on the Saugus*, Norman, University of Oklahoma Press, 1957.

A. Hasslacher, *Beiträge zur älteren Geschichte des Eisenhüttenwesen im Saargebiet*, Berlin, 1896.

J. Hodgkinson, 'The iron industry in the Weald in the period of the Seven Years' War, 1750-1770', unpublished M.A. dissertation, University of Brighton, 1993; http://www.wealdeniron.org.uk/thesis.htm

J. S. Hodgkinson, 'Notes on early 18th-century memoranda on the making of iron', *Wealden Iron*, Bulletin of the Wealden Iron Research Group, 2nd series, **15** (1995), p.

J. S. Hodgkinson, 'Crowhurst Forge, Surrey - a new site identified', *Wealden Iron*, Bulletin of the Wealden Iron Research Group, 2nd ser., **32** (2013), pp. 5-10.

J. S. Hodgkinson, 'A bloomforge in Frant: the case of Marriott's Croft', *Wealden Iron*, Bulletin of the Wealden Iron Research Group, 2nd ser., **35** (2015), 44-54.

O. F. G. Hogg, *English artillery, 1326-1716*, London, Royal Artillery Institution, 1963.

W. L. Holman, *Descendants of Samuel Hills: a supplement to The Hills family in America*, Concord, Rumford, 1957.

J. R. Hooker, 'Notes on the organization and supply of the Tudor military under Henry VII', *Huntington Library Quarterly*, **23**, *1* (November 1959), pp. 19-31.

K. Horikoshi, 'L'industrie du fer dans la Lorraine pré-moderne', Doctoral thesis in history, University of Nancy II, 1992.

L. Ince, *The Knight family and the British iron industry,* 1695-1902, Cardiff, Merton, Priory Press, 1991.

E. W. Ives and others (eds.), *Wealth and power in Tudor England*, London, Athlone, 1978.

S. M. Jack, 'Sources for the History of the Wealden Iron Industry in the Public Record Office, part 3', *Wealden Iron*, Bulletin of the Wealden Iron Research Group, Second series, **2** (1982), p. 24.

K. Jacobs, *Das Aufkommen der Feuerwaffen am Niederrheine bis zum Jahre 1400*, Bonn, Hanstein, 1910

G. Jars, *Voyages métallurgiques*, Lyon, Rignault, 1774.

O. Johannsen, *Die Geschichte des Eisens*, Düsseldorf, Verlag Stahleisen, 3rd ed., 1953.

B. L. C. Johnson, 'The charcoal iron trade in the Midlands, 1690-1720', unpublished M.A thesis, University of Birmingham, 1950.

H. Kellenbenz (ed.), *Schwerpunkte der Eisengewinnung und Eisenverarbeitung in Europa, 1500-1650,* Köln, Böhlau, 1974.

G. H. Kenyon, *The glass industry of the Weald,* Leicester University Press, 1967.

P. W. King, 'Early statistics for the iron industry; a vindication', *Historical Metallurgy*, 30 (1996), pp. 23-46.

R. H. Kinvig and others (ed.), *Birmingham and its regional setting: a scientific survey*, Birmingham, British Association for the Advancement of Science, 1950.

L. A. Knafla (ed.), *Kent at law, 1602: the county jurisdiction: assizes and sessions of the peace*, London, HMSO, 1994.

H. L. Knau, "Renn- und Roheisenverhüttung – Osmundefrischen. Zur Geschichte der Eisen- und Stahlerzeugung im märkischen Sauerland" in G. Magnusson (ed.), *The importance of ironmaking: technical innovation and social change; papers presented at the Norberg Conference on May 8-13, 1995,* **1**, Jernkontorets, Stockholm, 1995, pp. 165-71.

I. Krulis-Randa, 'Le développement des fourneaux à fer et l'introduction du haut fourneau wallon en Bohême', *Revue d'Histoire de la Sidérurgie,* **8** (1967), pp. 245-275.

K. Kumlien, *Sverige och hanseaterna: studier i svensk politik och utrikeshandel,* Stockholm, Wahlström and Widstrand, 1953.

F. Lambarde, 'The Lewknor carpet', *Sussex Archaeological Collections,* **70** (1929), pp. 1-7.

P. Lardin, 'Les chantiers du bâtiment en Normandie orientale à la fin du Moyen Age (matériaux et ouvriers)', Doctoral thesis, University of Rouen, 1995.

C. Laurent and J. Lameere, *Recueil des Ordonnances des Pays-Bas*, 2e série, **1**, Ministère de la Justice, Bruxelles, 1893.

A. T. C. and E. M. Lavender, *Our Lavender forgemen*, pt. 1, published by the authors, 1999.

R. E. Leader, *History of the Company of Cutlers in Hallamshire vol. 2,* Sheffield, Pawson and Brailsford, 1906.

V. Leblond (ed.), *Documents relatifs à l'histoire économique de Beauvais et du Beauvaisis au XVIe siècle extraits des minutes notariales, 1, 1537-1550*, Paris, Champion, 1925.

V. Leblond and J. Tremblot (eds.), *Documents notariés relatifs à l'histoire économique du Beauvaisis et du Vexin Français: extraits des minutes de Chaumont-en-Vexin 1489-1505*, Paris, Dumont, 1927.

S. Lee (ed.), *Dictionary of National Biography*, **39**, London, Smith, Elder & Co., 1894.

J.-P. Leguay, 'Un aspect du travail dans les villes armoricaines au Moyen Age: la fabrication des canons et armes blanches' in P. Benoît and D. Cailleaux (eds.), *Hommes et travail du métal dans les villes médiévales*, Paris, Association pour l'édition et la diffusion des études historiques, 1988, pp. 185-226.

W. A. Leighton (ed.), 'The Register of Sir Thomas Botelar, Vicar of Much Wenlock', *Transactions of the Shropshire Archaeological Society*, First series, **6** (1883), pp. 93-132.

J. Lejeune, *La formation du capitalisme moderne dans la principauté de Liège au XVIe siècle*, Bibliothèque de la Faculté de philosophie et lettres de l'Université de Liège, **87,** Paris, Les Belles Lettres, 1939.

H. Lepage, 'Recherches sur l'industrie en Lorraine; chapitre 4', *Mémoires de la Société Royale des Sciences, Lettres et Arts de Nancy* (1851), pp. 228-429.

J. H. Lewis, 'The charcoal-fired blast-furnaces of Scotland; a review', *Proceedings of the Society of Antiquaries of Scotland*, **114** (1984), pp. 433-79.

J. M. Lindsay, 'The iron industry of the Highlands: charcoal blast furnaces', *Scottish Historical Review*, **56** (1977), pp. 49-63.

A. G. Little and F. M. Powicke (eds.), *Essays in medieval history presented to Thomas Frederick Tout*, Manchester University Press, 1925.

W. Llewellin, 'Sussex ironmasters in Glamorganshire', *Archaeologia Cambrensis*, 3rd series, **34** (1863), pp. 81-119.

G. I. H. Lloyd, *The cutlery trade; an historical essay in the economics of small scale production*, London, Longmans, 1913.

F. Lot, *Recherches sur les effectifs des armées françaises, des Guerres d'Italie aux Guerres de Religion, 1494-1562*, Paris, École Pratique des Hautes Études, 1962.

M. A. Lower, 'Historical and archaeological notices of the ironworks of the county of Sussex', *Sussex Archaeological Collections*, **2** (1849), pp. 169-220.

W. I. Macadam, 'Notes on the ancient iron industry of Scotland', *Proceedings of the Society of Antiquaries of Scotland*, new series, **21** (1887), pp. 89-131.

G. Magnusson, 'The medieval blast furnace at Lapphyttan' in C. Rockwell and M. Garcia (eds.), *Ironworks and iron monuments: Study, conservation and adaptive use*, Ironbridge Symposium 23-25 October 1984, Rome, ICCROM, 1985, pp. 51-66.

G. Magnusson (ed.), *The importance of ironmaking: technical innovation and social change; papers presented at the Norberg Conference on May 8-13, 1995*, **1**, Stockholm, Jernkontorets, 1995.

G. Magnusson (ed.), *The importance of ironmaking: technical innovation and social change; papers presented at the Norberg Conference on May 8-13, 1995*, **2**, Stockholm, Jernkontorets, 1996.

A. Mawer and F. M. Stenton, *The place names of Sussex vol. 2*, Cambridge University Press, 1930.

G. Mayhew, *Tudor Rye*, Falmer, Sussex University, 1987.

J. G. McDonnell, 'An account of the iron industry in upper Ryedale and Bilsdale, c. 1150- 1650', *The Ryedale Historian*, **6** (1972), p. 23-49.

D. M. Meades and R. G. Houghton, 'Iron Plat, Buxted, Sussex, furnace and forge site, survey 1990/1 (TQ/497240)', *Wealden Iron*, Bulletin of the Wealden Iron Research Group, 2nd series, **12** (1992), pp. 23-6.

A. Milet, 'Comptabilité publique sous la domination anglaise au XVe siècle', *Melanges*, Société de l'histoire de Normandie, 7th series, 1907, pp. 195-204.

M. Mollat, *Comptabilité du port de Dieppe au XVe siècle: ports, routes, et trafics*, IV. Centre de Recherches Historiques, Ecole Pratique des Hautes Etudes, VIe Section, Paris, Colin, 1951.

M. Mollat, *Le commerce maritime normand à la fin du Moyen Age; étude d'histoire economique et sociale*, Paris, Librarie Plon, 1952.

N. Monteillard, 'Artisans et artisanat du métal à Rouen' in P. Benoît and D. Cailleaux (eds.), *Hommes et travail du métal dans les villes médiévales*, Paris, AEDEH, 1988, pp. 109-26.

E. Tomàs i Morera (ed.), *La farga catalana en el marc de l'arqueologia siderúrgica : aquest libre conté les comunicacions presentades al Simposi Internacional sobre la Farga Catalana, celebrat a Ripoll del 13 al 17 de setembre de 1993*, Andorra la Vella, Govern d'Andorra, Ministeri d'Afers Socials i Cultura, 1995.

R. A. Mott, 'English bloomeries, 1329-1589', *Journal of the Iron and Steel Institute*, **198** (1961-2), pp. 149-61.

R. A. Mott, 'Kirkstall forge and monkish ironmaking', *Publications of the Thoresby Society*, **15**, *2* (1972), pp. 154-66.

R. A. Mott (ed. P. Singer), *Henry Cort, the great finer*, London, The Metals Society, 1983.

W. M. Myddleton (ed.), *Chirk castle accounts*, Manchester University Press, 1931.

P. Neu, *Eisenindustrie in der Eifel: Aufstieg, Blüte und Niedergang*, Köln, Rheinland Verlag, 1988.

D. C. Nicolle, *Arms and armour in the crusading era 1050-1350*, White Plains, Kraus, 1988

A. Ödman, 'Iron and castles in Scania', in A. Espleund, *Bloomery ironmaking during 2000 years,vol. 2, Seminar in Budalen, Sør-Trondelag, Norway, August 26th-30th 1991* Trondheim, Budalseminaret, 1992, pp. 45-54.

J. A. Owen, *The history of the Dowlais iron works 1759-1970,* Risca, Newport, Starling Press, 1977.

R. Parrott (ed. S. A. H. Burne), *An accountt who hath enjoyed the severall estates in the parish of Audley and Hamlett of Talk in the County of Stafford for 200 years last past, 1733*, Newcastle, Staffs., 1947.

R. A. Pelham, 'The growth of settlement and industry, c 1100-1700' in R. H. Kinvig and others (ed.), *Birmingham and its regional setting: a scientific survey*, Birmingham, British Association for the Advancement of Science, 1950, pp. 135-48.

E. Perroy, 'L'artillerie de Louis XI dans la campagne d'Artois (1477)', *Revue du Nord*, **26** (1943), pp. 171-96 and 293-315.

H. Pirchegger, *Das steirische Eisenwesen bis 1564*, Graz, Leykam Verlag, 1937.

F. Pirotte, 'L'industrie métallurgique de la terre de Durbuy de 1480-1625, ses rapports avec la métallurgie liégeoise', *Bulletin de l'Institut archéologique liégeois*, **79** (1966), pp. 145-210.

C. H. Pope, *The pioneers of Massachusetts*, Boston, The author, 1900.

N.-R. Potin de La Mairie, *Recherches historiques sur la ville de Gournay, vol. 1*, Gournay, Veuve Follope, 1842.

N.-R. Potin de La Mairie, *Supplément aux Recherches historiques sur la ville de Gournay*, Gournay, Veuve Follope, 1844.

D. Potter, *War and government in the French Provinces: Picardy, 1470-1560,* Cambridge University Press, 1993.

H. Quignon, 'Fondeurs et ferronniers liégeois en Beauvaisis XVe-XVIe siècles', *Compte-rendu des séances de la Société académique de l'Oise*, 1901, pp. 11-17.

A. Raistrick, *Dynasty of iron founders*, York, Sessions, 1953.

A. Raistrick and E. Allen, 'The south Yorkshire ironmasters (1690-1750)', *Economic History Review*, **9** (1939), pp. 168-85.

E.-J.-B. Rathery, *Des relations sociales et intellectuelles entre la France et l'Angleterre*, Paris, 1855.

J. E. Rehder, 'Primitive furnaces and the development of metallurgy', *Historical Metallurgy*, **20**, *2* (1986), pp. 87-92.

T. Rehren and M. Ganzelewski, 'Early blast furnace and finery slags from the Jubach, Germany,' in G. Magnusson (ed.), *The importance of ironmaking: technical innovation and social change; papers presented at the Norberg Conference on May 8-13, 1995*, **1**, Stockholm, Jernkontorets, 1995, pp. 172-9.

P. Riden, *A gazetteer of charcoal-fired blast furnaces in Great Britain in use since 1660*, Cardiff, Merton Priory Press, 1987.

P. Riden, *The Butterley Company 1790-1830*, 2nd ed., Chesterfield, Derbyshire Record Society, 1990.

P. Riden, 'The charcoal iron industry in the East Midlands, 1580-1780', *Derbyshire Archaeological Journal*, **111** (1991), p. 64-84.

P. Riden, 'Early ironworks in the lower Taff valley', *Morgannwg; The journal of Glamorgan history*, **36** (1992), pp. 69-93.

J. Rigault, 'Quelques mots sur l'émigration liégeoise en France sous Louis XI', *La Vie Wallonne*, **22**

(1948), pp. 32-6.

C. Rockwell and M. Garcia (eds.), *Ironworks and iron monuments: Study, conservation and adaptive use*, Ironbridge Symposium 23-25 October 1984, Rome, ICCROM, 1985.

D. Rouet, 'Une dépendance de l'abbaye Saint-Pierre-de-Préaux : le prieuré Sainte-Radegonde de Neufchâtel-en-Bray d'après les sources de l'abbaye de Préaux', *Annales de Normandie*, **49** (1999), pp. 515-538.

A. Salamagne, 'L'attaque des places-fortes au xve siècle à travers l'example des guerres anglo- et franco-bourguignonnes', *Revue historique*, **585**, *1* (1993), pp. 65-114.

A. Salamagne, 'A propos de l'adaptation de la fortification à l'artillerie vers les années 1400: quelques remarques sur les problèmes de vocabulaire, de typologie et de méthode', *Revue du Nord*, **75** (1993), pp. 809-46.

H. R. Schubert, *Geschichte der nassauischen Eisenindustrie von den Anfängen bis zur Zeit des 30-jährigen Krieges*, Marburg, Elwert, 1937.

H. R. Schubert (ed.), *Vom Ursprung und Werden der Buderus'schen Eisenwerke, Wetzlar*, **1**, München, Bruckmann, 1938.

H. R. Schubert, 'A Tudor furnace in Waterdown Forest', *Journal of the Iron and Steel Institute*, **169** (1951), pp. 241-2.

H. R. Schubert, *History of the British iron and steel industry from c. 450 B.C. to A.D. 1775*, London, Routledge, 1957.

W. F. Schuster, *Das alte Metall- und Eisenschmelzen: Technologie und Zusammenhänge*, Düsseldorf, Verein deutscher Ingenieure, 1969.

H. Scrivenor, *History of the iron trade, from the earliest record to the present period*, 2nd ed., London, Longman, 1854.

J. Sion, *Les paysans de la Normandie orientale*, Paris, Armand Colin, 1909.

R. D. Smith and R. R. Brown, *Bombards: Mons Meg and her sisters*, London, Royal Armouries, 1989.

R. D. Smith, 'Early cast-iron guns with particular reference to guns on the Isle of Man', *Journal of the Ordnance Society*, **3** (1991), pp. 25-45.

J. Smyth, *The Lives of the Berkeleys* (ed. J. Maclean), 3 vols, Gloucester, John Bellows, 1883-5.

M. Sönnecken, *Forshungen zur spätmittelalterlichen frühneuzeitlichen Eisendarstellung in Kierspe, Märkischer Kreis; ein Beitrag zur Entwicklungsgeschichte des Eisenhüttenwesens in Westfalen*, Düsseldorf, Verein deutscher Eisenhüttenleute, 1977.

H. Speight, *Upper Wharfedale*, London, Elliot Stock, 1900.

R. T. Spence, 'Mining and smelting in Yorkshire by the Cliffords, earls of Cumberland, in the Tudor and early Stuart period', *Yorkshire Archaeological Journal*, **64** (1992), pp. 157-83.

R. Sprandel, *Das Eisengewerbe im Mittelalter*, Stuttgart, Hiersemann, 1968.

E. Straker, *Wealden iron*, London, Bell, 1931.

J. M. Swank, *History of the Manufacture of Iron in All Ages*, Philadelphia, American Iron and Steel Association, 1892.

E. B. Teesdale, *The Queen's gunstonemaker; an account of Ralph Hogge, Elizabethan ironmaster and gunfounder*, Seaford, Lindel, 1984.

E. B. Teesdale, 'The 1574 lists of ironworks in the Weald; a re-examination', *Wealden Iron*, Bulletin of the Wealden Iron Research Group, 2nd series, **6** (1986), pp. 7-44.

E. B. Teesdale, *Gunfounding in the Weald in the sixteenth century*, London, Royal Armouries, 1992.

J. W. Thompson, *The wars of religion in France, 1559-1576; the Huguenots, Catherine de Medici, Philip II*, Chicago University Press, 1909.

G. Thuesen, 'Bergverksdrift i Oslo området', *Volund*, Oslo, Norsk Teknisk Museum, 1988.

F. Tremel, 'Das Eisenwesen in der Steiermark und in Tirol, 1500-1650', in H. Kellenbenz (ed.), *Schwerpunkte der Eisengewinnung und Eisenverarbeitung in Europa, 1500-1650*, Köln, Böhlau, 1974. pp. 285-308.

B. S. Trinder, 'A description of Coalbrookdale in 1801', *Transactions of the Shropshire Archaeological Society*, **58**, *3* (1967-8), pp. 244-258.

R. F. Tylecote, *The early history of metallurgy in Europe*, London, Longman, 1987.

J. Unwin 'The marks of Sheffield cutlers 1614-1878', *Historical Metallurgy*, **33** (1999), pp. 93-103.

J. Upton, 'Catsfield furnace; a new discovery', *Wealden Iron*, Bulletin of the Wealden Iron Research Group, 2nd series, **1** (1981), pp. 16-17.

M. Vale, *War and chivalry: warfare and aristocratic culture in England, France and Burgundy at the end of the Middle Ages*, Athens, University of Georgia Press, 1981.

J. van Laun, 'Seventeenth century ironmaking in south west Herefordshire', *Historical Metallurgy*, **13**, *2* (1979), pp. 55-68.

H. F. J. Vaughan, 'Wenlock Corporation Records', *Transactions of the Shropshire Archaeological Society*, 2nd series, **6** (1894), pp. 223-283.

R. Vaughan, *Philip the Bold: the formation of the Burgundian state*, London, Longman, 1962.

R. Vaughan, *John the Fearless: the growth of Burgundian power*, London, Longman, 1966

R. Vaughan, *Charles the Bold: the last Valois duke of Burgundy*, London, Longman, 1973

Victoria County History of Shropshire, vol. 2 (ed. A. T. Gaydon), Oxford University Press, 1973.

Victoria County History of Shropshire, vol. 3 (ed. G. C. Baugh), Oxford University Press, 1979.

Victoria County History of Shropshire, vol. 8 (ed. A. T. Gaydon), Oxford University Press, 1968.

Victoria County History of Shropshire, vol. 10 (ed. G. C. Baugh), Oxford University Press, 1998.

Victoria County History of Shropshire, vol. 11 (ed. G. C. Baugh), Oxford University Press, 1985.

Victoria County History of the county of Stafford, vol. 2 (ed. M. W. Greenslade and J. G. Jenkins), Oxford University Press, 1967.

Victoria County History of the county of Stafford, vol. 20 (ed. M. W. Greenslade), Oxford University Press, 1994.

J. H. L. Vogt, *De gamla norske jernverk*, Norges Geologisk Undersögelse, **46**, Kristiania, 1908.

R. Walker and others, 'Analytical study of composite shot from the Mary Rose', *Historical Metallurgy*, **23** (1989), pp. 84-90.

H. B. Walters, 'The Church Bells of Shropshire', *Transactions of the Shropshire Archaeological Society*, 3rd series, **2**, (1902), pp. 165-247.

G. Watts (ed.), *Titchfield; a history*, Titchfield History Society, 1982.

S. Watts, 'Shifnal ironworks accounts, 1583-90' in D. C. Cox (ed.), *Shropshire historical documents; a miscellany*, Shropshire Record Series, **4**, Keele, Centre for Local History, 2000, pp. 1-30.

T. A. Wertime, *The coming of the age of steel*, Leiden, Brill, 1961.

A. Weyhmann, 'Geschichte der älteren lothringischen Eisenindustrie', *Jahrbuch der Gesellschaft für Lothringische Geschichte*, **17** (1905), pp. 1-212.

C. Whittick, 'Re-dating an early document', *Wealden Iron*, Bulletin of the Wealden Iron Research Group, 2nd series, **22** (2002), pp. 18-21.

R. M. Willatts, 'Pre-Industrial revolution cast-iron grave slabs', *Wealden Iron*, Bulletin of the Wealden Iron Research Group, 2nd series, **8** (1988), 12-47.

C. Wilson, *England's apprenticeship, 1603-1763*, London, Longman, 1965.

B. C. Worssam, 'Geology and iron ore in the pays de *Bray*', *Wealden Iron*, Bulletin of the Wealden Iron Research Group, 2nd series, **10** (1990), p. 12-18.

R. Yakemtchouk, *Les transferts internationaux d'armes de guerre*, Paris, Pedone, 1980.

M. Yans, *Histoire économique du duché de Limbourg sous la maison de Bourgogne: les forêts et les mines*, Mémoires Classe des Lettres et des Sciences Morales et Politiques, **38**, *2*, Brussels, Palais des Académies, 1938.

J. Yernaux, *La métallurgie liégeoise et son expansion au XVIIe siècle*, Liège, Thone, 1939.

J. Yernaux, 'Retour de notre passé industriel: la sidérurgie ancienne dans la vallée de la Lienne' *Revue du Conseil économique wallon*, **63** (1963), 62-5.

M. Zell, *Industry in the countryside*, Cambridge University Press, 1994.

ARCHIVE LOCATIONS

Abbreviations, eg. (AEN), are used in footnotes

Belgium

Archives de l'État à Namur (AEN)
Archives Générales du Royaume à Bruxelles (AGR)

France

Archives communales et communautaires d'Amiens (ACA)
Archives départementales d'Eure-et-Loir, Chartres (ADEL)
Archives départementales de la Meuse, Bar-le-Duc
Archives départementales de la Seine-Maritime, Rouen (ADSM)
Archives départementales de l'Eure, Evreux (ADE)
Archives départementales de l'Oise, Beauvais (ADO)
Archives départmentales de l'Yonne, Auxerre
Archives municipales de Rouen (AMR)
Archives nationales de France, Paris (AN)

United Kingdom

Barnsley Archives
Canterbury Cathedral Library
Carmarthen Record Office
Cheshire Record Office, Chester
East Sussex Record Office, Brighton (ESRO)
Gloucestershire Record Office, Gloucester (GRO)
Hampshire Record Office, Winchester
Herefordshire Archives and Record Centre, Hereford (HARC)
Kent History and Library Centre, Maidstone (KHLC)
Lancashire Archives, Preston (LA)
Lichfield Record Office (LRO)
London Metropolitan Archives (LMA)
National Library of Wales, Aberystwyth (NLW)
Sheffield Archives (SA)
Shropshire Archives, Shrewsbury
Staffordshire Record Office, Stafford
Surrey History Centre, Woking
The British Library, London (BL)
The National Archives, Kew (TNA)
University of Nottingham Manuscripts and Special Collections (UNMASC)
West Glamorgan Archives Service, Swansea
West Sussex Record Office, Chichester (WSRO)
William Salt Library, Stafford

United States of America

Henry E. Huntington Library, San Marino, California (HEH)

INDEX OF PLACES AND SUBJECTS

Notes: Alphabetization is word-by-word. A page reference containing n indicates a note: e.g. 221n140 refers to note 140 on page 221. Roman page numbers refer to the Author's Preface. Historic counties are used in the index, and place names with two elements (e.g. East Grinstead) are indexed under the first element.

The text often has multiple mentions of places and ironworking sites in various different contexts. In the index priority is given to the most important mentions. Note that an index entry may refer to more than one reference on the same page.

Personal names are indexed here only in subheadings under places. For full coverage of persons see the separate index of personal names beginning on page 928.

E

INDEX OF PERSONAL NAMES

Notes: Alphabetization is word-by-word. A page reference containing n indicates a note: e.g. 739n103 refers to note 103 on page 739. Page numbers in bold type indicate major coverage. Roman page numbers refer to the Author's Preface. Note that an index entry may refer to more than one reference on the same page.

Minor mentions of individuals or families may not be indexed where the information is given in more detail elsewhere in the book. In Appendices 1 and 2, forgemasters and other employers of ironworkers are indexed, but not individual ironworkers.

All surnames are indexed but sections indexed as 'family' may include references to named individuals not separately indexed. References to individuals from the same family are grouped together in the index, but where there is no firm evidence that individuals with the same surname are related they have been given separate entries.

family **242–3**, 301
John Angell (fl. 1510–43) 125, 195, 242, 444
see also Russell
Angerfield
family 149–50, **322–4**
Angreville (d'Angreville) family 71, 125, 136, 137–8, 149–50, 168, 322–3
Colin Le Pellu (?Angreville) (fl. 1520) 132, 150, 323
Jehan Angreville (fl. 1480s–*c.* 1504) 71, 74, 113, 114, 136, 137, 138, 149, 186
Jehan Angreville alias Motin (?John Ongerfield) (fl. 1509–21) 116, 122, 149, 150, 186, 322–3, 775
Jehan Angreville alias Pellu (?John Angerfield) (fl. 1509–21) 149–50, 323
John Angerfield (d. 1590) 323, 478
Marguerite d'Engreville (fl. 1488) 74, 137
Nathaniel White alias Angerfield (fl. 1643) 700
Peter Angerfield (fl. 1559) 150, 323
Angreville (d'Angreville) *see* Angerfield
Angrome, William (fl. 1614) 729
Annable, Elizabeth (fl. 1682) 354
Annessett *see* Hunnisett
Ansell
Angel Ansell (fl. 1646), w. of John 692
John Ansill (fl. 1631) 341
Susan Ancell (fl. 1612) 341
Anthony, John (fl. 1549) 536–7
Aoustin, Jacques (fl. 1539) 108
Apsley, Henry (fl. 1600) 236
Arcano, Arcangelo (fl. 1538) 400, 444, 454, 455
Archon, family 109
Arenberg, counts of *see* La Marck
Armitage, Joseph (fl. 1647) 751
Armyshaw, ____ (Oakamoor, fl. 1590s) 721
Arnold, Finyce (fl. 1600) 240
Arthur
family **549–50**
Arter (?Actor/Hector) (collier, fl. 1550) 446, 549, 633
William Artur (fl. 1643) 739n103
Artys, Sarvase d' (16th cent.) 244
Asces or Astes, family **385–6**
Ashburnham
family 440
Alice Ashburnham (fl. 1541) 585
John Ashburnham (fl. 1549–80) 81, 381, 424, 428, 564, 598, 658, 749; aliens in lay subsidy rolls 824, 825
Sir John Ashburnham (d. 1620) 415
Thomas Ashburnham (fl. 1606) 492
Ashdown, Mary (fl. 1586), d. of Nicholas 315
Ashe, Martin (fl. 1585) 611
Asheforde, ____ (Hints, fl. 1595–6) 720
Ashenden, family 582
Ashforth, Stephen (fl. 1715) 484
Ashmore, Edward (fl. 1597) 723, 724
Ashmore, Thomas (fl. 1709) 318
Ashurste, Joan (fl. 1595) 285
Askew, George (d. 1574) 550
Aspes, Mary (fl. 1576) 631
Aspie, Anne (fl. 1639) 364, 721
Astell, John (fl. 1607) 706
Astes *see* Asces or Astes
Atherall, Alice (fl. 1578) 667
Atherton, John (fl. 1604) 237, 725
Atkins, Sarah (fl. 1656) 290
Atterall, Joan (fl. 1633) 567
Aubel, family 678
Aubert, Hursin (fl. 1534–46) 153
Aubery (Auvery)
family 88, 369
Engren Auveray (fl. 1540s) 44
Jehan Aubery (fl. 1540) 133, 186
Parnell Auverey (fl. 1561) 673
see also Awberie; Larby
Audierne, Denis (fl. 1526) 142
Audierne, Elias (fl. 1570) 90–1
Audierne, Pierre (fl. 1495) 47
Aufrey *see* Alfrey; Avery
Auger *see* Ogier
Austen, *see also* Aoustin; Awstin; Awstine
Austen, Anne (fl. 1655) 473
Austen, Henry (fl. 1621) 476
Austen, Robert (fl. 1638) 797
Austen, Sarah (fl. 1639) 298
Auvery *see* Aubery
Auxerre, counts of 46, 669–70
Averell
family **228–9**
Gilbert Averell (Verall) (fl. 1544) 88, 200, 228, 444
Avery
family 326, 554
see also Alfrey; Aubery
Awaigne, Gilles d' (fl. 1460) 29
Aware, Alice (fl. 1574) 468
Awberie, *see also* Aubery
Awberie, ____ (Oakamoor, fl. 1607) 721
Awcock, Richard (fl. 1587) 577
Awcock, Thomas (fl. 1577) 422
Awcocke, John (fl. 1579) 217
Awford, Anne (fl. 1717) 238
Awger *see* Ogier
Awstin, Awstine, *see also* Austen
Awstin, William (fl. 1630) 685
Awstine, Joan (fl. 1562) 373
Awton, William (fl. 1596) 724, 753
Axoll, Katherine (fl. 1617) 578
Aylard
family 71, 222, 223, 685
see also Allard
Aynat, Thomas (probate 1620) 772
Aynet, Richard (fl. 1616) 405
Aynscombe
Anne Aynscombe (fl. 1624) 312
Stephen Aynscombe (fl. 1617) 477
Thomas Aynescombe (fl. 1618) 786
see also Ainscome; Enscombe
Azoult, Nicolas (fl. 1546) 82

B

Baart, Perette (16th cent.) 619
Baart *dit* Frerot, Jehan (15th cent.) 333
Bab(b), family 722, 732, 740
Bacheler, *see also* Batchellor
Bacheler, Mary (fl. 1669) 680
Bachellor, James (fl. 1621) 581
Bachelor, Goddard (fl. 1555) 617
Bachelour, Constance (fl. 1674) 683
Backall *see* Buckoll
Bacon, Sir Francis (d. 1657) 713
Bagnall, ____ (Oakamoor, fl. 1596) 721
Bailey *see* Bayley
Baillard, Baiard *see* Ballard
Baillet, Andrieu (fl. 1511) 53
Baillet, Guillaume (fl. 1552) 177
Baillet, Henry (fl. 1507) 52
Bailleul, Jacques de (fl. 1538) 181
Bailleul, Jehan de (fl. 1534) 131
Bakaell, Philippe (fl. 1544) 504
Baker
Agnes Baker (fl. 1585) 552
Alice Baker (fl. 1599) 807
Elizabeth Baker (fl. 1677) 483
John Baker (fl. 1611) 630
John Baker (Battle, d. 1587) 441, 443, 446, 596
John Baker (Gildredge, fl. 1638) 652
John Baker (Hamsell, fl. 1571) 362
John Baker (Mayfield, fl. 1618) 786
John Baker (Speldhurst and Withyham, 1581–1638) 563

Baker (*continued*)
John Baker (Withyham, d. 1555) 241, 429, 440, 443, 445–6, 767; aliens in lay subsidy rolls 831, 832; immigrants listed in Westminster denization roll (1544) 814, 818
Katherine Baker (fl. 1584) 697
Margaret Baker (fl. 1612) 807
Sir Richard Baker (d. 1594) 222, 429, 597, 598
Robert Baker (d. 1585) 209–10, 443, 767
Robert Baker (fl. 1603) 552
Robert Baker (fl. 1677) 483
Roger Baker (fl. 1638) 806–7
Sarah Baker (fl. 1693) 629
William Baker (fl. 1598) 642
William Baker (fl. 1677) 483
Balden (?Barden), William (16th cent.) 601
Balding, Clemens (fl. 1585) 299
Baldock, Elizabeth (fl. 1641) 478
Baldock, Mary (fl. 1612) 631
Baldocke, John (fl. 1575) 243
Baleden, Richard (fl. 1592) 676
Ball, ____ (Oakamoor, fl. 1599) 721
Ballan, John (fl. 1584) 676
Ballard
family **552**
George Ballard (fl. 1583) 507, 508
Jane Ballard (fl. 1575) 222
Simon Ballard (fl. 1497) 196, 198
Bamber, Jane (fl. 1572) 283
Bamforth, family 306, 337, 611, 728, 731, 732–3, 735, 737, 739
Banckes, Thomas (fl. 1581) 572
Banford *see* Bamforth
Banister, Margaret (fl. 1575), w. of Thomas 310
Bankes, Nicholas (fl. 1575) 586
Banks, Bridget (fl. 1590) 395
Bannester, James (fl. 1579) 217
Bannister, Thomas (fl. 1559) 338
Bannson, Lewes (fl. 1550) 585
Barate, Jehan (fl. 1486) 77
Barate, Jehan (fl. 1513) 131
Barbançon, count of *see* Ligne
Barbe *see* Barby
Barbesallee, Godeffrin (Marche, fl. 1416) 18n33
Barbier, Jehan (fl. 1477) 166
Barby
family 614–15
Elizabeth Barby (fl. 1610) 525
John Barbe (fl. 1564) 81, 156, 377, 470, 471, 615
William Barby (Barbie) (fl. 1562) 471
Bardel, Sarah (fl. 1681) 229
Barden *see* Balden; Lamy alias Barden
Bare, Pierre (fl. 1541) 169
Barfoot, Peter (fl. 1773) 646
Barham
family 440
Elizabeth Barham (fl. 1609) 213
John Barham (d. 1558) 206, 232, 246, 247, 423, 429, 441, 453; immigrants listed in Westminster denization roll (1544) 816
Richard Barham (fl. 1559) 658
Stephen Barham (fl. 1547) 543
see also Borayne
Barker, Isabel (fl. 1587) 239
Barker, John (fl. 1673) 732
Barker, William (fl. 1555) 403
Barley, Thomas (fl. 1620) 737
Barlow, Lewis (fl. 1590s) 721
Barnard *see* Barnet
Barnby, family 738
Barne, William (fl. 1612) 396
Barnes, John (fl. 1606) 268
Barnes alias Browne, Parnell (fl. 1606) 268
Barnet
family **583–4**, 717, 719, 725
John Barnet (fl. 1595) 259
Thomas Barnet (fl. 1554) 207
Barnowe, Leonard (fl. 1574) 293
Barr *see* Briseboys alias Barr
Barrentyne
Drew Barrentyne (d. 1588) 455, 456, 694
Sir William Barrentyne (1481–1549) 261, 422, 440, 455; aliens in lay subsidy rolls 841; immigrants listed in Westminster denization roll (1544) 816–17
Barrett, Sir Edward (fl. 1618) 738
Barrett, John (fl. 1631) 354
Barritte, Thomas (fl. 1583) 473
Barry, Jane (fl. 1672) 468
Barry, John (fl. 1672) 468
Bartelett *see* Bartlett
Bartell, Jane (fl. 1584) 323
Barth, Caspar (d. 1607) 591
Bartholomew alias Ponting
family 221, **361–5**, 559–60, 613, 721–2, 740–1
Dionise Ponting (fl. 1611) 359
Jane Bartholomew, later Mannings (fl. 1760) 624
Joan Pounting (fl. 1615) 259
John Bartholomew (probate 1597) 559, 773
John Bartholomew alias Pounteine (fl. 1616) 363, 765
Julian (Gillian) Bartholomew (d. 1635) 227
Mary Bartholomew (fl. 1695) 336
Mary Ponting (fl. 1611) 213
Peter Bartholomew (fl. 1562–89) 362–3, 560, 762
Peter Pontinge (fl. 1581) 794
see also Jordan
Bartle, Thomas (fl. 1545) 379
Bartlett
family 645
Avery Bartlet (fl. 1608) 296
Henry Bartlet (fl. 1583) 262
John Bartelett (fl. 1625) 375
Robert Bartlet (fl. 1623) 227
Bartley, Margaret (fl. 1545) 379
Bartner, Catherine (fl. 1569) 243
Barton, family (Midlands and Yorkshire) 610, 721, 741
Barton, Peter (fl. 1524) 156
Barton alias Gillet
family **320–1**
Nicholas Bartyn (fl. 1521) 63, 320
Baseden, Margaret (fl. 1603) 654
Bassage, Mercy (fl. 1589) 276
Basset
family 568
Edward Bassett (probate 1620) 568, 774
Elizabeth Bassett (fl. 1558) 233
Jehan Basset (fl. 1483) 68–9
John Bassett (fl. 1594) 380
Margaret Bassett (fl. 1593) 234
Thomas Bassett (fl. 1619) 787
William Bassett (fl. 1591) 674
see also Low
Bassock, family 568
Bastard, Laurens (fl. 1530s/40s) 44
Baster (Bastard), Gellet (fl. 1537) 775
Batchellor, *see also* Bachellor
Batchellor, Thomas (fl. 1635) 335
Bates, Margaret (fl. 1631) 792
Baude, Peter (d. 1546) 79, 133, 400, 439, 444
Baudin, Jehan (fl. 1504) 138
Baudin, Laurens (fl. 1539) 108
Baudin, Pierre, alias Vigor (fl. 1505) 147, 148
Baudouyn, Nicollas (fl. 1546) 180
Baudouyn, Robert (fl. 1553) 71
Baudouyn, Thomassin (fl. 1540) 171
Bawdon (Baughden), Gervaise (fl. 1614–23) 731

family 721
see also Booth
Botting
family **313–14**
Hugh Botting (fl. 1558) 599
Joan Botting (fl. 1599) 314, 779
John Bottinge (Butting) (fl. 1519–44) 313, 445, 446
Mary Botting (fl. 1628) 585
Peter Botten (Botton) (fl. 1543) 313, 445
Bouaffles, Thomas de (fl. 1554) 119, 145, 146, 170
Bouceleu
family 394, 569
Alizon Bouceleu (fl. 1536) 121
Roumain Bouceleu (fl. 1520) 121, 393
Bouchart, Guillaume (fl. 1501) 93
Boué, Simon (fl. 1568) 108
Bouffioulx, Hanekart de *see* Hanekart le Fondeur
Boulbie, George (fl. 1618) 733
Boulenger, Jehan (fl. 1500) 99
Boullainvillier, Antoine (de) (fl. 1514) 103, 106
Bouncklie, family 531
Bound, Joan (fl. 1601) 494
Bourbon, Henri de, Prince of Condé (1552–88) 83, 86
Bourbon, Louis de, Prince of Condé (1530–69) 75, 77, 78, 80, 82, 83
Bourbon, Nicholas, the elder (fl. 1505–50), *Ferraria* 62, 253
Bourbon, Nicholas, the younger (fl. 1517) 24, 62, 253, 440
Bourdet (Bourdel)
family 89, 103, 106–7, 131–3, 150, 186, 318, 323, 334, 380, 499
Guillaume Bourdet, identified as Gilham Nuffyld (fl. 1530–44) and William Burdett (d. 1574) v–vi, 102, 106, 132, 186, 334, 452, 499
see also Borde; Nevill alias Burdett
Bourgoise *see* Burgess
Bourgtheroulde (Boutheroulde), Monsieur de (16th cent.) 101, 181
Bourguygnon *see* Burgonyon
Bourne, Thomas (fl. 1590) 122, 639
Bourse, Ant(h)oine (fl. 1486) 78, 97–9, 171, 183
Bourse, Clement (fl. 1437) 43
Bourse, Guillaume (15th cent.) 97, 183
Bourse, Jacques (16th cent.) 101
Bourse, Jehan (fl. 1486–94) 98–9, 100, 101, 102, 106, 107, 180
Bousselowe
John (fl. 1550) 569
see also Bouceleu
Boutelleu *see* Bouceleu
Bouteraye *see* Buttery
Boutheroulde *see* Bourgtheroulde
Bouvet *see* Bonnet
Bower, ____ (fl. 1603) 613
Bowier *see* Bowyer
Bowle, Alice (fl. 1627) 344
Bowlie *see* Bully
Bowmer (Bowman), William (fl. 1620) 306, 737
Bowmer, George 732
Bowmer, Gilbert (fl. 1564–1617) 306, 737
Bowyer
family 440, 442, **788–9**, 801
Denise Bowyer (fl. 1540s) 199, 223, 232, 442, 776, 788; aliens in lay subsidy rolls 839
Henry Bowyer (d. 1589) 208, 599, 600
John Bowyer (Bowier) (fl. 1512–44) 199, 244, 442, 788; immigrants listed in Westminster denization roll (1544) 819
William Bowyer (d. 1544) 442
William Bowyer (fl. 1636) 490
Box, Godfrey (d. 1604) 713
Boxall, Mary (fl. 1641) 375
Boxe, Denise (fl. 1561) 645
Boxold, Alice (fl. 1632) 331
Boycott, Francis (fl. 1661) 347
Boycott, William (fl. 1634) 347, 727
Boyer, Lawrence (d. 1598) 729
Boyle, Cardo (fl. 1519–44) 147, 149, 300, 309–10
Boyle, Richard, later 1st earl of Cork (1566–1643) 713, 741–2, 748
Boynam, William (fl. 1724) 651
Boyne, John (fl. 1588) 611
Boys, James (fl. 1590) 473
Boysard, Bussard or Billing
family **466–8**, 758
Anne Billnes (Billins) (fl. 1618) 467, 783
Awdryn Blynd alias Billing (fl. 1579) 359
Elizabeth Billin (d. 1602) 575–6
Isabell Billinge (fl. 1599) 474
Mary Blynd (fl. 1582) 639
Michael Bossard (fl. 1649) 433
Braband (Brabon), family 550, 580, 788
Brabant, Arnould de (fl. 1477) 36
Bracpoole, Annes (fl. 1594) 302
Braddow, Braddy *see* Bradwall
Braden, Thomas (fl. 1577) 222
Bradfold, Antony (fl. 1618) 678–9
Bradforth, Lionel (fl. 1615–21) 737
Bradshaigh, Sir Roger (fl. 1716) 307–8
Bradshaw, Francis (d. 1608) 725
Bradwall (Braddow, Braddy)
family 683, 730, 732
Robert Braydow (d. 1571) 610
see also Brydale
Brailsford, family 732
Bramall, Hanna (fl. 1688) 740
Brand, Grace (fl. 1585) 556, 733
Brandon, Edward (fl. 1676) 732
Brasier, Marchie (fl. 1628) 468
Bray, Edward (fl. 1574–80) 369, 615, 654, 700
Bray, Edward (fl. 1622) 369
Bray, Elizabeth (fl. 1610) 481
Bray, John (fl. 1571–6) 542
Bray, Susan (fl. 1626) 702
Bray (Braie), Joan (fl. 1582) 382
Braydow *see* Bradwall
Breame, Mary (fl. 1643) 650
Bredes, Bormeyne (fl. 1539) 538
Breecher, Roger (fl. 1568) 468, 598
Breke, Vincent (fl. 1503) 197
Bretheul, Jehan de (15th cent.) 53
Briant, Elizabeth (fl. 1625) 797
Briant, Richard (fl. 1592) 410
Briday *see* Brydale
Bridger, Alice (fl. 1610) 655
Bridger, Elizabeth (fl. 1610) 332
Bridger, Elizabeth (fl. 1620) 343–4
Bridger, Joan (fl. 1601) 548
Bridger, John (fl. 1610) 655
Bridges, Captain ____ (fl. 1649) 752–3
Bridoul
family 146–7, 682
Germain Bridoul (fl. 1540s) 48
Jehan Bridoul (fl. 1495–1520) 89, 120, 146, 147, 148
Jehan Bridou(l) (fl. 1506) 180–1
Jehan Bridoul (fl. 1527) 89
Marin Bridoul (fl. 1527) 89
Noël Bridoul (fl. 1563) 80
Pierre Bridou (fl. 1504) 140
Pierre Bridoul (fl. 1538) 144, 393
see also Brydale
Bridoullet
family 78, 80–1, 142, 682
Jehan Bridoullet (fl. 1486–1512) 69, 75, 77–8, 84, 86, 100, 101, 104, 124, 160, 161, 164, 169, 178, 183

Burden, Mary (fl. 1655) 633
Burden, Mildred (fl. 1616) 650
Burder
family **379–80**
Anne Border (fl. 1583), d. of Robert 687
Anthony Burder (Burdell) (fl. 1544) 88, 89, 379–80
see also Nevill alias Burdett
Burdet, Francis (fl. 1621) 738
Burdett *see* Nevill alias Burdett
Burdewe *see* Borde
Burford *see* Purford
Burgain, Thomas and Francis (d. 1723) 730
Burge, Anne (fl. 1688) 643
Burgen, Ann (fl. 1602) 809
Burgess
family **705**
Elizabeth Burges (fl. 1614) 562
George Burgess (fl. 1569) 608
Henry Burges (fl. 1621) 582
Isabel Burges (fl. 1581) 385
John Burges (fl. 1638) 652
Nicholas Burges (fl. 1567) 595, 705
Stephen Burges (fl. 1593) 358
William Burgesse (fl. 1573) 610
Burgo, Kilian (fl. 1601) 591
Burgon, John (fl. 1654) 569
Burgonyon, family **629**
Burgundy, dukes of *see* Charles the Bold; John the Fearless; Philip the Bold; Philip the Good
Burkham, Alice (fl. 1629) 409
Burkhard, Meister (fl. 1471) 37
Burleigh, Lord *see* Cecil
Burlett, family **797**
Burley, Mary (fl. 1628) 372
Burmer, Margery (fl. 1567) 321
Burnett, William (fl. 1577) 661
Burr, John (fl. 1596) 778
Burrell
Andrew Burrell (fl. 1611) 741
Catherine Burrell (fl. 1567) 656
Elizabeth Burrell (fl. 1611) 497
Ninian Burrell (fl. 1540–62) 440, 451, 470, 598; aliens in lay subsidy rolls 829
Ninian Burrell (1540–1614) 599
Thomas Burrell (fl. 1549) 451
William Burrell (fl. 1613) 713, 741
Burrow, Margaret (fl. 1621) 631
Bursbe *see* Briseboys alias Barr
Burstow, Henry (fl. 1664) 379
Burte, John (fl. 1639) 477
Burton, Ann (fl. 1662) 584
Busleiden, Gabriel de (fl. 1547) 436
Buss
family **669–73**, 714
Alice Buss (fl. 1609) 517
Audrin Bysse (?Busse) (fl. 1575) 662
Joan Busse (16th cent.) 524
Lawrence Busse (probate 1596) 774
Lorentz Buss (d. 1575) 591
Walter Busse (fl. 1617) 213
see also Beuse
Bussard *see* Boysard, Bussard or Billing
Bussett, Alice (fl. 1560) 486
Busshop *see* Bishop
Butcher, Agnes (fl. 1581) 522
Butcher, Anthony (fl. 1640) 406
Butcher, Bridget (fl. 1594) 331
Butcher, Joan (fl. 1616) 727
Butcher, John (fl. 1622) 676
Butcher, Mercy (fl. 1610) 319
Butcher, Thomas (fl. 1643) 650
Butler, Elizabeth (fl. 1721) 413
Butler, Joan (fl. 1625) 416
Butson (Bodson), Jan de (17th cent.) 742
Butten
family 314
see also Botting
Butterfield, family 332–3
Buttery (Bouteraye)
family 157, 159, **332–3**, 600, 720, 733
Lewis Botery (Buttery, Buttre) (fl. 1522–44) 159, 332, 600
Robert Boutheraye (fl. 1488) 159
Butting, Button *see* Botting
Byckerton, Sibil (fl. 1568) 293
Byfflet, Francis (fl. 1567) 783
Bygnoll, Bygood *see* Vigor, Bigod or Bugo
Byllard, family **384**
Bylwarn, Peter (fl. 1552) 384, 680–1
Byman, Peter (fl. 1552) 651
Byne
family 502, **551**
Richard Byne (fl. 1532) 203
Simon Byne (fl. 1616) 620
Thomas Byne (fl. 1671) 782
see also Bine
Byrley, Margaret (fl. 1576) 794
Byshoppenden, Joan (fl. 1589) 661
Bysse *see* Buss
Bywood, Margaret (fl. 1641) 623

C
Cachecoll, ____ (Robertsbridge, fl. 1542–44) 579–80
Cachelow *see* Catchloe, Ketchlow or Ketslow
Cacherie
family 310, **375–6**, 579, 648
James and Peter Cachery (Cacherie) alias de Mergeyes (fl. 1524–52) 71, 72, 375–6
Cad (Cade, Cat), Thomas (fl. 1577) 233, 761
Cade, Jane (fl. 1628) 344
Cade, Joan (fl. 1562) 535
Cade, Thomas (fl. 1608) 630
Caen, Jehan de (fl. 1514) 53–4, 78, 182
Caen, Nicolas de (fl. 1529) 54, 182
Caffe or Taffte, family **799**
Caffie, Agnes (fl. 1582) 414
Caffinch, Caffynch *see* Cavenche
Cage, Edward (fl. 1589) 736
Caille(u), Adrien (fl. 1545) 146, 177
Caiman, Margaret (fl. 1572) 382
Calear *see* Carler
Callis *see* Roberts alias Callis
Calober *see* Colbor or Calober
Calton, Grace (fl. 1648) 731
Cambier, Jean (fl. 1449) 25, 27–8
Candeville, Jean (Jehan) de (fl. 1461–86) 35, 55, 68, 69, 72, 78, 95, 97–9, 106, 171, 183
Canellier, Jehan (fl. 1501) 109
Canonne, Pierre de (fl. 1566) 51, 58, 182
Canonne, Thomas de (fl. 1547) 51, 58, 102, 182
Canterbury, archbishops of *see* Morton; Warham
Capel
family **387–8**
John Capell (d. 1559) 597
Capelin, Caplin, Capline *see* Chaplin
Capp, Richard (fl. 1617) 341
Capper, family **631–2**
Caquelard, Denis (fl. 1509) 117n354
Caradas, Nicolle (fl. 1518) 67
Carbonet, John (fl. 1514–44) 61, 274
Card, Alice (fl. 1569) 282
Carde, Kyrwyn (fl. 1552) 658
Carden, Cardo *see* Kydevilde
Care
family 686
Nicholas Care (fl. 1610) 630
Careden, Thomas (fl. 1657) 345
Carey
family **282**
see also Kerwyn
Carill *see* Caryll

Thomas Creasy (Cressie) (d. 1627) 482, 637, 772
Cressingham, Richard (fl. 1667) 503
Crevel, Adam (16th cent.) 109
Crevel, Adrien (16th cent.) 129
Crevel, Raoullin (fl. 1540) 181
Crevel, Thomas (fl. 1555) 130
Crewe, Richard (17th cent.) 488
Criel, Laurens (fl. 1462) 104–5
Crier, Marie (fl. 1580) 469
Crippen
family **699**
John Crippin (fl. 1643) 739n103
Cripps, John (fl. 1630) 685
Crips, Edward (d. 1633) 699
Crisford, Thomas (fl. 1606) 268
Croche, Richard (fl. 1505) 93
Crofts, Christopher (fl. 1593) 729
Crompe, Margery (17th cent.) 541
Cromwell, Richard (fl. 1537) 454–5
Cromwell, Thomas (d. 1540) 253, 429, 431, 440, 441, 446, 454
Crop, John (fl. 1610) 328
Cropper, family **419**
Crosse
family 716, 722, 724, 730, 737–8, 740, 744
Mary Crosse (fl. 1666) 364
Crouche, Bartholomew (fl. 1607) 403
Croucher, Joan (fl. 1608) 351
Crowe, Sackville (fl. 1619) 236, 372, 616
Crowe, William (16th cent.) 632
Crowhurst, Agnes (fl. 1610) 490
Crowhurst, James (fl. 1635) 490
Crowley, Ambrose (fl. 1682) 759, 760
Crownage, Simon (fl. 1612) 788
Croy, de, family 158
Crump, Francis (d. 1571) 605
Cruttenden
family 247, 620
Henry Cruttenden (fl. 1627) 647
Robert Cruttenden (d. 1586/7) 537, 538
Cuddington, Allen (fl. 1592) 472
Cuddington, John (fl. 1621) 259
Cuignart, Robin (fl. 1477) 166
Culpeper
Alexander Culpeper (fl. 1574) 373, 597
John Colpeper (fl. 1559) 360
Thomas Colpeper (fl. 1574) 476
Thomas Culpeper (d. 1541) 446
Thomas Culpeper (fl. 1664) 493
Thomas Culpepper (fl. 1552) 596
Cumber, Elizabeth (fl. 1675) 469
Cumberford, William (fl. 1597) 724
Cumberland, earls of *see* Clifford
Cundy, Edward (fl. 1621) 738
Cupper, Richard (fl. 1563) 604
Curbiton, Mathew (fl. 1559) 605
Curd, family 300
Curleggo, John (fl. 1551) 556, 658
Curlyffe, Leonard (fl. 1551) 657–8
Cussin, Joan (fl. 1620) 474
Cuttyng, Robert (fl. 1510) 87

D
Dabancourt, family 65, 66, 67, **326**
Dabat
family **698–9**
Mary Dobet (fl. 1576) 645
Dacre, Lord *see* Fiennes
Dad, John and Joan (fl. 1616) 633
Daggnet, Mary (fl. 1556) 338
Daglon, Guillam (fl. 1560) 378, 379
Daix *see* Day
Dakyn, *see also* Dayken
Dakyn, Thomas (d. 1644) 722
Dale, family 345
Dallanton, family **796**
Dalton, Mary (fl. 1679) 787
Damery, Nicholas (fl. 1541) 678
Damesell, William (fl. 1546) 167n579
Damper, Joan (fl. 1620) 787
Dampierre, counts of 10–18
Dan(ne), family 797
Dance, John (fl. 1645) 504
Danekin le Feron (Jausse, fl. 1414) 16, 87
Dangerfield *see* Angerfield
Daniell
family **584–5**
Denys Daniell (fl. 1607) 568
Hester Daniel (fl. 1579) 217
Mary Daniel (fl. 1637) 361
Dannequin *see* Dennequyn
Danvers, Sir John (fl. 1590) 734
Danviers, Gérard (fl. 1356) 11
Danyel, Volant (fl. 1520) 85
Darby, *see also* Derby
Darby, Abraham (d. 1717) 228, 348
Darby, Alice (fl. 1571) 524
Darby, Robert (fl. 1592) 722
Darendel
Anthoine Darendel (fl. 1528) 142, 143, 144
Jehannot Darendel (fl. 1500) 99
Laurens Darendel (fl. 1526) 78, 141, 142, 174
Mariette Darendel (16th cent.) 141
Darrell
family 601–2
Christopher Darrell (fl. 1554–74) 440, 601–2
Henry Darrell (16th cent.) 206
Richard Darrell (fl. 1588) 281
Sarah Darral (fl. 1777) 324
Thomas Darrell (fl. 1545–8) 441, 454, 761
Thomas Darrell (fl. 1574) 597
William Darrell (fl. 1574) 608–9
Darret, Mary (fl. 1597) 574
Darvie, John (fl. 1524) 420, 469–70
Daubeney, Clement (fl. 1618) 713
Davice, Roger (fl. 1617) 727
David, Jean (fl. 1579) 164
Davie, Gyles (fl. 1656) 330
Davis, Devereux (fl. 1693) 407
Davis, Elizabeth (fl. 1749) 215
Davis, Mary (fl. 1710) 407
Davis, Richard (fl. 1710) 407
Davis, William (fl. 1675) 220
Davison, William (fl. 1590) 419
Davy
family 645
Alice Davy (fl. 1629) 487
Eleanor Davy (fl. 1586) 651
Mercy Davy (Davis) (fl. 1575) 327, 329n343
Seth Davy (fl. 1630) 481
Davyes, Lancelot (fl. 1612) 396
Daw(e)
family 647, 681
Constance Daw (fl. 1654) 389
Thomas Dawe (fl. 1597) 785
see also Downe
Dawes
family **681**
Jeffrey Dawes (d. 1657) 730
Margaret Dawes (fl. 1639) 809
William and Margaret Dawes (fl. 1720) 718, 719
Day, 'Fayther' (fl. 1525) 249
Day (Deix/Daix), Jacques (15th cent.) 36
Daye, Ann (fl. 1610) 642
Daye, Ann (fl. 1663) 730
Dayken, *see also* Dakyn
Dayken, ____ (Oakamoor, fl. 1605) 721
Deakin, family 487
Deamond *see* Diamond
Deane, Anne (fl. 1653) 346
Deane, Hannah (fl. 1733) 270
Deane, John (fl. 1677) 346
Deaven, Mary (fl. 1641) 688
Debewe
family 102, **667**, 787–8

Nicholas Grant (?Grout) (fl. 1645) 630
Richard Grant (fl. 1680s) 359, 731
Grantpierre, Pierre (fl. 1565) 202, 594
Grate, John (fl. 1551–2) 356–7
Gratwick, Richard (fl. 1571) 615
Gratwick, Roger (fl. 1576) 485, 600, 615
Graunt *see* Grant
Graves, Pierre de (fl. 1526) 185
Graye, Ralph (fl. 1600) 236
Grayling, Margaret (fl. 1601) 230
Greaves, William (fl. 1574) 610
Green, *see also* Grene
Green, Mary (18th cent.) 628
Green, Thomas, aliens in lay subsidy rolls 832
Greene, family 647
Greene, Elizabeth (fl. 1558) 558
Greene, Elizabeth (fl. 1661) 354
Greene, John (fl. 1599) 408
Greene, Mathew (fl. 1644) 364
Greene, Richard (fl. 1574) 396, 397
Greenfield, Mary (fl. 1607) 497
Greenfilde, Joan (fl. 1592) 689
Greengow *see* Gringo
Grégoir, family 41
Gregorie, family 721
Gregory, ____ (Loscoe Furnace, fl. 1592) 722
Gregory, Humphrey (fl. 1616) 727
Grene, William (fl. 1586) 733
Greneleafe, Susan (fl. 1576) 502
Grengoe *see* Gringo
Gresham, John (fl. 1567) 595
Gresham, Sir Thomas (d. 1579) 585, 589, 595, 614
Gressent, Jehan (fl. 1509) 100
Greville, Fulke (fl. 1591) 605
Grewe, family 357, **531–2**
Griaunt
family **542**
Clement Gryans (Griaunt) (fl. 1550) 451, 542
Griel *see* Le Griel
Grimault, Denis (16th cent.) 49
Gringo
family **644–7**, 716, 771
Elizabeth Greengow (fl. 1616), m. Edward Tullet 498
Elizabeth Greengow (fl. 1616), m. Thomas Hersie 514
Elizabeth Gringo (fl. 1622) 330
Joan Gringo (fl. 1579) 473
Joan Gringoe (fl. 1629) 650
Philip Grengoe (d. 1623) 498, 645
Grint
family 417, 542
Daniel Grint (fl. 1611) 245
Grodoeuvre, François (fl. 1631) 44
Grosmenil and Bouelles, lord of 101, 126
Grosvenor, William (fl. 1589) 717
Grouchy, Louis de (fl. 1456) 111
Groulart, Thomson (fl. 1544) 40
Grove, Sarah (fl. 1763) 392
Grove, William (fl. 1710) 407
Grove, William and Margaret (fl. 1720) 718, 719
Grover, James (17th cent.) 756
Growshe, ____ (Bexhill, fl. 1572) 631
Growte
family **356–9**, 618, 717, 719, 731
Charles Growt (fl. 1639) 669
Parnell Growte (fl. 1599) 793
William Growte (fl. 1591) 674
Grubar, Thomas (fl. 1596) 735
Gryans *see* Griaunt
Gryffen, Richard ap (fl. 1597) 221
Gryffith, Ann (fl. 1629) 806
Gryffyn, Margaret (fl. 1607) 504
Gryndegore, Gryngoe *see* Gringo
Gue *see* Gewe
Guerard
family 113, 133–4, 138, 186, 399
Adrian Guerard (fl. 1564) 136, 174
Aubery Guerard (fl. 1504–26) 111n327, 133, 137, 142, 186
Guillaume Guerard (fl. 1478) 166
see also Gerard; Gerard or Jarrett
Guildford
family 477
Frances Guylford (fl. 1613) 745
Sir Henry Guildford (1489–1532) 432
Sir Richard Guildford (d. 1506) 190, 432
Guillam *see* Gilham
Guillemotte (Guillaume, Willemot) le Fondeur (Vaux, fl. 1451) 35, 131, 487
Guise *see* Degoye
Guise, dukes of 164, 713
Gumrie
family 38–9, 158–9, **509–11**
Jehan de Gommery(e) (fl. 1472–8) 38, 157, 158–9, 509
John Gombrye (Gumrye) (fl. 1572) 328, 510
Margaret Gomerye (fl. 1559) 128, 328
Gunn, ____ (Hints, fl. 1595–6) 720
Gunter
family 620, 637, 745, 772
Richard Gunter (fl. 1608) 637, 789
Richard Gunter (fl. 1656) 666
Thomas Gunter (fl. 1593–1639) 744, 745
Gunwen, Gunwyn *see* Devall alias (G)ounyon
Gurr
George Gurr (fl. 1626) 329
John Gurr (fl. 1621) 409, 615
Mary Gurr (fl. 1642) 409
Guttell, Priscilla (fl. 1626) 339
Guye, Guyes, de Guye *see* Degoye
Guylford *see* Guildford
Guyot, Guillaume (fl. 1536) 94–5
Guyot, Jehan (fl. 1536) 100
Guyson, Colin (fl. 1418) 16, 702
Gybrig, John (d. 1561) 799
Gyles *see* Giles
Gyllam *see* Gilham
Gyllat, Gyllett *see* Gillet
Gyllman, Wishawe (17th cent.) 742
Gynney, Joan (fl. 1552) 261
Gyssop, Alice (fl. 1609) 277
Gytard, Elizabeth (fl. 1576) 621

H

Habburley, Thomas (d. 1561) 605
Habchyll, Anne (fl. 1578) 675
Hacker (Acor), Pantellus (fl. 1566) 776
Hacket, Thomas (fl. 1610) 495
Hackwood, family 290
Hacqueville, family 56
Haddock (Harrock), family 720, 721, 724, 727
Hadlow, ____ (Robertsbridge, fl. 1551) 464
Hadnoll, Stephen (fl. 1554) 603, 604, 605, 606, 607
Hafar, Joan (fl. 1567) 478
Hague, Hannah (fl. 1764) 337
Haige, Mary (fl. 1709) 337
Haigh, Rebecca (fl. 1740) 299, 739
Hain, Haines *see* Gayne
Haincques (Hainques)
family 54–5, 60, 122, 387, 507
Georges Hainque (fl. 1545) 55
Jacquemin (Jaquemin) Haincques (Hainques) (fl. 1487) 32, 54, 55, 182, 387
see also Haynk or Jenkes
Haler, Ruth (fl. 1622) 332
Hales, ____ (fl. 1677) 346
Hales, Denise (fl. 1639) 633
Halfpenny, Isaac and William (fl. 1639) 669

Hauneng (?Haunyng), John (fl. 1550s) 644, 680
Hautot, Jean de (14th cent.) 45
Haward *see* Heyward
Hawkins, John (fl. 1575) 547
Hawkins, Thomas (fl. 1549) 451
Hawksley *see* Haukshey; Hauksley
Hawkyns, ____ (Panningridge, fl. 1549) 460
Haws, Susan (fl. 1618) 683
Hawsee, Thomas (fl. 1563) 294
Hawthorne, William (fl. 1551) 601
Hay
Agnes (Ann) Hay (Hey) (fl. 1598) 345, 737
Sir George Hay (d. 1634) 743, 745
John Hay (fl. 1550) 598; aliens in lay subsidy rolls 833
John Hay (d. 1670) 745
Richard Hay (fl. 1697) 341
Thomas Hay (16th cent.) 776
William Haye (fl. 1549) 598
William Hayes (fl. 1670) 731
see also La Haye
Hayfield, George (fl. 1725) 732
Hayford, Dennys (fl. 1690) 279, 760
Haylor, John (fl. 1616) 797
Hayne, Haynes *see* Gayne
Haynk or Jenkes
family 32, 54–5, 122, **387**, 507, 508
Marion Haynke (fl. 1524) 245
Thiery Henk (Henck, Henrique) (fl. 1420–55) 32, 55, 122, 387
see also Haincques (Hainques)
Hayward *see* Heyward
Heade, Mary (fl. 1613) 572
Hearsee, Richard (fl. 1593) 568
Heath
family **690**, 731
John Heathe (fl. 1567) 601
Richard Heath (fl. 1592) 800
Heather, Agnes (fl. 1639) 511
Hedall, Heddall, Hedoll, Hedowell *see* Addes, Judd or Powell
Heeley *see* Hiley
Hees, John (fl. 1593–4) 721
Heiley, John and Mary (fl. 1686) 718, 719
Helies *see* Ellis
Heliot, Helion *see* Elliot
Hellande, Guillaume de, bishop of Beauvais (fl. 1454) 425
Hellery, Rachel (fl. 1656) 481
Hellifield, Luke (fl. 1714) 587
Heluys, Pierre (fl. 1512) 85
Hemande, Peter (fl. 1595) 212
Hembrey *see* Hambrey
Hemsley, Elizabeth (fl. 1654) 680
Hemsworth, George (fl. 1618) 738
Henberry *see* Hambrey
Henck *see* Haincques; Haynk or Jenkes
Henesye, Henisett *see* Hanosse (Hanozet); Hunnisett
Henfry, John (fl. 1733) 365
Henk *see* Haynk or Jenkes
Henley, ____, Lady Henley (fl. 1569) 579
Henley, John (fl. 1524–5) 226, 247, 420
Henley, Umfray (fl. 1524) 226
Hennes, Meister (Eisenschmitt, 15th cent.) 37
Henold, Lawrence (fl. 1554–58) 619, 763
Henri II, king of France 591
Henri le Fondeur (Ermeton, fl. 1371) 17, 32
Henri le Martelleur (Ermeton, fl. 1456) 29
Henrique, *see also* Haynk or Jenkes
Henrique le Feron (Maître Henrique) (Ermeton, fl. 1407), and son Hubert 32
Henry V, king of England 15, 22, 24, 25, 26
Henry VII, king of England, and ironfounding in the Weald 189–95
as Henry Tudor 189–90
Henry VIII, king of England 62, 244, 252, 431–2, 434, 440
guns purchased 25, 244
visits to Weald (1538–9) 431–2, 441, 454–5
Henry le Allemant (Jouet, fl. 1402) 21
Henry le Feron (Henry/Hennedric Laffineur) (fl. 1451) 30, 34, 38, 50, 51, 52, 163, 182
Henshall, Richard (fl. 1687) 347
Hensley, family 715
Hepden, Herbert (fl. 1626) 580
Hepden, John (fl. 1552) 620
Hepden (Epden), Thomas (fl. 1586–1600) 537, 538
Herbert family, earls of Pembroke 608
Herbille, family 321
Hereford, viscounts *see* Devereux
Herichon
family 90, 91, 521, 583
see also Harrison
Hermen, Jehan (fl. 1467) 157, 159
Hermeu, Loys (fl. 1541) 177
Hermier, Gervaiz (fl. 1473/4) 165
Heron, John (fl. 1491) 192–3
Heron, Loys (fl. 1539) 175
Hersie *see* Harshaw
Herston, Guyllam (fl. 1543) 521, 583
Hervy *see* Harvey
Hese *see* Hussey
Heth, John (fl. 1555) 614
Heue *see* Huet (Hue)
Heuse, Jehan (fl. 1518) 67
Heuze, Jehan (fl. 1512) 78, 84, 164, 168
Hewashe *see* Hussey
Hewes, *see also* Hughes
Hewes, Elizabeth (fl. 1623) 807
Hewgate
family 529, **704**
'Hewgate Fownder' (fl. 1572) 79, 204, 606, 704
see also Holgate; Huggett
Hewgynson, Christian (fl. 1561) 702
Hewson, John (fl. 1559) 224
Hey *see* Hay
Heymann le Fondeur (Jausse, fl. 1373) 17
Heyward
family 442–3, **653–5**
Ann Hayward (fl. 1597) 504
Dorothy Haward (fl. 1561) 214
Jane Haward (fl. 1585) 311
Joan Hayward (fl. 1577) 636
Richard Heyward (d. 1560) 605
William Heyward (fl. 1574) 615
Hider, family 581
Hiesse, Simon 84
Hiesse alias des Mazis
Hutyn Hiesse *dit* des Mais (fl. 1500) 81
Jehan Hiesse *dit* des Mais (fl. 1493), and widow Mahiote 78, 83–4, 85, 86, 164, 178, 184
Higgins, John (d. 1624) 778
Higham, ____ (Etchingham, fl. 1644) 647
Hiley (Heeley), John (fl. 1599–1607) 720, 725
Hill, Anne (fl. 1639) 739
Hill, Avis (fl. 1602) 332
Hill, Gregory (fl. 1579) 277
Hillie, Joan (fl. 1576) 319
Hillman, Ann (fl. 1738) 628
Hills, Jane (fl. 1611) 330
Hills, John (fl. 1570) 581
Hills, Philip (fl. 1565) 762
Hills, Richard (fl. 1635) 213n103
Hills, William (fl. 1641) 360

Hinckes
family 387, 508
see also Haynk or Jenkes
Hoad, family 683
Hobson, Hugh (fl. 1647) 317, 722
Hoby, Catherine (fl. 1610) 285
Hochard *see* Hussey
Hocqueberg, Jeanne de (fl. 1518) 158
Hodeng, Jehanne de (15th cent.) 97, 98, 106, 183
Hodge, Abiah (fl. 1640) 577
Hodgetts, Mary (fl. 1652) 643
Hodgson, Robert (fl. 1562–70) 439, 471, 595, 614
Hodson, Parratt (fl. 1616) 664
Hoffer, Peircy (fl. 1671) 787
Hogan, Thomas (fl. 1550) 444
Hogens, Thomas (fl. 1549) 777
Hogge
Margaret Hogge (fl. 1572–80) 292, 645, 690
Ralph Hogge (d. 1585) 79, 564, 589–90, 595, 761, 762–3
Hoggelet, family 248
Hoke *see* Hook
Holbeame, Richard (fl. 1545) 441
Holbeck, Richard (fl. 1605) 727
Holborne, Alice (fl. 1620) 300
Holgate
family **529**
John Holgatt (d. 1535) 203, 529, 775
see also Hewgate; Huggett
Holier, ____ (Hints, fl. 1595–6) 720
Holland
family **425–7**, 735
Agnes Holland (fl. 1634) 583
Catherine Hollan(d) (fl. 1597) 414
Constance Holland (fl. 1573) 561
Elizabeth Hollande (fl. 1588) 498
Toussaint (Toussains) Holland (d. 1597) 426, 653
Holloway, Jarrett (fl. 1711) 614
Holman
family 677
Bridget Holman (fl. 1638) 787
Thomas Holman (fl. 1586) 537
Holmden, Simon (fl. 1604) 746
Holmes
family **486**
Ann Holmes (fl. 1611) 279, 740
Gilham Holmes (fl. 1528) 247, 452, 486, 501
John Holme (fl. 1600) 721
see also Homan
Holstoke *see* Coulstock
Holt, George (fl. 1738) 732
Holte, Ann (fl. 1601) 642
Homan
family **677**
Joan Homan (fl. 1606) 794
see also Holmes
Homberg, Hans von (fl. 1539) 431, 434
Home *see* Homan
Homesby, John (fl. 1569) 777
Homo, Olivier (fl. 1404) 169
Homsby, John (fl. 1621) 581
Homson, Elizabeth (fl. 1569) 574
Homwood, John (fl. 1560) 599
Honwyne *see* Devall alias (G)ounyon
Honysett *see* Hunnisett
Hood, Robert (fl. 1625) 493
Hoode, William (fl. 1629) 342
Hook
family 745–6, 752, 754–5
Henry Hooke (fl. 1633) 508
Joan Hooke (fl. 1609), w. of Thomas 345
John Hoke (?Hooke) (fl. 1541) 437, 453, 745–6
John Hooke (probate 1558) 774
Richard Hook (fl. 1628) 744, 746
Hopkins, ____ (Robertsbridge, fl. 1551) 764
Hopkins, ?Thomas (fl. 1594) 720–1, 724
Hopkins, Thomas (fl. 1599) 724
Hopkyns, ____ (Oakamoor, fl. 1608) 721
Horcholle *see* Harshaw
Horden *see* Harding
Horshall *see* Harshaw
Horsmonden, Anne (fl. 1574) 417
Hoschett, Hosher *see* Hussey
Hosmer, Henry (fl. 1587) 281
Hosmer, William (fl. 1629) 640
Hoth, Harry and Robert (fl. 1567) 562
Hoth, Nicholas (fl. 1589) 665
Hothelye, Richard (fl. 1589) 553
Hother, Richard (fl. 1559) 205
Hotsowe, Gyllowe de (17th cent.) 742
Houchard, Houzard *see* Hussey
Houel, Guillaume (fl. 1478–86) 55, 97–8, 171, 183
Houel, Jehan (fl. 1478) 55
Hough *see* Haugh
Houghton, Richard (fl. 1586) 611
Houseman, Izabell (fl. 1539) 275
Houssaye, Housset *see* Hussey
Howard
family, dukes of Norfolk, ironworks in Yorkshire 731, 738, 739, 740
Thomas Howard, 3rd duke of Norfolk (1473–1554) 198, 429, 432, 439, 440, 444, 454–5; aliens in lay subsidy rolls (1543) 842; immigrants listed in Westminster denization roll (1544) 521–2, 815, 817
Howell, Sir John (17th cent.) 424
Howell, Sampson (fl. 1629) 307
Howtinge, William (fl. 1601) 788
Hoyse *see* Hussey
Huache, Jehan (16th cent.) 153
Hubbard, John (fl. 1701) 271
Huckstepe, Elizabeth (fl. 1631) 352
Hudson, Mary (fl. 1731) 628
Hudson, Thomas (fl. 1509) 191, 195
Huesh, Robert (fl. 1616) 715
Huet (Hue)
Collenet Hue alias Le Blanc (fl. 1519) 78–9
Guillaume Duquiefdelaville alias Huet (fl. 1462) 110, 147, 300
Marin Huet (fl. 1545–55) 79
Marquis and Benoist Hue (fl. 1540s) 79
Michel Huet (fl. 1568) 79
Nicolas Huet (Heue, Hue, Hué) alias Le Blanc (fl. 1537) 78–9, 85, 145, 173, 174, 177, 179, 183–4, 204, 565
Huggat, Christopher (fl. 1558) 323
Huggett
family 79–80, 202, **203–7**
Clement Huggett (16th cent.) 202, 203, 584
Hannah Hugget (fl. 1708) 803
Isaac Hugatt (fl. 1616) 648
John Hugget (16th cent.) 789
see also Hewgate; Holgate; Huet; Huguet
Hughes, *see also* Hewes
Hughes, John (fl. 1618–24) 727
Hugues alias Voleaume (Précy, fl. 1401) 21
Huguet, Jenenot (Jehan) (fl. 1489) 155, 156, 202, 203
Huit, Silvester (b. 1571) 610
Hull, Hugh (fl. 1598) 721
Humel, Jean (fl. 1547) 49
Humfrey
family **580–2**
Anne Humphrey (fl. 1633) 309
Catherine Humfry (fl. 1632) 686
Rachel Humphrey (fl. 1600) 481
Robert Umfrye (fl. 1559) 338
Winifred Humphrey (fl. 1630) 493

Hune *see* Homan
Hunnisett
family 6, **292–4**, 644, 680, 772
Adrian Annessett (Hanysete, Hunnisett) (fl. 1523–50) 6, 93, 292–3, 419, 775
Anne Henwysey (Hunniset) (fl. 1561) 616
Clement Hunisett (probate 1617) 294, 772, 773, 778
Jakes Hunnisett (Hanysite) (fl. 1517–43) 6, 39, 292–3
Joan Henisett (fl. 1604) 649
John Annesett (fl. 1542) 93, 293
Peter Clarke alias Honysett (d. 1632) 294, 478
see also Hanosse (Hanozet)
Hunt, Bridget (fl. 1614), d. of Richard 268–9
Hunt, Catherine (fl. 1634) 803
Hunt, Jane (fl. 1575) 325
Hunt, Stephen (d. 1589) 714
Hunt, William (fl. 1541) 386
Huntingdon, earls of *see* Hastings
Huntley, Robert (fl. 1579) 339
Hurley, John (fl. 1605) 716
Hushe, Husher *see* Hussey
Hushyer, John (fl. 1670s) 765
Husse, John (fl. 1559) 508
Hussey
family **532–5**
Abigail Ussall (?Vassall or Hussey) (fl. 1637) 707, 727
Constance Hussey (d. *c.* 1526) 261
Elizabeth Husher (fl. 1640) 783
Elizabeth Hussey (fl. 1619) 329
Joan Husshe (fl. 1566) 467
John Hussey (d. 1660) 759
Maria Hussey (fl. 1735) 273
Peter Hushe (Hese, Hewashe) (fl. 1540s) 447, 532
Quintin Husher (probate 1627) 533, 774
Robert Hewashe (fl. 1588) 575, 673
Susan Husher (fl. 1588) 297
Thomas Hussey (fl. 1720s) 742
William Hosher (fl. 1562) 597
Huswiffe, John (d. 1566) 224, 534
Hutt, family 626
Huttemann, Lambert (fl. 1552–3) 434
Hüttenhenn, Johannes (fl. 1614) 592–3
Hutton, Elizabeth (fl. 1777) 709
Huysson, family **702**
Hyder, William (fl. 1569) 223
Hyland, Joan (fl. 1578) 698
Hylles, Elizabeth (fl. 1558) 806
Hyndall *see* Addes, Judd or Powell
Hytche, Robert (fl. 1590) 734

I
Ibbs, Margaret (fl. 1646) 364
Iden, Alice (fl. 1625) 784
Iden, Elizabeth (fl. 1577) 415
Iden, Elizabeth (fl. 1605) 788
Iden, Elizabeth (fl. 1625) 548
Iden, Elizabeth (fl. 1631) 352
Iden, William (fl. 1618) 352
Ifeld, Alice (fl. 1566) 521
Ilands, Mary (fl. 1589) 621
Ilman or Ilmaunt
family 263
Thomas Ilman (fl. 1567) 600, 640
William Ilman (fl. 1574) 476
Infield, Richard (fl. 1612) 796
Inggs, Thomas (fl. 1663) 732
Inglett, Katherine (fl. 1564) 503
Ingram, Sarah (fl. 1712) 292
Inold, William (fl. 1537) 209, 778
Ireland, Rachel (fl. 1600) 497
Isaack, Joan (fl. 1585) 576
Isted
family 440
Joan Isted (fl. 1544) 239, 241, 248, 441, 446; aliens in lay subsidy rolls 831, 832; immigrants listed in Westminster denization roll (1544) 517–19, 814
Richard Isted (fl. 1525–41) 203, 248, 429, 441, 446
Thomas Isted (fl. 1583) 508, 538, 660

J
Jace *see* Jas (Jace, Jasse)
Jackett *see* Jakatt
Jackson, Randall (fl. 1593–4) 721
Jacques, Colin (fl. 1410) 35
Jacquet, Jacquette *see* Jakatt
Jaillant, ____ (fl. 1471–2) 38
Jakatt, family **386–7**
James
family **525**, 730
Alice James (fl. 1665) 579
Elizabeth James (fl. 1634), d. of Jonas 536
Francis Jayms (fl. 1541–3) 443, 525
John James (fl. 1648) 322
Robert James (fl. 1600) 722
Jamet *see* Jonnett
Jamotte, Henry, mayor of Beaufort (fl. 1560s) 33
Jan, Hens (fl. 1535) 433
Jarlett, family 296, 582, 714
Jarman, John (fl. 1560) 398
Jarman alias Mittell, Henry (17th cent.) 544
Jarmyn *see* Jerman
Jarnoll, Thomas (16th cent.) 219
Jarrett *see* Gerard or Jarrett
Jarvis, family **384**
Jas (Jace, Jasse)
François de Jas (Namur, 16th cent.) 33
Jean de Jasse (Jace) (Namur, 16th cent.) 33
Jasper
family **543**
William and Gyles de Jesper (17th cent.) 742
Jausse
Pholien de Jauce (fl. 1527) 33
Pierchon de Jausse (fl. 1450) 29, 30
Jayms *see* James
Jean le Bombardier (Jean 'de Briey') (fl. 1469) 36
Jean le Fondeur (Vaux, fl. 1445) 35, 36
Jean le Fondeur (Virton, fl. 1501) 36, 37
Jefferay, Thomas (fl. 1655) 547
Jeffery, Joan (d. 1707) 331
Jeffery (Jeffrey), Bartholomew (fl. 1543–74) 240, 304, 394, 440, 447, 453, 598, 777
aliens in lay subsidy rolls 831, 832
Jeffery (Jeffries)
family 513
John Jeffries (fl. 1604) 513, 725
Robert Jeffrey (Jeffery) (fl. 1619) 513, 727
Jeffery alias Druet, William (fl. 1604) 809
Jeffray, ____ ('Mr Jeffray', 17th cent.) 424
Jelite, Phillis (fl. 1630) 651
Jellett, Jellot *see* Barton alias Gillet; Gillet alias Duforde
Jellie, Jelly *see* Jolly
Jemmett *see* Jonnett
Jenkes *see* Haynk or Jenkes
Jenkin, family **420**
Jenkynges, Bridget (fl. 1609) 807
Jenne, James (fl. 1543) 342, 468, 558
Jenner, Joan (fl. 1614) 664
Jenson, ____ (Middleton, fl. 1593) 720
Jerman (Jarmyn)
family 715n13
see also Jarman

Jerratt *see* Gerard or Jarrett
Jerre, Aleyn (fl. 1549) 551–2
Jervice, Elizabeth (fl. 1649) 236
Jeselbe, Mary (fl. 1604) 575, 576, 752
Jesper *see* Jasper
Jewell, Anne (fl. 1612) 800
Jewell, John (fl. 1568) 777
Jewet, George and Richard (fl. 1558) 210
Jewkes, ____ (Hints, 18th cent.) 624
Jisbor, Joan (fl. 1561) 205
Joakes alias Fuller, family 782
Johanes, Margaret (fl. 1596) 374
John, duke of Bedford (1389–1435) 24–5
John the Fearless, duke of Burgundy 19, 21, 22, 24
Johnes, *see also* Jones
Johnes, Hawell (fl. 1655) 483, 740
Johnson
  family 316, 452, **564–5**, 721, 722, 730, 732, 733, 736, 802
  James Johnson (fl. 1749) 365
  John Johnson (fl. 1551) 602
  John Johnson (d. 1591) 79, 205, 452, 456, 564, 772, 778
  Katherine Jonson (d. 1591) 717, 719
  Marion Johnson (fl. 1562) 564, 778
  Mary Johnson (fl. 1691) 238
  Peter Johnson (fl. 1591) 663
  Robert Johnson (fl. 1657) 803
  Thomas Johnson (d. 1596) 564–5, 663, 746, 802
Joiner, George (fl. 1527) 428
Jolis *see* Jolly
Jolly
  family 99, 135–6, 254, 365, **388–92**, 601, 602, 720, 721, 722, 726, 730, 739
  Alice/Anne Jolly (Jelly) (fl. 1602) 291, 718
  Elizabeth Gelly (fl. 1633) 626
  Jacques Jollis (fl. 1526) 121
  Jehan Jolis (fl. 1487) 186
  Martha Jelly (fl. 1717) 484
  Noël Jolly (Jolye) (fl. 1545) 136, 146, 177
  Peter Jolly (Gellie) (d. 1594/5) 135, 225, 388–9, 499, 762, 764, 766, 767
  Peter Jollye (fl. 1596) 622
  Pierres Jollys (fl. 1564) 136, 174
Jolys *see* Jolly
Jones, *see also* Johnes
Jones, Ellen (fl. 1838) 274
Jones, Francis (fl. 1750) 627–8
Jones, Hugh and John (fl. 1629) 307
Jones, John and Martha (fl. 1754) 728
Jones, Lowrye (fl. 1642) 626
Jones, Richard (fl. 1633) 578
Jones, William and Martha (fl. 1755) 728
Jonnett, family **468–9**
Jonney, Gloves (?Sloves) (fl. 1551) 468
Jonson *see* Johnson
Jordan
  family 310–11, **559–61**, 658
  Edward Jorden (fl. 1592) 725
  John Jorden (Jurdaine) (fl. 1559) 338
  Katherine Jordan alias Bewley (fl. 1585–94) 389
  see also Bartholomew alias Ponting
Joseph, ____ (Norton, fl, 1592) 717
Joseph, Colart (fl. 1386) 22
  see also Colart le Kanonier
Joseph, Joan (fl. 1628) 216
Journée, Anthoine (fl. 1542) 176
Joyse, Alice (fl. 1601) 498
Judd, Judge *see* Addes, Judd or Powell
Jupp, Jane (fl. 1625) 408
Jurden (Jurdenne)
  family 559, **658**, 715, 716
  see also Jordan

K
Keay, Hugh (fl. 1699) 718, 719
Keete, William (fl. 1643) 650
Kellery, family **520**
Kemmerling alias Kolmuth, Wilhelm (fl. 1588–97) 593
Kemp
  family 744
  Joan Kemp (fl. 1608–9) 715, 716
  Simon Kempe (fl. 1546) 760
  Thomas Kempe (fl. 1558) 402
Kenchyard, William (fl. 1599) 714
Kenion (Kennion), George (fl. 1591–7) 479, 559
Kennad (Kennet)
  family **392–3**
  Mary Kennet (fl. 1595) 665
Kent, Agnes (fl. 1585) 651
Kent, John a' (fl. 1570) 581
Kenward
  family 392–3
  Joan Kenward (fl. 1610) 284, 285
  Richard Kenwarde (fl. 1613) 546
Kenyon, George (fl. 1577) 690, 763
Kerby *see* Kirby
Kerrin, Kerry *see* Kerwyn
Kervill *see* Kydevilde
Kerwyn
  family 282, **658–60**
  John Kerrin (Kyrrin) (fl. 1580–3) 282, 659
  Jordan Carye (Kerin) (fl. 1589) 340
Ketchley, Ketchlie, Ketslow *see* Catchloe, Ketchlow or Ketslow
Kidd, Elizabeth (fl. 1606) 309
Kidd, Thomsen (fl. 1639) 412
Kidder
  Joan Kidder (fl. 1623) 649
  see also Kydder
Kindgewood, Joan (fl. 1570) 212
King
  family **791–2**
  Elizabeth King (fl. 1595) 566
  Ellen Kinge (fl. 1609) 300
  Hellen King (fl. 1649) 374
  Peter King (d. 1608) 185, 259, 361, 791–2
  Thomas King (fl. 1630) 481
  see also Godard alias King
Kingswood, Mary (fl. 1594) 807
Kintail, Lord *see* Mackenzie
Kirbie, Eleanor (fl. 1653) 731
Kirby, family 736, **807**
Kirkam, Joyce (fl. 1583) 523, 729
Kirkby *see* Kirby
Kirrin, Kirring *see* Kerwyn
Kirshley, John (fl. 1568) 580
Kitchinam, Elizabeth (fl. 1577) 651
Knight
  Anthony Knight (fl. 1639) 669
  Elizabeth Knight (fl. 1571) 522
  Joan Knight (fl. 1610) 495
  Joan Knight (fl. 1621) 368
  Mary Knight (fl. 1613) 311
  Mary Knight (fl. 1615) 668
  see also Carles alias Knight
Knolles, Eleanor (fl. 1598) 278, 724, 753
Knowler, Katherine (fl. 1612) 675
Knowles, John (fl. 1601) 419
Knyvet, Sir Henry (fl. 1546) 455
Kock, David and Remacle (fl. 1583) 164, 713
Kollenbrenner, Hans (fl. 1439) 41
Kolmuth *see* Kemmerling alias Kolmuth
Krefting, Herman (fl. 1624) 613, 675
Kydder
  family 562
  see also Kidder
Kydevilde
  family **299–301**
  Cardo (Cardin, Cardot) Kydvilde

Lambert alias Gewe
family 527
see also Gewe
Lambkin, Anne (fl. 1620) 339
Lambley *see* Lamley
Lambourne, family **703**
Lamell *see* La Mell
Lamere, Peter (fl. 1551–2) 570
Lamley (Lambley), George (fl. 1608–17) 729
Lamot *see* La Mott alias Finch
Lamy alias Barden
family 148–9, **294–9**, 721, 726, 737, 775
____ (Widow Barden) (fl. 1638) 649
Alice Lame alias Barden (fl. 1600) 792
Charles Barden (1562–1632/3) 148, 296, 601, 667, 682–3
Dorothy Lammye (fl. 1584) 656
Elizabeth Bardin (fl. 1623) 317
Humphrey Lambe (fl. 1586) 268
Isambard (Izambard) Lamme (Lamy) alias Bardyne (fl. 1518–50) 147, 148, 294–5, 296, 602
Jehan Lamy alias Lamby (fl. 1462–95) 105, 136, 148
Joan Barden (fl. 1563) 504
Joan Barden (fl. 1598) 555
Joan Lamby (fl. 1572) 510
John Barden (fl. 1529) 229, 775
John Pynion/Barden (probate 1596) 774
Mathew Lambe (fl. 1637) 503
Rose Barden (fl. 1601) 668
Thomas Sudds alias Bardon (fl. 1601) 630, 667
see also Bordyn
L'Ancien *see* Lawnsyne/de Lawnse or Old
Lancin, Massin (fl. 1542) 169
Lanckeford, Stephen (fl. 1621) 581
Lane, Laney *see* Leaney alias Thomas
Langford, Margaret (fl. 1692) 238
Langley *see* Longley
Langlois (Langloys)
family 70, 93–5, 103
Ector Langloys (fl. 1551) 87
Gillet Langloys (fl. 1514) 151
Jean Langlois (Le Vaumin, 15th/16th cent.) 57
Quaism Langlois (Quesm Langloys), identified as Come (Cosmo) Langley 70–1, 93, 94, 474–5, 765
Robert Langloys (16th cent.) 108
see also Lenglois; Longley
Langridge, Mary (fl. 1636) 312
Larby
family 130–1, **368–70**
Aubery Larber (Oberie Larbie) (fl. 1557–71) 130, 226, 369, 602
Larchevesque, family 143, 649
Larchié, Jennin (fl. 1411) 35
Lardenois, family 643
Lardge, Agnes (fl. 1581) 277
Lardinois, Lambert (fl. 1474) 434
Larence, Bridget (fl. 1584) 630
Larmar, Edward (fl. 1616–20) 570
Lassoll
family **619**
Francis Lassells (fl. 1606) 619, 722
Myghell Lassoll (fl. 1552) 619, 764
Latornys, Peter (fl. 1551) 643
Lattenden, Dorothy (fl. 1632) 483
Latter *see* Leader (Ledder)
Lattre, Pierre de (d. 1586) 49–50, 60
Laughen, Laugham *see* Lawhen alias Collin
Laurens *see* Lawrence
Laurent (Laurens) (fl. 1484) 36
Lauris, family **570**
Laussell, family 716
Lavender
family **621–9**
James Lavender (fl. *c.* 1763–1839) 628, 782
Lavington *see* Lavender
Lavy, Sarah (fl. 1631) 623
Lawhen alias Collin
family **280–1**, 500
Alice Laughen (fl. 1591) 663
Anne Laffam (fl. 1661) 803
Anne Lahan alias Collins (fl. 1625) 473
Joan Laughen (fl. 1559) 124, 276
Lawmporthe, William (fl. 1558) 807
Lawnsyne/de Lawnse or Old
family 254, **559**, **668–9**, 746
John Lansum (Lancien) (fl. 1634) 375, 559, 668
Peter Lawnsyne (fl. 1580) 335, 559, 668
Walter Old (probate 1639) 668, 765, 768, 769, 770, 773
Lawrence
family 156, **239–40**, 570
Agnes Laurance (fl. 1597) 387
Agnes Lawrence (fl. 1616) 715
Elizabeth Lawrence (fl. 1677) 346
Giles Lawrence (?Gyles Myner) (fl. 1510–52) 156, 200, 239–40, 446
Guillaume Laurens (fl. 1505–12) 71, 156, 239
Maurice Lawrence (fl. 1585–93) 240, 720
Nicholas Lawrens (fl. 1539) 452
Thomas Lawrence (fl. 1677) 346
William Lawrence (fl. 1598) 721
see also Larence; Laurent
Layne *see* Leaney alias Thomas
Le Bages, family **423–4**
Le Bastier, Thibault (fl. 1508) 58
Le Blanc
family 66, 67, 69
Pierre Le Blanc (fl. 1554) 132, 318
see also Blanche; Blank; White
Le Blond
family 102, 800
Jehan Le Blond (cutler, fl. 1555) 109
Jehan Le Blond (locksmith, fl. 1542) 108
Jehan Le Blont (fl. 1487) 114
Pierre and Raoullin Le Blond (fl. 1573) 108
Thomas Le Blont (fl. 1486) 148
see also Blunden
Le Bon
Jehan Le Bon (fl. 1530s–40s) 108, 793
see also Good
Le Bouchier, Pierres (15th cent.) 70
Le Boullenger, Jehan (fl. 1566) 108
Le Boullenger, Laurent (16th cent.) 49
Le Boullenger, Michault (fl. 1505) 140
Le Boullenger, Nicolas (fl. 1529) 147
Le Boullenger, Raoullin (fl. 1552) 177
Le Bourgeois, Baptiste (16th cent.) 49
Le Brun, family (Bouelles) 421
Le Brun, Anthoine (fl. 1627) 746
Le Caron, *see also* Caron
Le Caron, Clement (fl. 1504) 100
Le Caron, Guillaume (fl. 1514) 53, 54, 182
Le Caron, Jehan (fl. 1505) 172, 181
Le Caron, Robert (fl. 1550) 49
Le Clerc
family 170
Guillaume Le Clerc (fl. 1516) 44
Jehan Le Clerc (fl. 1503–12) 106
Pierre Le Clerc (fl. 1530s) 145, 169, 170
Le Cognu, Jehan (fl. 1509) 140
Le Cointte, Jehan (fl. 1478) 166
Le Comte, Bertault (fl. 1534) 142, 143
Le Conroyeur, Theysse (fl. 1455) 98

Middleton, Arthur (Huggetts and Maynards Gate furnaces, fl. 1570) 204, 205, 595, 729n67
Middleton, Arthur (Ticknell, fl. 1610) 728–9
Middleton, David (16th cent.) 632
Middleton, David (fl. 1610) 729
Middleton, William (fl. 1586) 620
Middleton, William (fl. 1591) 371
Midhurst, Mary (fl. 1640) 659
Mier, Margaret (fl. 1581) 533
Miles
family **702**
Ann Mills (d. 1642) 800
John Miles (fl. 1640) 623
Margaret Miles (fl. 1623) 357
Nicholas Myles (fl. 1614) 270
Richard a' Myll (fl. 1560–66) 420, 599
Richard Miles (fl. 1599) 408
Thomas Myllles 721
Timothie Miles (fl. 1633) 364
Walter Milles (fl. 1599) 563
William Miles (fl. 1607) 789
William Mills (fl. 1609) 530
Millam alias Thousand
family **691–2**
Agnes Thousand (fl. 1594) 678
John Thousand (fl. 1592) 714
Katherine Myllam (fl. 1599) 335
Mary Milham (fl. 1620), d. of Anthony 700
Millard *see* Milward
Miller, Jane (fl. 1640) 356
Milles *see* Miles
Millet, Jacquet (fl. 1502) 93
Millington, Nicholas (probate 1638) 517, 774
Millom *see* Millam alias Thousand
Mills *see* Miles
Milner (Myllner), Collyn (fl. 1543–4) 582
Milton, Elizabeth (fl. 1613) 683
Milward
family **528**
John Milward alias Frengman (fl. 1531) 528, 619, 775
Mary Milward (fl. 1655), d. of Nathaniel 269
see also Clarke alias Milward
Minion or Monyon
family 308, 309, **544–6**, 718, 719, 720, 723
Peter Russell alias Mynion (d. 1613) 309, 545, 754
Minnage, family **635–7**
Minshowe *see* Message and Mason
Minshull, family 719
Minstrel *see* Harshaw
Minto, Mabel (fl. 1584) 732
Miriam, Anne (fl. 1610) 282
Mishaw, Mishawe *see* Message and Mason
Misho, Margaret (fl. 1562) 483
Miskyn, family **385**
Misse *see* Message and Mason
Missho, Joan (fl. 1605) 660
Missian, Jacob (d. 1565) 600
Missing, family 715n13
Mitchell
Christopher Mitchell (fl. 1617) 737
William Mitchell (fl. 1635) 737
see also Michell
Mittell
family 88, 127–8, **283–5**
Anthony Mittell (Mytyll) (fl. 1549) 88, 127, 283, 284
Henry Jarman alias Mittell (17th cent.) 544
Jarman Mittell (Mytyll) (d. 1585) 88, 127–8, 283–4, 544, 763, 772, 783
John Mettell (fl. 1617) 517
Philpott (Phllipot) Mettell (Mutel) (fl. 1524–44) 88, 127, 283, 399, 763
Mittenden, Joan (fl. 1664) 636
Mitton
family 283, 285
Agnes Mitten (fl. 1590) 276
Elizabeth Mitten (fl. 1641) 230
Henry Mitten (fl. 1630s) 285
James Mitten (fl. 1592) 219
Mobery, Mobrye *see* Maybury
Mocko *see* Makkowe
Mocumble
family 122–3, 200–1, **216–18**, 715
Mary Mocumble (fl. 1556) 234
Richard Mocumble (fl. 1556) 338
Rowland Mocumble (fl. 1544) 122, 123, 200, 201, 216
William Rowland alias Mocumble/Mocumber (d. 1579) 201, 216–17, 303, 421, 767–8, 770, 772
see also Rowland
Moddyll, *see also* Muddyll
Moddyll, Joan (fl. 1558) 263
Mohser, Caspar (fl. 1601) 594
Mole, Molet *see* Moolett
Moncke, Jane (fl. 1596) 678
Moncke, Joan (fl. 1571) 386
Moncke, Tomasyn (fl. 1572) 227
Mone *see* Moone
Mongommeray, Sir John de (fl. 1437) 43
Moniot, Guillaume de (17th cent.) 746
Monsloo *see* Munslowe
Mont, Christopher (fl. 1539) 431
Montague, viscounts *see* Browne
Monteagle, barons *see* Parker
Montholier *see* Mantellier
Montmorency, family 82
Monyon *see* Minion
Moolett
family 648, **804–5**
see also Mallet; Mallot
Moone
family 324
Agnes Moone (fl. 1621–22) 581
Andrew Moone (fl. 1621) 581
John Moone (16th cent.) 441
William Moone (fl. 1592) 564
Moonsell, David de (Demoyschell, Dumouchel) (fl. 1521–49) 151–3, 324, 445
Moor, Anne (fl. 1724) 804
Moore, *see also* More
Moore, Elizabeth (fl. 1641) 580
Moore, Richard (d. 1619) 330
Moore, Thomas (fl. 1597) 716
Moorey *see* Mowery
Morain, John (d. 1577) 605
Morall *see* Morrell
Morant
Bonne Morant (fl. 1489–94) 99, 101, 102, 106, 107
see also Morrant
More
family **557**, 558
William More (fl. 1574) 615, 654
see also Moor; Moore
Morel *see* Morrell
Mores *see* Moor; Moore; More
Moreway *see* Mowery
Morgaine, John (16th cent.) 600
Morgan, ____ (Dacre, fl. 1580) 367, 734
Morgan, Edmond (fl. 1574) 608
Morgan, John (fl. 1638) 806
Morgan, Stephen and Sarah (fl. 1728) 728
Morgyn, Mary (fl. 1580) 618
Morice *see* Morris
Morin, Jehan (fl. 1564) 108
Moris, Morisse *see* Morris
Morishurst, John (fl. 1593) 720
Morley
Anthony Morley (fl. 1562–74) 447, 456, 609, 632

Thomas Morley (fl. 1552) 124, 450, 480; aliens in lay subsidy rolls 832
William Morley (d. 1597) 609
Morley, barons *see* Parker
Morrall *see* Meryall; Morrell
Morrant
family 550
see also Morant
Morrell
family 46, 120, 121, 125–7, 186, **349–55**, 430, 605, 719, 730, 731, 737, 739, 740, 806
Didier Morel (fl. 1471) 35
Dorothy Morrell (fl. 1590) 412
George Morrall (fl. 1550) 286
Hugh Morall (fl. 1525–44) 126, 349–50, 351, 430, 602, 603, 604, 605
Humphrey Morrell (fl. 1599–1613) 353, 720
James Morrell (*c.* 1484–1544) 126, 349
Jehanne Morel (fl. 1546) 158
Joan Morell alias Laby (fl. 1553) 234
John Morrell (fl. 1532–50) 126, 127, 349, 351, 430, 444, 604
John Morrell (fl. 1584–1604) 353, 612, 722
John Morrell (fl. 1655) 336
Robinet Morel (fl. 1504) 121, 125
Simon Morrell (fl. 1589) 658
William Morrell (probate 1620) 351–2, 771, 773
see also Meryall
Morris
family 91, 92, 95, **285–7**, 514
Anthoine Moris (fl. 1462) 130
Anthony Morrys (fl. 1544) 91, 92, 285–6, 287
Sir Christopher Morris (Morice) (d. 1545) 443–4
Elizabeth Morris (fl. 1665) 411
Estienne Morisse (fl. 1534) 95
Francis Morris (fl. 1593–4) 721
George(s) Morisse (Morrys) (fl. 1543) 92, 186, 286, 287, 448, 487, 514, 557
John Morres (Oakamoor, fl. 1593–4) 721
John Morris (Battle, fl. 1563) 684
John Morris (Battle, fl. 1587) 402
Katherine Morris (fl. 1563) 684
Stephen Morris alias Usher (fl. 1659) 287, 514
Susan Morris (fl. 1682) 680
see also Harshaw; Morice
Morton, John, archbishop of Canterbury (d. 1500) 190–2, 195–6, 199
Morton, William (fl. 1576) 607
Moryow *see* Mowery
Mose, Parret (fl. 1587) 511
Mosson *see* Message and Mason
Moth, Motte *see* La Mott alias Finch
Motin *see* Angerfield
Motton
family **327**
Charles Motton (Mottynge, Motye) (fl. 1522–44) 61, 327, 442
Mouchard (Mouchart), Pierre(s) (fl. 1539–41) 108, 146, 175, 176, 185
Moumforth, Anne (fl. 1574) 488
Mounle, John de (fl. 1550) 531
Mounteneye (Mownteney), William (fl. 1501) 195, 209
Mowbery, Mowbray *see* Maybury
Mower, Margaret (fl. 1604) 509
Mowery, family 90, 448, **486–7**, 557
Mowle *see* Le Mowle
Moy, Philipot de (fl. 1520s) 127
Moyse, George (fl. 1613) 567
Muddyll, *see also* Moddyll
Muddyll, Richard (fl. 1534) 275, 778
Muglett
family 804–5
Frances Muglett (16th cent.) 213
see also Moolett
Muller, Jean (fl. 1590) 33
Mullet *see* Moolett
Mullinax, Margery (fl. 1638) 626
Muncke, Mary (fl. 1610) 672
Munnion *see* Minion or Monyon
Munnyer, Anne (Annis) (fl. 1613) 378
Munslow, John (fl. 1545) 604, 607
Munslowe (Monsloo), Thomas (fl. 1532–41) 603
Murhall, Murrall *see* Morrell
Mustel, Mutel *see* Mittell
Muttrell, Mary (fl. 1617) 806
Muza, Mercy (fl. 1616) 639
Mychelborne *see* Michelbourne
Mychell *see* Michell
Myclowe, family **558**
Myell, John (fl. 1613) 727
Myffaut, Jehan (fl. 1534) 143
Myles, Myll, Mylles *see* Miles
Myllam, Myllion *see* Millam alias Thousand
Mynault *see* Fry
Myngoes, Jeremy (fl. 1601) 722
Mynifee, William (fl. 1608) 385
Mynion *see* Minion or Monyon
Mynnage, Mynage, Mynidge *see* Minnage
Myschewe/Myshaw/Myshawe/Myshar *see* Message and Mason
Myskyn *see* Miskyn
Myston, John (fl. 1532) 603
Mytyll *see* Mittell

N
Naldrett, Edward (fl. 1580) 776
Namur, counts of 10–12, 13, 15, 17–18, 21
see also Willem I
Nantes, Jehan de (fl. 1477) 166
Nantier, Anthoine (fl. 1556) 86, 178
Napper, Jane (fl. 1589) 548
Napper, Matthew (fl. 1661) 659
Napper, Richard (fl. 1661) 659
Naset *see* Nazet
Nash, Marian (fl. 1635), widow of Stephen 481
Nash, Mary (fl. 1606) 510
Nassau, Lux von (fl. 1514) 435
Nayler or Clotear
family 254, **552–3**
Alice Naylor (fl. 1658) 495
John Nayler (fl. 1543) 453
John Nayler alias Clotear (fl. 1549–60) 453
Nazet
Colin Nazet (fl. 1480s–90s) 120–1
Jehanne Nazet (fl. 1494) 120–1
Pierres Nazet (Naset) (fl. 1480s–90s) 120–1, 149, 171
Neale, Henry (fl. 1655) 579
Neave *see* Neve
Neevett *see* Nevett
Neffe *see* Neve
Nele, William (fl. 1484–1525) 189–90, 192, 193, 249
Nelson, Elizabeth (fl. 1770) 681
Nelson, John (fl. 1593) 235
Nelson, Margery (fl. 1628) 578
Nepekar, Frances (fl. 1639) 745
Neston *see* Eason
Neve, family **561–2**
Nevell *see* Nevill
Nevers, count of *see* Philip, count of Nevers
Nevett
Amy Neevett (fl. 1617) 549, 727
Edward Nevet (fl. 1567–8) 204
William Nevett (fl. 1621) 727
Nevill, family, Lords Bergavenny 598, 600, 601, 777, 787
Sir Edward Nevill (fl. 1526) 428

201, 433
John Symard alias Pownsley (fl. 1511) 210, 246
Lambert Symar(t) (Seimar, Semer) alias Ponsley (fl. 1512, d. 1558) 196, 197, 201, 210, 246, 429, 430, 602, 603, 607, 616
Pauncelett Symart (fl. 1505–12) 196, 197, 199, 201, 202, 210, 246, 249
Peter Semer (Rievaulx, fl. 1578) 210, 701, 732
Symons
family **699–701**, 728
Elizabeth Simmons (fl. 1640) 682
Henry Simons (fl. 1593) 357–8, 695
Thomas Haskewe alias Symon (fl. 1581) 550
Thomas Simones (16th/17th cent.) 682
William Symons (fl. 1635) 425
Sympson, *see also* Simpson
Sympson, ____ (fl. 1590) 734
Sym(p)son, Elizabeth (fl. 1576), d. of John 210, 732
Syslye, Thomas (fl. 1613) 546

T
Taber
family **797**
John Taberer (fl. 1629) 729
see also Taverner
Taffte *see* Caffe or Taffte
Tailer *see* Taylor
Talbot
George Talbot, 6th earl of Shrewsbury (d. 1590) 590–1, 604, 607, 609–10, 611, 618, 717, 719
Gilbert Talbot, 7th earl of Shrewsbury (d. 1616) 731, 732
Talboy
family **413–14**
Alice Tarboyes (fl. 1539) 280, 413, 448
Gyllam Taylboy (fl. 1524) 283, 290, 413
Tamplier, Tampling *see* Turke alias Tomplin
Tancarville, counts of 63, 64, 65, 66
Tancre or Tanckerell
family 123, **280**
Agnes Tankerell (fl. 1611) 586
Michel Tanquerel (fl. 1477) 123, 166, 280
Roger Tancre (Tankerell, Tankerye, Tauncre) (fl. 1514–89) 123, 280, 448, 598, 673
Tanner, Anne (fl. 1652) 688
Tanner, Mary (fl. 1610) 331
Tantas, Tantoise *see* Gumrie
Tapsell, Elizabeth (fl. 1643) 693
Tarboyes *see* Talboy
Tarffe *see* Caffe or Taffte
Tarpe, *see also* Thorpe
Tarpe, Elizabeth (fl. 1632) 421
Tassell, family 90, 91, **648–9**
Tassen
family 93, **399**
Jordan Tassen (d. 1543) 93, 399, 775
Tasset, Elizabeth (fl. 1545) 315
Tatsust (?Toussains), Tomsyn (fl. 1598) 405
Taverner
Robert Taverner (fl. 1580s) 734
see also Taber
Taylboy *see* Talboy
Tayler, family 343
Taylor
family **529**
Agnes Taylor (fl. 1577) 419
Alexander Taylor (fl. 1593) 358
Elizabeth Taylor (fl. 1611) 276
Elizabeth Taylor (fl. 1641) 412
Elizabeth Taylor (fl. 1701) 354
Elizabeth Taylour (fl. 1636) 636
Elizabeth Taylour (fl. 1648) 634
Hester Tayler (fl. 1578) 509
Jane Taylor (fl. 1656) 474
John Taylor (fl. 1700) 579
Mary Taylor (fl. 1732) 731
Rebecca Tailer (fl. 1593) 486
Sara Taylor (fl. 1590) 797
Thomas Taylor alias Sargett or Sage (fl. 1657) 418
see also Tyler
Teaster, Joan (fl. 1592) 311
Telleth, Marcia (fl. 1556) 572
Tellow, Joan (fl. 1545) 379
Temple, Templier *see* Turke alias Tomplin
Tenate, Alice (fl. 1567) 660
Tench, Anne (fl. 1686) 731n80
Terrie, Stephen (fl. 1594) 235
Terse, Tersey *see* Torshy
Tester, Elizabeth (fl. 1630) 298
Thacker, Mary (fl. 1621) 301
Tharpe *see* Thorpe
Theissen, Pirotz (fl. 1585) 433
Theobald
family **650–1**
Thomas Theobull (fl. 1646) 583
Thibaut, Georges (fl. 1430) 25–6
Thieremand le Fondeur (Thy-le-Bauduin, fl. 1406) 17
Thierry (Tierry)
François Tierry (fl. 1555) 181
Jehan Thierry (Tierry) (fl. 1555) 180, 181
Thievenan (?Thiereman) Laffineur (Marche, fl. 1416) 18
Thirshurst, John (fl. 1645) 580
Thomas
family 375
Alice Thomas (fl. 1597) 382
Jehan Thomas (fl. 1541) 179
John Thomas (18th cent.) 348
Richard Thomas (fl. 1573) 352
Richard Thomas (fl. 1633) 554
see also Leaney alias Thomas
Thompson, John (fl. 1682) 270
Thompson, Margaret (fl. 1723) 587
Thornden, Edward and Elizabeth (fl. 1661) 659
Thornton, John (fl. 1589) 716
Thorp, Elizabeth (fl. 1675) 803
Thorpe, *see also* Tarpe
Thorpe, Christopher (16th cent.) 383
Thorpe, John (fl. 1574–94) 615, 645, 666
Thorpe (Tharpe), Katherine (fl. 1671) 354, 718
Thousand *see* Millam alias Thousand
Throckmorton, Clement (fl. 1550) 444
Throckmorton, Sir William (fl. 1612) 495
Thrushe *see* Drowsh
Thumann, Bartel (fl. 1589) 593–4
Thursfeld, ____ (Oakamoor, fl. 1607) 721
Thwaytes, Robert (fl. 1548) 611
Tibball, Tibboll *see* Theobald
Tibbits, Joyce (fl. 1737) 392
Tickner, Joan (fl. 1682) 336
Tickner, Sarah (fl. 1610) 219
Tickredg, Anne (fl. 1621) 804
Tidye, *see also* Tydie
Tidye, Elizabeth (fl. 1725) 575
Tierry *see* Thierry
Tiler *see* Tyler
Tillet *see* Tullet
Tilley, John (fl. 1587) 234
Timmis, Richard and Hannah (fl. 1743) 718, 719
Tingle
family 758
Thomas Tingell (Tyngell) (fl. 1599) 721, 758
Tipping, Mary (fl. 1689) 579

Walker, William (fl. 1690) 306
Wall, Martin (fl. 1593) 358
Wall, Mary (fl. 1782) 413
Waller
family 245, 596
John Waller (fl. 1558) 213
Thomas Waller (fl. 1582) 636
Wallis, John (fl. 1612) 298
Walpole, Catherine (fl. 1580) 332
Walpole, William (fl. 1574) 601
Walsh
family 100, 243, 462
Goddard Walsh (fl. 1551) 440, 447, 450, 485, 598; aliens in lay subsidy rolls 833
Joan Walsh (fl. 1542) 450, 464, 485, 598; aliens in lay subsidy rolls 833
John Walshe (fl. 1548) 200, 452
Robert Walsh (fl. 1562) 485
Thomas Walsh (d. 1540) 251, 429, 441, 450
Walsingham, Sir Francis (d. 1590) 736
Walsted
family 247–8
John Walstedde (fl. 1524) 247–8, 446; workers with John Walstedde at Heathfield 416–19
Walter or Waters
family **693**
Alice Waters (fl. 1575) 478
Dorothy Waters (fl. 1584) 207
Guillaume Ouatre (fl. 1474) 166
James Waters (fl. 1617) 505, 535–6
Jeremey Waters (fl. 1606) 715, 716
Joan Watters (fl. 1603) 641
John Walter (fl. 1543) 442
Margaret Waters (fl. 1594) 546
Marie Waters (fl. 1615) 637
Martha Waters (fl. 1630) 640
Moore Waters (fl. 1603) 706
Richard a'Water (fl. 1589) 265
Solomon Walter (fl. 1629) 697
Susan Water (fl. 1594) 671
William Waters (fl. 1570s) 452, 631
Walys, Joan (fl. 1542) 561
Ward
Elizabeth Ward (fl. 1609) 329
Henry Ward (17th cent.) 329
Mary Ward (fl. 1727) 273
Thomas and Joan Ward alias Hackwood 290
Wardle, Thomas (fl. 1593–4) 721
Warham, William, archbishop of Canterbury (d. 1532) 191, 246
Waring, Anne (fl. 1713) 413
Warner
family 199, 244, 405, 408
Charles Warner (Warnet) (d.1559) *see* Gerard or Jarrett, Charles
John Warner (fl. 1491) 192, 197, 199
Richard Warner (fl. 1518) 197
Thomas Warner (16th cent.) 208
Thomas Warner (fl. 1614) 586
William Warner (fl. 1547) 442, 776
Warnet
family 400, 405, 408, 542
Charles Warner (Warnet) (d.1559) *see* Gerard or Jarrett, Charles
Gyles Warnett (fl. 1590) 409, 735
Nicholas Warnet (Werett) (fl. 1549) 405, 542
Warrell *see* Worrell
Warry, Frances (fl. 1640) 408
Warwick, earl of *see* Dudley
Washer *see* Hussey
Wassell
family 716
Nicholas Wassell (fl. 1658) 231
see also Vassel
Waterhouse, Herbert (fl. 1611) 227
Waterman, Joan (fl. 1614) 684
Waters *see* Walter or Waters
Watkins
Thomas Watkins (fl. 1597) 221
Thomas Watkins (fl. 1727) 708
Thomas Watkins (Watkyns) (fl. 1601–4) 724, 725
Watkyne, Myell (fl. 1594) 720
Watkyne, Thomas (fl. 1594) 721
Watson, Mary (fl. 1741) 624
Watson, Ruth (fl. 1696) 540
Wauckley, Margaret (fl. 1595) 211
Wauklyn, *see also* Wakelin
Wauklyn, Clementia (fl. 1566) 660
Wayed (Wayde), family 737
Wayner, James (fl. 1559) 653
Weaste, Joan (fl. 1578) 392
Weaver, *see also* Wever
Weaver, Peter (fl. 1595) 694
Webb, Alice (fl. 1589) 332
Webb, Clare and John (fl. 1624) 501
Webb, John (fl. 1602) 357
Webbe, Thomas (fl. 1579) 217
Webster, Mary (fl. 1664) 368
Webster, Sir Whistler (1709–79) 624
Weekes
George a' Weekes (fl. 1582) 286, 479, 528
Henry a' Weke (fl. 1545) 295
John Weekes (fl. 1656) 640
Margaret Weekes (fl. 1588) 215–16
Richard a' Weekes (fl. 1605) 492
Richard Weekes (fl. 1544–60s) 81, 100, 224, 232, 249, 286, 429, 440, 449, 450, 453, 460, 463, 471, 598, 614; aliens in lay subsidy rolls 829, 830; immigrants listed in Westminster denization roll (1544) 520, 814
Richard Weekes (fl. 1657) 507
Weken (Wicking)
family 746–7, 758
John Wekyng the elder (John Wyking) (fl. 1579) 339
see also Wickens; Wiken
Welch, Joan (fl. 1611) 300
Welche, Agnes (fl. 1574) 243
Weld, Richard (fl. 1627) 659
Weldern (Wyldorne), Peter (fl. 1543–9) 529, 693–4
Weller, Alexander (17th cent.) 341
Weller, Elizabeth (fl. 1621) 364
Weller, John (fl. 1630) 508
Welles
family **792**
____ Wells (?Hawksden, fl. 1549) 464, 464n176, 465
William Well(e)s (fl. 1576–9) 472, 792
Welling, William (fl. 1623) 651
Wells *see* Welles
Welsted *see* Walsted
Wembourne, John (fl. 1543) 206
Wenham, George (fl. 1607) 620
Wenham, George (fl. 1627) 396
Wenham, John (fl. 1584) 660
Wenham, John (fl. 1624) 729
Wenham, Michael (fl. 1634) 268
Wenman, Edward (fl. 1591) 550
Wenmar, Francis (fl. 1596) 305
Werett (Warnet), Nicholas (fl. 1549) 405, 542
Wesson *see* Weston
West, Thomas (fl. 1627) 659
Westall, Harry (Henry) (fl. 1550) 226, 401, 614, 615, 761, 777, 810, 830
Westburne, Martha (fl. 1602) 223
Weste, Richard (fl. 1573) 615
Western, Thomas (fl. 1692) 637
Westmorland, earl of *see* Fane
Weston, Constance (fl. 1575) 789
Weston, John (fl. 1560s) 805
Weston, John (d. 1585) 291, 607
Weston, Michael (fl. 1551–74) 453, 595, 596
Weston, Richard (fl. 1560s) 805
Weston, Richard (fl. 1577) 618